$\sqrt[n]{a}$ is called the *n*th root of *a*:

(1.38)
- If *n* is an even positive integer, and *a* and *b* are positive real numbers for which $a = b^n$, then $\sqrt[n]{a} = b$.
- If *n* is an odd positive integer, and if *a* and *b* are real numbers for which $a = b^n$, then $\sqrt[n]{a} = b$.
- In either case, $\sqrt[n]{0} = 0$.

For any positive integer *n* and any positive real numbers *a* and *b*:

(1.39) $\sqrt[n]{ab} = (\sqrt[n]{a})(\sqrt[n]{b})$

(1.40) $\sqrt[n]{a/b} = \dfrac{\sqrt[n]{a}}{\sqrt[n]{b}}$ (1.41) $\sqrt[m]{\sqrt[n]{a}} = \sqrt[mn]{a}$

For any positive integer *n* and any real number *a*, if $\sqrt[n]{a}$ is a real number, then:

(1.42) $a^{1/n} = \sqrt[n]{a}$

(1.43) $a^{m/n} = (\sqrt[n]{a})^m = (a^{1/n})^m = (a^m)^{1/n} = \sqrt[n]{a^m}$

(5.1) $y = \log_b x$ if and only if $b^y = x$
$\log_b (b^y) = y$ and $b^{\log_b x} = x$ for $x > 0$, *y* real

(5.2) $\log_b (xy) = \log_b x + \log_b y$ (5.3) $\log_b (x/y) = \log_b x - \log_b y$

(5.4) $\log_b (x^p) = p \cdot \log_b x$

(5.5) $\log_b \sqrt[r]{x} = \dfrac{1}{r} \log_b x$

$(\log_a x)(\log_b a) = \log_b x$

(6.1) π radians $= 180°$ (6.2) $s = r\theta$

(6.3) $\dfrac{y}{r} = \sin \theta \qquad \dfrac{x}{r} = \cos \theta \qquad \dfrac{y}{x} = \tan \theta$

$\dfrac{r}{y} = \csc \theta \qquad \dfrac{r}{x} = \sec \theta \qquad \dfrac{x}{y} = \cot \theta$

(6.4) $\sin \theta \csc \theta = 1 \qquad \cos \theta \sec \theta = 1 \qquad \tan \theta \cot \theta = 1$

(6.5) $\sin \theta = \dfrac{\text{opp}}{\text{hyp}} \qquad \cos \theta = \dfrac{\text{adj}}{\text{hyp}} \qquad \tan \theta = \dfrac{\text{opp}}{\text{adj}}$

(6.6) $\cot \theta = \dfrac{\text{adj}}{\text{opp}} \qquad \sec \theta = \dfrac{\text{hyp}}{\text{adj}} \qquad \csc \theta = \dfrac{\text{hyp}}{\text{opp}}$

Any trigonometric function of an acute angle is equal to the corresponding cofunction of the complementary angle.

We define sin *s*, where *s* is a real number, to be sin θ, where θ is an angle whose radian measure is *s*. Similarly we define

(6.7) $\cos s = \cos \theta$, $\tan s = \tan \theta$, $\cot s = \cot \theta$, $\sec s = \sec \theta$, and $\csc s = \csc \theta$ for any real number *s*.

(6.8) The sine, cosine, secant, and cosecant functions have period 2π, or $360°$. The tangent and cotangent functions have period π, or $180°$.

(7.1) $\sin \theta \csc \theta = 1$ (7.2) $\cos \theta \sec \theta = 1$

(7.3) $\tan \theta \cot \theta = 1$ (7.4) $\tan \theta = \dfrac{\sin \theta}{\cos \theta}$

(7.5) $\cot \theta = \dfrac{\cos \theta}{\sin \theta}$ (7.6) $\cos^2 \theta + \sin^2 \theta = 1$

(7.7) $1 + \tan^2 \theta = \sec^2 \theta$ (7.8) $1 + \cot^2 \theta = \csc^2 \theta$

(7.9) $\quad \cos (A - B) = \cos A \cos B + \sin A \sin B$

(7.10) $\quad \cos \left(\dfrac{\pi}{2} - B \right) = \sin B$

(7.11) $\quad \sin \left(\dfrac{\pi}{2} - B \right) = \cos B$

(7.12) $\quad \cos (A + B) = \cos A \cos B - \sin A \sin B$

(7.13) $\quad \sin (A + B) = \sin A \cos B + \cos A \sin B$

(7.14) $\quad \sin (A - B) = \sin A \cos B - \cos A \sin B$

(7.15a) $\quad \cos 2\theta = \cos^2 \theta - \sin^2 \theta$

(7.15b) $\quad \cos 2\theta = 2 \cos^2 \theta - 1$

(7.15c) $\quad \cos 2\theta = 1 - 2 \sin^2 \theta$

(7.16) $\quad \sin 2\theta = 2 \sin \theta \cos \theta$

(7.17) $\quad \sin^2 \dfrac{\theta}{2} = \dfrac{1 - \cos \theta}{2}$

(7.18) $\quad \cos^2 \dfrac{\theta}{2} = \dfrac{1 + \cos \theta}{2}$

(7.19) $\quad \tan (A + B) = \dfrac{\tan A + \tan B}{1 - \tan A \tan B}$

(7.20) $\quad \tan 2\theta = \dfrac{2 \tan \theta}{1 - \tan^2 \theta}$

(7.21a) $\quad \tan \dfrac{\theta}{2} = \dfrac{1 - \cos \theta}{\sin \theta}$

(7.21b) $\quad \tan \dfrac{\theta}{2} = \dfrac{\sin \theta}{1 + \cos \theta}$

(7.22) $\quad \tan (A - B) = \dfrac{\tan A - \tan B}{1 + \tan A \tan B}$

(7.23) $\quad \sin A \cos B = \frac{1}{2}[\sin(A + B) + \sin (A - B)]$

(7.24) $\quad \cos A \sin B = \frac{1}{2}[\sin (A + B) - \sin (A - B)]$ $\left.\rule{0pt}{48pt}\right\}$ Product-to-sum formulas

(7.25) $\quad \cos A \cos B = \frac{1}{2}[\cos (A + B) + \cos (A - B)]$

(7.26) $\quad \sin A \sin B = \frac{1}{2}[\cos (A + B) - \cos (A - B)]$

(7.27) $\quad \sin x + \sin y = 2 \sin \dfrac{x + y}{2} \cos \dfrac{x - y}{2}$

(7.28) $\quad \sin x - \sin y = 2 \cos \dfrac{x - y}{2} \sin \dfrac{x - y}{2}$ $\left.\rule{0pt}{60pt}\right\}$ Sum-to-product formulas

(7.29) $\quad \cos x + \cos y = 2 \cos \dfrac{x + y}{2} \cos \dfrac{x - y}{2}$

(7.30) $\quad \cos x - \cos y = -2 \sin \dfrac{x + y}{2} \sin \dfrac{x - y}{2}$

(7.31) $\quad \sin (\theta + \alpha) = \dfrac{C}{\sqrt{A^2 + B^2}}$ is $A \sin \theta + B \cos \theta = C$ with

$\quad \cos \alpha = \dfrac{A}{\sqrt{A^2 + B^2}}$ and $\sin \alpha = \dfrac{B}{\sqrt{A^2 + B^2}}$

(8.1) $\quad \dfrac{a}{\sin A} = \dfrac{b}{\sin B} = \dfrac{c}{\sin C}$ or $\dfrac{\sin A}{a} = \dfrac{\sin B}{b} = \dfrac{\sin C}{c}$

(8.2) $\quad a^2 = b^2 + c^2 - 2bc \cos A$ or $\cos A = \dfrac{b^2 + c^2 - a^2}{2bc}$

(8.3) $\quad K = \frac{1}{2}ab \sin C = \frac{1}{2}ac \sin B = \frac{1}{2}bc \sin A$

(8.4) $\quad K = \dfrac{c^2 \sin A \sin B}{2 \sin C} = \dfrac{b^2 \sin A \sin C}{2 \sin B} = \dfrac{a^2 \sin B \sin C}{2 \sin A}$

(8.5) $\quad s = \dfrac{a + b + c}{2}$

(8.6) $\quad K = \sqrt{s(s - a)(s - b)(s - c)}$

College Algebra with Trigonometry

College Algebra with Trigonometry

Paul K. Rees
Professor Emeritus of Mathematics
Louisiana State University

Fred W. Sparks
Late Professor of Mathematics
Texas Tech University

Charles Sparks Rees
Professor of Mathematics
University of New Orleans

McGraw-Hill, Inc.
New York St. Louis San Francisco Auckland Bogotá Caracas Hamburg
Lisbon London Madrid Mexico Milan Montreal New Delhi Paris
San Juan São Paulo Singapore Sydney Tokyo Toronto

2 3 4 5 6 7 8 9 0   DOH   DOH   9 5 4 3 2 1

ISBN 0-07-051737-1

This book was set in Times Roman by York Graphic Services, Inc.
The editors were Karen M. Hughes and James W. Bradley;
the production supervisor was Leroy A. Young.
The cover was designed by Caliber Design Planning, Inc.
New drawings were done by Fine Line Illustrations, Inc.
R. R. Donnelley & Sons Company was printer and binder.

Library of Congress Cataloging-in-Publication Data

Rees, Paul Klein, (date).
    College algebra with trigonometry / Paul K. Rees, Fred W. Sparks,
Charles Sparks Rees.
        p.   cm.
    ''Portions . . . were previously published under the title of College
algebra''—T.p. verso.
    Includes index.
    ISBN 0-07-051737-1
    1. Algebra.   2. Trigonometry.   I. Sparks, Fred Winchell, (date).
    II. Rees, Charles Sparks.   III. Title.
QA154.2.R443   1991
512'.13—dc20   90-22514

About the Authors

Paul K. Rees earned his B.A. from Southwestern University in 1923, his M.A. from the University of Texas in 1925, and his Ph.D. from Rice University in 1933. After teaching 20 years at colleges in Texas, Mississippi, and New Mexico, he joined the mathematics department at Louisiana State University. In 1967, after 21 years at LSU, he retired with the title of Professor Emeritus of Mathematics.

Charles Sparks Rees earned his B.S. from Louisiana State University in 1962 and his M.S. and Ph.D. from the University of Kansas in 1963 and 1967, respectively. He currently teaches at the University of New Orleans.

Both Paul and Charles Rees are authors of numerous elementary mathematics textbooks.

The surviving authors dedicate this book to
Fred W. Sparks, friend and namesake,
Madge Sparks, his wonderful wife,
and their daughter, Mary Matthews,
and her family.

Contents

CHAPTER 13   The Conics   609

Preface

Organization

In this text, we cover all the standard topics for a college algebra and trigonometry text in a straightforward manner. This book has eight chapters in common with our *College Algebra*, which was published last year by McGraw-Hill. We have tried to make the text material easily readable while preserving its mathematical integrity. There are many examples which are worked in detail, and these have been coordinated closely with the problems at the end of each section. We try to show the student how a concrete situation leads to a general rule. Ample opportunity is given for students to practice, since we have more problems than almost every other book in this field.

Chapter 1 gives a review of many of the basic methods of algebra, including factoring, fractions, radicals, and rational exponents. Chapter 2, on equations and inequalities, includes quadratic equations as well as linear and fractional material. The section on complex numbers has been placed just before quadratic equations, since this is where it is first needed.

Chapter 3 first introduces graphs, and then treats certain modifications of some standard graphs. We also include a section which gives an introduction to the graphs of conics. We present graphs and then functions since we think the student can grasp the function concept more readily if it is associated with graphs. Ample time is spent on functions, function values, and graphs of functions.

Chapter 4 deals with polynomials in the first seven sections. We begin with quadratic functions, and then show how to graph polynomials both in factored form and as sums. Thus, students are more prepared for the material in Sections 4.3 to 4.7 on zeros of polynomials. Section 4.8 incorporates guidelines on graphing rational functions, and it includes not only horizontal and vertical asymptotes, but also linear ones.

Exponential and logarithmic functions are introduced in the first two sections of Chapter 5. These two concepts are reinforced and intertwined in Section 5.3 via the number e and the natural exponential and logarithmic functions. Calculations are given in Appendix I, in keeping with the common use today of calculators in place of tables. Appendix II includes tables of common logarithms as well as e^x and $\ln x$.

Trigonometry is presented in three chapters: Chapters 6, 7, and 8. In Chapter 6, we introduce the trigonometric functions by angles, and give the circle approach shortly afterward. This concrete approach is the one students find easiest to understand, and it also allows right-triangle applications to be given early, in Section 6.4.

In Chapter 7, we give the identities at a slower pace than do most books because there are so many identities to learn. Again our intent is to help the student as much as possible. The chapter closes with inverse functions and trigonometric equations.

Chapter 8 gives a variety of applications of trigonometry, beginning with the laws of sines and of cosines. The chapter also includes vectors, complex numbers, and polar coordinates. This concludes the trigonometric part of the book, except for the last half of Chapter 13.

Chapters 9 and 10 are kept separate to avoid having one immensely long chapter on systems of equations. We believe this makes it easier for teachers to choose and students to understand the material.

Chapter 11 treats arithmetic and geometric sequences, giving, as always, some actual applications. It closes with some practical material on interest and annuities since they are among the applications that every adult needs from time to time.

In Chapter 12 we have included several related topics, including permutations and combinations, the binomial theorem, and probability. Mathematical induction treats equations and inequalities.

Chapter 13 gives a detailed look at the conics for those who prefer this to the overview of conics given earlier in Chapter 3. It concludes with sections on rotation of axes and the use of the discriminant in classifying conics, and on the polar form of conics.

Special Features

The exercises are a normal lesson apart, and the problems in each exercise are in groups of four similar ones. This makes it a simple matter for even the inexperienced instructor to make a good assignment regularly. Most classes need only to be assigned every fourth problem, but many other problems are available for practice.

There are some 6400 problems in 87 regular and 13 review exercises. There are many routine problems which are closely keyed to the examples. We also include more challenging ones near the end of each exercise to keep up the student's interest and enthusiasm. Answers are given in the text for three-fourths of the regular problems and all the review problems. The review problems can be used as a supplement, for extra credit, as a self-test, as the basis for short quizzes, or as a preview of the chapter to see where extra work is needed.

We give applications of the mathematical methods presented in the book in a variety of areas, including anthropology, astronomy, biology, business, chemistry, demography, earth science, education, engineering, ichthyology, management, navigation, physics, political science, psychology, and sociology. Each applied problem is labeled as to the discipline it illustrates.

Learning Aids

We consistently keep a good balance among computation, applications, and theory. Some exercises include numerical problems to emphasize that the rules of algebra apply to honest-to-goodness real numbers as well as to variables.

Each chapter begins with a section-by-section outline, and then is followed by an overview of the material to be given in the chapter.

There are marginal notes to make it easy for the student to see which concept is being discussed. This is enhanced by the liberal use of boldface to highlight key terms. Many concepts and procedures are set apart in boxes for easy reference. A functional use of color is made throughout the book. There are many illustrations in the book to aid comprehension.

A chapter summary appears at the end of each chapter. This includes a list of key words and concepts and a compilation of all the main formulas from the chapter. The summary is followed by a review exercise.

The book may be used with or without a calculator. The ideas and techniques in the book do not depend on the use of a calculator. We try to allow its use for the jobs it does best—actual calculation and as a table of function values. Occasionally we ask specifically for an "exact" answer in order to emphasize the distinction between exact solutions and decimal approximations. There are rules on calculating with approximate, or rounded, numbers.

Supplements

There is a Student's Solution Manual which gives detailed solutions to the odd-numbered problems. There is also an Instructor's Resource Manual which gives answers (to the multiple-of-four problems) that are not in the text. This supplement also includes a list of extra problems for each chapter that may be used as a diagnostic test, a review, or a self-test for the chapter. McGraw-Hill is also offering software to accompany the book.

Acknowledgments

A considerable variety of people have helped to make this edition a better book than it would have been without their input. They include the following reviewers: Benjamin P. Bockstege, Broward Community College; B. F. Boudria, Stephen F. Austin State University; Barbara M. Brook, Camden County College; Julius M. Burkett, Stephen F. Austin State University; Michael W. Ecker, Pennsylvania State University; Leland J. Fry, Kirkwood Community College; Robert Gold, Ohio State University; Piotr Mikusinski, University of Central Florida; Julia R. Monte, Daytona Beach Community College; Gillian C. Raw, University of Missouri–St. Louis; John Snyder, Sinclair Community College; C. H. Tjoelker, California State

University–Sacramento; Ken Stewart Wagman, Gavilan College; and Lynn J. Wolfmeyer, Western Illinois University.

We would be remiss without thanking our Senior Editing Supervisor James W. Bradley, our Assistant Editor Karen M. Hughes, and Shelly Langman, who studied each version of the manuscript and thought, wrote, organized, and helped out in numerous ways.

Paul K. Rees
Charles Sparks Rees

1 Algebraic Concepts

Chapter 1 is an overview of fundamental ideas and methods in algebra, and it is essential that you master the material here before studying the rest of the book. Doing so will help you to develop real skills in the understanding and manipulation of numbers, and of symbols which represent numbers. Such skills have always been necessary in the traditional scientific subjects, and due in large part to the computer revolution they have also become important now in areas such as anthropology, biology, business, economics, education, geology, political science, psychology, and sociology among others. In fact, efficient manipulation of numbers is especially important with calculators and computers in order to save time and money. Besides, algebra can be fun; learning is one of life's greatest pleasures. Enjoy.

1.1 The Real Number System

In algebra we use symbols or letters to represent numbers, and so the rules of algebra depend on the rules of arithmetic. Real numbers are used throughout mathematics, and every real number written in base 10 uses some or all of the 10 digits 0, 1, 2, 3, 4, 5, 6, 7, 8, and 9. The number zero or 0 came into use much later than the other nine digits, and the use of 0 is a hallmark of our place-value notation, which we inherited from the Hindus via the Arabs. It allows us to distinguish between numbers such as 479 and 4709.

The **positive integers,** also called the **counting numbers,** or **natural numbers,** are the numbers

$$1, 2, 3, 4, 5, 6, 7, 8, 9, 10, 11, 12, 13, \ldots$$

If we include their negatives, as well as 0, we have the **integers**

$$\ldots, -4, -3, -2, -1, 0, 1, 2, 3, 4, \ldots$$

A **rational number** is a quotient m/n, where m and n are integers with $n \neq 0$. For instance, the numbers 31/2, 4/53, 707/1, 18/6, 0/44, and $-22/19$ are rational.

Any **real number** can be written as a decimal. If the digits *end* (terminate), as in

$$461.3351 \qquad 6.1 \qquad -75.57 \qquad 0.135246 \qquad -3.701$$

or if the digits form a *repeating pattern,* as in

$$16.232323 \cdots \qquad 90.1654654654 \cdots \qquad -4.0577777 \cdots$$

it can be shown that the real number is **rational.** Ordinary long division shows that the converse is true also. For instance, using long division will show that

2/7 must repeat after at most 6 digits.
13/29 must repeat after at most 28 digits.

We sometimes write a repeating decimal by putting a line over the part which repeats, such as

$$50.1987987987 \cdots = 50.1\overline{987}$$

Real numbers that are not rational are called **irrational numbers,** and they include

$$\sqrt{3} \qquad \sqrt[5]{8} \qquad \pi \qquad -\sqrt{71}$$

It follows that every irrational number must have an infinite number of digits in its decimal form, and these digits must not form a repeating pattern. Examples of irrational numbers in decimal form are

$$0.414114111411114 \cdots \qquad \text{and} \qquad -16.1718192021 \cdots$$

By definition, every real number is either rational or irrational. This and other relationships are shown in Fig. 1.1 on **the real number system.**

If m, n, and k are positive integers with $m = nk$, then n and k are called **factors** of m, or **divisors** of m. For instance, $28 = 28 \cdot 1 = 14 \cdot 2 = 7 \cdot 4$, and so 28 has the factors 1, 2, 4, 7, 14, and 28. Factoring is vital in order to simplify many algebraic expressions.

A positive integer $n > 1$ is **prime** if its only positive integer factors are 1 and n. Otherwise it is called **composite.** Thus 28 is composite, as are $123 = 3 \cdot 41$ and $551 = 19 \cdot 29$. Euclid proved that there are an infinite number of primes, and some very large ones have been found with the aid of computers.

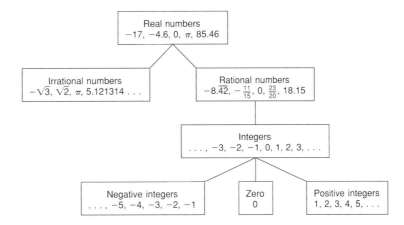

FIGURE 1.1

The prime numbers are the building blocks of the natural numbers. The **fundamental theorem of arithmetic** is the basis for this statement. That theorem says that every natural number can be factored into prime factors, and that this can be done in only one way except for the order of the factors. That is, the prime factors can be arranged in different orders, but the factors themselves are unique.

EXAMPLE 1 Factor the numbers below.

Solution (a) $35 = 5 \cdot 7 = 7 \cdot 5$.
(b) $105 = 3 \cdot 5 \cdot 7 = 5 \cdot 7 \cdot 3 = 7 \cdot 3 \cdot 5$, etc. The order of the factors is not important.
(c) $44 = 2 \cdot 2 \cdot 11 = 2 \cdot 11 \cdot 2 = 11 \cdot 2 \cdot 2$.

The numbers

$$1 + (2)(3)(5)(7)(11) \qquad \text{and} \qquad 1 + (2)(3)(5)(7)(11)(13)$$

are related to the proof that there are an infinite number of primes. The first number above is $1 + 2310 = 2311$, which is prime. The second one is $1 + 30,030$, which is composite since its prime factorization is $30,031 = (59)(509)$.

Algebra is based on the same rules as arithmetic, beginning with the **four fundamental operations** of addition, subtraction, multiplication, and division. In algebra we generalize calculations by using symbols (usually letters) to represent numbers. Real numbers have many properties which govern combining and comparing them. We shall begin with the following properties or axioms of real numbers. Together they are called the **field properties.** If a and b represent any real numbers, we write their product as

$$a \cdot b \qquad \text{or} \qquad a \times b \qquad \text{or} \qquad ab \qquad \text{or} \qquad (a)(b) \qquad \text{or} \qquad a(b)$$

Properties of real numbers

Properties of the real numbers include the following:

Closure property

$a + b$ and ab are real numbers.

Associative property

$(a + b) + c = a + (b + c)$ and $(ab)c = a(bc)$.

Identity properties

$a + 0 = a$ and $(a)(1) = a$ for all real a.

0 is called the **additive identity.**

1 is called the **multiplicative identity;**

Inverse properties

$a + (-a) = 0$ and $b(b^{-1}) = 1$ for $b \neq 0$.

For every real a, there is an **additive inverse** $-a$, and there is a **multiplicative inverse** b^{-1}, if $b \neq 0$.

Commutative properties

$a + b = b + a$ and $ab = ba$.

Distributive property

$a(b + c) = ab + ac$ for all reals a, b, and c.

Of these, the distributive property or law deserves special mention because it alone deals with both addition and multiplication in one equation. We will find it useful in much of our later work, especially in factoring, in multiplying, and in adding fractions.

▶ EXAMPLE 2   The calculations below illustrate the distributive law.

Solution
$$63(41 + 25) = 63(66) = 4158$$
$$63(41) + 63(25) = 2583 + 1575 = 4158$$
◢

The **multiplicative inverse** b^{-1} is defined only if $b \neq 0$, and it is often written $1/b$. Thus for instance $4^{-1} = 1/4 = 0.25$.

An **additive inverse,** $-a$, exists for any real number a, and it is also called the **negative** of a. NOTE *Note:* It is possible for $-a$ to be a negative or a positive real number, depending upon what value a has. For instance if $a = 3$, then $-a = -3$, which is negative. But with $a = -18$, $-a = -(-18)$, which we will soon see is equal to $+18$, or just 18.

The additive identity 0 plays a special role in multiplication, as illustrated in the theorem below.

Theorem

For all real numbers b,
$$(b)(0) = 0 \tag{1.1}$$

For all real numbers a and b,
$$\text{if } ab = 0, \text{ then } a = 0, \text{ or } b = 0, \text{ or both are zero} \tag{1.2}$$

The proofs of this theorem and some of the other properties in this section are outlined in Exercise 1.1.

▶ EXAMPLE 3   Find each product below.

Solution   If 0 is multiplied by any real number, the result is zero:

$$5(0) = 0 \qquad 0(-181.3) = 0 \qquad 0(0) = 0$$ ◢

▶ EXAMPLE 4   Solve the equation $(x)(x - 5) = 0$ by using the above theorem.

Solution   If $(x)(x - 5) = 0$, then either $x = 0$ or $x - 5 = 0$. Thus the solutions are 0 and 5.   ◢

In the field properties for real numbers, the operations defined are addition and multiplication. Two other operations may be defined by using addition and multiplication of inverses.

Subtraction

$$a - b \text{ is defined to be } a + (-b) \tag{1.3}$$

Division

$$a \div b \text{ is defined to be } a(b^{-1}) \text{ if } b \neq 0 \tag{1.4}$$

Other notations for division are a/b or $a(1/b)$. The number $1/b$ is called the **reciprocal** of b, for $b \neq 0$. Notice particularly that

NOTE   *Division by 0 is not defined*

Therefore $71/0$ and $-23.45/0$ are not defined; not even $0/0$ is defined. On the other hand

$$\frac{0}{b} = 0 \qquad \text{for every } b \neq 0$$

We sometimes write fractions or decimals using %, or percent. By definition, $x\%$ means $x/100$. Hence

$$6.5\% = 6.5/100 = 6.5(0.01) = 0.065$$

$$(7/8)\% = 0.875\% = 0.875/100 = 0.00875$$

Negatives, or additive inverses, have a number of important properties which are collected below.

Properties of negatives

$$-a = (-1)(a) \qquad (-a)(-b) = ab$$
$$-(-a) = a \qquad -(a + b) = -a - b$$
$$a(-b) = -(ab) \qquad -(a - b) = -a + b$$

For instance, $(-6)(-3) = 18$, and we may write either

$$-(5 - 7) = -5 + 7 = 2 \qquad \text{or} \qquad -(5 - 7) = -(-2) = 2$$

Some of the proofs of the properties of negatives are outlined in the exercises.

Laws of signs

> If a and b have the same sign, both positive or both negative, then ab and a/b are positive.
> If a and b have opposite signs, then ab and a/b are negative.

▶ **EXAMPLE 5**

$$(6)(19) = +114 \qquad (-11)(-13) = +143 \qquad (14)(-9) = -126$$

$$\frac{81}{27} = 3 \qquad \frac{-180}{-15} = +12 \qquad \frac{108}{-18} = -6$$

How should we calculate $3 + 4 \times 5$? If there were no rules to tell us whether to add or multiply first, it could be either

$$(3 + 4) \times 5 = 7 \times 5 = 35 \qquad \text{or} \qquad 3 + (4 \times 5) = 3 + 20 = 23$$

To avoid any possible uncertainty, the order of operations below has been agreed upon, which shows that 23 is the correct answer above. Sometimes the symbols brackets [ ] or braces { } are used, as well as parentheses ( ), to group certain terms together.

Order of operations

> (a) In calculations where there are no parentheses, first do any multiplications and divisions working from left to right, then any additions and subtractions working from left to right.
> (b) If there are parentheses, use the rules above within each set of parentheses, beginning with the innermost. In a fraction, work separately with the numerator and denominator.

▶ **EXAMPLE 6**   Do these calculations using the order of operations listed above.

Solution   (a) Doing multiplications and divisions first gives

$$19 - 2 \times 3 - 27 \div 3 = 19 - 6 - 9$$

Now working left to right gives

$$19 - 6 - 9 = 13 - 9 = 4$$

Notice that working right to left would have given $19 - 6 - 9 = 19 - (-3) = 22$.
(b) Working with the innermost parentheses first, and separately with the numerator and denominator, we have

$$\frac{3 + [14 - (22 - 18 \div 2) + 4 \times 6] - 2 \times 7}{4 - 15 + (3 - 8 \times 7) - (13 \times 3 - 5 + 9)}$$

$$= \frac{3 + [14 - (22 - 9) + 4 \times 6] - 14}{4 - 15 + (3 - 56) - (39 - 5 + 9)}$$

$$= \frac{3 + [14 - 13 + 24] - 14}{4 - 15 + (-53) - (34 + 9)} = \frac{3 + [1 + 24] - 14}{4 - 15 - 53 - 43}$$

$$= \frac{3 + 25 - 14}{-11 - 53 - 43} = \frac{28 - 14}{-64 - 43} = \frac{14}{-107}$$

The following two properties will be used extensively in solving equations.

If $a = b$, and c is any real number, then

$$a + c = b + c \qquad\qquad \textbf{(1.5i)}$$

$$ac = bc \qquad\qquad \textbf{(1.5ii)}$$

These rules allow equations to be simplified, and therefore solved easily. The rules illustrate the fact that

If we do something to one side of an equation, we
must do the same thing to the other side of the equation

It is important to realize that although $a = b$ implies $ac = bc$ for any real c, the converse is only true for $c \neq 0$. However, for any c, we have $a = b$ if and only if $a + c = b + c$.

NOTE   If $k \neq 0$, dividing by k is the same as multiplying by $1/k$. And subtracting r is the same as adding $-r$. Thus Eqs. (1.5i) and (1.5ii), allow us to use all four fundamental operations when working with equations.

◤ EXAMPLE 7   Solve $2x + 5 = 19$.

Solution

$$2x + 5 = 19 \qquad\qquad \text{given}$$

$$2x = 19 - 5 = 14 \qquad\qquad \text{adding } -5 \text{ to each side}$$

$$x = 14(\tfrac{1}{2}) = 7 \qquad\qquad \text{multiplying each side by } \tfrac{1}{2} \qquad\qquad ◢$$

The real numbers can be identified with points on a line, called the **number line,** or real line, or coordinate line. One way to do this is to draw a line and choose any point on it to represent 0. Choose another point to the right which represents 1. The distance from 0 to 1 sets up a unit of length which can be used to locate other points. Positive numbers correspond to points to the right of 0, negative ones to the left. See Fig. 1.2.

If a and b are real numbers and $a - b$ is positive, then a is said to be **greater** than b, and we write $a > b$. We could just as well say that b is **less** than a and write $b < a$. This can also be thought of geometrically (see Fig. 1.2):

$a > b$ *means that a is to the right of b on the number line.*

All of the following notations mean the same thing:

$$
\begin{array}{lll}
a - b \text{ is positive} & a > b & a - b > 0 \\
b - a \text{ is negative} & b < a & b - a < 0
\end{array}
$$

◤ EXAMPLE 8

$$
\begin{array}{lll}
7 < 22 & -7 < 43 & -80 < -53 \\
181 > 143 & 0 > -5 & -31 > -67
\end{array}
$$
◢

FIGURE 1.2

We write $a \leq b$ to indicate that a is **less than** or **equal to** b. For example,

$$5 \leq 5 \qquad 13 \leq 285 \qquad -17 \leq 8 \qquad -6 \leq -4$$

The distance on the number line from the point for 0 to the point for a is called the **absolute value** of a and is written as $|a|$. We have the following definition:

Absolute value

$$|a| = \begin{cases} a & \text{if } a \geq 0 \\ -a & \text{if } a < 0 \end{cases} \tag{1.6}$$

NOTE

By definition, the absolute value of every real number is either **positive** or **zero.**

◢ EXAMPLE 9

$$|3| = 3 \qquad |-21.6| = 21.6 \qquad |0| = 0$$

$$|5 - 12| = |-7| = 7 \qquad |\pi - 3| = \pi - 3 \approx 0.14$$ ◢

Either the algebraic or geometric definition of absolute value can be used to show the seven properties listed below.

Properties of absolute value

$$|-a| = |a| \tag{1.7}$$

$$|a - b| = |b - a| = \text{distance between } a \text{ and } b \tag{1.8}$$

$$|ab| = |a| \cdot |b| \tag{1.9}$$

$$\left| \frac{a}{b} \right| = \frac{|a|}{|b|} \qquad b \neq 0 \tag{1.10}$$

$$-|a| \leq a \leq |a| \tag{1.11}$$

$$|a - b| \geq \big||a| - |b|\big| \tag{1.12}$$

$$|a + b| \leq |a| + |b| \qquad \text{triangle inequality} \tag{1.13}$$

◢ EXAMPLE 10

$$|-267| = |267| = 267 \qquad \text{by (1.7)}$$

$$|4(-3)| = |-12| = 12 \qquad \text{and} \qquad |4| \cdot |-3| = 4 \cdot 3 = 12 \qquad \text{by (1.9)}$$

$$-|-32| \leq -32 \leq |-32| \qquad \text{with } a = -32 \text{ in (1.11)}$$

$$|-10 + 6| = |-4| = 4 \qquad \text{but} \qquad |-10| + |6| = 10 + 6 = 16 \qquad \text{by (1.13)}$$ ◢

The distance between two points on a number line can be expressed in terms of absolute value. For example, 6 is 4 units to the right of 2, and the distance between them is

$$4 = |6 - 2| = |2 - 6|$$

$A \longleftarrow d(A, B) = |a - b| \longrightarrow B$

$a \qquad\qquad\qquad b$

Let a and b be the coordinates of points A and B. Then the distance between A and B is $d(A, B) = |a - b|$.

It is always true that $|a - b| = |b - a|$.

Sets

When describing certain real numbers, or writing the solutions of equations or inequalities, it is sometimes helpful to use sets. A **set** is a collection of *elements*. We write $x \in A$ if x is a member, or element, of the set A. The set may be described either by **listing** or with **set-builder notation.**

EXAMPLE 11 Write the set of integers from 1 to 22 which are divisible by either 3 or 5.

Solution The set may be written using listing as

$$\{3, 5, 6, 9, 10, 12, 15, 18, 20, 21\}$$

and it may be written using set-builder notation as

$$\{x | x \text{ is an integer, } 1 \leq x \leq 22, x \text{ divisible by 3 or 5}\}$$

which is read ''the set of all x such that x is . . . or 5.''

Two sets are equal if every element of each set is an element of the other set. The **union** of the sets A and B is written $A \cup B$, and it is

$$A \cup B = \{x | x \in A \text{ or } x \in B \text{ or both}\}$$

The **intersection** of A and B is

$$A \cap B = \{x | x \in A \text{ and } x \in B\}$$

EXAMPLE 12 Find $A \cup B$ and $A \cap B$ if

$$A = \{1, 2, 3, 5, 8, 13\} \quad \text{and} \quad B = \{2, 3, 5, 7, 11, 13\}$$

Solution The union and intersection are

$$A \cup B = \{1, 2, 3, 5, 7, 8, 11, 13\}$$

and
$$A \cap B = \{2, 3, 5, 13\}$$

Intervals are subsets of the real number line which are used so frequently that they have a special notation. Using R for the set of real numbers, we write

$$(a, b) = \{x \in R | a < x < b\} \quad \text{open interval}$$

$$[a, b] = \{x \in R | a \leq x \leq b\} \quad \text{closed interval}$$

$$(a, b] = \{x \in R | a < x \leq b\} \quad \text{half-open interval}$$

$$[a, b) = \{x \in R | a \leq x < b\} \quad \text{half-open interval}$$

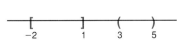

We may show the *open interval* (3, 5) and the *closed interval* [−2, 1] on the number line. This is done in the figure at the left. Similar notation is used for infinite intervals. For instance

$$(a, \infty) = \{x \in R | a < x\} = \{x | x > a\} \quad \text{open infinite interval}$$

$$[a, \infty) = \{x \in R | a \leq x\} = \{x | x \geq a\} \quad \text{closed infinite interval}$$

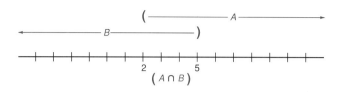

FIGURE 1.3

$$(-\infty, a) = \{x \in R | a > x\} = \{x | x < a\} \qquad \text{open infinite interval}$$

$$(-\infty, a] = \{x \in R | a \geq x\} = \{x | x \leq a\} \qquad \text{closed infinite interval}$$

Thus if $A = (2, \infty)$ and $B = (-\infty, 5)$, then $A \cap B = (2, 5)$. See Fig. 1.3.

Two especially important sets we have discussed earlier are given below in set notation:

Integers $\{\ldots, -3, -2, -1, 0, 1, 2, 3, \ldots\}$

Positive real numbers $\{x \in R | x > 0\} = (0, \infty)$

EXERCISE 1.1

Verify the calculations in Probs. 1 to 8. Notice the digit patterns.

1. $8(473) = 3784$
2. $15(93) = 1395$
3. $12 = 5796/483$
4. $12{,}345{,}679 = 98{,}765{,}432/8$
5. A positive integer is divisible by 4 if and only if its last two digits form a number divisible by 4. Use this test to check (a) 699,722,392 and (b) 886,775,442 for divisibility by 4.
6. A positive integer is divisible by 3 if and only if the sum of its digits is divisible by 3. Use this test to check (a) 667,135,297 and (b) 414,285,732 for divisibility by 3.
7. A positive integer is divisible by 11 if $x - y$ is divisible by 11, where x is the sum of the first, third, fifth, etc., digits, and y is the sum of the second, fourth, etc., digits. Use this test to check (a) 608,353,449 and (b) 597,595,581 for divisibility by 11.
8. A positive integer is divisible by 6 if and only if it is divisible by 2 and by 3. Use this test to check (a) 293,625,072 and (b) 596,007,402 for divisibility by 6.
9. Find $(67.2)(43.7) + 594.34$.
10. Find $(16.4 + 27.9)(50.4)$.
11. Find $(3036.54/45.8) - 21.5$.
12. Find $(935.48 - 33.22)/19.7$.
13. Show that subtraction is not commutative by showing that
$$6 - 9 \neq 9 - 6$$

14. Show that division is not commutative by showing that
$$8 \div 4 \neq 4 \div 8$$

15. Show that division is not associative by showing that
$$24 \div (6 \div 3) \neq (24 \div 6) \div 3$$

16. Show that subtraction is not associative by showing that
$$4 - (11 - 5) \neq (4 - 11) - 5$$

Perform the calculations in Probs. 17 to 36.

17. $(6)(-3)(2)$
18. $(-8)(-4)(3)$
19. $4(-3)/(-2)$
20. $(-5)(-6)/(-10)$
21. $(6) - (-4) + (-2)$
22. $(-7) + (-5) - (3)$
23. $(-11) - (8) - (-5)$
24. $(14) - (-3) + (6)$
25. $6 - 4 - (3 - 8)$
26. $5 - (-3 + 10) + 2$
27. $-3 + (-7 + 2) - 1$
28. $-7 - 4 - (-2 - 8)$
29. $|5| + |-3|$
30. $|-8| - |4|$
31. $-|-4| - |3|$
32. $-|7| + |5|$
33. $\dfrac{|3 - 7|}{|3| - 7}$
34. $\dfrac{-|-5|}{-|5|}$
35. $\dfrac{|-6| + |8|}{|-6 + 8|}$
36. $\dfrac{|10| - |-6|}{-10 - |-6|}$

Problems 37 to 40 are true–false.

37. The integers are closed under addition and multiplication.
38. The sum of two negative numbers is negative.
39. The set $\{0, 1\}$ is closed under multiplication.
40. The set $\{x | 0 \leq x \leq 1\}$ is closed under multiplication.

41. Is $4.123\overline{23}$ rational?

42. Is $2.3\overline{3} + 6.8$ rational?

43. Is $7.4 + (3/11)$ rational?

44. Is $0.010010001 + \cdots + 0.101101110 \cdots$ rational?

Write the exact value of each number in Probs. 45 to 48 without using absolute value signs.

45. $|4 - \pi|$ **46.** $|3 - \pi|$

47. $|x - 10|$ if $x < 6$ **48.** $|x^2 + 5|$

Solve the equations in Probs. 49 to 52.

49. $(x - 5)(x + 6) = 0$

50. $(x + 3)(x - 18) = 0$

51. $(x - 1)(x - 2)(x - 13) = 0$

52. $(x + 5)(x - 5)(x - 10) = 0$

In Probs. 53 to 56, arrange the numbers from smallest to largest.

53. $-5.3, -5.33, -5 + 0.33$

54. $-|6 + 2|, -|4| - |3|, -|-3| + 10$

55. $-(5 + 3), -5 + 3, 5 - 3$

56. $-(-6), -6.1, |-6.2|$

For all positive numbers x, y, and z we have

$$(x + y)(y + z)(z + x) \geq 8xyz$$

Verify this for the following values of x, y, and z.

57. $x = 2, y = 5, z = 6$ **58.** $x = 4, y = 2, z = 7$

Verify the inequality

$$(ab + cd)^2 \leq (a^2 + c^2)(b^2 + d^2)$$

in the following cases:

59. $a = 2, b = 4, c = 1, d = 5$

60. $a = 6, b = 3, c = 2, d = 4$

Verify the steps in each of the following proofs:

61. Show $a(0) = 0$ for every real number a:

$$a(0) = a(0 + 0) = a(0) + a(0)$$

Thus $0 = a(0)$.

62. Show that $-(a + b) = -a - b$:

$$(a + b) + [-(a + b)] = 0$$

and $(a + b) + (-a - b) = (a + b - a) - b$
$$= b - b = 0$$

63. Show that $a(-b) = -(ab)$:

$$(ab) + [-(ab)] = 0$$
$$(ab) + a(-b) = a(b - b) = a(0) = 0$$

64. Show that $|-a| = |a|$:

if $a \geq 0$, then $|-a| = -(-a) = a$ and $|a| = a$

if $a < 0$, then $|-a| = -a$ and $|a| = -a$

65. A rational number m/n, in lowest terms, has a terminating decimal expansion if and only if the integer n has no prime factors except 2 and 5. Verify this for 13/20 and 13/15.

66. Let P be the number of primes less than n. Show that P divides n for $n = 8$, $n = 30$, and $n = 33$.

67. If x and y are positive, then $(x + y)(xy + 1) \geq 4xy$. Verify this for $x = 1.8$, $y = 1.9$.

68. If a, b, c, and d are positive, then

$$(a + b)(b + c)(c + d)(d + a) \geq 16abcd$$

Verify this for $a = 3$, $b = 4$, $c = 5$, $d = 6$.

69. Show that $|x - a| < \delta$ if and only if $a - \delta < x < a + \delta$.

70. Write $5 < x < 11$ in the form $|x - a| < b$. *Hint:* Try

$$a = \frac{11 + 5}{2} \quad \text{and} \quad b = \frac{11 - 5}{2}$$

71. For any integer n, we have $n^3 - n$ always divisible by 6. Verify this for n equal to 7, 8, and 9.

72. Given a positive integer n, we will determine another one by using the following rule: If n is odd, we compute $3n + 1$, whereas if n is even, we compute $n/2$. Starting arbitrarily with $n = 6$ and using the rule successively gives the numbers 6, 3, 10, 5, 16, 8, 4, 2, 1, 4, 2, 1 and the pattern 4, 2, 1 will keep on occurring. It is a long-standing conjecture that no matter which positive integer n we begin with, the pattern 4, 2, 1 will occur (and keep on occurring repeatedly). Try it yourself beginning with your favorite positive integer n.

73. Show that if $a > b > 0$ and $c > d > 0$, then $ac > bd$.

74. Show that if $a > b > 0$, then $a \cdot a > b \cdot b$.

75. Show that if $0 < a < 1$, then $a \cdot a < a$.

76. Show that if $a < b$ and $c > 0$, then $ac < bc$.

In Probs. 77 to 80, suppose that $x > 0, y < 0$, and $z < 0$. What is the sign of these numbers?

77. $x - y$ and xz **78.** z/y and $y + z$

79. $xy + z$ and yz/x **80.** $(z - x)/y$ and $x(y + z)$

In Probs. 81 to 84, suppose that a, b, c, and d are real numbers with b and d nonzero. Answer these true-false questions:

81. $a(c + d) = ac + d$

82. $a - (b - c) = (a - b) - c$

83. $(d + b)^{-1} = d^{-1} + b^{-1}$

84. $(bd)^{-1} = b^{-1}d^{-1}$

85. Show that the sum of two rational numbers is rational.

86. Show that the sum of a rational number and an irrational number is irrational. *Hint:* Let b be rational and c be irrational, and suppose that $b + c$ is rational; show that this contradicts Prob. 85 by considering $b + (-b - c)$.

87. (a) Show that the sum of two irrationals can be irrational by using $5 + \sqrt{2}$ and $-5 + \sqrt{2}$.
(b) Show that the sum of two irrationals can be rational by using $7 - \sqrt{3}$ and $7 + \sqrt{3}$.

88. Show that

$$\tfrac{1}{2}(a + b + |a - b|)$$

is the larger of the two numbers a and b, and also that

$$\tfrac{1}{2}(a + b - |a - b|)$$

is the smaller of the two numbers a and b. Verify each statement above for $a = 68$ and $b = 73$.

In Probs. 89 and 90, find $A \cup B$ and $A \cap B$.

89. $A = \{12, 13, 15, 18, 22\}$ and $B = \{12, 14, 16, 18, 20\}$

90. $A = \{3, 7, 11, 15, 19, 23\}$ and $B = \{5, 8, 11, 14, 17, 20, 23\}$

91. List the elements in the set $\{x \mid 1 \leq x \leq 33$, and $x + 1$ has a remainder of 2 when divided by 4$\}$.

92. List the elements in the set $\{x \mid 12 \leq x \leq 43$, and $x + 2$ has a remainder of 2 when divided by 5$\}$.

In the next four problems, write the set in interval notation.

93. $\{x \mid 2 \leq x \leq 9\} \cap \{x \mid 5 < x \leq 13\}$

94. $\{x \mid 4 \leq x \leq 11\} \cup \{x \mid 10 \leq x < 12\}$

95. $\{x \mid 2 < x < \infty\} \cap \{x \mid -\infty < x \leq 8\}$

96. $\{x \mid 33 \leq x < \infty\} \cup \{x \mid 25 < x < \infty\}$

1.2 Integer Exponents

Exponents are used in a wide variety of applications of algebra to simplify and shorten the notation. Positive integer exponents are used to indicate products of repeated values. For example:

$$a^2 = a \cdot a \qquad a^3 = a \cdot a \cdot a \qquad a^4 = a \cdot a \cdot a \cdot a$$
$$7^2 = 49 \qquad 5^3 = 5 \cdot 5 \cdot 5 = 125 \qquad 3^4 = 3 \cdot 3 \cdot 3 \cdot 3 = 81$$

> If n is a positive integer and a is a real number, then
>
> $$a^n = a \cdot a : a \cdot a \cdots a \qquad\qquad (1.14)$$
>
> where there are n factors of a.

Base

The number a is called the **base,** and the positive integer n is called the **exponent.** We read a^n as "a to the n" or as "a to the nth power."

▶ **EXAMPLE 1** Find the value of these exponential expressions.

Solution

$$4^3 = 4 \cdot 4 \cdot 4 = 64$$
$$3^5 = 3 \cdot 3 \cdot 3 \cdot 3 \cdot 3 = 243$$
$$(-2)^4 = (-2)(-2)(-2)(-2) = 16$$
$$(-7)^3 = (-7)(-7)(-7) = -343$$
$$(2a)^3 = (2a)(2a)(2a) = 8 \cdot a^3 = 8(a^3) = 8a^3$$

◀

Be careful

Notice the difference between $(2a)^3$ and $2a^3$. As in Example 1

$$(2a)^3 = 8 \cdot a^3 = 8(a^3), \text{ whereas } 2a^3 = 2 \cdot a^3 = 2(a^3).$$

Similarly there is a difference between

$$-5^4 = -(5^4) = -625$$

and

$$(-5)^4 = (-5)(-5)(-5)(-5) = +625$$

Furthermore, $(3 + 4)^2 = 7^2 = 49$, but $3^2 + 4^2 = 9 + 16 = 25$.

The next example is not only an illustration of property (1.17) below, but it also gives an indication as to why (1.17) is true. A proof of (1.17) will be given after the laws of exponents are stated.

EXAMPLE 2 Write $a^3 \cdot a^5$ as a power of a.

Solution

$$a^3 \cdot a^5 = (a \cdot a \cdot a)(a \cdot a \cdot a \cdot a \cdot a)$$
$$= a \cdot a \cdot a \cdot a \cdot a \cdot a \cdot a \cdot a = a^8$$

We shall now state the definitions of a^n for the cases when n is a positive integer, when $n = 0$, and when n is a negative integer, and then follow that with the laws of exponents. These laws are

true for all integers m and n

whether the integers are positive, negative, or zero. They are in fact true when m and n are any real numbers, as we shall see in Chap. 5 on exponents and logarithms.

Definitions

$a^n = a \cdot a \cdots a$	with n factors, where n is any positive integer	**(1.14)**
$a^0 = 1$	if $a \neq 0$	**(1.15)**
$a^{-n} = \dfrac{1}{a^n}$	if n is any positive integer and $a \neq 0$	**(1.16)**

EXAMPLE 3 $5^0 = 1$ and $(-3)^0 = 1$, but 0^0 is not defined.

EXAMPLE 4 $\qquad 3^{-2} = \dfrac{1}{3^2} = \dfrac{1}{9} \quad$ and $\quad 5^{-3} = \dfrac{1}{5^3} = \dfrac{1}{125}$

Laws of exponents

Suppose that m and n are any integers. Then

$a^m a^n = a^{m+n}$	add exponents	**(1.17)**
$\dfrac{a^m}{a^n} = a^{m-n}$	if $a \neq 0$; subtract exponents: numerator minus denominator	**(1.18)**
$(a^m)^n = a^{mn}$	multiply exponents	**(1.19)**
$a^n b^n = (ab)^n$	multiply bases	**(1.20)**
$\dfrac{a^n}{b^n} = \left(\dfrac{a}{b}\right)^n$	if $b \neq 0$; divide bases	**(1.21)**

Notice that in the first three laws above, each side uses the **same base.** It is only then that we add, subtract, or multiply exponents, as stated after each law. Similarly, in the last two laws, each side used the **same exponent,** and it is only then that we multiply or divide bases.

▶ **EXAMPLE 5**

$$2^3 \cdot 2^4 = 2^7 = 128 \qquad \text{and} \qquad (2^3)(5^3) = 10^3 = 1000$$

but

$$(2^3)(5^4) \neq 10^7$$ ◢

In order to prove (1.17), we will first consider the product $a^m a^n$, where m and n are positive integers. Later in the section, we will carry out the proof when m and n are negative. Since a^m is the product of m a's and a^n is the product of n a's, it follows that

$$\begin{array}{c} \overset{m \text{ factors}}{} \qquad \overset{n \text{ factors}}{} \\ a^m \cdot a^n = [(a)(a)(a) \cdots (a)][(a)(a) \cdots (a)(a)] \\ = (a)(a)(a) \cdots (a)(a) \qquad m+n \text{ factors of } a \\ = a^{m+n} \end{array}$$

since a^{m+n} is the product of $(m + n)$ a's. Hence we have

$$a^m a^n = a^{m+n} \tag{1.17}$$

for m and n positive integers. Thus, in multiplication, we *add exponents if the bases are the same.* For instance

$$a^3 \cdot a^8 = a^{11} \qquad \text{and} \qquad 2^6 \cdot 2^4 = 2^{10} = 1024$$

Why is a^0 defined to be 1?

Property (1.17) was stated and proved for positive integers m and n. We want it to be true for all integers, both negative and zero as well as positive. For instance if we take $n = 0$ in (1.17), then we have

$$a^m \cdot a^0 = a^{m+0}, \text{ which means that } a^m \cdot a^0 = a^m.$$

Now if $a \neq 0$, we may divide the last equation by a^m, giving $a^0 = 1$. Therefore for consistency we define

Zero as an exponent

$$a^0 = 1 \qquad \text{for } a \neq 0 \tag{1.15}$$

Thus $9^0 = 1$, $(3x)^0 = 1$, and $(x + y)^0 = 1$, but

remember that 0^0 is not defined.

Notice that we *defined* $a^0 = 1$, if $a \neq 0$, and we did so in order that the laws of exponents would remain valid when zero is an exponent.

Definition of a^{-n}

If n is a positive integer, then $-n$ is negative, and if we use $m = -n$ in (1.17), we have

$$a^{-n} \cdot a^n = a^{-n+n} = a^0 = 1$$

If $a \neq 0$, we may divide by a^n, giving $a^{-n} = 1/a^n$. So again for consistency, we *define*

Negative exponents

$$a^{-n} = \frac{1}{a^n} \qquad \text{for } a \neq 0 \tag{1.16}$$

Notice that

$$a^{-1} = \frac{1}{a} \qquad \text{and} \qquad a^{-n} = (a^{-1})^n = \frac{1}{a^n}$$

We shall now further illustrate the laws of exponents.

► **EXAMPLE 6** Simplify the following expressions.

Solution

$$3^2 3^3 = 3^5 = 243 \qquad \text{adding exponents}$$

$$7^5/7^3 = 7^2 = 49 \qquad \text{subtracting exponents}$$

$$(2^3)^2 = 2^6 = 64 \qquad \text{multiplying exponents}$$ ◄

► **EXAMPLE 7** Simplify the following expressions.

Solution

$$\left(\frac{2}{3}\right)^4 = \frac{2^4}{3^4} = \frac{16}{81} \qquad\qquad \left(\frac{a}{b}\right)^n = \frac{a^n}{b^n}$$

$$(2^3 \cdot 3^2)^2 = 2^6 \cdot 3^4 = (64)(81) = 5184$$

$$(3x^2y^3)(4xy^5) = 3 \cdot 4x^2xy^3y^5$$

$$= 12x^3y^8 \qquad \text{by the commutative law}$$ ◄

Once again, the laws of exponents hold for all real numbers as long as everything is defined. We shall now prove that $(a^m)^n = a^{mn}$ if m and n are positive integers:

$$(a^m)^n = a^m \cdot a^m \cdot a^m \cdots a^m \qquad \text{with } n \text{ factors of } a^m$$

$$= a^{m+m+\cdots+m} \qquad \text{adding exponents}$$

$$= a^{mn} \qquad \text{definition of the product } mn$$

This formula should be remembered in words also:

To raise a power to another power, multiply exponents **(1.19)**

The expressions $(a^m)^n$ and $a^{(m^n)}$ are different. For instance

$$(2^3)^2 = 8^2 = 64 \qquad \text{but} \qquad 2^{(3^2)} = 2^9 = 512$$

A complete proof of each of the theorems for integer exponents can be done using mathematical induction (Chap. 12). Here, however, we shall give an argument for (1.17) only in the case where m and n are negative integers. In that case $-m$ and $-n$ are *positive integers*, and so by definition of negative exponents

$$a^m \cdot a^n \qquad m \text{ and } n \text{ are negative}$$

$$= \frac{1}{a^{-m}} \cdot \frac{1}{a^{-n}} \qquad -m \text{ and } -n \text{ are positive}$$

$$= \frac{1}{a^{-m-n}} \qquad \text{adding the exponents } -m \text{ and } -n$$

$$a^m \cdot a^n = \frac{1}{a^{-(m+n)}} \qquad \text{properties of negatives}$$

$$= a^{m+n} \qquad \text{definition of negative exponent}$$

The laws of exponents treat the product $a^m b^n$, and the quotient a^m/b^n, in the cases where the exponents are the same, and also where the bases are equal. Do not confuse the two.

EXAMPLE 8   Use the laws of exponents to simplify the following expression.

Solution

$$\left\{ \frac{4a^3b^4}{3c^2d^3} \right\}^4 \cdot \left\{ \frac{9c^5d}{2a^2b^5} \right\}^2$$

$$= \frac{4^4(a^3)^4(b^4)^4}{3^4(c^2)^4(d^3)^4} \cdot \frac{9^2(c^5)^2d^2}{2^2(a^2)^2(b^5)^2} \qquad \text{by (1.20) and (1.21)}$$

$$= \frac{256a^{12}b^{16}}{81c^8d^{12}} \cdot \frac{81c^{10}d^2}{4a^4b^{10}} \qquad \text{multiplying exponents}$$

$$= \frac{64a^8b^6c^2}{d^{10}} \qquad \text{subtracting exponents}$$

The rules below are direct consequences of the laws of exponents, and they are very helpful when actually working with positive and negative exponents:

$$\frac{a^m}{a^n} = a^{m-n} = \frac{1}{a^{n-m}} \qquad (abc)^n = a^n b^n c^n$$

$$\frac{a^{-n}}{b^{-n}} = \frac{b^n}{a^n} \qquad \text{or equivalently} \qquad \left(\frac{a}{b}\right)^{-n} = \left(\frac{b}{a}\right)^n$$

EXAMPLE 9   Use the laws of exponents to evaluate the expressions below.

Solution   (a)

$$3^{-9}3^43^2 = 3^{-9+4+2} = 3^{-3} = (\tfrac{1}{3})^3 = \tfrac{1}{27}$$

(b)

$$\frac{5^3 \cdot 5^{-7}}{5^{-4} \cdot 5^{11} \cdot 5^{-2}} = \frac{5^{3-7}}{5^{-4+11-2}} = \frac{5^{-4}}{5^5} = \frac{1}{5^5 \cdot 5^4} = \frac{1}{5^9}$$

(c)

$$\frac{2^3 \cdot 4^{-2}}{4^5 \cdot 8^{-2}} = \frac{2^3(2^2)^{-2}}{(2^2)^5 \cdot (2^3)^{-2}} = \frac{2^3 \cdot 2^{-4}}{2^{10} \cdot 2^{-6}}$$

$$= 2^{3-4-10+6} = 2^{-5} = \frac{1}{32}$$

The examples above illustrate the following fact which helps to simplify expressions with exponents:

> Any *factor* in the numerator (denominator) of a fraction may be moved to the denominator (numerator) of the fraction provided that the sign of the exponent is changed.

▶ **EXAMPLE 10**   Write $2c^{-1}d^{-4}e^2/3c^{-3}d^2e^{-1}$ with only positive exponents.

Solution 1   Moving factors with negative exponents from the numerator, or the denominator, to the other, as in the comment after Example 9:

$$\frac{2c^{-1}d^{-4}e^2}{3c^{-3}d^2e^{-1}} = \frac{2c^3e^2e^1}{3c^1d^4d^2}$$

$$= \frac{2c^{3-1}e^{2+1}}{3d^{4+2}} = \frac{2c^2e^3}{3d^6}$$

Solution 2   Subtracting exponents first, by (1.18), gives

$$\frac{2c^{-1}d^{-4}e^2}{3c^{-3}d^2e^{-1}} = \tfrac{2}{3} \cdot c^{-1-(-3)}d^{-4-2}e^{2-(-1)}$$

$$= \tfrac{2}{3} \cdot c^2d^{-6}e^3 \qquad \text{arithmetic}$$

$$= \frac{2c^2e^3}{3d^6} \qquad \text{definition of negative exponent} \qquad ◀$$

Order of operations
    In Sec. 1.1, we saw that multiplications and divisions should be done before any additions and subtractions. When exponents are involved, the exponents should be applied first of all. For instance, when $x = 2$, the expression $7x^3$ is evaluated like this:

$$7x^3 = 7(x^3) = 7(2^3) = 7(8) = 56$$

Scientific Notation

Scientific work often involves very large or very small numbers. The speed of light is

$$186{,}000 \text{ mi/s} = 1.86(10^5) \text{ mi/s}$$

The mass of a hydrogen atom is (23 zeros)

$$0.00000000000000000000001673 \text{ g} = 1.673(10^{-24}) \text{ g}$$

And a nonscientific example is the national debt, which is currently over $\$2{,}000{,}000{,}000{,}000 = 2(10^{12})$ dollars. Scientific notation is a convenient way to write numbers and compare their magnitudes.

> The positive number N is in scientific notation if N is written $m(10^c)$ where $1 \le m < 10$, and c is an integer (positive, negative, or zero).

EXAMPLE 11

N	m	Scientific notation
647.22	6.4722	$6.4722(10^2)$
0.008189	8.189	$8.189(10^{-3})$
5,000,000,000	5	$5(10^9)$
0.00000003303	3.303	$3.303(10^{-8})$

Calculators

Many calculators use scientific notation in the form ''2.81643 17'' or ''2.81643E17,'' for instance, and either one means $2.81643(10^{17})$. Thus the product (7.42 8)(4.06 11) may be displayed as ''3.01252 20,'' meaning $3.01252(10^{20})$.

If a number represents an approximation, it should not be treated as an exact value. The digits which are known to be correct are called **significant digits.**

The digits 1, 2, 3, 4, 5, 6, 7, 8, and 9 are always significant if used in connection with a measurement, as are any zeros between any two of these digits. Zeros on the right of the last nonzero digit may or may not be significant. Zeros on the left of the first nonzero digit are an aid in placing the decimal point and are never significant. Such zeros occur between the decimal and the first nonzero digit in positive numbers less than $\frac{1}{10}$.

EXAMPLE 12   Write the significant digits in the numbers 238.71, 2.051, 0.038, and 4960.

Solution

N	Significant digits in N
238.71	2, 3, 8, 7, 1
2.051	2, 0, 5, 1
0.038	3, 8
4960	4, 9, 6 (and maybe the zero)

In the form 4960, we must be told if the last zero in 4960 is significant. The scientific notation is $4.960(10^3)$ if the last zero is significant, and $4.96(10^3)$ otherwise.

Do not confuse *significant digits* with *decimal place accuracy,* i.e., the number of digits to the right of the decimal point. The number 84.35 has four significant digits, but only two decimal places of accuracy. Also, the number 0.00251 has three significant digits but five decimal places of accuracy.

Approximate numbers occur all the time in measurements such as the weight of a compound, the height of a mountain, the time of the winner in a race, or an earnings estimate for the next quarter. If a digit is doubtful, we round off to eliminate it. When we round off 4.3269 to three significant digits, we are trying to find the number with three significant digits which is closest to 4.3269. It is either 4.32 or 4.33, and since

$$|4.3269 - 4.32| = 0.69 \qquad \text{and} \qquad |4.3269 - 4.33| = 0.31$$

then 4.3269 rounded to three significant digits is 4.33. We simply discarded the 6 and 9 in 4.3269, and increased the 2 to a 3 since 6 is at least 5, as explained next.

Rounding off

> Suppose that a number has more than *n* significant digits, and we want to round it off to *n* significant digits. We first discard all digits beyond the *n*th one.
> (a) If the first digit discarded is 5, 6, 7, 8, or 9, increase the last digit kept by 1 (above we increased 2 to 3).
> (b) If the first digit discarded is 0, 1, 2, 3, or 4, do not change the last digit kept.

For instance,

$$51.3624 \ rounded \ to \ 4 \ digits \ is \ 51.36$$
$$7.8163 \ rounded \ to \ 3 \ digits \ is \ 7.82$$
$$6358 \ rounded \ to \ 2 \ digits \ is \ 6400, \ or \ 6.4(10^3)$$

In the number 6400, we had to insert two zeros on the right, which are not significant digits, in order to make the number be the correct size.

Rounding off should *not* be done digit by digit. For instance, suppose that 6.1247 is to be rounded to three significant digits. Doing it correctly, we discard 47 and have 6.12. Doing it digit by digit gives first 6.125, and then 6.13. However 6.1247 is closer to 6.12 than it is to 6.13.

Rules for calculation

Suppose, for instance, that a rectangle has length *a* and width *b*. Now

$$If \ a \ is \ rounded \ to \ 2.16, \ then \ 2.155 \leq a < 2.165$$

and

$$If \ b \ is \ rounded \ to \ 7.32, \ then \ 7.315 \leq b < 7.325$$

and thus

$$(2.155)(7.315) \leq ab < (2.165)(7.325)$$
$$15.763825 \leq ab < 15.858625$$

All we can conclude is that the area *ab* is about 15.8. For this reason, the rules below are commonly used for calculating with rounded numbers.

Calculating with rounded numbers

> When multiplying or dividing rounded numbers, round the answer to the least number of **significant digits** in any of the given data.
>
> When adding or subtracting rounded numbers, round the answer to the same number of **decimal places** as there are in the least accurate of the given numbers.

▶ **EXAMPLE 13** (a) $(48.2) \cdot (61.37) = 2958.034$, which should be rounded off to three significant digits, namely, 2960 or $2.96(10^3)$.
(b) For $m = 1.81(10^{14})$, $M = 6.93(10^{15})$, $d = 2.98(10^9)$, we have

$$\frac{mM}{d^2} = \frac{(1.81)(6.93)10^{14+15}}{(2.98)^2(10^9)^2} \approx 1.41247(10^{11})$$

which should be rounded off to three significant digits, namely $1.41(10^{11})$.
(c) $1.2345 + 2.345 + 6.8 = 10.3795$, which should be rounded off to 10.4 since 6.8

has only one decimal place of accuracy.

(d) $180.373 - 145.22 + 166.9225 = 202.0755$, which should be rounded off to 202.08 since 145.22 has only two decimal places of accuracy. ◀

EXERCISE 1.2

Simplify the following expressions using the laws of exponents.

1. $2^3 2^4$ 2. $5^5/5^3$ 3. $(2^3)^2$ 4. $(5/2)^3$
5. $(3x^2y)(2xy^3)$ 6. $(-7x^2y^3)(2x^3y^4)$
7. $(2x^4y^2)(-3x^3y^5)$ 8. $(-2x^2y^5)(-3x^3y^0)$
9. $\dfrac{12x^5y^4}{3x^2y^3}$ 10. $\dfrac{27x^6y^7}{3x^3y^4}$ 11. $\dfrac{18x^4y^3}{3x^3y^2}$
12. $\dfrac{24x^5y^6}{6x^3y^4}$ 13. $(2a^2bc^3)^3$ 14. $(3a^3b^2c^4)^2$
15. $(5ab^2c^4)^4$ 16. $(7a^3b^2c^4)^3$ 17. $\left(\dfrac{a^3b^2}{2c^3d^4}\right)^2$
18. $\left(\dfrac{a^4b^3c}{2d^2}\right)^3$ 19. $\left(\dfrac{2x^4y^3}{3w^2z}\right)^2$ 20. $\left(\dfrac{3x^3y^5}{2p^2q^3}\right)^4$
21. $(2a^2b^3)^2(3ab^0)^4$ 22. $(3a^3b)^3(2a^2b^3)^2$
23. $(5cd^2)^2(2c^2d^3)^3$ 24. $(3x^2y^3)^3(5x^2y)^4$
25. $\dfrac{2u^2v^3}{3w^4} \cdot \dfrac{6w^2u}{8u^2v^2}$ 26. $\dfrac{15b^2c^5}{16d^3} \cdot \dfrac{4b^4d^3}{5c^6}$
27. $\dfrac{3x^2y^3}{7x^4z^2} \cdot \dfrac{28y^3}{33x^4z^3}$ 28. $\dfrac{7b^4c^3}{8d^2} \cdot \dfrac{16b^3d^3}{21c^4d^5}$
29. $\left(\dfrac{c^4d^3}{a^4}\right)^2\left(\dfrac{a^3}{c^2d}\right)^3$ 30. $\left(\dfrac{3a^2}{b^3c^0}\right)^4\left(\dfrac{bc^2}{9a^4}\right)^2$
31. $\left(\dfrac{4a^2b^5}{c^3}\right)^2\left(\dfrac{c^5}{12a^3b}\right)^3$ 32. $\left(\dfrac{6a^4}{b^2c^5}\right)^3\left(\dfrac{bc^2}{2a^3}\right)^4$

In Probs. 33 to 56, simplify and express the results without zero or negative exponents.

33. 3^{-3} 34. $5^{-3}5^2$ 35. $3^{-3}3^{-1}$
36. $(2^{-3})^{-2}$ 37. $\dfrac{3p^{-3}q^{-4}}{6^{-1}p^2q^{-2}}$ 38. $\dfrac{9^{-2}p^{-4}q^0}{3^{-3}p^{-3}q^{-2}}$
39. $\dfrac{2a^{-2}b^{-1}}{3^{-1}a^3b^{-4}}$ 40. $\dfrac{3^{-2}a^{-2}b^{-3}}{6^{-1}a^{-4}b^{-2}}$ 41. $(a^{-2}/b^{-3})^2$
42. $(a^{-4}/b)^{-3}$ 43. $(a^3/b^{-1})^{-2}$ 44. $(a^3/b^2)^{-4}$
45. $(a^{-1}b^{-2})^2$ 46. $(a^{-2}b)^{-2}$ 47. $(a^3b^{-1})^{-3}$
48. $(a^{-4}b^3)^3$ 49. $\left(\dfrac{a^2n^0t^{-2}}{a^{-2}nt^{-5}}\right)^{-1}$
50. $\left(\dfrac{b^{-2}u^3g^{-4}}{bu^{-2}g^{-1}}\right)^2$ 51. $\left(\dfrac{s^{-2}a^2t^{-1}}{s^2a^{-1}t^2}\right)^2$

52. $\left(\dfrac{a^2p^{-3}c^{-1}}{a^{-1}p^{-4}c^0}\right)^{-2}$ 53. $b^2 + \dfrac{1}{b^{-2}}$

54. $3a^{-2} - \dfrac{2}{a^2}$ 55. $c^3 - \dfrac{2}{c^{-3}}$ 56. $2a^{-1} - \dfrac{2}{a}$

57. *Anthropology*   In statistical studies of migration, the relatedness between any pair of populations in this system after t generations is

$$r = 1 - \left(\dfrac{Ny - 1}{N - 1}\right)^t$$

where N = the number of populations and $0 < y < 1$. Find r for $N = 12$, $y = \frac{1}{4}$, and $t = 8$.

58. *Earth science*   In working with the atomic scattering factor for hydrogen, we need the expression

$$I = \dfrac{2ab}{(a^2 + b^2)^2}$$

Find I if $b = 3a$.

59. *Psychology and calculator*   In a learning experiment with probability p in the nth trial, the average latency (interval between stimulus and response) is

$$L = \dfrac{k}{1 - (1 - p)(1 - b)^{n-1}}$$

Calculate L if $k = 1.65$, $p = 0.11$, and $b = 0.10$ for $n = 4$ and then for $n = 12$.

60. *Anthropology and calculator*   The diffusion of water into obsidian is governed by the equation $M^2 = Kt$, where M is the depth in micrometers, t is the time in years, and $K = 0.00354$. What is t if $M = 1.62$?

In Probs. 61 to 76, assume the given numbers are approximations, and do the indicated calculations.

61. $(6.92 \times 10^4)(1.13 \times 10^7)$
62. $(8.11 \times 10^{14})(3.26 \times 10^{16})$
63. $(5.53 \times 10^9)(1.72 \times 10^{12})$
64. $(6.88 \times 10^{23})(7.09 \times 10^{19})$
65. $(7.1 \times 10^{10})(8.42 \times 10^{15})$
66. $(8.2 \times 10^5)(9.411 \times 10^6)$
67. $(6.93 \times 10^{31})(1.071 \times 10^{27})$
68. $(4.45 \times 10^{18})(1.7921 \times 10^{22})$

69. $18.45 + 17.53$ **70.** $142.633 + 118.051$
71. $432.1 + 653.8$ **72.** $2.449 + 2.646$
73. $31.7 + 28.443$ **74.** $72.45 + 69.8$
75. $6.518 + 8.01$ **76.** $7.5689 + 4.71$

77. The amount of light that can penetrate a depth of x meters in an ocean is given by $10(0.4)^x$. What is the amount of light

$$\text{at 1 m?} \qquad \text{at 3 m?}$$

78. If the half-life of a medical substance is 5 days, then the amount remaining after n days is approximately $(0.87)^n$. How much remains after 4 days?

79. *Medicine* The amount of a drug in the body t hours after an initial dose of 20 mg is given by $20(0.7)^t$. Estimate the amount of the drug in the body 12 h after it is taken. After 24 h.

80. *Investment* If the value of an investment in a rare coin increases at 10 percent per year, then its value t years after being purchased for P dollars is $P(1.1)^t$. How much is a coin purchased for \$130 worth after 5 years?

81. If $n \geq 2$ is a positive integer, then 4^n may be written as a sum of consecutive odd integers. Do this for the numbers

$$4^2 = 16 \qquad 4^3 = 64 \qquad 4^4 = 256$$

Hint: Start with 7, 31, and 127, respectively.

82. If $n \geq 2$ is a positive integer, then 5^n may be written as a sum of consecutive odd integers. Do this for the numbers

$$5^2 = 25 \qquad 5^3 = 125 \qquad 5^4 = 625$$

Hint: Start with 1, 21, and 121, respectively.

83. Show that

$$(1^5 + 2^5 + 3^5) + (1^7 + 2^7 + 3^7) = 2(1 + 2 + 3)^4$$

84. Show that

$$(1^5 + 2^5 + 3^5 + 4^5) + (1^7 + 2^7 + 3^7 + 4^7)$$
$$= 2(1 + 2 + 3 + 4)^4$$

In Probs. 85 and 86, use x, x^2, x^4, x^8, x^{16}, and x^{32} as factors at most once each.

85. Write x^{46} as a product using each factor above at most once.

86. Write x^{55} as a product using each factor above at most once.

In Probs. 87 and 88, use x, x^3, x^9, and x^{27} at most once each. Each may be used in either numerator or denominator, but not in both. For instance

$$x^7 = \frac{x \cdot x^9}{x^3}$$

87. Write x^{33} as a quotient as explained above.
88. Write x^{19} as a quotient as explained above.
89. It can be shown that the average value of x^2 on the interval $[0, 2]$ is $\frac{4}{3} \approx 1.33$. Calculate the value of the average below:

$$\frac{0.25^2 + 0.75^2 + 1.25^2 + 1.75^2}{4}$$

90. It can be shown that the average value of x^3 on the interval $[1, 2]$ is $\frac{15}{4} = 3.75$. Calculate the value of the average below:

$$\frac{1.1^3 + 1.3^3 + 1.5^3 + 1.7^3 + 1.9^3}{5}$$

1.3 Polynomials and Algebraic Expressions

The area of a circle with radius r is πr^2. The irrational number π has a well-known specific value, approximately 3.1415927. The symbol r represents the radius of the circle, and it may be any positive real number.

This illustrates the following definitions. If a symbol is used to represent only one value from a given set, it is called a **constant.** If a symbol is used to represent any element from a given set, it is called a **variable.** The result of applying the four fundamental operations of addition, subtraction, multiplication, and division (except division by 0) to a collection of constants and variables is called an **algebraic expression.** In Sec. 1.6 and later, we shall also allow the extraction of roots. We will normally use letters from near the beginning of the alphabet as constants, while letters from near the end of the alphabet will typically be variables. Thus a, b, and c will ordinarily represent constants, and x, y, and z will generally stand for variables.

EXAMPLE 1 The following are algebraic expressions:

$$a + 3x \qquad 32a^2 - 5ay \qquad \frac{2p}{1 + 5q}$$

$$1 - \frac{v^2}{c^2} \qquad 4.6pv^2 \qquad (1 - x^3)^2(1 + x^2)^3$$

If a specific real number is substituted for each variable is an algebraic expression, the real number obtained is called the **value** of the expression for those specific real numbers. For example, the value of

$$32x^2 - 5yz \qquad \text{for } x = 2,\ y = 4,\ z = 6$$

is found by substitution, and it is

$$32(2^2) - 5(4)(6) = 32(4) - 120 = 128 - 120 = 8$$

Since algebraic expressions are symbols which represent real numbers,

We may use all of the rules governing real numbers

In particular, the distributive law as well as $(-a)(-b) = ab$ and $-(a - b) = -a + b$ are used repeatedly.

Symbols of Grouping

A **term** of an algebraic expression is a product where each factor is either a real number or a variable raised to a power. The real number factor is called the **numerical coefficient,** or just the **coefficient.** For example,

$$3x^2y + 4xyz^3$$

has two *terms* with *coefficients* 3 and 4, and

$$\frac{6}{x} + 11x - 24x^4$$

has three terms. If the exponents are all positive integers, the expression is called a **polynomial.** We will study polynomials later in this chapter.

Symbols of grouping, such as ( ) or [ ] or { }, are often used to indicate that the sum or difference of several terms is to be considered as an entity (one quantity). If grouping symbols preceded by a plus sign are removed from (or inserted in) an expression, the signs of the terms remain as they were. If, however, grouping symbols preceded by a minus sign are removed (or inserted), then *the sign of each term must be changed.* In effect, each term inside the grouping symbols is multiplied by -1 since

$$a - (b + c) = a + (-1)(b + c) = a - b - c$$

For instance,

$$2x + (3y - 4z) = 2x + 3y - 4z$$

and
$$2x - (3y - 4z) = 2x - 3y + 4z$$

NOTE   If grouping symbols are preceded by a coefficient, each term inside the symbols must be multiplied by that coefficient when the symbols are removed. This is simply an application of the distributive law. For instance,

$$-3(2x - 5y) = -6x + 15y \qquad \text{and} \qquad 5x(2 - 7x) = 10x - 35x^2$$

EXAMPLE 2   Verify that all of the following expressions are equal.

Solution
$$2x - 6y + 2p - 4q$$
$$2x - 6y - (-2p + 4q)$$
$$2x - 6y + (2p - 4q)$$
$$2x - (6y - 2p + 4q)$$
$$2(x - 3y + p - 2q)$$

Two terms are called **similar,** or **like,** if they differ at most in their coefficients. For instance, $2x^2y$ and $-5x^2y$ are similar terms, as are $14x^3$ and $-61x^3$, but $2x^2y$ and $2xy$ are not.

EXAMPLE 3   Remove both sets of parentheses from

$$2x + 3(2x - 5y) - 2(-4x + 3y - 5z)$$

and collect similar terms.

Solution   The first set of parentheses is preceded by a $+3$; hence no sign changes are needed in removing them. The second set is preceded by a -2; hence, all signs in the parentheses must be changed when the parentheses are removed. Consequently, removing parentheses we have

$$2x + 6x - 15y + 8x - 6y + 10z = 16x - 21y + 10z$$

Sometimes grouping symbols are *nested,* meaning that one set of grouping symbols is contained in another set. When the symbols are removed from an expression of this type, it is advisable to

Remove the innermost symbols first

since we then work with a smaller number of terms at a time.

EXAMPLE 4   Remove the symbols of grouping in

$$3a - [4b + 2(6a - b) - 3(a - 5b - 1) - 7]$$

Solution   We work first with the parentheses since they are inside the brackets:

$$3a - [4b + 12a - 2b - 3a + 15b + 3 - 7]$$

$$= 3a - [17b + 9a - 4] \qquad \text{collecting terms}$$

$$= 3a - 17b - 9a + 4 \qquad \text{removing [ ]}$$

$$= -6a - 17b + 4 \qquad \text{collecting terms}$$

EXAMPLE 5   Remove the grouping symbols from the expression

$$3x^2 - \{2x^2 - xy - [x(x - y) - y(2x - y)] + 4xy\} - 3y^2$$

Solution   We start with the given expression and explain the successive steps in removing the symbols of grouping:

$$3x^2 - \{2x^2 - xy - [x(x - y) - y(2x - y)] + 4xy\} - 3y^2 \qquad \text{given expression}$$

$$= 3x^2 - \{2x^2 - xy - [x^2 - xy - 2xy + y^2] + 4xy\} - 3y^2 \qquad \begin{array}{l}\text{applying the distributive law} \\ \text{to the expression in ( )}\end{array}$$

$$= 3x^2 - \{2x^2 - xy - [x^2 - 3xy + y^2] + 4xy\} - 3y^2 \qquad \begin{array}{l}\text{adding similar terms} \\ \text{inside | |}\end{array}$$

$$= 3x^2 - \{2x^2 - xy - x^2 + 3xy - y^2 + 4xy\} - 3y^2 \qquad \text{removing [ ]}$$

$$= 3x^2 - \{x^2 + 6xy - y^2\} - 3y^2 \qquad \text{adding similar terms in \{ \}}$$

$$= 3x^2 - x^2 - 6xy + y^2 - 3y^2 \qquad \text{removing \{ \}}$$

$$= 2x^2 - 6xy - 2y^2 \qquad \text{adding similar terms}$$

If parentheses are preceded by a coefficient, remember that each term inside the parentheses is to be multiplied by that coefficient, including its sign.

EXAMPLE 6   Remove the grouping symbols and collect terms in

$$2[-3x + 4y - 5(2x - 3y) + 9x(3x - 2y)]$$

Solution $2[-3x + 4y - 5(2x - 3y) + 9x(3x - 2y)] \qquad \text{given expression}$

$$= 2[-3x + 4y - 10x + 15y + 27x^2 - 18xy] \qquad \text{removing parentheses}$$

$$= 2[-13x + 19y + 27x^2 - 18xy] \qquad \text{collecting terms}$$

$$= -26x + 38y + 54x^2 - 36xy \qquad \text{removing [ ]}$$

PROBLEMS   Problems 1 to 28 may be done now.

Polynomials

Certain types of algebraic expressions occur so frequently that they are given special names. A **polynomial** (in one variable) is an expression

Polynomial

$$a_n x^n + a_{n-1} x^{n-1} + \cdots + a_2 x^2 + a_1 x + a_0$$

where $a_n, a_{n-1}, \ldots, a_0$ are real numbers, called the **coefficients,** and n is a nonnegative integer. For instance, the expressions

$$2x^3 + 5x^2 - 17x + 613$$
$$11x^6 - 53x^5 + 4.1x^3 - 16.9x$$
$$x^4 - x + 88$$

are all polynomials.

A polynomial with one term is called a **monomial,** with two terms is called a **binomial,** and with three terms is called a **trinomial.**

If $a_n \neq 0$, then a_n is called the **leading coefficient** and n is the **degree** of the polynomial in x. Thus the degree is the highest exponent which occurs on the variable. For instance, 6 is the degree of $15x^6 - 35x^4 + 1$, and its leading coefficient is 15. Also, 4 is the degree of $x^4 - x^3 + x^2 - x + 1$, whose leading coefficient is 1.

To add polynomials, we add similar terms. To multiply polynomials, we first use the distributive law along with the laws of exponents, and then add similar terms.

▶ **EXAMPLE 7** Find the product $(3x + 2)(7x^2 + 5x + 4)$.

Solution

$$(3x)(7x^2 + 5x + 4) + (2)(7x^2 + 5x + 4) \qquad \text{distributive axiom}$$
$$= 21x^3 + 15x^2 + 12x + 14x^2 + 10x + 8 \qquad \text{multiplying}$$
$$= 21x^3 + 29x^2 + 22x + 8 \qquad \text{adding similar terms} \qquad ◀$$

Certain products occur often and so deserve special mention. Each of the ones below can be justified directly by multiplication. The first one below uses the FOIL method, so named because the terms are the products of the First, Outside, Inside, and Last members of the given binomials.

FOIL

$$(ax + by)(cx + dy) = acx^2 + adxy + bcxy + bdy^2$$
$$ \text{F} \qquad \text{O} \qquad \text{I} \qquad \text{L}$$

The FOIL method is used only for the product of two binomials.

Square of a sum $\qquad\qquad (x + y)^2 = x^2 + 2xy + y^2 \qquad\qquad$ **(1.22)**

Square of a difference $\qquad (x - y)^2 = x^2 - 2xy + y^2 \qquad\qquad$ **(1.23)**

Product of sum and difference $\quad (x + y)(x - y) = x^2 - y^2 \qquad\qquad$ **(1.24)**

Cube of a sum $\qquad\qquad (x + y)^3 = x^3 + 3x^2y + 3xy^2 + y^3 \qquad$ **(1.25)**

Cube of a difference $\qquad\quad (x - y)^3 = x^3 - 3x^2y + 3xy^2 - y^3 \qquad$ **(1.26)**

Square of a trinomial $\qquad (x + y + z)^2 = x^2 + y^2 + z^2 + 2xy + 2xz + 2yz \qquad$ **(1.27)**

▶ **EXAMPLE 8** Find the product of $3x - 7$ and $4x - 1$.

Solution By the FOIL method we have

$$(3x - 7)(4x - 1) = (3x)(4x) + (3x)(-1) + (-7)(4x) + (-7)(-1)$$
$$ \text{F} \qquad\quad \text{O} \qquad\qquad \text{I} \qquad\qquad \text{L}$$

$$= 12x^2 - 3x - 28x + 7$$
$$= 12x^2 - 31x + 7 \qquad\qquad ◀$$

EXAMPLE 9   Find $(2a + 5b)^2$.

Solution
$$(2a + 5b)^2 = (2a)^2 + 2(2a)(5b) + (5b)^2 \qquad \text{square of a sum}$$
$$= 4a^2 + 20ab + 25b^2$$

▶ EXAMPLE 10   Find the power $(3x - 4y)^2$.

Solution
$$(3x - 4y)^2 = (3x)^2 - 2(3x)(4y) + (4y)^2 \qquad \text{square of a difference}$$
$$= 9x^2 - 24xy + 16y^2$$

▶ EXAMPLE 11   Find the product $(3x + 5y)(3x - 5y)$.

Solution
$$(3x + 5y)(3x - 5y) = (3x)^2 - (5y)^2 \qquad \text{product of sum and difference}$$
$$= 9x^2 - 25y^2$$

▶ EXAMPLE 12   Find $(2x + y + a)(2x - y + a)$ by writing it as the product of a sum and difference.

Solution
$$(2x + y + a)(2x - y + a) \qquad \text{given}$$

$$= [(2x + a) + y][(2x + a) - y] \qquad \begin{array}{l}\text{written as the product of} \\ \text{the sum and difference of } 2x + a \text{ and } y\end{array}$$

$$= (2x + a)^2 - y^2 \qquad \text{the difference of two squares}$$

$$= 4x^2 + 4xa + a^2 - y^2 \qquad \text{square of a sum}$$

Use the formula for the cube of a difference to find $(2x - 5y)^3$.

▶ EXAMPLE 13
$$(2x - 5y)^3 \qquad \text{cube of a difference}$$

Solution
$$= (2x)^3 - 3(2x)^2(5y) + 3(2x)(5y)^2 - (5y)^3 \qquad \text{expanding}$$
$$= 8x^3 - 60x^2y + 150xy^2 - 125y^3$$

▶ EXAMPLE 14   Find $(x + 2y - 3z)^2$ as the square of a trinomial.

Solution
$$(x + 2y - 3z)^2 \qquad \text{square of a trinomial}$$

$$= x^2 + 4y^2 + 9z^2 + 4xy - 6xz - 12yz \qquad \text{formula (1.27)}$$

PROBLEMS   Problems 29 to 88 may be done now.

The Division Algorithm for Polynomials

An algorithm is simply a step-by-step procedure. The division algorithm shows how to systematically use multiplication and addition of polynomials to divide one polynomial by another one. Recall from arithmetic that when we divide m by n, both positive integers, we may write

$$m = n \cdot q + r \qquad (1)$$

where q is the quotient and the remainder r satisfies $0 \leq r < n$. For instance, with $m = 38$, $n = 9$, $q = 4$, and $r = 2$ in Eq. (1), we may write either

$$\tfrac{38}{9} = 4 + \tfrac{2}{9} \qquad \text{or} \qquad 38 = 9 \cdot 4 + 2$$

The division algorithm for polynomials provides a relation similar to Eq. (1).

The division algorithm is stated below without proof. A good indication of the reasoning behind it is given in Prob. 101 of Exercise 1.3.

> Suppose that P and D are polynomials with the degree of D smaller than the degree of P, and $D \neq 0$. Then there are unique polynomials Q, the quotient, and R, the remainder, with
>
> $$P = D \cdot Q + R$$
>
> where either $R = 0$ or R has smaller degree than D.

The restriction on the degrees of P and D is not necessary, but otherwise there is no need to divide. We may write either

$$P = D \cdot Q + R \qquad \text{or} \qquad \frac{P}{D} = Q + \frac{R}{D}$$

The degree of P is the sum of the degrees of D and Q.

Here are the steps for finding the quotient Q and remainder R. The process is sometimes called **long division.**

Polynomial division

1. Arrange the terms in P and D in descending powers of the variable. If a coefficient in P is 0, leave a space or insert the 0.
2. Divide the first monomial term in P by the first term in D to get the first term in the quotient Q.
3. Multiply D by the first term in the quotient and subtract the product from P.
4. With the divisor remaining the same, treat the result in step 3 as the new P and then repeat steps 2 and 3.
5. Continue this process until a remainder is obtained that has a lower degree than D.

The computation can be checked by using the relation $P = D \cdot Q + R$.

▶ **EXAMPLE 15** Find the quotient and remainder if

$$6x^2 + 5x - 1 \text{ is divided by } 2x - 1$$

Solution Here $P = 6x^2 + 5x - 1$ and $D = 2x - 1$. We begin by dividing $6x^2$ by $2x$, getting $3x$ as the first term in the quotient:

$$
\begin{array}{r}
3x + 4 \\
2x - 1 \overline{)6x^2 + 5x - 1} \\
\underline{6x^2 - 3x} \\
8x - 1 \\
\underline{8x - 4} \\
3
\end{array}
$$

$6x^2/2x = 3x$ and also $8x/2x = 4$

$= (2x - 1)3x$

subtracting

$= (2x - 1)4$

subtracting

This gives $Q = 3x + 4$ and $R = 3$. The result may be written as either

$$6x^2 + 5x - 1 = (2x - 1)(3x + 4) + 3$$

or $\qquad \dfrac{6x^2 + 5x - 1}{2x - 1} = 3x + 4 + \dfrac{3}{2x - 1}$

▶ **EXAMPLE 16**   Divide $P = 6x^4 - 6x^2 - 3 + 8x - x^3$ by $D = -2 + 2x^2 + x$.

Solution   We arrange the terms in both polynomials in descending powers of x and proceed as indicated below. The terms of the quotient come from dividing $2x^2$ into $6x^4$, then into $-4x^3$, and finally into $2x^2$:

$$
\begin{array}{r}
3x^2 - 2x + 1 \\
2x^2 + x - 2 \overline{)6x^4 - x^3 - 6x^2 + 8x - 3} \\
\underline{6x^4 + 3x^3 - 6x^2} \\
- 4x^3 + 8x - 3 \\
\underline{- 4x^3 - 2x^2 + 4x} \\
2x^2 + 4x - 3 \\
\underline{2x^2 + x - 2} \\
3x - 1
\end{array}
$$

$6x^4/2x^2 = 3x^2$ and $-4x^3/2x^2 = 2x$

and $2x^2/2x^2 = 1$

$= (2x^2 + x - 2)(3x^2)$

subtracting

$= (2x^2 + x - 2)(-2x)$

subtracting

$= (2x^2 + x - 2)(+1)$

subtracting

The quotient is $Q = 3x^2 - 2x + 1$ and the remainder is $R = 3x - 1$, and again we have $P = D \cdot Q + R$, which may be written as either

$$6x^4 - x^3 - 6x^2 + 8x - 3 = (2x^2 + x - 2)(3x^2 - 2x + 1) + 3x - 1$$

or $\qquad \dfrac{6x^4 - x^3 - 6x^2 + 8x - 3}{2x^2 + x - 2} = 3x^2 - 2x + 1 + \dfrac{3x - 1}{2x^2 + x - 2}$

▶ **EXAMPLE 17**   Divide $16x^3 + 4x^2 + 19$ by $4x + 5$.

Solution   Since the term involving x is missing, we may either leave a blank space for that term, or else write in the term with a **zero coefficient.** We choose to do the latter since it forces us to remember all of the terms and use them in the division. The terms of the quotient come from dividing $4x$ into $16x^3$, then into $-16x^2$, and finally into $20x$:

$$
\begin{array}{r}
4x^2 - 4x + 5 \\
4x + 5 \overline{)16x^3 + 4x^2 + 0x + 19} \\
\underline{16x^3 + 20x^2} \\
- 16x^2 \\
\underline{- 16x^2 - 20x} \\
20x + 19 \\
\underline{20x + 25} \\
-6
\end{array}
$$

dividing $4x$ into $16x^3$, $-16x^2$, and $20x$

$= (4x + 5)(4x^2)$

subtracting

$= (4x + 5)(-4x)$

subtracting

$= (4x + 5)(5)$

subtracting

Therefore

$$16x^3 + 4x^2 + 19 = (4x + 5)(4x^2 - 4x + 5) + (-6)$$

which may be written in the form

$$\frac{16x^3 + 4x^2 + 19}{4x + 5} = 4x^2 - 4x + 5 + \frac{-6}{4x + 5}$$ ◢

PROBLEMS   Problems 89 to 108 may be done now.

When the divisor D has the form $x - r$ for a real number r, the long division process may be shortened significantly by using synthetic division, which is explained in Sec. 4.3.

EXERCISE 1.3

Find the value of each algebraic expression in Probs. 1 to 4.

1. $3a + 14b - ab$ for $a = 5$ and $b = 2$
2. $(16a + 5b) \div (1 - 4a)$ for $a = -1$ and $b = 5$
3. $(x^2 + 1)/(x + 1)$ for $x = 4$
4. $(x + 4)^2 - (x + 2)^2$ for $x = -2$

Remove parentheses and combine terms in Probs. 5 to 8.

5. $-5(3x + t) - 4(2x - 5t) + 2(-x - t)$
6. $4(-2n - 5b + 4a) - 3(-3n - 7b + 5a)$
7. $2x(3a + b) - y(a - b) + a(-x - 2y) - 3b(2x + y)$
8. $a(c - d) + b(d - c) - c(a - b) - d(-a - b)$

Complete the equations by inserting the appropriate expressions inside the parentheses.

9. $6x - 5y + 3z = 6x + (\quad)$
10. $4x + 3y - 2z = 4x - (\quad)$
11. $-2x + 3a + 5b = 3a - (\quad)$
12. $4a + 2t + 3g = 3g - (\quad)$

Remove the symbols of grouping in each of Probs. 13 to 28 and then combine similar terms.

13. $2a + [3a - 2(a - 2b) - 3a]$
14. $3a + [5a - (2a - b)] + 3b$
15. $2a - [2c - 3b - (2a + 4c - 3b) - 2a] - (c - b)$
16. $5a - (2b - 3c) -$
$\qquad [3a - 4b - (a - b - 2c) + c] - 2(a - b) + c$
17. $2\{2a - b[2a - c(2a - 1) + 2ac] - c\}$
18. $2a\{a^2 - a[2a - 3(a + 2) + 1] - a^2\}$
19. $4[3a - 2(a + 2b)] - 3\{a^2 - [3b + a(a - b)]\}$
20. $2a^3 - 5a\{a^2 + 3[3a - 4(a - 2) + 3] - a^2\}$
21. $2x + 2\{y - [4x - (z + 2y)] + z\} - 2y$
22. $3a - \{b - 2[c - 3b + 2(c - a) + b] + 2a\}$
23. $6d - 4e - \{2f + 2[-d + e - 2(d - f)] + e\} + e$
24. $2g - 3\{h - 4[i + 2(g - h + 2i) - g] + 2h\} + 3i$

25. $3 + x[-6 + x(4 + x)]$
26. $-2 + x[5 - x(-7 + x)]$
27. $-1 + x\{6 + x[-4 + x(3 + x)]\}$
28. $5 - x\{-5 + x[4 + x(1 - x)]\}$

Add the expressions in each of Probs. 29 to 32.

29. $2ab^2 + 3ab + 5a^2b$, $3ab^2 - 4ab - 3a^2b$, $4ab^2 + 7ab - 8a^2b$
30. $4xy - 3xy^2 + 2xy^3$, $-7xy + 8xy^2 + 3xy^3$, $2xy - 3xy^2 - 2xy^3$
31. $3p^2q + 4pq + 5pq^2$, $-7p^2q - 6pq + 3pq^2$, $5p^2q + 4pq - 7pq^2$
32. $7r^2s + 2rs + 3s^2$, $-9r^2s - 7rs - 2s^2$, $3r^2s + 5rs + s^2$

In each of Probs. 33 to 36, subtract the second expression from the first.

33. $2a + b - 3c$, $3a + 2b + 4c$
34. $7a - 5b + 8c$, $6a - 6b + 9c$
35. $5x + 2y - 6z$, $7x - 2y + 3z$
36. $7a - 3k + 4p$, $8a - 4k - 2p$

Find the products in Probs. 37 to 88.

37. $-2x^2y^3(3xy^2 - 2x^2y)$ **38.** $-3xy^2(2x^2y^3 - 5x^3y)$
39. $5x^3y^4(2xy^2 - 4x^3y)$ **40.** $7x^2y^4(3x^3y^2 - 2x^5y^3)$
41. $2x^2y(3y - 2x) - 3xy^2(2x - y)$
42. $3xy(2x + 3x^2y) - 2x^2y(4 - xy)$
43. $5xy^3(2x^2y - 3xy^3) - 4x^2y(2xy^3 - 7y^5)$
44. $7x^2y(2xy^3 - 3x^2y^2) - 4xy^3(3x^2y - 5x^3)$
45. $(2x^2 + 3xy - 3y^2)(x^2 - 3xy + 2y^2)$
46. $(2x^2 - xy + 3y^2)(3x^2 - xy - 2y^2)$
47. $(5x^2 + 2xy + y^2)(2x^2 - xy + 3y^2)$
48. $(x^2 - 3xy + 2y^2)(x^2 + 3xy - y^2)$
49. $(2x + 3)(4x + 5)$ **50.** $(3x + 5)(2x - 3)$
51. $(5x - 2)(2x - 5)$ **52.** $(4x - 3)(3x - 2)$
53. $(3x + 4y)(2x - 5y)$ **54.** $(4x - 7y)(7x + 4y)$

55. $(5x + 7y)(6x - 5y)$ **56.** $(6x - 7y)(7x + 5y)$
57. $(2a + b)^2$ **58.** $(3a + 2b)^2$
59. $(6a + 5b)^2$ **60.** $(7a + 4b)^2$
61. $(x + 2y)^3$ **62.** $(3x + 5y)^3$
63. $(2x + x^2)^3$ **64.** $(3x^2 + x)^3$
65. $(5x - y)^3$ **66.** $(6x - 5y)^3$
67. $(7x - 2)^3$ **68.** $(5x - 4)^3$
69. $(x + 4)(x - 4)$ **70.** $(x + 7)(x - 7)$
71. $(3x + 5)(3x - 5)$ **72.** $(2x + 3)(2x - 3)$
73. $(2x - 5y)(2x + 5y)$ **74.** $(3x + 4y)(3x - 4y)$
75. $(7x + 6y)(7x - 6y)$ **76.** $(8x - 5y)(8x + 5y)$
77. $(2a^2 - 3b^2)(2a^2 + 3b^2)$
78. $(2a^2 + 5b^2)(2a^2 - 5b^2)$
79. $(5a^2 + 7b^3)(5a^2 - 7b^3)$
80. $(6a^3 + 7b^2)(6a^3 - 7b^2)$
81. $(x + y + z)^2 = [(x + y) + z]^2$
82. $(2x - y + z)^2$
83. $(x - y + 3z)^2$ **84.** $(2x + y - z)^2$
85. $[(x^3 + x) + (x^2 - 1)][(x^3 + x) - (x^2 - 1)]$
86. $[(x^2 + x) + (x^3 + 1)][(x^2 + x) - (x^3 + 1)]$
87. $[(2x^4 + x) + (x^3 - 2x^2)][(2x^4 + x) - (x^3 - 2x^2)]$
88. $[(x^5 - 3x) + (3x^3 - 1)][(x^5 - 3x) - (3x^3 - 1)]$

Find the quotient and remainder if the first expression is divided by the second.
89. $6x^3 + 5x^2 - 4x + 4$, $2x + 3$
90. $6x^3 - 5x^2 + 7x - 1$, $3x - 1$
91. $6x^3 - 22x + 9$, $2x - 4$
92. $8x^3 + 10x + 1$, $4x + 2$
93. $2x^4 + 7x^3 + 2x - 1$, $x^2 + 3x - 1$
94. $3x^4 - 4x^2 + 8x + 3$, $3x^2 + 6x + 2$
95. $6x^4 + x^3 + x^2 - 7x - 9$, $3x + 2$
96. $3x^4 + 11x^3 - 7x - 2$, $3x + 2$

Show that the remainder is zero if the first expression is divided by the second.
97. $x^9 + x^5 + x^2 + 1$, $x^2 - x + 1$
98. $x^7 - x^6 + x^5 + 2x^4 - 2x^3 + x^2 + x - 1$, $x^2 - x + 1$
99. $x^8 + x^6 - x^2 - 1$, $x^2 + x + 1$
100. $x^7 + 3x^6 - 2x^4 + x^3 + x - 4$, $x^2 + x + 1$

101. *The basis for polynomial division* Suppose that $6x^2 + 5x - 1 = (2x - 1)$ (quotient) + remainder, where the degree of the remainder is smaller that the degree of the term $2x - 1$, which is 1.
(a) Why is the quotient of the form $ax + b$?
(b) Why is $6x^2 = (2x)(ax)$? Why is $a = 3$?

(c) Show that from $6x^2 + 5x - 1 = (2x - 1)(3x + b)$ + remainder, it follows that $8x = 2bx$, and hence $b = 4$.
(d) Show that from $6x^2 + 5x - 1 = (2x - 1)(3x + 4)$ + remainder, it follows that the remainder is 3.

102. Verify the following calculation, which is used in showing that the product of two odd integers is odd:
$$(2n + 1)(2k + 1) = 2(2nk + n + k) + 1$$

103. Verify the following calculation, which is used in showing that the integer n is a multiple of 3 if and only if n^2 is a multiple of 3:
$$(3k + 2)^2 = 3(3k^2 + 4k + 1) + 1$$

104. Show that the sum of two squares times the sum of two squares is a sum of two squares by verifying that
$$(a^2 + b^2)(c^2 + d^2) = (ac - bd)^2 + (ad + bc)^2$$
Write $(3^2 + 4^2)(2^2 + 7^2)$ as a sum of two squares.

105. *Production* Under certain circumstances, the cost of producing x items is
$$(50 + 3x)^3$$
Expand this product. Find the cost of producing five items without expanding.

106. *Advertising* Assume that, in thousands, if $\$x$ is spent on advertising, the sales will be
$$75\left(1 - \frac{2}{3 + x}\right)\left(1 + \frac{2}{3 + x}\right)$$
Expand this, using the difference of two squares. Find the sales if $x = 1$ and if $x = 3$.

107. *Profit* Assume that the profit, if x items are sold, is
$$(x - 24)(60 - x)$$
Expand this product.

108. *Profit* Assume that the profit, if x items are sold, is
$$(x - 30)(75 - x)$$
Expand this product.

1.4 Factoring

When adding, multiplying, and simplifying expressions, and when using the zero factor law to solve quadratic equations, it is often desirable to write a polynomial as the product of other polynomials. If this is done, the polynomials that are multiplied together are called **factors** of the original polynomial. Rewriting a polynomial as a product is called **factoring.**

In this section, we will be interested only in numerical **coefficients which are integers.** Thus $x - 4$ and $x + 4$ are allowed as factors of $x^2 - 16$ since the coefficients 1, 4, and -4 are integers and

$$(x - 4)(x + 4) = x^2 - 16$$

However, $x - \sqrt{5}$ and $x + \sqrt{5}$ are not allowed as factors of $x^2 - 5$ even though $(x - \sqrt{5})(x + \sqrt{5}) = x^2 - 5$.

A polynomial with integer coefficients is **irreducible,** or **prime,** if it cannot be expressed as the product of two polynomials, each with positive degree and integer coefficients. Thus $x^2 - 5$ is irreducible since it cannot be written in the form $(x - a)(x - b)$ where a and b are integers. A polynomial with real coefficients is **factored into prime factors** if it is expressed as the product of prime factors. For example since

$$(x - 1)(x - 2)(x - 3) = x^3 - 6x^2 + 11x - 6$$

and $x - 1$, $x - 2$, and $x - 3$ are all prime, then the left-hand side is the prime factorization of the right-hand side.

It is customary to use the distributive law if possible to remove any integral factor from each numerical coefficient. Thus, for instance, we would write the prime factorization of $5x^2 - 20$ as $5(x - 2)(x + 2)$ rather than $(5x - 10)(x + 2)$.

Common Factors

If each term of a polynomial is divisible by the same term (often a monomial), this term is called a **common factor** of the terms of the polynomial. Such a polynomial can be factored by expressing it as the product of the common factor and the sum of the quotients obtained by dividing each term of the polynomial by the common factor. This procedure is justified by the *distributive axiom*. If either factor thus obtained is not prime, we continue factoring by use of one or more of the methods discussed later. For example,

$$ab + ac - ad = a(b + c - d) \qquad \text{by the distributive law}$$

EXAMPLE 1   Factor $9x^2y^2 + 6xy^3 + 21x^3y^2 + 3xy^2$ by using a common factor.

Solution   The common factor is $3xy^2$, and

$$9x^2y^2 + 6xy^3 + 21x^3y^2 + 3xy^2 = 3xy^2(3x + 2y + 7x^2 + 1)$$

▶ **EXAMPLE 2**   Factor $a(x^2 + y^2) - a(x^2 - xy - y^2)$ by using common factors.

Solution
$$a(x^2 + y^2) - a(x^2 - xy - y^2)$$
$$= a(x^2 + y^2 - x^2 + xy + y^2) \qquad \text{the common factor is } a$$
$$= a(2y^2 + xy) \qquad \text{combining similar terms}$$
$$= ay(2y + x) \qquad \text{the common factor is } y$$ ◀

▶ **EXAMPLE 3**   Factor $(x - 1)(x + 2) - (x - 1)(2x - 3)$ by finding a common binomial factor.

Solution
$$(x - 1)(x + 2) - (x - 1)(2x - 3) \qquad \text{given}$$
$$= (x - 1)[(x + 2) - (2x - 3)] \qquad \text{common factor of } x - 1$$
$$= (x - 1)(x + 2 - 2x + 3) \qquad \text{remove parentheses}$$
$$= (x - 1)(-x + 5) \qquad \text{combining similar terms}$$ ◀

Factoring Formulas

The following formulas can be used to factor many expressions. Each formula can be verified by multiplying the terms in the right-hand side of the equation. Some of the formulas occurred in the last section as product formulas.

Factoring formulas

Difference of squares	$x^2 - y^2 = (x - y)(x + y)$	**(1.28)**
Sum of cubes	$x^3 + y^3 = (x + y)(x^2 - xy + y^2)$	**(1.29)**
Difference of cubes	$x^3 - y^3 = (x - y)(x^2 + xy + y^2)$	**(1.30)**
Square of sum	$x^2 + 2xy + y^2 = (x + y)^2$	**(1.31)**
Square of a difference	$x^2 - 2xy + y^2 = (x - y)^2$	**(1.32)**

▶ **EXAMPLE 4**   Factor (1) $49a^2 - 16b^2$, (2) $(a + 3b)^2 - 4$, and (3) $x^2 - (y + z)^2$ by using the difference-of-squares formula.

Solution (1) $\quad 49a^2 - 16b^2 = (7a)^2 - (4b)^2 \qquad$ laws of exponents
$$= (7a + 4b)(7a - 4b) \qquad \text{difference of squares}$$

(2) $\quad (a + 3b)^2 - 4 = (a + 3b)^2 - 2^2 \qquad$ since $4 = (2)(2)$
$$= (a + 3b + 2)(a + 3b - 2) \qquad \text{difference of squares}$$

(3) $\quad x^2 - (y + z)^2 = [x + (y + z)][x - (y + z)] \qquad$ difference of squares
$$= (x + y + z)(x - y - z) \qquad \text{remove parentheses}$$ ◀

$x^2 + y^2$

Note that the *sum* of two squares cannot in general be factored using integer coefficients and real numbers. Also

$$x^3 + y^3 \neq (x + y)^3 \qquad \text{and} \qquad x^3 - y^3 \neq (x - y)^3$$

► **EXAMPLE 5** Factor (1) $8x^3 + 27y^3$ and (2) $27a^3 - 64b^6$.

Solution (1) $8x^3 + 27y^3 = (2x)^3 + (3y)^3$ sum of cubes
$$= (2x + 3y)[(2x)^2 - (2x)(3y) + (3y)^2]$$
$$= (2x + 3y)(4x^2 - 6xy + 9y^2)$$

(2) $27a^3 - 64b^6 = (3a)^3 - (4b^2)^3$ difference of cubes
$$= (3a - 4b^2)[(3a)^2 + (3a)(4b^2) + (4b^2)^2]$$
$$= (3a - 4b^2)(9a^2 + 12ab^2 + 16b^4)$$ ◄

► **EXAMPLE 6** Factor (1) $4x^2 - 12xy + 9y^2$, (2) $9a^2 + 24ab + 16b^2$, and (3) $(2a - 3b)^2 - 8(2a - 3b) + 16$ as squares of a sum or difference.

Solution (1) Since $4x^2 = (2x)^2$, $9y^2 = (3y)^2$, and $12xy = 2(2x)(3y)$, we have
$$4x^2 - 12xy + 9y^2 = (2x - 3y)(2x - 3y) = (2x - 3y)^2$$

(2) $9a^2 + 24ab + 16b^2 = (3a + 4b)^2$ square of a sum

(3) $(2a - 3b)^2 - 8(2a - 3b) + 16$ square of a difference
$$= [(2a - 3b) - 4]^2 = (2a - 3b - 4)^2$$

Sometimes one or more of the factors can be factored further, as in the next example.

► **EXAMPLE 7** Factor $x^8 - y^8$.

Solution $x^8 - y^8 = (x^4)^2 - (y^4)^2$ laws of exponents
$$= (x^4 + y^4)(x^4 - y^4)$$ difference of squares
$$= (x^4 + y^4)(x^2 + y^2)(x^2 - y^2)$$ difference of squares again
$$= (x^4 + y^4)(x^2 + y^2)(x + y)(x - y)$$ and once more ◄

PROBLEMS Problems 1 to 44 may be done now.

Factors of the Quadratic Trinomial $ax^2 + bx + c$

We are looking for factorizations of $ax^2 + bx + c$ which have the form $(px + q)(rx + s)$; and **we assume that all coefficients are integers.** Thus we need integers p, q, r, and s for which

$$pr = a \qquad ps + qr = b \qquad qs = c$$

In order to do this efficiently, it often helps to write the factors of a in pairs, and also the factors of c in pairs, since we need $pr = a$ and $qs = c$.

Note that factoring $ax^2 + bx + c$ is very similar to factoring $ax^2 + bxy + cy^2$.

For instance,

$$2x^2 - x - 15 = (x - 3)(2x + 5)$$

and $$2x^2 - xy - 15y^2 = (x - 3y)(2x + 5y)$$

Knowing the pattern of signs of a, b, and c also helps by eliminating some of the possibilities. We may as well assume that $a > 0$, since otherwise we can begin by factoring out -1. For instance,

$$-5x^2 + 8x + 4 = -(5x^2 - 8x - 4)$$

Now if $c > 0$, the signs in each factor of $ax^2 + bx + c$ must be alike:

$$(\ + \ )(\ + \ ) \qquad \text{if } b > 0$$
$$(\ - \ )(\ - \ ) \qquad \text{if } b < 0$$

However, if $c < 0$, the signs in the factors are different:

$$(\ + \ )(\ - \ ) \qquad \text{or} \qquad (\ - \ )(\ + \ )$$

▶ **EXAMPLE 8**   (a) For $x^2 + 11xy + 24y^2$, all signs are positive, the form must be $(x + \ \ )(x + \ \ )$, and the factored form is

$$(x + 3y)(x + 8y)$$

(b) For $x^2 - 13xy + 36y^2$, the sign of the last term is positive and the sign of the middle term is negative, and so the form must be $(x - \ \ )(x - \ \ )$. The actual factorization is

$$(x - 4y)(x - 9y)$$ ◢

▶ **EXAMPLE 9**   Factor $3x^2 - 10xy - 8y^2$.

Solution   Since the coefficient of y^2 is negative, the factors must have the form $(3x - \ \ )$ $(x + \ \ )$ or $(3x + \ \ )(x - \ \ )$, with the second terms chosen so that their product is $-8y^2$. The correct factorization is

$$(3x + 2y)(x - 4y) = 3x^2 - 10xy - 8y^2$$

Notice that also $3x^2 - 10xy - 8y^2 = (-3x - 2y)(-x + 4y)$, since $(-1)(-1) = 1$. Taking $y = 1$ shows

$$3x^2 - 10x - 8 = (3x + 2)(x - 4)$$ ◢

The next example shows an alternative way to factor $ax^2 + bxy + cy^2$ by using a common factor.

▶ **EXAMPLE 10**   To factor $3x^2 - 10xy - 8y^2$, look for two numbers whose product is $(3)(-8) = -24$ and whose sum is -10. We can use -12 and 2 since their product is $(-12)(2) = -24$ and their sum is $-12 + 2 = -10$. Now writing $-10xy$ as $-12xy + 2xy$ gives

$$3x^2 - 10xy - 8y^2 = [3x^2 - 12xy] + [2xy - 8y^2]$$

$$= (3x)(x - 4y) + (2y)(x - 4y) \qquad \text{common factors of } 3x \text{ and } 2y$$

$$= (x - 4y)(3x + 2y) \qquad \text{common factor of } x - 4y$$ ◢

It is often desirable to know whether a quadratic trinomial is factorable. In Chap. 2, we will establish the following result.

> For a, b, and c integers, $ax^2 + bx + c$ is factorable with integer coefficients if and only if
>
> $$b^2 - 4ac \text{ is a nonnegative perfect square}$$

EXAMPLE 11   Factor these trinomials, if possible.

$$(1)\ 7x^2 - 12x + 4 \quad \text{and} \quad (2)\ 6x^2 - 13x + 6.$$

Solution   (1) $b^2 - 4ac = (-12)^2 - 4(7)(4) = 144 - 112 = 32$, which is not a perfect square; so $7x^2 - 12x + 4$ is not factorable.
(2) $b^2 - 4ac = (-13)^2 - 4(6)(6) = 169 - 144 = 25 = 5^2$; hence $6x^2 - 13x + 6$ is factorable. There are many possibilities to try; however, the middle signs must be the same because of the $+$ sign in the constant term $+6$. Further, they must both be minus because of the minus sign in $(-13x)$. The possibilities are

$$(6x -\ )(x -\ ) \quad \text{and} \quad (3x -\ )(2x -\ )$$

and the factors are $(2x - 3)(3x - 2) = 6x^2 - 13x + 6$.   ◢

If a trinomial can be made a perfect square by *adding* a perfect square term, then the given trinomial can be factored as a difference of two squares by adding and subtracting the same perfect square.

EXAMPLE 12   Factor $4x^4 + 8x^2y^2 + 9y^4$.

Solution
$$4x^4 + 8x^2y^2 + 9y^4$$

$$= 4x^4 + 8x^2y^2 + 9y^4 + 4x^2y^2 - 4x^2y^2 \qquad \text{adding and subtracting } 4x^2y^2$$

$$= 4x^4 + 12x^2y^2 + 9y^4 - 4x^2y^2 \qquad \text{combining similar terms}$$

$$= (2x^2 + 3y^2)^2 - (2xy)^2 \qquad \text{perfect squares}$$

$$= (2x^2 + 3y^2 + 2xy)(2x^2 + 3y^2 - 2xy) \qquad \text{difference of squares} \quad ◢$$

If $ax^2 + bx + c$ can be factored with real coefficients, then the method shown in the next example always works with no trial and error. It is based on "completing the square," which will be treated fully in Chap. 2. This merely involves adding and subtracting the same term, exactly the same technique used in Example 12 above.

EXAMPLE 13
$$18x^2 - 33x + 14$$

$$= 18(x^2 - \tfrac{33}{18}x + \tfrac{14}{18}) \qquad \text{factoring out coefficient of } x^2$$

$$= 18(x^2 - \tfrac{11}{6}x + \tfrac{7}{9}) \qquad \text{simplifying fractions}$$

For the next step, we add and subtract the square of half the coefficient of x. This is the heart of the method called "completing the square." Since here half of the coefficient of x is $-\frac{11}{12}$, we will add and subtract $\frac{121}{144}$:

$$= 18\left(x^2 - \frac{11}{6}x + \frac{121}{144} + \frac{7}{9} - \frac{121}{144}\right) \qquad \text{adding and subtracting } \tfrac{121}{144}$$

$$= 18\left[\left(x - \frac{11}{12}\right)^2 + \frac{112 - 121}{144}\right] \qquad \text{first three terms are a perfect square}$$

$$= 18\left[\left(x - \frac{11}{12}\right)^2 - \left(\frac{3}{12}\right)^2\right] \qquad \text{arithmetic}$$

$$= 18\left(x - \frac{11}{12} - \frac{3}{12}\right)\left(x - \frac{11}{12} + \frac{3}{12}\right) \qquad \text{difference of two squares}$$

$$= 6\left(x - \frac{7}{6}\right) \cdot 3\left(x - \frac{2}{3}\right) = (6x - 7)(3x - 2)$$

Remember, we only claimed that no trial and error is necessary. Nothing was said about the time required. ◢

PROBLEMS   Problems 45 to 76 may be done now.

Factoring by Grouping

Some polynomials can be factored by first properly grouping the terms.

▶ **EXAMPLE 14**   Factor $4c^2 - a^2 + 2ab - b^2$.

Solution

$$4c^2 - a^2 + 2ab - b^2$$

$$= 4c^2 - (a^2 - 2ab + b^2) \qquad \text{inserting parentheses}$$

$$= 4c^2 - (a - b)^2 \qquad \text{square of a difference}$$

$$= (2c)^2 - (a - b)^2 \qquad \text{law of exponents}$$

$$= [2c + (a - b)][2c - (a - b)] \qquad \text{difference of squares}$$

$$= (2c + a - b)(2c - a + b) \qquad \text{removing parentheses} \qquad ◢$$

▶ **EXAMPLE 15**   Factor $ax + ay + bx + by$.

Solution   Grouping the first two terms and the last two terms gives

$$ax + ay + bx + by = a(x + y) + b(x + y)$$
$$= (x + y)(a + b) \qquad ◢$$

When factoring an expression, see first if there is a common factor in all the terms. Then try to see which standard form will allow the factoring to be completed.

EXERCISE 1.4

Remove the common factors in Probs. 1 to 12.

1. $3x + 9$ **2.** $7x - 28$
3. $5x + 30$ **4.** $6x - 18$
5. $x^2 + 3x$ **6.** $x^2 - 4x$
7. $x^3 + 6x^2$ **8.** $x^3 - 3x^2$
9. $3x(x - 1) - (x - 1)^2$
10. $(2x + 3)7x + 5(2x + 3)$
11. $x^2(3x + 4) + 3x(3x + 4) + 2(3x + 4)$
12. $(2x - 1)12x + 4(2x - 1) + 9(2x - 1)x^2$

Factor the expression in each of Probs. 13 to 44.

13. $a^2 - x^2$ **14.** $9 - y^2$
15. $x^2 - 25$ **16.** $y^2 - 36$
17. $16y^2 - 25a^2$ **18.** $64x^2 - 49y^2$
19. $16x^2 - 81y^2$ **20.** $49y^2 - 36x^2$
21. $x^2 - (y + 1)^2$ **22.** $4x^2 - (3y + 2)^2$
23. $(2x - 3)^2 - 9y^2$ **24.** $(5x + 2)^2 - (2y + 7)^2$
25. $x^3z - 8y^3z$ **26.** $27a^3c^2 + b^3c^2$
27. $8ka^3 + 125kb^3$ **28.** $27x^3w^3 - 512y^3w^3$
29. $(x + y)^3 - 1$ **30.** $(2x - y)^3 - 8$
31. $(3x + 2y)^3 + 27$ **32.** $(x - 3y)^3 + 64$
33. $16x^4 - y^4$ **34.** $x^4 - 81y^4$
35. $81x^4 - 625y^4$ **36.** $16x^4 - 81y^4$
37. $4a^2b - 4ab + b$ **38.** $9b^2d + 6bd + d$
39. $25x^2 + 10x + 1$ **40.** $100x^2 - 20x + 1$
41. $4x^2 - 12x + 9$ **42.** $9x^2y^2 + 24xy^2 + 16y^2$
43. $25kx^2 + 60xk + 36k$ **44.** $64x^2 - 80x + 25$

Test the expression in each of Probs. 45 to 76 to see if it is factorable with integer coefficients. Factor those that can be so factored and give the value of $b^2 - 4ac$ for the others. Look for common factors first.

45. $3x^2 + 7x + 2$ **46.** $2x^2 + 5x + 2$
47. $6x^2 + 7x - 3$ **48.** $4x^2 - 1\,x + 12$
49. $7x^3 - 10x^2 + 3x$ **50.** $3x^4 + 13x^3 - 10x^2$
51. $4x^5 + 4x^4 - 3x^3$ **52.** $5x^4 + 6x^3 - 8x^2$
53. $2x^2 + 7x - 2$ **54.** $x^2 + 4x + 5$
55. $5x^2 + 6x + 7$ **56.** $5x^2 + 4x + 1$
57. $2x^2 + 9x - 9$ **58.** $3x^2 + 8x + 2$
59. $4x^2 + 9x - 5$ **60.** $3x^2 + 11x - 8$
61. $x^2 + 4x - 5$ **62.** $5x^2 + 4x - 1$
63. $2x^2 - 3x - 9$ **64.** $4x^2 + 9x + 5$
65. $2x^2 - xy - 28y^2$ **66.** $3x^2 - xy - 24y^2$
67. $5x^2 - 9xy - 18y^2$ **68.** $15x^2 + 11xy - 12y^2$
69. $20x^2 + 3xy - 35y^2$ **70.** $24x^2 + 26xy - 15y^2$

71. $42x^2 + 5xy - 25y^2$ **72.** $45x^2 + 2xy - 15y^2$
73. $30x^2 + 7xy - 49y^2$ **74.** $54x^2 - 3xy - 35y^2$
75. $30x^2 + 37xy - 12y^2$ **76.** $30x^2 - xy - 99y^2$

Factor the expression in each of Probs. 77 to 92.

77. $xy + x + 3y + 3$ **78.** $xy - 2x + 4y - 8$
79. $xy + 4x - 3y - 12$ **80.** $xy - 3x - 5y + 15$
81. $2x^2 + 4xy - x - 2y$ **82.** $3x^2 - 12xy + 2x - 8y$
83. $2x^2 - 3xy + 4x - 6y$ **84.** $6x^2 - 8xy - 9x + 12y$
85. $3x^3 + 2x^2 - 3x - 2$ **86.** $2x^3 + 4x - x^2 - 2$
87. $2x^3 - 5x^2 + 6x - 15$ **88.** $2x^3 - 6x^2 - x + 3$
89. $x^2 + 4xy + 4y^2 - z^2$ **90.** $4x^2 + y^2 - 9z^2 - 4xy$
91. $x^2 - 9y^2 - z^2 + 6yz$ **92.** $9x^2 - 4y^2 - z^2 - 4yz$

93. The statements below are a proof of the following simplified version of Fermat's last theorem: If x, y, z, and n are positive integers with $x < y < z \le n$, then $x^n + y^n \ne z^n$. Verify each step.

$$z^n - y^n = (z - y)(z^{n-1} + yz^{n-2} + y^2z^{n-3} + \cdots + y^{n-2}z + y^{n-1})$$
$$> (1)(x^{n-1} + x^{n-1} + x^{n-1} + \cdots + x^{n-1} + x^{n-1})$$
$$= n(x^{n-1}) > x^n$$

94. Show that
$$(ax + c)(ay + b) + ad - bc = a(axy + bx + cy + d)$$

95. If tic-tac-toe is placed in three dimensions on a cube which is $k \times k \times k$, the number of winning lines is
$$\frac{(k + 2)^3 - k^3}{2}$$
Simplify the expression above.

96. Simplify the expression
$$\frac{(x + h)^3 - x^3}{h}$$

97. *Psychology* Assume that the learning curve
$$18t^2 - t^3$$
gives the score of a rat after t weeks of learning. Factor the above expression, and also factor
$$18b^2 - b^3 - (18a^2 - a^3)$$

98. *Advertising* Assume that, in thousands, if \$$x$ is spent on advertising, the sales will be

$$75\left(1 - \frac{4}{(3 + x)^2}\right)$$

Factor this using the difference of two squares. Find the sales if $x = 0$ and if $x = 2$.

99. *Profit* Suppose the profit from selling x items is $(x - 40)(90 - x)$. Find in factored form the following difference in profits:

$$(b - 40)(90 - b) - (a - 40)(90 - a)$$

100. *Profit* If the profit from selling x items is $(x - 30)(100 - x)$, find in factored form the following difference in profits:

$$(b - 30)(100 - b) - (a - 30)(100 - a)$$

101. *Economics* Suppose that in a certain region, the number of households with an income above \$70,000 is $60(x^2 + 6x + 10)$, where x is the number of years after 1990. Factor the difference

$$60(b^2 + 6b + 10) - 60(a^2 + 6a + 10)$$

102. *Falling body* Suppose that the height of an object after t seconds is

$$-16t^2 + 40t + 850$$

Factor the difference

$$-16t^2 + 40t + 850 - (-16T^2 + 40T + 850)$$

103. *Supply* If the price is p, the supply is $p^2 + 10p - 600$. Factor this expression.

104. *Demand* If the price is p, the demand is $-p^2 - 30p + 2800$. Write this in factored form.

105. *Psychology* In the theory of learning in psychology, probabilities t and p and a constant b are related by

$$t = (1 - b)p$$

Show that this equation may be rewritten as

$$1 - t = (1 - b)(1 - p) + b$$

106. *Profit* Suppose that, in thousands, if x is the amount sold then the profit is $18x^2 + 12x$. Write this in factored form. Also factor the following difference in profits:

$$18b^2 + 12b - (18a^2 + 12a)$$

107. This problem occurs in mathematical induction proofs, which are treated in Chap. 12 of this book. It has been modified slightly to eliminate fractions. Start with the left-hand side, and simplify it to the form on the right.

$$n(n + 1)(2n + 1) + 6(n + 1)^2$$
$$= (n + 1)(n + 2)(2n + 3)$$

108. Same instructions as in Prob. 107, except use

$$n^2(n + 1)^2 + 4(n + 1)^3 = (n + 1)^2(n + 2)^2$$

1.5 Fractional Expressions

A **fractional expression** is a quotient of algebraic expressions; remember that division by zero is not defined. We will usually work with quotients of polynomials in this section, and these are called **rational expressions,** or **fractions.** Since the values of fractional expressions are real numbers, all of the properties of real numbers hold. For example, the order of adding or multiplying two rational expressions does not matter. There are some new properties too, which are now stated.

Properties of fractions

Assume there is *no division by zero* below.

$$\frac{a}{b} = \frac{c}{d} \text{ if and only if } ad = bc \qquad \text{equivalent fractions} \qquad \textbf{(1.33)}$$

$$\frac{a}{b} = \frac{ak}{bk} \text{ for any } k \neq 0 \qquad \text{fundamental principle of fractions} \qquad \textbf{(1.34)}$$

$$\frac{a}{b} = \frac{-a}{-b} = -\frac{-a}{b} = -\frac{a}{-b} \qquad \text{signs of fractions} \qquad \textbf{(1.35)}$$

and

$$-\frac{a}{b} = \frac{-a}{b} = \frac{a}{-b} = -\frac{-a}{-b}$$

$$\frac{a}{b} \cdot \frac{c}{d} = \frac{ac}{bd} \qquad \text{product of fractions} \qquad \textbf{(1.36)}$$

$$\frac{a}{d} + \frac{c}{d} = \frac{a+c}{d} \qquad \text{sum of fractions} \qquad \textbf{(1.37)}$$

The fundamental principle of fractions (1.34) is true since, by the rule for equivalent fractions (1.33) we know that

$$\frac{a}{b} = \frac{ak}{bk} \text{ is equivalent to } (a)(bk) = (b)(ak)$$

and the last equation is true since each side is equal to *abk*.

EXAMPLE 1 Show that the fractions below are equivalent.

Solution Either the rule for equivalent fractions or the fundamental principle of fractions may be used.

(a) Using the rule for equivalent fractions gives

$$\frac{4x}{9y} = \frac{28xz}{63yz} \text{ since } (4x)(63yz) = (9y)(28xz) = 252xyz$$

(b) By the fundamental principle of fractions

$$\frac{20gmt}{32amt} = \frac{5g(4mt)}{8a(4mt)} = \frac{5g}{8a}$$

The fundamental principle of fractions, *ak/bk = a/b*, can be used in two ways. We can simplify a fraction by **removing a common factor** by division from the numerator and the denominator. On the other hand, many situations are best handled if we **introduce a common factor** into both the numerator and denominator by multiplication.

Removing a Common Factor: *ak/bk = a/b*

A rational expression is said to be in **lowest terms** if the numerator and denominator have no common factors except 1. We say that such an expression has been **simplified** or **reduced to lowest terms.** Consequently, to reduce a given fraction to lowest terms, we remove from the numerator and denominator each *factor* that is common to both. This is sometimes called **removing,** or **canceling,** the common factor, and it is merely a rewording of the fundamental principle of fractions

$$\frac{a \cdot k}{b \cdot k} = \frac{a}{b}$$

▶ **EXAMPLE 2**   Reduce $\dfrac{35a^4b^2}{42a^3b^3}$ to lowest terms.

Solution   The common factor is $7a^3b^2$; hence

$$\frac{35a^4b^2}{42a^3b^3} = \frac{5a \cdot 7a^3b^2}{6b \cdot 7a^3b^2} = \frac{5a}{6b}$$

after removing $7a^3b^2$ from numerator and denominator.   ◢

NOTE   Only common *factors*, not common terms which are *added*, can be removed. Thus

$$\frac{a + b + c}{a + b + d} \neq \frac{c}{d} \qquad \text{but} \qquad \frac{(a + b)c}{(a + b)d} = \frac{c}{d}$$

because $a + b$ **is not a factor** of both the numerator and denominator in the first expression, while $a + b$ **is a common factor** in the second. For the same reason

$$\frac{2x + 5}{2y - 3} \neq \frac{x + 5}{y - 3} \qquad \text{and} \qquad \frac{x^2 + 5x - 9}{4y + 5x + 7} \neq \frac{x^2 - 9}{4y + 7}$$

NOTE   You must factor the numerator and denominator of a fraction so that the **common factors** can be clearly identified.

▶ **EXAMPLE 3**   Reduce $\dfrac{x^3 + x^2 - 6x}{x^3 - 3x^2 + 2x}$ to lowest terms.

Solution   We first factor the numerator and denominator of the fraction:

$$\frac{x^3 + x^2 - 6x}{x^3 - 3x^2 + 2x} = \frac{x(x^2 + x - 6)}{x(x^2 - 3x + 2)} \qquad \text{common factor of } x$$

$$= \frac{x(x - 2)(x + 3)}{x(x - 2)(x - 1)} \qquad \text{factoring}$$

$$= \frac{x + 3}{x - 1} \qquad \text{removing } x \text{ and } x - 2 \qquad ◢$$

If a factor of both the numerator and the denominator differ only in their signs, then their quotient is -1. This is demonstrated in the next example.

▶ **EXAMPLE 4**   Simplify the following fraction.

Solution
$$\frac{b(x - 2y)}{2y - x} = \frac{-b(2y - x)}{2y - x} = -b \qquad ◢$$

Introducing a Common Factor: $a/b = ak/bk$

In many operations, such as dividing complex numbers (Chap. 2), adding fractions (later in this section), rationalizing the denominator or numerator of some radical expressions (Sec. 1.6), working with negative exponents, and simplifying complex fractions, a given expression must have a certain form. We can often accomplish this by multiplying both members of the fraction by the same expression.

In Example 5, we show how to make the denominator a perfect cube, an essential step in rationalizing monomial denominators *in Sec. 1.6.*

EXAMPLE 5 Multiply the numerator and denominator by the same factor to make the denominator a perfect cube.

Solution
$$\frac{5x}{12y^2} = \frac{5x \cdot [2 \cdot 3^2 \cdot y]}{2^2 \cdot 3 \cdot y^2 \cdot [2 \cdot 3^2 \cdot y]} = \frac{90xy}{2^3 \cdot 3^3 \cdot y^3} = \frac{90xy}{(6y)^3}$$

EXAMPLE 6 Write $\dfrac{2}{x - y}$ as an equivalent fraction with $x^3 - y^3$ as its denominator. This type of operation will be essential when adding fractions *later in this section.*

Solution Since $x^3 - y^3 = (x - y)(x^2 + xy + y^2)$, we write

$$\frac{2}{x - y} \cdot \frac{x^2 + xy + y^2}{x^2 + xy + y^2} = \frac{2(x^2 + xy + y^2)}{x^3 - y^3}$$

Example 7 uses the fundamental principle of fractions in both ways. First we introduce a common factor, and then we remove a different common factor.

EXAMPLE 7 Simplify the fraction $(|2x + 1| - 7)/(x - 3)$.

Solution
$$\frac{|2x + 1| - 7}{x - 3} = \frac{|2x + 1| - 7}{x - 3} \cdot \frac{|2x + 1| + 7}{|2x + 1| + 7}$$

Now we use the fact that $|t|^2 = t^2$, with $t = 2x + 1$, and get

$$\frac{(2x + 1)^2 - 49}{(x - 3)(|2x + 1| + 7)} = \frac{4x^2 + 4x - 48}{(x - 3)(|2x + 1| + 7)}$$

$$= \frac{4(x - 3)(x + 4)}{(x - 3)(|2x + 1| + 7)} = \frac{4(x + 4)}{|2x + 1| + 7}$$

PROBLEMS Problems 1 to 12 may be done now.

Multiplication and Division of Fractions

In words, rule (1.36) on multiplying fractions says the following:

The product of rational expressions is a rational expression where the numerator is the product of the numerators of the given expressions, and the denominator is the product of the given denominators.

This product should be reduced to lowest terms. For this reason, the members of the fractions should be factored, if possible, before the product is formed. Then the **factors** that are common to the members of the product can be detected easily and should be removed before forming the product.

EXAMPLE 8   Find the following product of fractions.

Solution
$$\frac{11x^2w^4}{14y^3} \cdot \frac{21y^2w^8}{22x^5} = \frac{11x^2w^4 \cdot 7 \cdot 3y^2w^8}{7 \cdot 2y^3 \cdot 2 \cdot 11x^5} = \frac{3w^{12}}{4yx^3}$$

EXAMPLE 9   Find the product of

$$\frac{a^2 - 4b^2}{2a^2 - 7ab + 3b^2} \qquad \frac{6a - 3b}{2a + 4b} \qquad \text{and} \qquad \frac{a^2 - 4ab + 3b^2}{a^2 - ab - 2b^2}$$

Solution
$$\frac{a^2 - 4b^2}{2a^2 - 7ab + 3b^2} \cdot \frac{6a - 3b}{2a + 4b} \cdot \frac{a^2 - 4ab + 3b^2}{a^2 - ab - 2b^2}$$

$$= \frac{(a - 2b)(a + 2b)}{(2a - b)(a - 3b)} \cdot \frac{3(2a - b)}{2(a + 2b)} \cdot \frac{(a - b)(a - 3b)}{(a + b)(a - 2b)} \qquad \text{factoring}$$

$$= \frac{3(a - 2b)(a + 2b)(2a - b)(a - 3b)(a - b)}{2(a - 2b)(a + 2b)(2a - b)(a - 3b)(a + b)} \qquad \begin{array}{l}\text{by the commutative}\\ \text{axiom and (1.36)}\end{array}$$

$$= \frac{3(a - b)}{2(a + b)} \qquad \begin{array}{l}\text{removing } (a - 2b), (a + 2b),\\ (a - 3b), \text{ and } (2a - b)\end{array}$$

EXAMPLE 10   Find the product of

$$\frac{x^2 - 3x + 2}{2x^2 + 3x - 2} \qquad \frac{2x^2 + 5x - 3}{x^2 - 1} \qquad \text{and} \qquad \frac{3x^2 + 6x}{2x - 4}$$

Solution
$$\frac{x^2 - 3x + 2}{2x^2 + 3x - 2} \cdot \frac{2x^2 + 5x - 3}{x^2 - 1} \cdot \frac{3x^2 + 6x}{2x - 4}$$

$$= \frac{(x - 2)(x - 1)}{(2x - 1)(x + 2)} \cdot \frac{(2x - 1)(x + 3)}{(x - 1)(x + 1)} \cdot \frac{3x(x + 2)}{2(x - 2)} \qquad \text{factoring}$$

$$= \frac{3x(x + 3)}{2(x + 1)} \qquad \text{removing common factors}$$

Division   To divide by a fraction c/d, we

Multiply by its reciprocal d/c

This is also sometimes stated as ''invert and multiply.'' Here is the reason for this procedure:

$$\frac{a/b}{c/d} = \frac{\dfrac{a}{b} \cdot \dfrac{d}{c}}{\dfrac{c}{d} \cdot \dfrac{d}{c}} = \frac{\dfrac{ad}{bc}}{\dfrac{cd}{cd}} = \frac{ad/bc}{1} = \frac{a}{b} \cdot \frac{d}{c}$$

EXAMPLE 11 Divide $\dfrac{x^2 - 3x + 2}{2x^2 - 7x + 3}$ by $\dfrac{x^2 - x - 2}{2x^2 + 3x - 2}$.

Solution

$$\frac{x^2 - 3x + 2}{2x^2 - 7x + 3} \div \frac{x^2 - x - 2}{2x^2 + 3x - 2}$$

$$= \frac{x^2 - 3x + 2}{2x^2 - 7x + 3} \cdot \frac{2x^2 + 3x - 2}{x^2 - x - 2} \qquad \text{multiplying by the reciprocal}$$

$$= \frac{(x - 2)(x - 1)(2x - 1)(x + 2)}{(2x - 1)(x - 3)(x - 2)(x + 1)} \qquad \text{factoring}$$

$$= \frac{(x - 1)(x + 2)}{(x - 3)(x + 1)} \qquad \text{removing } (x - 2) \text{ and } (2x - 1)$$

PROBLEMS Problems 13 to 36 may be done now.

Addition and Subtraction of Rational Expressions

If two rational expressions, or fractions, have the same denominator, it is easy to add or subtract them by Eq. (1.37):

$$\frac{a}{d} + \frac{b}{d} = \frac{a + b}{d} \qquad \frac{a}{d} - \frac{b}{d} = \frac{a - b}{d}$$

We simply keep the same denominator, and add or subtract the numerators. This is a result of the distributive law.

EXAMPLE 12 Add the fractions below, which have the same denominator.

Solution

$$\frac{4}{21} + \frac{2}{21} + \frac{8}{21} = \frac{14}{21} = \frac{2}{3}$$

EXAMPLE 13 Combine the following fractions.

Solution Since they have the same denominator, we only have to combine their numerators:

$$\frac{5a}{2xy} + \frac{2b}{2xy} - \frac{5b - 9a}{2xy} = \frac{5a + 2b - (5b - 9a)}{2xy} = \frac{14a - 3b}{2xy}$$

If the rational expressions to be added or subtracted do not all have the same denominator, we begin by rewriting them as equivalent fractions, where the denominator of each one is the **lcd (least common denominator).** The lcd is the least common multiple of the denominators, which means that it is a multiple of each denominator and that its degree is as small as possible. We may find the lcd of several rational expressions as shown below.

Finding the lcd

1. Factor each denominator into prime factors.
2. Write the product of all of the different prime factors.
3. Give each prime factor the largest exponent it has in any of the given denominators.

▶ **EXAMPLE 14**   Find the lcd if the denominators are $(x - 2)^4(x + 1)$, $(x - 2)(x + 1)^3(x - 1)$, and $(x - 2)^2(x - 1)^2$.

Solution   The different factors are $x - 2$, $x + 1$, and $x - 1$ and their greatest exponents are 4, 3, and 2, respectively. Consequently, the lcd is $(x - 2)^4(x + 1)^3(x - 1)^2$.   ◀

▶ **EXAMPLE 15**   Convert each of the fractions $\dfrac{a}{xy}$, $\dfrac{3b}{x^3y}$, and $\dfrac{2c}{xy^2}$ to an equivalent rational expression with the lcd as its denominator.

Solution   The lcd is x^3y^2; hence, we multiply the members of the given fractions by x^2y, y, and x^2, respectively, giving

$$\frac{a \cdot x^2y}{xy \cdot x^2y} = \frac{ax^2y}{x^3y^2} \qquad \frac{3b \cdot y}{x^3y \cdot y} = \frac{3by}{x^3y^2} \qquad \text{and} \qquad \frac{2c \cdot x^2}{xy^2 \cdot x^2} = \frac{2cx^2}{x^3y^2} \qquad ◀$$

▶ **EXAMPLE 16**   Combine $1/2x + 1/5y + (8x - 2y)/20xy$ into a single fraction.

Solution   The lcd for the given fractions is $20xy$; hence, we multiply each member of the first fraction by $20xy/2x = 10y$ and each member of the second fraction by $20xy/5y = 4x$, and thus have

$$\frac{1}{2x} \cdot \frac{10y}{10y} + \frac{1}{5y} \cdot \frac{4x}{4x} + \frac{8x - 2y}{20xy} = \frac{1}{20xy}(10y + 4x + 8x - 2y)$$

$$= \frac{12x + 8y}{20xy} \qquad \text{combining}$$

$$= \frac{3x + 2y}{5xy} \qquad \text{reducing to lowest terms} \qquad ◀$$

▶ **EXAMPLE 17**   Combine $2/(2x - y) + 3/(2x + y) - 9x/(4x^2 - y^2)y$ into a single fraction.

Solution   The factored form of the third denominator is $(2x - y)(2x + y)y$; furthermore, each of the other denominators is a factor of this one. Therefore, $(2x - y)(2x + y)y$ is the lcd. Consequently, we multiply the members of the first fraction by $(2x + y)y$, the members of the second fraction by $(2x - y)y$, and have

$$\frac{2}{2x - y} \cdot \frac{y(2x + y)}{y(2x + y)} + \frac{3}{2x + y} \cdot \frac{y(2x - y)}{y(2x - y)} - \frac{9x}{(4x^2 - y^2)y}$$

$$= \frac{4xy + 2y^2 + 6xy - 3y^2 - 9x}{(4x^2 - y^2)y} = \frac{10xy - y^2 - 9x}{(4x^2 - y^2)y} \qquad ◀$$

▶ **EXAMPLE 18**   Find $\dfrac{1}{x^2 + 8x + 16} - \dfrac{1}{x^2 + 4x} + \dfrac{1}{x^3 + x^2}$.

Solution   The denominators are $(x + 4)^2$, $x(x + 4)$, and $x^2(x + 1)$, and so the lcd is $x^2(x + 4)^2(x + 1)$. The sum is therefore

$$\frac{x^2(x + 1)}{(x + 4)^2[x^2(x + 1)]} - \frac{x(x + 4)(x + 1)}{x(x + 4)[x(x + 4)(x + 1)]} + \frac{(x + 4)^2}{x^2(x + 1)[(x + 4)^2]}$$

$$= \frac{x^3 + x^2}{x^2(x + 4)^2(x + 1)} - \frac{x^3 + 5x^2 + 4x}{x^2(x + 4)^2(x + 1)} + \frac{x^2 + 8x + 16}{x^2(x + 4)^2(x + 1)}$$

$$= \frac{x^3 + x^2 - x^3 - 5x^2 - 4x + x^2 + 8x + 16}{x^2(x + 4)^2(x + 1)}$$

$$= \frac{-3x^2 + 4x + 16}{x^2(x + 4)^2(x + 1)}$$

◀

PROBLEMS   Problems 37 to 68 may be done now.

Complex Fractions

A **complex fraction** is a fraction in which either the numerator or denominator or both involve a rational expression. We have two ways to simplify a complex fraction. One procedure is to write the numerator and denominator each as a rational expression, then perform the division by multiplying the numerator by the reciprocal of the denominator. The other way is to multiply both the numerator and denominator by the lcd of the various denominators.

▶ EXAMPLE 19   Simplify.

$$\frac{\dfrac{2}{x + y} - \dfrac{1}{x - y}}{\dfrac{4(x - y)}{x + y} - \dfrac{x + y}{x - y}}$$

Solution 1   We first rewrite the numerator as a single fraction:

$$\frac{2}{x + y} \cdot \frac{x - y}{x - y} - \frac{1}{x - y} \cdot \frac{x + y}{x + y} = \frac{2x - 2y}{x^2 - y^2} - \frac{x + y}{x^2 - y^2} = \frac{x - 3y}{x^2 - y^2}$$

Then the denominator is also rewritten as a single fraction:

$$\frac{4(x - y)}{x + y} \cdot \frac{x - y}{x - y} - \frac{x + y}{x - y} \cdot \frac{x + y}{x + y} = \frac{4(x^2 - 2xy + y^2)}{x^2 - y^2} - \frac{x^2 + 2xy + y^2}{x^2 - y^2}$$

$$= \frac{3x^2 - 10xy + 3y^2}{x^2 - y^2}$$

Now we can find the given quotient:

$$\frac{x - 3y}{x^2 - y^2} \div \frac{3x^2 - 10xy + 3y^2}{x^2 - y^2} = \frac{x - 3y}{x^2 - y^2} \cdot \frac{x^2 - y^2}{3x^2 - 10xy + 3y^2}$$

$$= \frac{x - 3y}{(3x - y)(x - 3y)} = \frac{1}{3x - y}$$

Solution 2   With this procedure, we multiply the numerator and denominator by the lcd $(x - y)(x + y)$, and obtain

$$\frac{\dfrac{2}{x + y} - \dfrac{1}{x - y}}{\dfrac{4(x - y)}{x + y} - \dfrac{x + y}{x - y}} \cdot \frac{(x - y)(x + y)}{(x - y)(x + y)}$$

$$= \frac{2(x - y) - (x + y)}{4(x - y)(x - y) - (x + y)(x + y)} \qquad \text{multiplying each term by lcd}$$

$$= \frac{2x - 2y - x - y}{4(x^2 - 2xy + y^2) - (x^2 + 2xy + y^2)} \qquad \text{simplifying}$$

$$= \frac{x - 3y}{3x^2 - 10xy + 3y^2} \qquad \text{similar terms}$$

$$= \frac{x - 3y}{(3x - y)(x - 3y)} = \frac{1}{3x - y} \qquad \text{factoring and canceling} \qquad \blacktriangleleft$$

PROBLEMS   Problems 69 to 84 on complex fractions may be done now, as well as the rest of the problems.

EXERCISE 1.5

Reduce the fraction in each of Probs. 1 to 12 to lowest terms.

1. $8x^2y^3/2xy$

2. $18x^3y^2/9x^4y$

3. $9x^5yz^3/15x^3y^2z^3$

4. $12x^4y^3z/27x^2y^4z^3$

5. $\dfrac{x^2 + x - 6}{x^2 + 2x - 3}$

6. $\dfrac{x^2 + x - 2}{x^2 - x - 6}$

7. $\dfrac{2x^2 + 3x - 2}{2x^2 + 5x + 2}$

8. $\dfrac{3x^2 - x - 2}{2x^2 + x - 3}$

9. $\dfrac{(x + 2)(x^2 - 4x + 4)}{(x - 1)(x^2 + 5x + 6)}$

10. $\dfrac{(x - 3)(x^2 - x - 6)}{(x + 2)(x^2 - 4x + 3)}$

11. $\dfrac{(2x - 1)(x^2 + 2x - 8)}{(x + 4)(2x^2 + x - 1)}$

12. $\dfrac{(3x + 2)(x^2 - x - 2)}{(x - 2)(3x^2 - x - 2)}$

Perform the indicated operations in the following problems and reduce to lowest terms.

13. $\dfrac{3x^3y^2}{4x^2z^3} \cdot \dfrac{8y^3z^2}{15x^2y^7} \div \dfrac{3z}{16x^2y^5}$

14. $\dfrac{7x^2y^3}{6w^4v^2} \cdot \dfrac{9xw^3}{21y^2v} \div \dfrac{5x^4}{8y^2w}$

15. $\dfrac{11x^2w^4}{14yv^3} \cdot \dfrac{21v^2w^2}{33xy^2} \div \dfrac{3w^6}{2y^3}$

16. $\dfrac{3x^5y^4}{12v^3w^2} \cdot \dfrac{21yw}{17x^2v^2} \div \dfrac{7x^3}{68y^4}$

17. $\dfrac{xy + 2xz}{3y + 6z} \cdot \dfrac{5y + 10z}{3xy + 6xz}$

18. $\dfrac{2x^2 + 5xy}{6x - 2y} \cdot \dfrac{3xw - yw}{2xy + 5y^2}$

19. $\dfrac{2x^2 - 3xy}{2y^2 - 3xy} \cdot \dfrac{3xy - 2y^2}{3xy - 2x^2}$

20. $\dfrac{2x + 6y}{2v^2 - vw} \cdot \dfrac{6vw - 3w^2}{2xy + 6y^2}$

21. $\dfrac{4x^2 - y^2}{x + 2y} \div \dfrac{4x^2 + 2xy}{xy + 2y^2}$

22. $\dfrac{x^2 - 16}{x - 5} \div \dfrac{2x - 8}{xy - 5y}$

23. $\dfrac{2x^2 + 3xy}{3xy - 2y^2} \div \dfrac{4x^2 - 9y^2}{3x^2 - 2xy}$

24. $\dfrac{x^2 - 4y^2}{x^2 + xy - 2y^2} \div \dfrac{x^2 - 2xy}{x^2 - y^2}$

25. $\dfrac{w^2 + 3w}{z^2 - 2z} \cdot \dfrac{wz^2 - 2wz}{w^2 - 9} \cdot \dfrac{w - 3}{z^2}$

26. $\dfrac{p^2 + 5pq}{q^2 - q} \cdot \dfrac{q^2 - 1}{p^3q + 5p^2q^2} \cdot \dfrac{q^3}{pq + p}$

27. $\dfrac{3x^2 - 7xy}{x^2y^3 - 49y^5} \cdot \dfrac{3x + 21y}{3x^4 - 7x^3y} \cdot \dfrac{x^3yz^2}{xz - 7yz}$

28. $\dfrac{3x + y}{xy - 3xz} \cdot \dfrac{x^2yz}{x - 2y} \cdot \dfrac{y^3 - 9yz^2}{2yz + 6z^2}$

29. $\dfrac{x^2 - y^2}{x^2y} \cdot \dfrac{xy - 2y^2}{x - y} \cdot \dfrac{xy^3}{x^2 - xy - 2y^2}$

30. $\dfrac{xy - xz + y^2 - yz}{yz} \cdot \dfrac{2yz - z^2}{xz - xy} \cdot$

31. $\dfrac{xy + 2xz + y^2 + 2yz}{xy + 2xz} \cdot \dfrac{\dfrac{x^2y}{2xy - xz - 2y^2 + yz}}{\dfrac{xy + xz}{x^2 + xy + xz + yz}} \cdot$

$\dfrac{\dfrac{x^2 - xy - xz + yz}{xy - xz - yz + z^2}}{}$

32. $\dfrac{2xy - xz + 4y^2 - 2yz}{y - 2x} \cdot \dfrac{\dfrac{2xy - y^2}{x^2 + xy - 2y^2}}{\dfrac{x^2 - xy + xz - yz}{z^3 - 2yz^2}} \cdot$

33. $\dfrac{x^3 + y^3}{x^2 + 3xy + 2y^2} \cdot \dfrac{x^2 - xy - 6y^2}{x^2 - 2xy - 3y^2} \div$

$\dfrac{\dfrac{x^2 - xy + y^2}{2x^2 + 2xy}}{}$

34. $\dfrac{x^2 - xy - 2y^2}{x^3 - y^3} \cdot \dfrac{x^2 + xy + y^2}{x^2 - 4y^2} \div \dfrac{x^2 + 4xy + 3y^2}{x^2 + xy - 2y^2}$

35. $\dfrac{x^3 + 8y^3}{x^2 - 4y^2} \cdot \dfrac{x^2 - xy - 2y^2}{x^2 - 2xy + 4y^2} \div \dfrac{x^2 - 2xy - 3y^2}{x^2 - 3xy}$

36. $\dfrac{27x^3 - y^3}{3x^2 - 4xy + y^2} \cdot \dfrac{x^2 + 2xy - 3y^2}{9x^2 + 3xy + y^2} \div \dfrac{x^2 - 9y^2}{xy + 3y^2}$

Perform the additions indicated in Probs. 37 to 68 and then reduce to lowest terms.

37. $\dfrac{2x + 1}{6x + 1} + \dfrac{7x - 5}{6x + 1} + \dfrac{9x - 3}{6x + 1}$

38. $\dfrac{2x}{x^2 + 11} + \dfrac{5 - 3x}{x^2 + 11} - \dfrac{6 + 7x}{x^2 + 11}$

39. $\dfrac{3a + b}{d - 1} - \dfrac{4c - 3a}{d - 1} + \dfrac{6b - 5c}{d - 1}$

40. $\dfrac{4a + 5}{b + 13} - \dfrac{3a - b}{b + 13} - \dfrac{6 + 4b}{b + 13}$

41. $\dfrac{4b}{3a} - \dfrac{5a}{2b} + \dfrac{9a^2 - 8b^2}{6ab}$

42. $\dfrac{3a}{2b} - \dfrac{2b}{3a} - \dfrac{9a^2 - 4b^2}{6ab}$

43. $\dfrac{5a}{3b} - \dfrac{2b}{5a} + \dfrac{9b^2 - 22a^2}{15ab}$

44. $\dfrac{3b}{7a} - \dfrac{a}{2b} + \dfrac{3a^2 - 2b^2}{14ab}$

45. $\dfrac{2x - y}{3x + y} + \dfrac{5x}{2y}$

46. $\dfrac{3x + 4y}{2x + y} - \dfrac{2y}{x}$

47. $\dfrac{3x}{2y} - \dfrac{3x - 2y}{3x + 2y}$

48. $\dfrac{3x}{5y} - \dfrac{5x + 2y}{2x - y}$

49. $\dfrac{x + 2y}{x - y} - \dfrac{x - 2y}{x + y}$

50. $\dfrac{3x - 2y}{2x - y} - \dfrac{2x + y}{3x - y}$

51. $\dfrac{5x - 2y}{3x - 8y} + \dfrac{3x - 3y}{2x - 5y}$

52. $\dfrac{2x + 7y}{5x - 3y} + \dfrac{5x + 3y}{2x - 7y}$

53. $\dfrac{r + s}{rs} - \dfrac{1}{s} + \dfrac{s}{r(r - s)}$

54. $\dfrac{s}{r + s} - \dfrac{r^2}{s(r + s)} + \dfrac{2r}{s}$

55. $\dfrac{s}{r} - \dfrac{2rs}{r(r - 2s)} + \dfrac{r}{r - 2s}$

56. $\dfrac{r^2 - 3s^2}{r(r + 3s)} + \dfrac{3s}{r} + \dfrac{2s}{r + 3s}$

57. $\dfrac{6x}{x^2 - y^2} + \dfrac{2x}{y(x + y)} - \dfrac{3}{x - y}$

58. $\dfrac{2}{3x - 2y} - \dfrac{3y}{x(3x + 2y)} - \dfrac{8y}{9x^2 - 4y^2}$

59. $\dfrac{2x}{y(x + 2y)} + \dfrac{4}{x - 2y} + \dfrac{8x}{x^2 - 4y^2}$

60. $\dfrac{x}{x + 3} - \dfrac{6x + 6}{x^2 - 9} + \dfrac{x + 1}{x - 3}$

61. $\dfrac{3}{(x + 2y)(x - y)} + \dfrac{2}{(x - 2y)(x - y)} - $

$\dfrac{4}{(x + 2y)(x - 2y)}$

62. $\dfrac{2}{(a + 3b)(a + b)} - \dfrac{3}{(a + 3b)(a - 2b)} + $

$\dfrac{5}{(a + b)(a - 2b)}$

63. $\dfrac{4}{(a + 5b)(a - 4b)} + \dfrac{1}{(a - 4b)(a - b)} +$

$$\dfrac{\dfrac{2}{(a + 5b)(a - b)}}{}$$

64. $\dfrac{2}{(a + b)(a + 2b)} - \dfrac{5}{(a - 3b)(a + 2b)} +$

$$\dfrac{4}{(a - 3b)(a + b)}$$

65. $\dfrac{3}{x + 1} + \dfrac{2}{(x + 1)^2} - \dfrac{5}{(x + 1)^3}$

66. $\dfrac{4}{x - 2} - \dfrac{3}{(x - 2)^2} + \dfrac{1}{(x - 2)^3}$

67. $\dfrac{x}{(x + 3)^2} - \dfrac{2x + 1}{(x + 3)(x - 1)}$

68. $\dfrac{2x + 5}{(x - 4)^2} + \dfrac{x - 1}{(x - 4)(x + 2)}$

Simplify these complex fractions.

69. $\dfrac{1 + \dfrac{x}{x + y}}{1 - \dfrac{3x}{x - y}}$

70. $\dfrac{2 - \dfrac{x}{2x + y}}{2 - \dfrac{5x}{x - y}}$

71. $\dfrac{a - 2 + \dfrac{a - 2}{a + 2}}{a - \dfrac{3a + 12}{a + 2}}$

72. $\dfrac{a + \dfrac{8a}{2a - 1}}{a + 2 - \dfrac{6}{2a + 3}}$

73. $\dfrac{\dfrac{2}{p + q} - \dfrac{1}{p - 2q}}{2 - \dfrac{p + q}{p - 2q}}$

74. $\dfrac{\dfrac{1 - 2p}{1 + 3p} - \dfrac{1}{1 - p}}{1 - \dfrac{10}{1 + 3p}}$

75. $\dfrac{6 + \dfrac{7}{x} + \dfrac{2}{x^2}}{2 + \dfrac{7}{x} + \dfrac{3}{x^2}}$

76. $\dfrac{3 - \dfrac{11}{x} + \dfrac{6}{x^2}}{4 - \dfrac{13}{x} + \dfrac{3}{x^2}}$

77. $\dfrac{\dfrac{2}{3x + 5} - \dfrac{1}{7}}{x - 3}$

78. $\dfrac{\dfrac{3}{4x - 5} - \dfrac{1}{5}}{x - 5}$

79. $\dfrac{\dfrac{1}{x^2 + 6} - \dfrac{1}{10}}{x + 2}$

80. $\dfrac{\dfrac{1}{x^2 - 5} - \dfrac{1}{11}}{x + 4}$

81. $\dfrac{1}{3 + \dfrac{1}{2 + \dfrac{1}{x}}}$

82. $\dfrac{1}{4 + \dfrac{1}{3 + \dfrac{1}{x - 2}}} + 5$

83. $\dfrac{1}{5 + \dfrac{1}{2 + \dfrac{1}{x + 4}}} + 3$

84. $\dfrac{1}{8 + \dfrac{1}{5 + \dfrac{1}{x + 1}}}$

Simplify the expressions in Probs. 85 to 86. *Note:* Problems similar to these will occur in Chap. 2 in this book, where the topic of equations with fractions is discussed.

85. $\left(\dfrac{3}{x + 5} - \dfrac{4}{2x + 1}\right)(x + 5)(2x + 1)$

86. $\left(\dfrac{7}{x + 9} + \dfrac{5}{6x - 5}\right)(x + 9)(6x - 5)$

Simplify the expressions in Probs. 87 and 88. *Note:* Problems similar to these may occur when working with inequalities.

87. $\dfrac{x - y}{x - 2y} - \dfrac{x + y}{x + 2y}$ **88.** $\dfrac{3x + 2y}{2x + y} - \dfrac{3x - 2y}{2x - y}$

Verify the statements in Probs. 89 and 90.

89. $x = x/2 + x/3 + x/8 + x/24$

90. $z = z/3 + z/5 + z/6 + z/7 + z/10 + z/30 + z/42$

91. *Business/rule of 78* If depreciation is calculated according to the sum-of-the-digits method, then the fractions used in the n years have numerators n, $n - 1$, $n - 2$, . . . , 2, 1 and each denominator is

$$\dfrac{n(n + 1)}{2}$$

Calculate these fractions for $n = 12$, and find their sum. When interest is calculated in a similar way, it is called ''the rule of 78'' because each denominator is 78.

92. *Management* Suppose that the total cost of orders is the ordering cost plus carrying cost, or

$$75x + \dfrac{4680}{x}$$

The minimum value of this occurs when x is nearly 8. Calculate the total cost for (a) $x = 5$, (b) $x = 8$, and (c) $x = 10$.

93. If a, b, and c are positive numbers, and if x, y, and z are the numbers a, b, c written in any order, then

$$\frac{a}{x} + \frac{b}{y} + \frac{c}{z} \geq 3$$

Verify this for any three positive numbers you choose.

94. Show that

$$\frac{x}{x+1} + \frac{x+1}{x+2} + \frac{x+2}{x} =$$
$$\frac{3(x^3 + 3x^2 + 2x) + 3x + 4}{x^3 + 3x^2 + 2x}$$

and thus the sum on the left is always ≥ 3 if $x > 0$.

95. *Inventory control* Suppose that total annual inventory cost is $3x + 480,000/x$. Find the difference in these inventory costs.

$$3x + \frac{480,000}{x} - \left(3y + \frac{480,000}{y}\right)$$

96. *Can the cost be cut?* Suppose that a can with a top and a bottom is to be a right circular cylinder with a volume of 100 in^3. If its radius is r, the surface area is

$$2\pi r^2 + \frac{200}{r}$$

The actual minimum value of the surface area occurs for $r = \sqrt[3]{50/\pi} \approx 2.52$. Find the surface area (and thus the material needed to build the can) for (a) $r = 2$, (b) $r = 2.5$, and (c) $r = 3$.

97. Suppose two cans are made, each like the one in Prob. 96, and that the radii are a and b. Find and simplify the following difference in surface areas:

$$2\pi b^2 + \frac{200}{b} - \left(2\pi a^2 + \frac{200}{a}\right)$$

98. Show that

$$\frac{a-b}{1+ab} + \frac{b-c}{1+bc} + \frac{c-a}{1+ac} =$$
$$\frac{a-b}{1+ab} \cdot \frac{b-c}{1+bc} \cdot \frac{c-a}{1+ac}$$

99. In a sense which can be made precise using more advanced mathematics, the average value of $1/x^2$ on the interval $[1, 2]$ is $1/2$. Calculate the value of the average below:

$$\frac{\dfrac{1}{(7/6)^2} + \dfrac{1}{(9/6)^2} + \dfrac{1}{(11/6)^2}}{3}$$

100. It can be shown that the average value of $1/x^2$ on the interval $[1.5, 4.5]$ is $4/9$. Simplify the average below, leaving h in the answer:

$$\frac{1}{3}\left[\frac{1}{(3-h)^2} + \frac{1}{3^2} + \frac{1}{(3+h)^2}\right]$$

Simplify the expressions in Probs. 101 and 102, which can occur when working with partial fractions in Chap. 9 of this book.

101. $\left[\dfrac{3}{x-2} + \dfrac{7}{(x-2)^2} + \dfrac{4x-5}{x^2+3}\right](x-2)^2(x^2+3)$

102. $\left[\dfrac{6}{x+3} + \dfrac{7}{(x+3)^2} + \dfrac{3}{4x-5}\right](x+3)^2(4x-5)$

1.6 Radicals

For positive integers n, we have already defined the nth power of b, namely b^n. In this section we will use the equation $a = b^n$ to define the nth root of a, and we begin with $n = 2$.

Square root

If a is a *positive real* number, then
$$\sqrt{a} = b \text{ if and only if } a = b^2 \text{ and } b > 0. \text{ Also, } \sqrt{0} = 0.$$

Thus for $a > 0$, we have $\sqrt{a} > 0$ by definition. This is sometimes called the **principal square root** of a. For $a < 0$, $\sqrt{a}$ is not defined as a real number.

The notation for the square root of 49 is $\sqrt{49}$. Its value is defined to be 7 since $7^2 = 49$ and $7 > 0$. Although $(-7)^2 = 49$, we use $\sqrt{49}$ only for $+7$, not for -7. The reason is so that we will have just one value for $\sqrt{49}$. We may, of course, write $-\sqrt{49}$ if we want the negative value -7. Also the value of $\pm\sqrt{49}$ is ± 7. Notice that -49 has no real square root since $b^2 \geq 0$ for every real number b, and thus $b^2 = -49$ has no real number solutions.

It follows by definition that $(\sqrt{a})^2 = a$ for $a \geq 0$.

EXAMPLE 1   Find the value of each expression below, if it is defined.

Solution

$$\sqrt{169} = 13 \qquad (\text{not } -13 \text{ and not } \pm 13)$$
$$-\sqrt{169} = -13$$
$$\pm\sqrt{169} = \pm 13$$
$$\sqrt{1{,}234{,}321} = 1111 \qquad \text{since } 1111 > 0 \text{ and } 1111^2 = 1{,}234{,}321$$
$$\sqrt{-144} \text{ is not defined because } -144 < 0$$

Cube roots

A cube root may be positive, negative, or zero. This follows from, for instance,

$$2^3 = 8 \qquad \text{and} \qquad (-5)^3 = -125 \qquad \text{and } 0^3 = 0$$

Here is the definition for cube roots:

> For *any real* numbers a and b,
> $$\sqrt[3]{a} = b \text{ if and only if } a = b^3$$

In particular, $\sqrt[3]{0} = 0$.

EXAMPLE 2   Find the value of $\sqrt[3]{343}$ and $\sqrt[3]{-1728}$.

Solution

$$\sqrt[3]{343} = 7 \qquad \text{since } 343 = 7^3$$
$$\sqrt[3]{-1728} = -12 \qquad \text{because } -1728 = (-12)^3$$

Thus there is a **basic distinction** between square roots and cube roots. Square roots are defined only for positive real numbers and zero. Cube roots are defined for all real numbers. The same pattern holds for nth roots whenever n is any positive integer—the key distinction is whether n is even or odd.

$\sqrt[n]{a}$ is called the nth root of a

> If n is an even positive integer, and a and b are **positive real numbers** for which $a = b^n$, then we write $\sqrt[n]{a} = b$.
> If n is an odd positive integer, and if a and b are **real numbers** for which $a = b^n$, then we write
> $$\sqrt[n]{a} = b \tag{1.38}$$
> In either case, $\sqrt[n]{0} = 0$.

We use the symbol $\sqrt{a}$ to mean $\sqrt[2]{a}$.

The definitions of square roots, cube roots, and *n*th roots yield real numbers. If $\sqrt[n]{a}$ exists, it is a unique real number. The easiest way to see this is to use the graph of $y = x^n$, which we will not have until Chap. 3.

If complex numbers are allowed, every complex number has *n* complex *n*th roots. Complex numbers will be treated in Sec. 2.3, just before quadratic equations.

EXAMPLE 3 Find the value of each expression below, if it is defined.

Solution

$$\sqrt[4]{81} = 3 \qquad \text{since } 3^4 = 81 \text{ and } 3 > 0$$
$$\sqrt[7]{-1} = -1 \qquad \text{since } (-1)^7 = -1$$
$$\sqrt[6]{1/64} = 1/2 \qquad \text{since } (1/2)^6 = 1/64 \text{ and } 1/2 > 0$$
$$\sqrt[5]{32/243} = 2/3 \qquad \text{since } (2/3)^5 = 32/243$$
$$\sqrt[8]{-2174} \text{ is not defined as a real number}$$

For any positive integer *n*, the symbol $\sqrt[n]{a}$ is called a **radical** of order *n*. Sometimes $\sqrt[n]{a}$ is called the **principal *n*th root** of *a* to emphasize that

$$\sqrt[n]{a} \text{ is defined to be positive if } a > 0$$

The number *a* is called the **radicand,** $\sqrt{}$ is called the **radical sign,** *n* is the **index** of the radical, and $\sqrt[n]{a}$ is called a **radical expression** or the *n*th root of *a*.
Whenever $\sqrt[n]{a}$ is defined, it is true by definition that

$$(\sqrt[n]{a})^n = a$$

The chart below summarizes the definition of $\sqrt[n]{a}$.

	$a < 0$	$a = 0$	$a > 0$
n even	Not defined	$\sqrt[n]{0} = 0$	$\sqrt[n]{a} > 0$
n odd	$\sqrt[n]{a} < 0$	$\sqrt[n]{0} = 0$	$\sqrt[n]{a} > 0$

We have to consider not only $(\sqrt[n]{a})^n$, but also $\sqrt[n]{a^n}$. For instance,

$$\sqrt[4]{2^4} = \sqrt[4]{16} = 2 \qquad \text{and} \qquad \sqrt[3]{(-4)^3} = \sqrt[3]{-64} = -4$$

If *n* **is odd,** things work nicely since for every real *a*:

$$\sqrt[n]{a^n} = a$$

This is also true for any positive *a*, whether *n* is even or odd. As in the table above, the problem occurs when $a < 0$ and *n* is even. For instance if $a = -3$ and $n = 4$,

$$\sqrt[n]{a^n} = \sqrt[4]{(-3)^4} = \sqrt[4]{81} = +3 \qquad \text{while } a = -3$$

And similarly for $a = -6$ and $n = 2$,

$$\sqrt{a^2} = \sqrt{(-6)^2} = \sqrt{36} = +6 \qquad \text{while } a = -6$$

If *n* is even, it is true that

$$\sqrt{a^2} = |a| \qquad \text{and also} \qquad \sqrt[n]{a^n} = |a|$$

since all of these radicals are positive, or zero. Thus we have two possible solutions to our dilemma. Either we treat all situations and use absolute values whenever necessary, or we treat only some situations and use simpler notation. We shall use the following practice, which is very common at this level.

> Assume that all variables in radicals are positive.

With this assumption, and n any positive integer, we have

$$(\sqrt[n]{a})^n = a = \sqrt[n]{a^n}$$

NOTE   We will use this property to simplify radicals.

EXAMPLE 4   Find the value of each expression below.

Solution   (a) $\sqrt[3]{-343} = -(\sqrt[3]{7^3}) = -7$ (b) $\sqrt[5]{243} = \sqrt[5]{3^5} = 3$
(c) $\sqrt[4]{a^4} = a$ (d) $\sqrt{x^6} = \sqrt{(x^3)^2} = x^3$
(e) $\sqrt[3]{b^6} = \sqrt[3]{(b^2)^3} = b^2$

There are three laws of radicals that we will use extensively.

Laws of radicals

> For any positive integer n and any positive real numbers a and b
>
> $$\sqrt[n]{ab} = (\sqrt[n]{a})(\sqrt[n]{b}) \tag{1.39}$$
>
> $$\sqrt[n]{\frac{a}{b}} = \frac{\sqrt[n]{a}}{\sqrt[n]{b}} \tag{1.40}$$
>
> $$\sqrt[m]{\sqrt[n]{a}} = \sqrt[mn]{a} \tag{1.41}$$

We will prove only the first of these laws. Letting $x = \sqrt[n]{a}$ and $y = \sqrt[n]{b}$ gives $x^n = a$ and $y^n = b$ by definition. Thus, by the laws of exponents

$$ab = (x^n)(y^n) = (x \cdot y)^n$$

Then, by definition of roots, we obtain

$$\sqrt[n]{ab} = xy = \sqrt[n]{a}\sqrt[n]{b}$$

If the radicand contains a factor that is raised to a power greater than or equal to the index of the radical, we can use law (1.39) to simplify the radical expression.

EXAMPLE 5   Simplify each radical below.

Solution   (a) $\sqrt{125} = \sqrt{5^3} = \sqrt{5^2 \cdot 5} = \sqrt{5^2}\sqrt{5} = 5\sqrt{5}$

(b) $\sqrt[3]{-192} = -\sqrt[3]{64 \cdot 3} = -\sqrt[3]{4^3 \cdot 3}$
$\qquad = -\sqrt[3]{4^3} \cdot \sqrt[3]{3} = -4 \cdot \sqrt[3]{3}$

(c) $\sqrt[4]{128a^6b^9} = \sqrt[4]{16a^4b^8(8a^2b)} = 2ab^2 \cdot \sqrt[4]{8a^2b}$

We will now illustrate another use of law (1.39) by combining two radicals.

▶ **EXAMPLE 6** Combine and simplify the radicals below.

Solution (a) $\sqrt{8x^3y} \cdot \sqrt{6x^2y^5}$
$$= \sqrt{(8x^3y)(6x^2y^5)} = \sqrt{48x^5y^6}$$
$$= \sqrt{16x^4y^6(3x)} = 4x^2y^3 \cdot \sqrt{3x}$$

(b) $\sqrt[3]{9a^5b^2} \cdot \sqrt[3]{-81a^2b^7}$
$$= -\sqrt[3]{(9^3)a^7b^9} = -\sqrt[3]{(9^3)a^6b^9(a)}$$
$$= (-9a^2b^3) \cdot \sqrt[3]{a}$$ ◢

If a radical expression has a coefficient, it is sometimes desirable to rewrite the expression with the coefficient as a part of the radicand. We do this in part (a) below by using the fact that $x = \sqrt{x^2}$ if $x > 0$. Similarly, $x = \sqrt[3]{x^3}$ for any real number x.

▶ **EXAMPLE 7** Use Eq. (1.39), for the radical of a product, in both parts below.

Solution (a) $2a\sqrt{4ab} = \sqrt{(2a)^2} \cdot \sqrt{(4ab)} = \sqrt{4a^2 \cdot 4ab} = \sqrt{16a^3b}$
(b) $(4x)\sqrt[3]{2y} = \sqrt[3]{(4x)^3} \cdot \sqrt[3]{2y} = \sqrt[3]{64x^3(2y)} = \sqrt[3]{128x^3y}$ ◢

We can rewrite the product or quotient of *two radicals of the same order* as a single radical with the help of Eqs. (1.39) and (1.40). For example, $\sqrt[4]{a}/\sqrt[4]{b} = \sqrt[4]{a/b}$. Radicals of different orders can be handled easily with rational exponents, as explained in Sec. 1.7.

▶ **EXAMPLE 8** Write each expression below as a single radical.

Solution (a) $\dfrac{\sqrt{128a^3b^5}}{\sqrt{2ab^2}} = \sqrt{\dfrac{128a^3b^5}{2ab^2}}$
$$= \sqrt{64a^2b^3} = \sqrt{(64a^2b^2)b} = 8ab\sqrt{b}$$

(b) $\dfrac{\sqrt[3]{625x^{10}y^7z^{11}}}{\sqrt[3]{-5x^2yz^4}} = \sqrt[3]{\dfrac{625x^{10}y^7z^{11}}{-5x^2yz^4}}$
$$= -\sqrt[3]{125x^8y^6z^7} = -\sqrt[3]{(5x^2y^2z^2)^3 \cdot x^2z}$$
$$= (-5x^2y^2z^2)\sqrt[3]{x^2z}$$ ◢

▶ **EXAMPLE 9** In each of the following expressions, insert the factor at the left of the radical sign into the radicand. Then arrange the original expressions in order from smallest to largest.

Solution
$$3\sqrt{3} = \sqrt{3^2 \cdot 3} = \sqrt{3^3} = \sqrt{27}$$
$$2\sqrt{6} = \sqrt{2^2 \cdot 6} = \sqrt{4 \cdot 6} = \sqrt{24}$$
$$4\sqrt{2} = \sqrt{4^2 \cdot 2} = \sqrt{16 \cdot 2} = \sqrt{32}$$

Since $24 < 27 < 32$, the desired order is

$$2\sqrt{6} < 3\sqrt{3} < 4\sqrt{2}$$ ◢

Adding Radicals

The distributive law may be used to add two or more radical expressions with the **same index and same radicand.**

▶ **EXAMPLE 10**   Combine $\sqrt{108} + \sqrt{48} - \sqrt{3}$ into a single radical expression.

Solution
$$\sqrt{108} + \sqrt{48} - \sqrt{3} = \sqrt{36 \cdot 3} + \sqrt{16 \cdot 3} - \sqrt{3}$$
$$= 6\sqrt{3} + 4\sqrt{3} - \sqrt{3}$$

Now since $\sqrt{3}$ is a common factor, the above expression becomes
$$(6 + 4 - 1)\sqrt{3} = 9\sqrt{3}$$

◀

▶ **EXAMPLE 11**   Simplify the radical expression
$$\sqrt{8a^3b^3} + \sqrt[3]{ab} - \sqrt[3]{8a^4b^4} - \sqrt[4]{4a^2b^2}$$

Solution   In this problem, no two radicands are identical and we have radical expressions of orders 2, 3, and 4. The radical expression $\sqrt[4]{4a^2b^2}$, however, can be converted to a lower order in this way:
$$\sqrt[4]{4a^2b^2} = \sqrt[4]{(2ab)^2} = \sqrt{[\sqrt{(2ab)^2}]} = \sqrt{2ab}$$

We therefore can complete the solution as below:
$$\sqrt{8a^3b^3} + \sqrt[3]{ab} - \sqrt[3]{8a^4b^4} - \sqrt[4]{4a^2b^2}$$
$$= \sqrt{(2ab)^2 2ab} + \sqrt[3]{ab} - \sqrt[3]{(2ab)^3 ab} - \sqrt{2ab}$$

factoring powers in radicands

$$= 2ab\sqrt{2ab} - \sqrt[3]{ab} - 2ab \cdot \sqrt[3]{ab} - \sqrt{2ab}$$

radical of a product

$$= 2ab\sqrt{2ab} - \sqrt{2ab} - \sqrt[3]{ab} - 2ab \cdot \sqrt[3]{ab}$$

by the commutative axiom

$$= (2ab - 1)\sqrt{2ab} - (1 + 2ab)\sqrt[3]{ab}$$

by the distributive axiom

◀

PROBLEMS   Problems 1 to 48 may now be done.

Rationalizing the Denominator

It is frequently desirable to convert a radical expression with a fractional radicand to a form in which no radical appears in the denominator. This simplifies the expression for further work or calculation. The process is called **rationalizing the denominator.**

Monomial denominator   If the denominator of the radicand is a monomial, we can use the laws of radicals, along with $\sqrt[n]{a^n} = a$, to change the denominator into a perfect nth power.

▶ **EXAMPLE 12**   Rationalize the denominator of $\sqrt{8a/3bc^3d^2}$.

Solution   To rationalize the denominator of $\sqrt{8a/3bc^3d^2}$, we multiply the denominator and numerator inside the radical by the expression with lowest exponents that will convert the denominator into a perfect square. In this case, the correct expression is $3bc$:

$$\sqrt{\frac{8a}{3bc^3d^2}} = \sqrt{\frac{8a(3bc)}{3bc^3(3bc)d^2}}$$

$$= \sqrt{\frac{2^2 \cdot 2 \cdot 3abc}{(3bc^2d)^2}} = \frac{2\sqrt{6abc}}{3bc^2d}$$

▲

▶ **EXAMPLE 13**   Rationalize the denominator of the expression below.

Solution

$$\sqrt[3]{\frac{4xy^2}{5x^5y^7}} = \sqrt[3]{\frac{4xy^2(25xy^2)}{5x^5y^7(25xy^2)}} = \sqrt[3]{\frac{100x^2yy^3}{(5x^2y^3)^3}}$$

$$= \frac{(y)\sqrt[3]{100x^2y}}{5x^2y^3} = \frac{\sqrt[3]{100x^2y}}{5x^2y^2}$$

▲

PROBLEMS   Problems 49 to 64 may now be done.

Binomial denominators   A similar process can be used if the denominator of a fraction is the sum or difference of two terms, at least one of which is a radical of order 2. In such cases, we rationalize the denominator by the method illustrated below.

▶ **EXAMPLE 14**   Rationalize the denominator in $4/(\sqrt{5} - 3)$.

Solution   Since $(\sqrt{5} - 3)(\sqrt{5} + 3) = 5 - 9 = -4$, we multiply the numerator and denominator of the given fraction by $\sqrt{5} + 3$, thereby eliminating the radical from the denominator:

$$\frac{4}{\sqrt{5} - 3} = \frac{4(\sqrt{5} + 3)}{(\sqrt{5} - 3)(\sqrt{5} + 3)}$$

$$= \frac{4(\sqrt{5} + 3)}{5 - 9} = -\sqrt{5} - 3$$

▲

NOTE   Had the denominator been $\sqrt{8} - \sqrt{3}$, for instance, we would have multiplied both numerator and denominator by $\sqrt{8} + \sqrt{3}$. In fact if a and b are positive, then the two facts below allow us to rationalize the denominator in many cases:

$$(\sqrt{a} + \sqrt{b})(\sqrt{a} - \sqrt{b}) = a - b \tag{i}$$

and also

$$(c + \sqrt{d})(c - \sqrt{d}) = c^2 - d \tag{ii}$$

Sometimes it is desirable to rationalize the numerator instead of the denominator.

▶ **EXAMPLE 15**   The following technique is used in calculus. Rationalize the numerator in the fraction $(\sqrt{x + h} - \sqrt{x})/h$.

Solution

$$\frac{\sqrt{x + h} - \sqrt{x}}{h} = \frac{(\sqrt{x + h} - \sqrt{x})(\sqrt{x + h} + \sqrt{x})}{h \cdot (\sqrt{x + h} + \sqrt{x})}$$

In the numerator we now use Eq. (i) above with $a = x + h$ and $b = h$.

$$= \frac{(x + h) - x}{h(\sqrt{x + h} + \sqrt{x})}$$

$$= \frac{h}{h(\sqrt{x + h} + \sqrt{x})} = \frac{1}{\sqrt{x + h} + \sqrt{x}}$$ ◢

PROBLEMS   Problems 65 to 80 may now be done, as well as the rest of the problems.
Above we used $(\sqrt{a} + \sqrt{b})(\sqrt{a} - \sqrt{b}) = a - b$. By way of contrast, in Chap. 2 when solving radical equations we will need to find $(\sqrt{a} + \sqrt{b})^2 = a + 2\sqrt{ab} + b$. For instance,

$$(\sqrt{2x - 1} + \sqrt{x + 4})^2 = 2x - 1 + 2\sqrt{(2x - 1)(x + 4)} + x + 4$$

NOTE   For a and b positive, $\sqrt{ab} = \sqrt{a}\sqrt{b}$. For sums, however,

$$\sqrt{a + b} \le \sqrt{a} + \sqrt{b}$$

with equality only when a or $b = 0$. For example,

$$\sqrt{9 + 16} = \sqrt{25} = 5 \qquad \text{but} \qquad \sqrt{9} + \sqrt{16} = 3 + 4 = 7$$

To "simplify a radical expression" means to:

(a)   Remove all possible factors from under the radical sign.
(b)   Rationalize each denominator.
(c)   Reduce the index of each radical, if possible.
(d)   Perform all indicated addition, subtraction, multiplication, and division.

It is an interesting fact that the set of numbers of the form $a + b\sqrt{2}$ with a and b rational form a field if we use ordinary addition and multiplication. We shall not prove this, but instead make two calculations and related comments:

$$(3 + 5\sqrt{2})(7 - 3\sqrt{2}) = 21 - 9\sqrt{2} + 35\sqrt{2} - 15(2) = -9 + 26\sqrt{2}$$

This shows that the product of $3 + 5\sqrt{2}$ and $7 - 3\sqrt{2}$ has the form $a + b\sqrt{2}$ with a and b rational. Furthermore

$$\frac{1}{8 + 3\sqrt{2}} = \frac{1}{8 + 3\sqrt{2}} \cdot \frac{8 - 3\sqrt{2}}{8 - 3\sqrt{2}} = \frac{8 - 3\sqrt{2}}{64 - 18} = \frac{4}{23} + \frac{-3}{46}\sqrt{2}$$

showing that $8 + 3\sqrt{2}$ has a multiplicative inverse which also has the form $a + b\sqrt{2}$ with a and b rational.

EXERCISE 1.6

State whether each number is real.

1. $\sqrt{12}$ **2.** $\sqrt[4]{-6}$ **3.** $\sqrt[3]{-81}$ **4.** $\sqrt[5]{77}$

Remove all possible factors from the radicands in Probs. 5 to 16.

5. $\sqrt{18}$ and $\sqrt{105}$
6. $\sqrt{162}$ and $\sqrt{175}$
7. $\sqrt{192}$ and $\sqrt[3]{-135}$
8. $\sqrt[3]{32}$ and $\sqrt[4]{405}$
9. $\sqrt{63a^7b^4}$
10. $\sqrt{147a^6b^5}$

11. $\sqrt{175a^0b^4}$
12. $\sqrt{180a^7b^3}$
13. $\sqrt[3]{-24a^3b^9}$
14. $\sqrt[3]{108a^6b^7}$
15. $\sqrt[4]{243a^6b^5}$
16. $\sqrt[5]{96a^7b^{10}}$

In Probs. 17 to 28, combine into a single radical and then remove all possible factors from the radicand.

17. $\sqrt[3]{2} \cdot \sqrt[3]{648}$
18. $\sqrt[4]{15} \cdot \sqrt[4]{27}$
19. $\sqrt{15}\sqrt{27}$
20. $\sqrt[5]{48} \cdot \sqrt[5]{20}$

21. $\sqrt{3xy^2}\sqrt{18x^3y}$ 22. $\sqrt{11x^3y^3}\sqrt{77xy^2}$
23. $\sqrt{6x^2y}\sqrt{30xy^3}$ 24. $\sqrt{8x^2y^3}\sqrt{18xy}$
25. $\sqrt[3]{4x^4y^2}\sqrt[3]{6x^2y}$ 26. $\sqrt[3]{16x^5y^3}\sqrt[3]{10x^3y}$
27. $\sqrt[4]{24xy^3}\sqrt[4]{18x^2y^2}$ 28. $\sqrt[4]{45x^3y^5}\sqrt[4]{72x^2y^3}$

Write the expression in Probs. 29 to 36 as a single radical.

29. $\sqrt{\sqrt{2}}$ 30. $\sqrt[3]{\sqrt{5}}$ 31. $\sqrt{\sqrt[3]{3}}$ 32. $\sqrt[3]{\sqrt{7}}$

33. $\sqrt{\sqrt[3]{a^2}}$ 34. $\sqrt[4]{\sqrt{a}}$ 35. $\sqrt[5]{\sqrt[4]{a^2}}$ 36. $\sqrt[3]{\sqrt[3]{a^4}}$

In Probs. 37 to 48, remove all possible factors from each radicand, and then combine terms by addition and subtraction.

37. $\sqrt{3} - \sqrt{48} + \sqrt{12}$
38. $\sqrt{5} - \sqrt{45} + \sqrt{80} + \sqrt{125}$
39. $\sqrt[3]{16} + \sqrt[3]{2} - \sqrt[3]{128}$
40. $\sqrt[3]{40} + \sqrt[3]{135} - \sqrt[3]{5}$
41. $\sqrt{18} + \sqrt[3]{128} + \sqrt{8} - \sqrt[3]{54}$
42. $\sqrt{27} + \sqrt[3]{54} - \sqrt{12} + \sqrt[3]{16}$
43. $\sqrt{50} - \sqrt{375} + \sqrt{72} + \sqrt[3]{24}$
44. $\sqrt[3]{81} + \sqrt[3]{256} - \sqrt[3]{24} - \sqrt[3]{108}$
45. $\sqrt{4a^2b} - \sqrt{25ab^2} + \sqrt{a^2b} + \sqrt{16ab^2}$
46. $\sqrt{2r^3t} - \sqrt{r^3t^2} + \sqrt{18rt^5} + \sqrt{r^5t^6}$
47. $\sqrt[3]{8c^5d} + \sqrt[3]{27c^4d^5} + \sqrt[3]{27c^2d^4} - \sqrt[3]{c^7d^5}$
48. $\sqrt[3]{3g^4m^2} - \sqrt[3]{8g^2m^4} - \sqrt[3]{24gm^8} + \sqrt[3]{27g^5m}$

Rationalize the monomial denominators in these problems, and then remove all possible factors from the radicand.

49. $\sqrt{\dfrac{3x^5}{5y}}$ 50. $\sqrt{\dfrac{3x}{8y^3}}$

51. $\sqrt{\dfrac{2x^3}{50y^5}}$ 52. $\sqrt{\dfrac{8x^7}{27y^3}}$

53. $\sqrt{\dfrac{243x^5y^8}{147xy^5}}$ 54. $\sqrt{\dfrac{24x^3y^9}{54xy^4}}$

55. $\sqrt{\dfrac{7x^8y^4}{6x^6y}}$ 56. $\sqrt{\dfrac{64x^5y^9}{98xy^7}}$

57. $\sqrt[3]{\dfrac{27x^5y^{12}}{4x^2y^{14}}}$ 58. $\sqrt[3]{\dfrac{125x^7y}{18x^5y^2}}$

59. $\sqrt[4]{\dfrac{8x^7y^4}{27x^2y^6}}$ 60. $\sqrt[5]{\dfrac{7xy^{13}}{16x^8y^{16}}}$

61. $\sqrt{\dfrac{147x^9y^2}{243x^4y^{-3}}}$ 62. $\sqrt{\dfrac{17x^5y^{-1}}{6x^{-3}y^{-8}}}$

63. $\sqrt{\dfrac{9x^{-2}y^7}{98x^{-6}y^{-3}}}$ 64. $\sqrt{\dfrac{49x^5y^{-9}}{24x^{-3}y}}$

Rationalize the binomial denominators in Probs. 65 to 76.

65. $\dfrac{2}{1 - \sqrt{3}}$ 66. $\dfrac{7}{\sqrt{2} - 3}$

67. $\dfrac{3}{2 + \sqrt{5}}$ 68. $\dfrac{1}{\sqrt{7} - 2}$

69. $\dfrac{6}{\sqrt{5} - \sqrt{2}}$ 70. $\dfrac{2}{\sqrt{3} - \sqrt{7}}$

71. $\dfrac{5}{\sqrt{10} - \sqrt{5}}$ 72. $\dfrac{12}{\sqrt{13} - \sqrt{7}}$

73. $\dfrac{2 + \sqrt{3}}{\sqrt{5} - \sqrt{3}}$ 74. $\dfrac{1 + 2\sqrt{5}}{\sqrt{3} + \sqrt{5}}$

75. $\dfrac{\sqrt{3} + 2\sqrt{2}}{\sqrt{2} - \sqrt{3}}$ 76. $\dfrac{\sqrt{14} - 2}{\sqrt{7} - \sqrt{2}}$

77. Rationalize the numerator and simplify the expression

$$\dfrac{\sqrt{x + h + 3} - \sqrt{x + 3}}{h}$$

78. Rationalize the numerator and simplify the expression

$$\dfrac{\sqrt{2x + 2h - 5} - \sqrt{2x - 5}}{h}$$

79. Rationalize the numerator and simplify the expression

$$\dfrac{\sqrt{3x - 2} - \sqrt{10}}{x - 4}$$

80. Rationalize the numerator and simplify the expression

$$\dfrac{\sqrt{5x + 1} - 4}{x - 3}$$

81. *Area of a triangle* Heron's formula for the area of a triangle with sides of length a, b, and c is

$$\sqrt{s(s - a)(s - b)(s - c)}$$

where $a + b + c = 2s$. Find the area of a triangle with sides of length 8, 9, and 11 cm.

82. *Physics* Kepler's third law states that the square of the time required for a planet to make a circuit about the sun is a constant times the cube of the mean distance between the sun and the planet. Find the time in *days* for Mars to make a circuit about

the sun if the mean distances of the Earth and Mars from the sun are 93 and 141 million miles, respectively. Use 365 days in an Earth year.

83. *Earth science*   The velocity for compressional waves is $V_1 = \sqrt{(L + 2m)/p}$ and for shear waves is $V_2 = \sqrt{m/p}$. Find the ratio V_1/V_2 of compressional to shear velocity.

84. *Earth science*   The vertical gravitational attraction of a buried cylinder is

$$g = \sqrt{L^2 + (x - r)^2} - \sqrt{L^2 + (x + r)^2}$$

Express g by rationalizing the numerator.

Calculator

In Probs. 85 to 88, use a calculator to find the root to two decimal places.

85. $\sqrt{114.7}$ **86.** $\sqrt[3]{-278.4}$
87. $\sqrt[4]{788.1}$ **88.** $\sqrt[5]{112.9}$

Calculator
89. Using a calculator, find these numbers to two decimal places:

$$\sqrt{2 + \sqrt{2}}$$
$$\sqrt{2 + \sqrt{2 + \sqrt{2}}}$$
$$\sqrt{2 + \sqrt{2 + \sqrt{2 + \sqrt{2}}}}$$

Repeating this pattern gives numbers closer and closer to 2.

90. Using a calculator, find these numbers to two decimal places:

$$\sqrt{6 + \sqrt{6}}$$
$$\sqrt{6 + \sqrt{6 + \sqrt{6}}}$$
$$\sqrt{6 + \sqrt{6 + \sqrt{6 + \sqrt{6}}}}$$

Repeating this pattern gives numbers closer and closer to 3.

91. Using a calculator, find these numbers to three decimal places:

$$\sqrt{12 + \sqrt{12}}$$
$$\sqrt{12 + \sqrt{12 + \sqrt{12}}}$$
$$\sqrt{12 + \sqrt{12 + \sqrt{12 + \sqrt{12}}}}$$

Repeating this pattern gives numbers closer and closer to 4.

92. Using a calculator, find these numbers to three decimal places:

$$\sqrt{20 + \sqrt{20}}$$
$$\sqrt{20 + \sqrt{20 + \sqrt{20}}}$$
$$\sqrt{20 + \sqrt{20 + \sqrt{20 + \sqrt{20}}}}$$

Repeating this pattern gives numbers closer and closer to 5.

Problems 93 to 96 refer to the fact that if $a > 0$ and $a^2 \geq b > 0$

$$\sqrt{a + \sqrt{b}} = \sqrt{\frac{a + \sqrt{a^2 - b}}{2}} + \sqrt{\frac{a - \sqrt{a^2 - b}}{2}}$$

93. Verify the above equation for $a = 3$ and $b = 2$.
94. Verify the above equation for $a = 4$ and $b = 5$.
95. Verify the above equation for $a = 5$ and $b = 11$.
96. Prove that the equation above is true with the stated conditions for a and b. *Hint:* Square the right-hand side, and then simplify it to $a + \sqrt{b}$.
97. Show $\sqrt[3]{26 + 15\sqrt{3}} + \sqrt[3]{26 - 15\sqrt{3}} = 4$. *Hint:* Begin with $(2 + \sqrt{3})^3$.
98. Show $\sqrt[3]{26 + 15\sqrt{3}} - \sqrt[3]{26 - 15\sqrt{3}} = 2\sqrt{3}$. *Hint:* Begin with $(2 - \sqrt{3})^3$.
99. Show $\sqrt[3]{\sqrt{243} + \sqrt{242}} - \sqrt[3]{\sqrt{243} - \sqrt{242}} = 2\sqrt{2}$. *Hint:* Begin with $(\sqrt{2} + \sqrt{3})^3$.
100. Show $\sqrt[3]{7 + 5\sqrt{2}} + \sqrt[3]{7 - 5\sqrt{2}} = 2$. *Hint:* Calculate $(1 + \sqrt{2})^3$.
101. Show that

$$\frac{1}{\sqrt{m} + \sqrt{n} + \sqrt{p}} = \frac{(\sqrt{m} + \sqrt{n} - \sqrt{p})(m + n - p - 2\sqrt{mn})}{m^2 + n^2 + p^2 - 2mn - 2mp - 2np}$$

102. Show that if $a > 1$, then

$$\sqrt{a + \frac{a}{a^2 - 1}} = a\sqrt{\frac{a}{a^2 - 1}}$$

and

$$\sqrt{6 + \frac{6}{35}} = 6\sqrt{\frac{6}{35}}$$

103. *You can "hear"* $\sqrt{2}$ The frequency of any note is twice the frequency of the note one octave lower. On a piano each octave is broken into 12 steps (from one note to the adjacent one). Thus the frequency of any note is found by multiplying by $\sqrt[12]{2}$ the frequency of the note just lower. Hence starting at middle C and going successively to C$^\sharp$, D, D$^\sharp$, E, F, and F$^\sharp$ multiplies the frequency of middle C by $(\sqrt[12]{2})^6 = \sqrt{2}$. Therefore playing C and F$^\sharp$ simultaneously allows you to "hear" $\sqrt{2}$. For each pair of notes below, give both the exact value and a good rational approximation for the ratio of their frequencies (larger to smaller):
(a) C and E   (b) C and F   (c) C and G

104. *A radical inequality*   Verify these inequalities, which provide a good rational approximation to $\sqrt{3}$:

$$1.7 < \sqrt{3} < 1.75$$
$$-0.05 < \sqrt{3} - 1.75 < 0$$
$$0 < 1.75 - \sqrt{3} < 0.05$$
$$0 < 1.75^2 - 3.5\sqrt{3} + 3 < 0.05^2$$
$$0 < 6.0625 - 3.5\sqrt{3} < 0.0025$$
$$\frac{6.06}{3.5} < \sqrt{3} < \frac{6.0625}{3.5}$$
$$\frac{303}{175} < \sqrt{3} < \frac{97}{56}$$

Calculator

105. In a certain sense the average value of $\sqrt{x}$ on the interval [0, 1] is 2/3. Calculate the value of the average below:

$$\frac{\sqrt{0.1} + \sqrt{0.3} + \sqrt{0.5} + \sqrt{0.7} + \sqrt{0.9}}{5}$$

106. *Power line cost*   A power line is to be run from a generator, down a straight shoreline, then out to a platform in the lake. Suppose that the total cost is

$$600(5 - x) + 900\sqrt{x^2 + 4}$$

where x is the distance on shore from the point that the line goes out into the lake to the point on shore closest to the platform. The actual minimum cost occurs for $x = \sqrt{16/5} = 4\sqrt{5}/5 \approx 1.79$. Calculate the cost if x is (a) 1.5, (b) 1.8, (c) 2.0.

1.7 Rational Exponents

So far we have defined a^x only when x is an integer, either positive or negative or zero. In this section we extend the definition of a^x so as to include rational exponents. In the property $(a^m)^n = a^{mn}$, if we let $m = 1/n$, then $mn = 1$ and thus

$$(a^{1/n})^n = a$$

Furthermore, by the definition of a radical, we have

$$(\sqrt[n]{a})^n = a$$

So to be consistent with previous work, we make the following definition:

For any positive integer n and any real number a, if $\sqrt[n]{a}$ is a real number, then

$$a^{1/n} = \sqrt[n]{a} \qquad \textbf{(1.42)}$$

EXAMPLE 1   Find the value of each exponential expression.

Solution

$$289^{1/2} = \sqrt{289} = 17$$
$$(-243)^{1/5} = \sqrt[5]{-243} = -3$$
$$27^{1/3} = \sqrt[3]{27} = 3$$
$$(-16)^{1/4} = \sqrt[4]{-16} \quad \text{which is not defined}$$

For general rational exponents $m/n = m(1/n)$, we still want the laws of exponents to hold, and thus we require that

$$a^{m/n} = (a^{1/n})^m = (\sqrt[n]{a})^m$$

We want to show that this is equal to $(a^m)^{1/n}$, that is, that $(a^{1/n})^m$ is an nth root of a^m:

$$[(a^{1/n})^m]^n = (a^{1/n})^{mn} \qquad \text{multiply exponents}$$
$$= (a^{1/n})^{nm} \qquad \text{commutative law}$$
$$= [(a^{1/n})^n]^m \qquad \text{power of a power}$$
$$= a^m \qquad \text{definition of } a^{1/n}$$

Now both $(a^m)^{1/n}$ and $(a^{1/n})^m$ are nth roots of a^m, and it can be shown that they have the same sign. Thus we make the following definition:

> For all integers m, all positive integers n, and all nonzero real numbers a for which $a^{1/n}$ exists, we define
>
> $$a^{m/n} = (\sqrt[n]{a})^m = (a^{1/n})^m = (a^m)^{1/n} = \sqrt[n]{a^m} \qquad \textbf{(1.43)}$$

Equation (1.43) gives the basic relationship between rational exponents and radicals. It also has applications in calculus, where it is used to write expressions in exponential form so that they can be more readily handled.

We will not prove that all of the laws of exponents stated in Sec. 1.1 can be extended to rational exponents as defined in Eq. (1.43). We will now see how to use the properties to evaluate expressions involving rational exponents, as illustrated in the following examples.

EXAMPLE 2   Evaluate $4^{5/2}$, $8^{-2/3}$, and $(-32)^{3/5}$ by using the definition of rational exponents.

Solution

$$4^{5/2} = (\sqrt{4})^5 = 2^5 = 32 \qquad \text{or} \qquad 4^{5/2} = 4^2 \cdot 4^{1/2} = 16 \cdot \sqrt{4} = 32$$
$$8^{-2/3} = (\sqrt[3]{8})^{-2} = 2^{-2} = 1/2^2 = 1/4$$
$$(-32)^{3/5} = (\sqrt[5]{-32})^3 = (-2)^3 = -8$$

NOTE   The first expression above may be evaluated by writing

$$4^{5/2} = \sqrt{4^5} = \sqrt{1024} = 32$$

This however involves larger numbers than the first line above. Therefore it is usually advisable to use the form

$$(\sqrt[n]{a})^m \text{ or equivalently } (a^{1/n})^m$$

▶ **EXAMPLE 3**   Express (i) $3a^{1/2}b^{5/2}$ and (ii) $a^{3/4}b^{-5/3}$ in radical form.

Solution   (i)

$$3a^{1/2}b^{5/2} = 3(ab^5)^{1/2} \qquad \text{multiply exponents}$$

$$= 3 \cdot \sqrt{ab^5} \qquad \text{definition of rational exponent}$$

(ii)

$$a^{3/4}b^{-5/3} = \frac{a^{3/4}}{b^{5/3}} \qquad \text{negative exponent}$$

Writing the exponents with a common denominator gives

$$\frac{a^{9/12}}{b^{20/12}} = \sqrt[12]{\frac{a^9}{b^{20}}}$$

▶ **EXAMPLE 4**   Find the product of $3a^{1/2}$ and $2a^{2/3}$.

Solution

$$(3a^{1/2})(2a^{2/3}) = 6a^{1/2+2/3}$$
$$= 6a^{(3+4)/6} = 6a^{7/6}$$

▶ **EXAMPLE 5**   Find the quotient of $8x^{1/2}y^{5/6}$ and $5x^{1/4}y^{1/3}$.

Solution

$$\frac{8x^{1/2}y^{5/6}}{5x^{1/4}y^{1/3}} = \frac{8x^{1/2-1/4}y^{5/6-1/3}}{5} = \frac{8x^{1/4}y^{3/6}}{5} = \frac{8x^{1/4}y^{1/2}}{5}$$

▶ **EXAMPLE 6**   Simplify the expression

$$\left(\frac{4x^4y^{3/4}z^2}{9x^2y^{1/4}z}\right)^{1/2}$$

using the laws of exponents, and write the result without zero or negative exponents.

Solution

$$\left(\frac{4x^4y^{3/4}z^2}{9x^2y^{1/4}z}\right)^{1/2} = \left(\frac{4}{9} \cdot \frac{x^4}{x^2} \cdot \frac{y^{3/4}}{y^{1/4}} \cdot \frac{z^2}{z}\right)^{1/2}$$

$$= \left(\frac{4x^2 \cdot y^{1/2} \cdot z}{9}\right)^{1/2}$$

$$= \frac{2x \cdot y^{1/4} \cdot z^{1/2}}{3}$$

NOTE   It sometimes shortens the work to remember that if r is a positive rational number, then

$$\left(\frac{a}{b}\right)^{-r} = \left(\frac{b}{a}\right)^{r}$$

▶ **EXAMPLE 7**   Simplify the expression

$$\left(\frac{4x^2y^{3/4}z^{1/6}}{32x^{-1}y^0z^{-5/6}}\right)^{-1/3}$$

and write the result without zero or negative exponents, and without fractional exponents in the denominator.

Solution

$$\left(\frac{4x^2y^{3/4}z^{1/6}}{32x^{-1}y^0z^{-5/6}}\right)^{-1/3} = \left(\frac{4}{32} \cdot \frac{x^2}{x^{-1}} \cdot \frac{y^{3/4}}{y^0} \cdot \frac{z^{1/6}}{z^{-5/6}}\right)^{-1/3}$$

$$= \left(\frac{x^3y^{3/4}z}{8}\right)^{-1/3}$$

$$= \left(\frac{8}{x^3y^{3/4}z}\right)^{1/3}$$

$$= \frac{2}{xy^{1/4}z^{1/3}} \cdot \frac{y^{3/4}z^{2/3}}{y^{3/4}z^{2/3}}$$

$$= \frac{2y^{3/4}z^{2/3}}{xyz}$$

◢

Expressions which look similar must be handled carefully to give the right value. For instance,

$$\sqrt[5]{(x + y)^3} = (x + y)^{3/5}$$

which is different from

$$\sqrt[5]{x^3 + y^3} = (x^3 + y^3)^{1/5}$$

and both of the above are different from

$$\sqrt[5]{x^3} + \sqrt[5]{y^3} = x^{3/5} + y^{3/5}$$

▶ **EXAMPLE 8**   Write each of these expressions using rational exponents:

(a) $\sqrt{x^2 + 4}$ (b) $\sqrt[3]{\dfrac{x^6}{4x + 3}}$

Solution   (a) $\sqrt{x^2 + 4} = (x^2 + 4)^{1/2}$

(b) $\sqrt[3]{\dfrac{x^6}{4x + 3}} = \left(\dfrac{x^6}{4x + 3}\right)^{1/3} = \dfrac{x^2}{(4x + 3)^{1/3}} = x^2(4x + 3)^{-1/3}$ ◢

Notice that

$$\sqrt{(x^2 + 16)^3} = (x^2 + 16)^{3/2}$$

and these are *not* equal to

$$(x^2)^{3/2} + 16^{3/2} = x^3 + 4^3 = x^3 + 64$$

▶ **EXAMPLE 9**   Show that $\sqrt[3]{38 + 17\sqrt{5}} + \sqrt[3]{38 - 17\sqrt{5}} = 4$ by using $(2 + \sqrt{5})^3$.

Solution   Multiplying the factors, or using the formula for the cube of a sum, shows that

$$(2 + \sqrt{5})^3 = (2 + \sqrt{5})(9 + 4\sqrt{5}) = 38 + 17\sqrt{5}$$

and also

$$(2 - \sqrt{5})^3 = (2 - \sqrt{5})(9 - 4\sqrt{5}) = 38 - 17\sqrt{5}$$

It follows that

$$\sqrt[3]{38 + 17\sqrt{5}} + \sqrt[3]{38 - 17\sqrt{5}} = (2 + \sqrt{5}) + (2 - \sqrt{5}) = 4$$ ◀

Rational exponents can be used to simplify certain expressions with radicals. For instance,

$$\sqrt[3]{x} \cdot \sqrt[4]{x} \cdot \sqrt[5]{x} \cdot \sqrt[6]{x} \cdot \sqrt[20]{x} = x^{1/3+1/4+1/5+1/6+1/20} = x^1 = x$$

Also we have

$$\sqrt{x} \cdot \sqrt[3]{y} = x^{1/2}y^{1/3} = x^{3/6}y^{2/6} = \sqrt[6]{x^3y^2}$$

and finally

$$\sqrt{x^3y^5} \cdot \sqrt[3]{x^2y^4} = (x^3y^5)^{1/2} \cdot (x^2y^4)^{1/3}$$
$$= x^{3/2}y^{5/2}x^{2/3}y^{4/3} = x^{13/6}y^{23/6}$$
$$= x^2x^{1/6}y^3y^{5/6} = x^2y^3\sqrt[6]{xy^5}$$

EXERCISE 1.7

Rewrite each number or expression in Probs. 1 to 36 without exponents or radicals.

1. $25^{1/2}$
2. $49^{1/2}$
3. $64^{1/3}$
4. $64^{1/6}$
5. $27^{2/3}$
6. $32^{3/5}$
7. $64^{4/3}$
8. $9^{3/2}$
9. $8^{-1/3}$
10. $4^{-3/2}$
11. $16^{-3/4}$
12. $27^{-4/3}$
13. $(4/25)^{3/2}$
14. $(64/27)^{4/3}$
15. $(243/32)^{2/5}$
16. $(81/625)^{3/4}$
17. $(49/81)^{-1/2}$
18. $(216/125)^{-1/3}$
19. $(125/27)^{-2/3}$
20. $(81/625)^{-3/4}$
21. $\sqrt{8^4}$
22. $\sqrt[3]{125^2}$
23. $\sqrt[4]{4^3}$
24. $\sqrt[6]{8^2}$
25. $\sqrt{16a^2b^4}$
26. $\sqrt{9a^4b^6}$
27. $\sqrt{49a^6b^8}$
28. $\sqrt{36a^0b^6}$
29. $\sqrt{27p^3q^6}$
30. $\sqrt{16p^6q^4}$
31. $\sqrt[4]{16p^8q^4}$
32. $\sqrt[5]{243p^5q^{10}}$
33. $\sqrt{\dfrac{25a^2}{b^4c^6}}$
34. $\sqrt[3]{\dfrac{8a^6}{b^3c^9}}$
35. $\sqrt[4]{\dfrac{a^8b^4}{81c^0}}$
36. $\sqrt[5]{\dfrac{a^{10}b^0}{32c^5}}$

Rewrite the expression in each of Probs. 37 to 44 in radical form.

37. $x^{1/5}y^{3/5}$
38. $x^{2/3}y^{1/3}$
39. $x^{2/3}y^{5/6}$
40. $x^{1/2}y^{3/4}$
41. $x^{2/3}y^{-1/4}$
42. $x^{-1/2}y^{2/3}$
43. $x^{-3/5}y^{-2/3}$
44. $x^{-3/2}y^{2/3}$

Simplify the expressions in each of Probs. 45 to 76 using the laws of exponents, and express each result

without zero or negative exponents, and with no fractional exponents in the denominator.

45. $(3x^{1/3})(2x^{1/2})$
46. $(2x^{1/4})(5x^{1/3})$
47. $(3x^{1/2})(4x^{1/5})$
48. $(7x^{1/6})(3x^{1/5})$
49. $\dfrac{12x^{2/3}y^{1/2}}{3x^{1/3}y^{3/4}}$
50. $\dfrac{6x^{3/5}y^{-1/3}}{2x^{2/5}y^{1/2}}$
51. $\dfrac{15x^{1/4}y^{-1/2}}{3x^{-1/4}y}$
52. $\dfrac{27x^{4/5}y^{-1}}{9x^{4/3}y^0}$
53. $(64x^{3/8}y^{-3/5})^{1/3}$
54. $(81a^{-4}b^{4/3})^{-1/4}$
55. $(243^{-1}a^{5/3}b^{-5/7})^{1/5}$
56. $(36x^{-2}y^{6/7})^{-1/2}$
57. $\left(\dfrac{8x^3y^{-4/3}}{27x^{-6}y}\right)^{-2/3}$
58. $\left(\dfrac{x^{5/6}y^{-5/4}}{243x^0y^{-5/3}}\right)^{-1/5}$
59. $\left(\dfrac{64x^{-1}y^6}{x^0y^{3/2}}\right)^{-1/6}$
60. $\left(\dfrac{36a^0b^3}{25a^{-1}b^{2/3}}\right)^{-1/2}$
61. $(16x^6y^4)^{1/2}(27x^9y^6)^{-1/3}$
62. $(625a^4b^8)^{-1/4}(243a^{-10}b^5)^{1/5}$
63. $(8a^6b^9)^{-2/3}(4a^4b^6)^{1/3}$
64. $(16x^{-4}y^2)^{1/2}(125^{-1}xy^{-3})^{1/3}$
65. $(4x + 1)(\tfrac{1}{2})(5x + 3)^{-1/2}(5) + (5x + 3)^{1/2}(4)$
66. $(x + 3)(\tfrac{1}{2})(5 - 3x)^{-1/2}(-3) + (5 - 3x)^{1/2}$
67. $(3x + 2)(\tfrac{3}{4})(2x - 5)^{-1/4}(2) + 3(2x - 5)^{3/4}$
68. $(2x - 5)(\tfrac{1}{4})(3x + 4)^{-3/4}(3) + 2(3x + 4)^{1/4}$
69. $(2x - 1)^{2/3}(\tfrac{1}{2})(x + 1)^{-1/2} + (\tfrac{2}{3})(2x - 1)^{-1/3}(2)(x + 1)^{1/2}$
70. $(5x + 2)^{2/3}(\tfrac{1}{2})(x + 1)^{-1/2} + (\tfrac{2}{3})(5x + 2)^{-1/3}(5)(x + 1)^{1/2}$

71. $(2x + 3)^{1/4}(\frac{3}{2})(3x - 1)^{-1/2} + (3x - 1)^{1/2}(\frac{1}{2})(2x + 3)^{-3/4}$

72. $(3x + 5)^{2/3}(3)(4x - 3)^{-1/4} + 2(3x + 5)^{-1/3}(4x - 3)^{3/4}$

73. $\left(\dfrac{x^{1/(b-2)}}{x^{1/(b+2)}}\right)^{(b^2-4)/b}$ **74.** $\left(\dfrac{x^{a+5b}}{x^{3b}}\right)^{a/(a+2b)}$

75. $\left(\dfrac{x^{a+3b}}{x^a}\right)^a\left(\dfrac{x^{a-2b}}{x^{-2b}}\right)^b$ **76.** $\left(\dfrac{x^{a-5b}}{x^{-4b}}\right)^{b/(a^2-b^2)}$

77. Find the value of t for $r = \frac{1}{3}\sqrt{5}$ and $N = 27$ if

$$t = \frac{r\sqrt{N-2}}{\sqrt{1-r^2}}$$

78. Calculate e for $n = 2783$ and $m = 2117$ if

$$e = \frac{201\sqrt{n+m}}{n-m}$$

79. Solve $R = k(S - S_0)^c$ for S.

80. Calculate the value of $a\sqrt{2\pi(k^2 + s^2)}/2A$ if $a = 6.83$, $k = 60$, $s = 63$, and $A = 0.215$.

81. *Business and calculator*   The production of pencils is governed by

$$Q = 650x^p y^{1-p}$$

where $0 < p < 1$, x is labor cost, and y is equipment value. Find Q if $x = 18$, $y = 75$ for (a) $p = 0.65$ and (b) $p = 0.93$.

82. *Earth science and calculator*   A study of sedimentary-rock velocities V showed that for sandstone and shale,

$$V = 125.3(ZT)^{1/6}$$

where Z is depth in feet and T is age in years. Find V if $Z = 6000$ ft and $T = 12,860,000$ years.

83. *Cost analysis*   Suppose that the cost of producing x units each day is

$$\frac{75 + (3x + 10)^{3/2}}{x}$$

Find the cost if $x = 13$, and if $x = 18$.

84. *Calculus and calculator*   If earnings are $-300 + ax^n + 5a/x^m$, then the optimum value of x is

$$\left(\frac{5m}{n}\right)^{1/(m+n)}$$

Calculate the optimum value if $m = 3$ and $n = 4$.

In Probs. 85 to 92, write the expression using rational exponents.

85. $\sqrt{(x^2 + 25)^3}$

86. $\sqrt{(4x^2 + 49)^5}$

87. $\sqrt{(16x^2 - 1)^3}$

88. $\sqrt{(36x^2 + 81)^3}$

89. $\sqrt[4]{(x + 2y)^3}$ and $\sqrt[4]{x^3 + 2y^3}$

90. $\sqrt[5]{x^4} + \sqrt[5]{y^4}$ and $\sqrt[5]{(x + y)^4}$

91. $\sqrt[6]{(3x - y)^5}$ and $\sqrt[6]{3x^5} - \sqrt[6]{y^5}$

92. $\sqrt[7]{(x - 2y)^3}$ and $\sqrt[7]{x^3} - \sqrt[7]{2y^3}$

It is sometimes important to be able to write certain expressions as perfect squares. Do this in Probs. 93 to 96. (An advanced formula for arc length is one case where this technique is needed.)

93. $1 + \left(2x - \dfrac{1}{8x}\right)^2$ **94.** $1 + \left(x^{2/3} - \dfrac{1}{4x^{2/3}}\right)^2$

95. $1 + \left(\sqrt{x} - \dfrac{1}{4\sqrt{x}}\right)^2$ **96.** $1 + \left(\dfrac{x^2}{2} - \dfrac{1}{2x^2}\right)^2$

1.8 Key Concepts

Be certain that you understand and can use each of the following important words, ideas, and indicated procedures.

Axiom (p. 3)   Division (p. 5)
Theorem (p. 4)   Variable (p. 22)
Real numbers (p. 2)   Factor (p. 2)
Triangle inequality (p. 8)   Negative integers (p. 3)

Fundamental theorem of arithmetic (p. 3)
Natural numbers (p. 2)
Algebraic expression (p. 22)
Set (p. 9)
Binomial (p. 25)
Trinomial (p. 25)
Coefficient (pp. 22, 24)
Factorable (p. 35)
Common factor (p. 31)
Term (p. 22)
Fundamental principle of fractions (p. 39)
Equivalent fractions (p. 39)
Quotient of fractions (p. 42)
Least common denominator (p. 43)
Product of fractions (p. 41)
Complex fraction (p. 45)
Reduce to lowest terms (p. 40)
Exponent (p. 12)
Base (p. 12)
Negative exponent (p. 13)
Radical (p. 51)
Rational numbers (p. 2)
Irrational numbers (p. 2)
Absolute value (p. 8)
Subtraction (p. 5)
Cancellation laws (p. 40)
Constant (p. 22)
Prime (p. 2)
Composite (p. 2)

Exponent (p. 12)
Integers (p. 2)
Least common multiple (p. 43)
Similar terms (p. 23)
Intersection (p. 9)
Union (p. 9)
Monomial (p. 25)
Polynomial (p. 24)
Degree (p. 25)
Special products (p. 25)
Integer coefficients (p. 31)
Divisor (p. 2)
Signs of a fraction (p. 39)
Remainder (p. 27)
Sum of fractions (p. 43)
Cancellation (p. 40)
Power (p. 12)
Index (p. 51)
Rational exponent (p. 60)
Principal root (p. 50)
Square root (p. 49)
Radicand (p. 51)
Rationalize the denominator or numerator (p. 54)
Scientific notation (p. 17)
Cube root (p. 50)
Rounding off (p. 19)
Adding and multiplying approximate numbers (p. 19)
Laws of radicals (p. 52)

(1.1)   For all real numbers b, $(b)(0) = 0$

(1.2)   For all real numbers a and b, if $ab = 0$, then $a = 0$, or $b = 0$, or both are zero

(1.3)   Subtraction: $a - b$ is defined to be $a + (-b)$

(1.4)   Division: $a \div b$ is defined to be $a(b^{-1})$ if $b \neq 0$

(1.5)   If $a = b$, and c is any real number, then
(i) $a + c = b + c$, and (ii) $ac = bc$

(1.6) $|a| = \begin{cases} a & \text{if } a \geq 0 \\ -a & \text{if } a < 0 \end{cases}$

(1.7) $|-a| = |a|$

(1.8) $|a - b| = |b - a| = $ distance between a and b

(1.9) $|ab| = |a| \cdot |b|$

(1.10) $|a/b| = |a|/|b|$, $b \neq 0$

(1.11) $-|a| \leq a \leq |a|$

(1.12) $|a - b| \geq ||a| - |b||$

(1.13) $|a + b| \le |a| + |b|$, triangle inequality

(1.14) $a^n = a \cdot a \cdots a$, with n factors, where n is any positive integer

(1.15) $a^0 = 1$ if $a \ne 0$

(1.16) $a^{-n} = \dfrac{1}{a^n}$ if n is any positive integer and $a \ne 0$

Suppose that m and n are any integers. Then

(1.17) $a^m a^n = a^{m+n}$ add exponents

(1.18) $a^m/a^n = a^{m-n}$ if $a \ne 0$ subtract exponents

(1.19) $(a^m)^n = a^{mn}$ multiply exponents

(1.20) $(ab)^n = a^n b^n$ multiply bases

(1.21) $(a/b)^n = a^n/b^n$ if $b \ne 0$ divide bases

(1.22)   Square of a sum: $(x + y)^2 = x^2 + 2xy + y^2$

(1.23)   Square of a difference: $(x - y)^2 = x^2 - 2xy + y^2$

(1.24)   Product of sum and difference: $(x + y)(x - y) = x^2 - y^2$

(1.25)   Cube of a sum: $(x + y)^3 = x^3 + 3x^2 y + 3xy^2 + y^3$

(1.26)   Cube of a difference: $(x - y)^3 = x^3 - 3x^2 y + 3xy^2 - y^3$

(1.27)   Square of a trinomial $(x + y + z)^2 = x^2 + y^2 + z^2 + 2xy + 2xz + 2yz$

(1.28)   Difference of squares: $x^2 - y^2 = (x - y)(x + y)$

(1.29)   Sum of cubes: $x^3 + y^3 = (x + y)(x^2 - xy + y^2)$

(1.30)   Difference of cubes: $x^3 - y^3 = (x - y)(x^2 + xy + y^2)$

(1.31)   Square of a sum: $x^2 + 2xy + y^2 = (x + y)^2$

(1.32)   Square of a difference: $x^2 - 2xy + y^2 = (x - y)^2$

(1.33) $\dfrac{a}{b} = \dfrac{c}{d}$ if and only if $ad = bc$ equivalent fractions

(1.34)   For any $k \ne 0$, $\dfrac{a}{b} = \dfrac{ak}{bk}$ fundamental principle of fractions

(1.35) $\dfrac{a}{b} = \dfrac{-a}{-b} = -\dfrac{-a}{b} = -\dfrac{a}{-b}$

and

$-\dfrac{a}{b} = \dfrac{-a}{b} = \dfrac{a}{-b} = -\dfrac{-a}{-b}$ signs of fractions

(1.36) $\dfrac{a}{b} \cdot \dfrac{c}{d} = \dfrac{ac}{bd}$ product of fractions

(1.37) $\dfrac{a}{d} + \dfrac{c}{d} = \dfrac{a + c}{d}$ sum of fractions

$\sqrt[n]{a}$ is called the nth root of a. Thus

(1.38)   If n is an even positive integer, and a and b are **positive real numbers** for which $a = b^n$, then $\sqrt[n]{a} = b$.

If n is an odd positive integer, and if a and b are **real numbers** for which $a = b^n$, then $\sqrt[n]{a} = b$.

In either case, $\sqrt[n]{0} = 0$.

For any positive integer n and any positive real numbers a and b:

(1.39) $\sqrt[n]{ab} = (\sqrt[n]{a})(\sqrt[n]{b})$

$$(1.40) \quad \sqrt[n]{a/b} = \frac{\sqrt[n]{a}}{\sqrt[n]{b}}$$

$$(1.41) \quad \sqrt[m]{\sqrt[n]{a}} = \sqrt[mn]{a}$$

For any positive integer n and any real number a, if $\sqrt[n]{a}$ is a real number, then

$$(1.42) \quad a^{1/n} = \sqrt[n]{a}$$
$$(1.43) \quad a^{m/n} = (\sqrt[n]{a})^m = (a^{1/n})^m = (a^m)^{1/n} = \sqrt[n]{a^m}$$

EXERCISE 1.8 Review

1. Show that 460 is a composite number and give its prime factors.

2. What law is used in $21(13 + 4) = 21(13) + 21(4)$?

3. Why do we say that 17 is a prime number?

4. If $(2x - 3)(x + 5) = 0$, what is x?

5. What is the absolute value of
$$-\sqrt{64} - \sqrt{50} + \sqrt{32} + \sqrt{18} - \sqrt{8}?$$

6. Use the tests given in Probs. 6 and 7 of Exercise 1.1 to see if 28,271,463 is divisible by 3 and by 11.

7. Show that the sum of the divisors of 42, not including 42, is 1.5 times the sum of the divisors of 24, not including 24.

8. Evaluate $(17.1)(26.2) + 23.7$ and $17.1(26.2 + 23.7)$.

9. Is $\{1, -1\}$ closed under multiplication; under addition?

10. Which of the following are rational?
$$2/11 \qquad 3.141414 \cdots \qquad 2.12112111 \cdots$$

11. Evaluate -3^4 and $(-3)^4$.

12. Evaluate $[(2) \cdot (3)]^4$ and $(5/7)^3$.

13. Evaluate 3^{-2}, 2^{-3}, and $(-2)^{-3}$.

14. Find the product of $\left(\dfrac{3a^4b^3}{2cd^0}\right)^2$ and $\left(\dfrac{4c^2d}{3a^2b^2}\right)^3$.

15. Write $4^{-1}c^{-1}a^{-2}t^{-3}/2^{-3}c^{-3}at^0$ without negative exponents.

16. Put 583, 0.00583, 50.83, and 0.00203 in scientific notation.

17. Round 73.64, 73.65, 0.07366, and 736,600 off to 3 significant digits.

18. Find $(28.7)(39.6)$ and $28.7/39.6$ and round off each to the proper number of digits.

19. Assume the numbers are approximations and evaluate

$$(3.1416)(2.718) \qquad \text{and} \qquad 3.1416 + 2.718$$

20. Remove the grouping symbols from
$$2a - 3\{1 + 2a[3 - 4a(2a - 1) + 6a^2] - 2a\}$$

Find the following products.

21. $(3x - 2y)(5x + 4y)$

22. $(3x - 5y)(3x + 5y)$

23. $(3x - 5y)^3$

24. $(x - 2y + 3z)^2$

25. $(2x - 5y + 7z)(2x + 5y - 7z)$

26. Find the quotient and remainder if $3x^3 - 11x^2 + 14x + 11$ is divided by $x - 2$.

27. Find the product of $2x^2 - 5xy + y^2$ and $x^2 + 3xy - 2y^2$.

Factor the expressions in Probs. 28 to 30.

28. $27a^3 - 8b^3$

29. $(2a - b)^2 - 9$

30. $6a^2 - ab - 15b^2$

31. Is $6x^2 - x - 14$ factorable into real factors with integer coefficients? What are the factors or why are there none?

32. Factor $4x^2 - 4y^2 + 12y - 9$.

33. Factor $x^4 + 3x^2 + 4$.

34. Reduce $72x^5y^3/27x^2y^4$ to lowest terms.

35. Reduce $\dfrac{x^2 - x - 2}{x - 1} \cdot \dfrac{6x^2 + x - 2}{3x^2 - 4x - 4} \cdot \dfrac{2x^2 + x - 3}{2x^2 + x - 1}$ to lowest terms.

36. Find the sum of $\dfrac{2x^2 + x - 6}{3x^2 + 8x - 3}$ and $\dfrac{2x^2 - 5x - 3}{2x^2 + 9x + 9}$.

37. Simplify

$$\dfrac{\dfrac{3}{2x + 3} - \dfrac{5}{x + 2}}{\dfrac{3x + 1}{x + 2} + 1}$$

38. Perform the indicated operations and reduce to lowest terms

$$\frac{(x-3)x-4}{(x-9)x+20} \cdot \frac{(x+3)x-40}{(x^2-9)-8x} \div \frac{x+8}{x-9}$$

Evaluate the expression in each of Probs. 39 to 42.

39. $\sqrt{(-3)^2}$

40. $\sqrt[3]{(-3)^3}$

41. $\sqrt{(-9)(-8)}$

42. $\sqrt[4]{162/625}$

Remove all possible factors from the radicand.

43. $\sqrt[3]{72x^5y^3z^2}$

44. $\sqrt[5]{81x^3y^2}\,\sqrt[5]{21x^2y^9}$

45. Rationalize the denominator in $\dfrac{\sqrt{5}-2\sqrt{3}}{\sqrt{5}-\sqrt{3}}$.

46. Express $\sqrt{\sqrt[3]{6a}}$ as a single radical.

Perform the indicated addition and subtraction in Probs. 47 to 49 and remove all possible factors from the radicands.

47. $\sqrt[3]{6}+\sqrt[3]{48}+\sqrt[3]{162}-\sqrt[3]{750}$

48. $\sqrt{8a^3b^2}-\sqrt{18a^5}-\sqrt{8ab^2}$

49. $\sqrt[3]{375}+\sqrt{72}-\sqrt[3]{192}+\sqrt{98}$

50. Use the following area formula:

$$\sqrt{s(s-a)(s-b)(s-c)}$$

where $2s=a+b+c$ to find the area of the triangle with sides $a=7$, $b=13$, and $c=18$.

51. Rationalize the numerator in

$$\frac{\sqrt{2x+2h+3}-\sqrt{2x+3}}{h}$$

52. Evaluate $625^{1/2}$, $-125^{1/3}$, $-(125^{1/3})$, $-25^{1/2}$, $(-25)^{1/2}$.

53. Put $a^{2/5}b^{3/5}$ and $a^{-1/2}b^{1/3}$ in radical form.

54. Express $(625a^{-4}b^{4/3})^{-1/4}$ without negative exponents.

55. Express

$$-2(x+2)^{1/2}(2x-1)^{-1/3}+5(x+2)^{-1/2}(2x-1)^{2/3}$$

without negative exponents.

56. Simplify $[(x^{a^2-b^2})^{1/(a+b)}]^{a/(a-b)}$.

57. Evaluate $(5m/n)^{1/(m+n)}$ for $m=2$ and $n=3$.

58. Simplify

$$\frac{\dfrac{5}{3x+4}-\dfrac{1}{2}}{x-2}$$

59. Show $\sqrt{10+6\sqrt{3}}+\sqrt{10-6\sqrt{3}}=2$. *Hint:* Begin with $(1+\sqrt{3})^3$.

60. *Calculator* It can be shown that the average value of x^2 on the interval [1.5, 4.5] is 39/4. Calculate the value of the average below:

$$\frac{2^2+3^2+4^2}{3}$$

Write the expression below using rational exponents.

61. $\sqrt{(x^2+25)^3}$

Write this expression as a perfect square:

62. $1+\left(x^{3/5}-\dfrac{1}{4x^{3/5}}\right)^2$

63. If $n\ge 9$, then

$$\sqrt{n}^{\sqrt{n+1}}>\sqrt{(n+1)}^{\sqrt{n}}$$

Verify this for $n=9$.

64. Find

$$\cfrac{1}{1+\cfrac{1}{2+\cfrac{1}{1+\cfrac{1}{3}}}}$$

65. *Political science* In a model of negotiating, the equation

$$R=\frac{P-\dfrac{1}{m}}{Q-\dfrac{1}{m}}$$

occurs, where $P<Q$, P and Q measure goodness of fit, and m is a positive integer.
(a) Express R without complex fractions.
(b) Find R if $P=0.271$, $Q=0.547$, and $m=5$.

66. For $0<a<b$, it is true that

$$\frac{2ab}{a+b}<\sqrt{ab}<\frac{a+b}{2}<\sqrt{\frac{a^2+b^2}{2}}$$

Verify this for $a=8$ and $b=9$.

67. *A radical inequality* The following inequalities give an excellent approximation to $\sqrt{10}$. Verify each step.

$3 < \sqrt{10} < 3.2$ *Hint:* Square each term.

$0 < \sqrt{10} - 3 < 1/5$

$0 < (\sqrt{10} - 3)^4 < (1/5)^4$

and

$$(\sqrt{10} - 3)^4 = [(\sqrt{10} - 3)^2]^2$$
$$= (19 - 6\sqrt{10})^2 = 721 - 228\sqrt{10}$$

$0 < 721 - 228\sqrt{10} < 1/625$

$-721 < -228\sqrt{10} < -721 + 1/625$

$721 > 228\sqrt{10} > 721 - 1/625 = 450{,}624/625$

$721/228 > \sqrt{10} > 450{,}624/142{,}500$
$$= 112{,}656/35{,}625$$

Note that to six decimal places

$$112{,}656/35{,}625 = 3.162274$$
$$\sqrt{10} = 3.162278$$
$$721/228 = 3.162281$$

68. Show that

$$\frac{1}{\sqrt[3]{4} + \sqrt[3]{6} + \sqrt[3]{9}} = \sqrt[3]{3} - \sqrt[3]{2}$$

69. Show that if $\dfrac{1}{p} + \dfrac{1}{q} = 1$, then $p + q = pq$.

70. Show that if a, b, c, and d are positive distinct numbers,

$$\frac{ab}{cd} = \frac{a - b}{c - d}$$

if and only if

$$\frac{1}{a} + \frac{1}{d} = \frac{1}{b} + \frac{1}{c}$$

2 Linear and Quadratic Equations and Inequalities

For many people and many centuries, the study of algebra has been closely tied to the study of equations. An **equation** is a statement that two algebraic expressions are equal. In this chapter, we will discuss linear and quadratic equations, and also their related inequalities. Many real-world applications of mathematics can be solved using equations and inequalities. In fact, inequalities have become especially important in this century because they are so useful when applied to linear programming in business and other areas.

2.1 Linear Equations

In later chapters, we will study equations such as $2^x = 7$, $x^2 + 3y = 145$, and $x^3 - 7x^2 + 2x - 5 = 0$. In this chapter, we will study linear and quadratic equations in one variable, as well as inequalities.

A **linear equation** is one which can be written in the form

$$ax + b = 0 \qquad \text{with } a \neq 0$$

A **quadratic equation** is one which can be written in the form

$$ax^2 + bx + c = 0 \qquad \text{with } a \neq 0$$

The expressions on both sides of the equal sign are called the **sides,** or **members,** of the equation. The equation

$$6x - 5 = 2x + 7$$

is true if x is replaced by 3 since each side equals 13. However it is false if x is replaced by 4 since the sides are then 19 and 15. A number that makes the equation a true statement is called a **solution** or a **root** of the equation. We say that a root, or a solution, **satisfies the equation.** The set of all solutions of an equation is called the **solution set.** To **solve an equation** means to find all of its solutions.

Some equations are true for every value of the variable, or unknown, for which all expressions are defined. For example

$$4x^2 - 25 - (2x - 5)(2x + 5) = 0$$

and

$$\frac{3}{x - 2} - \frac{2}{x - 2} = \frac{1}{x - 2}$$

are true for every real value of x, with the exception that $x = 2$ is not allowed in the second equation since division by zero is not defined. An **identity** is an equation that is true for every value of the variable, for which all expressions are defined. Every allowable number is a solution of an identity.

If an equation is not an identity, we call it a **conditional equation.** The equation $x = 5$ is a conditional equation since it is true only if x has the value 5. The equation $x + 17 = x + 19$ is a conditional equation with no solutions. The equation $6x - 17 = 2x + 11$ is also conditional since it is satisfied by $x = 7$, but not for instance by $x = -4$.

The simpler the equation is in form, the easier it is to solve. For example, it is easy to see that $x = 4$ is a solution of $2x = 8$, while for the equation

$$7x - 45 = 5x - 37$$

the only way we can find the solution at this stage is to pick a number for x and then substitute to see if it satisfies the equation. Now if we substitute 4 for x in this equation and simplify, we get $28 - 45$ or -17 for the left side and $20 - 37$ or -17 for the right side. This means that $x = 4$ is in fact a root.

Two equations are **equivalent** if every solution of one is also a solution of the other one. Thus two equations are equivalent if and only if they have the same solution set.

We will make extensive use of the concept of equivalent equations to solve equations. Our goal is to replace an equation by successively simpler equivalent equations until we get one that is readily solved. To do this, we will use some of the properties of real numbers given earlier. Namely, we may

Add the same number to both sides of an equation.
Subtract the same number from both sides of an equation.

We may also multiply or divide both members by **the same nonzero number.** Remember that

$$\text{Dividing by } p \text{ is just multiplying by } \frac{1}{p}, \text{ if } p \neq 0$$

and also

$$\text{Subtracting } t \text{ is just adding } -t$$

In equation form, these statements are as follows:

$a = b$ is equivalent to $a + c = b + c$ for every c

$a = b$ is equivalent to $ac = bc$ for every $c \neq 0$

For instance the equations

$$x - 32 = 14 \quad \text{and} \quad x - 32 + 32 = 14 + 32$$

are equivalent and so are the equations

$$6x = 30 \quad \text{and} \quad \frac{6x}{6} = \frac{30}{6}$$

NOTE   It is important to distinguish between *working with an expression* and *solving an equation*. When working with a single expression, we may not simply add 6 to it, because then we would have changed its value. For instance

$$4x^2 + 3x + 2 \quad \text{and} \quad 4x^2 + 3x + 2 + 6$$

are not **equivalent expressions.** However, when solving an equation, we are working with two expressions, and, by the first rule above, it is legitimate to add 6 to each of the two expressions. For instance the equations

$$5x - 6 = 7 \quad \text{and} \quad 5x - 6 + 6 = 7 + 6$$

are **equivalent equations.**

We will now see how to solve the general linear equation $ax + b = 0$, if $a \neq 0$:

$ax + b = 0$	given
$ax + b - b = 0 - b$	subtracting b from both sides
$ax = -b$	combining terms
$\dfrac{ax}{a} = \dfrac{-b}{a}$	dividing by a since $a \neq 0$
$x = \dfrac{-b}{a}$	removing the common factor of a on the left-hand side **(2.1)**

This shows that if there is a solution, it must be $x = -b/a$. We verify that it is in fact a solution by calculating

$$ax + b = \frac{a(-b)}{a} + b = -b + b = 0$$

▶ EXAMPLE 1   Solve the equation $x - 3 = 4$.

Solution

$$x - 3 = 4 \qquad \text{given}$$
$$x = 7 \qquad \text{adding 3}$$ ◢

▶ EXAMPLE 2   Solve the equation $5x - 6 = 9$.

Solution

$$5x - 6 = 9 \qquad \text{given}$$
$$5x = 15 \qquad \text{adding 6}$$
$$x = 3 \qquad \text{dividing by 5}$$ ◢

▶ EXAMPLE 3   Solve the equation $4x = 7x - 6$.

Solution

$$4x = 7x - 6 \qquad \text{given}$$
$$6 = 7x - 4x \qquad \text{adding } 6 - 4x$$
$$6 = 3x \qquad \text{combining}$$
$$2 = x \qquad \text{dividing by 3}$$ ◢

▶ EXAMPLE 4   Solve the equation $6x - 7 = 2x + 1$.

Solution

$$6x - 7 = 2x + 1 \qquad \text{given}$$
$$6x - 2x = 1 + 7 \qquad \text{adding } 7 - 2x$$
$$4x = 8 \qquad \text{collecting}$$
$$x = 2 \qquad \text{dividing by 4}$$ ◢

When multiplying both members of an equation by the same expression, we usually **use the lcd** (least common denominator) of the denominators to get an equivalent equation with no fractions. We must however be careful

Not to multiply by 0 in any form

because the resulting equation will not be equivalent to the preceding one.

▶ EXAMPLE 5   Solve the equation $x/2 - \frac{2}{3} = 3x/4 + \frac{1}{12}$.

Solution   Since the lcd of the denominators is 12 and $12 \neq 0$, we will multiply each side by 12.

$$12\left(\frac{x}{2} - \frac{2}{3}\right) = 12\left(\frac{3x}{4} + \frac{1}{12}\right) \qquad \text{multiplying by the lcd, 12}$$
$$6x - 8 = 9x + 1 \qquad \text{distributive axiom}$$
$$6x - 9x = 1 + 8 \qquad \text{adding } 8 - 9x$$
$$-3x = 9 \qquad \text{combining}$$
$$x = -3 \qquad \text{dividing by } -3$$ ◢

▶ **EXAMPLE 6** Solve the equation

$$\frac{x}{x+1} + \frac{5}{8} = \frac{5}{2(x+1)} + \frac{3}{4} \tag{1}$$

where $x \neq -1$ in order to avoid division by 0.

Solution The least common denominator is $8(x+1)$, and we multiply both sides of the equation by the lcd in order to eliminate fractions.

$$8(x+1)\left(\frac{x}{x+1} + \frac{5}{8}\right) = 8(x+1)\left[\frac{5}{2(x+1)} + \frac{3}{4}\right]$$

$$8x + 5(x+1) = 4(5) + 6(x+1) \qquad \text{removing common factors from each term}$$

The two equations above are equivalent if $8(x+1) \neq 0$, which means $x \neq -1$.

$$8x + 5x + 5 = 20 + 6x + 6 \qquad \text{distributive axiom}$$

$$8x + 5x - 6x = 20 + 6 - 5 \qquad \text{adding } -6x - 5$$

$$7x = 21 \qquad \text{combining terms}$$

$$x = 3 \qquad \text{multiplying by } \tfrac{1}{7}$$

Thus the equation $x = 3$ is equivalent to the given equation, since the only restriction was $x \neq -1$. Therefore $x = 3$ is a solution, and it is the only one. In fact each side of (1) is $\frac{11}{8}$ when $x = 3$. ◢

▶ **EXAMPLE 7** Solve the equation

$$\frac{2x}{x-3} = 1 + \frac{6}{x-3}$$

Solution We will multiply by the lcd $x - 3$ and will therefore stipulate that $x \neq 3$.

$$2x = 1(x-3) + 6 \qquad \text{multiplying by } x - 3$$

$$2x = x - 3 + 6 \qquad \text{distributive axiom}$$

$$2x - x = -3 + 6 \qquad \text{subtracting } x$$

$$x = 3 \qquad \text{combining terms}$$

Thus if there is a solution of the original equation, it must be $x = 3$. However 3 can not be a solution of the given equation since replacing x by 3 involves division by 0. So the first equation has **no solution.** In other words, the first step, multiplying by $x - 3$, was in effect multiplying by 0. The number 3 in this example is called an **extraneous root** of the given equation because it is not a root of the given equation, although it is a root of a subsequent nonequivalent equation. ◢

REMEMBER Do not multiply each side of an equation by 0 in any form.

▶ **EXAMPLE 8** Solve $2/(x-5) + 5/(x-2) = 7/(x-2)(x-5)$, where we assume $x \neq 5$ and $x \neq 2$ to avoid division by zero.

Solution $$2(x - 2) + 5(x - 5) = 7 \qquad \text{multiplying by the lcd } (x - 2)(x - 5)$$

This is equivalent to the given equation since $(x - 2)(x - 5) \neq 0$.

$$2x - 4 + 5x - 25 = 7 \qquad \text{distributive axiom}$$

$$7x - 29 = 7 \qquad \text{combining terms}$$

$$7x = 36 \qquad \text{adding 29}$$

$$x = \frac{36}{7} \qquad \text{dividing by 7}$$

This is the solution since the lcd $(x - 5)(x - 2)$ is not zero for $x = \frac{36}{7}$. It can be checked in the original equation.   ◢

EXAMPLE 9   Solve $6/(2x - 1) - 1/(x - 3) = 2/(x + 2)$, where we assume $x \neq \frac{1}{2}$, $x \neq 3$, and $x \neq -2$ to avoid division by zero.

Solution $$6(x - 3)(x + 2) - 1(2x - 1)(x + 2) = 2(2x - 1)(x - 3) \qquad \begin{array}{l}\text{multiplying by the lcd}\\ (2x - 1)(x - 3)(x + 2)\end{array}$$

This is equivalent to the given equation since the lcd is not 0.

$$6(x^2 - x - 6) - (2x^2 + 3x - 2) = 2(2x^2 - 7x + 3) \qquad \text{multiplying the binomials}$$

$$6x^2 - 6x - 36 - 2x^2 - 3x + 2 = 4x^2 - 14x + 6 \qquad \text{distributive axiom}$$

$$4x^2 - 9x - 34 = 4x^2 - 14x + 6 \qquad \text{combining terms}$$

$$5x = 40 \qquad \text{adding } 14x + 34 - 4x^2$$

$$x = 8 \qquad \text{dividing by 5}$$

The solution of the given equation is $x = 8$ since this number does not make any denominator 0.   ◢

EXAMPLE 10   Solve $S = \pi r^2 + 2\pi rh$ for h.

Solution $$S = \pi r^2 + 2\pi rh \qquad \text{given}$$

$$S - \pi r^2 = 2\pi rh \qquad \text{subtracting } \pi r^2$$

$$\frac{S - \pi r^2}{2\pi r} = h \qquad \text{dividing by } 2\pi r \qquad ◢$$

EXERCISE 2.1

In Probs. 1 to 8, decide whether the equation is an identity or a conditional equation.

1. $x^2 - 9 = (x + 3)(x - 3)$
2. $x^2 - 5 = (x - 3)(x - 2)$
3. $(3x - 2)^2 = 9x^2 - 6x + 4$
4. $x^3 - 1 = (x - 1)(x^2 + x + 1)$
5. $x/2 + x/4 = x/6$
6. $x/2 - x/3 = x/6$
7. $\dfrac{2x^2 - 5x}{2} = \dfrac{-x(5 - 2x)}{2}$

8. $\dfrac{x}{5} + \dfrac{5}{x} = \dfrac{x^2 - 25}{5x}$

In Probs. 9 to 12, state whether the two equations are equivalent or not.

9. $7x - 2 = 4x + 3$
$3x = 1$

10. $8x + 5 = 5x + 8$
$3 = 3x$

11. $2x = 17$
$x = 17 - 2$

12. $5 + 3x = 11$
$3x = \frac{11}{5}$

Find the solution of the equation in each of Probs. 13 to 64.

13. $3x = 5x + 4$

14. $5x = 8x + 3$

15. $7x = 4x + 9$

16. $5x = 6x - 9$

17. $3(y + 2) = 8y + 1$

18. $3(y + 4) - 2(y - 1) = 13$

19. $5(y + 2) = 7(y + 1) + 1$

20. $6(y - 1) - 5(y + 2) = -14$

21. $x/2 + 3 = 2x/5 + 4$

22. $7x/8 + 9 = x/2 + 6$

23. $5x/6 - 7 = x/2 - 3$

24. $5 - 3x/4 = 2x/3 + 22$

25. $\dfrac{2w - 3}{3} = w - 3$

26. $\dfrac{3w + 4}{2} = 3w - 4$

27. $\dfrac{3w + 5}{4} = 2w - 5$

28. $\dfrac{5w - 7}{3} = 2w - 5$

29. $\dfrac{3x - 2}{5} + 3 = \dfrac{4x - 1}{3}$

30. $\dfrac{2x - 3}{3} + 1 = \dfrac{3x + 2}{5}$

31. $\dfrac{2x - 9}{3} - 2 = \dfrac{x - 3}{3}$

32. $\dfrac{5x + 1}{8} + 3 = \dfrac{3x + 1}{2}$

33. $\dfrac{3t + 7}{2} + 3t - 7 = \dfrac{2t + 3}{5}$

34. $\dfrac{3t + 10}{2} - t - 4 = \dfrac{3t + 6}{4}$

35. $\dfrac{5t + 7}{2} = \dfrac{3t + 5}{4} + 2t + 3$

36. $\dfrac{4t + 5}{5} = \dfrac{3t - 15}{2} + 2t - 5$

37. $\dfrac{2}{3x + 1} = \dfrac{1}{x}$

38. $\dfrac{2}{3x + 1} = \dfrac{5}{8x + 1}$

39. $\dfrac{11}{6x + 1} = \dfrac{2}{x + 1}$

40. $\dfrac{8}{5x - 4} = \dfrac{5}{3x - 1}$

41. $\dfrac{p + 1}{p - 2} = \dfrac{p - 1}{p - 3}$

42. $\dfrac{p + 1}{p - 5} = \dfrac{p + 4}{p - 4}$

43. $\dfrac{p + 5}{p - 1} = \dfrac{p + 2}{p - 2}$

44. $\dfrac{p + 4}{p - 3} = \dfrac{p + 2}{p - 4}$

45. $\dfrac{2x + 5}{4x + 1} = \dfrac{3x + 5}{6x - 1}$

46. $\dfrac{4x - 3}{2x - 3} = \dfrac{8x + 5}{4x + 1}$

47. $\dfrac{2x - 5}{4x - 1} = \dfrac{3x - 4}{6x + 9}$

48. $\dfrac{6x - 8}{9x + 8} = \dfrac{2x - 3}{3x + 2}$

49. $\dfrac{4}{x - 2} - \dfrac{3}{x + 1} = \dfrac{8}{(x - 2)(x + 1)}$

50. $\dfrac{1}{x + 5} + \dfrac{1}{2x + 9} = \dfrac{2}{(x + 5)(2x + 9)}$

51. $\dfrac{1}{2x + 3} - \dfrac{3}{x - 3} = \dfrac{3}{(2x + 3)(x - 3)}$

52. $\dfrac{2}{x + 2} + \dfrac{1}{2x - 1} = \dfrac{5}{(x + 2)(2x - 1)}$

53. $\dfrac{2}{z + 1} + \dfrac{3}{2z - 3} = \dfrac{6z + 1}{2z^2 - z - 3}$

54. $\dfrac{5}{3z - 1} - \dfrac{1}{5z - 7} = \dfrac{11z - 1}{15z^2 - 26z + 7}$

55. $\dfrac{5}{2z + 1} + \dfrac{4}{z - 1} = \dfrac{12z + 6}{2z^2 - z - 1}$

56. $\dfrac{9}{2z + 3} - \dfrac{2}{z - 1} = \dfrac{z + 9}{2z^2 + z - 3}$

57. $\dfrac{4}{2x - 3} + \dfrac{5}{5x - 4} = \dfrac{3}{x + 2}$

58. $\dfrac{4}{3x - 2} - \dfrac{1}{2x - 3} = \dfrac{5}{6x + 3}$

59. $\dfrac{4}{3x - 1} - \dfrac{3}{2x + 3} = \dfrac{-1}{6x - 24}$

60. $\dfrac{3}{x + 3} - \dfrac{2}{2x - 5} = \dfrac{6}{3x - 13}$

61. $\dfrac{x + 7}{(2x - 3)(x + 1)} = \dfrac{8x - 9}{2x - 3} - \dfrac{4x + 9}{x + 2}$

62. $\dfrac{3x + 8}{(x + 1)(x + 3)} = \dfrac{x + 3}{x + 1} - \dfrac{2x + 3}{2x + 5}$

63. $\dfrac{5x + 20}{(3x - 5)(x + 1)} = \dfrac{2x - 7}{x - 5} + \dfrac{6x - 6}{3x - 5}$

64. $\dfrac{15x - 79}{(3x + 1)(x - 1)} = \dfrac{x - 5}{x - 1} - \dfrac{x - 6}{x + 3}$

In Probs. 65 to 68, find the value of b for which $x = 5$ is a solution of the equation.

65. $\dfrac{x - 3}{b + 2} + \dfrac{x - 2}{b + 6} = \dfrac{x}{b + 4}$

66. $\dfrac{x - 3}{b + 6} + \dfrac{2x - 8}{2b - 9} = \dfrac{x - 2}{b - 1}$

67. $\dfrac{x - 3}{b + 5} + \dfrac{x + 1}{3b + 5} = \dfrac{2x - 6}{b + 3}$

68. $\dfrac{x - 2}{3b + 7} - \dfrac{x - 4}{2b + 18} = \dfrac{1}{2b - 2}$

Find the solution of the equation in each of Probs. 69 to 76 for the letter given at the right of the comma.

69. $C = \frac{5}{9}(F - 32),\ F$

70. $C = \dfrac{Ak}{4\pi d},\ d$

71. $\dfrac{p}{q} = \dfrac{f}{q - f},\ f$

72. $\dfrac{1}{p} + \dfrac{1}{q} = \dfrac{2}{R},\ q$

73. $m = \dfrac{c(1 - p)}{1 - d},\ p$

74. $I = \dfrac{Ne}{R + Nr},\ r$

75. $S = \dfrac{a - ar^n}{1 - r},\ a$

76. $M = \dfrac{L}{F}\left(\dfrac{25}{f} + 1\right),\ f$

Solve the equation in each of Probs. 77 and 78 by adding the expressions on each side of the equal sign before multiplying by the lcd.

77. $\dfrac{1}{x + 3} - \dfrac{1}{x + 1} = \dfrac{1}{x + 4} - \dfrac{1}{x + 2}$

78. $\dfrac{1}{x + 5} - \dfrac{1}{x + 8} = \dfrac{1}{x + 3} - \dfrac{1}{x + 6}$

79. *Anthropology* In the study of agricultural terraces in Ecuador, the following equations arise. Solve each of them for H.

(a) $z = \dfrac{WHx}{x^2 + W^2}$

(b) $H(W - x)^2 = W^2(H - 2z)$

(c) $\dfrac{H}{W} = \dfrac{H - y - z}{W - x}$

80. *How thick is Scotch tape?* When tape is wrapped around a circular core, its length L, thickness T, inner radius a, and outer radius b are related by

$$L = \dfrac{\pi}{T}(b^2 - a^2)$$

Find the thickness if $L = 3290$ cm, $a = 1.78$ cm, and $b = 3.14$ cm. Use $\pi = 3.1416$.

Show that the equations in Probs. 81 to 84 have no solutions.

81. $\dfrac{x}{x - 4} + 1 = \dfrac{4}{x - 4}$

82. $\dfrac{2x}{x - 3} - 11 = \dfrac{6}{x - 3}$

83. $\dfrac{3y}{y + 4} = 7 - \dfrac{12}{y + 4}$

84. $\dfrac{6y}{y + 7} = 10 - \dfrac{42}{y + 7}$

Some borrowers are fortunate and frugal enough to be able to repar a loan before the due date. If this is the case, the borrower ordinarily receives a rebate on the finance charges. One method for determining the refund is called "the rule of 78." If that method is used, the refund is given by

$$r = \dfrac{fn(n + 1)}{q(q + 1)}$$

where r is the refund, f the original finance charge, n is the number of payments still to be made, and q is the original number of payments. Find the refund under the conditions given in each of Probs. 85 to 88.

85. $f = \$900,\ q = 12,\ n = 4$

86. $f = \$1200,\ q = 24,\ n = 9$

87. $f = \$1500,\ q = 18,\ n = 6$

88. $f = \$600,\ q = 15,\ n = 10$

89. Find the error in the following "proof" that $1 = -1$. *Hint:* Which two consecutive equations are not equivalent?

$$x = 1$$
$$x^2 = 1^2$$
$$x^2 - x = 1 - x$$
$$x(x - 1) = -1(x - 1)$$
$$x = -1$$

2.2 Applications

A stated problem, or word problem, or applied problem, is a description of a situation that involves both known and unknown quantities and relationships between them. A problem involving only one unknown can be solved by use of a single equation.

As is true for any skill, the process of solving a stated problem by using equations requires considerable practice to become adept at it. Most people find the following approach helpful. It may be applied not only in this section, but in all cases where a problem is stated and must be "translated into an equation" and then solved.

1. Read the problem carefully and make sure the situation is thoroughly understood.
2. Identify the quantities, both known and unknown, that are involved in the problem.
3. Select one of the unknown quantities and represent it by a variable (letter), and then express any other unknowns in terms of this variable, if possible.
4. Search the problem for information that tells what quantities or combinations of them are equal.
5. Often, making a sketch helps to carry out step 4.
6. Write an equation using the algebraic expressions found in step 5. Carrying through the calculations with an initial guess sometimes helps to clarify the relationship between variables.
7. Solve the equation obtained in step 6.
8. Check the solution in the *original problem*. This step is critical since we want a solution of the stated problem rather than of the equation that we write.

The following examples illustrate how various English statements can be represented by linear equations:

(a) "x is 25 more than y" or
"x is greater than y by 25" or
"the value of x decreased by 25 is y" or
"y is 25 less than x"
Equation: $x = 25 + y$ or $x - y = 25$

(b) "The sum of x and y is 380"
"y is 380 diminished by x"
"The values of x and y total 380"
Equation: $x + y = 380$ or $y = 380 - x$

(c) "The sum of four consecutive integers is 178."
Equation: $x + (x + 1) + (x + 2) + (x + 3) = 178$, where x is the smallest of the four integers.

(d) "x is twice y" or "y is half of x"
Equation: $x = 2y$ or $y = x/2$

(e) "x is 17 less than twice y"
Equation: $x = 2y - 17$

(f)   "Kaye's age is 3 more than twice what it was 10 years ago."
Equation: $x = 3 + 2(x - 10)$, where x is Kaye's age now.

(g)   "$106.50 is the interest earned on $1800 if part of it is invested at 5 percent and the rest at $6\frac{1}{2}$ percent."
Equation: $106.50 = 0.05x + 0.065(1800 - x)$, where x dollars are at 5 percent $= 0.05$ and $1800 - x$ dollars are at $6\frac{1}{2}$ percent $= 0.065$.

It often helps to organize the data in a table, as in the examples later in this section.

Pick a number

Sometimes you can understand the problem better if you *select any number* for the variable and then calculate the various quantities using this number instead of the variable. The benefit is that you will then know when and what to add, multiply, etc. In part (f) above, one could arbitrarily choose Kaye's age to be 19 since it is clearly more than 10. Then the following **numerical calculations**

Kaye's current age	Her age 10 years ago	Twice her age 10 years ago	3 more than twice her age 10 years ago
19	9	18	21

can be rewritten replacing 19 by x:

| x | $x - 10$ | $2(x - 10)$ | $2(x - 10) + 3$ |

Frequently there is a formula which represents the relationship between the unknowns. The first applications that we will consider are problems involving motion. The fundamental formula used for these problems is

Motion problems

$$d = rt$$

where d represents distance, r represents rate or velocity or speed, and t represents time. When this formula is used, d and r must use the same unit of distance (for example, miles and miles per hour) and r and t must use the same unit of time (for example, miles per hour and hours). If the formula is solved for r or t, we get two additional forms of the formula

$$r = \frac{d}{t} \quad \text{and} \quad t = \frac{d}{r}$$

▶ **EXAMPLE 1**   Suppose that a trip from the dormitory to the lake at 30 mi/h takes 12 min longer than the return trip at 48 mi/h. How far apart are the dormitory and the lake?

Solution   Units used must be the same; so we use

$$12 \text{ min} = \tfrac{12}{60} \text{ h} = \tfrac{1}{5} \text{ h}$$

since the speeds are given in miles per hour. Then the equation is

$$\frac{d}{30} = \frac{d}{48} + \frac{1}{5}$$

where d is the distance of the trip in miles and each of the fractions represents time in hours, using $t = d/r$ from above. Instead of finding the lcd of 30, 48, and 5, the arithmetic is easier if we first just multiply each side by 30:

$$30\left(\frac{d}{30}\right) = 30\left(\frac{d}{48} + \frac{1}{5}\right)$$

$$d = \frac{5d}{8} + 6 \qquad \text{simplifying each fraction}$$

$$8d = 5d + 48 \qquad \text{multiplying by 8}$$

$$3d = 48 \qquad \text{subtracting } 5d$$

$$d = 16 \qquad \text{dividing by 3}$$

The distance is 16 mi. Check in the original problem:

The time to the lake at 30 mi/h is $\frac{16}{30} = \frac{32}{60}$, or 32 min

The time from the lake at 48 mi/h is $\frac{16}{48} = \frac{1}{3} = \frac{20}{60}$, or 20 min

which is indeed 12 min quicker.　◢

EXAMPLE 2 A hiking club made a trip of 380 km to a base camp in 7 h. They traveled 4 h on a paved highway and the remainder of the time on a wilderness trail. If the average velocity on the trail was 25 km/h less than that on the highway, find the average velocity and distance traveled on each part of the trip.

Solution We begin with a sketch of the situation in Fig. 2.1 and then present the data in a table.

	Time, h	Velocity, km/h	Distance, km
On highway	4	x	$4x$
On trail	$7 - 4 = 3$	$x - 25$	$3(x - 25)$
Total	7		380

The unknown quantities are the two velocities and the distance on each part of the trip. The known quantities are 380 km, the total distance; 7 h, the total time; 4 h, the time spent on the highway; and 25 km/h, the amount by which the velocity on the highway exceeds that on the trail. The time spent on the trail was 7 h − 4 h = 3 h, and the total distance is equal to the sum of the distances traveled on each of the two parts.

If we let

$$x = \text{speed on the highway} \qquad \text{km/h}$$

then

$$x - 25 = \text{speed on the trail}$$

Furthermore, as in the table

$$4x = \text{distance traveled on the highway} \qquad \text{km}$$

4 h at x km/h	3 h at $(x - 25)$ km/h
Paved highway	Wilderness trail

FIGURE 2.1

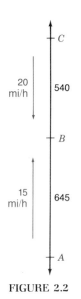

FIGURE 2.2

$$3(x - 25) = \text{distance traveled on the trail} \quad \text{km}$$

Quantities that are equal:

$$\text{Distance on highway} + \text{distance on trail} = 380$$

$$4x \quad + \quad 3(x - 25) \quad = 380$$

This is the desired equation, and we solve it below:

$$4x + 3x - 75 = 380 \qquad \text{distributive axiom}$$

$$4x + 3x = 380 + 75 \qquad \text{adding 75}$$

$$7x = 455 \qquad \text{combining terms}$$

$$x = 65 \qquad \text{dividing by 7}$$

Thus 65 km/h is the velocity on the highway, and 40 km/h is the velocity on the trail, since $65 - 25 = 40$.

Check in the original problem:

$$4 \text{ h} \times 65 \text{ km/h} = 260 \text{ km} \qquad \text{traveled on the highway}$$

$$3 \text{ h} \times 40 \text{ km/h} = 120 \text{ km} \qquad \text{traveled on the trail}$$

$$260 \text{ km} + 120 \text{ km} = 380 \text{ km}$$

EXAMPLE 3   Three airports, A, B, and C, are located on a north-south line. B is 645 mi north of A, and C is 540 mi north of B. A pilot flew from A to B, delayed 2 h, and continued to C. The wind was blowing from the south at 15 mi/h during the first part of the trip, but during the delay it changed to the north with a velocity of 20 mi/h. If each flight required the same time, find the airspeed of the plane. See Fig. 2.2.

Solution   We proceed as follows. Let

$$x = \text{airspeed} \quad \text{mi/h}$$

Then

$$x + 15 = \text{speed of the plane from } A \text{ to } B \qquad \text{mi/h}$$

and

$$x - 20 = \text{speed of the plane from } B \text{ to } C \qquad \text{mi/h}$$

Furthermore,

$$\frac{645}{x + 15} = \text{number of hours required for first flight}$$

$$\frac{540}{x - 20} = \text{number of hours required for second flight}$$

The key to this problem is that these two periods of time are equal. Using this information, we have the equation

$$\frac{645}{x + 15} = \frac{540}{x - 20}$$

We may now solve the equation in the following way:

$$(x - 20)(x + 15)\left(\frac{645}{x + 15}\right) = (x - 20)(x + 15)\left(\frac{540}{x - 20}\right) \qquad \text{multiplying by the lcd } (x + 15)(x - 20)$$

$$(x - 20)645 = (x + 15)540 \qquad \text{canceling factors}$$

$$645x - 12,900 = 540x + 8100 \qquad \text{multiplying}$$

$$105x = 21,000 \qquad \text{combining terms}$$

$$x = 200 \qquad \text{dividing by 105}$$

Therefore the airspeed is 200 mi/h.

Check $x + 15 = 200 + 15 = 215$, which is the velocity of the plane during the first flight; distance/speed $= \frac{645}{215} = 3$; so the first flight required 3 h. Furthermore, $x - 20 = 200 - 20 = 180$ and distance/speed $= \frac{540}{180} = 3$; so the second flight required 3 h. Consequently, the airspeed of 200 mi/h satisfies the conditions of the problem. ◢

Work problems   Problems that involve the rate of doing certain tasks can often be solved by first finding the fractional part of the task done by each individual, or machine, in one unit of time. For instance, if a job takes 7 h to do, then $\frac{1}{7}$ of it can be done in 1 h. We then find a relation between the fractional parts. If this method is used, the unit 1 represents the entire job that is to be done.

▶ **EXAMPLE 4**   A farmer can plow a field in 4 days by using a tractor. A hired hand can plow the same field in 6 days by using a smaller tractor. How many days will be required for the plowing if they work together?

Solution   We let

$$x = \text{number of days required to plow the field working together}$$

Then for the part of the field plowed by each in 1 day,

$$\tfrac{1}{4} = \text{the part plowed in 1 day by the farmer}$$

$$\tfrac{1}{6} = \text{the part plowed in 1 day by the hired hand}$$

and $\dfrac{1}{x} = \text{the part plowed in 1 day by the two of them}$

We now make use of the fact that the part plowed in 1 day by the farmer plus the part plowed in 1 day by the hired hand equals the part plowed in 1 day by the two:

$$\frac{1}{4} + \frac{1}{6} = \frac{1}{x}$$

This is the desired equation, and we solve it as follows:

$$12x\left(\frac{1}{4} + \frac{1}{6}\right) = 12x\left(\frac{1}{x}\right) \qquad \text{multiplying by the lcd} = 12x$$

$$3x + 2x = 12 \qquad \text{by distributive axiom}$$

$$5x = 12 \qquad \text{combining terms}$$

$$x = \tfrac{12}{5} \qquad \text{dividing by 5}$$

Check   They will plow the field in $\frac{12}{5}$ days working together, and thus they complete $\frac{5}{12}$ of it in 1 day. Furthermore, the hired hand plows one-sixth of it in 1 day, and the farmer plows one-fourth; thus

$$\frac{1}{6} + \frac{1}{4} = \frac{2+3}{12} = \frac{5}{12}$$

   **EXAMPLE 5**   If, in Example 4, the hired hand worked 1 day with the smaller machine and then was joined by the employer with the larger one, how many days were required for them to finish the plowing?

Solution   Since the hired hand plowed one-sixth of the field in 1 day, five-sixths remained unplowed. We let

$$x = \text{number of days required for the two to finish the job}$$

Then we multiply the part of the field plowed by each in 1 day by the number of days required for the two to finish the job and get

$$\frac{x}{4} = \text{the part plowed by the farmer}$$

$$\frac{x}{6} = \text{the part plowed by the hired hand}$$

Setting the sum of these equal to the part of the field still to be plowed after the hired hand worked alone for one day, we get

$$\frac{x}{4} + \frac{x}{6} = \frac{5}{6}$$

We now solve this equation as follows:

$$12\left(\frac{x}{4} + \frac{x}{6}\right) = 12\left(\frac{5}{6}\right) \qquad \text{multiplying by the lcd}$$

$$3x + 2x = 10 \qquad \text{distributive axiom}$$

$$5x = 10 \qquad \text{combining terms}$$

$$x = 2 \qquad \text{dividing by 5}$$

They finish the plowing in 2 days.

Check   In 2 days, the farmer plowed $2(\frac{1}{4}) = \frac{1}{2}$ of the field, and the hired hand plowed $2(\frac{1}{6}) = \frac{1}{3}$ of it. So the two of them together plowed $\frac{1}{3} + \frac{1}{2} = \frac{5}{6}$ of it.

Mixture problems   Another application concerns mixture problems. Many problems involve the combination of certain substances of known strengths, usually expressed in percentages, into a mixture of required strength. Others involve the mixing of certain products at specified prices. If the problem primarily concerns mixing products of different prices to get a product to sell for a given price, we use the fact that the sum of the values of the products that are mixed is equal to the value of the mixture.

EXAMPLE 6 How many pounds of coffee worth $2.50 per pound should be mixed with 140 lb worth $3.50 per pound in order to get a mixture to sell at $3.20 per pound?

Solution We will let

$$x = \text{the number of pounds of the \$2.50 coffee}$$

$$140 = \text{the number of pounds of the \$3.50 coffee}$$

Now consider the total values of the different coffees in dollars. The lower-priced one is worth $2.50x$, the higher-priced grade is worth $3.50(140) = 490$, and the mixture is worth $(140 + x)3.20 = 448 + 3.2x$. Consequently, equating the sum of the values of the parts in the mixture and the value of the total mixture, we find that the desired equation is

$$2.50x + 490 = 3.20x + 448$$

$$0.70x = 42 \qquad \text{collecting terms}$$

$$x = 60 \qquad \text{dividing by 0.70}$$

Therefore, we must add 60 lb of the $2.50 grade in order to obtain a mixture to sell at $3.20 per pound.

EXAMPLE 7 How many gallons of a liquid that is 74 percent alcohol must be combined with 5 gal of another that is 90 percent alcohol to obtain a mixture that is 84 percent alcohol?

Solution If we let x represent the number of gallons of the first liquid, then the amount of alcohol in it is $0.74x$. The data in the problem can be expressed in a table as below.

	Number of gallons	Percentage of alcohol	Number of gallons of alcohol
First liquid	x	74	$0.74x$
Second liquid	5	90	$0.90 \cdot 5 = 4.5$
Mixture	$x + 5$	84	$0.84(x + 5)$

The number of gallons of alcohol in the first liquid + the number of gallons of alcohol in the second liquid = the number of gallons of alcohol in the mixture.

$$0.74x + 4.5 = 0.84(x + 5)$$

$$0.74x + 4.5 = 0.84x + 4.2 \qquad \text{distributive axiom}$$

$$-0.10x = -0.3 \qquad \text{combining terms}$$

$$x = 3 \qquad \text{dividing by } -10$$

Hence, the required amount of the first mixture is 3 gal.

Check

$$(0.74 \times 3) + 4.5 = 2.22 + 4.5 = 6.72$$

$$0.84(3 + 5) = 0.84(8) = 6.72 \qquad \blacktriangleleft$$

In addition to the types of problems discussed above, there are a wide variety that can be solved by means of equations. The fundamental approach to all such applications is the same. We must first find two equal expressions, one or both of which involve the unknown quantity. The unknown should be the quantity requested in the problem. We will outline three more applications below and give the general principle or formula to be used in solving each one.

Lever

Many problems in physics and mechanics involve a *lever*. A lever is a rigid bar supported at a point, called the *fulcrum*, which is usually between the two ends of the bar. If two weights W_1 and W_2 at distances L_1 and L_2, respectively, from the fulcrum are balanced on a lever, then

$$W_1L_1 = W_2L_2$$

The weights in Fig. 2.3 balance since $21(4) = 12(7)$, both being 84. Furthermore, if a force F at a distance D from the fulcrum will just balance a weight R that is a distance d from the fulcrum, then $FD = Rd$.

Simple interest

Investment problems frequently can be solved by using the simple interest formula

$$I = Prt$$

where P is the principal, r is the interest rate, and t is the time. At 8.75 percent, the interest on $900 for 2 years is $157.50 since

$$(\$900)(0.0875)(2) = \$157.50$$

Number system

If we use the place value in our *number system*, we see that $1000T + 100h + 10t + u$ is the number with T as the thousands digit, h the hundreds digit, t the tens digit, and u the units digit. For example, $3456 = 3(1000) + 4(100) + 5(10) + 6$. There are of course many more formulas that are useful in solving equations.

Even the simplest linear equations can be extremely useful. Suppose that an ecologist wants to estimate the number n of fish in a lake to determine whether to

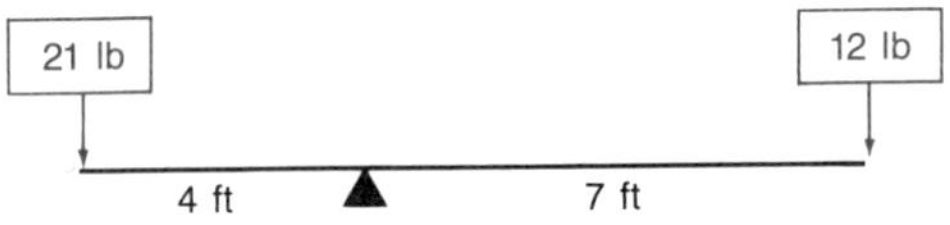

FIGURE 2.3

restock it. A common method is to fish part of the lake with a net, band the fish caught, and then release them. If 90 fish are caught and banded, then

$$\frac{\text{Total number of fish in the lake}}{\text{Number of banded fish}} = \frac{n}{90}$$

The same thing is then done the next day to give a new sample. If 84 fish are caught and 7 of these have bands from the day before, then

$$\frac{\text{Total number of fish in the sample}}{\text{Banded fish in the sample}} = \frac{84}{7}$$

Assuming that the two samples were done similarly and that each is representative of the whole fish population in the lake, then $n/90 = \frac{84}{7}$, and hence $n = 90(\frac{84}{7}) = 90(12) = 1080$. Thus there are about 1080 fish in the lake.

EXERCISE 2.2

In Probs. 1 to 8, write a linear equation that represents the problem, and solve that equation.

1. Find three consecutive integers whose sum is 75.
2. One fall, the Hookings spent $224 outfitting their two children for school. If the clothes for the older child cost $1\frac{1}{3}$ the cost of those for the younger, how much did they spend for each child?
3. The population of Mattville was 41,209 in 1984. If this population was 5015 less than twice the population of Mattville in 1978, what was the population increase in those 6 years?
4. Dr. Dixit jogged a total of 6600 yd in three nights. If each night he increased his distance 440 yd, how far did he jog on the first night?
5. The Kitchen family spent $625 buying a band instrument for each of their two children. If one instrument cost $195 more than the other, how much did each instrument cost?
6. The winning candidate for president of the freshman class received 2898 votes. If that was 210 more than half the votes cast, how many freshmen voted.
7. Ellen noticed that she had worked one-third of the problems in her math assignment and that when she had worked two more problems, she would be halfway through the assignment. How many problems were in the assignment?
8. John agreed to work on his uncle's ranch 3 months one summer for $650 and a used car. At the end of 2 months, he was needed at home, so his uncle paid him $200 and the car. What was the value of the car?
9. Sal has 316 more stamps in his collection than Bruce, and together they have 2736 stamps. How many stamps does each have?
10. Eight less than half of the students in the sophomore class at a certain college have their own cars. If 258 cars are owned by sophomores, how many sophomores are there?
11. A student has test scores of 75, 83, 68, 71, and 58 on hour tests. If the final counts $\frac{1}{3}$ of the course grade and the hour tests determine the other $\frac{2}{3}$, what must the student make on the final to have an average of 75 for the course?
12. The equation $C = 5(F - 32)/9$ gives the relation between Fahrenheit and Celsius temperatures. Find

the temperature at which the reading is the same on both thermometers.

13. The Intelligence Quotient is represented by IQ and is given by $IQ = 100m/c$, where m is the mental age and c is the chronological age. Find the mental age of a 10-year-old with an IQ of 120.

14. For a fetus more than 12 weeks old, $L = 1.53t - 6.7$, where L is the length in centimeters and t is the age in weeks. Find the age of a fetus that is 17.78 cm in length.

15. Gordon figured that when he saved $21 more, he would have one-fourth of the money for the camera he wanted. How much does the camera cost if he had already saved one-sixth of the amount?

16. One vacation season Sara and Rachel earned $160 taking care of one neighbor's yard and feeding another neighbor's dog. How much did they earn doing the yard work if that amount was $40 more than they earned feeding the dog?

17. On a trip Jennifer noticed that her car averaged 21 mi/gal of gas except for the days she used the air conditioning, and then it averaged only 17 mi/gal. If she used 91 gal of gas to drive 1751 mi, on how many of those miles did she use the air conditioning?

18. Maria invested a portion of $31,750 at 9 percent and the remainder at 10 percent. If the total income from the money is $3020, how much did she invest at each rate?

19. The Chans spent $1488 on carpeting for their new home. The carpeting used in the living room cost $13 per square yard and that used in the bedrooms cost $10 per square yard. If the bedroom area used 20 yd^2 more than the living room, how much did the Chans spend on each type of carpet?

20. At the beginning of the summer, Maude and Marilyn each earned $26.40 per day from their summer jobs. After a time, Maude was assigned more responsibility and then earned $29.60 per day. If they each worked 65 days and together earned a total of $3528, how long did Maude work at the higher rate?

21. Ellis collected $8200 in 1 year by renting two apartments. Find the rent charged for each if one rented for $50 per month more than the other and if the more expensive one was vacant for 2 months.

22. Nguyen has an income of $30,000 from the business he inherited. He pays a total income tax of 28 percent and invests part of the amount left at 10 percent

and the remainder at 12 percent. How much is at each rate if the total income from these two investments is $2360?

23. A firm wants to invest $50,000. Part of it is invested in a fund that pays 12.5 percent and the remainder in one that pays 14 percent. Find the sum at each rate if the annual income from the two is $6640.

24. A mountain resort that featured skiing in the winter was partially staffed by college students in the summer. One summer there were 3 times as many students employed as there were year-round employees. When September came, 40 of the students went back to school and 30 nonstudents were hired for the winter. If there were then twice as many nonstudents as students, how many people staffed the resort in the winter?

25. Fred is 3 years older than his sister Mary. In 7 years she will be six-sevenths of his age. How old are they?

26. The petty-cash drawer of a small office contained $16.25. If there were twice as many nickels as quarters and as many dimes as nickels and quarters combined, how many coins of each type were there?

27. Janice drove 30 mi to work each day and picked up a friend on the way. If she was able to average 40 mi/h on the trip and drove 15 min longer with the friend than without him, how far did she live from her friend's house?

28. Charles and Paul enter the Center Point–Comfort Hill Country Run. Charles runs at 8 mi/h and Paul at 6 mi/h. If they start together, how long before Charles is $\frac{1}{4}$ mi ahead of Paul?

29. John can run a certain course in 9 min and Henry can run it in 6 min. If they start at opposite ends and run toward one another, how long will they run before they meet?

30. Dominic rode his motorbike 20 min to Helen's home, and then the two drove in a car 30 min to a beach 35 mi from Dominic's home. If the car speed was 10 mi/h faster than that of the motorbike, how fast did the car travel?

31. Two students are 350 m apart and begin walking toward one another at constant rates. One travels at 1.6 m/s and the other at 1.9 m/s. How long will they walk until they meet? How far has each of them gone?

32. A bicycle club left the campus to ride to a park

24 mi away for an outing. Lynn left from the same place by car with picnic supplies $1\frac{1}{2}$ h later, traveled at a speed 4 times as fast, and arrived at the park at the same time as the cyclists. How fast did Lynn drive?

33. A jumbo jet left an airport at the same time as a small private plane that followed the same flight plan during the first hour of its flight. The speed of the jet was 5 times that of the small one, and at the end of the hour it was 500 mi ahead. What was the speed of the large plane?

34. Walt and Gail left a stable for a ride to a mountain lookout. On the way up, they averaged 3 mi/h. On the way back along the same trail, they averaged $5\frac{1}{4}$ mi/h, and the return trip took $\frac{5}{7}$ h less time than the outward trip. How long was the entire horseback ride?

35. Jo Beth left her college town on a bus that traveled 60 mi/h. Three hours later, her father left home driving at a speed of 50 mi/h to meet the bus. If the college was 345 mi from Jo Beth's home and the father met the bus as it arrived at the station, how long did the father drive to meet the bus?

36. Two brothers took turns washing the family car on weekends. John could usually wash the car in 45 min, whereas Jim took 30 min for the job. One weekend they were in a hurry to go to a football game; so they worked together. How long did it take them?

37. Lyman can mow the family yard in 75 min, while Jean can mow it in 60 min. If they work together, how long will be needed for the job?

38. Mrs. Windell spent 1 h addressing one-third of the family Christmas cards, and Mr. Windell spent $1\frac{1}{4}$ h addressing another third. Continuing the addressing together, how long did they take to finish the rest of the cards?

39. A three-person maintenance crew could clean a certain building in 4 h, whereas a four-person crew could do the job in 3 h. If one worker of the four-person crew was an hour late, how long did the job take?

40. Three people using word processors worked together preparing a group of form letters. Koonce could have done them alone in 2 h, Schaeffer in 3 h, and Yeldell in 2 h. How long did they need to do the letters working together?

41. A chemical mixing tank can be filled by two hoses. One requires 42 min to fill the tank, and the other 30 min. If both hoses are used, how much time is needed to fill the tank?

42. Jean, Carol, and Linda were on a committee to compile and staple the pages of their club newsletter. Each worker could have done the job alone in 4 h. Jean started at 3:30 P.M., Carol came at 3:45, and Linda joined the work at 4. What time did they finish?

43. Dave, Joe, and Sabrina were assigned the job of cataloging the music for their school band. Dave could have completed the assignment in 2 h alone, Sabrina in 3 h, and Joe in 4 h. They started work together, but Sabrina left at the end of a half hour and Joe at the end of an hour. How long did Dave work *alone* to finish the cataloging?

44. A swimming pool can be filled in 6 h and requires 9 h to drain. If the drain was accidentally left open for 6 h while the pool was being filled, how long did filling the pool require?

45. The intake pipe to a reservoir is controlled by an automatic valve that closes when the reservoir is full and opens again when three-fourths of the water has been drained. The intake pipe can fill the reservoir in 6 h, and the outlet can drain it in 16 h. If the outlet is open continuously, how much time elapses between two consecutive times when the reservoir is full?

46. How many pounds of chocolates costing $4.60 per pound may be mixed with 6 lb of chocolates costing $5 per pound to produce a mixture that can be sold for $4.90 per pound?

47. Keith paid $21.43 for a collection of seven tapes. Some were on sale for $3.94, and some for $1.89. How many of each type did he buy?

48. There were 11,000 people at a recent National Collegiate Athletic Association track meet who paid a total of $79,000 in entrance fees. Students paid $5 each, and nonstudents paid $8 each. How many of each type attended?

49. How much candy that is worth $5 per pound must be mixed with 60 lb that is worth $4 per pound to get a special Christmas mixture to sell for $4.40 per pound?

50. A contractor mixed two batches of concrete that were 9.3 and 11.3 percent cement to obtain 4500 lb of concrete that was 10.8 percent cement. How many pounds of each type of concrete was used?

51. British sterling is 7.5 percent copper by weight. How many grams of silver must be mixed with 150 g of an alloy that is 10 percent copper in order to make sterling?

52. At what rate must a car that is 20 ft long travel in order to pass, in 5 s, a truck that is 35 ft long and traveling in the same direction at 55 mi/h? Time starts when the front of the car is even with the rear of the truck, and it ends when the rear of the car is even with the front of the truck.

53. The minimum standard for a shipment of gravel is that 85 percent of the gravel should drop through a screen of a certain size. One load of 6 yd^3 tested at only 65 percent. How much gravel testing at 90 percent must be added to the 65 percent load to make it acceptable?

54. How much 20% hydrochloric acid must be mixed with 40 ml of 8% acid to form the 12% acid that is needed in an experiment?

55. Only 5 percent of the area of a city could be developed into parks, whereas in the unincorporated area outside the city limits 25 percent of the area could be developed into parks. If the city covered an area of 300 mi^2, how many square miles of suburbs had to be annexed so the city could develop 15 percent of its total area as parks?

56. Olie is told that the installation of insulation in the attic and walls of his home will decrease his heating costs by 15 percent. How long will be required for the installation to pay for itself if the cost is $1440 and heating costs are currently $160 per month?

57. Lynn, a chemist, mixed 40 ml of 8% hydrochloric acid with 60 ml of 12% hydrochloric acid solution. She used a portion of this solution and replaced it with distilled water. If the new solution tested 5.2% hydrochloric acid, how much of the original mixture did she use?

58. A small plane was scheduled to fly from Los Angeles to San Francisco. The flight was against a head wind of 10 mi/h. Threat of mechanical failure forced the plane to turn back, and it returned to Los Angeles with a tail wind of 10 mi/h, landing $1\frac{1}{2}$ h after it had taken off. If the plane had a uniform airspeed of 150 mi/h, how far had it gone before turning back?

59. A group of tourists took a sightseeing bus trip of 240 mi and then boarded a plane, which took them to their next stop 550 mi away. The average speed of the plane was 16.5 times that of the bus, and their travel time was 6 h and 50 min. Find the average bus speed and the average plane speed.

60. One pipe can fill a swimming pool in 6 h and another in 8 h. If the first runs for 2 h and then the second is opened, how long before the pool is full?

61. Sam rode his bicycle 15 mi with a tail wind of 8 mi/h, but in the same time rode only 3 mi of the return trip with the same wind now against him. How fast would he have traveled with no wind?

62. A rancher drove 40 km/h on a gravel road to the highway, on which she traveled at 60 km/h until she reached a city that was 110 km from home. If the trip took 2 h, how far was the ranch from the highway?

63. Mr. Tramel traveled 870 mi to attend a company conference. He drove his car 30 mi to an airport and flew the rest of the way. If his plane speed was 12 times that of the car and he flew 48 min longer than he drove, how long did he fly?

64. Hartowski has $10,000 invested at 7.4 percent. How much can he invest at 5 percent in order to make 6.6 percent on his total investment?

65. Jane Mendelau has $18,000 invested and gets an income of $1470. Part of the investment pays 10 percent, and the remainder pays 7 percent. How much is invested at each rate?

66. Gowdy invested $2400 in the common stock of one company and $1280 in the stock of another. The price per share of the second was four-fifths the price per share of the first. The next day the price of the more expensive stock advanced $1.50 per share, the price of the other declined $0.75 per share, and as a result, the value of his investment increased $30. Find the price per share of the more expensive stock.

67. Mrs. Johnson planned to spend $780 for fabric for her store. She found her fabric on sale at 20 percent less per yard than she expected and was able to buy 40 extra yards for a total cost of $832. How much fabric had she planned to buy, and what was the original cost per yard?

68. The treasurer of Wilbanks and Co. has some $10 bills and some $20 bills. How many of each type does she have if there are n altogether and they have a value of v?

2.3 Complex Numbers

Definition of i

In Sec. 1.6 we did not define $\sqrt[n]{a}$ if n is even and a is negative. For instance $\sqrt[4]{-16}$ and $\sqrt{-9}$ were not defined. In particular, we did not define $\sqrt{a}$ if a is negative since there is no *real* number whose square is negative. Thus we cannot solve an equation such as $x^2 = -121$ using only real numbers. We may, however, extend the real number system to a larger system, called the **complex number system,** which will provide solutions for any equation encountered in this book. To do this, we define the imaginary number i by

$$i^2 = -1 \quad \text{or} \quad i = \sqrt{-1}$$

We want the ordinary rules of arithmetic to apply to i as well as to real numbers. Therefore, we will have to work with numbers such as $9i + 2i$ and $-35i$, as well as $5 + 2i$ and $8 - 23i$. The set of numbers of the form

$$a + bi$$

Complex number

where a and b are real and $i = \sqrt{-1}$ is called the set of **complex numbers.** The number a is called the **real part** of $a + bi$, and b is called the **imaginary part** of $a + bi$. The imaginary number bi is sometimes referred to as a **pure imaginary number.**

The following statements describe some special types of complex numbers:

> If $b = 0$, then $a + bi$ is the real number $a + 0i = a$.
> If $a = 0$ and $b \neq 0$, then $a + bi$ is the imaginary number bi.

The real numbers and imaginary numbers are subsets of the set of complex numbers.

EXAMPLE 1 Give some examples of complex numbers, including real numbers and imaginary numbers.

Solution Each of the numbers

$$3 + 7i \qquad -8.1 - 65i \qquad 32 - i \qquad -9 + 0i$$

is a complex number since it has the form $a + bi$ where a and b are real numbers. The complex numbers

$$5 \qquad -14.7 \qquad \pi \qquad \tfrac{83}{11}$$

have $b = 0$ and are also real numbers, while the complex numbers

$$-6i \qquad 17.8i \qquad 10i \qquad i\sqrt{2}$$

have $a = 0$ and are imaginary numbers. ◀

Definition of equality

> If a, b, c, and d are real numbers, then
> $$a + bi = c + di \qquad \text{if and only if } a = c \text{ and } b = d$$

▶ **EXAMPLE 2**   Find a and d so that $a + 5i = 16 - di$.

Solution   If $a + 5i = 16 - di = 16 + (-d)i$, then we must have $a = 16$ and $5 = -d$, hence $d = -5$.   ◢

In addition to i being defined as $\sqrt{-1}$, we define

$$\sqrt{-p} = i\sqrt{p} \qquad \text{if } p \text{ is a positive number}$$

For instance

$$\sqrt{-144} = \sqrt{(-1)(144)} = i\sqrt{144} = 12i$$
$$\sqrt{-18} = i\sqrt{18} = i\sqrt{9 \cdot 2} = 3i\sqrt{2}$$

Notice that above we wrote $i\sqrt{144}$ and not $\sqrt{144}i$, in order to avoid confusion about what is under the radical sign.

The rule $\sqrt{ab} = \sqrt{a} \cdot \sqrt{b}$ is true for a and b positive. The definition of i assures us that it also holds if one of the numbers a and b is positive and the other is negative. For instance with $a = 16$ and $b = -25$

$$\sqrt{ab} = \sqrt{(16)(-25)} = \sqrt{-400} = i\sqrt{400} = 20i$$

and

$$\sqrt{a} \cdot \sqrt{b} = \sqrt{16} \cdot \sqrt{-25} = 4(i\sqrt{25}) = 4(5i) = 20i$$

However the rule fails if a and b are both negative, as the following example with $a = -9$ and $b = -4$ shows:

$$\sqrt{ab} = \sqrt{(-9)(-4)} = \sqrt{36} = 6 = +6$$

whereas

$$\sqrt{a} \cdot \sqrt{b} = \sqrt{-9} \cdot \sqrt{-4} = (3i)(2i) = 6i^2 = 6(-1) = -6$$

We can now define the addition, subtraction, and multiplication of complex numbers. Division will be defined a bit later in this section.

Addition

Subtraction

Multiplication

For real numbers a, b, c, and d, we define

$$(a + bi) + (c + di) = (a + c) + (b + d)i$$
$$(a + bi) - (c + di) = (a - c) + (b - d)i$$
$$(a + bi)(c + di) = (ac - bd) + (ad + bc)i$$

Instead of actually memorizing these definitions, it helps to simply treat $a + bi$ as a first-degree polynomial with i replacing x. Addition and subtraction of complex numbers is then exactly like polynomial addition and subtraction. Multiplication is just like polynomial multiplication, except that we replace i^2 by -1.

▶ **EXAMPLE 3**   Perform the indicated additions.

Solution   (a) $(3 + 4i) + (-8 + 7i) = 3 - 8 + 4i + 7i$
$$= -5 + (4 + 7)i = -5 + 11i$$
(b) $(16 - 7i) + (5i) = 16 - 2i$
(c) $(4) + (15 + 8i) = 19 + 8i$ ◢

▶ **EXAMPLE 4** Perform the indicated subtractions.

Solution (a) $(8 + 3i) - (5 - 2i) = 8 + 3i - 5 + 2i$
$$= 8 - 5 + (3 + 2)i = 3 + 5i$$
(b) $(13) - (-9 + 44i) = 22 - 44i$
(c) $(6.3 - 7i) - (5.1 - 7i) = 6.3 - 5.1 - 7i + 7i = 1.2$ ◀

▶ **EXAMPLE 5** Find the following products: (a) $(2 + 3i)(5 + 7i)$, (b) $i(5 + 12i)$, (c) $(3 + 4i)(5 - 12i)$.

Solution (a) $(2 + 3i)(5 + 7i) = 2(5 + 7i) + 3i(5 + 7i)$
$$= 10 + 14i + 15i + 21i^2$$
$$= 10 + 29i - 21 = -11 + 29i$$
(b) $i(5 + 12i) = 5i + 12i^2 = -12 + 5i$
(c) $(3 + 4i)(5 - 12i) = 15 - 36i + 20i - 48i^2$
$$= 15 - 16i + 48 = 63 - 16i$$ ◀

If $a + bi$ is a complex number, then the **conjugate** of $a + bi$ is $a - bi$. The notation $\overline{a + bi}$ is used for the conjugate of $a + bi$, so

Definition

$$\overline{a + bi} = a - bi$$

Before finding the quotient of two complex numbers, we shall first find the product of a complex number $a + bi$ and its conjugate $a - bi$:

$$(a + bi)(a - bi) = a^2 - abi + abi - b^2i^2 = a^2 + b^2$$

which shows that the product of a complex number and its own conjugate is a real number. In fact, this product is the sum of the square of the real part and the square of the imaginary part of the complex number. For instance

$$(3 + 5i)(3 - 5i) = 3^2 + 5^2 = 9 + 25 = 34$$

Division

> To find the quotient of two complex numbers, we multiply both members of the fraction by the conjugate of the denominator.

Doing this makes the denominator a real number.

▶ **EXAMPLE 6** Find the quotient if $-11 + 29i$ is divided by $2 + 3i$.

Solution
$$\frac{-11 + 29i}{2 + 3i} = \frac{-11 + 29i}{2 + 3i} \cdot \frac{2 - 3i}{2 - 3i}$$

$$= \frac{-22 + 33i + 58i - 87i^2}{4 + 9}$$

$$= \frac{65 + 91i}{13} = 5 + 7i$$

This is consistent with Example 5, where we found that

$$(2 + 3i)(5 + 7i) = -11 + 29i$$ ◀

▶ **EXAMPLE 7**   Find the quotient if $4 + 7i$ is divided by i.

Solution
$$\frac{4 + 7i}{i} = \frac{(4 + 7i)(-i)}{i(-i)} = \frac{-4i - 7i^2}{1} = \frac{-4i + 7}{1} = 7 - 4i$$

Alternative solution
$$\frac{4 + 7i}{i} = \frac{4}{i} + \frac{7i}{i} = \frac{4i}{i^2} + 7 = -4i + 7 = 7 - 4i$$ ◢

▶ **EXAMPLE 8**   Find the quotient if $7 + 24i$ is divided by $3 + 4i$.

Solution
$$\frac{7 + 24i}{3 + 4i} = \frac{7 + 24i}{3 + 4i} \cdot \frac{3 - 4i}{3 - 4i}$$

$$= \frac{21 - 28i + 72i - 96i^2}{9 + 16}$$

$$= \frac{21 + 96 + 44i}{25} = \frac{117 + 44i}{25}$$

This can be checked by showing that the product of $3 + 4i$ and $(117 + 44i)/25$ is $7 + 24i$. ◢

▶ **EXAMPLE 9**   Show that $i^{27} = -i$.

Solution
$$i^{27} = i^{24} \cdot i^2 \cdot i = (i^4)^6 \cdot (-1)(i) = (1^6)(-i) = -i$$ ◢

▶ **EXAMPLE 10**   Evaluate $x^2 + 10x + 74$ for the value $x = -5 + 7i$.

Solution
$$(-5 + 7i)^2 + 10(-5 + 7i) + 74 = 25 - 70i + 49i^2 - 50 + 70i + 74$$

$$= 25 - 49 - 50 + 74 - 70i + 70i$$

$$= 99 - 99 - 70i + 70i = 0$$ ◢

▶ **EXAMPLE 11**   By definition i is a square root of -1. Show that $\dfrac{\sqrt{2} + i\sqrt{2}}{2}$ is a square root of i.

Solution
$$\frac{\sqrt{2} + i\sqrt{2}}{2} \cdot \frac{\sqrt{2} + i\sqrt{2}}{2} = \frac{2 + 2(2i) - 2}{4} = \frac{4i}{4} = i$$ ◢

The **absolute value** of a complex number $a + bi$ is defined as
$$|a + bi| = \sqrt{a^2 + b^2}$$

For instance
$$|5 - 12i| = \sqrt{5^2 + 12^2} = \sqrt{169} = 13$$

$$|-4 + 7i| = \sqrt{4^2 + 7^2} = \sqrt{16 + 49} = \sqrt{65} \approx 8.1$$

If $a + bi$ is a real number, then $b = 0$ and this definition of absolute value agrees with our earlier definition of the absolute value of a real number. In fact for $b = 0$
$$|a + bi| = \sqrt{a^2 + b^2} = \sqrt{a^2} = |a|$$

One of the most important inequalities in mathematics is the **triangle inequality,** which says that if z and w are any two complex numbers, then

$$|z + w| \leq |z| + |w|$$

EXAMPLE 12   Verify the triangle inequality for $z = 4 + 9i$ and $w = 2 + 7i$.

Solution   If $z = 4 + 9i$ and $w = 2 + 7i$, then $z + w = 6 + 16i$ and

$$|z + w| = \sqrt{36 + 256} = \sqrt{292} \approx 17.09$$
$$|z| + |w| = \sqrt{16 + 81} + \sqrt{4 + 49}$$
$$= \sqrt{97} + \sqrt{53} \approx 9.85 + 7.28 = 17.13$$

Hence $|z + w| \leq |z| + |w|$ becomes $17.09 \leq 17.13$.

The set of complex numbers $a + bi$, with addition and multiplication as defined in this section, is a field. That is, all of the field properties given in Chap. 1 are satisfied. Some of these field properties are treated at the end of this exercise. Polynomials whose coefficients are complex numbers, such as $9x^2 + (2 - i)x + 5i$, have been studied extensively and play an important role in applications.

EXERCISE 2.3

Perform the indicated operations in Probs. 1 to 32.

1. $(2 + 3i) + (7 + 2i)$ **2.** $(5 + 4i) + (4 + 3i)$

3. $(3 - 2i) - (4 + i)$ **4.** $(3 - 6i) - (2 - 3i)$

5. $(3 - 4i) - (4 - 3i)$ **6.** $(9 + 5i) - (-4 + 3i)$

7. $(-5 - 8i) - (6 - 9i)$ **8.** $(6 - 5i) + (5 - 6i)$

9. $(3 + 2i)(3 - 4i)$ **10.** $(4 - 5i)(2 + 9i)$

11. $(3 - 2i)(3 + 2i)$ **12.** $(4 + 5i)(4 + 5i)$

13. $(4 - 6i)(3 + 7i)$ **14.** $(7 + 6i)(6 - 7i)$

15. $(3 - 7i)(3 - 5i)$ **16.** $(7 - 5i)(5 + 7i)$

17. $\dfrac{2 - 3i}{4 + 5i}$ **18.** $\dfrac{1 - 8i}{8 + i}$

19. $\dfrac{4 - 5i}{7 - 6i}$ **20.** $\dfrac{5 - 3i}{5 + 2i}$

21. $\dfrac{4 + 7i}{4 - 7i}$ **22.** $\dfrac{13i}{3 + 2i}$

23. $\dfrac{14 + 48i}{7 - i}$ **24.** $\dfrac{14 - 48i}{7 + i}$

25. $\dfrac{2 + 3i}{2 - 3i} + \dfrac{4 - 3i}{4 + 3i}$ **26.** $\dfrac{4 + i}{4 - 3i} - \dfrac{4 - i}{4 + 3i}$

27. $\dfrac{3 + 4i}{2 - i} + \dfrac{3 - 4i}{2 + i}$ **28.** $\dfrac{3 + 2i}{1 + 5i} - \dfrac{1 + 5i}{3 + 2i}$

29. $|4 + 3i|$ **30.** $|3 - 4i|$

31. $|-5 + 12i|$ **32.** $|-7 - 24i|$

Verify the fact that $|z|^2 = z\bar{z}$ in each of Probs. 33 to 36.

33. $3 + 5i$ **34.** $5 - 2i$

35. $1 - 7i$ **36.** $4 + 3i$

Prove the statement in each of Probs. 37 to 40 for

$$z = a + bi \quad \text{and} \quad w = c + di$$

37. $\overline{z + w} = \bar{z} + \bar{w}$ **38.** $\overline{z - w} = \bar{z} - \bar{w}$

39. $\overline{zw} = \bar{z}\bar{w}$ **40.** $z + \bar{z}$ is real

For any two complex numbers $z = a + bi$ and $w = c + di$, the triangle inequality holds.

$$|z + w| \leq |z| + |w|$$

Verify this in the specific cases in Probs. 41 to 44.

41. $z = 3 + 5i$, $w = 6 - 4i$

42. $z = 18 + 7i$, $w = -11 + i$

43. $z = 6 + 5i$, $w = -12 - 10i$

44. $z = -8 + 3i$, $w = 4 - 9i$

Verify the statements in Probs. 45 to 48, where n is any positive integer.

45. $i = i^5 = i^9 = i^{13} = i^{37} = i^{4n+1}$

46. $-1 = i^2 = i^6 = i^{10} = i^{38} = i^{4n+2}$

47. $-i = i^3 = i^7 = i^{11} = i^{39} = i^{4n+3}$
48. $1 = i^4 = i^8 = i^{12} = i^{40} = i^{4n}$

Find x and y so that the statements in Probs. 49 to 56 are true. Use the definition that

$a + bi = c + di$ if and only if $a = c$ and $b = d$

49. $x + 2i + 2 = 5 + yi$ **50.** $x - 5i = 4 + 2i - yi$
51. $y + ix - 3i = 2 + 3i$ **52.** $5 + x + i = 2 + yi$
53. $(x + iy)(1 + 3i) = -1 + 7i$
54. $(x - 2iy)(3 + i) = 20$
55. $(x - iy)(3 - 5i) = -6 - 24i$
56. $(x - iy)(2 + 3i) = 4 + 6i$
57. Show that the value of $x^2 - 10x + 29$ is 0 if $x = 5 + 2i$.
58. Show that the value of $x^2 + 14x + 58$ is 0 if $x = -7 + 3i$.
59. Show that the value of $x^2 - 12x + 37$ is 0 if $x = 6 - i$.
60. Show that the value of $x^2 - 16x + 289$ is 0 if $x = 8 + 15i$.
61. Let $z = (-1 + i\sqrt{3})/2$. Show that

$$z^3 = 1   \text{and}   1 + z + z^2 = 0$$

62. Let $w = (-1 - i\sqrt{3})/2$. Show that

$$w^3 = 1   \text{and}   1 + w + w^2 = 0$$

63. Let $z = (1 + i)/\sqrt{2}$ and show that

$$z^4 = -1$$

64. Let $w = (-1 + i)/\sqrt{2}$ and show that

$$w^4 = -1$$

Problems 65 to 68 deal with some of the field properties of the complex numbers.
65. As an example of the associative law of multiplication, calculate both

$$(1 - 2i)(3 + i) \cdot (5 + 3i)$$

and $$(1 - 2i) \cdot (3 + i)(5 + 3i)$$

and show that they have the same value.
66. As an example of the commutative law of multiplication, calculate both

$$(3 - 4i) \cdot (6 + 5i)   \text{and}   (6 + 5i) \cdot (3 - 4i)$$

and show that they have the same value.
67. As an example of the distributive law, calculate both

$$(4 - 3i) \cdot [(6 + 7i) + (-2 + i)]$$

and $(4 - 3i) \cdot (6 + 7i) + (4 - 3i) \cdot (-2 + i)$

and show that they have the same value.
68. If $a + bi \neq 0$, show that the multiplicative inverse of $a + bi$ is $\dfrac{a - bi}{a^2 + b^2}$ by calculating that

$$(a + bi) \left(\frac{a - bi}{a^2 + b^2} \right) = 1$$

2.4 Quadratic Equations

Although many problems can be solved, or approximated well, by linear equations, there are numerous other problems which can only be solved by nonlinear equations. Quadratic equations occur frequently because they accurately describe many actual situations. They have exact solutions which can be found in a straightforward manner.

Quadratic equation

An equation of the form

$$ax^2 + bx + c = 0 \tag{1}$$

in which a, b, and c are constants, $a \neq 0$, is called a **quadratic equation.**

Equation (1) is called the **standard form** of a quadratic equation. The equations

$$4x^2 + 3x + 1 = 0 \qquad 2x^2 + 5x + 6 = 7x^2 - 2x$$

$$9x^2 - 5x = 2x + 8 \qquad 2x + \frac{x}{4} - x^2 = 7 + 5x$$

are quadratic equations, but only the first one is in standard form.

Factoring

If $ax^2 + bx + c$ can be factored, we may use the following **zero factor property** to solve the equation $ax^2 + bx + c = 0$.

Zero factor property

> Let p and q be real numbers. Then $pq = 0$ if and only if $p = 0$ or $q = 0$ or both.

There are several methods for solving a quadratic equation. The one we will present first is **solution by factoring.** In order to use it, it is absolutely essential that

NOTE

One side of the equation must be zero

If, for instance, $x(x - 1) = 4$, we *cannot* conclude that x or $x - 1$ is ± 1, ± 2, or ± 4, the factors of 4. Later in this section, we will learn how to show that the roots of $x(x - 1) = 4$ are irrational.

▶ **EXAMPLE 1** Solve the following quadratic equations by factoring:
(a) $12x^2 + 23x = -5$ (b) $8x^2 + 5x = 0$ (c) $9x^2 + 16 = 24x$

Solution (a)

$$12x^2 + 23x + 5 = 0 \qquad \text{making one member 0}$$
$$(3x + 5)(4x + 1) = 0 \qquad \text{factoring}$$
$$3x + 5 = 0 \quad \text{or} \quad 4x + 1 = 0 \qquad \text{zero factor property}$$
$$x = -\tfrac{5}{3} \quad \text{or} \quad x = -\tfrac{1}{4} \qquad \text{solutions}$$

(b)
$$8x^2 + 5x = 0 \qquad \text{given equation}$$
$$x(8x + 5) = 0 \qquad \text{factoring}$$
$$x = 0 \quad \text{or} \quad 8x + 5 = 0 \qquad \text{zero factor property}$$
$$x = -\tfrac{5}{8} \qquad \text{solutions are 0 and } -\tfrac{5}{8}$$

In the equation $8x^2 + 5x = 0$ above, it is very tempting to write

$$8x^2 = -5x \qquad \text{adding } -5x$$

$$8x = -5 \qquad \text{dividing by } x$$

$$x = -\tfrac{5}{8} \qquad \text{dividing by 8}$$

NOTE *The root $x = 0$ was lost when we divided by x.* We found only the root $x = -\tfrac{5}{8}$, whereas $x = 0$ is also a root of the given equation, as shown above.

(c)
$$9x^2 + 16 = 24x \qquad \text{given}$$
$$9x^2 - 24x + 16 = 0 \qquad \text{making one side 0}$$
$$(3x - 4)(3x - 4) = 0 \qquad \text{factoring}$$

Setting each factor equal to zero gives the solution $x = \tfrac{4}{3}$. In this case, both factors give the same solution. ◀

The possible solutions we find for a quadratic equation **should be checked** by substituting each one for the variable in the given equation. In part (a) of Example 1, we found $-\tfrac{5}{3}$ and $-\tfrac{1}{4}$ as possible solutions. If we replace x by the value $-\tfrac{5}{3}$, we get

$$12(-\tfrac{5}{3})^2 + 23(-\tfrac{5}{3}) = 12(\tfrac{25}{9}) - \tfrac{115}{3} = \tfrac{300}{9} - \tfrac{345}{9} = -\tfrac{45}{9} = -5$$

for the left member. Since that is also the value of the right member, the possible solution is in fact an actual solution. Other values can be checked in a similar manner.

If an equation has the form $x^2 = d$, $d > 0$, then

$$x^2 - d = 0$$

$$(x - \sqrt{d})(x + \sqrt{d}) = 0 \qquad \text{factoring}$$

$$x - \sqrt{d} = 0 \qquad x + \sqrt{d} = 0 \qquad \text{zero factor property}$$

$$x = \sqrt{d} \qquad x = -\sqrt{d}$$

This leads to the following **square root property:**

Square root property

If $x^2 = d$, $d > 0$, then $x = \pm\sqrt{d}$.

EXAMPLE 2   Solve $(x + 5)^2 = 23$.

Solution

$$(x + 5)^2 = 23 \qquad \text{given}$$

$$x + 5 = \pm\sqrt{23} \qquad \text{square root property}$$

$$x = -5 \pm \sqrt{23} \qquad \text{adding } -5$$

Completing the Square

We will need to work with expressions of the form

$$x^2 + kx$$

several times in the book. If we add $(k/2)^2$, we have

$$x^2 + kx + \left(\frac{k}{2}\right)^2 = \left(x + \frac{k}{2}\right)^2$$

which is the square of $x + k/2$. This process is called **completing the square,** and in order to do it we need to

NOTE   *Have 1 as the coefficient of x^2*

EXAMPLE 3   Solve the equation $x^2 - 6x + 2 = 0$ by completing the square.

Solution

$$x^2 - 6x \qquad\quad = -2 \qquad\qquad \text{subtracting 2}$$

$$x^2 - 6x + 9 = -2 + 9 \qquad\quad \text{completing the square by adding } (-\tfrac{6}{2})^2, \text{ or 9}$$

$$(x - 3)^2 = 7 \qquad\qquad\quad \text{left side is a square}$$

$$x - 3 = \pm\sqrt{7} \qquad\qquad \text{square root property}$$

$$x = 3 \pm \sqrt{7} \qquad\qquad \text{solving for } x$$

If we had begun with $5x^2 - 10x + 8 = 0$ in Example 3, then we would have first divided both members of the equation by 5 to make the coefficient of x^2 equal to 1.

The standard form, $ax^2 + bx + c = 0$, of the quadratic equation can be solved by completing the square as above.

$$ax^2 + bx + c = 0 \qquad\qquad \text{given, } a \neq 0$$

$$ax^2 + bx = -c \qquad \text{adding } -c$$

$$x^2 + \frac{b}{a}x = -\frac{c}{a} \qquad \text{dividing by } a,\ a \neq 0$$

$$x^2 + \frac{b}{a}x + \left(\frac{b}{2a}\right)^2 = -\frac{c}{a} + \left(\frac{b}{2a}\right)^2 \qquad \text{adding } \left(\frac{b}{2a}\right)^2$$

In the last step, we completed the square in the left member, after obtaining 1 as the coefficient of x^2. The last equation above can thus be put in the form

$$\left(x + \frac{b}{2a}\right)^2 = \frac{b^2}{4a^2} - \frac{c}{a} \qquad \text{expressing the left member as a square}$$

$$\left(x + \frac{b}{2a}\right)^2 = \frac{b^2 - 4ac}{4a^2} \qquad \text{using a common denominator on the right}$$

$$\left(x + \frac{b}{2a}\right)^2 = \left(\frac{\sqrt{b^2 - 4ac}}{2a}\right)^2 \qquad \text{writing the right member as a perfect square}$$

$$x + \frac{b}{2a} = \pm\frac{\sqrt{b^2 - 4ac}}{2a} \qquad \text{square root property and } \sqrt{(2a)^2} = |2a| = \pm 2a$$

$$x = \frac{-b}{2a} \pm \frac{\sqrt{b^2 - 4ac}}{2a} \qquad \text{adding } \frac{-b}{2a}$$

This result gives us the quadratic formula.

Quadratic formula

> The solutions of the quadratic equation $ax^2 + bx + c = 0$, $a \neq 0$ are
> $$x = \frac{-b \pm \sqrt{b^2 - 4ac}}{2a} \qquad\qquad (2.2)$$

NOTE   As a general rule, we may solve a quadratic equation most simply and quickly if we first try to factor the equation. If it can not be readily factored, the quadratic formula is the next best way. The formula works not only for integers a, b, and c, but for any real numbers. In fact, it works even if the coefficients are complex numbers.

As we have seen above, completing the square can be used directly to solve a quadratic equation. However it is most useful in working with circles, parabolas, ellipses, and hyperbolas, in solving polynomial equations of degree 4, and in finding the maximum or minimum value of a quadratic function.

▶ EXAMPLE 4   Solve the equation $30x^2 + 49x + 20 = 0$ by the quadratic formula.

Solution   To solve $30x^2 + 49x + 20 = 0$ by the quadratic formula, we first write $a = 30$, $b = 49$, and $c = 20$ and obtain

$$x = \frac{-(49) \pm \sqrt{(49)^2 - 4(30)(20)}}{2(30)} \qquad \text{quadratic formula}$$

$$= \frac{-49 \pm \sqrt{2401 - 2400}}{60}$$

$$x = \frac{-49 \pm 1}{60} = \frac{-50}{60} \text{ or } \frac{-48}{60} = \frac{-5}{6} \text{ or } \frac{-4}{5} \quad \blacktriangleleft$$

The equation in Example 4 could have been solved by factoring, but it might have taken more time to find the factors than to have used the quadratic formula.

NOTE   If it is properly applied, the quadratic formula will always give the two correct solutions to the quadratic equation $ax^2 + bx + c = 0$. These two solutions may be the same number repeated.

▶ **EXAMPLE 5**   Solve the equation $4x^2 = 8x - 5$ by the quadratic formula.

Solution   The first step in solving the given equation is to convert it to an equivalent equation in standard form, which is $4x^2 - 8x + 5 = 0$. Therefore we see that $a = 4$, $b = -8$, and $c = 5$.

$$x = \frac{-(-8) \pm \sqrt{(-8)^2 - 4(4)(5)}}{2(4)} \qquad \text{quadratic formula}$$

$$= \frac{8 \pm \sqrt{64 - 80}}{8} = \frac{8 \pm \sqrt{-16}}{8}$$

$$= \frac{8 \pm 4i}{8} = \frac{1}{2}(2 \pm i)$$

Hence the solutions are the conjugate complex numbers $(2 \pm i)/2$.

Check   We must use the fact that $i^2 = -1$ in checking these solutions since they are complex numbers. Checking $x = (2 + i)/2$ yields

$$4x^2 = \frac{4(2 + i)^2}{2^2} = (2 + i)^2 = 4 + 4i + i^2 = 3 + 4i$$

$$8x - 5 = \frac{8(2 + i)}{2} - 5 = 4(2 + i) - 5 = 8 + 4i - 5 = 3 + 4i \quad \blacktriangleleft$$

▶ **EXAMPLE 6**   Solve $2x^2 + 2x = 1$ by using the quadratic formula.

Solution $2x^2 + 2x - 1 = 0$ \qquad\qquad adding -1

$$x = \frac{-2 \pm \sqrt{4 - 4(2)(-1)}}{2(2)} \qquad \text{quadratic formula with } a = 2, b = 2, c = -1$$

$$= \frac{-2 \pm \sqrt{12}}{4} = \frac{-2 \pm 2\sqrt{3}}{4}$$

$$= \frac{-1 \pm \sqrt{3}}{2} \quad \blacktriangleleft$$

▶ **EXAMPLE 7**   Solve $x^2 + 4ix - 5 = 0$.

Solution   The coefficient of x is the imaginary number $4i$. Using $a = 1$, $b = 4i$, and $c = -5$ in the quadratic formula gives

$$x = \frac{-4i \pm \sqrt{(4i)^2 - 4(1)(-5)}}{2(1)} \qquad \text{quadratic formula}$$

$$= \frac{-4i \pm \sqrt{-16 + 20}}{2}$$

$$= \frac{-4i \pm 2}{2} = -2i \pm 1$$

Discriminant

In the quadratic formula, the expression $b^2 - 4ac$ occurs under the radical sign. We write $D = b^2 - 4ac$ and call it the **discriminant.** Its sign gives us information about the roots of $ax^2 + bx + c = 0$, if a, b, and c are real.

> Suppose that $ax^2 + bx + c = 0$ and a, b, and c are real.
> (1) If $D = 0$, then there is a double root, the real number $-b/2a$.
> (2) If $D > 0$, then there are two roots, real and unequal.
> (3) If $D < 0$, then there are two roots which are complex numbers, conjugates of each other.

Suppose now that a, b, and c are not only real but integers and $D \geq 0$. From (2) above, there are two real roots, and they are unequal. Since D is an integer here and the quadratic formula involves $\sqrt{D}$ and integers, it follows that the solutions are rational if and only if $\sqrt{D}$ is an integer. This is equivalent to D being the square of an integer. Hence the following statement is true:
(4) Suppose that $D \geq 0$ and a, b, and c are integers. Then the roots are rational if and only if D is the square of an integer. An equivalent statement is that the roots are irrational if and only if D is not the square of an integer.

▶ **EXAMPLE 8**   Calculate the discriminant and use it to discuss the nature of the roots of the quadratic equations below.

Solution

Equation	D = discriminant	Nature of the roots
$4x^2 - 4x\sqrt{5} + 5 = 0$	$D = 80 - 80 = 0$	Real, both $= -\dfrac{b}{2a} = \dfrac{\sqrt{5}}{2}$
$5x^2 + 2x - 9 = 0$	$D = 184 > 0$	Real, irrational, and unequal
$\sqrt{2}x^2 + 3x + \sqrt{5} = 0$	$D = 9 - 4\sqrt{10} < 0$	Complex conjugates
$3x^2 - 7x - 6 = 0$	$D = 121 = 11^2 > 0$	Rational and unequal

If, in the quadratic formula, we let r be the root $(-b + \sqrt{b^2 - 4ac})/2a$ and s be the root $(-b - \sqrt{b^2 - 4ac})/2a$, then

$$r = \frac{-b + \sqrt{D}}{2a} \qquad \text{and} \qquad s = \frac{-b - \sqrt{D}}{2a}$$

We can now show that the sum and the product of the roots of a quadratic equation are simple combinations of the coefficients in the equation. For example, the sum of the two roots is

$$r + s = \frac{-b + \sqrt{D}}{2a} + \frac{-b - \sqrt{D}}{2a} = \frac{-2b}{2a} = \frac{-b}{a}$$

Furthermore the product is

$$rs = \left(\frac{-b + \sqrt{D}}{2a}\right) \cdot \left(\frac{-b - \sqrt{D}}{2a}\right) = \frac{(-b)^2 - (\sqrt{D})^2}{(2a)^2}$$

$$= \frac{b^2 - D}{4a^2} = \frac{b^2 - (b^2 - 4ac)}{4a^2} = \frac{4ac}{4a^2} = \frac{c}{a}$$

Therefore we have the following rules for finding the sum and the product of the roots of the quadratic equation $ax^2 + bx + c = 0$:

Sum and product of the roots

$$r + s = \frac{-b}{a} \qquad\qquad (2.3)$$

$$rs = \frac{c}{a} \qquad\qquad (2.4)$$

▶ **EXAMPLE 9**   Use the equations above to find the sum and the product of the roots of the quadratic equations given below.

Solution

Equation	Sum of roots	Product of roots
$x^2 - 3x + 2 = 0$	$-\dfrac{b}{a} = \dfrac{-(-3)}{1} = 3$	$\dfrac{c}{a} = \dfrac{2}{1} = 2$
$2x^2 + 8x - 5 = 0$	$-\dfrac{b}{a} = \dfrac{-8}{2} = -4$	$\dfrac{c}{a} = \dfrac{-5}{2}$
$\sqrt{2}x^2 + 5x - \sqrt{8} = 0$	$-\dfrac{b}{a} = \dfrac{-5}{\sqrt{2}}$	$\dfrac{c}{a} = \dfrac{-\sqrt{8}}{\sqrt{2}} = -\sqrt{4} = -2$

▶ **EXAMPLE 10**   Find a quadratic equation with roots $\frac{4}{3}$ and $-\frac{7}{5}$.

Solution   If $x = \frac{4}{3}$, then $3x - 4 = 0$. If $x = -\frac{7}{5}$, then $5x + 7 = 0$. Thus

$$0 = (3x - 4)(5x + 7) = 15x^2 + x - 28$$

We can also use information about the sum and the product of the roots to find the original equation.

▶ **EXAMPLE 11**   Find a quadratic equation for which the sum of the roots is 4 and the product is 7.

Solution   We know that $-b/a = 4$ and $c/a = 7$, and thus $b = -4a$ and $c = 7a$. Any value for a may be used, except 0, and choosing $a = 1$ gives $b = -4$ and $c = 7$. The equation is $x^2 - 4x + 7 = 0$.

▶ **EXAMPLE 12** Solve the equation $3x^2 - 7xy - 6y^2 = 4$ for y.

Solution Writing the equation in the form $0 = 6y^2 + 7xy + 4 - 3x^2$ allows us to solve for y, using the quadratic formula with $a = 6$, $b = 7x$, and $c = 4 - 3x^2$.

$$y = \frac{-7x \pm \sqrt{(7x)^2 - 4(6)(4 - 3x^2)}}{2(6)}$$

$$= \frac{-7x \pm \sqrt{49x^2 - 96 + 72x^2}}{12}$$

$$= \frac{-7x \pm \sqrt{121x^2 - 96}}{12}$$ ◢

EXERCISE 2.4

Solve the equation in each of Probs. 1 to 52.
1. $x^2 - 9 = 0$
2. $x^2 - 25 = 0$
3. $4x^2 - 1 = 0$
4. $16x^2 - 49 = 0$
5. $x^2 - 3x = 0$
6. $x^2 - 4x = 0$
7. $3x^2 = 6x$
8. $5x^2 = -15x$
9. $x^2 + 1 = 0$
10. $x^2 + 36 = 0$
11. $9x^2 = -25$
12. $16x^2 = -9$
13. $x^2 - 5x + 6 = 0$
14. $x^2 + x - 2 = 0$
15. $x^2 + x - 12 = 0$
16. $x^2 + 2x - 24 = 0$
17. $x(x - 7) = -12$
18. $x(x - 2) = 3$
19. $x(x - 1) = 12$
20. $x(x - 8) = -15$
21. $(2x + 1)(x - 4) = -7$
22. $(2x - 1)(x - 1) = 3$
23. $(3x + 1)(x - 2) = -4$
24. $(3x - 1)(x + 1) = 7$
25. $6x^2 + x = 2$
26. $6x^2 + 5x = 6$
27. $12x^2 - 5 = 17x$
28. $10x^2 - 9 = -9x$
29. $5x^2 - 17x + 6 = 0$
30. $3x^2 - 7x + 2 = 0$
31. $7x^2 - 17x + 6 = 0$
32. $2x^2 - 9x + 4 = 0$
33. $x^2 - 2x - 2 = 0$
34. $x^2 - 4x - 1 = 0$
35. $x^2 - 6x + 7 = 0$
36. $x^2 - 10x + 18 = 0$
37. $4x^2 - 8x + 1 = 0$
38. $9x^2 - 18x + 7 = 0$
39. $9x^2 - 12x + 1 = 0$
40. $2x^2 - 10x + 11 = 0$
41. $x^2 - 8x - 5 = 0$
42. $x^2 + 4x - 6 = 0$
43. $2x^2 - 6x - 7 = 0$
44. $6 = 3x^2 - 2x$
45. $x^2 - 4x + 13 = 0$
46. $x^2 - 6x + 13 = 0$
47. $x^2 - 8x + 20 = 0$
48. $x^2 - 10x + 34 = 0$
49. $2x^2 - 6x + 5 = 0$
50. $9x^2 - 12x + 5 = 0$
51. $25x^2 - 30x + 13 = 0$
52. $4x^2 - 20x + 41 = 0$

Calculate the discriminant, determine the nature of the roots, and find their sum and product.
53. $x^2 - 5x + 6 = 0$
54. $12x^2 - 5x - 2 = 0$

55. $x^2 - 6x + 9 = 0$
56. $9x^2 + 12x + 4 = 0$
57. $x^2 - 6x - 9 = 0$
58. $4x^2 + 2x - 5 = 0$
59. $4x^2 + 2x + 5 = 0$
60. $x^2 - 2x + 9 = 0$

Find a quadratic equation that has the given solutions.
61. 2, 1
62. 3, −1
63. $-\frac{2}{3}, \frac{4}{5}$
64. $-\frac{1}{2}, \frac{3}{7}$
65. $2 + \sqrt{5}, 2 - \sqrt{5}$
66. $3 + \sqrt{2}, 3 - \sqrt{2}$
67. $5 + 2i, 5 - 2i$
68. $3 + 4i, 3 - 4i$

In Probs. 69 to 72, find the solutions to two decimal places.
69. $1.67x^2 + 5.22x + 2.94 = 0$
70. $2.53x^2 - 3.02x - 3.86 = 0$
71. $-3.73x^2 + 8.77x - 4.31 = 0$
72. $-2.97x^2 - 1.34x + 3.79 = 0$

Solve the equations in Probs. 73 to 76 with the quadratic formula.
73. $x^2 - 6ix - 13 = 0$
74. $x^2 - 8ix - 25 = 0$
75. $x^2 + 4ix - 13 = 0$
76. $x^2 + 10ix - 26 = 0$

77. *Management* If earnings are $-0.0025x^2 + 27x - 66{,}000$, find the number of units x which produce earnings of 6900.

78. *Finance* A certain debt will be repaid after n months where

$$416 = \frac{n}{2}[2(11) + (n - 1)2]$$

How many months will repayment take?

79. *Chemistry and calculator* The heat of vaporization in calories per mole is given by

$$A + BT + CT^2$$

For hexafluorobenzene, $A = 12,587.5$, $B = -10.3365$, and $C = -1.0917$. Find the heat of vaporization for $T = 25°C$.

80. *Chemistry* The equation $2\pi r(V_2 - V_3) + \pi r^2 pgh = 0$ occurs in physical chemistry in connection with free energy of a liquid at equilibrium. Solve it for r.

81. *Anthropology* In the study in population stability of intermarriage of two groups, the equation

$$x^2 - (B + C)x + BC - AD = 0$$

arises. (a) Find its solutions. (b) Show that both roots are real if A, B, C, and D are all positive.

82. *Biology* The equation $4x^2 - 2x - 1 = 0$ is used in determining Mendelian heredity. Find its roots.

83. *Chemistry* The ionization constant K_v, volume V, and dissociation α are connected by

$$K_v = \frac{4\alpha^2}{(1 - \alpha)V}$$

Find α if $K_v = 1$ and $V = 10$.

84. *Chemistry* The equation $K = x^2/(a - x)(b - x)$ is used in connection with equilibrium in liquid flow. Solve for x if $a = b = 1$ and $K = 4$.

In Probs. 85 to 92, solve the equation for the stated variable.

85. $3x^2 + 8xy + 8y^2 = 2$ for y
86. $6x^2 - 3xy + 2y^2 = -1$ for y
87. $2x^2 + 5xy - 8y^2 = 4$ for x
88. $x^2 - 4xy + 5y^2 = -3$ for x
89. $s = -16t^2 + vt$ for t
90. $A = \pi r^2 + 2\pi rh$ for r
91. $S = n(n + 1)/2$ for n
92. $\dfrac{x^2}{a^2} - \dfrac{y^2}{b^2} = 1$ for y

In Probs. 93 to 96, find three roots for each equation by first factoring as a sum or difference of cubes.

93. $x^3 - 64 = 0$ **94.** $x^3 + 27 = 0$
95. $8x^3 + 125 = 0$ **96.** $8x^3 - 1 = 0$
97. When does the cost equal the revenue if the cost is $-x^2 + 15x + 16$ and the revenue is $7x - 4$?
98. Solve the equation

$$4^3 + 4(4)^2 - 5(4) + 2 - [2^3 + 4(2)^2 - 5(2) + 2]$$
$$= (4 - 2)(3x^2 + 8x - 5)$$

2.5 Equations Which Lead to Quadratic Equations

The equation $x^4 - 5x^2 - 36 = 0$ is not quadratic in x. However if we substitute t for x^2, then $t^2 = x^4$ and the equation becomes

$$t^2 - 5t - 36 = 0$$

which is a quadratic equation in t. We will complete the solution to this problem in Example 1. An equation is said to be in **quadratic form** if

$$at^2 + bt + c = 0$$

where $a \neq 0$ and t is an algebraic expression in some variable.

▶ **EXAMPLE 1** Solve the equation $x^4 - 5x^2 - 36 = 0$ for x.

Solution The given equation can be expressed in quadratic form by substituting t for x^2, and hence also t^2 for x^4. Thus, the given equation becomes

$$t^2 - 5t - 36 = 0$$

$$(t - 9)(t + 4) = 0 \qquad \text{factoring}$$

$$t = 9, -4$$

Therefore using $t = x^2$ gives

$$x^2 = 9, -4$$

and $$x = \pm 3, \pm 2i$$ ◢

▶ **EXAMPLE 2**   Solve $(x^2 - 3x)^2 - 2(x^2 - 3x) - 8 = 0$.

Solution   We can rewrite the given equation in quadratic form by substituting t for $x^2 - 3x$. We thus obtain $t^2 - 2t - 8 = 0$, which we solve by factoring.

$$(t - 4)(t + 2) = 0$$

$$t = 4, -2$$

We can now find the values of x by using $x^2 - 3x$ for t:

$$x^2 - 3x = 4 \qquad 0 = x^2 - 3x - 4 = (x - 4)(x + 1)$$

and $$x^2 - 3x = -2 \qquad 0 = x^2 - 3x + 2 = (x - 2)(x - 1)$$

The solutions are $x = 4, -1, 2$, and 1. Each solution should be checked by substituting it in the original equation. ◢

There are other types of equations that can be rewritten in quadratic form. One of these is a radical equation.

A **radical equation** is an equation in which one or both members contain a radical that has the variable in the radicand. We can often solve the equation by using the following result:

> If P and Q are algebraic expressions and n is a positive integer, then every solution of $P = Q$ is also a solution of $P^n = Q^n$.

We will normally use this result with $n = 2$ by isolating a square root, then squaring and simplifying. We may repeat the process if necessary.

Although the above property is true, its converse is not. Thus if $x = 3$, then $x^2 = 3^2 = 9$. However if $a^2 = 7^2$, then a may be either 7 or -7. Each possible root of a radical equation

NOTE   *Must always be checked in the original equation*

Any root of $P^n = Q^n$ which is not a root of $P = Q$ is called an **extraneous root.**

Sometimes the very form of an equation shows that it has no roots. Such is the case with $\sqrt{x + 3} + \sqrt{x - 2} = -3$, since the left member is positive and the right member is negative.

▶ **EXAMPLE 3**   Solve $x + 1 = \sqrt{4x + 9}$.

Solution
$$(x + 1)^2 = (\sqrt{4x + 9})^2 \qquad \text{squaring}$$

$$x^2 + 2x + 1 = 4x + 9 \qquad \text{expanding}$$

$$x^2 - 2x - 8 = 0 \qquad \text{combining terms}$$

$$(x - 4)(x + 2) = 0 \qquad \text{factoring}$$

$$x = 4 \quad \text{or} \quad x = -2 \qquad \text{possible solutions}$$

To check, we first use $x = 4$:

$$x + 1 = 4 + 1 = 5 \quad \text{and} \quad \sqrt{4x + 9} = \sqrt{16 + 9} = \sqrt{25} = 5$$

and so $x = 4$ is a solution. If, however, we take $x = -2$:

$$x + 1 = -2 + 1 = -1 \quad \text{and} \quad \sqrt{4x + 9} = \sqrt{-8 + 9} = 1$$

and so $x = -2$ is not a solution.   ◢

    In Example 3 the radical was already on a side by itself. In Example 4, the first step is to isolate the radical.

▶ **EXAMPLE 4**   Solve the equation $\sqrt{5x - 11} - \sqrt{x - 3} = 4$.

Solution

$$\sqrt{5x - 11} = \sqrt{x - 3} + 4 \qquad \text{isolating } \sqrt{5x - 11}$$

We will now square each side. The left side is easy since $(\sqrt{5x - 11})^2 = 5x - 11$. For the right side we must use $(a + b)^2 = a^2 + 2ab + b^2$ with $a = \sqrt{x - 3}$ and $b = 4$. The result is

$$5x - 11 = x - 3 + 8\sqrt{x - 3} + 16 \qquad \text{squaring}$$

$$4x - 24 = 8\sqrt{x - 3} \qquad \text{isolating } 8\sqrt{x - 3}$$

$$x - 6 = 2\sqrt{x - 3} \qquad \text{dividing by 4}$$

$$x^2 - 12x + 36 = 4(x - 3) \qquad \text{squaring}$$

$$x^2 - 12x + 36 = 4x - 12 \qquad \text{distributive axiom}$$

$$x^2 - 16x + 48 = 0 \qquad \text{combining terms}$$

$$(x - 12)(x - 4) = 0 \qquad \text{factoring}$$

$$x = 12, 4 \qquad \text{solution by factoring}$$

Check

$$\sqrt{60 - 11} - \sqrt{12 - 3} = \sqrt{49} - \sqrt{9} = 7 - 3 = 4 \qquad \text{12 is a solution}$$

$$\sqrt{20 - 11} - \sqrt{4 - 3} = \sqrt{9} - \sqrt{1} = 3 - 1 = 2 \qquad \text{4 is not a solution}$$

Since the right-hand member of the given equation is not 2, 4 is not a root, and the only solution of the given equation is 12.   ◢

▶ **EXAMPLE 5**   Solve the equation $\sqrt{x + 1} + \sqrt{2x + 3} - \sqrt{8x + 1} = 0$.

Solution

$$\sqrt{x + 1} + \sqrt{2x + 3} = \sqrt{8x + 1} \qquad \text{isolating } \sqrt{8x + 1}$$

We square each side now, again using $(a + b)^2 = a^2 + 2ab + b^2$ on the left-hand side.

$$x + 1 + 2\sqrt{(x + 1)(2x + 3)} + 2x + 3 = 8x + 1 \qquad \text{squaring}$$

$$2\sqrt{2x^2 + 5x + 3} = 5x - 3 \qquad \text{isolating the radical and combining terms}$$

$$4(2x^2 + 5x + 3) = 25x^2 - 30x + 9 \qquad \text{squaring both sides}$$

$$17x^2 - 50x - 3 = 0 \qquad \text{combining terms}$$

$$(17x + 1)(x - 3) = 0 \qquad \text{factoring}$$

$$x = 3 \text{ and } -\tfrac{1}{17} \qquad \text{possible solutions}$$

Checking will show that $x = 3$ is a root of the original equation and that $-\tfrac{1}{17}$ is not.

The radical equations in the last three examples have each had one actual root and one extraneous root. In the next example, the given equation has two roots.

EXAMPLE 6   Solve $3\sqrt{x - 3} = x - 1$.

Solution

$$3\sqrt{x - 3} = x - 1 \qquad \text{given}$$

$$9(x - 3) = x^2 - 2x + 1 \qquad \text{squaring each side: on the left use } (3a)^2 = 9a^2$$

$$0 = x^2 - 11x + 28 \qquad \text{collecting terms}$$

$$0 = (x - 4)(x - 7) \qquad \text{factoring}$$

The solutions are 4 and 7. Checking 4 gives

$$3\sqrt{4 - 3} = 3(1) = 3 \qquad \text{and} \qquad 4 - 1 = 3$$

while checking 7 gives

$$3\sqrt{7 - 3} = 3\sqrt{4} = 3(2) = 6 \qquad \text{and} \qquad 7 - 1 = 6$$

Both 4 and 7 are solutions.

EXAMPLE 7   Solve $\sqrt[3]{x^2 + 5x - 9} = 3$.

Solution

$$\sqrt[3]{x^2 + 5x - 9} = 3 \qquad \text{given}$$

$$x^2 + 5x - 9 = 27 \qquad \text{cubing}$$

$$x^2 + 5x - 36 = 0 \qquad \text{collecting terms}$$

$$(x - 4)(x + 9) = 0 \qquad \text{factoring}$$

The solutions are 4 and -9, and both of them check when substituted in the original equation.

The equations in the next two examples involve fractions. Some equations involving fractions can be changed into quadratic equations by multiplying both sides of the equation by the lcd.

EXAMPLE 8   Solve $1/(2x - 5) + 1/(x - 1) = 1$.

Solution

$$1(x - 1) + 1(2x - 5) = (x - 1)(2x - 5) \qquad \text{multiplying by the lcd } (2x - 5)(x - 1)$$

$$3x - 6 = 2x^2 - 7x + 5 \qquad \text{distributive axiom}$$

$$0 = 2x^2 - 10x + 11 \qquad \text{combining terms}$$

$$x = \frac{10 \pm \sqrt{100 - 4(2)(11)}}{4} \qquad \text{quadratic formula}$$

$$= \frac{10 \pm \sqrt{12}}{4} = \frac{10 \pm 2\sqrt{3}}{4} \qquad \text{simplifying the radicand}$$

$$= \frac{5 + \sqrt{3}}{2}, \frac{5 - \sqrt{3}}{2} \qquad \text{possible solutions}$$

NOTE   We must be sure to omit any solutions that would result in division by zero. Since the only such values are $\frac{5}{2}$ and 1, the two possible solutions above are actually solutions.

► EXAMPLE 9   Solve the equation $\dfrac{2x + 1}{3x + 4} = \dfrac{3x - 1}{9x - 8}$, if $x \neq -\frac{4}{3}$ and $x \neq \frac{8}{9}$.

Solution

$$(2x + 1)(9x - 8) = (3x - 1)(3x + 4) \qquad \text{multiplying by lcd}$$

$$18x^2 - 7x - 8 = 9x^2 + 9x - 4 \qquad \text{distributive axiom, FOIL}$$

$$9x^2 - 16x - 4 = 0 \qquad \text{combining terms}$$

$$(9x + 2)(x - 2) = 0 \qquad \text{factoring}$$

$$x = -\tfrac{2}{9} \quad \text{and} \quad x = 2 \qquad \text{solution by factoring}$$

Again, we must make sure that the solutions do not result in division by zero in the given equation. Since neither does, $-\frac{2}{9}$ and 2 are the solutions.

Many equations that involve absolute values can be solved by the method above for radical equations, using $t^2 = |t|^2$.

► EXAMPLE 10 $|2x - 5| + |2x - 3| = 4$.

Solution

$$|2x - 5| = 4 - |2x - 3| \qquad \text{isolating } |2x - 5|$$

$$4x^2 - 20x + 25 = 16 - 8|2x - 3| + 4x^2 - 12x + 9 \qquad \text{squaring both sides of the equation, using } |t|^2 = t^2 \text{ and } (a - b)^2 = a^2 - 2ab + b^2$$

$$-8x = -8|2x - 3| \qquad \text{combining similar terms}$$

$$x = |2x - 3| \qquad \text{dividing by } -8$$

$$x^2 = 4x^2 - 12x + 9 \qquad \text{squaring}$$

$$0 = 3x^2 - 12x + 9 \qquad \text{combining terms}$$

$$0 = x^2 - 4x + 3 = (x - 3)(x - 1) \qquad \text{factoring}$$

$$x = 3, 1 \qquad \text{solution by factoring}$$

Both of these roots check, but as usual they should be checked in the original equation. The reason is that squaring, which was done in the solution, can give extraneous roots.

EXERCISE 2.5

Solve each of the following equations for x.

1. $x^4 - 5x^2 + 4 = 0$ 2. $x^4 - 5x^2 - 36 = 0$
3. $x^4 - 8x^2 - 9 = 0$ 4. $x^4 + 13x^2 + 36 = 0$
5. $4x^{-4} - 7x^{-2} - 36 = 0$
6. $36x^{-4} - 77x^{-2} - 9 = 0$
7. $16x^{-4} + 32x^{-2} - 9 = 0$
8. $9x^{-4} + 5x^{-2} - 4 = 0$
9. $100x^{-4/3} - 409x^{-2/3} + 36 = 0$
10. $36x^{4/3} - 13x^{2/3} + 1 = 0$
11. $x^{4/3} - 34x^{2/3} + 225 = 0$
12. $36x^{4/3} - 25x^{2/3} + 4 = 0$
13. $(x^2 - 3x)^2 - 2(x^2 - 3x) - 8 = 0$
14. $(x^2 - 2x)^2 - 2(x^2 - 2x) - 3 = 0$
15. $(x^2 + 4x)^2 - 4(x^2 + 4x) - 32 = 0$
16. $(2x^2 - 3x)^2 - (2x^2 - 3x) - 2 = 0$
17. $\left(\dfrac{x+1}{x-3}\right)^2 - \dfrac{x+1}{x-3} - 2 = 0$
18. $2\left(\dfrac{x-3}{x+1}\right)^2 + \dfrac{x-3}{x+1} - 1 = 0$
19. $\left(\dfrac{x-2}{3x+1}\right)^2 - 4\dfrac{x-2}{3x+1} + 3 = 0$
20. $3\left(\dfrac{x+3}{2x-1}\right)^2 - 4\dfrac{x+3}{2x-1} + 1 = 0$
21. $\dfrac{x+2}{x-2} - 3 - 4\dfrac{x-2}{x+2} = 0$
22. $\dfrac{x+3}{x+1} - 5 + 4\dfrac{x+1}{x+3} = 0$
23. $\dfrac{2x-3}{x-4} - 7 + 6\dfrac{x-4}{2x-3} = 0$

24. $\dfrac{3x+2}{2x-1} - 10 + 9\dfrac{2x-1}{3x+2} = 0$
25. $\dfrac{3x+4}{4x+1} = \dfrac{6x-5}{2x+7}$ 26. $\dfrac{2x-3}{3x-2} = \dfrac{x-1}{2x}$
27. $\dfrac{3x+5}{3x-1} = \dfrac{5x+3}{x+1}$ 28. $\dfrac{4x+3}{3x+4} = \dfrac{2x+1}{x+2}$
29. $\sqrt{x+2} = 3x - 4$ 30. $\sqrt{3x+1} = 2x - 1$
31. $\sqrt{5x+9} = 2x + 3$ 32. $\sqrt{3x+7} = x + 3$
33. $\sqrt{5x+1} = \sqrt{2x+1} + 2$
34. $\sqrt{3x+1} + 1 = \sqrt{4x+5}$
35. $\sqrt{3x+12} - 1 = \sqrt{5x+9}$
36. $\sqrt{x+2} + 1 = \sqrt{3x+3}$
37. $\sqrt{x+1} + \sqrt{3x+4} = \sqrt{5x+9}$
38. $\sqrt{3x+1} + \sqrt{3x-2} = \sqrt{4x+5}$
39. $\sqrt{3x+7} + \sqrt{2x+6} = \sqrt{11-5x}$
40. $\sqrt{2x+3} - \sqrt{x-2} = \sqrt{x+1}$
41. $\sqrt[3]{5x-1} = 4$ 42. $\sqrt[3]{5x-9} = 3$
43. $\sqrt[3]{x^2+x-4} = 2$ 44. $\sqrt[4]{x^2-2x+8} = 2$
45. $|x+3| - 1 = |x+1|$ 46. $|x+2| + 1 = |x+7|$
47. $|2x+3| - |2x-2| = 1$
48. $|3x+5| - |1+3x| = 3$

In Probs. 49 to 52, find three roots for each equation by first factoring as a sum or difference of cubes and then using the quadratic formula.

49. $(x+2)^3 - 64 = 0$ 50. $(2x-3)^3 + 8 = 0$
51. $8(x-4)^3 + 27 = 0$ 52. $8(3x+2)^3 - 1 = 0$

2.6 Applications

Just as many problems can be solved by using linear equations, there are numerous ones that can be solved by using quadratic equations. We can use the same basic procedures used in solving linear equations in Sec. 2.2.

These are some of the formulas that help in translating the problem from English to an equation:

1. Distance = rate multiplied by time

$$d = rt \quad \text{or} \quad \text{kilometers} = \frac{\text{kilometers}}{\text{hour}} \text{(hours)}$$

2. Work done = rate of working multiplied by time worked

$$w = rt \quad \text{or} \quad \text{number of cars produced} = \frac{\text{cars}}{\text{day}} \text{(days)}$$

3. Simple interest = principal times rate times time

$$I = Prt \quad \text{or} \quad \text{dollars} = (\text{dollars}) \left(\frac{\text{percent}}{\text{year}} \right) \text{(years)}$$

4. Revenue = cost per item times number of items

$$R = CI \quad \text{or} \quad \text{dollars} = \frac{\text{dollars}}{\text{item}} \text{(items)}$$

5. Area of a rectangle = length times width

$$A = lw \quad \text{or} \quad \text{square meters} = (\text{meters})(\text{meters})$$

6. $W_1 L_1 = W_2 L_2$ in a fulcrum, or (weight)(length) is a constant.

7. $100h + 10t + u$ is the number with h hundreds, t tens, and u units. For instance, $742 = 100(7) + 10(4) + 2$.

▶ EXAMPLE 1   (a) If the sum of two numbers is 40, then we can represent one of them by x. The other one must be $40 - x$ since $x + (40 - x) = 40$.
(b) A pecan orchard yields 120 kg of pecans per tree when there are 8 trees per acre. Every extra tree per acre decreases production per tree by 10 kg. Since

$$\frac{\text{kg of pecans}}{\text{tree}} \cdot \frac{\text{trees}}{\text{acre}} = \frac{\text{kg of pecans}}{\text{acre}}$$

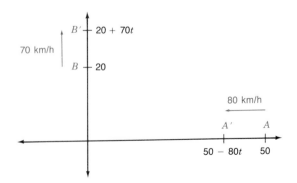

FIGURE 2.4

the production with 8 trees is $(120)8 = 960$ kg/acre. If x trees are added, then there are $8 + x$ trees, the production per tree is $120 - 10x$, and the total production is

$$(120 - 10x)(8 + x)$$

(c) Two cars A and B driving on perpendicular roads are moving at 80 and 70 km/h, and they are 50 and 20 km from the intersection, respectively. After t hours, car A has gone $80t$ km toward the intersection and car B has gone $70t$ km away from it. So their new positions are $A' = 50 - 80t$ and $B' = 20 + 70t$, as shown in Fig. 2.4 (facing page). By the pythagorean theorem, which states that the square of the hypotenuse of a right triangle is equal to the sum of the squares of the two sides, the distance d between the cars is

$$\sqrt{(50 - 80t)^2 + (20 + 70t)^2} \text{ km}$$

◢

EXAMPLE 2   A rectangular building was constructed so that its depth is twice its frontage. The building is divided into two parts by a partition that is 30 ft from and parallel to the front wall. If the rear portion of the building contains 3500 ft^2, find the dimensions of the building.

Solution   In problems describing physical objects, it is advisable to draw a diagram, such as Fig. 2.5 for this problem. We will let x equal one of the unknown dimensions. For example,

$$x = \text{frontage of the building} \qquad \text{ft}$$

Then
$$2x = \text{depth of the building} \qquad \text{ft}$$

and
$$2x - 30 = \text{depth of the rear portion} \qquad \text{ft}$$

Since the area of a rectangle is equal to the product of its length and its width, the area of the rear portion of the building is $x(2x - 30)$ ft^2. Furthermore, since we know that this area is 3500 ft^2, we have

$$x(2x - 30) = 3500$$

We solve the equation as follows:

$$2x^2 - 30x = 3500 \qquad \text{distributive axiom}$$
$$2x^2 - 30x - 3500 = 0 \qquad \text{adding } -3500$$
$$(x - 50)(2x + 70) = 0 \qquad \text{factoring}$$
$$x = 50, \ -35 \qquad \text{solutions}$$

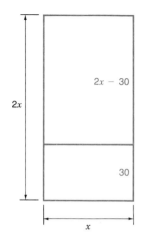

FIGURE 2.5

The solutions are 50 and -35, but the dimensions of the building must be positive. Thus, we reject -35, and the dimensions are

$$x = 50 \qquad \text{frontage in feet}$$

$$2x = 100 \qquad \text{depth in feet}$$

Check
$$2x - 30 = 100 - 30 = 70$$

and
$$50 \text{ ft} \times 70 \text{ ft} = 3500 \text{ ft}^2$$ ◢

▶ **EXAMPLE 3** The times required for two students to paint a square yard of the floor of their dorm room differ by 1 min. Together, they can paint 27 yd^2 in 1 h. How long does it takes each to paint 1 yd^2?

Solution We can express our answers as fractions of an hour or in minutes. We let x = number of minutes for the faster student to paint 1 yd^2. Then $x + 1$ = the number of minutes required by the other. Consequently,

$$\frac{1}{x} = \begin{array}{l} \text{fractional part of 1 yd}^2 \text{ painted} \\ \text{by the first student in 1 min} \end{array}$$

and
$$\frac{1}{x + 1} = \begin{array}{l} \text{fractional part of 1 yd}^2 \text{ painted} \\ \text{by the other student in 1 min} \end{array}$$

Consequently
$$\frac{1}{x} + \frac{1}{x + 1} = \begin{array}{l} \text{fractional part of 1 yd}^2 \text{ painted} \\ \text{by both students in 1 min} \end{array}$$

Since, however, together they painted 27 yd^2 in 60 min (1 h), they covered $\frac{27}{60} = \frac{9}{20}$ yd^2 in 1 min. Therefore,

$$\frac{1}{x} + \frac{1}{x + 1} = \frac{9}{20} \tag{1}$$

This is the desired equation, and we solve it as follows:

$$(20x + 20) + 20x = 9x^2 + 9x \qquad \text{multiplying by the lcd } 20x(x + 1)$$

$$0 = 9x^2 - 31x - 20 \qquad \text{combining terms}$$

$$0 = (9x + 5)(x - 4) \qquad \text{factoring}$$

$$x = -\tfrac{5}{9}, 4 \qquad \text{solutions}$$

We reject $-\frac{5}{9}$, however, since a negative time has no meaning in this problem. Therefore, we have

$$x = 4 \qquad \text{number of minutes for faster student to paint 1 yd}^2$$

$$x + 1 = 5 \qquad \text{number of minutes required by the slower student}$$

Check
$$5 \text{ min} - 4 \text{ min} = 1 \text{ min}$$

▶ **EXAMPLE 4** In Example 1(c), when are the cars $34\sqrt{2}$ km apart?

Solution From Example 1(c) and Fig. 2.4, we know that the distance is

$$\sqrt{(50 - 80t)^2 + (20 + 70t)^2}$$

Thus we need to solve the equation

$$34\sqrt{2} = 10\sqrt{(5 - 8t)^2 + (2 + 7t)^2}$$

$$2(34)^2 = 100(25 - 80t + 64t^2 + 4 + 28t + 49t^2) \qquad \text{squaring}$$

$$2(1156) = 100(113t^2 - 52t + 29) \qquad \text{collecting terms}$$

$$0 = 11{,}300t^2 - 5200t + 2900 - 2312 \qquad \text{zero on one side}$$

$$0 = 11{,}300t^2 - 5200t + 588$$

$$0 = 2825t^2 - 1300t + 147 \qquad \text{dividing by 4}$$

The quadratic formula gives

$$x = \frac{1300 \pm \sqrt{(1300)^2 - 4(2825)(147)}}{2(2825)}$$

$$= \frac{1300 \pm \sqrt{28{,}900}}{2(2825)} = \frac{1300 \pm 170}{2(2825)} = \frac{1130}{5650} \text{ or } \frac{1470}{5650}$$

The answers in hours are $\frac{1130}{5650} = \frac{1}{5}$ and $\frac{1470}{5650} = \frac{147}{565}$. In minutes these answers are exactly 12 and ≈ 15.6. ◢

In Sec. 4.1 we will present a general method for determining the maximum or minimum value of quadratic expressions such as the one above.

EXERCISE 2.6

In Probs. 1 to 16, write a quadratic equation that represents the problem, and then solve the equation.

1. Find two consecutive integers whose product exceeds their sum by 19.
2. Find two consecutive odd integers whose product exceeds 3 times their sum by 15.
3. Find two numbers that differ by 8 and whose product is 273.
4. Divide 67 into two parts whose product is 1120.
5. The difference between the square of a positive number and 7 times the number is 18. Find the number.
6. Find a negative number such that the sum of its square and 5 times the number is 14.
7. If the length of the side of a square is increased by 6 units, the area is multiplied by 4. Find the original side length.
8. Two numbers differ by 9, and the sum of their reciprocals is $\frac{5}{12}$. Find the numbers.
9. The tens digit of a certain number is 3 more than the units digit. The sum of the squares of the two digits is 117. Find the number.
10. The tens digit of a certain number is 4 more than the units digit. The sum of the squares of the two digits is 26. Find the number.
11. Wesley purchased some shares of stock for $1560. Later, when the price had gone up $24 per share, he sold all but 10 of the shares for $1520. How many shares had he bought?
12. Dorothy drives 10 mi, then increases her speed by 10 mi/h and drives another 25 mi. Find her original speed if she drove for 45 min.
13. Two brothers washed the family car in 24 min. When they each washed the car alone, the younger brother took 20 min longer to do the job than the older brother. How long did the older brother take to wash the car?
14. Mr. Billings received dividends of $72 one year from some stock. Mrs. Billings received $50 from some other stock which was worth $200 less and

whose rate was 1 percent less. Find the higher rate.

15. Two planes P and Q are flying at the same altitude on perpendicular paths. Suppose that when $t = 0$, plane P is flying north at 400 km/h from a point 100 km due south of the intersection of the paths, and plane Q is flying west at 300 km/h from a point 200 km due east of the intersection. After how many hours will they be 100 km apart? See figure.

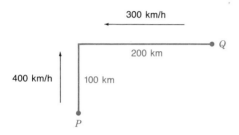

16. Karl and Clara are riding bicycles on perpendicular roads. Suppose that Karl is 9 km from the intersection and riding toward it at 20 km/h, and Clara is 7 km from it and riding away from it at 25 km/h. After how many hours will they be 13 km apart? See figure.

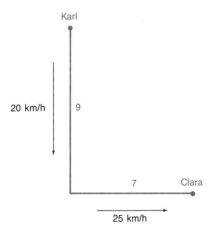

Solve the remaining problems with the help of a quadratic equation.

17. A farmer wants to make a rectangular garden of 7500 ft^2, and she has 250 ft of fencing. There is already a fence on one side. What dimensions should her garden have? See figure.

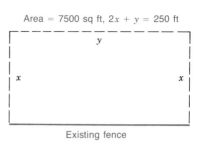

Area = 7500 sq ft, $2x + y = 250$ ft

Existing fence

18. A small business wants to construct a rectangular building with a perimeter of 300 m and an area of 5400 m^2. What are the dimensions of the building?

19. The area of a triangle is 30 ft^2. Find the base and altitude if the latter exceeds the former by 7 ft.

20. The area of a triangular island is 67,500 yd^2. Find the base if it is 150 yd more than the altitude.

21. To make a straight sidewalk from her house to her garage, Lenore used 54 ft of forming, into which she poured 24 ft^3 of concrete to form a slab 4 in thick. What were the dimensions of the sidewalk?

22. The Braun's living room is 13 by 16 ft, and they want to carpet it, except for a border of uniform width. What dimensions should the carpet be if they can afford only 108 ft^2? See figure.

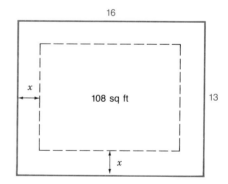

23. Both Warren and Rachel walked the entire 10 mi of the charity walk. What was Rachel's speed if it was 1 mi/h less than Warren's and she took $\frac{1}{2}$ h more than he for the walk?

24. Mr. Buckley purchased $4\frac{1}{4}$ lb of grass seed to plant a rectangular lawn. Find the dimensions of the area to be planted if the length exceeds the width by 35 ft and if a pound of seed is required for 1000 ft^2.

25. Find the dimensions of a right triangle if the shortest side is 3 less than the middle one and 6 less than the hypotenuse.

26. Find the dimensions of a right triangle if the hypotenuse is 2 more than twice the shortest side and 4 more than the other side.

27. Find the dimensions of a right triangle if the area is 120 and one leg is 4 more than twice the other leg.

28. Find the dimensions of a right triangle if the area is 84 and one leg is 3 more than 3 times the other leg.

29. A manufacturer wants to make a can of height $\frac{21}{8}$ in that will hold 42π in^3. What must the radius of the can be?

30. Running shoes in lots of 50 or fewer pairs can be bought for $18 per pair. The price decreases by 1.5 cents per pair for the excess over 50 pairs bought at one time up to 400 pairs. How many pairs can be bought for $4464?

31. The Celsius temperature T at which water boils at an elevation of h m above sea level is given by

$$h = 1000(100 - T) + 580(100 - T)^2$$

(a) For which elevation does it boil at 98.6°C?

(b) For which temperatures does it boil at an elevation of 1 km?

32. Two oil spills are each circular, and their centers are 6 km apart. Find each radius if the sum of the areas is 20π. Assume the circles are tangent.

Economics

A demand function $D(x)$ gives a price per unit at which x items can be sold. (x may represent 1 unit or 1000 units or even 100,000 units.) A revenue function $R(x) = x \cdot D(x)$ gives the amount of money received if x items are sold. The cost function $C(x)$ gives the total cost of producing x items. The profit is

$$P(x) = R(x) - C(x)$$

33. What value of x makes the profit 2 if
$$D(x) = -3x + 18 \qquad \text{and} \qquad C(x) = 9x + 4$$

34. What value of x makes the profit 6 if
$$D(x) = 20 - 2x \qquad \text{and} \qquad C(x) = 10x + 3$$

35. What value of x makes the profit 39 if
$$D(x) = 22 - 5x \qquad \text{and} \qquad C(x) = -x^2 + 7x + 6$$

36. What value of x makes the profit 7 if
$$D(x) = -4x + 33 \qquad \text{and} \qquad C(x) = -x^2 + 9x + 2$$

2.7 Inequalities

As described in Sec. 2.1, an equation is a statement that two expressions are equal. An **inequality** is a statement that one expression is greater than, greater than or equal to, less than, or less than or equal to another. We will use the following four properties of inequalities in working with real numbers.

Suppose that a, b, and c are real numbers.

If $a < b$ and $b < c$, then $a < c$	(1)
If $a < b$, then $a + c < b + c$	(2)
If $a < b$ and $c > 0$, then $ac < bc$	(3)
If $a < b$ and $c < 0$, then $ac > bc$	(4)

Remember that dividing by t is the same as multiplying by $1/t$, for $t \neq 0$. And since subtracting d is the same as adding $-d$, we know that

If $a < b$, then $a - d < b - d$

▶ **EXAMPLE 1**   Verify the following operations with inequalities.

Solution   By (1): since $-5 < -1$ and $-1 < 13$, then $-5 < 13$.
By (2): since $-6 < -5$, then $-6 + 11 < -5 + 11$.
By (3): since $7 < 15$ and $2 > 0$, then $14 < 30$.
By (4): since $7 < 15$ and $-3 < 0$, then $-21 > -45$.   ◀

We may use $\leq$ and $\geq$ in the same manner as $<$ and $>$ are used. For instance $13 \leq 15$ implies that

$$13 + 7 \leq 15 + 7 \quad\text{and}\quad 13(3) \leq 15(3) \quad\text{since } 3 > 0$$

If an inequality involves a variable, then a **solution** is a value of the variable that makes the inequality a true statement. The set of all solutions is the **solution set.** If two inequalities have the same solution set, they are called **equivalent inequalities.**

NOTE   **To solve an inequality,** we write it as a sequence of equivalent and successively simpler inequalities by using the laws above. The goal is to isolate x, that is, to solve for x, or whatever the variable is.

▶ **EXAMPLE 2**   Solve the inequality $12x + 1 < 3 + 5x$.

Solution
$$12x - 5x < 3 - 1 \qquad \text{adding } -5x - 1$$
$$7x < 2 \qquad \text{combining terms}$$
$$x < \tfrac{2}{7} \qquad \text{dividing by 7, } 7 > 0$$

We combined terms above in such a way that the coefficient of x would be positive. Had we chosen the method below, we would have gotten a negative number times x:

$$1 - 3 < 5x - 12x \qquad \text{adding } -3 - 12x$$
$$-2 < -7x \qquad \text{combining terms}$$
$$\frac{-2}{-7} > x \qquad \text{dividing by } -7, -7 < 0$$

In the last step, we divided by -7 and thus had to change the sense of the inequality. The solution is, as above, $x < \tfrac{2}{7}$. See Fig. 2.6.   ◀

Whereas the solution of an equation is usually one or more numbers, the solution of an inequality is usually one or more intervals. The notation is repeated here for easy reference:

Open interval
$$(a, b) = \{x | a < x < b\}$$

Closed interval
$$[a, b] = \{x | a \leq x \leq b\}$$

Note that the endpoints are not included in an open interval:

$$(a, \infty) = \{x | x > a\} \qquad (-\infty, a) = \{x | x < a\}$$

FIGURE 2.6

$$[a, \infty) = \{x | x \ge a\} \qquad (-\infty, a] = \{x | x \le a\}$$

Accordingly, the solution to Example 2 can be written in the form $(-\infty, \frac{2}{7})$, which is a short way of describing all of the real numbers less than $\frac{2}{7}$. The symbols ∞ and $-\infty$ themselves are not real numbers.

EXAMPLE 3 Solve the inequality $\frac{1}{6}x - \frac{3}{4} \le \frac{3}{8}x + \frac{1}{2}$.

Solution

$$24(\tfrac{1}{6}x - \tfrac{3}{4}) \le 24(\tfrac{3}{8}x + \tfrac{1}{2}) \qquad \text{multiplying by the lcd, 24}$$

$$4x - 18 \le 9x + 12 \qquad \text{distributive axiom}$$

$$4x - 9x \le 12 + 18 \qquad \text{adding } -9x + 18$$

$$-5x \le 30 \qquad \text{combining terms}$$

$$x \ge -6 \qquad \text{dividing by } -5, \; -5 < 0$$

The solution is $[-6, \infty)$. See Fig. 2.7

Nonlinear Inequalities

If we are given a nonlinear inequality, we may often use factoring to reduce it to two or more linear inequalities. We must then find the common solution to all of these linear inequalities. One method that helps is to use a number line. Another aid is a sign chart, which shows the sign of each factor on each interval.

The basis for our solutions is that, for instance, the product of two positive numbers is positive. In fact

(positive) · (positive) is positive

(negative) · (negative) is positive

(positive) · (negative) is negative

Get 0 on one side of the inequality

In order to use these facts, it is essential to rewrite the inequality in an equivalent form with

0 alone on one side of the inequality

EXAMPLE 4 Solve the inequality $(x + 6)(x - 2) > 6x - 9$.

Solution

$$x^2 + 4x - 12 > 6x - 9 \qquad \text{multiplying left side}$$

$$x^2 - 2x - 3 > 0 \qquad \text{combining terms}$$

$$(x + 1)(x - 3) > 0 \qquad \text{factoring}$$

Setting each factor equal to zero and solving give $x = 3$ and $x = -1$. These two numbers divide the number line into three intervals. We now find the sign of $x + 1$, of $x - 3$, and of their product in each interval.

FIGURE 2.8

Number line $\quad\quad\quad\quad\quad\quad$ $-1\quad\quad\quad 3$			
Interval	$(-\infty, -1)$	$(-1, 3)$	$(3, \infty)$
Sign of $(x + 1)$	$-$	$+$	$+$
Sign of $(x - 3)$	$-$	$-$	$+$
Sign of $(x + 1)(x - 3)$	$+$	$-$	$+$

Sign chart

This chart is called a **sign chart,** and it shows that

$$(x + 1)(x - 3) > 0 \quad\quad \text{if } x < -1 \text{ or } x > 3$$

The solution can be written in interval notation as

$$(-\infty, -1) \cup (3, \infty)$$

which is shown in Fig. 2.8.

Alternative Solution

Instead of a sign chart, we may use **test values.** Both of these methods require that only 0 be on one side of the inequality sign. As above, the inequality $(x - 3)(x + 1) > 0$ determines the three intervals $(-\infty, -1)$, $(-1, 3)$, and $(3, \infty)$. Now because $(x - 3)(x + 1)$ is zero *only* at $x = 3$ and $x = -1$, it follows that $(x - 3)(x + 1)$ will have the same sign in the whole interval $(-\infty, -1)$. The same is true for each of the intervals. Therefore we may determine the sign of $(x - 3)(x + 1)$ in each interval by using *any number* in that interval.

Determining the sign of $(x - 3)(x + 1)$

Number line $\quad\quad\quad\quad\quad$ $-1\quad\quad\quad\quad\quad\quad\quad 3$			
Number in each interval $\quad\quad -2$	0		5
Interval	$(-\infty, -1)$	$(-1, 3)$	$(3, \infty)$
A number in the interval	-2	0	5
Test value at that number	$(-5)(-1) = 5$	$(-3)(1) = -3$	$(2)(6) = 12$
Sign in the interval	Positive	Negative	Positive

▶ **EXAMPLE 5**   Solve the inequality $(2x + 1)/(x - 3) > 3$.

Solution

In order to isolate 0 on one side of the inequality, we subtract 3 from both sides:

$$\frac{2x + 1}{x - 3} - 3 > 0$$

$$\frac{(2x + 1) - 3(x - 3)}{x - 3} > 0 \quad\quad \text{subtracting, using the lcd } x - 3$$

$$\frac{10 - x}{x - 3} > 0 \quad\quad \text{combining terms}$$

FIGURE 2.9

We will complete the solution by using test values on the intervals $(-\infty, 3)$, $(3, 10)$, and $(10, \infty)$.

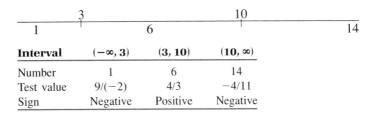

Determining the sign of
$(10 - x)/(x - 3)$

Interval	$(-\infty, 3)$	$(3, 10)$	$(10, \infty)$
Number	1	6	14
Test value	$9/(-2)$	$4/3$	$-4/11$
Sign	Negative	Positive	Negative

The solution is therefore $(3, 10)$. See Fig. 2.9.

Alternative Solution   It is tempting to multiply both sides of the inequality by the lcd $x - 3$ and get $2x + 1 > 3(x - 3)$. This is **incorrect** since $x - 3$ may be positive or negative, and, where it is negative, the sense of the inequality is changed.

A **correct** way to change this from a fractional inequality to an *equivalent* quadratic inequality is to multiply both sides by the *positive* expression $(x - 3)^2$. This does not change the sense of the inequality.

$$\left(\frac{2x + 1}{x - 3}\right)(x - 3)^2 > 3(x - 3)^2 \qquad \text{multiplying by } (x - 3)^2$$

$$(2x + 1)(x - 3) > 3(x^2 - 6x + 9) \qquad \text{simplifying}$$

$$2x^2 - 5x - 3 > 3x^2 - 18x + 27 \qquad \text{multiplying}$$

$$0 > x^2 - 13x + 30 \qquad \text{combining terms}$$

$$0 > (x - 3)(x - 10) \qquad \text{factoring}$$

We will complete the solution by using a sign chart.

| Number line | | 3 | 10 | |

Interval	$(-\infty, 3)$	$(3, 10)$	$(10, \infty)$
Sign of $(x - 3)$	$-$	$+$	$+$
Sign of $(x - 10)$	$-$	$-$	$+$
Sign of product	$+$	$-$	$+$

The sign chart shows that $(x - 10)(x - 3) < 0$ if $3 < x < 10$, which gives the interval $(3, 10)$.

NOTE   The solution and alternative solution of Example 5 show that

$$\frac{x - 10}{x - 3} < 0 \qquad \text{and} \qquad (x - 3)(x - 10) < 0$$

have the same solutions.

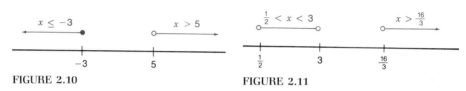

FIGURE 2.10   FIGURE 2.11

EXAMPLE 6   Solve the inequality $(x + 3)/(x - 5) \geq 0$.

Solution   We must be careful here to use $\geq$ (not $>$), and we have to remember that x can not be 5 since division by 0 is not defined. We will use a sign chart.

Number line		-3	5	
Interval	$(-\infty, -3)$	$(-3, 5)$	$(5, \infty)$
Sign of $(x + 3)$	$-$	$+$	$+$
Sign of $(x - 5)$	$-$	$-$	$+$
Sign of $(x + 3)/(x - 5)$	$+$	$-$	$+$

Remembering that we want the quotient to be positive or zero, but x cannot be 5, we see the solution is

$$(-\infty, -3] \cup (5, \infty)$$

See Fig. 2.10.

EXAMPLE 7   Solve the inequality $(2x - 1)(x - 3)(3x - 16) > 0$.

Solution   This inequality involves three different factors and hence four intervals. The values of x that determine the intervals are $\frac{1}{2}$, 3, and $\frac{16}{3}$. We will use a sign chart.

Number line		$\frac{1}{2}$	3	$\frac{16}{3}$	
Interval	$(-\infty, \frac{1}{2})$	$(\frac{1}{2}, 3)$	$(3, \frac{16}{3})$	$(\frac{16}{3}, \infty)$
Sign of $(2x - 1)$	$-$	$+$	$+$	$+$
Sign of $(x - 3)$	$-$	$-$	$+$	$+$
Sign of $(3x - 16)$	$-$	$-$	$-$	$+$
Sign of product	$-$	$+$	$-$	$+$

The solution is $(\frac{1}{2}, 3) \cup (\frac{16}{3}, \infty)$. See Fig. 2.11.

Inequalities with more terms can also be solved. Consider

$$\frac{x^2 - 4x + 3}{x^2 + 3x - 10} < 0$$

or $$\frac{(x - 3)(x - 1)}{(x + 5)(x - 2)} < 0$$

Multiplying both sides by the positive expression $[(x + 5)(x - 2)]^2$ shows that this is equivalent to

$$(x - 3)(x - 1)(x + 5)(x - 2) < 0$$

Putting -5, 1, 2, and 3 on a number line and using a sign chart shows that the solution is $(-5, 1) \cup (2, 3)$.

EXERCISE 2.7

Solve each of the following inequalities:

1. $3x < 6$
2. $5x > 15$
3. $-2x > 14$
4. $-4x < -12$
5. $4x - 5 > x + 1$
6. $7x - 4 > 3x - 8$
7. $6x + 7 < 3x - 2$
8. $11x + 2 < 3x - 4$
9. $7x + 2 \le 5x + 6$
10. $5x + 8 \le 2x - 1$
11. $9x - 3 \ge 7x + 5$
12. $8x - 1 \ge 5x + 8$
13. $3x + 1 > 6x - 2$
14. $4x - 3 > 8x + 5$
15. $2x - 7 < 7x + 3$
16. $x + 6 < 5x - 2$
17. $\dfrac{3}{4}x - \dfrac{5}{8} < \dfrac{1}{2}x + \dfrac{3}{8}$
18. $\dfrac{5}{6}x - \dfrac{3}{4} < \dfrac{1}{3}x + \dfrac{1}{4}$
19. $\dfrac{7}{8}x + \dfrac{1}{2} > \dfrac{1}{4}x - \dfrac{1}{8}$
20. $\dfrac{3}{4}x + \dfrac{1}{3} > \dfrac{2}{3}x + \dfrac{1}{2}$
21. $\dfrac{1}{2}x - \dfrac{1}{3} \le \dfrac{3}{4}x + \dfrac{7}{6}$
22. $\dfrac{1}{6}x + \dfrac{1}{3} \ge \dfrac{1}{2}x + \dfrac{2}{3}$
23. $\dfrac{4}{7}x + \dfrac{3}{4} \ge \dfrac{1}{2}x + \dfrac{1}{4}$
24. $\dfrac{5}{9}x + \dfrac{5}{6} \le \dfrac{1}{2}x + \dfrac{1}{2}$
25. $(x - 2)(x + 1) > 0$
26. $(x - 4)(x - 2) > 0$
27. $(x + 2)(x + 3) \ge 0$
28. $(x - 2)(x - 5) \ge 0$
29. $(2x + 3)(5x - 2) \le 0$
30. $(2x - 7)(7x + 2) \le 0$
31. $(5x - 3)(2x + 7) < 0$
32. $(3x + 5)(2x - 3) < 0$
33. $-x^2 + 4x - 3 < 0$
34. $-x^2 - x + 6 > 0$
35. $-x^2 + 6x - 9 > 0$
36. $-x^2 + 4x + 5 < 0$
37. $3x^2 \ge 2x - 5$
38. $-11x \ge 2x^2 + 12$
39. $6x^2 - 6 \le 5x$
40. $12 \le 6x^2 + x$
41. $\dfrac{x - 1}{x + 3} > 0$
42. $\dfrac{x + 4}{x - 2} < 0$
43. $\dfrac{2x + 1}{x + 3} < 0$
44. $\dfrac{4x - 3}{2x + 5} > 0$
45. $\dfrac{x + 5}{x - 1} \ge 2$
46. $\dfrac{1 - x}{3 + x} \le 4$
47. $\dfrac{2x + 7}{8x - 5} > -3$
48. $\dfrac{2 - 3x}{2 + 3x} < -4$
49. $\dfrac{x^2 - x + 2}{x - 1} < x + 3$
50. $\dfrac{x^2 + 2x + 3}{x + 1} < x + 2$
51. $\dfrac{2x^2 + 5x - 1}{2x - 1} \le x + 2$
52. $\dfrac{3x^2 + 8x - 2}{3x - 4} \le x - 2$
53. $(x + 1)(2x - 1)(3x + 4) > 0$
54. $(x - 3)(3x + 1)(2x + 3) > 0$
55. $(3x - 7)(7x + 3)(x + 2) \ge 0$
56. $(2x + 5)(x - 3)(2x - 3) \ge 0$
57. $(x - 4)(x + 2)(2x + 1)(3x - 5) \le 0$
58. $(x - 1)(3x - 8)(x + 2)(5x - 1) \le 0$
59. $(x + 3)(2x - 7)(7x + 2)(x - 4) < 0$
60. $(x - 2)(4x - 7)(x + 1)(2x - 7) < 0$
61. $(x - 1)(2x + 1) < (3x + 1)(x + 2)$
62. $(x + 3)(x - 5) > (2x + 1)(x - 4)$
63. $(2x + 3)(3x - 2) > (4x - 1)(x - 4)$
64. $(x - 5)(x + 2) < (2x - 5)(x - 2)$
65. Find k so that $(k + 1)x^2 - 2kx + 3 = 0$ has two real solutions.
66. Find k so that $(k + 2)x^2 + 5x + 2k - 1 = 0$ has two real solutions.
67. Find k so that $x^2 + (k - 1)x + 3k = 0$ has two complex solutions.
68. Find k so that $kx^2 + (k + 1)x + k + 2 = 0$ has two complex solutions.
69. *Physics* If a shot is fired upward with a velocity of 100 m/s, its height after t s is $-5t^2 + 100t$ m. During what time is it at least 250 m high?
70. *Area* If the length of a rectangle is 4 m more than its width, find all possible lengths so that the area of the rectangle will be at least 25 m².
71. *Economics* If a company sells x items, its total cost is $145x + 245$ and its total income is $2x^2 - 144x + 100$. How many items will it take to show a profit?
72. *Management* If the earnings of a small business are $-x^2 + 160x - 4800$, find the number of units x which produce earnings that are at least 1200.
73. If F and C are the degrees in Fahrenheit and Celsius, then $F = 1.8C + 32$. Which values of C correspond to $68 \le F \le 86$?

74. Suppose that resistances R, R_1, and R_2 satisfy the equation

$$\frac{1}{R} = \frac{1}{R_1} + \frac{1}{R_2}$$

If $R_1 = 15$, find the values of R_2 which make $R \le 10$.

75. Suppose that the force F required to stretch a certain spring a distance of x is $F = 6.5x$. Which values of F will make $\frac{1}{8} \le x \le \frac{7}{8}$?

76. *Management* To determine when to change from double declining balance to straight-line depreciation, solve the following inequality for t:

$$\frac{1}{N - t + 1} \ge \frac{2}{N}$$

77. Suppose $0 < a < b$. Show that $1/a > 1/b$.

78. Suppose $0 < a < b$. Show that $a^2 < b^2$.

79. Suppose $0 < a < b$ and $0 < c < d$. Show that $ac < bd$.

80. Suppose $0 < a < b$. Show that $\sqrt{ab} < (a + b)/2$.

2.8 Equations and Inequalities That Involve Absolute Values

We will now consider some equations and inequalities that involve absolute values. To solve them, we will use the definition of the absolute value of a real number, and so we shall repeat it here.

$$|a| = \begin{cases} a & \text{if } a \ge 0 \\ -a & \text{if } a < 0 \end{cases}$$

▶ **EXAMPLE 1** Solve $|t| = k$, where k is some positive constant.

Solution If $t \ge 0$, then $|t| = t$ and so the given equation becomes $t = k$. However, if $t < 0$, then $|t| = -t$ and so the equation $|t| = k$ becomes $-t = k$, which gives $t = -k$. Therefore the solutions are $t = \pm k$. Note that there are no solutions to the equation $|x| = -2$ since the left-hand side is never negative, whereas the right-hand side is negative. ◀

▶ **EXAMPLE 2** Solve $|3x + 1| = 16$.

Solution Using Example 1 with $t = 3x + 1$ and $k = 16$ gives

$$3x + 1 = 16 \qquad \text{or} \qquad 3x + 1 = -16$$
$$3x = 15 \qquad\qquad\qquad 3x = -17$$
$$x = 5 \qquad\qquad\qquad x = -\tfrac{17}{3}$$

Alternative Solution Another way to solve $|3x + 1| = 16$ is to recall that $|a - b|$ is the distance between a and b. Dividing each side by 3 gives

$$\left|\tfrac{1}{3}(3x + 1)\right| = \tfrac{1}{3}(16)$$
$$\left|x - (-\tfrac{1}{3})\right| = \tfrac{16}{3}$$

This equation means that the distance from x to $-\tfrac{1}{3}$ is $\tfrac{16}{3}$. From Fig. 2.12, we see that

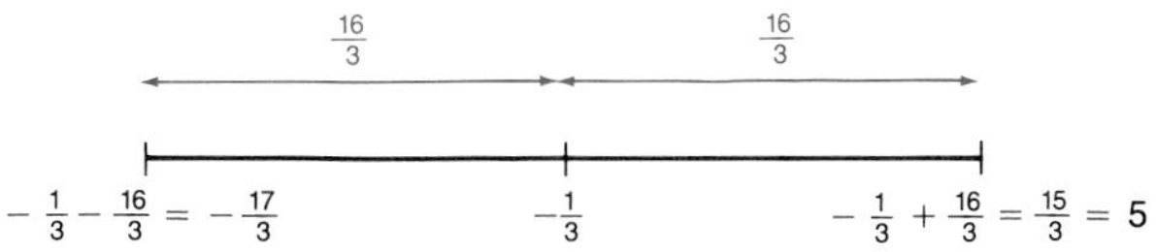

FIGURE 2.12

$$x = -\frac{1}{3} - \frac{16}{3} = -\frac{17}{3} \qquad \text{or} \qquad x = -\frac{1}{3} + \frac{16}{3} = \frac{15}{3} = 5$$

EXAMPLE 3 Solve $|5x - 3| = |2x + 9|$.

Solution Using the definition of absolute value shows that $|t| = |u|$ if and only if $t = \pm u$. Accordingly

$$5x - 3 = 2x + 9 \qquad \text{or} \qquad 5x - 3 = -(2x + 9) = -2x - 9$$

$$3x = 12 \qquad\qquad\qquad 7x = -6$$

$$x = 4 \qquad\qquad\qquad x = -\tfrac{6}{7}$$

Alternative Solution Since $|t|^2 = t^2$, we can square both sides and get

$$(5x - 3)^2 = (2x + 9)^2$$

$$25x^2 - 30x + 9 = 4x^2 + 36x + 81$$

$$21x^2 - 66x - 72 = 0$$

$$7x^2 - 22x - 24 = 0$$

$$(7x + 6)(x - 4) = 0$$

$$x = -\tfrac{6}{7} \qquad \text{or} \qquad x = 4$$

Both roots check in the given equation.

The methods used to solve equations that involve absolute values can be extended to inequalities involving absolute values.

The expression $|ax + b|$ is $ax + b$ if $ax + b$ is positive and is $-(ax + b)$ if $ax + b$ is negative. Thus $|ax + b| < c$ is equivalent to the two inequalities

$$ax + b < c \qquad \text{and} \qquad -(ax + b) < c$$

$$ax + b > -c \qquad \text{multiplying by } -1$$

By combining these two inequalities, we get the following result:

> The inequality $|ax + b| < c$, for $c > 0$, is equivalent to
>
> $$-c < ax + b < c$$

We will use this property to solve inequalities involving absolute values.

EXAMPLE 4 Solve $|3x - 4| \le 5$.

Solution

$$-5 \le 3x - 4 \le 5 \qquad \text{equivalent inequality}$$

$$-1 \le 3x \le 9 \qquad \text{adding } 4$$

$$-\tfrac{1}{3} \le x \le 3 \qquad \text{dividing by 3, } 3 > 0$$

EXAMPLE 5   Solve $|-2x + 7| < 9$.

Solution

$$-9 < -2x + 7 < 9 \qquad \text{equivalent inequality}$$

$$-16 < -2x < 2 \qquad \text{subtracting } 7$$

$$\frac{-16}{-2} > x > \frac{2}{-2} \qquad \text{dividing by } -2, -2 < 0$$

$$8 > x > -1$$

This can be written as the equivalent inequality $-1 < x < 8$, and so the solution is the interval $(-1, 8)$. We could have replaced $|-2x + 7|$ by $|2x - 7|$ at the beginning. This would have avoided the later division by a negative number, which required us to change the sense of the inequality.

The solution of $|-2x + 7| \le 9$ differs from that of $|-2x + 7| < 9$ only in that the endpoints -1 and 8 must also be included in the solution.

The solutions of $|-2x + 7| > 9$ are precisely the real numbers not included in the solution of $|-2x + 7| \le 9$. Therefore the solutions are **complements.** Thus, from Example 5, the solution to $|-2x + 7| > 9$ is all x such that $x < -1$ or $x > 8$. This discussion generalizes into the following statement:

> The solution of the inequality $|ax + b| > c$ is the complement of the solution of $|ax + b| \le c$, for $c > 0$. In other words
>
> $$|ax + b| > c \text{ is equivalent to } ax + b > c \text{ or } ax + b < -c$$

EXAMPLE 6   Solve $|3x + 2| > 4$.

Solution

In keeping with the statement in the box above, the solution of the given inequality is the complement of the solution of $|3x + 2| \le 4$.

$$|3x + 2| \le 4$$

$$-4 \le 3x + 2 \le 4$$

$$-6 \le 3x \le 2$$

$$-2 \le x \le \tfrac{2}{3}$$

The solution of $|3x + 2| \le 4$ is $[-2, \tfrac{2}{3}]$. Thus the solution of the given problem is the complement of $[-2, \tfrac{2}{3}]$, which is $(-\infty, -2) \cup (\tfrac{2}{3}, \infty)$. See Fig. 2.13.

| $x < -2$ | $x > \tfrac{2}{3}$ | $x < 0$ | $x > 2$ |

FIGURE 2.13   **FIGURE 2.14**

▶ **EXAMPLE 7** Solve $|3x - 2| > |x + 2|$.

Solution For positive numbers a and b, $a > b$ if and only if $a^2 > b^2$. Furthermore, $|t|^2 = t^2$. Hence the inequality is equivalent to

$$(3x - 2)^2 > (x + 2)^2$$

$$9x^2 - 12x + 4 > x^2 + 4x + 4 \qquad \text{squaring}$$

$$8x^2 - 16x > 0 \qquad \text{combining terms}$$

$$x^2 - 2x > 0 \qquad \text{dividing by } 8 > 0$$

$$x(x - 2) > 0 \qquad \text{factoring}$$

This inequality may be solved with a sign chart as shown below, or with test values.

Number line		0	2	
Interval	$(-\infty, 0)$	$(0, 2)$	$(2, \infty)$
Sign of x	$-$	$+$	$+$
Sign of $x - 2$	$-$	$-$	$+$
Sign of $x(x - 2)$	$+$	$-$	$+$

The solution is $(-\infty, 0) \cup (2, \infty)$. See Fig. 2.14. ◀

Some inequalities can be seen by inspection to have no solution. This is the case with

$$|6x - 5| < -2$$

since the left-hand side is always positive or zero, but the right-hand side is negative.

EXERCISE 2.8

Solve each of the following equations and inequalities:

1. $|x| = 3$
2. $|x| = 1$
3. $|-x| = 3$
4. $|-x| = -1$
5. $|x - 2| = 3$
6. $|x - 1| = 0$
7. $|-x + 2| = 4$
8. $|x + 3| = 6$
9. $|3x - 2| = 4$
10. $|2x + 3| = 9$
11. $|5x - 1| = 9$
12. $|-5x + 1| = 9$
13. $|-3x + 7| = 5$
14. $|-7x - 13| = 1$
15. $|4x - 6| = -2$
16. $|-4x - 2| = 6$
17. $|x - 2| = |x + 1|$
18. $|x - 3| = |-x + 1|$
19. $|x - 3| = |-x + 3|$
20. $|x + 4| = |x - 6|$
21. $|2x - 5| = |x + 4|$
22. $|3x + 7| = |2x - 3|$
23. $|4x + 3| = |3x + 4|$
24. $|5x - 2| = |3x + 4|$
25. $|x| < 2$
26. $|x| < 5$
27. $|x| > 3$
28. $|x| > 7$
29. $|x + 3| < 4$
30. $|x - 2| < 6$
31. $|x - 5| \leq 3$
32. $|x + 7| \leq 5$
33. $|2x - 1| \geq 5$
34. $|3x - 5| \geq 1$
35. $|3x + 4| > 2$
36. $|5x - 7| > -3$
37. $|-x + 2| < 3$
38. $|-2x - 1| \leq 5$
39. $|-3x + 5| \geq 2$
40. $|-5x + 3| > 2$
41. $|x + 2| < |x - 4|$
42. $|x - 1| < |x - 3|$
43. $|2x - 3| < |2x + 1|$
44. $|2x - 1| > |-2x + 1|$
45. $|3x - 4| \geq |3x + 6|$
46. $|3x + 2| \leq |2x + 3|$
47. $|4x + 1| \geq |2x - 3|$
48. $|5x - 2| \geq |3x + 4|$

2.9 Key Concepts

Make sure you understand each of the following important words and ideas.

Equation (p. 71)
Root (p. 72)
Solution (p. 72)
Solution set (p. 72)
Conditional equation (p. 72)
Identity (p. 72)
Equivalent equations (p. 72)
Linear equation in one variable
  (p. 72)
$a = b$ and $a + c = b + c$ are
  equivalent (p. 73)
$a = b$ and $ac = bc$, $c \neq 0$ are
  equivalent (p. 73)
How to solve stated problems (pp. 79,
  110)
Complex numbers (p. 91)
Quadratic equation (p. 96)

Solution by factoring (p. 97)
Completing the square (p. 98)
Solution by the quadratic formula
  (p. 99)
Use of the discriminant to determine
  the nature of the roots (p. 101)
Sum and product of the roots (p. 102)
Writing an equation given its roots
  (p. 102)
Equations and problems leading to
  quadratic equations (pp. 104, 109)
Fractional equation (p. 107)
Inequality (p. 115)
Equivalent inequalities (p. 116)
Nonlinear inequalities (p. 117)
Sign chart and test values (p. 118)

(2.1) $x = \dfrac{-b}{a}$ is the solution to $ax + b = 0$, if $a \neq 0$

(2.2) $x = \dfrac{-b \pm \sqrt{b^2 - 4ac}}{2a}$ quadratic formula

(2.3) $r + s = \dfrac{-b}{a}$ sum of the roots

(2.4) $rs = \dfrac{c}{a}$ product of the roots

$a < b$ is equivalent to

$$a + c < b + c \qquad \text{for any real } c$$

$$ac < bc \qquad \text{for } c > 0$$

$$ac > bc \qquad \text{for } c < 0$$

EXERCISE 2.9   Review

Are the following pairs of equations or inequalities
equivalent?

1. $3x = 2x + 7$
        $1.5x = 7$
2. $2x + 5 = 7x + 10$
        $x + 11 = 3x + 15$
3. $|2x + 1| = 7$
        $2x + 1 = 7$
4. $-5x < 15$
        $x < -3$
5. $(3x - 1)/(8 - x) > 0$
        $(3x - 1)(8 - x) > 0$
6. $7x + 3 < 4x + 6$
        $2x + 9 > 5x + 6$

Solve the equations in Probs. 7 to 44.

7. $3x - 2 = x + 4$
8. $5x + 3 = 2x - 3$
9. $5(x + 3) = 4(2x + 1) + 5$

10. $3(x - 1) = 4(x - 3) + 4$
11. $2(x - 3)/3 = (x + 6)/6$
12. $5(3x - 8)/8 = (x + 12)/2$
13. $4(2x/3 - 9/4) = 3(3x/5 + 4/3)$
14. $2(7x/9 - 3/2) = 3(x/3 + 7/3)$
15. $\dfrac{23x + 7}{5} = \dfrac{4x + 5}{3} + x + 2$
16. $\dfrac{2x - 6}{3} = \dfrac{3x - 6}{2} - x + 5$
17. $\dfrac{x + 2}{x - 2} = \dfrac{x + 8}{x}$　　18. $\dfrac{6x + 2}{2x - 1} = \dfrac{3x + 7}{x + 1}$
19. $\dfrac{2}{x + 2} + \dfrac{1}{x - 2} = \dfrac{16}{x^2 - 4}$
20. $\dfrac{12}{x - 8} - \dfrac{7}{x - 5} = \dfrac{56}{x^2 - 13x + 40}$
21. $16x^2 = 1$　　　　22. $16x^2 = x$
23. $6x^2 - 5x - 4 = 0$　　24. $9x^2 + 18x + 2 = 0$
25. $x^2 - 4x + 1 = 0$　　26. $4x^2 + 12x + 3 = 0$
27. $x^2 - 4x + 7 = 0$　　28. $4x^2 - 20x + 34 = 0$
29. $16x^2 + 8x + 5 = 0$　　30. $24x^2 - 2x - 15 = 0$
31. $7(x - 5)^2 + 189 = 0$　　32. $x^4 - 10x^2 + 9 = 0$
33. $2(x^2 - 4x)^2 - 5(x^2 - 4x) - 3 = 0$
34. $x - 3\sqrt{x} - 4 = 0$
35. $\sqrt{3x + 1} = x - 1$
36. $\sqrt{4x - 3} + \sqrt{2x - 2} = 5$
37. $\dfrac{2x + 2}{2x - 3} = \dfrac{3x + 2}{x + 3}$
38. $\dfrac{4}{x - 1} + \dfrac{6}{x - 2} = 3$
39. $|x + 3| = 4$　　　40. $|-2x + 1| = 7$
41. $|x + 2| = |2x + 1|$　　42. $|5x - 4| = |2x + 8|$
43. Solve $F = 32 + 9C/5$ for C.
44. Solve $S = (n/2)(a + L)$ for L.

Solve the inequalities in Probs. 45 to 58.
45. $3x - 5 > x + 1$　　46. $5x + 2 > 8x - 4$
47. $4x + 3 < x + 6$　　48. $7x - 9 < 2x + 11$
49. $(2x - 1)(3x + 7) < 0$
50. $(5x - 8)(3x + 1) > 0$
51. $\dfrac{5x + 9}{6x - 5} > 0$　　52. $\dfrac{3x - 7}{7x + 3} < 0$
53. $(x + 2)(x - 4)(2x + 9) < 0$
54. $(3x + 8)(2x - 5)(5x + 3) > 0$
55. $|x + 3| < 4$　　　56. $|-2x + 1| > 7$
57. $|x + 2| > |2x + 1|$　　58. $|5x - 4| < |2x + 11|$

59. The correct formula for converting from Celsius to Fahrenheit temperature is $F = 1.8C + 32$, but a much easier approximate mental calculation is obtained by using

$$f = 2C + 30$$

Show that $|F - f| < 5°$ if $5° < F < 95°$.
60. Divide 48 into two parts so that their product is 287.
61. Divide 48 into two parts so that their product is 576.
62. Find the value of $6 - 3x - 2x^2$ when x is the average of the roots of $6 - 3x - 2x^2 = 0$.
63. Find the sum and product of the roots of the equation

$$-3x^2 + 8x - 14 = 0$$

64. Find the sum and product of the roots of the equation

$$5x^2 + 6x - 9 = 0$$

65. Find k so that there are two real roots of

$$(k - 2)x^2 + 4x - 2k + 1 = 0$$

66. Solve the inequality $10x^2 - 29x + 10 < 0$.
67. Solve the inequality $16x^2 - 24x + 11 > 0$.
68. Find the quadratic equation whose roots are $\frac{4}{3}$ and $-\frac{3}{5}$.
69. Find the quadratic equation whose roots are $2 \pm 3i$.
70. Is the quadratic $24x^2 + 106x - 105$ factorable with rational coefficients in the factors?

71. *Physics*　A projectile is $S = -5t^2 + 18t + 20$ m high after t s.
   (a) When is it 25 m high?
   (b) When is it 36.2 m high, which is its maximum height?
72. Show that the roots of $ax^2 + bx + c = 0$ are the reciprocals of the roots of $cx^2 + bx + a = 0$, if $a \neq 0$ and $c \neq 0$.
73. Show that the two roots of $ax^2 + bx + a = 0$ are reciprocals of each other.
74. Show that the roots of $ax^2 + bx + c = 0$ are the negatives of the roots of $ax^2 - bx + c = 0$.
75. Show that the average of the roots of $ax^2 + bx + c = 0$ is the x coordinate of the maximum or minimum point of $y = ax^2 + bx + c$.
76. Show that the sum of the roots equals the product of the roots in the equation $ax^2 + bx - b = 0$.
77. Suppose that a, b, and c are rational. Show that

$$ax^2 + bx + c = 0$$

cannot have one rational root and one irrational root. *Hint:* Suppose p is rational, y is irrational, and $ap^2 + bp + c = 0 = ay^2 + by + c$. Then $ap^2 - ay^2 = by - bp$. Solve this for y, and arrive at a contradiction. (This proves the statement.)

78. Assume that $ax^2 + bx + c$ has a, b, and c rational. Let $D = b^2 - 4ac$. Why is it true that

(i) D is a perfect square if and only if $ax^2 + bx + c$ can be factored with rational coefficients in the factors?

(ii) $D = 0$ if and only if $ax^2 + bx + c$ is the perfect square $(px + q)^2$ with p and q rational?

79. Show that the roots of $ax^2 + bx + c = 0$, given by the quadratic formula (2.2) may also be written

$$x = \frac{2c}{-b \pm \sqrt{b^2 - 4ac}}$$

This is very useful in numerical work if a is close to zero, since in that case the standard formula involves division by a, which is a very small number, leading to a possibly large error.

3 Graphs and Functions

Graphs are frequently used in national magazines and newspapers to present information about things such as the world's busiest airports (O'Hare in Chicago is first, Heathrow in London is sixth), about advertising-dollar receivers in the United States (newspapers are first, radio is fourth), and about NCAA men's golf team title winners (Yale is first, Houston is second). The function concept is very closely connected to graphs, and functions are at the heart of mathematics. Both graphs and functions provide a lot of information in a format that is easy to understand. Extensive applications occur in this chapter using lines and circles, as well as functions and variation. There are problems from areas such as business, education, anthropology, geometry, photography, navigation, and the sciences.

3.1 The Cartesian Coordinate System

Many relationships between two variables are shown by graphs. Some of the many examples are blood pressure and time, profit and production, ACT score and raw score on the test, area and radius of a circle, and distance and time. A two-dimensional coordinate system is used to draw graphs. This is an extension of the one-dimensional number line introduced in Chap. 1.

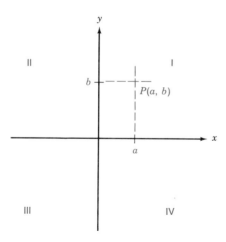

FIGURE 3.1

The rectangular coordinate system presented here is the most commonly used method for the plane. Another standard method is polar coordinates, which uses trigonometry. Our present method was invented by the French mathematician and philosopher René Descartes (1596–1650), and it is called the **cartesian** or **rectangular coordinate system** for the plane. To set up this system, we first draw two perpendicular number lines in the plane. The unit of length on these lines may be the same or different. The two lines are called the **coordinate axes,** and their point of intersection is called the **origin.** Usually one line, the **x axis,** is drawn horizontally with positive direction to the right. Then the **y axis** is drawn vertically with positive direction upward. The coordinate axes divide the plane into four parts called **quadrants,** and they are numbered I, II, III, and IV in a counterclockwise direction as in Fig. 3.1.

If a and b are real numbers, then (a, b) is called an **ordered pair** if the order in which they are written makes a difference.

$$(a, b) = (c, d) \quad \text{means} \quad a = c \text{ and } b = d \quad (3.1)$$

For instance $(4, 1) \neq (1, 4)$; and $(-12, b) = (-12, 33)$ if and only if $b = 33$.

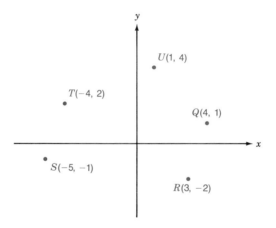

FIGURE 3.2

Every point in a coordinate plane can be assigned a specific ordered pair of numbers. Starting with the point P, as in Fig. 3.1, draw vertical and horizontal lines through P. These lines will cut the x axis at a and the y axis at b. We assign to P the ordered pair (a, b). Conversely, starting with the ordered pair (a, b), we locate a point in the plane by drawing a vertical line through a on the x axis and a horizontal line through b on the y axis. The point is found at the intersection of these two lines. See points $Q(4, 1)$, $R(3, -2)$, $S(-5, -1)$, and $T(-4, 2)$ in Fig. 3.2. Note $Q(4, 1) \neq U(1, 4)$.

NOTE   We have thus established a **1-1 correspondence** between the set of all points in the plane and the set of all ordered pairs of real numbers. The notation "1-1" is read "one-to-one." For each point there is one ordered pair, and for each ordered pair there is one point. Because of the correspondence, we often use the ordered pair as a name for the corresponding point. The two numbers in the ordered pair are called the **coordinates** of the point, the first one being the **abscissa** or **x coordinate,** and the second the **ordinate** or **y coordinate.** Notice that the *abscissas are positive in the first and fourth quadrants*; thus $(\frac{3}{7}, \frac{2}{9})$ and $(5.63, -81.22)$ are in quadrants I and IV, respectively. *Ordinates are positive in the first and second quadrants*; $(24, 7.1)$ and $(-6, 13)$ are in quadrants I and II, respectively.

◢ **EXAMPLE 1**   Describe in words the set of points in the plane with coordinates $(7, y)$.

Solution   Each x coordinate is 7, but the y coordinate can be any real number. This describes the vertical line 7 units to the right of the y axis.   ◢

NOTE   The standard notation $P(a, b)$ or (a, b) for a point opens the door to possible confusion since (a, b) also has been used for the open interval from a to b. It will usually be very clear from the situation which one is meant.

The Distance Formula

The pythagorean theorem may be used to find a formula for the distance between any two points in the plane. To begin, suppose that two points have the same x coordinate, say $(12, 19)$ and $(12, 3)$. Then the points are both on the same vertical line, and the distance between them is

$$|19 - 3| = |3 - 19| = 16$$

Similarly, the following statements are true. See Fig. 3.3.

Vertical
Horizontal

> The distance between (x_2, y_1) and (x_2, y_2) is $|y_2 - y_1|$.
> The distance between (x_2, y_1) and (x_1, y_1) is $|x_2 - x_1|$.

Recall the following fact from plane geometry. The pythagorean theorem and its converse say that a triangle with sides a, b, and c (c the largest) is a right triangle if and only if $a^2 + b^2 = c^2$. We will apply this theorem to the two points $P_1(x_1, y_1)$ and $P_2(x_2, y_2)$, as in Fig. 3.3.

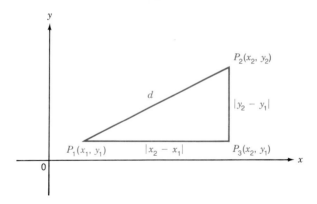

FIGURE 3.3

Now consider any two points $P_1(x_1, y_1)$ and $P_2(x_2, y_2)$, again as in Fig. 3.3. The point $P_3(x_2, y_1)$ is determined by a horizontal line through P_1 and a vertical line through P_2, and thus these three points form a right triangle. As above

The distance from P_3 to P_2 is $\left| y_2 - y_1 \right|$

The distance from P_3 to P_1 is $\left| x_2 - x_1 \right|$

Since $|t|^2 = t^2$ for any real number t, we use the pythagorean theorem to find that

$$(P_1 P_2)^2 = (P_1 P_3)^2 + (P_3 P_2)^2$$
$$= (x_2 - x_1)^2 + (y_2 - y_1)^2$$

The distance formula

> The distance d between the two points $P_1(x_1, y_1)$ and $P_2(x_2, y_2)$ in a coordinate plane is
>
> $$d = \sqrt{(x_2 - x_1)^2 + (y_2 - y_1)^2} \qquad (3.2)$$

EXAMPLE 2   Find the distance between $(3, -8)$ and $(-2, 4)$.

Solution   Using the distance formula, we see that the distance is

$$\sqrt{[3 - (-2)]^2 + (-8 - 4)^2} = \sqrt{25 + 144} = \sqrt{169} = 13$$

NOTE   Whether we write $(x_2 - x_1)^2$ or $(x_1 - x_2)^2$ is immaterial since $(x_2 - x_1)^2 = (x_1 - x_2)^2 = |x_1 - x_2|^2$. The same is true for y values.

EXAMPLE 3   Find the distance between $(-7, 14)$ and $(-1, 12)$.

Solution   The distance is

$$\sqrt{(-7 + 1)^2 + (14 - 12)^2} = \sqrt{36 + 4} = \sqrt{40} = \sqrt{4(10)} = 2\sqrt{10}$$

This is the *exact* distance. A decimal *approximation* by calculator is 6.32456.

EXAMPLE 4   Show that the triangle with vertices $A(17, 4)$, $B(12, 7)$, and $C(23, 14)$ is a right triangle.

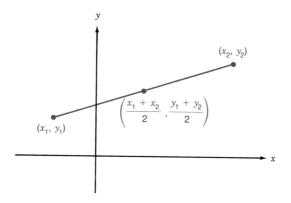

FIGURE 3.4

Solution By the distance formula

$$[d(A, B)]^2 = (17 - 12)^2 + (4 - 7)^2 = 25 + 9 = 34$$

$$[d(B, C)]^2 = (12 - 23)^2 + (7 - 14)^2 = 121 + 49 = 170$$

$$[d(A, C)]^2 = (17 - 23)^2 + (4 - 14)^2 = 36 + 100 = 136$$

Since $34 + 136 = 170$, then the converse of the pythagorean theorem says that it is a right triangle with the $90°$ angle at the point $A(17, 4)$. ◢

Midpoint Formula

We will now give the formula for the midpoint of the line segment joining any two points in the plane. See Fig. 3.4.

Midpoint formula

> If (x_1, y_1) and (x_2, y_2) are two given points, then the **midpoint of the line segment** joining them is
>
> $$\left(\frac{x_1 + x_2}{2}, \frac{y_1 + y_2}{2}\right) \qquad (3.3)$$

Although we could give a proof now using similar triangles, we will delay proving this result until Sec. 3.5 when we study the straight line. See Prob. 85 in Exercise 3.7. For now, you should verify by the distance formula that the distance from M to P_1 equals the distance from M to P_2, where M is the midpoint given in Eq. (3.3) and P_1 and P_2 are the given points.

▶ **EXAMPLE 5** Find the midpoint of the line segment with endpoints $(12, 7)$ and $(-4, 21)$.

Solution By the midpoint formula we have

$$\left(\frac{12 - 4}{2}, \frac{7 + 21}{2}\right) = \left(\frac{8}{2}, \frac{28}{2}\right) = (4, 14) \qquad ◢$$

▶ **EXAMPLE 6** The points $A(5, 1)$, $B(11, 2)$, $C(8, 7)$, and $D(2, 6)$ taken in the given order are the vertices of a parallelogram. Show that the diagonals AC and BD bisect each other.

Solution   We only need to show that the midpoints of *AC* and *BD* are the same point (midpoint implies bisect):

$$\text{Midpoint of } AC \text{ is } \left(\frac{5+8}{2}, \frac{1+7}{2}\right) = \left(\frac{13}{2}, \frac{8}{2}\right) = \left(\frac{13}{2}, 4\right)$$

$$\text{Midpoint of } BD \text{ is } \left(\frac{11+2}{2}, \frac{2+6}{2}\right) = \left(\frac{13}{2}, \frac{8}{2}\right) = \left(\frac{13}{2}, 4\right)$$

◀

EXERCISE 3.1

In which quadrant is the given point?
1. $(18, -5)$ 2. $(6, 111)$
3. $(-43, 61)$ 4. $(-99, -55)$
5. $(-10, -66)$ 6. $(14, -92)$
7. $(-17, -76)$ 8. $(-19, 45)$

Plot the points in Probs. 9 to 16.
9. $(-6, 4)$ 10. $(-4, -3)$
11. $(0, 2)$ 12. $(6, -1)$
13. $(3, 3)$ 14. $(-2, -3)$
15. $(5, -4)$ 16. $(-4, 0)$

Describe in words the given set of points in the plane.
17. All $(x, 0)$ with x real
18. All $(0, y)$ with y negative
19. All (x, y) with $x > 0$, $y < 0$
20. All $(x, 4)$ with x real
21. $y > 5$ 22. $xy > 0$
23. $x = -2$ 24. $xy = 0$

In Probs. 25 to 36, find the distance between the two points, and also the midpoint of the line segment joining them.
25. $(6, 4)$ and $(-8, 2)$ 26. $(8, -5)$ and $(4, 3)$
27. $(9, 4)$ and $(-3, 8)$ 28. $(5, 7)$ and $(7, -5)$
29. $(3, 7)$ and $(8, -5)$
30. $(-4, -8)$ and $(-12, 7)$
31. $(6, -2)$ and $(-1, 22)$
32. $(10, 0)$ and $(-10, -21)$
33. $(-11, -3)$ and $(-5, 2)$
34. $(5, 5)$ and $(8, -2)$
35. $(-9, 4)$ and $(4, 6)$
36. $(2, -5)$ and $(-7, -1)$

In Probs. 37 to 40, find the other endpoint of the line segment having the given midpoint and endpoint.
37. midpoint $(7, 3)$, endpoint $(2, 4)$

38. midpoint $(6, -2)$, endpoint $(1, 2)$
39. midpoint $(\frac{1}{2}, 4)$, endpoint $(3, -3)$
40. midpoint $(5, -1)$, endpoint $(\frac{1}{2}, 2)$

In Probs. 41 to 44, show that the given points are the vertices of a right triangle. What is the area of the triangle?
41. $(3, 7)$, $(5, 4)$, $(8, 6)$
42. $(4, 0)$, $(9, 3)$, $(-2, 10)$
43. $(5, -1)$, $(2, 5)$, $(-1, -4)$
44. $(0, 7)$, $(-6, 2)$, $(-1, -4)$

In Probs. 45 to 48, use the distance formula to show that the given points are on the same line.
45. $F(1, 5)$, $S(2, 7)$, $T(4, 11)$
46. $F(-2, -3)$, $S(2, -1)$, $T(8, 2)$
47. $F(0, 1)$, $S(3, 3)$, $T(9, 7)$
48. $F(2, 2)$, $S(-8, -2)$, $T(7, 4)$
49. If A is $(-1, 2)$ and B is $(7, 8)$, find the point that is $\frac{3}{4}$ of the way from A to B. *Hint:* Use the midpoint formula twice.
50. If A is $(1, -5)$ and B is $(9, 11)$, find the point that is $\frac{7}{8}$ of the way from A to B. *Hint:* Use the midpoint formula three times.
51. Show that $ABCD$ is a square where $A = (4, 3)$, $B = (7, 5)$, $C = (5, 8)$, and $D = (2, 6)$. *Hint:* Use the distance formula to show that all four sides have equal length and that the angle at A is a right angle.
52. Show that $ABCD$ is a rhombus where $A = (-4, 3)$, $B = (5, 6)$, $C = (8, 15)$, and $D = (-1, 12)$. *Hint:* Use the distance formula to show that all four sides have equal length.
53. The points $A(1, 1)$, $B(7, 2)$, $C(9, 6)$, and $D(3, 5)$ taken in the given order are the vertices of a parallelogram. Show that the diagonals AC and BD bisect each other.
54. The points $A(-4, -3)$, $B(2, -5)$, $C(5, 3)$, and

$D(-1, 5)$ taken in the given order are the vertices of a parallelogram. Show that the diagonals AC and BD bisect each other.

55. Show that $A(9, 5)$ is equidistant from $P(8, -2)$ and $Q(2, 6)$, but is not their midpoint.

56. Show that the midpoint of the hypotenuse of a right triangle is equidistant from all three vertices. *Hint:* Place the right triangle in the plane so that its vertices are

$$A(2a, 0) \qquad B(0, 2b) \qquad \text{and} \qquad O(0, 0)$$

57. Write an equation, not containing radicals, which is satisfied by all points (x, y) which are 3 units from $(5, -10)$.

58. Write an equation, not containing radicals, which is satisfied by all points (x, y) which are equidistant from $(-2, 5)$ and $(3, -6)$.

59. Show that the distance from M to P_1 equals the distance from M to P_2, where $P_1 = (x_1, y_1)$, $P_2 = (x_2, y_2)$, and

$$M = \left(\frac{x_1 + x_2}{2}, \frac{y_1 + y_2}{2} \right)$$

60. Use the distance formula to show that if $P(x, y)$ is equidistant from $Q(1, 4)$ and $R(6, 2)$, then $10x - 4y = 23$. Show that the midpoint $S(\frac{7}{2}, 3)$ satisfies this equation, as do

$$T(-1, -\tfrac{33}{4}) \qquad \text{and} \qquad V(3.9, 4)$$

3.2 Graphs

In our visually oriented culture, pictures are an essential means of communication. Just think of the various weather maps appearing daily in the newspapers and on TV, maps which show temperatures, moisture, the jet stream, and other interesting items. By using the rectangular coordinate system, we can produce a geometric picture of an equation, an inequality, or any set of ordered pairs of real numbers. This picture is called a graph, and in this chapter we shall concentrate on the graph of an equation.

Graph of an equation

> The **graph of an equation** is the set of all points $P(x, y)$ whose coordinates x and y satisfy the equation.

In this section, we will draw the graph of an equation by plotting, or locating, points in the plane. After plotting a sufficient number of points, **connect them in a reasonable order.** It helps to make a **table of values** with increasing x values or y values. A pattern will usually emerge if enough points are included and if nearby points are joined together.

In later sections and chapters of this book, we will encounter equations that can be graphed both quickly and accurately by recognizing certain standard forms. We will also learn how to make several basic modifications of them. There are more advanced methods, but they require calculus.

▶ **EXAMPLE 1** Sketch the graph of the equation $3x + 4y = 12$.

Solution Later in this chapter, we will be able to identify this as the equation of a straight line. Although two points are sufficient to determine a line, we will use four points here since this is our first example. We first choose several values of x, not all close together, and then use the equation to find the corresponding values of y. See Fig. 3.5.

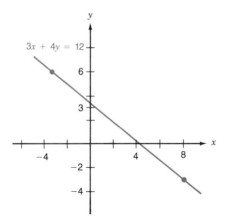

FIGURE 3.5

x	-4	0	4	8
y	6	3	0	-3

The **graph of the equation $y = x$** is shown in Fig. 3.6. This is a *basic graph* which will occur again. Try to graph it yourself by making a table of values.

Points that are especially useful are located where the graph crosses the x axis or the y axis. The x coordinate of a point where the graph crosses the x axis is called an **x intercept.** Similarly, the y coordinate of a point where the graph crosses the y axis is called a **y intercept.** In Example 1, the x intercept is 4 and the y intercept is 3.

> Find the x intercepts by setting $y = 0$ in the equation and solving for x. Similarly find the y intercept by setting $x = 0$ and solving for y.

A graph may have no intercepts, one, or more than one.

EXAMPLE 2   Sketch the graph of the equation $y = x^2 - 2x - 2$.

Solution   This time we *need* several points since the graph is not a straight line. We make our table of values by choosing values for x and then finding the corresponding y from

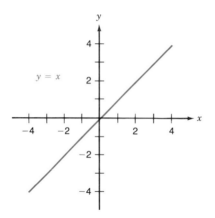

FIGURE 3.6

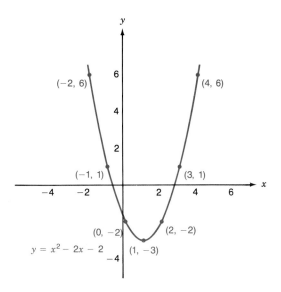

FIGURE 3.7

the equation. Afterwards we plot the points just identified and connect them with a smooth curve. The curve in Fig. 3.7 is a portion of the complete graph, which would extend indefinitely far both left and right.

x	-2	-1	0	1	2	3	4
y	6	1	-2	-3	-2	1	6

The graph in Example 2 is called a **parabola,** which will be treated at length in Chap. 4. Parabolas can open upward as in Fig. 3.7, downward, to the right, or to the left. Figure 3.8 shows the graph of $y = x^2$. This is a *basic graph* which will occur again. Try to graph it yourself by making a table of values.

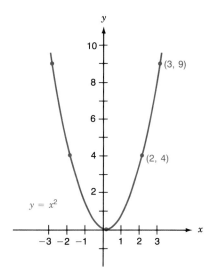

FIGURE 3.8

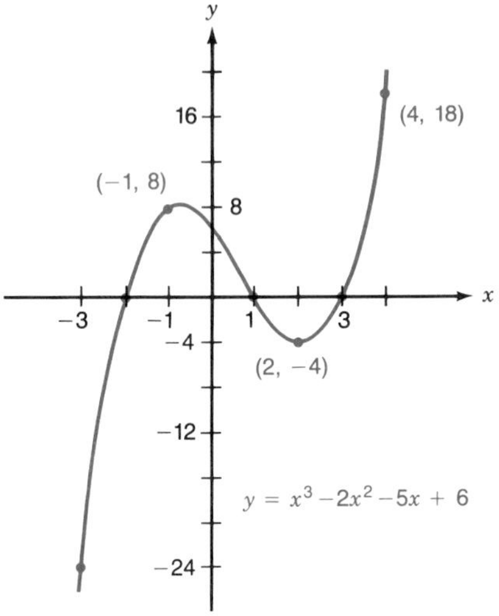

FIGURE 3.9

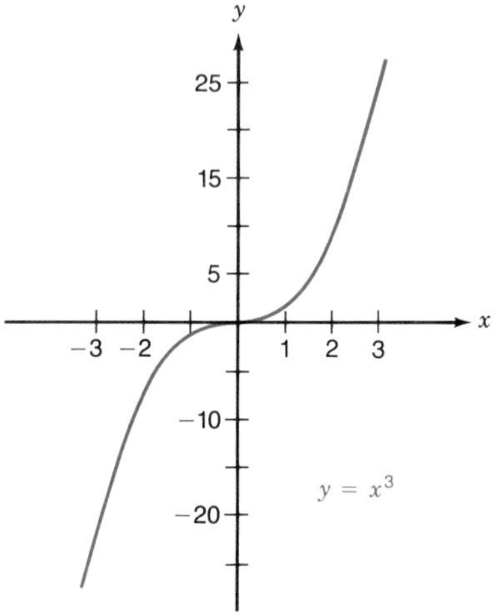

FIGURE 3.10

EXAMPLE 3 Sketch the graph of the equation $y = x^3 - 2x^2 - 5x + 6$.

Solution We plot points from the table of values below, being careful to choose values for x which are spread out enough. This is the graph of a cubic, which we will see again in the next chapter. The x intercepts are -2, 1, and 3, and the y intercept is 6. There is no largest or smallest y value. See Fig. 3.9.

x	-3	-2	-1	0	1	2	3	4
y	-24	0	8	6	0	-4	0	18

Remember that **different scales** can be used on the two axes. In Fig. 3.10, we show another *basic graph,* $y = x^3$. Try to sketch the graph yourself.

EXAMPLE 4 Sketch the graph of the equation $y = x^4 - 10x^2 + 9$.

Solution The table of values is given below, and the graph is shown in Fig. 3.11. This is the equation of a polynomial, which will be discussed in the next chapter. In fact all of the graphs so far in this section are graphs of polynomials. There is no largest y value here, but there is a smallest one. Methods from calculus show that it is -16 and that it occurs for $x = \pm\sqrt{5}$.

x	0	± 1	± 2	$\pm\sqrt{5} \approx \pm 2.236$	± 3	$\pm\sqrt{12} \approx \pm 3.464$
y	9	0	-15	-16	0	33

An important expression in areas such as the theory of numbers is $[x]$, which represents the greatest integer that is less than or equal to x. For instance, $[\frac{1}{2}] = 0$, $[3.45] = 3$, $[2] = 2$, $[-3.45] = -4$, and $[-\frac{1}{3}] = -1$.

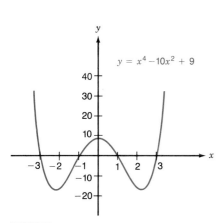

FIGURE 3.11

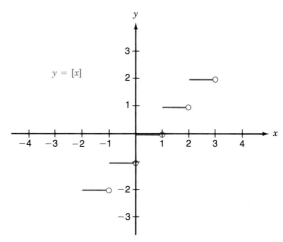

FIGURE 3.12

▶ **EXAMPLE 5** Draw the graph of the equation $y = [x]$.

Solution We can give a table of values in this form, using intervals:

x in	$[-2, -1)$	$[-1, 0)$	$[0, 1)$	$[1, 2)$	$[2, 3)$
y	-2	-1	0	1	2

The graph is shown in Fig. 3.12. The open circle on the right of each segment means that the point is not on the graph. ◢

▶ **EXAMPLE 6** Sketch the graph of $y = \sqrt{x}$ and $y = |x|$.

Solution In the table of values on page 140, notice that $\sqrt{x}$ is not defined for $x < 0$. The graphs are shown in Figs. 3.13 and 3.14. In Fig. 3.13, the graph of $y = \sqrt{x}$ is represented by the solid curve only. However, the solid and dashed parts together make up the graph of $y^2 = x$. This is due to the fact that $\sqrt{x}$ is never negative.

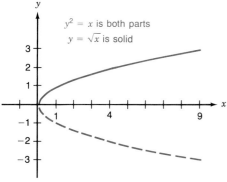

FIGURE 3.13

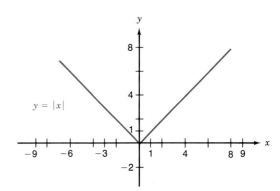

FIGURE 3.14

x	-9	-6	-3	0	1	4	9
$\sqrt{x}$				0	1	2	3
$|x|$	9	6	3	0	1	4	9

The graph of $y = |x|$ is actually parts of two lines; it is the graph of $y = x$ for $x \geq 0$ and of $y = -x$ for $x < 0$. ◢

Circles

In order to sketch the graph of $x^2 + y^2 = 169$, notice first that x^2 must be less than or equal to 169, and thus $-13 \leq x \leq 13$. The same is true of y. We will use some of these values of x to make the following table of values. See Fig. 3.15 for the graph.

x	0	± 5	± 12	± 13
y	± 13	± 12	± 5	0

◢

The graph in Fig. 3.15 is a circle with center at the origin and radius 13. We can generalize this result to a circle with any center and any radius. By definition, a **circle** is the set of all points in a plane that are equidistant from a fixed point. If the center is the point $C(h, k)$ and the radius is the positive number r, then the point $P(x, y)$ will be on the circle if $d(C, P) = r$. Using the distance formula for $d(C, P)$, we have

$$\sqrt{(x - h)^2 + (y - k)^2} = r$$

After squaring both sides, we have the result below.

Standard form

The *standard form* for the equation of a circle with center (h, k) and radius r is

$$(x - h)^2 + (y - k)^2 = r^2 \tag{3.4}$$

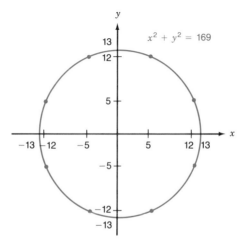

FIGURE 3.15

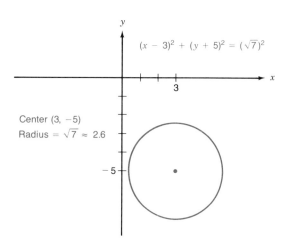

$(x - 3)^2 + (y + 5)^2 = (\sqrt{7})^2$

Center $(3, -5)$
Radius $= \sqrt{7} \approx 2.6$

FIGURE 3.16

▶ **EXAMPLE 7**   Describe the graph of the equation $(x - 3)^2 + (y + 5)^2 = 7$.

Solution   The graph of the equation $(x - 3)^2 + (y + 5)^2 = 7 = (\sqrt{7})^2$ is a circle with center $(3, -5)$ and radius $\sqrt{7}$. See Fig. 3.16.   ◀

If the equation is not given in standard form, we can put it in standard form by **completing the square** in the x terms and y terms separately. Squaring the terms on the left-hand side of Eq. (3.4) and then combining terms produces the following result.

General form

> The *general form* of the equation of a circle is
> $$ax^2 + ay^2 + cx + dy + e = 0$$

Note especially that x^2 and y^2 have the *same coefficient* in the general form of the equation of a circle.

▶ **EXAMPLE 8**   Write $2x^2 + 2y^2 + 8x - 10y - 3 = 0$ in standard form, and draw the graph.

Solution   We first divide by 2, the common coefficient of x^2 and y^2 in order to make their coefficients 1:

$$x^2 + y^2 + 4x - 5y - \tfrac{3}{2} = 0 \qquad \text{dividing by 2}$$

$$x^2 + 4x + y^2 - 5y = \tfrac{3}{2} \qquad \text{grouping } x \text{ and } y \text{ terms}$$

Remember that we **complete the square** by *adding the square of half the coefficient* of x (or of y) to both sides of the equation to produce an equation equivalent to the given one:

$$x^2 + 4x + (\tfrac{4}{2})^2 + y^2 - 5y + (-\tfrac{5}{2})^2 = \tfrac{3}{2} + (\tfrac{4}{2})^2 + (-\tfrac{5}{2})^2$$

$$x^2 + 4x + 4 + y^2 - 5y + \tfrac{25}{4} = \tfrac{3}{2} + 4 + \tfrac{25}{4}$$

$$(x + 2)^2 + \left(y - \frac{5}{2}\right) = \frac{6 + 16 + 25}{4} = \frac{47}{4}$$

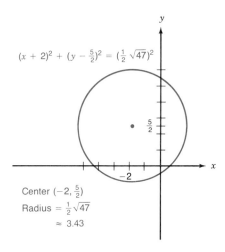

$(x + 2)^2 + (y - \frac{5}{2})^2 = (\frac{1}{2}\sqrt{47})^2$

Center $(-2, \frac{5}{2})$
Radius $= \frac{1}{2}\sqrt{47}$
≈ 3.43

FIGURE 3.17

Thus the circle has its center at $(-2, \frac{5}{2})$ and a radius of

$$\sqrt{\tfrac{47}{4}} = \tfrac{1}{2}\sqrt{47} \approx 3.43 \qquad \text{using a calculator}$$

See Fig. 3.17 for the graph.

If, after completing the square, the equation is

$$(x - h)^2 + (y - k)^2 = E$$

where E is negative, there is *no graph*. If $E = 0$, then (h, k) is the only point on the graph.

Circles are very important in trigonometry, and in other areas of mathematics as well. This is especially true of the **unit circle** $x^2 + y^2 = 1$, whose radius is 1 and center is $(0, 0)$. It is shown in geometry that a circle with radius r has area πr^2 and circumference $2\pi r$.

EXERCISE 3.2

Draw the graphs of the equations in Probs. 1 to 28.

1. $3x + 5y = 15$
2. $x - 4y = 8$
3. $-4x + 3y = 6$
4. $6x + y = 6$
5. $4y = x^2 + 4x + 8$
6. $4y = -x^2 + 2x - 7$
7. $2y = x^2 + 2x - 1$
8. $8y = x^2 + 6x - 15$
9. $2x = -y^2 + 4y - 8$
10. $4x = y^2 + 2y + 9$
11. $8x = y^2 + 2y - 15$
12. $-6x = y^2 - 4y + 10$
13. $y = x^3 - 2x^2 - x + 2$
14. $y = x^3 + x^2 - 4x - 4$
15. $4y = x^3 + 3x^2 + 3x - 8$
16. $3y = x^3 - 3x^2 + 4x + 1$
17. $2y = x^4 - 13x^2 + 36$
18. $4y = 4x^4 - 25x^2 + 21$

19. $y = x^4 - 15x^2 - 10x + 24$
20. $y = x^4 - 9x^2 - 4x + 12$
21. $y = x + |x|$
22. $y = x|x|$
23. $y = |x + 2| + |x - 1|$
24. $y = |2x + 1| + |2x - 3|$
25. $y = \sqrt{-x}$
26. $y = \sqrt{3x}$
27. $y = [2x]$
28. $y = 2[x]$

Write the standard form of the equation for each of the circles described here.

29. Center $(3, -5)$, radius 4
30. Center $(-12, -7)$, radius 11
31. Center $(-4, 2)$, radius 7

32. Center (6, 5), radius 8
33. Center (7, 4), through (4, 8)
34. Center (3, −3), through (−2, 9)
35. Opposite ends of a diameter at (4, 5) and (8, −7)
36. Opposite ends of a diameter at (−3, −10) and (7, 2)

Graph the circles in Probs. 37 to 52. Put the equations in standard form if they are not given that way.

37. $(x - 4)^2 + (y - 5)^2 = 4$
38. $(x - 2)^2 + (y + 3)^2 = 9$
39. $(x + 5)^2 + (y - 1)^2 = 1$
40. $(x + 2)^2 + (y + 2)^2 = 16$
41. $x^2 + (y + 3)^2 = 4$
42. $(x - 4)^2 + (y - 3)^2 = 25$
43. $(x - 6)^2 + y^2 = 36$
44. $(x - 5)^2 + (y + 12)^2 = 169$

45. $x^2 + y^2 + 6x + 4y = 3$
46. $x^2 + y^2 + 8x - 12y = -27$
47. $x^2 + y^2 - 4x + 8y = 5$
48. $x^2 + y^2 - 2x - 10y = -1$
49. $2x^2 + 2y^2 + 4x - 8y = 8$
50. $3x^2 + 3y^2 + 12x + 24y = -12$
51. $5x^2 + 5y^2 - 10x - 20y = -5$
52. $6x^2 + 6y^2 - 12x + 24y = 24$

Graph the equations in Probs. 53 to 56.

53. $y = x/|x|$
54. $y = 2^x$
55. $y = 6/(1 + x^2)$
56. $y = x - [x]$
57. It is true that $[x + y] \geq [x] + [y]$ for all real numbers x and y. Verify this for the numbers

$$x = 6.5, \ y = 4 \qquad x = 13.7, \ y = 8.6$$

3.3 Introduction to the Conics

In Chap. 13, we will cover the conics in detail, giving information about vertices, foci, asymptotes, and other data. Our aim here is merely to become familiar with certain common types of graphs which will occur frequently in the book.

In Example 2 of Sec. 3.2, we graphed a parabola. In addition we drew the graphs of $y = x^2$ and $x = y^2$, which are also parabolas. We also saw how to draw circles. Circles, ellipses, parabolas, and hyperbolas all belong to the family of curves known as the **conics.** The name conic is due to the fact that each conic is the intersection of a cone with a plane. Various prototypes of conics are listed below.

Equations of conics

> The graph of the equation:
> (i) $Ax^2 + Cy^2 = K$ is an **ellipse** if A, C, and K are positive.
> (ii) $Ax^2 + Ay^2 = K$ is a **circle** if A and K are positive.
> (iii) $Ax^2 - Cy^2 = K$ is a **hyperbola** if A, C, and K are positive.
> (iv) $By^2 - Dx^2 = K$ is a **hyperbola** if B, D, and K are positive.
> (v) $xy = K$ is a **hyperbola** if $K \neq 0$.
> (vi) $y = ax^2 + bx + c$ and $x = ay^2 + by + c$ are **parabolas** if $a \neq 0$.

The following loose descriptions are given only as memory aids. Since we have already discussed circles, we may think of an ellipse as a "squashed" or "flattened" circle, or as egg-shaped. A parabola has an elongated U shape, and it may open up, down, left, or right. By way of contrast, every hyperbola has two separate parts. Although each part resembles a parabola, it is definitely not one. Each part in fact gets closer and closer to a straight line, the farther out on the hyperbola you go.

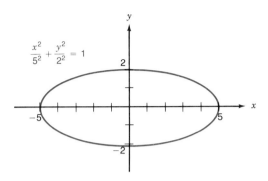

FIGURE 3.18

▶ **EXAMPLE 1** Draw the graph of $4x^2 + 25y^2 = 100$, or $x^2/5^2 + y^2/2^2 = 1$.

Solution From (i) above, the graph is an ellipse since the coefficients of x^2 and y^2 have the same sign. Since $4x^2 \leq 100$, then $x^2 \leq 25$, and thus $-5 \leq x \leq 5$. Similarly all of the y values are between -2 and 2. The graph does not exist if $|x| > 5$ or if $|y| > 2$. A table of values is shown below. See Fig. 3.18.

x	± 5	± 4	± 3	0
y	0	$\pm\frac{6}{5} = \pm 1.2$	$\pm\frac{8}{5} = \pm 1.6$	± 2

◀

The origin is called the **center** of the ellipse in Example 1. Each ellipse and hyperbola in this section has its *center at the origin*. In Sec. 3.4, we will see how to move the graph and put its center at any point in the plane. We know from our work in the last section on circles that each of the circles described in (ii) above has its center at the origin. A parabola does not have a center.

▶ **EXAMPLE 2** Draw the graph of $49x^2 + 9y^2 = 441$, or $x^2/3^2 + y^2/7^2 = 1$.

Solution This graph is also an ellipse since the coefficients of x^2 and y^2 are positive. The second form of the equation above shows that $|x| \leq 3$ and $|y| \leq 7$. The center is at the origin. These facts plus the table of values below allow us to draw the ellipse in Fig. 3.19.

x	± 3	± 2	0
y	0	$\approx \pm 5.2$	± 7

◀

▶ **EXAMPLE 3** Draw the graph of $xy = 6$.

Solution From part (v), the graph is a hyperbola, and thus it has two separate parts. Since the product of x and y positive, they have the same sign, and so the graph is in the first and third quadrants. Neither x nor y can be 0.

Writing $y = 6/x$ shows that as x gets larger and larger, y gets smaller and smaller. Therefore the portion of the graph in the first quadrant approximates the positive x axis, which is a straight line. There are three other portions which also approximate straight lines. These facts plus the table of values below allow us to draw the graph in Fig. 3.20.

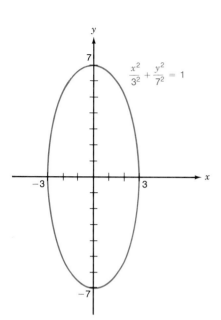

FIGURE 3.19

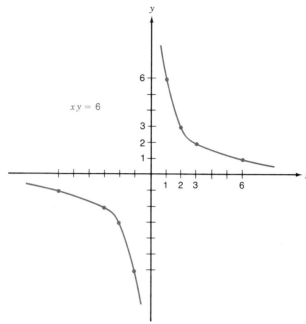

FIGURE 3.20

x	-6	-3	-2	-1	1	2	3	6
y	-1	-2	-3	-6	6	3	2	1

A hyperbola may have an equation $xy = 6$ as in Example 3, or $x^2 - 4y^2 = 4$ as in Example 4, or other forms also. In all cases, the parts of the graph further and further away from the origin approach straight lines. These lines are called **asymptotes,** and they will be treated in detail in Chap. 13.

EXAMPLE 4   Draw the graph of $x^2 - 4y^2 = 4$, or $x^2/2^2 - y^2/1^2 = 1$.

Solution   The graph is a hyperbola since the coefficients of x^2 and y^2 have opposite signs. Writing the equation in the form

$$x^2 = 4 + 4y^2$$

shows that there is no restriction on y, but x^2 must be at least 4, and so $|x| \geq 2$. The center is at the origin, but it is not a point on the hyperbola. It will be shown in Chap. 13 that the asymptotes can be found by replacing the constant term in the given equation by 0 and getting $x^2 - 4y^2 = 0$. We thus have $(x - 2y)(x + 2y) = 0$, and the lines which the hyperbola approaches are $y = x/2$ and $y = -x/2$. These facts plus the table of values below allow us to draw the graph in Fig. 3.21.

x	± 2	$\pm\sqrt{8} \approx \pm 2.8$	$\pm\sqrt{20} \approx \pm 4.5$	$\pm\sqrt{40} \approx \pm 6.3$
y	0	± 1	± 2	± 3

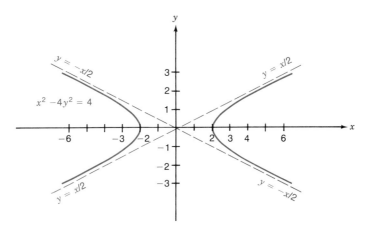

FIGURE 3.21

The graph of $x^2 - 4y^2 = 4$ above is a hyperbola with two x intercepts, but no y intercepts. On the other hand, the graph of $4y^2 - 49x^2 = 196$, for instance, is a hyperbola with two y intercepts, but no x intercepts. The difference is due to the signs of the coefficients of x^2 and y^2.

In Example 2 of the last section, we saw that the graph of $y = x^2 - 2x - 2$ is a parabola which opens up. In the next example, we graph a parabola which opens to the right.

EXAMPLE 5   Draw the graph of $x = y^2 - 3y - 4$.

Solution   Writing the equation as $x = (y - 4)(y + 1)$ shows that the y intercepts are 4 and -1, whereas, taking $y = 0$, we see that the x intercept is -4. The graph is a parabola, and the table of values shows that it opens to the right. See Fig. 3.22.

x	14	0	-4	-6	-6	-4	0	14
y	-3	-1	0	1	2	3	4	6

If you know the type of conic from the form of the equation, if its center (if any) is at the origin, and if you find the intercepts, then a short table of values will allow you to draw a reasonable graph quickly.

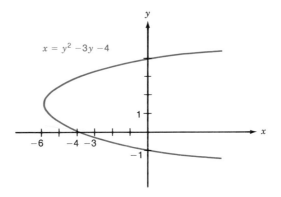

FIGURE 3.22

EXERCISE 3.3

Draw the graphs of these equations.

1. $4x^2 + 9y^2 = 36$ **2.** $9x^2 + y^2 = 9$
3. $x^2 + 36y^2 = 36$ **4.** $49x^2 + 4y^2 = 196$
5. $25x^2 + 16y^2 = 400$ **6.** $16x^2 + y^2 = 16$
7. $9x^2 + 25y^2 = 225$ **8.** $25x^2 + 4y^2 = 100$
9. $x^2 - 4y^2 = 9$ **10.** $4x^2 - 25y^2 = 16$
11. $9y^2 - 36x^2 = 36$ **12.** $36y^2 - 16x^2 = 9$
13. $25x^2 - 9y^2 = 81$ **14.** $16x^2 - 144y^2 = 49$

15. $81y^2 - 364x^2 = 36$ **16.** $9y^2 - 36x^2 = 64$
17. $xy = 4$ **18.** $xy = 7$
19. $xy = -3$ **20.** $xy = -1$
21. $y = 2x^2 - x - 10$ **22.** $y = -3x^2 + 4x + 7$
23. $x = 3y^2 + 7y - 6$ **24.** $x = -2y^2 - 3y$
25. $x = y^2 - 6y + 12$ **26.** $x = -y^2 - 2y + 1$
27. $y = -x^2 - 2x + 2$ **28.** $y = x^2 + 4x + 6$

3.4   Symmetry and Translation of Graphs

Algebra and geometry

The interplay between algebra (equations) and geometry (graphs) is the hallmark of the use of the rectangular coordinate system to draw the graph of an equation. This allows properties of either one to be expressed in terms of the other, and we gain the benefits of being able to look at one situation in two ways.

If the graph of $y = |x|$ in Fig. 3.14 were cut in half along the y axis, then each half would be a mirror image of the other. The same property is true for the W-shaped graph in Fig. 3.11.

> The graph of an equation is
>
> *Symmetric with respect to the y axis*
>
> if replacing x by $-x$ yields an equivalent equation (algebra). In this case, the point (x, y) is on the graph if and only if $(-x, y)$ is also on the graph (geometry).

The points (x, y) and $(-x, y)$ are the same distance from the y axis. The points P and R in Fig. 3.23a, and the points Q and S as well, are symmetric with respect to the y axis. See also Fig. 3.23b.

▶ **EXAMPLE 1**   The graph of each of the following equations is symmetric with respect to the y axis.

Solution   (a) $y = |x|$; see Fig. 3.14.
(b) $y = x^4 - 10x^2 + 9$; see Fig. 3.11.
(c) The ellipse $4x^2 + 25y^2 = 100$; see Fig. 3.18.
(d) $x^2 + y^6 x^{14} + y^{13} = 3$, since $(-x)^2 = x^2$ and $(-x)^{14} = x^{14}$; the graph of this one will not be drawn. ◀

As above, we define another symmetry property by both equation and graph.

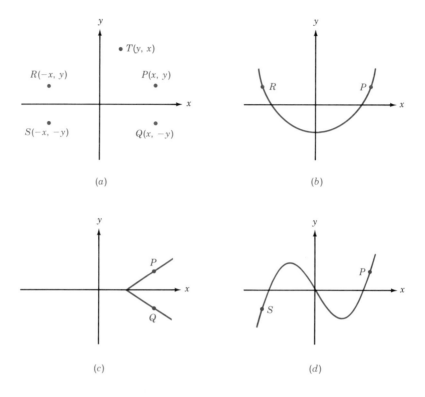

FIGURE 3.23

See points P and Q in Fig. 3.23a, which are the same distance from the x axis. This is also true for the points R and S in Fig. 3.23a. See also Fig. 3.23c.

EXAMPLE 2 Each of the following graphs is symmetric with respect to the x axis.

Solution (a) The circle $x^2 + y^2 = 169$; see Fig. 3.15.
(b) The parabola $x = y^2$; see Fig. 3.13.
(c) See Fig. 3.31 for $x = |y|$.
(d) See Fig. 3.30 for $(x + 3)^2 + y^2 = 1$.
(e) The graph of $y^4 + y^2 + 1 = x^5 + x^3 + x^2$, which will not be drawn here. ◢

The graph of an equation is

Symmetric with respect to the origin

if replacing x and y by $-x$ and $-y$, respectively, yields an equivalent equation (algebra). In this case, the point $(-x, -y)$ is on the graph if and only if (x, y) is on the graph (geometry).

See points P and S in Fig. 3.23a. If the line segment between P and S were drawn, it would be bisected by the origin. The points Q and R are also symmetric with respect to the origin, as in Fig. 3.23a. See also Fig. 3.23d.

EXAMPLE 3   Each of the following graphs is symmetric with respect to the origin.

Solution   (a) The circle $x^2 + y^2 = 169$; see Fig. 3.15.
(b) The ellipse $4x^2 + 25y^2 = 100$; see Fig. 3.18.
(c) The cubic $y = x^3$; see Fig. 3.10. Replacing (x, y) with $(-x, -y)$ gives $-y = (-x)^3 = -x^3$, which is equivalent to the given equation $y = x^3$.
(d) The hyperbola $xy = 6$; see Fig. 3.20. Replacing (x, y) by $(-x, -y)$ gives $(-x)(-y) = 6$, which is equivalent to $xy = 6$.   ◢

> The graph of an equation is
>
> $$\text{Symmetric with respect to the line } y = x$$
>
> if interchanging x and y yields an equivalent equation (algebra). In this case, the point (y, x) is on the graph if and only if (x, y) is on the graph (geometry).

See points P and T in Fig. 3.23a. Problem 53 is also relevant.

EXAMPLE 4   The graph of each of the equations below is symmetric with respect to the line $y = x$.

Solution   (a) The circle $x^2 + y^2 = 169$; see Fig. 3.15.
(b) The line $x + y = 5$ since interchanging x and y gives $y + x = 5$, which is clearly equivalent to $x + y = 5$.
(c) The hyperbola $xy = 6$; interchanging x and y gives $yx = 6$, an equation equivalent to $xy = 6$. See Fig. 3.20.
(d) The graph of the equation $|x| + |y| = 2$; interchanging x and y gives the same equation again. The graph of this equation is symmetric with respect to the x axis, to the y axis, to the origin, and to the line $y = x$. See Fig. 3.24.

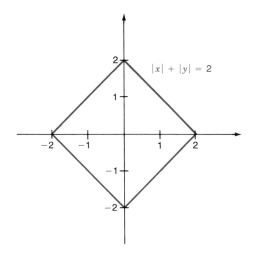

FIGURE 3.24

x	-2	-1	0	1	2
y	0	± 1	± 2	± 1	0

The above discussion of symmetry is summarized in the table below.

The graph of an equation is symmetric with respect to the	If we get an equivalent equation when (x, y) is replaced by
x axis	$(x, -y)$
y axis	$(-x, y)$
Origin	$(-x, -y)$
Line $y = x$	(y, x)

In discussing symmetry, we speak of one graph at a time. In discussing reflection below, we refer to two graphs at a time.

We can use the tests for symmetry to obtain related graphs from a given one. For instance, given the graph of an equation, we can replace (x, y) by $(x, -y)$ in the equation to get a new equation of a graph which is the original graph reflected through the x axis. That is, the new graph is the mirror image of the given graph, through the x axis. If the plane were folded along the x axis, then the two graphs would match exactly.

EXAMPLE 5   Discuss the graph of $2x + 3y = 6$ and its reflection through the x axis.

Solution   The graph of $2x + 3y = 6$ is the solid line shown in Fig. 3.25. Replacing (x, y) by $(x, -y)$ we obtain $2x - 3y = 6$, whose graph is shown dashed in the figure. Each graph is the reflection of the other through the x axis.

In a similar way, we can get a new graph which is the reflection of a given graph through the y axis, the origin, or the line $y = x$. Again we summarize the information in a table.

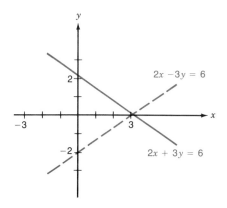

FIGURE 3.25

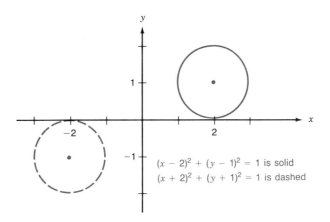

$(x - 2)^2 + (y - 1)^2 = 1$ is solid
$(x + 2)^2 + (y + 1)^2 = 1$ is dashed

FIGURE 3.26

To reflect a graph through the	Replace (x, y) in the given equation by
x axis	$(x, -y)$
y axis	$(-x, y)$
Origin	$(-x, -y)$
Line $y = x$	(y, x)

▶ **EXAMPLE 6**   Discuss the graphs of the equations

$$(x - 2)^2 + (y - 1)^2 = 1 \qquad \text{and} \qquad (x + 2)^2 + (y + 1)^2 = 1$$

Solution   The graph of the equation $(x - 2)^2 + (y - 1)^2 = 1$ is a circle. If we replace (x, y) with $(-x, -y)$, we get

$$(-x - 2)^2 + (-y - 1)^2 = 1 \qquad \text{or} \qquad (x + 2)^2 + (y + 1)^2 = 1$$

Each graph is the reflection of the other through the origin. See Fig. 3.26.   ◢
   Reflecting a graph through the x axis will be treated more completely in Sec. 3.5 on the graph of a function.

▶ **EXAMPLE 7**   Discuss each pair of equations below in terms of reflection through the x axis.

Solution   (a) The equations $2x + 3y = 6$ and $2x - 3y = 6$ from Example 5 can be written as

$$y = -\frac{2x - 6}{3} \qquad \text{and} \qquad y = \frac{2x - 6}{3}$$

The graph of either one is found by reflecting the graph of the other one through the x axis.
(b) The graph of $y = -x^2$ is found from the graph of $y = x^2$ by reflecting it through the x axis. See Fig. 3.27.   ◢

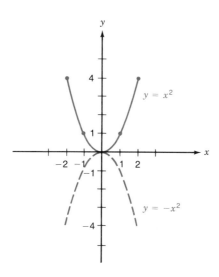

FIGURE 3.27

Translation

We shall now discuss translating a graph, that is, shifting it horizontally or vertically. First, we consider the equations $y = x^2$, $y - 3 = x^2$, and $y = (x - 4)^2$. Their graphs are shown in Figs. 3.28 and 3.29. In each figure, the graph of $y = x^2$ is shown solid.

As we can see, the graph of $y = x^2$ is translated or shifted 3 units up in the first figure, and it is moved 4 units to the right in the second. Although we could graph each equation by plotting points, it is clearly easier to merely shift the graph of $y = x^2$ the correct distance in the proper direction. The rules for translation of graphs are shown below.

Translating, or shifting, with $b > 0$

Replacing	Translates the graph b units
x by $x - b$	To the right
x by $x + b$	To the left
y by $y - b$	Up
y by $y + b$	Down

EXAMPLE 8   Write the equation if the graph of $x^2 + y^2 = 1$ is translated by 3 units to the left.

Solution   To translate the graph of $x^2 + y^2 = 1$ by 3 units to the left, we replace x by $x + 3$ and have $(x + 3)^2 + y^2 = 1$, which is a circle with center at $(-3, 0)$. See Fig. 3.30.

EXAMPLE 9   Write the equation if the graph of $x = |y|$ is translated by 4 units to the left and 1 unit up.

Solution   In the equation $x = |y|$, we replace x by $x + 4$ and y by $y - 1$. This gives us $x + 4 = |y - 1|$. The graph is simultaneously shifted 4 units to the left and 1 unit up. See Fig. 3.31.

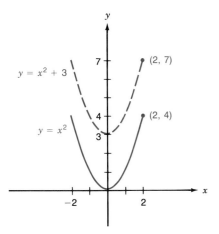

FIGURE 3.28

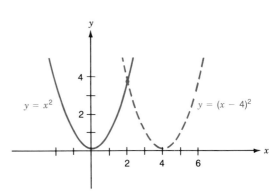

FIGURE 3.29

EXERCISE 3.4

In Probs. 1 to 4, write the coordinates of a point which is symmetric to the given point with respect to (a) the x axis and (b) the origin.

1. $(3, -5)$ 2. $(-2, 1)$
3. $(-3, -8)$ 4. $(5, 16)$

In Probs. 5 to 8, write the coordinates of a point that is symmetric to the given point with respect to (a) the y axis and (b) the line $y = x$. See Fig. 3.23.

5. $(3, 2)$ 6. $(4, -1)$
7. $(-5, 6)$ 8. $(-7, 0)$

In Probs. 9 to 16, state which of the four symmetry properties is shown by the graph of the given equation.

9. $x^2 - 4y^2 = 4$ 10. $x^2 - 4y = 4$
11. $x + y = 7$ 12. $xy = -1$
13. $(3x^6 - x^2)(2y + 1) = 31$
14. $(x + 1)^2 + (y + 1)^2 = 9$
15. $x^4y^7 + x^7y^4 = 3$ 16. $x^8y^9 - x^6y^5 = 23$

In Probs. 17 to 20, write the equation whose graph is the graph of $xy(x - y) = 7$ reflected as stated.

17. Through the y axis   18. Through the origin
19. Through the line $y = x$
20. Through the x axis

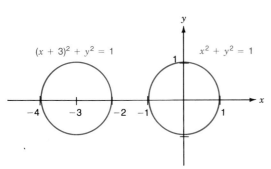

FIGURE 3.30

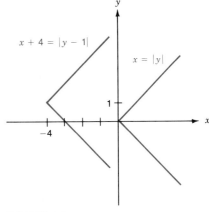

FIGURE 3.31

In Probs. 21 to 28, write the equation for the stated translation.

21. $x^2 + (y - 5)^2 = 4$ shifted 3 units to the right
22. $(x - 2)^2 - (y + 3)^2 = 11$ shifted 4 units to the left
23. $xy + x = 5$ shifted 1 unit up
24. $6x + 3y = 10$ shifted 7 units down
25. $7x - 2y = 3$ shifted right 3 units, down 2 units
26. $xy = 15$ shifted right 3 units, up 5 units
27. $x^2 + 3x + 2y = 4$ shifted left 2 units, up 3 units
28. $(x - 1)^2 = 4y$ shifted left 1 unit, down 2 units

In Probs. 29 to 36, draw the graphs of both equations on the same set of axes. The second is a translation of the first.

29. $y = x^3$ and $y = (x - 2)^3$
30. $2y = x^2$ and $2y = (x + 3)^2$
31. $3x + 5y = 15$ and $3x + 5(y + 2) = 15$
32. $y = x^4$ and $y - 3 = x^4$
33. $y = |x|$ and $y + 4 = |x - 2|$
34. $y = |x|$ and $y - 2 = |x - 1|$
35. $x = y^2$ and $x + 1 = (y - 3)^2$
36. $x = y^3$ and $x + 2 = (y + 1)^3$

In Probs. 37 to 40, use the same set of axes to draw the graph of $(x - 3)^2 + (y - 1)^2 = 1$ and the given equation (which is a reflection of the previously written circle).

37. $(-x - 3)^2 + (y - 1)^2 = 1$
38. $(x - 3)^2 + (-y - 1)^2 = 1$
39. $(-x - 3)^2 + (-y - 1)^2 = 1$
40. $(y - 3)^2 + (x - 1)^2 = 1$

Draw the graphs in Probs. 41 to 52.

41. $y = (x + 3)^2$
42. $y = (x + 2)^3$
43. $x = (y - 1)^4$
44. $x = (y + 2)^3$
45. $y + 1 = |x - 4|$
46. $y - 2 = -|x + 3|$
47. $x - 3 = -|y + 1|$
48. $x + 4 = |y - 2|$
49. $-y = (x - 3)^2$
50. $-x = y^3$
51. $-x = |y|$
52. $-y = |x - 2|$

53. Suppose that $a \neq b$, and let $P = (a, b)$, $T = (b, a)$, and $U = (x, y)$. Show that if the distance from P to U is the same as the distance from T to U, then $x = y$. *Hint:* Use the distance formula.

3.5 Functions

In graphing equations so far in ths chapter, we have considered equations such as

$$3x + 4y = 36$$

$$y - 3 = x^2 + 2x$$

$$x^2 + y^2 = 4$$

The first two equations are fundamentally different from the third. In each of the first two equations, if a specific number is used in place of x, then the equation can be solved for *exactly one* value of y. For instance, if we take $x = 4$ in the first equation, then we obtain

$$3(4) + 4y = 36 \qquad \text{or} \qquad y = 6$$

In the second equation, if we let $x = 5$, then

$$y = 25 + 10 + 3 = 38$$

However in the third equation, if we let $x = 1$, then

$$1 + y^2 = 4 \qquad \text{or} \qquad y^2 = 3$$

which has the *two* solutions $y = +\sqrt{3}$ and $y = -\sqrt{3}$.

Equations which determine exactly one value of y if a specific x is given define *functions*. In other words, given a value of x, the equation provides a way to find a unique y.

There are methods other than equations to make one object correspond to another. We could assign to each chair in a room the weight of that chair in kilograms. An example which does not use numbers assigns to each person that person's birthplace.

The function concept is at the heart of mathematics, and we will now present a definition of a function by using sets:

> A **function** f from a set A to a set B is a correspondence, or rule, which assigns to each element a of A exactly one element b of B.

The set A is called the **domain** of the function. The name of a function is often taken to be f, but g or h or any symbol may be used. If an element b of the set B corresponds to the element a of the set A, we call b the **value** of f at a, or the **image** of a under f, and we write

$$f(a) = b$$

which is read "f of a equals b." This does *not* mean "f times a," but it is instead a method of saying that b corresponds to a. The set of all such values b in B which actually correspond to some a in the domain is called the **range** of f. Thus the range is a subset of B.

These correspondences, or functions, can be illustrated using **diagrams.** The diagram in Fig. 3.32, for instance, represents a function since any given element of the domain is assigned precisely one element of the range. In fact

$$f(w) = r \qquad f(x) = r \qquad f(y) = s \qquad f(z) = t$$

Moreover, this function illustrates several important facts:

(i) An element of the range may be used more than once (see r in Fig. 3.32).

(ii) Some elements in the set B may not be in the range; this is true of q.

(iii) An element of the domain A never corresponds to more than one element of the range.

In contrast to (iii), note that (i) can be rephrased:

(i') *An element of the range may correspond to more than one element of* A.

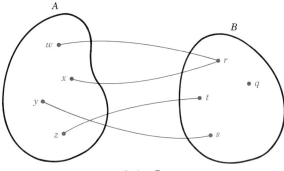

$$f: A = B$$

$$f(w) = r, f(x) = r, f(y) = s, f(z) = t$$

FIGURE 3.32

We can illustrate (i) by letting A be the set of all books in the Library of Congress, and B be the set of all positive integers from 1 to 1,111,111 and assigning to each book in A its number of pages (presuming all books have at most 1,111,111 pages). Surely there are at least two books with, for instance, 222 pages. This example illustrates (ii) as well, since it is unlikely that there is any book with, say, 333,333 pages.

Fact (iii) is simply a restatement of the definition of a function.

Sometimes the notation

$$f: A \longrightarrow B \qquad \text{or} \qquad A \xrightarrow{f} B$$

is used to denote a function f from a set A to a set B. If

$$f: A \longrightarrow B \qquad \text{and} \qquad g: A \longrightarrow B$$

we say that **f and g are equal** if $f(a) = g(a)$ for every element a in the domain A. In other words, the values of equal functions are the same no matter how the rules are given.

The correspondence defining a function can be given by an equation, a formula, a chart, a rule, a table, or simply a list of the ordered pairs of the function.

In this book, A and B are usually sets of real numbers, and the correspondence is usually given by means of an equation. We shall assume that the domain is the **largest possible set** for which the expression is defined. Generally this means no division by zero and no square roots of negative numbers are allowed.

EXAMPLE 1   What is the domain of the function defined by the equation $y = \sqrt{3x - 4}$?

Solution   Since the square root of a negative number is not a real number, we need $3x - 4 \geq 0$. This gives $x \geq \frac{4}{3}$, which may be written as the interval $[\frac{4}{3}, \infty)$.   ◢

EXAMPLE 2   For the function f defined by the equation $y = x^2 - 6x + 14$, show that 6 is in the range, but 4 is not in the range.

Solution   The number $y = 6$ is in the range since there are solutions to the equation $6 = x^2 - 6x + 14$. In fact this equation is equivalent to $0 = x^2 - 6x + 8 = (x - 4)(x - 2)$, which has the solutions 4 and 2. As a check

$$f(4) = 4^2 - 6(4) + 14 = 16 - 24 + 14 = 6$$

and

$$f(2) = 2^2 - 6(2) + 14 = 4 - 12 + 14 = 6$$

Thus 4 and 2 both correspond to 6, and this is permitted for a function. However $y = 4$ is *not* in the range, for, if it were, we could solve the equation

$$4 = x^2 - 6x + 14$$

But this is equivalent to $0 = x^2 - 6x + 10$, and the quadratic formula shows there are no real solutions since

$$b^2 - 4ac = (-6)^2 - 4(1)(10) = 36 - 40 = -4$$

which is negative.   ◢

The **range** can sometimes be found algebraically by a method similar to that used in Example 2, but it is often easier to do it graphically, which will be done in the next section.

EXAMPLE 3   Decide whether each equation below defines a function of x.

Solution   (a) The equation $y = x^2$ does define y as a function of x since for any real number x, the value x^2 is a single real number. The domain is the set of all real numbers. (b) $y = \sqrt{x}$ defines a function with the domain being all $x \geq 0$. However $y^2 = x$ does not define a function of x, since $x = 49$ corresponds to both $y = 7$ and $y = -7$.

EXAMPLE 4   Show that the equation $x^4 + y^4 = 17$ does not define a function of x.

Solution   The equation $x^4 + y^4 = 17$ does not define a function since $x = 1$ corresponds to both $y = 2$ and $y = -2$.

NOTE   We often use the letters f, g, or h as the name of a function, and we write $y = f(x)$, $y = g(x)$, or $y = h(x)$. If the name of the function is f, then the image or value of f at x is written $f(x)$. Thus

f is the name of the function

and   *f(x) is the value of f at x*

With this notation, we call x the **independent variable,** which is an element of the domain. Furthermore, we call y the **dependent variable,** and it is an element of the range. The word *independent* is used because any element x of the domain can be chosen. The word *dependent* is used because once x is chosen, y is specified by the function; y depends on x. Letters other than x and y may also be used.

NOTE   Remember that $f(x)$ means f evaluated at x, not f times x.

EXAMPLE 5   Let $f(x) = 4x - 3$, and find $f(3)$, $f(-2)$, and $f(2t)$.

Solution   We find $f(3)$ by replacing x by 3. Just substitute 3 for x:

For $x = 3$ $f(3) = 4(3) - 3 = 12 - 3 = 9$

For $x = -2$ $f(-2) = 4(-2) - 3 = -8 - 3 = -11$

To find $f(2t)$, substitute $2t$ for x in $f(x) = 4x - 3$:

For $x = 2t$ $f(2t) = 4(2t) - 3 = 8t - 3$

EXAMPLE 6   Let $h(t) = 2t^2 - 3t + 6$. Find $h(4)$, $h(-4)$, and $h(a + b)$.

Solution   We find $h(4)$ by substituting 4 for t:

$$h(4) = 2(16) - 3(4) + 6 = 32 - 12 + 6 = 26$$

Similarly, for $t = -4$,

$$h(-4) = 2(16) - 3(-4) + 6 = 32 + 12 + 6 = 50$$

Finally, for $t = a + b$, we substitute again.

$$h(a + b) = 2(a + b)^2 - 3(a + b) + 6$$
$$= 2(a^2 + 2ab + b^2) - 3a - 3b + 6$$
$$= 2a^2 + 4ab + 2b^2 - 3a - 3b + 6 \qquad \blacktriangleleft$$

Remember, all we have to do is

Substitute in order to find function values

Instead of saying for instance that "f is the function defined by the equation $y = x^2 + 2x + 3$," we often use a verbal shorthand and say "the function $f(x) = x^2 + 2x + 3$." It is also common to say "the function $y = f(x)$."

EXAMPLE 7   If $f(x) = 1/(x + 1)$, find these function values.

Solution   (a) $f(3) = 1/(3 + 1) = \frac{1}{4}$
(b) $f(-1)$ is not defined since we cannot divide by 0
(c) $f(1/w) = \dfrac{1}{(1/w) + 1} = \dfrac{1}{(1/w) + 1} \cdot \dfrac{w}{w} = \dfrac{w}{1 + w}$

Note: $f(1/w) \neq 1/[f(w)] = \dfrac{1}{1/(w + 1)} = w + 1$

(d) $\qquad \dfrac{f(x + h) - f(x)}{h} = \dfrac{\dfrac{1}{x + h + 1} - \dfrac{1}{x + 1}}{h} \qquad$ for $h \neq 0$

Now multiply both numerator and denominator by the lcd $(x + 1)(x + h + 1)$ and get

$$= \dfrac{(x + 1) - (x + h + 1)}{h(x + 1)(x + h + 1)}$$
$$= \dfrac{-h}{h(x + 1)(x + h + 1)} = \dfrac{-1}{(x + 1)(x + h + 1)} \qquad \blacktriangleleft$$

There are many everyday applications of functions. The area of a circle of radius r is

$$A(r) = \pi r^2$$

If a car is going 90 km/h, its distance in t h is

$$D(t) = 90t$$

The cost, in millions of dollars, of building a 16-mi stretch of road is

$$C(x) = 3x + 5(16 - x)$$

if x mi cost \$3 million per mile and the remaining $(16 - x)$ mi cost \$5 million per mile because of different types of terrain.

Just as these examples use the four fundamental operations, we can also add, subtract, multiply, and divide function values if the range of each function is a subset of the reals. For instance, we define the sum S of the functions f and g by

$$S(x) = f(x) + g(x)$$

This function can also be written $f + g$ since by definition

$$(f + g)(x) = f(x) + g(x)$$

Do not confuse the definition of the function $f + g$ with the distributive law. We are evaluating functions, not multiplying real numbers.

NOTE   Another pitfall to avoid is saying that $f(x + y) = f(x) + f(y)$ no matter what the function is. This is usually not true.

In a manner similar to that used in defining the function $f + g$, we may define three other new functions using the four fundamental operations.

> We define the functions:
> $f + g$ by $(f + g)(x) = f(x) + g(x)$
> $f - g$ by $(f - g)(x) = f(x) - g(x)$
> fg by $(f \cdot g)(x) = f(x) \cdot g(x)$
> f/g by $(f/g)(x) = f(x)/g(x)$

Since $f(x)$ and $g(x)$ must both be defined, the *domain* of the first three functions is the intersection of the domains of f and g. For the function f/g we also require that $g(x) \neq 0$. For instance if $f(x) = \sqrt{x - 4}$ and $g(x) = \sqrt{7 - x}$, then

$$\text{The domain of } f \text{ is } [4, \infty)$$

$$\text{The domain of } g \text{ is } (-\infty, 7]$$

and the domain of $f + g$, $f - g$, and fg is $[4, 7]$. The domain of f/g is $[4, 7)$.

EXAMPLE 8   If $f(x) = 2x + 3$ and $g(x) = x^2 - 1$, find the following function values.

Solution

$$(f + g)(4) = f(4) + g(4) = (8 + 3) + (16 - 1) = 26$$

$$(f - g)(5) = f(5) - g(5) = (10 + 3) - (25 - 1) = -11$$

$$(fg)(-2) = f(-2) \cdot g(-2) = (-4 + 3) \cdot (4 - 1) = -3$$

$$\left(\frac{f}{g}\right)(0) = \frac{f(0)}{g(0)} = \frac{0 + 3}{0 - 1} = -3$$

If $f(x)$ is a polynomial, f is called a polynomial function. The function g is called **algebraic** if g can be written using the sum, difference, product, quotient, and roots of polynomial functions. Thus

$$g(x) = \sqrt[3]{\frac{5x^4 + 2}{x}} + \frac{x^3 - 4x^2}{(x - 1)\sqrt{x}}$$

is an algebraic function. A function that is not algebraic is called **transcendental.** Some examples of transcendental functions are exponential and logarithmic functions, which are explained in Chap. 5. Other examples are provided by trigonometric functions.

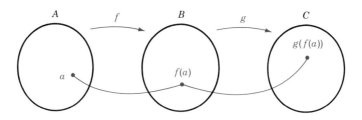

FIGURE 3.33

Composite Functions

In the remainder of this section, we will present another way to use two functions to get a third one. For instance when air is being pumped into a spherical balloon, the volume of the sphere depends on its radius, and the radius depends on the time, and so the volume depends on the time.

We can do a similar thing by assuming that f is a funcion from A to B and g is a function from B to C. See Fig. 3.33.

$$A \xrightarrow{f} B \xrightarrow{g} C$$

If we choose any element a in the set A, we may calculate $f(a)$, which will be in the set B. But g is a function from the set B to the set C, so we may now calculate $g(f(a))$. The net result is that we began with an element of A and produced an element of C. The function that does this is called the *composite function $g \circ f$*.

> If $f: A \to B$ and $g: B \to C$, the **composite** function $g \circ f: A \to C$ is defined by $(g \circ f)(x) = g(f(x))$.

EXAMPLE 9 If $f(x) = 5x - 4$ and $g(x) = 2x + 7$, then the domain and range of f is the reals, and similarly for g. Find the following composite-function values.

Solution

$$f(g(3)) = f(6 + 7) = f(13) = 65 - 4 = 61$$

$$g(f(3)) = g(15 - 4) = g(11) = 22 + 7 = 29$$

$$f(f(2)) = f(10 - 4) = f(6) = 30 - 4 = 26$$

$$f(g(4t)) = f(8t + 7) = 5(8t + 7) - 4 = 40t + 31$$

EXAMPLE 10 Find $(g \circ f)(x)$ if $f(x) = 3x + 2$ and $g(x) = x^2 + 3x + 7$.

Solution The definition of a composite function requires us to first calculate $f(x)$ and then substitute this value for x in the formula for $g(x)$. Doing this gives us

$$(g \circ f)(x) = g(f(x)) = g(3x + 2) \qquad \text{definition of } f$$

$$= (3x + 2)^2 + 3(3x + 2) + 7 \qquad \text{definition of } g$$

$$= 9x^2 + 12x + 4 + 9x + 6 + 7 \qquad \text{multiplying}$$

$$= 9x^2 + 21x + 17 \qquad \text{similar terms}$$

If $x = 2$, then $f(2) = 8$ and $g(8) = 64 + 24 + 7 = 95$, and also

$$(g \circ f)(2) = 9(4) + 21(2) + 17 = 36 + 42 + 17 = 95 \quad \blacktriangleleft$$

While it is quite possible for both $g \circ f$ and $f \circ g$ to be defined, they are rarely equal to each other. For instance, from Example 10, where $f(x) = 3x + 2$ and $g(x) = x^2 + 3x + 7$, we have

$$(f \circ g)(x) = f(g(x)) = f(x^2 + 3x + 7)$$

$$= 3(x^2 + 3x + 7) + 2 = 3x^2 + 9x + 23$$

and $\quad (g \circ f)(x) = g(f(x)) = g(3x + 2)$

$$= (3x + 2)^2 + 3(3x + 2) + 7$$

$$= 9x^2 + 12x + 4 + 9x + 6 + 7 = 9x^2 + 21x + 17$$

In this case we can use the two formulas to show that $(g \circ f)(x) = (f \circ g)(x)$ if and only if

$$9x^2 + 21x + 17 = 3x^2 + 9x + 23$$

which by the quadratic formula happens only when $x = -1 \pm \sqrt{2}$. Note that $(f \circ g)(1) = f(g(1)) = f(11) = 35$, but $(g \circ f)(1) = g(f(1)) = g(5) = 25 + 15 + 7 = 47 \neq 35$. Since the two composite functions do not *always* have the same function values, we conclude that

$$g \circ f \neq f \circ g$$

▶ **EXAMPLE 11** Suppose that a wire x cm long is shaped into a circle by a machine. Express the area of the circle as a function of x.

Solution If the radius of the circle is r, the area is

$$A = \pi r^2 = g(r)$$

Also, from plane geometry, $x =$ circumference $= 2\pi r$, and so

$$r = \frac{x}{2\pi} = f(x)$$

Therefore the area is

$$A = g(r) = g(f(x)) = \pi \left(\frac{x}{2\pi} \right)^2 = \frac{x^2}{4\pi} \quad \blacktriangleleft$$

In Sec. 3.7 on inverse functions, it will be important to have functions f and g for which $f \circ g = g \circ f$. In fact, we will require that

$$(f \circ g)(x) = x = (g \circ f)(x)$$

A special case of this is provided by the functions f and g where $f(x) = g(x) = (2x + 5)/(9x - 2)$ because we have

$$(f \circ g)(x) = (g \circ f)(x) = (f \circ f)(x) = f(f(x))$$

$$(f \circ g)(x) = f\left(\frac{2x + 5}{9x - 2}\right) = \frac{2\left(\dfrac{2x + 5}{9x - 2}\right) + 5}{9\left(\dfrac{2x + 5}{9x - 2}\right) - 2} \cdot \frac{9x - 2}{9x - 2}$$

$$= \frac{4x + 10 + 45x - 10}{18x + 45 - 18x + 4} = \frac{49x}{49} = x \qquad \blacktriangleleft$$

EXERCISE 3.5

In Probs. 1 to 8, find the largest possible domain of the function.

1. $f(x) = \sqrt{5x + 1}$ **2.** $f(x) = \sqrt[3]{12x - 7}$

3. $f(x) = \sqrt[4]{x^2 + 8}$ **4.** $f(x) = \sqrt{5 - 6x}$

5. $f(x) = \dfrac{4x}{x^2 - 4}$ **6.** $f(x) = \dfrac{|x|}{x}$

7. $f(x) = \dfrac{9}{x^2 + 9}$

8. $f(x) = \dfrac{x + 3}{2x^2 + 11x + 15}$

In Probs. 9 to 12, does the equation define y as a function of x?

9. $7y + x^3 = 4x - 32$ **10.** $y^4 = 16x$

11. $9y + 4/(2x + 65) = x^2 + 3xy$

12. $y - 41 = \sqrt{x} + \sqrt[3]{x}$

Find the function values in Probs. 13 to 36.

13. If $f(x) = 4x - 5$, find $f(3)$ and $f(-4)$.

14. If $f(x) = x^2 - 3x + 6$, find $f(1)$ and $f(-4)$.

15. If $f(x) = 2x^3 + x^2 - 8$, find $f(0)$ and $f(3)$.

16. If $f(x) = -2x^2 + 2x - 3$, find $f(4)$ and $f(-2)$.

17. If $f(x) = x^4 - 2x^2 + 3x$, find $f(2)$ and $f(-2)$.

18. If $f(x) = 2x^3 + 5x + 2$, find $f(-3)$ and $f(2)$.

19. If $f(x) = 6 - 5x$, find $f(-5)$ and $f(4)$.

20. If $f(x) = 4x^2 - 5x + 6$, find $f(0)$ and $f(-4)$.

21. If $g(x) = (3x + 2)/(x - 4)$, find $g(3)$ and $g(-4)$.

22. Find $h(0)$ and $h(3)$ if $h(x) = (x^2 + 3)/(2x - 5)$.

23. If $P(x) = (3x^2 - 2)/(7x + 1)$, find $P(2)$ and $P(-3)$.

24. Find $Q(5)$ and $Q(-4)$ if $Q(x) = (4x - 7)/(3x + 11)$.

25. If $f(t) = |3t - 17|$, find $f(5)$ and $f(-4)$.

26. If $f(s) = |s^2 - 32|$, find $f(-4)$ and $f(7)$.

27. If $f(n) = n^3 - n^2 + n - 1$, find $|f(0)|$ and $|f(2)|$.

28. If $f(k) = k^5 - k^4 + 2$, find $|f(2)|$ and $|f(-1)|$.

29. If $f(x) = 7x - 5$, find $f(3t)$ and $3f(t)$.

30. If $f(x) = x^2 + 3x + 1$, find $f(a + b)$ and $f(a) + f(b)$.

31. If $f(x) = (x + 3)/(2x - 1)$, find $f(1/x)$ and $1/f(x)$.

32. If $f(x) = 3x + 2$, find $f(x^2)$ and $[f(x)]^2$.

33. If $g(x) = 8x + 9$, find $[g(x + h) - g(x)]/h$.

34. Find $[h(x) - h(3)]/(x - 3)$ if $h(x) = x^2 + 5x + 2$.

35. If $f(x) = 2/(x + 3)$, find $[f(4 + h) - f(4)]/h$.

36. Find $[G(x) - G(4)]/(x - 4)$ if $G(x) = x^3$.

In Probs. 37 and 38, show that $f(-x) = f(x)$.

37. $f(x) = x^{14} + (3x + 4)/(2x - 3) - (4 - 3x)/(3 + 2x)$.

38. $f(x) = 2/x^6 + \sqrt{4 + 3x} + \sqrt{4 - 3x}$.

In Probs. 39 and 40, show that $f(-x) = -f(x)$.

39. $f(x) = x^{39} + (3x - 5)/(5x + 2) + (3x + 5)/(2 - 5x)$.

40. $f(x) = x^{17} + |x^2 + 2x + 3| - |x^2 - 2x + 3|$.

For part (b) in Probs. 41 to 43, solve $y = f(x)$ for x, then note the restrictions imposed on y.

41. Let $f(x) = 2x^2 - 8x + 7$. (a) Show that 17 is in the range of f. (b) Show that y is in the range of f if $y \geq -1$.

42. Let $f(x) = (5x + 3)/(x - 4)$. (a) Show that -18 is in the range of f. (b) Show that y is in the range of f if $y \neq 5$.

43. Let $f(x) = 4 + \sqrt{x}$. (a) Show that 21 is in the range of f. (b) Show that y is in the range of f if $y \geq 4$.

44. Let $f(x) = |x|/x$. (a) Show that 1 is in the range of f. (b) Show that the range of f is $\{-1, 1\}$.

Operations on functions

Find the values in Probs. 45 to 52 if $f(x) = x^2 + 3$ and $g(x) = x - 1$.

45. $(f + g)(4)$ **46.** $(f - g)(-3)$

47. $(fg)(0)$ **48.** $(f/g)(5)$

49. $(fg)(-6)$ **50.** $(f/g)(1)$

51. $(f - g)(8)$ **52.** $(f + g)(-7)$

Composite functions

Find the values of the composite functions in Probs.

53 to 64 if $f(x) = 5x - 1$, $g(x) = 2x^2 - 7$, and $h(x) = 1/(x + 1)$.

53. $(f \circ g)(1)$

54. $(g \circ h)(0)$

55. $(f \circ h)(4)$

56. $(g \circ f)(-5)$

57. $(h \circ g)(x)$

58. $(h \circ f)(x)$

59. $(f \circ g)(x)$

60. $(g \circ h)(x)$

61. $(f \circ f)(x)$ and $(f \circ f)(-1)$

62. $(g \circ f)(x)$ and $(g \circ f)(3)$

63. $(h \circ g)(x)$ and $(h \circ g)(-2)$

64. $(f \circ g)(x)$ and $(f \circ g)(-4)$

65. If $Q(x) = ax^2 + bx + c$, find $Q((-b + \sqrt{b^2 - 4ac})/2a)$.

66. If $L(x) = ax + b$, find $L(-b/a)$.

67. Let $C(x) = (5^x + 5^{-x})/2$ and $S(x) = (5^x - 5^{-x})/2$. Show that

$$[C(x)]^2 - [S(x)]^2 = 1$$

68. If $K(x) = 1.23$, find $K(4.56/7.89)$.

69. Let $F(x) = x^2 - 5x + 5$. Show that

$$|F(x)| = 1 \qquad \text{for } x = 1, 2, 3, 4$$

70. $H(x) = (x + 2)(x + 1)(x)(x - 1)(x - 2)(x - 3) - 5$. Show that
(a) $H(x) = -5$ for $x = -2, -1, 0, 1, 2, 3$
(b) $H(x) = (x^2 - x - 1)(x^4 - 2x^3 - 6x^2 + 7x + 5)$

71. *Geometric mean* Let $G(x) = a^{1-x}b^x$. Show that

$$G(0) = a \qquad G(1) = b \qquad G(\tfrac{1}{2}) = \sqrt{ab}$$

72. *Arithmetic mean* If $A(x) = (1 - x)a + xb$, show that

$$A(0) = a \qquad A(1) = b \qquad A\left(\frac{1}{2}\right) = \frac{a + b}{2}$$

Two variables

In Probs. 73 to 76, we give some functions of two variables, which are also evaluated by substitution. For instance, if $f(x, y) = x^2 + 3y$, then $f(5, 4) = 25 + 12 = 37$.

73. If $f(x, y) = 2x^2 + 3xy - 5y^2$, find $f(2, -3)$.

74. Show $f(a, b) = f(1, b/a)$ if $f(x, y) = xy/(x^2 + y^2)$.

75. If $f(x, y) = (x^3 - y^3)(x^2 + y^2)^{-1}$, show that

$$f(12, 18) = 6 \cdot f(2, 3)$$

76. Let $f(x, y) = 4x^2 - 16xy + 21y^2$. Show that

$$f(tx, ty) = t^2 f(x, y)$$

77. *Agriculture* The number of bees in a hive at the end of w weeks is $H(w) = 2700 + 1000w$ for w from 0 to 8, at which time the bees swarm. Find the number of bees in the hive at the end of 2, 4, and 8 weeks.

78. *Management* The earnings of a store, in units of $100,000, are

$$E(x, y) = 3x + 5y + 2xy + 5 - x^2 - y^2$$

where x is investment in inventory in millions of dollars and y is floor space in units of 10,000 ft^2. Find the earnings if the inventory is $7,000,000 and floor space is 40,000 ft^2.

79. *Marketing* The cost of a report is

$$C(x, y) = 4.16x + 0.43y + 0.012xy$$

where x is the number of pages in the report and y is the number of copies of the report. Find the cost if there are 33 pages and 425 copies.

80. *Geometry* If the volume of a right circular cylinder is 10 cm^3 and the radius of the base is r, the total surface area is

$$S(r) = 2\pi r^2 + \frac{20}{r}$$

Find the surface area if the radius is 4.

81. Let $a > 0$ and $a \neq 1$, and define

$$g(x) = -x\sqrt{a} + \frac{b}{1 - \sqrt{a}}$$

Show that $g(g(x)) = ax + b$.

82. Suppose that

$$f(x) = (x - a)(x - b) + q(x - a) + p$$

Show that $p = f(a)$, and then find q in terms of a, b, and f.

83. The average value of $f(x) = x^2 + x - 20$ on the interval $[1, 7]$ is 3. Calculate the value of the average below.

$$\frac{f(2) + f(4) + f(6)}{3}$$

84. The average value of $g(x) = 1/x^2$ on the interval $[\tfrac{3}{2}, \tfrac{7}{2}]$ is $\frac{4}{21} \approx 0.19$. Calculate the value of the average below.

$$\frac{g(2) + g(3)}{2}$$

Solve the equations in Probs. 85 to 88.

85. $f(5) - f(2) = (5 - 2) \cdot g(x)$ where

$f(x) = x^3 + 5x^2 - 6x - 2$ $g(x) = 3x^2 + 10x - 6$

86. $h(3) - h(1) = (3 - 1) \cdot p(x)$ where

$h(x) = 2x^3 - 6x^2 + x - 4$ $p(x) = 6x^2 - 12x + 1$

87. $f(4) - f(0) = (4 - 0) \cdot g(x)$ where

$$f(x) = \frac{3x + 1}{x + 2} \qquad g(x) = \frac{5}{(x + 2)^2}$$

88. $f(6) - f(3) = (6 - 3) \cdot g(x)$ where

$$f(x) = \frac{4x + 3}{2x - 3} \qquad g(x) = \frac{-18}{(2x - 3)^2}$$

3.6 The Graph of a Function

If f is a function, the values of the function can be given in a table of values. This assigns to each x in the domain exactly one y, where $y = f(x)$. The set of all points $P(x, y)$ in the plane determined in this way is called the *graph* of f.

> The **graph of the function f** is the graph of the equation $y = f(x)$.

If, for instance, $f(x) = 3x - 7$, then the graph of f is the graph of the equation $y = 3x - 7$. Another way to state the definition is to say that the graph of a function is the set

$$\{(x, f(x)) | x \in \text{domain of } f\}$$

We may apply the same rules for the graphs of functions that we used earlier for translation (or shifting), symmetry, and reflection of graphs of equations.

> If we know the graph of f and $b > 0$, then the graph of
> (a) $y = f(x) + b$ is found by translating the graph of $y = f(x)$ up by b units.
> (b) $y = f(x) - b$ is found by translating the graph of $y = f(x)$ down b units.
> (c) $y = -f(x)$ is found by reflecting the graph of $y = f(x)$ in the x axis.

▶ **EXAMPLE 1**   Draw the graphs of $f(x) = \sqrt{x}$, $g(x) = \sqrt{x} + 2$, and $h(x) = -\sqrt{x}$.

Solution   The graph of f, given in Fig. 3.13, is the top half of a parabola opening to the right. Figure 3.34 repeats the graph of f, shifts it up 2 for g, and reflects it through the x axis for h.   ◀

Suppose that the graph of $y = f(x)$ is symmetric with respect to the origin. This means that if (x, y) is on the graph, then $(-x, -y)$ is on it also. It follows that if $y = f(x)$, then

$$-y = f(-x) \qquad \text{and thus} \qquad y = -f(-x)$$

Since we began with $y = f(x)$, we can conclude that $-f(-x) = f(x)$. Such a function is called *odd*.

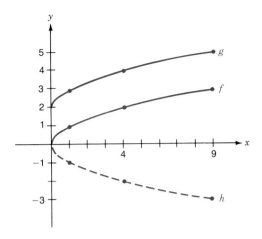

FIGURE 3.34

Odd function

If the graph of f is symmetric with respect to the origin, the function f is called **odd** and

$$f(-x) = -f(x)$$

In a similar way, we define an even function:

Even function

If the graph of f is symmetric with respect to the y axis, the function f is called **even** and

$$f(-x) = f(x)$$

See Fig. 3.35 for the graph of an odd function and Fig. 3.36 for the graph of an even function.

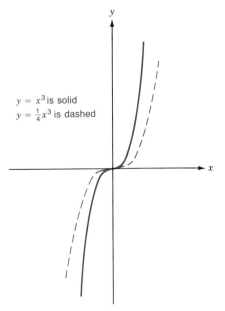

$y = x^3$ is solid
$y = \frac{1}{4}x^3$ is dashed

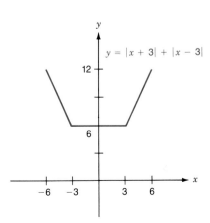

$y = |x + 3| + |x - 3|$

FIGURE 3.35

FIGURE 3.36

EXAMPLE 2   Which of the following functions is odd and which is even?
(a) $f(x) = x^4$ (b) $f(x) = x/(x + 1)$ (c) $f(x) = x^7$

Solution   (a) $f(-x) = (-x)^4 = x^4 = f(x)$, and so f is even.
Some other even functions are $g(x) = x^{12}$ and

$$h(x) = \frac{x^2}{3 + x} + \frac{x^2}{3 - x}$$

(b) $f(-x) = -x/(-x + 1)$, and this is not equal to $f(x) = x/(x + 1)$ or to $-f(x) = -x/(x + 1)$. Thus f is neither even nor odd.
(c) $f(-x) = (-x)^7 = -(x^7) = -f(x)$ and f is odd.
Some other odd functions are

$$G(x) = x^{39} \quad \text{and} \quad H(x) = \sqrt{x^2 + x^3} - \sqrt{x^2 - x^3}$$

If we know the graph of $y = f(x)$, the graph of $y = k \cdot f(x)$ is found by multiplying each $f(x)$ value by k. If $|k| < 1$, this brings the point closer to the x axis, assuming that the point was not on it to begin with. For instance if each value of $f(x) = x^3$ is multiplied by $\frac{1}{4}$, we get $g(x) = \frac{1}{4}x^3$. See Fig. 3.35. However, if $|k| > 1$, then each point on the graph of kf is further away from the x axis than the corresponding point on the graph of f, for a given value of x.

EXAMPLE 3   Show that

$$f(x) = |x + 3| + |x - 3|$$

is even, and draw the graph of f.

Solution
$$f(-x) = |-x + 3| + |-x - 3| \qquad \text{replacing } x \text{ by } -x$$
$$= |x - 3| + |x + 3| \qquad \text{using } |t| = |-t|$$
$$= f(x) \qquad \text{hence } f \text{ is even}$$

Because f is even, we only need a table of values for $x \geq 0$ since the graph of f is symmetric with respect to the y axis. By using the definition of absolute value, we can see that

If $0 \leq x \leq 3$, *then* $f(x) = (x + 3) + (3 - x) = 6$

and   *If* $x \geq 3$, *then* $f(x) = (x + 3) + (x - 3) = 2x$

See Fig. 3.36.

x	0	1	2	3	4	5	6	7
y	6	6	6	6	8	10	12	14

For the graph of f in Fig. 3.36, as we move from left to right, the graph first falls, then remains constant, and finally rises. We speak of the function f as *decreasing*, being *constant*, or *increasing* on the respective intervals. This is a geometrical interpretation of the following definition:

Increasing and decreasing functions

Suppose that f is a function defined on an interval I, and x_1 and x_2 are values in I with $x_1 < x_2$. Then
f **is increasing on** I means $f(x_1) \leq f(x_2)$ whenever $x_1 < x_2$
f **is decreasing on** I means $f(x_1) \geq f(x_2)$ whenever $x_1 < x_2$
f **is constant on** I means $f(x_1) = f(x_2)$ for all x_1 and x_2

Again, we are referring to what happens to the function values as we move **from left to right.** Note that if f is constant on an interval, then the graph is a horizontal line on that interval. Such is the case if $f(x) = 3$ for all x. Figure 3.35 shows that $f(x) = x^3$ is increasing on $(-\infty, \infty)$. Increasing and decreasing functions will be especially important in Sec. 3.8, which treats inverse functions.

Finding the **range of a function** algebraically can be difficult. Perhaps the simplest method is to graph the function and then estimate the range. From Fig. 3.35, the range of $f(x) = x^3$ is $(-\infty, \infty)$. Moreover, from Fig. 3.36, the range of $f(x) = |x + 3| + |x - 3|$ is $[6, \infty)$.

The function $f(x) = |x + 3| + |x - 3|$ of Example 3 can be defined without absolute values by using the definition $|t| = t$ if $t \geq 0$ and $|t| = -t$ if $t < 0$. The chart below shows the value of the two terms of $f(x)$ in the intervals $(-\infty, -3)$, $(-3, 3)$, and $(3, \infty)$.

Number line

	-3	3	
$|x + 3|$	$-x - 3$	$x + 3$	$x + 3$
$|x - 3|$	$-x + 3$	$-x + 3$	$x - 3$

Their sum is the value of f, and it can be described as

$$f(x) = \begin{cases} -2x & \text{if } x \leq -3 \\ 6 & \text{if } -3 < x < 3 \\ 2x & \text{if } x \geq 3 \end{cases}$$

Functions arising from actual physical situations are often defined, as above, in more than one piece as determined by critical temperatures, pressures, masses, or times for instance. In business this may occur when a company charges cheaper prices per unit for high-volume sales.

▶ EXAMPLE 4 Draw the graph of g if

$$g(x) = \begin{cases} x/4 & \text{if } 0 \leq x \leq 4 \\ -x^2 + 12x - 31 & \text{if } 4 < x < 7 \\ (15 - x)/2 & \text{if } 7 \leq x \leq 15 \end{cases}$$

Solution The graphs of the first and third parts are parts of two different lines with slopes $\frac{1}{4}$ and

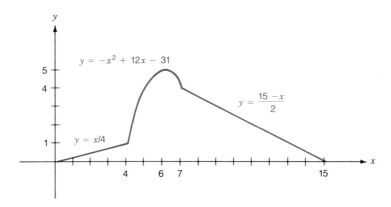

FIGURE 3.37

$-\frac{1}{2}$. The graph of the middle part is a portion of a parabola. The complete graph is in Fig. 3.37. For the graph of this function, all of the pieces "match up" at their endpoints, but this is not always the case. The range is [0, 5].

Often the simplest way to graph a function is to **do it in stages,** beginning with a basic graph.

EXAMPLE 5   Sketch the graph of $h(x) = -2|x - 4| + 3$.

Solution   In Fig. 3.38 we progressively show the following graphs:

$$y = |x|$$ which is a basic graph

$$y = |x - 4|$$ translate to the right by 4

$$y = 2|x - 4|$$ each point is twice as far from the x axis

$$y = -2|x - 4|$$ reflect through the x axis

$$y = -2|x - 4| + 3$$ translate up by 3

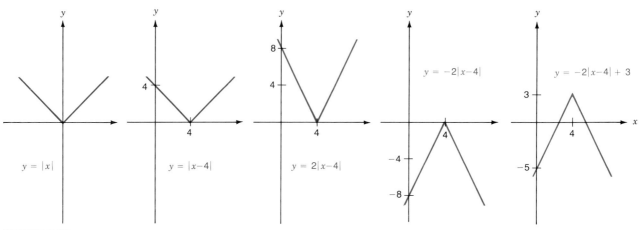

FIGURE 3.38

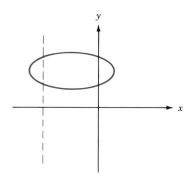

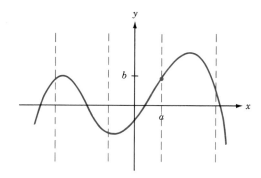

FIGURE 3.39

This *is not* the graph of a function

This *is* the graph of a function

These stages could have been done in a different order. For instance, we could have graphed $y = |x|$, then $y = -|x|$, then $y = -2|x|$, then $y = -2|x - 4|$, and finally $y = -2|x - 4| + 3$.

When the graph of an equation is known, there is an easy way to tell if it is the graph of a function. This method is called the **vertical-line test** for a function.

Vertical-line test

> If each vertical line intersects a graph at most once, then the graph is the graph of a function.

The vertical-line test is based on the definition of a function. It requires that for any value a in the domain, there is exactly one value b in the range which corresponds to it. Thus the vertical line passing through a on the x axis can only touch the graph of the function at one point, namely (a, b). See Fig. 3.39.

Here is an alternative, and more formal, definition of a function:

> A function is a set of ordered pairs (x, y) such that if the first elements are the same, then the second elements are also the same.

Another way to say this is

$$\text{If } x_1 = x_2, \text{ then } y_1 = y_2$$

or, equivalently, $\quad\quad\quad\quad$ *If $y_1 \neq y_2$, then $x_1 \neq x_2$*

We shall use this formulation and a horizontal-line test in Sec. 3.8 when we discuss inverse functions.

EXERCISE 3.6

Draw the graphs of these functions.

1. $f(x) = \sqrt{x} - 2$
2. $f(x) = [x] + 3$
3. $f(x) = |x| - 4$
4. $f(x) = 1/x + 2$
5. $g(x) = -[x]$
6. $g(x) = -x^3$
7. $g(x) = -1/x$
8. $g(x) = -|x|$
9. $h(x) = 2\sqrt{x}$
10. $h(x) = 3/x$
11. $h(x) = x^2/4$
12. $h(x) = [x]/2$
13. Show that $E(x) = 12|x|/(x^2 + 1)$ is even and draw the graph.

14. Show that $f(x) = x^4/5 - 4x^2 - 5$ is even and draw the graph.

15. Show that $G(x) = x^3 - 8x$ is odd and draw the graph.

16. Show that $H(x) = (x^3 - 6x)/(x^2 + 11)$ is odd and draw the graph.

Find the range of the functions in Probs. 17 to 20. Use the graph.

17. $f(x) = 6x/(x^2 + 1)$
18. $f(x) = |x + 1| + |x - 2|$
19. $f(x) = -x^2 + 4x + 3$
20. $f(x) = 4\sqrt{9 - x^2}$

On which intervals is the function increasing, decreasing, or constant?

21. $g(x) = |x + 2| + |2x - 1|$
22. $g(x) = 2x^3 - 3x^2 - 12x + 4$
23. $g(x) = |x|/x$ 24. $g(x) = 8x/(x^2 + 4)$

Draw the graphs in Probs. 25 to 36.

25. $P(x) = \begin{cases} x/2 + 1 & \text{for } x \leq 2 \\ 4 - x & \text{for } x > 2 \end{cases}$

26. $Q(x) = \begin{cases} x^3 & \text{if } x < 1 \\ -1 & \text{if } x \geq 1 \end{cases}$

27. $R(x) = \begin{cases} -2 & \text{for } x < 0 \\ x^2 & \text{for } 0 \leq x \leq 3 \\ 5 - x & \text{for } x > 3 \end{cases}$

28. $S(x) = \begin{cases} -x^2 & \text{if } x < 0 \\ x^3 & \text{if } 0 \leq x \leq 2 \\ 12 - x^2 & \text{if } x > 2 \end{cases}$

29. $f(x) = 3\sqrt{x - 2} + 4$
30. $f(x) = 4|x + 1| - 3$
31. $f(x) = -1/(x - 3) + 1$
32. $f(x) = -(x + 2)^3 - 2$
33. $g(x) = 3(x + 2)^2 - 3$
34. $g(x) = -4[x - 4] + 4$ (this is the bracket function)
35. $h(x) = -3|x - 2| + 1$
36. $h(x) = -2/(x - 2) - 2$

In Probs. 37 to 40, draw the graph of $y = f(2x)$ and $y = f(x/2)$.

37. $f(x) = 4x - 3$ 38. $f(x) = x^2 - 1$
39. $f(x) = 1/(x - 2)$ 40. $f(x) = \sqrt{1 - x^2}$

3.7 Linear Functions

Perhaps the simplest type of function, and one of the most useful, is the linear function.

Linear function

> A function f is a **linear function** if
> $$f(x) = ax + b$$
> where a and b are real numbers.

If a is 0 above, then $f(x) = b$, which is a constant function. We will see later in this section that the graph of a linear function is a straight line. Every **straight line** is determined by any two distinct points on it.

Slope

> If a line is not vertical and $P_1(x_1, y_1)$ and $P_2(x_2, y_2)$ are distinct points on the line, then the **slope of the line** is
> $$m = \frac{y_2 - y_1}{x_2 - x_1} \tag{3.5}$$

The slope is defined only if the line is not vertical, and thus
$$x_2 - x_1 \neq 0$$

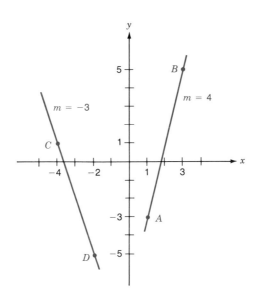

FIGURE 3.40

▶ **EXAMPLE 1** Find the slope of the line through the points

(a) $A(1, -3)$ and $B(3, 5)$ (b) $C(-4, 1)$ and $D(-2, -5)$

Solution Using the first point in each case as P_1 gives

(a) $m = \dfrac{5 - (-3)}{3 - 1} = \dfrac{8}{2} = 4$ (b) $m = \dfrac{(-5) - 1}{(-2) - (-4)} = \dfrac{-6}{2} = -3$

See Fig. 3.40. ◀

In the slope formula, **either point may be used as P_1** because

$$m = \frac{y_2 - y_1}{x_2 - x_1} = \frac{y_1 - y_2}{x_1 - x_2}$$

Other notations are sometimes used for the slope formula. Writing

$$y_2 - y_1 = \text{change in } y = \text{rise}$$

$$x_2 - x_1 = \text{change in } x = \text{run}$$

we have $\qquad m = \dfrac{\text{change in } y}{\text{change in } x} = \dfrac{\text{rise}}{\text{run}}$

The slope of a **vertical line** is not defined because the formula would require division by zero, and that is never allowed. The slope of a **horizontal line** is zero since $y_1 = y_2$ for any two points on it and

$m = 0$ $$m = \frac{y_2 - y_1}{x_2 - x_1} = \frac{0}{x_2 - x_1} = 0$$

In the slope formula,

Any two distinct points on the line may be used

The points P_1 and P_2 as in Fig. 3.41, and also points Q_1 and Q_2, can be used to draw

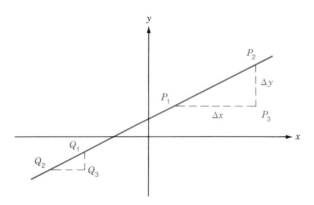

FIGURE 3.41

the right triangles $P_1P_2P_3$ and $Q_1Q_2Q_3$. The two triangles are **similar,** which means the *ratios of corresponding sides* of the triangles are equal. So the slope

$$m = \frac{\text{change in } y}{\text{change in } x}$$

is the same for either triangle.

Positive and negative slopes   If the slope of a line is positive, the y coordinate of the line increases as we go from left to right. If the slope is negative, the y coordinate of the line decreases. See Figs. 3.40 and 3.42. The larger $|m|$ is, the steeper the line is. The closer $|m|$ is to 0, the more nearly the line is to being horizontal.

We can write the slope formula as

$$y_2 - y_1 = m(x_2 - x_1)$$

This expression shows us that if we begin at any point on the line, move horizontally any distance $x_2 - x_1$, and then move vertically a distance of $m(x_2 - x_1)$, we will again be on the line.

EXAMPLE 2   Suppose that the slope for a line is $\frac{1}{2}$. If we begin with any point on the line, then
(i) A change of 6 in x followed by a change in y of $\frac{1}{2}(6) = 3$ will bring us back to the line.

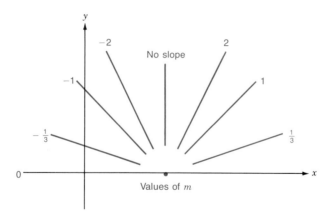

FIGURE 3.42

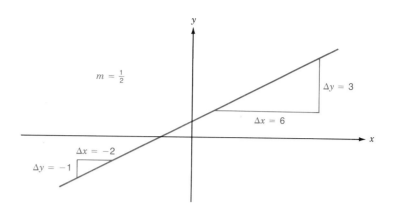

FIGURE 3.43

(ii) Similarly, if the change in x is -2, then the corresponding change in y is $\frac{1}{2}(-2) = -1$. See Fig. 3.43.

If (x_1, y_1) and (x_2, y_2) are specific points on a nonvertical line and (x, y) is any other point on the line, then both

$$\frac{y - y_1}{x - x_1} \quad \text{and} \quad \frac{y_2 - y_1}{x_2 - x_1}$$

are expressions for the slope; hence they are equal. Multiplying each of these by $(x - x_1)$ gives a standard form for the equation of a line.

Two-point form

$$y - y_1 = \frac{y_2 - y_1}{x_2 - x_1}(x - x_1) \qquad (3.6)$$

is called the **two-point form** of the equation of the line through the points (x_1, y_1) and (x_2, y_2). Either point may be used as (x_1, y_1).

EXAMPLE 3 Find an equation of the line through $(6, -4)$ and $(1, -1)$.

Solution Using $(x_1, y_1) = (6, -4)$,

$$y - (-4) = \frac{-1 - (-4)}{1 - 6}(x - 6)$$

$$y + 4 = \frac{3(x - 6)}{-5}$$

$$-5(y + 4) = 3(x - 6)$$

$$-5y - 20 = 3x - 18$$

$$0 = 3x + 5y + 2$$

Using $(x_1, y_1) = (1, -1)$,

$$y - (-1) = \frac{-4 - (-1)}{6 - 1}(x - 1)$$

$$y + 1 = \frac{-3(x - 1)}{5}$$

$$5(y + 1) = -3(x - 1)$$

$$5y + 5 = -3x + 3$$

$$3x + 5y + 2 = 0$$

Using $m = (y_2 - y_1)/(x_2 - x_1)$ with the two-point form gives us a new standard form for the equation of a straight line.

Point-slope form

> The **point-slope form** of the equation of the line through the point (x_1, y_1) and with slope m is
>
> $$y - y_1 = m(x - x_1) \tag{3.7}$$

▶ **EXAMPLE 4** Find an equation of the line through $(\frac{4}{3}, 4)$ with slope 6.

Solution Using $(x_1, y_1) = (\frac{4}{3}, 4)$ and $m = 6$ in the point-slope form gives

$$
\begin{aligned}
y - 4 &= 6(x - \tfrac{4}{3}) &&\text{by (3.7)} \\
y - 4 &= 6x - 8 &&\text{multiplying} \\
0 &= 6x - y - 4 &&\text{combining terms}
\end{aligned}
$$ ◀

The y intercept b is the y coordinate of the point where a line crosses the y axis. If we use $(x_1, y_1) = (0, b)$ in the point-slope form, we have

$$y - b = m(x - 0) = mx$$

This proves the following result:

Slope-intercept form

> The **slope-intercept form** of the equation of the line with slope m and y intercept b is
>
> $$y = mx + b \tag{3.8}$$

NOTE The slope-intercept form given in (3.8) makes graphing very easy. All we need to do is solve the equation of a line for y. Then the *coefficient of x is the slope*, and *the constant term* is the y intercept.

▶ **EXAMPLE 5** Find the slope and y intercept of $2x + 3y + 6 = 0$.

Solution We first solve for y.

$$
\begin{aligned}
2x + 3y + 6 &= 0 &&\text{given} \\
3y &= -2x - 6 &&\text{transposing} \\
y &= -\tfrac{2}{3}x - 2 &&\text{dividing by 3}
\end{aligned}
$$

Hence $m = -\frac{2}{3}$ is the slope and $b = -2$ is the y intercept. The graph of $2x + 3y + 6 = 0$ is shown in Fig. 3.44. ◀

Parallel and Perpendicular Lines

Parallel lines

> Two nonvertical lines $y = m_1x + b_1$ and $y = m_2x + b_2$ are **parallel** if and only if
>
> $$m_1 = m_2 \tag{3.9}$$

Although we will not prove this, it is evident geometrically when we recall from the definition of slope that if x changes by 1, then y changes by m_1 and m_2, respectively,

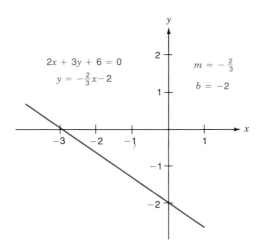

FIGURE 3.44

for the two lines. Thus corresponding changes are equal when $m_1 = m_2$. See Fig. 3.45 for parallel lines with slope 2.

There is also a simple characterization of perpendicular lines in terms of their slopes.

Perpendicular lines

> The two lines $y = m_1x + b_1$ and $y = m_2x + b_2$ are **perpendicular** if and only if
>
> $$m_1m_2 = -1 \qquad \textbf{(3.10)}$$

Proof We assume here, of course, that $m_1 \neq 0$ and $m_2 \neq 0$; so neither line is horizontal nor vertical. In Fig. 3.46, suppose that the two perpendicular lines meet at $P = (a, b)$. If Q is chosen 1 unit to the right of P, then $Q = (a + 1, b)$. The points R and S are chosen on the two given lines, and also on the vertical line through Q. From the

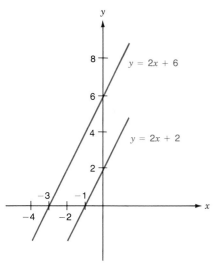

FIGURE 3.45

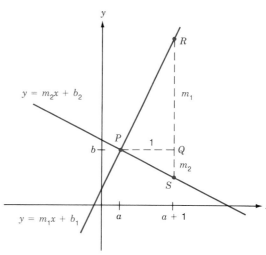

FIGURE 3.46

definition of slope, $QR = m_1$ and $SQ = m_2$, and thus $R = (a + 1, b + m_1)$ and $S = (a + 1, b + m_2)$. Therefore $SR = m_1 - m_2$, and, using the pythagorean theorem,

$$PR = \sqrt{1 + m_1^2} \quad \text{and} \quad PS = \sqrt{1 + m_2^2}$$

Since PRS is a right triangle, $PR^2 + PS^2 = SR^2$: that is, by substitution

$$(1 + m_1^2) + (1 + m_2^2) = (m_1 - m_2)^2$$

$$1 + m_1^2 + 1 + m_2^2 = m_1^2 - 2m_1m_2 + m_2^2$$

$$2 = -2m_1m_2$$

$$-1 = m_1m_2$$

These steps may be reversed to show the converse. In fact, the converse is the form we will use most often:

If $m_1m_2 = -1$, then the lines are perpendicular

Writing $m_1m_2 = -1$ as $m_1 = -1/m_2$ shows that the slopes of perpendicular lines are **negative reciprocals** of each other.

EXAMPLE 6   Are the following pairs of lines parallel, perpendicular, or neither?
(a) Through (2, 5) and (4, 9) and through (3, −1) and (6, 5)
(b) Through (4, 0) and (2, −1) and through (2, 5) and (5, 11)
(c) Through (12, 5) and (10, 4) and through (−1, 0) and (0, −2)

Solution   (a) $m_1 = \dfrac{9 - 5}{4 - 2} = \dfrac{4}{2} = 2, \quad m_2 = \dfrac{5 - (-1)}{6 - 3} = \dfrac{6}{3} = 2$

$$m_1 = m_2 \quad \text{hence parallel}$$

(b) $m_1 = \dfrac{0 - (-1)}{4 - 2} = \dfrac{1}{2}, \quad m_2 = \dfrac{5 - 11}{2 - 5} = \dfrac{-6}{-3} = 2 \quad \text{neither}$

(c) $m_1 = \dfrac{5 - 4}{12 - 10} = \dfrac{1}{2}, \quad m_2 = \dfrac{-2 - 0}{0 - (-1)} = -2$

$$m_1m_2 = -1 \quad \text{so perpendicular}$$

REMEMBER   A *vertical line* has no slope, and the equation of a vertical line is $x = $ constant. A *horizontal line* has slope 0, and its equation is $y = $ constant.
      We have now seen several forms of the equation of a line. The form $Ax + By + C = 0$ includes each of these. In fact, we have shown that the following is true:

(a) Every line is the graph of an equation $Ax + By + C = 0$.
(b) If A and B are not both 0, the graph of the equation $Ax + By + C = 0$ is a line.

      For (a), if the line is vertical, the equation is $x = k$. If the line is not vertical, the equation is $y = mx + b$. Both of these are represented by the general form $Ax + By + C = 0$.

For (b), if $B \neq 0$, then solving for y gives $y = (-A/B)x + (-C/B)$, whose graph is the line with slope $-A/B$ and y intercept $-C/B$. If $B = 0$, then solving for x gives $x = -C/A$, whose graph is a vertical line.

There are many actual situations which are described accurately by linear functions of the form $f(x) = ax + b$. Graphs of such functions are straight lines, and two points on a line enable you to find the function.

▶ **EXAMPLE 7**   Water freezes at 32°F or 0°C, and it boils at 212°F or 100°C. Express °F as a linear function of °C.

Solution   If x is °C and $f(x)$ is °F, we are looking for a and b for which $f(x) = ax + b$. We are given $f(0) = 32$ and $f(100) = 212$, and thus

$$32 = a(0) + b \qquad \text{and} \qquad 212 = a(100) + b$$

The first equation gives $b = 32$. Using the second equation with $b = 32$ gives

$$212 = 100a + 32 \qquad 100a = 180 \qquad a = \tfrac{180}{100} = \tfrac{9}{5}$$

The linear function is therefore $f(x) = \tfrac{9}{5}x + 32$, and its graph is the line with slope $\tfrac{9}{5}$ and y intercept 32. A change of 5°C means a change of 9°F. Incidentally the calculation of $\tfrac{9}{5}x + 32$ can be easily accomplished mentally by starting with x, then doubling that, subtracting 10 percent from the result, and finally adding 32.   ◀

EXERCISE 3.7

Find the slope of the line through the two given points in each of Probs. 1 to 4.
1. (2, 7) and (4, 9)
2. (6, 3) and $(-3, 8)$
3. $(5, -1)$ and $(2, -2)$
4. $(-3, 5)$ and $(2, 0)$

Find the equation of the line through the given pair of points in each of Probs. 5 to 12.
5. (4, 3) and (2, 5)
6. (7, 5) and (9, 1)
7. (4, 7) and $(-2, 3)$
8. (0, 6) and $(-2, 8)$
9. $(-5, -1)$ and (3, 3)
10. $(6, -2)$ and $(-2, 6)$
11. $(-6, -8)$ and $(-4, -3)$
12. $(-1, -3)$ and $(3, -1)$

Find the equation of the line described in each of Probs. 13 to 20.
13. Through (3, 2), slope 3
14. Through (5, 1), slope -3
15. Through $(-2, -3)$, slope $-\tfrac{2}{5}$
16. Through $(-4, 0)$, slope $-\tfrac{3}{4}$
17. Slope 4, y intercept 2
18. Slope $-\tfrac{1}{2}$, y intercept 5
19. Slope -5, y intercept -7
20. Slope $\tfrac{2}{5}$, y intercept -3

Find the slope and y intercept of the line determined by the equation in each of Probs. 21 to 24.
21. $2x - y = 4$
22. $3x + y = 5$
23. $x - 2y = 7$
24. $3x + 5y = 9$

The equation of the line with a and b as x and y intercepts is

$$\frac{x}{a} + \frac{y}{b} = 1$$

This is called the **intercept form** of the equation of a straight line. Find the x and y intercepts of the following lines by using the intercept form.
25. $x/3 + y/5 = 1$
26. $x/4 - y/7 = 1$
27. $16x + 3y = 24$
28. $3x + 4y = 24$

Are the following pairs of lines parallel, perpendicular, or neither?
29. $6x + 3y = 4$
     $2x + y = -5$
30. $4x - 11y = 8$
     $11x + 4y = 3$
31. $8x - 2y = 5$
     $x + 4y = 15$
32. $5x + 15y = 8$
     $6x + 2y = 1$

33. $-7x + 21y = 6$
$6x + 2y = 7$

34. $8x + 5y = 3$
$-8x + 5y = 6$

35. $-x + 6y = 18$
$2x - 12y = -9$

36. $6x - 9y = 14$
$-4x + 6y = -15$

Show that the three points in each problem are on the same line by using slopes.

37. $(-2, -10)$, $(1, -1)$, $(2, 2)$
38. $(-1, 8)$, $(0, 3)$, $(2, -7)$
39. $(-3, -7)$, $(1, 3)$, $(7, 18)$
40. $(-3, 12)$, $(-1, 5)$, $(3, -9)$
41. Find an equation of the line through $(4, 5)$ which is perpendicular to the line $7x + 6y = -3$.
42. Find an equation of the line through $(-6, 3)$ which is perpendicular to the line $5x - 10y = 3$.
43. Find an equation of the line through $(1, 4)$ which is parallel to the line $-4x + 6y = 2$.
44. Find an equation of the line through $(3, -5)$ which is parallel to the line $3x + 6y = 7$.
45. Find an equation of the line through $(3, 2)$ with equal, nonzero intercepts.
46. Find an equation of the line with the same x intercept as the line $2x - 9y = 14$ and the same slope as the line $x - y = 21$.
47. Find an equation of the line with the same y intercept as $2x + 5y = -25$ and twice the slope of $9x - 3y = 4$.
48. Find an equation of the line whose y intercept is twice its x intercept and is also 3 times its slope.

The distance between the point (x_1, y_1) and the line $Ax + By + C = 0$ is

$$\frac{|Ax_1 + By_1 + C|}{\sqrt{A^2 + B^2}}$$

Use this to find the distance between the following points and lines.

49. $(3, 5)$; $2x + 4y - 1 = 0$
50. $(4, -1)$; $3x + 7y - 12 = 0$
51. $(-3, 2)$; $5x + y = 7$
52. $(5, 1)$; $x - 3y = -8$

Graph the following lines by using the slope-intercept form.

53. $y = 3x + 1$
54. $y = -2x - 3$
55. $2y = x - 5$
56. $3y = -2x + 2$
57. $6x + 5y + 14 = 0$
58. $5x + 6y - 23 = 0$
59. $-4x + y + 6 = 0$
60. $3x - 7y + 15 = 0$

61. If f is a linear function such that $f(4) = 7$ and $f(7) = 16$, find the equation for $f(x)$.
62. Find an equation for the perpendicular bisector of the line segment joining $(4, -3)$ and $(8, 5)$.
63. Find an equation for the altitude through A in the triangle with vertices $A(1, 5)$, $B(2, -1)$, and $C(5, 0)$.
64. Show that the equation of the line through $(a, 0)$ and $(0, b)$ can be put in the form

$$\frac{x}{a} + \frac{y}{b} = 1$$

In Probs. 65 to 68, use the distance formula to find a linear equation satisfied by all points $P(x, y)$ which are equidistant from the two given points.

65. $(3, 8)$ and $(-1, 4)$
66. $(11, -3)$ and $(4, 7)$
67. $(-2, 5)$ and $(-4, -14)$
68. $(1, -9)$ and $(12, -4)$

In Probs. 69 to 72, use the fact that the equation of the tangent line to the circle $x^2 + y^2 = r^2$ at the point (a, b) is $ax + by = r^2$. This can be proved by using the result that the tangent line is perpendicular to the radius drawn to the point of tangency.

69. Find the equation of the tangent line to $x^2 + y^2 = 169$ at $(-5, 12)$.
70. Find the equation of the tangent line to $x^2 + y^2 = 25$ at $(3, -4)$.
71. Find the equation of the tangent line to $x^2 + y^2 = 289$ at $(8, 15)$.
72. Find the equation of the tangent line to $x^2 + y^2 = 841$ at $(20, 21)$.

In Probs. 73 to 76, use slopes to show that the three points are the vertices of a right triangle.

73. $P_1(-9, 4)$, $P_2(2, 3)$, $P_3(-4, -2)$
74. $P_1(4, 1)$, $P_2(1, -3)$, $P_3(9, -9)$
75. $P_1(-2, 2)$, $P_2(1, 10)$, $P_3(14, -4)$
76. $P_1(4, 2)$, $P_2(7, 4)$, $P_3(0, 8)$

In Probs. 77 to 80, find the slope of the line through $(x, f(x))$ and $(x + h, f(x + h))$, and simplify your answer.

77. $f(x) = x^2 + 5$
78. $f(x) = 4/x$
79. $f(x) = x^3$
80. $f(x) = 1/x^2$

In Probs. 81 to 84, assume that a linear function describes the situation accurately.

81. *Production* If a company can make 8 grandfather clocks for $10,100 and 22 of them for $16,400, how much does it cost to make x of them?

82. *Tax life* If a computer system has a scrap value of $12,000 after its tax life of 15 years and if it cost $132,000, what is its tax value after x years?

83. *Sales* If the number of bicycles sold in the first year by a company is 6720 and it sells 8320 in its sixth year, how many does it sell in year x?

84. *Thermal expansion* If the length of a metal rod is 108.75 cm at 25°C and is 109.08 cm at 36°C, what is its length at x°C?

85. This problem shows that the midpoint of the line segment joining (a, b) and (c, d) is $((a + c)/2, (b + d)/2)$.

(i) Show that the equation of the line passing through (a, b) and (c, d) is

$$(y - b)(c - a) = (d - b)(x - a)$$

(ii) Show that the equation of the perpendicular bisector of the line segment joining (a, b) and (c, d) is

$$2cx + 2dy + a^2 + b^2 = 2ax + 2by + c^2 + d^2$$

by simplifying

$$\sqrt{(x - a)^2 + (y - b)^2} = \sqrt{(x - c)^2 + (y - d)^2}$$

(iii) Show that $((a + c)/2, (b + d)/2)$ is on the lines in (i) and (ii).

3.8 Inverse Functions

For the function $f(x) = 3x + 1$, or $y = 3x + 1$, we know how to find $f(4)$ by substitution: $f(4) = 3(4) + 1 = 13$. That is, given a value for x, we can find a value for y. However, suppose we have a value given for y, can we find x? For the function above, the answer is yes. In particular, if we are given $y = -5$, we just solve the equation

$$-5 = 3x + 1$$

$$-6 = 3x$$

$$-2 = x$$

In this section we want to investigate the general problem of solving $y = f(x)$ for x. Moreover, we want the solution to be a single, well-defined real number x for any given y. We will shortly see how to do this and when it can be done.

▶ **EXAMPLE 1** Solve the equation $y = f(x) = 3x + 1$ for x.

Solution We solve for x by writing

$$y - 1 = 3x$$

$$\frac{y - 1}{3} = x$$ ◢

When using x and y as the variables, we normally write x as the independent variable. Thus in Example 1 we could have interchanged x and y, leading to a final equation of

$$\frac{x - 1}{3} = y$$

This is the reason for the second step below in the rules for *finding the inverse of a function,* if it exists.

Finding the inverse of a function

(a) $y = f(x)$ is given.
(b) Interchange x and y and get $x = f(y)$.
(c) Solve for y, and write the solution as $y = f^{-1}(x)$. We call f^{-1} the **inverse function of f.**

Substituting the value from (c) into the equation in (b) gives

$$x = f(y) = f(f^{-1}(x))$$

We will use this form later. Remember that the -1 in $f^{-1}(x)$ is not an exponent; thus $f^{-1}(x)$ and $1/f(x)$ are different things entirely.

▶ **EXAMPLE 2**   Find the inverse function for $f(x) = (2x + 1)/(x - 3)$, if it exists.

Solution

$$y = \frac{2x + 1}{x - 3} = f(x) \qquad \text{given}$$

$$x = \frac{2y + 1}{y - 3} = f(y) \qquad \text{interchange } x \text{ and } y$$

In order to have an inverse *function,* we want a given x to correspond to exactly one value of y:

$$xy - 3x = 2y + 1 \qquad \text{multiplying by } y - 3$$

$$xy - 2y = 1 + 3x \qquad \text{transposing}$$

$$y = \frac{1 + 3x}{x - 2} \qquad \text{solving for } y$$

Thus we were able to solve for a unique y, if $x \neq 2$. The inverse function is

$$f^{-1}(x) = \frac{3x + 1}{x - 2} \qquad \text{if } x \neq 2 \qquad ◀$$

Note in Example 2 that $f^{-1}(x) = (3x + 1)/(x - 2)$, which is different from $1/f(x) = (x - 3)/(2x + 1)$.

▶ **EXAMPLE 3**   Show that an inverse function for $f(x) = x^2 + 2x + 5$ does not exist.

Solution

$$y = x^2 + 2x + 5 \qquad \text{given}$$

$$x = y^2 + 2y + 5 \qquad \text{interchange } x \text{ and } y$$

$$0 = y^2 + 2y + (5 - x) \qquad \text{preparing to solve for } y$$

$$y = \frac{-2 \pm \sqrt{4 - 4(5 - x)}}{2} \qquad \text{quadratic formula with } a = 1, b = 2, c = 5 - x$$

First of all, this provides a solution only if $0 \leq 4 - 4(5 - x) = -16 + 4x$, that is,

$x \geq 4$. Second, when there is a solution, there are two solutions, using either the $+$ or $-$ sign. However this gives two values, not just one value as we need for a function. Hence

An inverse function does not exist

even though we were able to solve for y.

The question thus arises: When can we find an inverse function to a given function $y = f(x)$? The answer is that an inverse function exists if and only if f is one-to-one.

Definition

f is a **one-to-one function** means

$$\text{If } x_1 \neq x_2, \text{ then } y_1 \neq y_2 \qquad (1)$$

For a function, we require that each x correspond to exactly one y. For a function to be one-to-one, we also require that different x values correspond to different y values. Condition (1) is equivalent to the statement

$$\text{If } y_1 = y_2, \text{ then } x_1 = x_2 \qquad (2)$$

This says precisely that the inverse is a function. Using $f(x)$ notation, we have this alternative definition for a one-to-one function:

One-to-one function

$$\text{If } x_1 \neq x_2, \text{ then } f(x_1) \neq f(x_2)$$
or
$$\text{If } f(x_1) = f(x_2), \text{ then } x_1 = x_2$$

A function f will be one-to-one if it is **increasing** on an interval or if it is **decreasing** on an interval. Therefore

NOTE

If f is increasing on an interval, f has an inverse

If f is decreasing on an interval, f has an inverse

The function f with $f(x) = x^2$ is not one-to-one because different x values can produce the same y value. In fact

$$x = -12 \text{ gives } f(-12) = (-12)^2 = 144$$

$$x = 12 \text{ gives } f(12) = 12^2 = 144$$

However we can restrict the domain to the interval $[0, \infty)$, thereby getting a new function, say, F. By definition $F(x) = x^2$ is defined only for $x \geq 0$. For these values of x,

$$x_1 < x_2 \qquad \text{implies} \qquad x_1^2 < x_2^2$$

since the latter inequality is equivalent to

$$0 < x_2^2 - x_1^2 = (x_2 - x_1)(x_2 + x_1)$$

But $x_2 - x_1 > 0$ since $x_1 < x_2$ is assumed, and $x_2 + x_1 > 0$ since the domain requires that $x_1 \geq 0$ and $x_2 > 0$. Hence $(x_2 - x_1)(x_2 + x_1)$ is the product of positive numbers. Thus F is increasing, hence one-to-one, and so has an inverse function F^{-1}. The right half of the parabola $y = x^2$ in Fig. 3.8 also indicates that F is increasing, and so one-to-one. We find F^{-1} in the usual way:

$$y = x^2 \qquad \text{(x \ge 0) definition of } F$$

$$x = y^2 \qquad \text{interchange } x \text{ and } y \text{ (now } y \ge 0\text{)}$$

$$\sqrt{x} = y \qquad \text{solve for } y$$

Hence $F^{-1}(x) = \sqrt{x}$. Note that y is $+\sqrt{x}$, not $\pm\sqrt{x}$, since $y \ge 0$. The function F has the property that $F^{-1}(F(x)) = x$ and $F(F^{-1}(x)) = x$ since

$$F^{-1}(F(x)) = F^{-1}(x^2) = \sqrt{x^2} = x \qquad \text{(recall } x \ge 0\text{)}$$

$$F(F^{-1}(x)) = F(\sqrt{x}) = (\sqrt{x})^2 = x$$

This is always true for any one-to-one function f and its inverse function f^{-1}, and it could have been taken as the *definition* of the inverse function:

$$f(f^{-1}(x)) = x \qquad \text{and} \qquad f^{-1}(f(x)) = x \tag{3.11}$$

Thus f^{-1} undoes what f does, and so f and f^{-1} are inverses with respect to composition of functions. We may use the condition (3.11) to check whether our solution for f^{-1} really is the inverse function of the function f.

Using g for f^{-1} simplifies the notation implicit in the definition (3.11) of an inverse function.

> Suppose $f: A \to B$ is a one-to-one function with domain A and range B and $g: B \to A$ is a function with domain B and range A. Then g is called the **inverse function of f** if
>
> $$f(g(x)) = x \qquad \text{for every } x \text{ in } B$$
>
> and $\qquad\qquad g(f(x)) = x \qquad \text{for every } x \text{ in } A$

These last two conditions can also be written using **composite-function** notation, namely

$$(f \circ g)(x) = x \qquad \text{and} \qquad (g \circ f)(x) = x$$

for every x in the respective domains.

NOTE   It follows, by definition really, that the domain of f is the range of f^{-1}, and the range of f is the domain of f^{-1}, as illustrated in Fig. 3.47.

◤ EXAMPLE 4   For $f(x) = (x - 1)^3$:

(i) Show f is one-to-one   (ii) Find $f^{-1}(x)$

(iii) Show $f(f^{-1}(x)) = x = f^{-1}(f(x))$ (iv) Graph f and f^{-1}

Solution   (i) The simplest way to show f is one-to-one is to use graphs. The graph of f is just a horizontal translation of the graph of $y = x^3$, which as shown in Fig. 3.10, is clearly increasing. Hence f is increasing, and so one-to-one. We could also show algebraically that f is one-to-one, but it is more difficult.

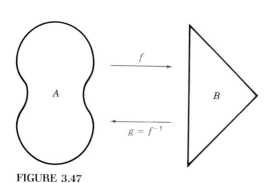

FIGURE 3.47

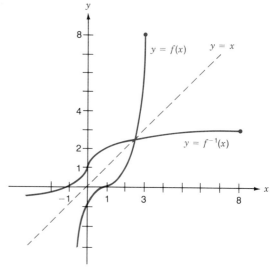

FIGURE 3.48

(ii)

$$y = (x - 1)^3 \qquad \text{given}$$

$$x = (y - 1)^3 \qquad \text{interchanging } x \text{ and } y$$

$$\sqrt[3]{x} = y - 1 \qquad \text{taking cube roots}$$

$$\sqrt[3]{x} + 1 = y = f^{-1}(x) \qquad \text{inverse function}$$

(iii)

$$f(f^{-1}(x)) = f(\sqrt[3]{x} + 1)$$

$$= [(\sqrt[3]{x} + 1) - 1]^3 = (\sqrt[3]{x})^3 = x$$

$$f^{-1}(f(x)) = f^{-1}[(x - 1)^3]$$

$$= \sqrt[3]{(x - 1)^3} + 1 = (x - 1) + 1 = x$$

(iv) Here is a table of values for f:

x	−1	0	1	2	3
$f(x)$	−8	−1	0	1	8

A table of values for f^{-1} can be made from this by interchanging the x and $f(x)$ values:

x	−8	−1	0	1	8
$f^{-1}(x)$	−1	0	1	2	3

See Fig. 3.48.

As the graphs above illustrate, the graph of $y = f^{-1}(x)$ is the reflection of the graph of $y = f(x)$ through the line $y = x$. This results from interchanging x and y to find $f^{-1}(x)$. Recall from the discussion of symmetry in Sec. 3.4 that (a, b) and (b, a) are symmetric with respect to the line $y = x$. Of course (a, b) is a point on the graph of f if and only if (b, a) is a point on the graph of f^{-1}.

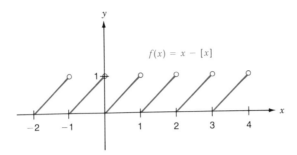

$f(x) = x - [x]$

FIGURE 3.49

There is an easy graphical method which tells us whether a function is one-to-one and, thus, whether an inverse function exists.

Horizontal-line test

A function f is one-to-one if every horizontal line intersects the graph of f in at most one point.

NOTE　The vertical-line test tells whether a graph is the graph of a function. The horizontal-line test tells whether a function is one-to-one.

In this section we have considered functions which are one-to-one, increasing, or decreasing in order to study inverse functions. Another special type of function is a **continuous function.** A complete description of a continuous function comes in a calculus course where limits are considered. For the purposes of this discussion, though, it is enough to say that the graph of a continuous function has no holes or gaps. Every polynomial function is continuous. So is $f(x) = |x|$, even though its graph has a corner at the origin. However the function $g(x) = 1/x$ for $x \neq 0$ and $g(0) = 0$ is not continuous. Neither is the function $h(x) = |x|/x$ for $x \neq 0$ and $h(0) = 0$. You should draw their graphs and try to see why.

Additional special functions we have studied are even functions and odd functions (Sec. 3.5). They are important because every function can be written as the sum of an even function and an odd function. In fact (see Prob. 57)

$$f(x) = \frac{f(x) + f(-x)}{2} + \frac{f(x) - f(-x)}{2} = \text{even} + \text{odd}$$

In Example 5, Sec. 3.2, we saw the graph of $y = [x]$, where $[x]$ is the greatest integer which is less than or equal to x. The graph of $f(x) = x - [x]$ is shown in Fig. 3.49, and it has an interesting property. The function is called **periodic** because its values repeat at regular intervals. In fact, $f(x + 1) = f(x)$ for all x. Notice that on the real line, this function is not continuous, not increasing, not decreasing, not even, and not odd. It is, though, increasing and continuous on the open interval $(0, 1)$.

EXERCISE 3.8

Is the function in Probs. 1 to 8 one-to-one? Use any method.

1.　$y = \sqrt{x}$

2.　$y = x^2$

3.　$y = x^3$

4.　$y = \sqrt[3]{x}$

5.　$y = |x|$

6.　$y = [x]$

7.　$y = x$

8.　$y = 1/x$

In Probs. 9 to 24, find the inverse of $y = f(x)$.

9. $y = 3x + 2$

10. $y = 5x - 1$

11. $y = -2x + 7$

12. $y = -4x - 3$

13. $y = (x + 4)/3$

14. $y = (2x - 1)/7$

15. $y = 3x - \frac{1}{4}$

16. $y = x/8 + 2$

17. $y = (x + 1)^3$

18. $y = x^3 - 3$

19. $y = x^5 + 4$

20. $y = 2x^5 - 5$

21. $y = 6/x$

22. $y = 4x/(3 + x)$

23. $y = 1/(2x - 3)$

24. $y = 5/(3x + 1)$

25. If $f(x) = 3x - 1$, find $f(2)$ and $f^{-1}(2)$.

26. If $f(x) = 2x + 7$, find $f(-3.5)$ and $f^{-1}(-3.5)$.

27. If $f(x) = 4x - 3$, find $f(1)$ and $f^{-1}(1)$.

28. If $f(x) = -3x + 5$, find $f(3)$ and $f^{-1}(3)$.

In Probs. 29 to 32, let $f(x) = 3^x$. Find $f^{-1}(t)$ for the given value of t. Use the fact that if $f^{-1}(t) = w$, then $t = f(w)$.

29. $t = 3$

30. $t = 81$

31. $t = \frac{1}{9}$

32. $t = \frac{1}{243}$

In Probs. 33 to 36, graph $y = f(x)$ and $y = f^{-1}(x)$. Verify the fact that the domain and range of f^{-1} are the range and domain, respectively, of f.

33. $y = 2x - 4$ for $0 \le x \le 6$

34. $y = 1/x$ for $\frac{1}{8} \le x \le 8$

35. $y - 1 = (x + 1)^3$ for $-3 \le x \le 1$

36. $y = \sqrt{x}$ for $0 \le x \le 9$

In Probs. 37 to 40, show that $f(f^{-1}(x)) = x$ and $f^{-1}(f(x)) = x$.

37. $f(x) = 3x + 5$

38. $f(x) = 3/x$

39. $f(x) = 3/(x + 5)$

40. $f(x) = 1/(3x + 5)$

Show that the functions in Probs. 41 to 44 are increasing. Do it graphically or algebraically.

41. $f(x) = x^2 + 2x + 5$ on $(-1, \infty)$

42. $f(x) = 3x + 5$

43. $f(x) = x^3 + 2x$

44. $f(x) = -1/x$ for $x > 0$

45. Let $f(x)$ and $g(x)$ be odd functions. Show that $f(x) + g(x)$ is odd and $f(x)g(x)$ is even.

46. Let $f(x)$ be odd and $g(x)$ be even. Show that $f(x)g(x)$ is odd.

47. Let $f(x)$ be the remainder when x is divided by 3. What is the smallest positive value of k such that $f(x + k) = f(x)$ for all x?

48. Show that the sum of two increasing functions is increasing. Show that the product of two increasing positive functions is increasing.

The number p is called a **fixed point** of the function f if $f(p) = p$. Find at least one fixed point for each function in Probs. 49 to 52.

49. $f(x) = 4x - 9$

50. $f(x) = \sqrt{x}$

51. $f(x) = 2x^2 - 2x - 20$

52. $f(x) = \dfrac{4x + 8}{15x + 2}$

53. Let $h(x) = (6x + 7)/(5x - 6)$. Show that $h^{-1}(x) = h(x)$. Find $h(h(2))$.

54. Let $M(x) = (x + 9)/(x - 1)$. Show that $M^{-1}(x) = M(x)$. Find $M^{-1}(M^{-1}(x))$.

55. Let $f(x) = (ax + b)/(cx - a)$. Show that $f(f(x)) = x$; hence $f^{-1}(x) = f(x)$.

56. Let $g(x) = (1 - x^{2/3})^{3/2}$. Show that $g(g(x)) = x$ and that $g^{-1}(x) = g(x)$.

57. Let $y = f(x)$ be any function defined for all real x, whether or not f^{-1} exists. Show that it is the sum of an even function and an odd function. *Hint:* Begin with

$$f(x) = \frac{f(x) + f(-x)}{2} + \frac{f(x) - f(-x)}{2}$$

3.9 Variation

In the numerous applications of mathematics to science, certain basic formulas or relationships occur repeatedly. The key to many of these formulas is a function f defined by some equation $y = f(x)$. There are special names for certain types of functions.

Equation	Terminology
$y = kx$	y **varies directly** as x
	y is directly proportional to x
$y = kx^n$	y varies directly as the nth power of x
	y is directly proportional to the nth power of x
$y = k/x$	y **varies inversely** as x
	y is inversely proportional to x
$y = k/x^n$	y varies inversely as the nth power of x
	y is inversely proportional to the nth power of x
$y = kxw$	y **varies jointly** as x and w
	y is jointly proportional to x and w

Letters other than y, x, w, and k may be used. In each case above, the number k is a constant, and it is called the **constant of variation** or the constant of proportionality.

(a) If the weight w of a piece of pipe varies directly as its length L, then $w = kL$.

(b) The area A of a circle varies directly as the square of its radius r. So $A = kr^2$, where in this case we know that $k = \pi$.

(c) *Boyle's law* states that the volume V of a confined mass of gas at a constant temperature varies inversely as the pressure P. Thus, $V = k/P$, or $PV = k$.

If more than one kind of variation is involved, then the variation is referred to as **combined variation.** Thus if y varies jointly as x and z and inversely as w, then $y = kxz/w$. Also, *Newton's law of gravitation* states that the gravitational attraction between two bodies varies directly as the product of their masses and inversely as the square of the distance between their centers of gravity. If we let G, M, m, and d represent the gravitational attraction, the two masses, and the distance, respectively, then the law states

Newton's law of gravitation

$$G = \frac{kMm}{d^2}$$

NOTE   In variation problems, the actual *constant of variation* does not need to be calculated unless we want to write the function involved. See Examples 1 and 3. The constant can be evaluated if a complete set of values of the variables is known.

   **EXAMPLE 1**   The pressure on the bottom of a swimming pool varies directly as the depth. If the pressure is 125 lb/ft^2 when the water is 2 ft deep, find the pressure when it is $4\frac{1}{2}$ ft deep.

Direct variation

Solution   (a) In this solution, we **find the value of k.** Letting P = pressure and d = depth, then P varies directly as d, and hence

$$P = kd$$

Since $P = 125$ when $d = 2$, then

$$125 = k(2)$$

$$k = \tfrac{125}{2} = 62.5$$

$$P = 62.5d \qquad \text{\small P as a function of d}$$

Consequently, if $d = 4\frac{1}{2} = \frac{9}{2}$, then

$$P = (62.5)(\tfrac{9}{2}) = 281.25 \text{ lb/ft}^2$$

Alternative Solution

(b) In this solution, we **do not find** *k*. The equation $P = kd$ may be written $P/d = k$, meaning that P/d is a constant. Hence

$$\frac{P_1}{d_1} = \frac{P_2}{d_2}$$

$$\frac{125}{2} = \frac{P_2}{\frac{9}{2}}$$

$$P_2 = \frac{125(\frac{9}{2})}{2} = 281.25 \text{ lb/ft}^2 \qquad \blacktriangleleft$$

▶ **EXAMPLE 2**

Direct variation

The horsepower required to propel a ship varies directly as the cube of its speed. If the horsepower required for a speed of 15 knots is 10,125, find the horsepower required for a speed of 20 knots.

Solution If we let

$$P = \text{required horsepower}$$

$$s = \text{speed, in knots}$$

then, since *P* varies directly as s^3, we have

$$P = ks^3 \qquad (1)$$

We are given that $P = 10,125$ for $s = 15$ knots, and substituting these values in (1), we get

$$10,125 = k(15^3)$$

and

$$k = \frac{10,125}{15^3} = \frac{10,125}{3375} = 3$$

Now we substitute $k = 3$ and $s = 20$ in (1) and obtain

$$P = 3(20^3) = 3(8000)$$

$$= 24,000 \text{ hp} \qquad \blacktriangleleft$$

▶ **EXAMPLE 3**

Inverse variation

If the volume of a mass of gas at a given temperature is 56 in^3 when the pressure is 18 lb/in^2, use Boyle's law to find the volume when the pressure is 16 lb/in^2.

Solution As given just after the definitions, Boyle's law states that $V = k/P$ or $PV = k$, meaning that *PV* is a constant.

(a) Without finding *k*, we may write

$$P_1V_1 = P_2V_2$$

$$(56)(18) = (16)V_2$$

$$V_2 = \frac{56(18)}{16} = 63 \text{ in}^3$$

Alternative Solution   (b) If we want to find k, we may write $V = k/P$ and thus

$$18 = \frac{k}{56} \quad \text{and} \quad k = 56(18) = 1008$$

It follows that

$$V = \frac{1008}{P} \qquad \text{V as a function of } P$$

$$V = \frac{1008}{16} = 63 \text{ in}^3 \qquad \text{V when } P = 16$$

 EXAMPLE 4   The weight of a rectangular block of metal varies jointly as its length, width, and

Joint variation   thickness. If the weight of a 12- by 8- by 6-in block of aluminum is 18.7 lb, find the weight of a 16- by 10- by 4-in block.

Solution   We let

$$W = \text{weight} \qquad \text{lb}$$
$$l = \text{length} \qquad \text{in}$$
$$w = \text{width} \qquad \text{in}$$
$$t = \text{thickness} \qquad \text{in}$$

Then, since the weight varies jointly as the length, width, and thickness, we have

$$W = klwt$$

When $l = 12$ in, $w = 8$ in, and $t = 6$ in, then $W = 18.7$ lb. Therefore,

$$18.7 = k(12)(8)(6) = 576k$$

and

$$k = \frac{18.7}{576}$$

If we substitute $k = 18.7/576$, $l = 16$, $w = 10$, and $t = 4$ in the equation $W = klwt$, we obtain

$$W = \frac{18.7}{576}(16)(10)(4)$$

$$= 20.8 \text{ lb}$$

as the weight of the 16- by 10- by 4-in block. You should note in this example that k is the weight of 1 in^3 of aluminum.

EXAMPLE 5   The amount of coal used by a steamship traveling at a uniform speed varies jointly as

Joint variation   the distance traveled and the square of the speed. If a steamship uses 45 tons of coal traveling 80 mi at 15 knots, how many tons will it use if it travels 120 mi at 20 knots?

Solution   If we let

$$T = \text{the number of tons used}$$
$$s = \text{the distance in miles}$$

and

$$v = \text{the speed in knots}$$

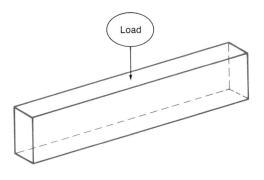

Load

FIGURE 3.50

then $\qquad T = k(sv^2) \qquad$ definition of joint variation $\qquad$ (1)

Hence, when $T = 45$, $s = 80$, and $v = 15$, we have

$$45 = k(80)(15^2)$$

Therefore, $\qquad k = \dfrac{45}{(80)(225)} = \dfrac{1}{400}$

Substituting this value for k in (1), we have

$$T = \tfrac{1}{400}(sv^2) \qquad \text{\textit{T} as a function of \textit{s} and \textit{v}}$$

Now, when $s = 120$ and $v = 20$, it follows that

$$T = \tfrac{1}{400}(120)(20^2)$$

$$= \tfrac{48000}{400} = 120 \text{ tons}$$

▶ **EXAMPLE 6**

Combined variation

The load which can be safely put on a beam with a rectangular cross section that is supported at each end varies jointly as the product of the width and the square of the depth and inversely as the length of the beam between supports. If the safe load of a beam 3 in wide and 6 in deep with supports 8 ft apart is 2700 lb, find the safe load of a beam of the same material that is 4 in wide and 10 in deep with supports 12 ft apart. See Fig. 3.50.

Solution We let $\qquad\qquad w = $ width of beam $\qquad$ in

$\qquad\qquad d = $ depth of beam $\qquad$ in

$\qquad\qquad l = $ length between supports $\qquad$ ft

$\qquad\qquad L = $ safe load $\quad$ lb

Then $\qquad\qquad L = \dfrac{kwd^2}{l}$

According to the first set of data, when $w = 3$, $d = 6$, and $l = 8$, then $L = 2700$. Therefore

$$2700 = \dfrac{k(3)(6^2)}{8}$$

$$k = \frac{8(2700)}{3(6^2)} = \frac{2(2700)}{3^3} = 200 \qquad \text{value of } k$$

Consequently, if $w = 4$, $d = 10$, $l = 12$, and $k = 200$, we have

$$L = \frac{200(4)(10^2)}{12} = 6666\tfrac{2}{3} \qquad \blacktriangleleft$$

Direct variation problems have equations such as $y = kx$, which can also be written as $y/x = k$. This is stated as "y is **directly proportional** to x." If one set of values for x and y is a and b and another set is c and d, then (assuming no division by zero)

$$\frac{b}{a} = k = \frac{d}{c}$$

which is equivalent to

$$\frac{a}{b} = \frac{c}{d} \tag{2}$$

An equation such as this is called a **proportion.** See Probs. 49 to 52 for some equivalent proportions.

EXERCISE 3.9

Express the statements in Probs. 1 to 4 as equations.
1. m varies directly as n^2.
2. s varies inversely as t.
3. p varies jointly as q and r^3.
4. w varies directly as x and inversely as the square of y.
5. If y varies directly as x and is 10 when $x = 5$, find the value of y if $x = 7$.
6. If w varies directly as x and is 10 when $x = 5$, find the value of w if $x = 3$.
7. Given that y varies inversely as x. If $y = 3$ when $x = 4$, find the value of y when $x = 6$.
8. If w varies inversely as y and is equal to 2 when $y = 3$, find the value of w if $y = 6$.
9. If y varies jointly as x and w and is 30 when $x = 2$ and $w = 3$, find the value of y if $x = 4$ and $w = 5$.
10. Given that x varies jointly as w and y and also that $x = 24$ when $w = 3$ and $y = 4$, find the value of x if $w = 4$ and $y = 5$.
11. Given that w varies directly as the product of x and y and inversely as the square of z. If $w = 9$ when $x = 6$, $y = 27$, and $z = 3$, find the value of w when $x = 4$, $y = 7$, and $z = 2$.
12. Suppose p varies directly as b^2 and inversely as s^3. If

p is $\tfrac{3}{4}$ when $b = 6$ and $s = 2$, find b when p is 6 and s is 4.

13. *Geometry* The volume of a right circular cylinder varies jointly as the height and the square of the radius. If the volume of a right circular cylinder of radius 4 in and height 7 in is 352 in^3, find the volume of another of radius 8 in and height 14 in.

14. *Physics* In comparing Celsius and Fahrenheit thermometers, it has been found that the Celsius reading varies directly as the difference between the Fahrenheit reading and 32°F. If a Celsius thermometer reads 100° when a Fahrenheit one reads 212°, what will the Celsius read when the Fahrenheit reads 100°?

15. *Engineering* The intensity of light varies inversely as the square of the distance from the source. Compare the intensity on a screen that is 5 ft from a given source with that on a screen 7 ft from the source.

16. *Photography* The time necessary to make an enlargement from a photographic negative varies directly as the area. If 6 s are required for an enlargement that is 4 by 5 in, how many seconds are

required to make an enlargement that is 8 by 10 in from the same negative?

17. *Engineering* The amount of oil used by a ship traveling at a uniform speed varies jointly as the distance traveled and the square of the velocity. If a certain ship used 600 bbl of oil on a 300-mi trip at 20 knots, how much oil would it use on a trip of 100 mi at 10 knots?

18. *Athletics* If an athlete jumps 22.7 ft when taking off at 9.25 m/s, how far will the jump be if the takeoff is at 9.5 m/s? Assume the jump is proportional to the square of the takeoff velocity.

19. *Physics* The wind force on a flat vertical surface varies jointly as the area of the surface and the square of the wind velocity. If the pressure on 1 ft^2 is 1 lb when the wind velocity is 15 mi/h, find the force on an 8- by 10-ft sign in a storm with a wind velocity at 60 mi/h.

20. *Navigation* On the ocean, the square of the distance in miles to the horizon varies as the height in feet that the observer is above the surface of the water. If a 6-ft man on a surfboard can see 3 mi, how far can he see if he is in a plane that is 1000 ft above the water?

21. *Strength of a beam* The strength of a rectangular horizontal beam that is supported at the ends varies jointly as the width w and the square of the depth d and inversely as the length L. Compare the strengths of two beams if one of them is 20 ft long, 4 in wide, and 6 in deep and the other is 10 ft long, 2 in wide, and 4 in deep.

22. *Engineering* The horsepower required to propel a ship varies as the cube of its speed. Find the ratio of the power required at 14 knots to that required at 7 knots.

23. *Physics* The kinetic energy of a body varies as the square of its velocity. Find the ratio of the kinetic energy of a car at 20 mi/h to that of the same car at 50 mi/h.

24. *Physics* As a body falls from rest, its velocity varies as the time in flight. If the velocity of a body at the end of 2 s is 64.4 ft/s, find the velocity at the end of 5 s.

25. *Physics* If a body is above the surface of the earth,

its weight varies inversely as the square of the distance of the body from the center of the earth. If a man weighs 160 lb on the surface of the earth, how much will he weigh 200 mi above the surface? Assume the radius of the earth is 4000 mi.

26. *Engineering* The current I varies as the electromotive force E and inversely as the resistance R. If in a system a current of 20 A flows through a resistance of 20 Ω (ohms) with an electromotive force of 100 V, find the current that 150 V will send through the system.

27. *Physics* The illumination produced on a surface by a source of light varies directly as the candlepower of the source and inversely as the square of the distance between the source and the surface. Compare the illumination produced by a 512-cd (candela) lamp that is 8 ft from a surface with that of a 72-cd lamp 2 ft from the surface.

28. *Physics* If other factors are equal, the centrifugal force on a circular curve varies inversely as the radius of the turn. If the centrifugal force is 18,000 lb for a curve of radius 50 ft, find the centrifugal force on a curve of radius 150 ft.

29. If y varies jointly as x and w and is 72 for $x = 9$ and $w = 4$, find the value of y for $x = 18$ and $w = 1.5$.

30. *Economics* The simple interest earned in a given time varies jointly as the principal and the rate. If $300 earned $45 at a 6 percent rate, how much would be earned by $500 at 5 percent in the same time?

31. *Volume* The volume of a regular pyramid varies jointly as the altitude and the area of the base. If the volume of a regular pyramid of altitude 5 in and base 9 in^2 is 15 in^3, find the volume of another of altitude 4 in and base area 6 in^2.

32. *Engineering* The crushing load of a circular pillar varies directly as the fourth power of the diameter and inversely as the square of the height of the pillar. If 256 tons is needed to crush a pillar 8 in in diameter and 20 ft high, find the load needed to crush a pillar 10 in in diameter and 15 ft high.

33. *Engineering* The mechanical advantage of a jackscrew varies directly as the length of the lever arm. If the mechanical advantage of a jackscrew is 192 when a 3-ft lever arm is used, what is the mechanical advantage for a 2-ft arm?

34. *Aerodynamics*   If the other factors are fixed, the lift on a wing of a plane varies with the density of the air. If the density of air at sea level is 0.08 lb/ft^3 and the lift on a wing is 2500 lb, find the lift at the altitude where the density is 0.06 lb/ft^3.

35. *Physics*   For a given load, the amount a wire stretches varies inversely as the square of the diameter. If a wire with a diameter of 0.6 in is stretched 0.006 in by a given load, how much will a wire of the same material with a diameter of 0.2 in be stretched by the same load?

36. *Engineering*   Under the same load, the sag of beams of the same material, length, and width varies inversely as the cube of the thickness. If a beam 4 in thick sags $\frac{1}{64}$ in when a load is placed on it, find the sag of a beam 2 in thick under the same load.

37. *Education*   The Wechsler score W on a test is $W(z) = 10 + 3z$, where z is the standard deviation. (a) Find z in terms of W. (b) Find z if $W = 8$.

38. *Earth science*   The integrated intensity reflected by a perfect crystal is

$$I = \frac{L^2 F \sqrt{0.69/\pi}}{0.64V}$$

for an angle of 20°. What is the effect on I if L is doubled and V is halved?

39. *Biology*   The volume V of the body of any animal is given by $V = kL^3$, where L is one of its linear dimensions. Find the relative body size of two animals if their lengths are 12 and 21 in.

40. *Radiation of heat*   According to the Stefan-Boltzmann law, the heat radiation from an object is proportional to the fourth power of its Kelvin temperature. For a certain object the radiation is 215.81 at 294 K. Find the radiation if the temperature is 333 K.

41. *Pizza price*   The cost of a pizza of a certain type varies directly as the square of the radius. If a pizza of radius 6 in costs \$6, find the cost of one of radius 9 in.

42. *Period of a pendulum*   The period of time required for one complete oscillation of a pendulum varies directly as the square root of its length. If a pendu-

lum 1 ft long has a period of 1.06 s, what is the period of a pendulum 3 ft long?

43. *Blood flow*   Suppose that the rate of blood flow through major arteries in liters per second is jointly proportional to the fourth power of the radius R and blood pressure P. During moderate exercise, blood flow often doubles. If the radius increases by $\frac{1}{12}$, what is the new blood pressure?

44. *Time for fruit to ripen*   Assume that the time required for fruit to ripen is inversely proportional to the Fahrenheit temperature and that it takes 24 days at 76°F. How long will be required if the temperature is 80°F?

45. *Normal weight*   The normal weight for a human varies directly as the cube of the height. Find the normal weight for a person 68 in tall if 180 is the normal weight for a person 74 inches tall.

46. *Normal shoe size*   The square of the normal shoe size of a female varies directly as the cube of her height. Find the normal shoe size for a female 62 in tall if 8 is the normal shoe size for a female 68 in tall.

47. *Mass mailing*   Suppose that the time required to do a mass mailing is inversely proportional to the number of machines working on it. If 3 machines take 10 h, how long will 5 machines take?

48. *Number of letters*   Suppose that the number of personal letters mailed between two cities varies directly as the population of each city and inversely as the distance between them. If 25,000 personal letters are mailed between cities with populations of 30,000 and 80,000 which are 200 miles apart, how many personal letters are mailed between cities with populations of 20,000 and 120,000 which are 400 miles apart?

In Probs. 49 to 52, show that the given proportion is equivalent to $a/b = c/d$, assuming that there is no division by zero. Use the fundamental principle of fractions, then show that the result is equivalent to $ad = bc$.

49. $\dfrac{a + b}{b} = \dfrac{c + d}{d}$

50. $\dfrac{a - b}{b} = \dfrac{c - d}{d}$

51. $\dfrac{a + b}{a - b} = \dfrac{c + d}{c - d}$

52. $\dfrac{a}{b} = \dfrac{a + c}{b + d}$

3.10 Key Concepts

Be certain that you understand and can use the following important words and ideas.

Coordinate axes (p. 130)
Origin (p. 130)
Ordered pair (p. 130)
Graph (p. 135)
Intercept (p. 136)
Circle (p. 140)
Parabola (p. 143)
Ellipse (p. 143)
Hyperbola (p. 143)
Symmetry (p. 150)
Reflection (p. 151)
Translation (p. 152)
Domain (p. 155)
Range (p. 155)
Function (p. 155)
Function value (p. 155)

Composite function (p. 160)
Increasing function (p. 167)
Decreasing function (p. 167)
Vertical-line test for a function (p. 169)
Slope (p. 170)
Equations of a line (p. 174)
Inverse function (p. 180)
One-to-one function (p. 181)
Graph of inverse function (p. 183)
Horizontal-line test for one-to-one function (p. 184)
Direct variation (p. 186)
Inverse variation (p. 186)
Joint variation (p. 186)
Combined variation (p. 186)

(6.1) $(a, b) = (c, d)$ if and only if $a = c$ and $b = d$

(6.2) Distance $= \sqrt{(x_2 - x_1)^2 + (y_2 - y_1)^2}$

(6.3) Midpoint $= \left(\dfrac{a + c}{2}, \dfrac{b + d}{2} \right)$

(6.4) $(x - h)^2 + (y - k)^2 = r^2$ Circle

(6.5) Slope $= m = \dfrac{y_2 - y_1}{x_2 - x_1}$

(6.6) $y - y_1 = \dfrac{y_2 - y_1}{x_2 - x_1}(x - x_1)$ Two-point form

(6.7) $y - y_1 = m(x - x_1)$ Point-slope form

(6.8) $y = mx + b$ Slope-intercept form

(6.9) $m_1 = m_2$ Parallel lines

(6.10) $m_1 m_2 = -1$ Perpendicular lines

(6.11) $f(f^{-1}(x)) = x = f^{-1}(f(x))$ Inverse functions

EXERCISE 3.10   Review

1. Does the equation define a function of x? (a) $x^2 + y^2 = 6$, (b) $x + y^2 = 6$, (c) $x^2 + y = 6$, and (d) $x + y = 6$.

2. If $f(x) = 3x - 4$, find $f(2)$, $f(-2)$, and $f(2t)$.

3. If $g(x) = x^2 - 4x + 1$, find $g(3)$, $g(1)$, and $g(g(0))$.

4. If $f(x) = 4x - 1$ and $g(x) = 1/(x^2 + 1)$, find $f(g(0))$ and $g(f(0))$.

5. Find the distance between the points $(8, 13)$ and $(-12, -8)$.

6. Are the points $(2, 1)$, $(-1, 5)$, and $(5, -2)$ all on the same line?

7. Find the equation of the line through $(1, -4)$ and $(3, 1)$.

8. Find the equation of the line through $(3, -7)$ and parallel to $6x + 2y = 1$.

9. Find the equation of the line which has x intercept 5 and which is perpendicular to $7x - 2y = 13$.

10. Find the distance from the point $(4, 1)$ to the line $3x - 4y + 7 = 0$.

11. Is $f(x) = \sqrt{25 - x^2}$ one-to-one?

12. If $f(x) = 4x - 3$, find $f(-1)$ and $f^{-1}(-1)$.

13. Find $f^{-1}(x)$ if $f(x) = (2x - 1)/(x + 3)$.

14. Show that if $f(x) = -x + 5$, then $f^{-1}(x) = f(x)$.

15. If $f(x) = 6x - 5$, show that $(f^{-1})^{-1} = f$ by finding $f^{-1}(x)$ and then finding the inverse of $f^{-1}(x)$.

16. Find the midpoint of the line segment which joins $(\frac{4}{5}, \frac{2}{3})$ and $(-\frac{1}{3}, \frac{2}{5})$.

17. Show that in any triangle, the line joining the midpoints of two sides is parallel to the third side.

Graph the following equations and functions.

18. $y = x + |x| + 1$

19. $x = y^2 - 4y + 3$

20. $y = -5x + 1$ and $y = x/5 + 1$

21. $x = 3y$ and its inverse

22. $y = x^3 + 1$ and its inverse

23. $y + 1 = -4(x - 2)^2$

24. $y = (x - 1)^4$ and $y - 1 = x^4$

25. $x = y^2 + 1$ and $x = (y + 1)^2$

In Probs. 26 to 37, tell what letter of the alphabet the graph most resembles.

26. $(x - 4)^2 + (y - 5)^2 = 9$

27. $x = 1$

28. $y = 2(x - 4)^2$

29. $y = 4x^4 - 65x^2 + 16$

30. $y = |x + 5|$

31. $|y + 2| = |x - 3|$

32. $-y = 4x^4 - 65x^2 + 16$

33. $x = y^4 - 26y^2 + 25$

34. $x + 3 = (y + 5)^2$ 35. $y = x^3 - 16x$

36. $x = y^3 - 9y$ 37. $-x = y^3 - 25y$

38. *Symmetry of a quadratic* Show that the graph of $y = ax^2 + bx + c = f(x)$ is symmetric about the vertical line $x = -b/2a$ by proving that for any $h > 0$

$$f\left(-\frac{b}{2a} + h\right) = f\left(-\frac{b}{2a} - h\right)$$

39. *Symmetry of a cubic* Show that the graph of $y = ax^3 + bx^2 + cx + d = f(x)$ is symmetric about the

point $(-b/3a, f(-b/3a))$ by showing that for any $h > 0$

$$\frac{f\left(-\dfrac{b}{3a} + h\right) + f\left(-\dfrac{b}{3a} - h\right)}{2} = f\left(-\frac{b}{3a}\right) \quad (*)$$

Another way to express Eq. $(*)$ is to write

$$g(-h) = -g(h)$$

where $g(h) = f(-b/3a + h) - f(-b/3a)$.

40. *Education* The Dale-Chall reading score is

$$R(x, y) = 0.1579x + 0.0496y + 3.6365$$

where x is the percentage of words outside the Dale list of 3000 easy words and y is the average sentence length in words. Find $R(28, 11.3)$.

41. *Education* The Flesch readability formula is

$$r(W, S) = 206.8 - 0.85W - 1.015S$$

where W is the average number of syllables per 100 words and S is the average number of words per sentence. Calculate $r(178, 8.3)$.

42. *Psychology* Weber's law in psychology states that $D/S = c$, where D is the minimum amount of stimulus change required to produce a sensation difference, S is the magnitude of the stimulus, and c is a constant. Calculate D if $S = 4000$ and $c = 0.20$.

43. *Agriculture* The amount y of potassium absorbed by Zea mays (corn) leaf is a linear function of time t up to 4 h. Thus $y = at$, where a is called the rate of absorption and is 18 μmoles (micromoles) per unit of leaf in darkness and 4.0 μmoles in a light intensity of 2×10^4 1m/m^2 (lm = lumens). How long in darkness is required for the same absorption by a leaf as in 1 h of 2×10^4 lm/m^2 of light?

44. *Photography* The exposure time necessary to obtain a good negative varies directly as the square of the f numbers of the camera shutter. If $\frac{1}{25}$ s is required when the shutter is set at $f/16$, what exposure is required under the same conditions if the shutter is set at $f/8$?

45. *Physics* The force of attraction between two spheres varies directly as the product of their masses and inversely as the square of the distance between

them. Compare the attraction between two bodies with masses m_1 and m_2 that are separated by the distance d with that between two other bodies of masses $2m_1$ and $8m_2$ that are separated by the distance $4d$.

46. *Energy* If the kinetic energy of a body varies as the square of its velocity, compare the kinetic energy of a car traveling at 10 mi/h with that of the same car traveling at 50 mi/h.

47. *Motion of the planets* One of Kepler's laws states that the square of the time required by a planet to make one revolution about the sum varies directly as the cube of the average distance of the planet from the sun. If Mars is $1\frac{1}{2}$ times as far from the sun, on the average, as the earth, find the approximate length of time required for it to make a revolution about the sun. Use 1 year = 365 days.

48. *Satellites* The gravitational attraction of the earth for an object varies inversely as the square of the distance of the object from the center of the earth. If a space satellite weighs 100 lb on the earth's surface, how much does it weigh when it is 1000 mi from the earth's surface? (Assume the radius of the earth to be 4000 mi.)

4 Polynomial and Rational Functions

Polynomial functions are basic to algebra because they are formed from the real numbers with only the four fundamental operations. Rational functions are quotients of polynomials. Polynomial and rational functions are useful because they represent many more complicated situations and functions very well. Applications include satellite dishes, projectile paths, economics, geometry, ecology, weather, biology, and others.

The chapter begins by working with quadratic functions, which are the simplest type of polynomial functions except for the linear functions studied in the last chapter. We then prepare for a detailed study of polynomials of higher degree, written either as a sum or product, by learning how to graph them. The product method allows us to draw accurate graphs with little actual plotting of points. We then show how to find rational, irrational, and complex zeros of polynomial functions. This will enable us to factor any polynomial into the product of linear and quadratic terms. Rational functions and inequalities are also presented.

4.1 Quadratic Functions

Some of the most important functions in applications are the polynomial functions, which are defined below. Although we will occasionally allow the coefficients a_i to be complex numbers, the main focus of this chapter is polynomials with real coefficients.

Polynomial function

> A function is a polynomial function of degree n if
>
> $$f(x) = a_n x^n + a_{n-1} x^{n-1} + \cdots + a_2 x^2 + a_1 x + a_0$$
>
> where the coefficients a_i are real numbers, $a_n \neq 0$, and n is a positive integer.

For instance, $f(x) = 3x^4 - 17x^3 - 4.6x^2 + 9x - \sqrt{5}$ is a polynomial function of degree 4, while $g(x) = x^9 + x^6 - 4x^5 - 2x^3 - 2$ is a polynomial function of degree 9.

In Sec. 3.7 we studied linear functions $f(x) = ax + b$, which are polynomial functions with $n = 1$. Polynomial functions with $n > 2$ will be discussed later in this chapter. If $n = 2$, then f is called a **quadratic function.**

Quadratic function

> A function f is a quadratic function if $f(x) = ax^2 + bx + c$ where a, b, and c are real numbers and $a \neq 0$.

The graph of a quadratic function is called a **parabola.** The most basic aid in graphing a parabola is knowing whether $a > 0$ (the graph opens upward) or $a < 0$ (the graph opens downward). The two simplest quadratic functions are $f(x) = x^2$ and $g(x) = -x^2$. Their graphs are obtained by plotting points from the following table of values, and the graphs are shown in Figs. 4.1 and 4.2.

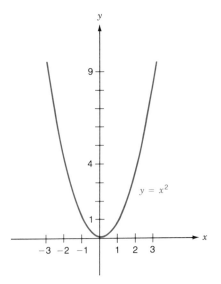

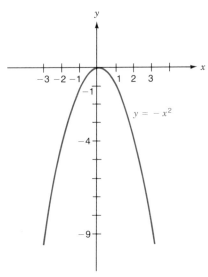

FIGURE 4.1   FIGURE 4.2

x	-3	-2	-1	0	1	2	3
$y = x^2$	9	4	1	0	1	4	9

The graph of $f(x) = x^2$ was one of the basic graphs given in Sec. 3.2. Notice that either graph is the reflection of the other through the x axis. Each graph is also symmetric about the y axis since $(-x)^2 = x^2$. The lowest, or highest, point for each of the graphs is the origin $(0, 0)$. The graphs of $y = 3x^2$ and $y = \frac{1}{4}x^2$ are shown dashed in Figs. 4.3 and 4.4, along with a solid $y = x^2$. These show how changing the coefficient a in $y = ax^2$ alters the shape of the graph for a given x. If $|a| > 1$, the graph of $y = ax^2$ is narrower than the graph of $y = x^2$. If $0 < |a| < 1$, it is wider than the graph of $y = x^2$.

There are several ways to modify the function $f(x) = x^2$:

$$f(x) = ax^2 \qquad \text{multiply by a constant, positive or negative} \qquad \textbf{(1)}$$

$$f(x) = x^2 + k \qquad \text{add a constant, positive or negative} \qquad \textbf{(2)}$$

$$f(x) = (x - h)^2 \qquad \text{replace } x \text{ by } x - h, \ h \text{ positive or negative} \qquad \textbf{(3)}$$

$$f(x) = a(x - h)^2 + k \qquad \text{do a combination of the above changes} \qquad \textbf{(4)}$$

The stretching effect of (1) on the graph has already been discussed above. The result of (2) is to translate (or shift) the graph up or down, while (3) results in translating the graph to the left or right. Note that (2) can be rewritten as $f(x) - k = x^2$. Thus the graph of $y = ax^2$ is translated

Vertically by replacing y by y − k
Horizontally by replacing x by x − h

as we saw in Sec. 3.4.

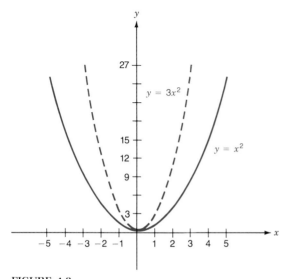

FIGURE 4.3

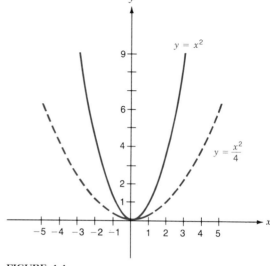

FIGURE 4.4

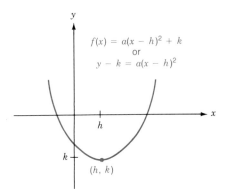

FIGURE 4.5

With (4), of course, any combination of the effects above may be produced. See Fig. 4.5, where $a > 0$, and thus the graph opens up. There the point (h, k) is the lowest point on the graph of $f(x) = a(x - h)^2 + k$, and it is called the **vertex.** Notice that by the definition of the graph of a function, the graph of $f(x) = a(x - h)^2 + k$ is identical with the graph of $y - k = a(x - h)^2$.

If we consider the quadratic function $f(x) = ax^2 + bx + c$ and complete the square, we have

$$f(x) = a\left(x^2 + \frac{bx}{a} + \frac{c}{a}\right) \qquad \text{factoring out } a$$

$$= a\left(x^2 + \frac{bx}{a} + \frac{b^2}{4a^2} + \frac{c}{a} - \frac{b^2}{4a^2}\right) \qquad \text{adding and subtracting } b^2/4a^2$$

Factoring the first three terms and adding the last two gives

$$f(x) = a\left[\left(x + \frac{b}{2a}\right)^2 + \frac{4ac - b^2}{4a^2}\right] \tag{5}$$

This has the form

Standard form of the equation of a parabola

$$f(x) = a(x - h)^2 + k$$

where $\qquad h = \dfrac{-b}{2a} \qquad$ and $\qquad k = f(h) = f\left(\dfrac{-b}{2a}\right) = \dfrac{4ac - b^2}{4a}$

Sign of a

From this we can draw several conclusions. The graph opens up if $a > 0$ and down if $a < 0$. If $a < 0$, for instance, the vertex (h, k) is the highest point on the graph because the graph opens downward. The larger $|a|$ is, the "narrower" the graph is. Finally, using the form $f(x) = a(x - h)^2 + k$, then substitution shows that for any real t

Value of |a|

Symmetry about x = h = −b/2a

$$f(h + t) = at^2 + k$$

$$f(h - t) = at^2 + k$$

Maximum or minimum for
$x = h = -b/2a$

The *symmetry about the vertical line* $x = h$ or $x = -b/2a$ follows since $h + t$ and $h - t$ are both $|t|$ units from the line $x = h = -b/2a$, and their function values are equal. Since a, b, and c are constants, the value of $f(x)$ from (5) above is

$$f(x) = a\left[\left(x + \frac{b}{2a}\right)^2 + \frac{4ac - b^2}{4a^2}\right]$$

and if $x = -b/2a$, then $x + b/2a$ is zero. Thus $f(x)$ has a maximum if $a < 0$ and a minimum if $a > 0$. This extreme value is

$$f(h) = f\left(\frac{-b}{2a}\right) = \frac{4ac - b^2}{4a}$$

x intercepts

We can find the points, if any, where the graph crosses the x axis by factoring or by using the quadratic formula to solve the quadratic equation $ax^2 + bx + c = 0$. Recall that the solutions are

$$x = \frac{-b \pm \sqrt{b^2 - 4ac}}{2a}$$

The average of the x intercepts is $-b/2a$, which is the x coordinate of the maximum or minimum point.

NOTE

Since we are interested only in real values of x and y when graphing, we can see that if $b^2 - 4ac < 0$, then the graph does not cross the x axis because the equation $ax^2 + bx + c = 0$ has no real solutions. See Figs. 4.7 and 4.9.

We will now summarize the above discussion about quadratic functions.

> The graph of the quadratic function
>
> $$f(x) = ax^2 + bx + c = a(x - h)^2 + k \qquad a \neq 0$$
>
> (1) Is a parabola opening upward if $a > 0$ and downward if $a < 0$.
> (2) Has a vertex (h, k), where $h = -b/2a$ and $k = f(h) = f(-b/2a)$.
> (3) Has an axis of symmetry which is the vertical line $x = -b/2a$.
> (4) Is narrower than the graph of $f(x) = x^2$, if $|a| > 1$ and
>   is wider than the graph of $f(x) = x^2$, if $0 < |a| < 1$.

If $f(x) = ax^2 + bx + c$, $a \neq 0$, then we may write it in standard form by completing the square or by finding h and k as in (2) above. See Example 1.

► **EXAMPLE 1** Draw the graph of $f(x) = 4x^2 - 8x - 21$.

Solution Since $a = 4 > 0$, the graph opens up. Also $f(x) = (2x + 3)(2x - 7)$, and thus the x intercepts are $-\frac{3}{2}$ and $\frac{7}{2}$, while the y intercept is -21. The vertex (h, k) has

$$h = \frac{-b}{2a} = \frac{-(-8)}{8} = 1$$

and

$$k = f(1) = 4 - 8 - 21 = -25$$

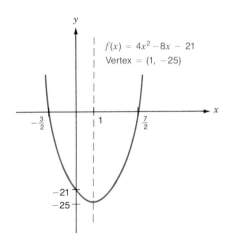

FIGURE 4.6

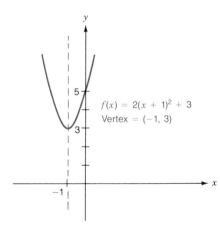

FIGURE 4.7

Therefore the minimum value is -25. Furthermore the vertical line $x = 1$ is the axis of symmetry. See Fig. 4.6. ◄

EXAMPLE 2 Rewrite the function $f(x) = 2x^2 + 4x + 5$ in standard form, and then sketch the graph.

Solution Since $a = 2 > 0$, the graph opens up. Putting $x = 0$ shows that the y intercept is 5. There are no x intercepts because $2x^2 + 4x + 5 = 0$ has no real solutions since $b^2 - 4ac = 16 - 40 < 0$. The vertex (h, k) has

$$h = \frac{-b}{2a} = \frac{-4}{2(2)} = -1$$

$$k = f(-1) = 2(1) + 4(-1) + 5 = 3$$

and hence the standard form is

$$f(x) = 2(x + 1)^2 + 3$$

The graph is thus a parabola with vertex at $(-1, 3)$ and axis of symmetry $x = -1$. Another way to see that there are no x intercepts is to note that the graph opens upward and the vertex is at $(-1, 3)$. See Fig. 4.7. ◄

EXAMPLE 3 Sketch the graph of $f(x) = 9x^2 - 12x - 1$.

Solution This is a parabola which opens upward since $a = 9 > 0$. The vertex is (h, k) where $h = -b/2a = -(-12)/2(9) = \frac{2}{3}$ and

$$k = f(\tfrac{2}{3}) = 9(\tfrac{2}{3})^2 - 12(\tfrac{2}{3}) - 1$$

$$= 9(\tfrac{4}{9}) - 8 - 1 = 4 - 9 = -5$$

and so the vertex is $(\frac{2}{3}, -5)$, which is the lowest point on this graph. The axis of symmetry is the vertical line $x = \frac{2}{3}$. The x intercepts can be found by solving $9x^2 - 12x - 1 = 0$.

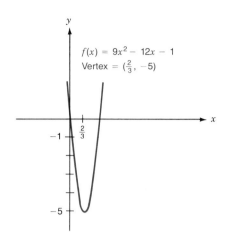

FIGURE 4.8

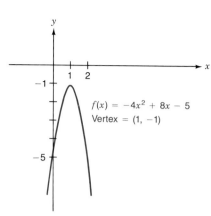

FIGURE 4.9

$$x = \frac{-(-12) \pm \sqrt{144 - 4(9)(-1)}}{18} = \frac{12 \pm \sqrt{180}}{18} = \frac{2 \pm \sqrt{5}}{3}$$

These values are approximately 1.4 and -0.1. The y intercept is -1. The graph is given in Fig. 4.8, and a table of values is shown below:

x	$\frac{2}{3}$	0 or $\frac{4}{3}$	$-\frac{2}{3}$ or 2
$f(x)$	-5	-1	11

▶ **EXAMPLE 4**   Draw the graph of $f(x) = -4x^2 + 8x - 5$.

Solution   The parabola opens downward since $a = -4 < 0$. The axis of symmetry is $x = -b/2a = -8/2(-4) = 1$. The maximum value is thus

$$f(1) = -4 + 8 - 5 = -1$$

and so the vertex, or highest point, is $(1, -1)$. Since

$$b^2 - 4ac = 64 - 4(-4)(-5) = 64 - 80 < 0$$

there are no x intercepts. The y intercept is -5, and the graph is shown in Fig. 4.9.

◀

NOTE   If we interchange x and y in $y = ax^2 + bx + c$, we get the equation $x = ay^2 + by + c$. This is also a parabola, and it opens to the right if $a > 0$ and to the left if $a < 0$. Here x is a function of y.

▶ **EXAMPLE 5**   Sketch the graph of $x = -(y - 2)^2 + 1$.

Solution   This equation may also be written

$$x = 1 - (y^2 - 4y + 4) = -y^2 + 4y - 3$$

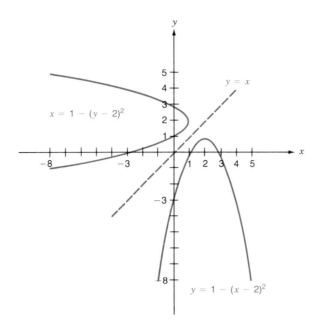

FIGURE 4.10

Its graph is a parabola which opens to the left, and its vertex is $(1, 2)$, where of course x is 1 and y is 2. The axis of symmetry is the horizontal line $y = 2$. When $y = 0$, we have $x = -3$. If $x = 0$, then $(y - 2)^2 = 1$; so $y - 2 = \pm 1$, and y is equal to either 3 or 1. These are the y intercepts. The graph is shown in Fig. 4.10. It is the reflection through the line $y = x$ of the graph of $y = -(x - 2)^2 + 1$. ◢

EXAMPLE 6   Find the maximum value of $f(x) = -x^2 + 6x + 17$.

Solution   For this function, $-b/2a = -6/(-2) = 3$, and so the maximum value is

$$f(3) = -9 + 18 + 17 = 26$$ ◢

EXAMPLE 7   If a young experimenter shoots a rocket upward with a velocity of 160 m/s from the ground, its height after t seconds is

$$f(t) = -5t^2 + 160t$$

Find the maximum height of the projectile.

Solution   In this case, $-b/2a = -160/(-10) = 16$, and the maximum height is

$$f(16) = -5(256) + 160(16) = 256(-5 + 10) = 256(5) = 1280$$ ◢

EXAMPLE 8   In Example 1(c) of Sec. 2.6, we saw that the distance between two cars is

$$\sqrt{(50 - 80t)^2 + (20 + 70t)^2}$$

assuming that they are on perpendicular roads. One car is 50 km from the intersection and driving at 80 km/h toward it, and the other car is 20 km from the intersection and driving at 70 km/h away from it. When are the cars closest together?

Solution   Instead of minimizing the distance d between them, we minimize d^2, since these minimum values will occur at the same time and d^2 does not involve a square root. We have

$$d = \sqrt{(50 - 80t)^2 + (20 + 70t)^2} \qquad \text{given in Example 1(c)}$$

$$d^2 = (50 - 80t)^2 + (20 + 70t)^2 \qquad \text{squaring}$$

$$= 100[(5 - 8t)^2 + (2 + 7t)^2] \qquad \text{factoring out } 10^2 = 100$$

$$= 100(25 - 80t + 64t^2 + 4 + 28t + 49t^2) \qquad \text{squaring}$$

$$= 100(113t^2 - 52t + 29) \qquad \text{collecting terms}$$

The minimum distance occurs for $t = -b/2a = \frac{26}{113}$ h, or almost 14 min since $(\frac{26}{113})(60) = 13.8$. ◢

Parabolas occur frequently in nature, for instance in the orbits of some atomic particles. They are used in making flashlights, headlights for cars, and dishes that receive signals from satellites. A cross section through the extreme point is a parabola. The reason parabolas are used is that rays which come in parallel to the axis of symmetry are all reflected off the surface and then pass through a common point (called the *focus*). This same property makes them useful in picking up sound from a distance—say, sideline microphones at a football game being televised.

Another use for parabolas is in describing the path of a projectile, if we ignore air resistance. Some types of telescopes use parabolic mirrors. Parabolic reflectors are also believed to be the basis for the ability the Greeks had to sometimes set an enemy ship on fire from the land.

Parabolas, ellipses, and hyperbolas are treated at length in Chap. 13.

Theory of chaos   The quadratic function $f(x) = kx(1 - x)$, with $0 \leq x \leq 1$, has played an important role in the recent development of the theory of *chaos* or *fractals,* and in the *Mandelbrot set*. It originated in modifying the linear growth model $y = kx$ by introducing a damping factor $1 - x$, giving $f(x) = kx(1 - x) = kx - kx^2$. Its maximum value occurs for $x = -b/(2a) = \frac{1}{2}$, and the maximum value is $f(\frac{1}{2}) = k/2 - k/4 = k/4$. Thus for any value of k with $0 < k < 4$, we will have $0 \leq f(x) \leq 1$ whenever $0 \leq x \leq 1$, and of course $f(0) = 0 = f(1)$. It follows that we may create a chain of calculations, called an *iterative process,* by choosing a value x_1 between 0 and 1, then finding $x_2 = f(x_1)$, then $x_3 = f(x_2)$, then $x_4 = f(x_3)$, etc. The behavior of this chain of values depends on the value of k and on x_1. We will illustrate this by choosing the functions

$$f(x) = 2x(1 - x) \qquad \text{where } k = 2$$

and $$g(x) = 3x(1 - x) \qquad \text{where } k = 3$$

and $$h(x) = 3.2x(1 - x) \qquad \text{where } k = 3.2$$

Using $x_1 = 0.3$ with $f(x)$ gives the values $x_2 = f(0.3) = 0.42$, $x_3 = f(0.42) = 0.4872$, $x_4 = f(0.4872) = 0.499672$, $x_5 = f(0.499672) = 0.499999$. Further calculation would give values even closer to 0.5, and it can be shown that the same thing happens for any starting value x_1 we use as long as $0 < x_1 < 1$. Notice that $f(\frac{1}{2}) = \frac{1}{2}$.

The behavior for $g(x)$ is similar to that of $f(x)$, but the values approach $\frac{2}{3}$, and they do so rather slowly. Notice that $g(\frac{2}{3}) = \frac{2}{3}$.

The behavior for $h(x)$ is more complicated. It can be shown that for most starting values x_1 with $0 < x < 1$, the values x_1, x_3, x_5, etc., all approach one number, and the values x_2, x_4, x_6, etc., all approach another number. Using $x_1 = 0.8$ gives

$$x_1 = 0.8 \qquad\qquad x_2 = 0.512$$

$$x_3 = 0.7995392 \qquad x_4 = 0.512884$$

$$x_5 = 0.7994688 \qquad x_6 = 0.5130189$$

$$x_7 = 0.7994576 \qquad x_8 = 0.5130404$$

Further calculations show that the values 0.7994554 and 0.5130445 eventually repeat alternately.

Certain values of k between 3.2 and 4 would give functions which have 4, or 8, or 16, etc., values which are approached. The theory of chaos has been used to study economics, noise in telephone line transmission, population change, the coastline of Britain, and many other topics.

EXERCISE 4.1

Draw the graph of the parabola in Probs. 1 to 20.
1. $y = 2x^2$
2. $y = -3x^2$
3. $y = 6x^2$
4. $y = -4x^2$
5. $y = \dfrac{x^2}{2}$
6. $y = \dfrac{x^2}{5}$
7. $y = \dfrac{-x^2}{3}$
8. $y = \dfrac{-x^2}{7}$
9. $y = (x + 3)^2$
10. $y = -(x - 4)^2$
11. $y = -(x + 1)^2$
12. $y = (x - 2)^2$
13. $y - 2 = -(x + 1)^2$
14. $y + 1 = -(x - 1)^2$
15. $y - 1 = (x + 3)^2$
16. $y + 2 = (x - 3)^2$
17. $y - 2 = 2(x - 3)^2$
18. $y + 3 = 3(x - 1)^2$
19. $y - 4 = -3(x + 1)^2$
20. $y + 1 = -2(x - 2)^2$

Put the equation in each of Probs. 21 to 24 in standard form.
21. $y = 4x^2 - 8x + 6$
22. $y = 6x^2 - 24x + 27$
23. $y = -3x^2 + 18x - 28$
24. $y = -4x^2 - 8x$

Find the axis of symmetry and the vertex in each of Probs. 25 to 32.
25. $y = 4x^2 - 16x + 17$
26. $y = 2x^2 - 12x + 16$
27. $y = -3x^2 + 6x - 4$
28. $y = -4x^2 - 24x - 34$
29. $x = -2y^2 + 12y - 15$
30. $x = -3y^2 - 12y - 11$
31. $x = 4y^2 - 16y + 15$
32. $x = 2y^2 - 12y + 14$

Sketch the graphs in Probs. 33 to 40.
33. $y = 2x^2 - 4x + 6$
34. $y = -6x^2 - 12x - 11$
35. $y = 3x^2 + 18x + 30$
36. $y = 2x^2 - 12x + 16$
37. $x = -3y^2 - 6y + 2$
38. $x = 2y^2 - 8y + 4$
39. $x = 4y^2 + 16y + 19$
40. $x = -y^2 + 6y - 10$

If a projectile is thrown or shot with a velocity v m/s from a height H meters above ground, its height after t seconds is

$$f(t) = -5t^2 + vt + H$$

Use this in Probs. 41 to 44 to find the maximum height of the projectile and the number of seconds before it hits the ground.
41. $f(t) = -5t^2 + 40t + 25$
42. $f(t) = -5t^2 + 52t + 17$
43. $f(t) = -5t^2 + 36t + 42$
44. $f(t) = -5t^2 + 64t + 14$

Find the maximum or minimum value of each of the following.
45. $2x^2 - 5x - 8$
46. $-5x^2 - x + 8$
47. $-6x^2 + 4x - 5$
48. $7x^2 + 3x + 6$
49. $2x^2 + 6x - 1$
50. $3x^2 - 3x + 5$
51. $-x^2 + 5x + 4$
52. $-3x^2 + 1$
53. Find the maximum value of the product $x(1 - x)$.
54. Which two numbers have a sum of 24 and as large a product as possible?

55. *Satellite dish* A satellite dish, in storage, has parabolic cross sections and is resting on its vertex. A point on the rim is 4 ft high and is 6 ft horizontally from the vertex. How high is a point which is 3 ft horizontally from the vertex?

56. *Mileage* Suppose that if a car is driven at x mi/h, its mileage in mi/gal is $2x - x^2/36$. What speed gives the highest mi/gal?

57. *Management* The income of a chartered bus with seating capacity for 40 passengers is given by

$$R(x) = 6000 + 60(40 - x) - (40 - x)^2$$

where x is the number of seats taken. Find the maximum income and the number of passengers that produce it.

58. *Sales* A small radio sells 21 units per week when priced at \$56. The sales increase 4 units per week for each \$4 decrease in price. What price will bring in the largest weekly income?

59. *Growth rate of sales* Suppose that the growth rate of sales is

$$R(x) = 0.15x(30 - x)$$

if x is the present sales. What sales figure makes the growth rate a maximum?

60. Suppose that r and s are real numbers and $p > 0$. Use a graph to explain why there are real solutions to

$$(x - r)(x - s) = p$$

Are there any solutions between r and s?

Projectile above sloping ground
In Probs. 61 to 64, assume that if a golfer hits the ball from level ground, its height above level ground after x yards is

$$g(x) = 0.005x(200 - x)$$

Suppose however that the ground in fact slopes down according to the equation $6y + x = 0$.

61. What is the height of the ball above the sloping ground?

62. What is the value of x when the ball hits the ground?

63. What is the distance measured along the sloping ground from where it was hit to where it lands?

64. What is the maximum height of the ball above the sloping ground?

65. Suppose that

$$f(x) = \frac{(x - s)(x - t)}{(r - s)(r - t)}A + \frac{(x - r)(x - t)}{(s - r)(s - t)}B + \frac{(x - r)(x - s)}{(t - r)(t - s)}C$$

Show that $f(r) = A$, $f(s) = B$, and $f(t) = C$.

4.2 Graphs of Polynomial Functions

In this section we will graph polynomial functions, which have the form

$$f(x) = a_n x^n + a_{n-1}x^{n-1} + \cdots + a_2 x^2 + a_1 x + a_0$$

where each a_i is real. We have already seen that if $f(x)$ has degree $n = 1$, then the graph of f is a straight line, whereas if $f(x)$ has degree $n = 2$, then the graph of f is a parabola. We will now consider graphs of polynomials $f(x)$ with degree $n \geq 3$.

The **range** of the polynomial function depends on whether n is even or odd and also on the value of the leading coefficient a_n.

Range of a polynomial

  (i) If n is even and $a_n > 0$, the range is the interval $[m, \infty)$, where m is the minimum value of the function. A typical example is $f(x) = x^2$, whose graph is in Fig. 4.1.

  (ii) If n is even and $a_n < 0$, the range is the interval $(-\infty, M]$, where M is the maximum value of the function. A typical example is $f(x) = -x^2$, whose graph is in Fig. 4.2.

  (iii) If n is odd, the range is the set of real numbers $(-\infty, \infty)$. In this case, there is no maximum or minimum value. A typical example is $f(x) = x^3$, whose graph is in Fig. 3.9.

We have already graphed polynomial functions of degrees 1, 2, 3, and 4 in Chap. 3 by plotting points. The information in this chapter allows us to graph polynomials of any degree more easily and better. One especially useful aid in graphing is the corollary at the end of Sec. 4.4, which gives a standard factored form for every polynomial.

Factored polynomials

Every polynomial with real coefficients can be written as the product of linear and irreducible quadratic factors, each factor having real coefficients.

A quadratic factor $ax^2 + bx + c$ is irreducible if $b^2 - 4ac < 0$. We will use the factored form in this section because it is so helpful. Since no irreducible quadratic factor will ever be 0 for a real value of x, it follows that:

$$f(x) = 0 \ only \ at \ the \ values \ of \ x$$

$$where \ the \ linear \ factors \ are \ equal \ to \ 0$$

For instance, suppose $f(x) = (x - 4)(x^2 + 5x + 7)$. Then $x^2 + 5x + 7$ is irreducible since $b^2 - 4ac = 25 - 4(7) = -3 < 0$, and it has the same sign for all values of x. Since $x^2 + 5x + 7$ has the positive value 7 when $x = 0$, then it is positive for all real values of x. It follows that $f(x)$ is zero only when the linear factor $x - 4$ is zero, namely for the value $x = 4$.

To properly graph a polynomial function, including the location of all turning points, requires a knowledge of calculus. It is shown there that every polynomial function is continuous and has a graph which is a smooth, unbroken curve with no corners, holes, gaps, or breaks. The number of x intercepts is at most n, where n is the degree of f. The graph has at most $n - 1$ **turning points,** which can be either maximum points (peaks) or minimum points (valleys). Finally, as $|x|$ becomes arbitrarily large, so does $|f(x)|$. However, we can accurately sketch the graph using the techniques outlined above.

▶ **EXAMPLE 1**   Sketch the graph of

$$f(x) = (x + 2)(x - 1)(x - 4) = x^3 - 3x^2 - 6x + 8$$

Solution   This is a polynomial of degree 3 which has x intercepts only at -2, 1, and 4. These three values determine the four intervals

$$(-\infty, -2) \qquad (-2, 1) \qquad (1, 4) \qquad (4, \infty)$$

We can find the sign of $f(x)$ in each of these intervals by using any value of x in that interval. The sign of $f(x)$ at that value then tells us whether the graph in that whole interval is above or below the x axis. The chart below, along with the intercepts, serves as a table of values at key points.

Interval	Value of x	Value of $f(x)$	Position of graph
$(-\infty, -2)$	-3	$f(-3) = -28$	Below x axis
$(-2, 1)$	0	$f(0) = 8$	Above x axis
$(1, 4)$	2	$f(2) = -8$	Below x axis
$(4, \infty)$	5	$f(5) = 28$	Above x axis

Since the degree of $f(x)$ is 3, which is odd, the range is $(-\infty, \infty)$. There are two turning points, one of them on the interval $(-2, 1)$ and the other on the interval $(1, 4)$. See Fig. 4.11.

Cubics, or third-degree polynomials, have particularly nice graphs because of their symmetry, as shown in Fig. 4.11 for instance. In the review section of the last chapter, you were asked to show that if

$$f(x) = ax^3 + bx^2 + cx + d$$

then for every positive number h,

$$\frac{1}{2}\left[f\left(\frac{-b}{3a} + h\right) + f\left(\frac{-b}{3a} - h\right)\right] = f\left(\frac{-b}{3a}\right)$$

This shows that the graph of a third-degree polynomial function f is **symmetric with respect to the point**

$$\left(\frac{-b}{3a}, f\left(\frac{-b}{3a}\right)\right) \tag{1}$$

which means that if the graph of f is translated horizontally and/or vertically to a position such that the point in (1) above is at the origin, then the *translated graph* is symmetric with respect to the origin. In Example 1, $f(x) = x^3 - 3x^2 - 6x + 8$, and thus $a = 1$, $b = -3$, $c = -6$, and $d = 8$. Because

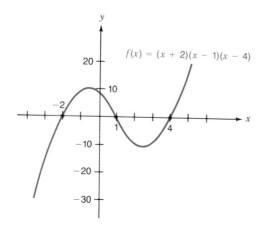

$$f(x) = (x + 2)(x - 1)(x - 4)$$

FIGURE 4.11

$$\frac{-b}{3a} = -\frac{-3}{3} = 1 \qquad \text{and} \qquad f(1) = 0$$

the graph in Fig. 4.11 is symmetric about the point $(1, 0)$.

We again will work with a cubic function in Example 2, and thus its graph is also symmetric about a point. This function is the product of linear and quadratic factors.

EXAMPLE 2   Sketch the graph of

$$f(x) = (x + 4)(x^2 + 2x + 2) = x^3 + 6x^2 + 10x + 8$$

Solution   We know that $x^2 + 2x + 2$ is irreducible since $(2)^2 - 4(1)(2) = 4 - 8 = -4 < 0$, and thus $f(x) = 0$ only for $x = -4$. This one value determines the two intervals

$$(-\infty, -4) \qquad (-4, \infty)$$

We can find the sign of $f(x)$ in each of these intervals by using any value of x in that interval:

Interval	Value of x	Value of $f(x)$	Position of graph
$(-\infty, -4)$	-5	$f(-5) = -17$	Below x axis
$(-4, \infty)$	-3	$f(-3) = 5$	Above x axis

For $f(x) = x^3 + 6x^2 + 10x + 8$, we have $a = 1$, $b = 6$, $c = 10$, and $d = 8$. Because

$$\frac{-b}{3a} = \frac{-6}{3} = -2 \qquad \text{and} \qquad f(-2) = 4$$

the graph is symmetric about the point $(-2, 4)$. The table of values below illustrates this symmetry since, for instance, $4 + 21 = 25$ and $4 - 21 = -17$. See Fig. 4.12.

x	-5	-4	-3	-2	-1	0	1
$f(x)$	-17	0	5	4	3	8	25

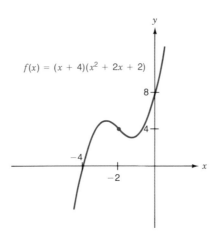

$f(x) = (x + 4)(x^2 + 2x + 2)$

FIGURE 4.12

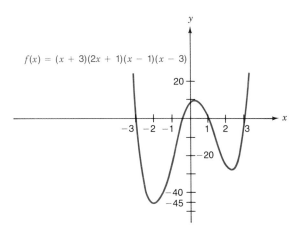

$f(x) = (x + 3)(2x + 1)(x - 1)(x - 3)$

FIGURE 4.13

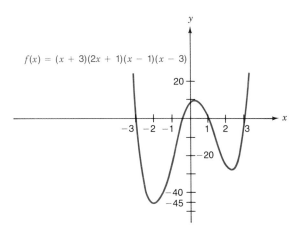

▶ **EXAMPLE 3**   Sketch the graph of $f(x) = (x + 3)(2x + 1)(x - 1)(x - 3)$.

Solution   This is a polynomial of degree 4 which has x intercepts only at -3, $-\frac{1}{2}$, 1, and 3. These values determine the intervals

$$(-\infty, -3) \qquad (-3, -\tfrac{1}{2}) \qquad (-\tfrac{1}{2}, 1) \qquad (1, 3) \qquad (3, \infty)$$

We can find the sign of $f(x)$ in each of these intervals by using any value of x in that interval. The sign of $f(x)$ at that value then tells us whether the graph in that whole interval is above or below the x axis:

Interval	Value of x	Value of $f(x)$	Position of graph
$(-\infty, -3)$	-4	$f(-4) = 245$	Above x axis
$(-3, -\frac{1}{2})$	-2	$f(-2) = -45$	Below x axis
$(-\frac{1}{2}, 1)$	0	$f(0) = 9$	Above x axis
$(1, 3)$	2	$f(2) = -25$	Below x axis
$(3, \infty)$	4	$f(4) = 189$	Above x axis

Since the degree of $f(x)$ is 4, which is even, and the leading coefficient is 2, which is positive, the range is $[m, \infty)$, where m is the minimum value of the function, about -45 in this case. From the graph, we see that there are three turning points. The graph is in Fig. 4.13.   ◢

▶ **EXAMPLE 4**   Sketch the graph of $f(x) = (x + 1)^2(x - 2)^3$.

Solution   The x intercepts of $f(x)$ are -1 and 2. The chart below, along with the intercepts, serves as a table of values at key points:

Interval	Value of x	Value of $f(x)$	Position of graph
$(-\infty, -1)$	-2	-64	Below x axis
$(-1, 2)$	0	-8	Below x axis
$(2, \infty)$	3	$16(1)$	Above x axis

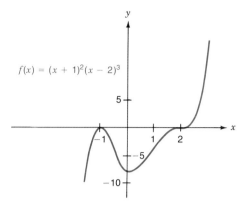

$$f(x) = (x + 1)^2(x - 2)^3$$

FIGURE 4.14

Notice that -1 is an x intercept, yet the graph is below the x axis on both sides of $x = -1$. Since the degree of $f(x)$ is 5, which is odd, the range is $(-\infty, \infty)$. There are at most four turning points, and Fig. 4.14 shows that there are in fact only two.

The **shape of the graph near the x intercepts** is approximately a horizontal translation of the graph of $y = ax^n$ for some coefficient a and exponent n. Thus

$$\textit{If } x \approx -1, \textit{ then } f(x) \approx (x + 1)^2(-1 - 2)^3 = -27(x + 1)^2$$

$$\textit{and} \qquad \textit{If } x \approx 2, \textit{ then } f(x) \approx (2 + 1)^2(x - 2)^3 = 9(x - 2)^3$$

Hence for values of x near -1, the graph is like a parabola which opens down. For values of x near 2, the graph is like a cubic which increases and has a "bend."

In Example 4, $f(x)$ had a factor $(x + 1)^2$ of power 2 and also a factor $(x - 2)^3$ of power 3. The next rule shows how to handle these situations in general:

> Suppose $f(x)$ has a factor $(x - c)^k$ with c real and k a positive integer. Then for x near c
>
> *If k is odd, the graph crosses the x axis*
>
> *If k is even, the graph touches the x axis, but does not cross it*

Note that this applies equally well when $k = 1$, which is odd. Example 5 further illustrates this rule.

EXAMPLE 5   Draw the graphs of $f(x) = (x + 1)(2x - 1)^2(x - 2)^2$

and $g(x) = (x + 1)(2x - 1)^2(x - 2)^3$

Solution   The only difference between the functions f and g is that g has one more factor of $x - 2$ than f does. Both have x intercepts at -1, $\frac{1}{2}$, and 2.

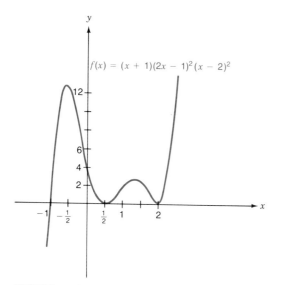

$f(x) = (x + 1)(2x - 1)^2(x - 2)^2$

FIGURE 4.15

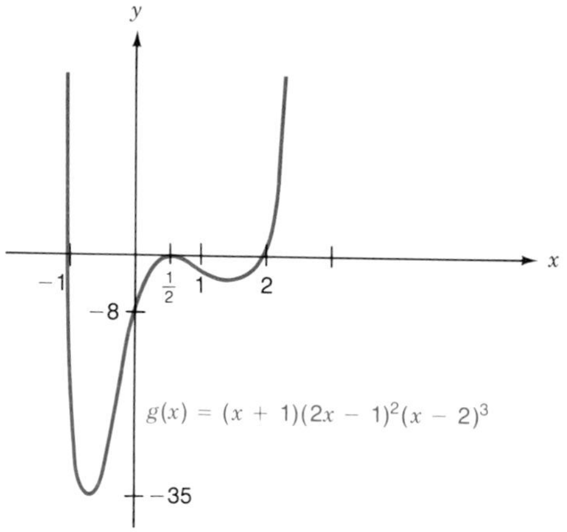

$g(x) = (x + 1)(2x - 1)^2(x - 2)^3$

FIGURE 4.16

Interval	Value of x	$f(x)$ and $g(x)$	Position w/r to x axis
$(-\infty, -1)$	-1.5	-98 and 343	f below and g above
$(-1, \frac{1}{2})$	0	4 and -8	f above and g below
$(\frac{1}{2}, 2)$	1	2 and -2	f above and g below
$(2, \infty)$	3	100 and 100	f above and g above

The degree of f is 5, which is odd, and so the range of f is $(-\infty, \infty)$. However, g has degree 6 with a positive leading coefficient, and its range turns out to be approximately $[-34, \infty)$. Notice that at $x = 2$, the graph of g crosses the x axis, while the graph of f just touches it without crossing. See Figs. 4.15 and 4.16. ◄

All but one of the examples so far have had only linear factors, sometimes raised to a power. When we have irreducible quadratic factors, we must remember that such factors are never zero and have the same sign for all real values of x.

EXAMPLE 6 Sketch the graph of $f(x) = (x^2 - x - 6)(3x^2 - 4x + 2)(x - 4)$.

Solution The first quadratic term is factorable since $x^2 - x - 6 = (x + 2)(x - 3)$. The second quadratic term is irreducible since its discriminant is $b^2 - 4ac = (-4)^2 - 4(3)(2) = 16 - 24 = -8$, which is negative. Therefore

$$f(x) = (x + 2)(x - 3)(3x^2 - 4x + 2)(x - 4)$$

and hence $f(x) = 0$ only for $x = -2$, $x = 3$, or $x = 4$. The chart below, along with the intercepts, serves as a table of values.

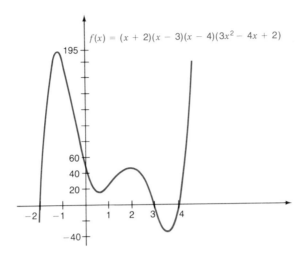

FIGURE 4.17

Interval	Value of x	Value of $f(x)$	Position of graph
$(-\infty, -2)$	-2.1	≈ -74	Below x axis
$(-2, 3)$	0 or 2	48	Above x axis
$(3, 4)$	3.6	-36	Below x axis
$(4, \infty)$	4.5	≈ 218	Above x axis

Since the degree $n = 5$ is odd, the range is $(-\infty, \infty)$. There are actually four turning points, at approximately $(-1.3, 195)$, $(0.7, 14)$, $(2, 48)$, and $(3.6, -36)$, which were found by substitution with a calculator every tenth. This was done just for accuracy, and you need not calculate values every tenth. However you will then have to make a reasonable guess as to where the turning points are. They can be found exactly with calculus. See Fig. 4.17. ◢

It can be shown that if

$$f(x) = a_n x^n + \text{(terms of lower degree)}$$

then for large values of $|x|$, the graph of $y = f(x)$ is approximately the same as the graph of $y = a_n x^n$. The reason for this depends on writing, for instance,

$$3x^3 - 6x^2 + 12x - 2 = 3x^3\left(1 - \frac{2}{x} + \frac{4}{x^2} - \frac{2}{3x^3}\right)$$

and noting that $1/x$, $1/x^2$, and $1/x^3$ approach 0 as $|x|$ gets larger and larger.

Polynomial inequalities in one variable can easily be solved visually if we first graph the related equation. For an inequality of the form $f(x) > 0$, we begin by graphing the equation $y = f(x)$, and then see where the graph is *above the x axis*. The solution is the corresponding values of x on the number line. For instance in Example 3, the solution to

$$f(x) > 0 \qquad \text{or} \qquad (x + 3)(2x + 1)(x - 1)(x - 3) > 0$$

is easily *seen* from Fig. 4.13 to be

$$(-\infty, -3) \cup (-\tfrac{1}{2}, 1) \cup (3, \infty)$$

EXERCISE 4.2

Draw the graphs of these polynomial functions.

1. $f(x) = (x - 2)(x - 1)(x + 2)$
2. $f(x) = -(2x + 3)(x - 1)(3x - 7)$
3. $f(x) = -(3x + 4)(2x - 1)(x - 2)$
4. $f(x) = (x + 3)(3x + 1)(2x - 5)$
5. $f(x) = -(3x + 5)(2x^2 - 6x + 5)$
6. $f(x) = (x - 2)(2x^2 + 5x + 4)$
7. $f(x) = (2x - 1)(x^2 - x + 7)$
8. $f(x) = -(x + 1)(3x^2 + 2x + 5)$
9. $f(x) = (x + 3)(x + 1)(x)(x - 2)$
10. $f(x) = -(x + 2)(2x + 1)(x - 1)(x - 4)$
11. $f(x) = (x - 2)(2x - 3)(x^2 + 2x + 2)$
12. $f(x) = -(x + 3)(x - 1)(x^2 - 5x + 7)$
13. $f(x) = -2x^4 + 13x^3 - 27x^2 + 13x + 15$
    $= -(2x + 1)(x - 3)(x^2 - 4x + 5)$
14. $f(x) = 3x^4 - 8x^3 + 11x^2 + 18x - 24$
    $= (3x + 4)(x - 1)(x^2 - 3x + 6)$
15. $f(x) = -x^4 + 15x^2 + 10x - 24$
    $= -(x + 3)(x + 2)(x - 1)(x - 4)$
16. $f(x) = x^4 + x^3 - 9x^2 - 9x$
    $= (x + 3)(x + 1)(x)(x - 3)$
17. $f(x) = (x + 4)(x^2 - x - 6)(x^2 - 1)$
18. $f(x) = -(x - 3)(x^2 + x - 2)(x^2 + 5x + 8)$
19. $f(x) = (x)(x^2 + 2x - 3)(x^2 - 2x - 8)$
20. $f(x) = -(x - 1)(x^2 + 3x + 2)(x^2 - 4x + 6)$
21. $f(x) = (x - 1)^2(x - 3)^3(x - 5)^2$
22. $f(x) = (x - 1)^2(x - 3)^2(x - 5)^2$
23. $f(x) = (x - 1)^3(x - 3)^2(x - 5)^3$
24. $f(x) = (x - 1)^3(x - 3)^3(x - 5)^2$
25. $f(x) = (x + 3)(x + 1)^2(x - 3)^3(x - 1)$
26. $f(x) = (x + 3)(x + 1)^3(x - 1)^3(x - 3)$
27. $f(x) = (x + 2)(x^2)(x - 1)^4(x - 2)^2$
28. $f(x) = (x + 2)(x^2)(x - 1)^3(x - 3)^3$
29. If a standard amount of a certain chemical is injected into the bloodstream, then the concentration after x seconds is
    $$C(x) = -0.001x^4 + 0.037x^3 + 0.117x^2 + 0.12x$$
    Graph $C(x)$, and estimate the times when the concentration is at least 200. Use $0 < x \le 40$.
30. The function
    $$D(x) = (-0.0008)(x^3 + x^2 - 72x)$$
    gives the percentage of alcohol in the blood x hours after drinking a standard amount of alcohol. Suppose that a person is legally drunk when the percent-

age is at least 0.10 percent. Use the graph of $D(x)$ to estimate the times when a person is legally drunk.

31. An open box is made from a 25 by 40 piece of metal by cutting out an x by x square from each corner, then turning up the edges. The volume is
    $$V(x) = x(25 - 2x)(40 - 2x)$$
    Use the graph of $V(x)$ to estimate the values of x for which the volume is at least 1950.

32. Suppose that during the first week in November, the temperature x hours after midnight is
    $$f(x) = (-0.05x)(x - 6)(x - 18) + 50$$
    in degrees Fahrenheit for $6 \le x \le 18$. Use the graph of $f(x)$ to estimate the times when the temperature is above 65°F.

Solve the inequalities in Probs. 33 to 40. Refer to the stated problem for the graph (in the answer section) or else graph the related equation here.

33. (Prob. 2) $-(2x + 3)(x - 1)(3x - 7) < 0$
34. (Prob. 10) $-(x + 2)(2x + 1)(x - 1)(x - 4) < 0$
35. (Prob. 18) $-(x - 3)(x^2 + x - 2)(x^2 + 5x + 8) > 0$
36. (Prob. 26) $(x + 3)(x + 1)^3(x - 1)^3(x - 3) > 0$
37. (Prob. 3) $y > -(3x + 4)(2x - 1)(x - 2)$
38. (Prob. 11) $y < (x - 2)(2x - 3)(x^2 + 2x + 2)$
39. (Prob. 19) $y > (x)(x^2 + 2x - 3)(x^2 - 2x - 8)$
40. (Prob. 27) $y < (x + 2)(x^2)(x - 1)^4(x - 2)$

Turning points for a cubic
Suppose that $f(x) = ax^3 + bx^2 + cx + d$. It can be shown that if $b^2 - 3ac \le 0$, there are no turning points. Furthermore there will be two turning points if $b^2 - 3ac > 0$, and these turning points will occur where
$$x = \frac{-b \pm \sqrt{b^2 - 3ac}}{3a}$$

Problems 41 and 42 give examples of a maximum value and a minimum value.

41. Let $f(x) = x^3 - 3x^2 - 6x + 8$, as in Example 1. Show that
    $$f(1 - \sqrt{3}) \ge f(1 - \sqrt{3} + h)$$
    for any h with $-1 \le h \le 1$. Thus $(1 - \sqrt{3}, f(1 - \sqrt{3}))$ is a maximum point.

42. Let $f(x) = x^3 - 3x^2 - 6x + 8$, as in Example 1. Show that

$$f(1 + \sqrt{3}) \leq f(1 + \sqrt{3} + h)$$

for any h with $-1 \leq h \leq 1$. Thus $(1 + \sqrt{3}, f(1 + \sqrt{3}))$ is a minimum point.

We have seen that quadratic functions have a symmetry property related to the line $x = -b/2a$ and that cubic functions have a symmetry property related to the point where $x = -b/3a$. There is no similar property for $x = -b/4a$ and all fourth-degree polynomial functions

$$f(x) = ax^4 + bx^3 + cx^2 + dx + e$$

as the next two problems show. It is, however, true that if $b = d = 0$, then the graph of $f(x) = ax^4 + cx^2 + e$ is symmetric with respect to the y axis.

43. Let $f(x) = x^4 + 4x^3 + 7x^2 + 6x + 5$

and $g(x) = x^4 + 4x^3 + 7x^2 + 3x + 5$

(a) Show that $-b/4a = -1$ for both f and g.
(b) Show that $f(-1 + h) = f(-1 - h)$ for all h.
(c) Show that $g(-1 + 3) \neq g(-1 - 3)$.

44. Let $f(x) = x^4 - 4x^3 + 5x^2 - 2x - 3$

and $g(x) = x^4 - 4x^3 + 5x^2 - 5x - 3$

(a) Show that $-b/4a = 1$.
(b) Show that $f(1 + h) = f(1 - h)$ for all h.
(c) Show that $g(1 + 2) \neq g(1 - 2)$.

45. The Chebychev polynomial

$$T(x) = x^2 - \tfrac{1}{2}$$

has the property that, for $-1 \leq x \leq 1$, the maximum value of $|T(x)|$ is $\tfrac{1}{2}$. Furthermore, if $P(x) = x^2 + ax + b$ is any polynomial with leading coefficient 1 and a and b real and $-1 \leq x \leq 1$, the maximum value of $|P(x)|$ is greater than $\tfrac{1}{2}$. Check this for several such polynomials $P(x)$, with $-1 \leq x \leq 1$.

4.3 The Remainder and Factor Theorems

For the next several sections, we will concentrate on polynomials of degree at least three, and see how to find function values, factors, and other information. The coefficients will often be rational, but they may also be any real numbers. Occasionally we will look at complex coefficients. We will make extensive use of functional notation. Recall that if $f(x) = 2x^3 + x^2 - 2x + 4$, then

$$f(-3) = 2(-3)^3 + (-3)^2 - 2(-3) + 4 = -54 + 9 + 6 + 4 = -35$$

$$f(5) = 2(5^3) + 5^2 - 2(5) + 4 = 250 + 25 - 10 + 4 = 269$$

and $f(c) = 2c^3 + c^2 - 2c + 4$

The Remainder Theorem

The computation involved in finding polynomial function values is greatly simplified if we use the following theorem.

Remainder Theorem   If a polynomial $f(x)$ is divided by $x - c$, then the remainder is equal to $f(c)$.

Proof In the long-division process, the following relation holds between the given polynomial $f(x)$, the divisor, the quotient, and the remainder:

$$f(x) = (\text{divisor})(\text{quotient}) + \text{remainder}$$

Hence, if $Q(x)$ is the quotient obtained by dividing $f(x)$ by the divisor $x - c$ and the remainder is R, we have

$$f(x) = (x - c)Q(x) + R$$

This equation is true for all values of x including $x = c$. Hence, if we substitute c for x, we have

$$f(c) = (c - c)Q(c) + R = (0)Q(c) + R = R$$

Thus the remainder is indeed equal to $f(c)$. ◢

EXAMPLE 1 Show that if we divide $x^3 - 2x^2 - 4x + 5$ by $x - 3$, using the long-division method. we get $x^2 + x - 1$ as the quotient and 2 as the remainder.

Solution

$$
\begin{array}{r}
x^2 + x - 1 \\
x - 3{\overline{\smash{\big)}\,x^3 - 2x^2 - 4x + 5}} \\
\underline{x^3 - 3x^2} \\
x^2 - 4x \\
\underline{x^2 - 3x} \\
-x + 5 \\
\underline{-x + 3} \\
2
\end{array}
$$

Note that the remainder 2 is independent of x. In this problem, $x - c = x - 3$, and so $c = 3$. Since

$$f(x) = x^3 - 2x^2 - 4x + 5$$

we have $f(3) = 3^3 - 2(3)^2 - 4(3) + 5 = 27 - 18 - 12 + 5 = 2$

in accord with the remainder theorem above. ◢

Synthetic Division

A short, simple method for long division is available when we divide a polynomial by $x - c$, as in the remainder theorem. A careful analysis of the long division in Example 1 above would show that the essentials are contained in the synthetic division below. The long division is repeated for easy reference. As the detailed rules below the division show:

The first line of the synthetic division consists of the coefficients of the polynomial

The third line is the sum of the first two lines; it gives the coefficients of the quotient, then the remainder

$$\begin{array}{r|rrrr} 3 & 1 & -2 & -4 & 5 \\ & & 3 & 3 & -3 \\ \hline & 1 & 1 & -1 & 2 \end{array}$$

$$\begin{array}{r} x^2 + x - 1 \\ x - 3 \overline{\smash{)}\ x^3 - 2x^2 - 4x + 5} \\ \underline{x^3 - 3x^2} \\ x^2 - 4x \\ \underline{x^2 - 3x} \\ -x + 5 \\ \underline{-x + 3} \\ 2 \end{array}$$

Rules for synthetic division

To use synthetic division to divide a polynomial

$$f(x) = a_n x^n + a_{n-1} x^{n-1} + \cdots + a_1 x + a_0 \qquad \text{by} \qquad x - c$$

1. With the polynomial in *decreasing* powers of x, *write the coefficients,* including any zeros, in the first row. To the left of the first row, write the number c from the divisor $x - c$:

$$\begin{array}{r|rrrrrr} c & a_n & a_{n-1} & a_{n-2} & \cdots & a_1 & a_0 \end{array}$$

2. Bring down the first coefficient to the third row.
   Multiply it by c and put it in the second row under the second coefficient. *Add* this product to the number above it in the first row and write the sum in the third row.
   Continue this multiply-and-add procedure.

$$\begin{array}{r|rrrrrr} c & a_n & a_{n-1} & a_{n-2} & \cdots & a_1 & a_0 \\ & & ca_n & & & & \\ \hline & a_n & a_{n-1} + ca_n & & & & \text{rem} \end{array}$$

3. *Interpret* the third row. The last number in the third row is the remainder; the other numbers, from left to right, are the coefficients of the quotient, which is of degree one less than the given polynomial.

► **EXAMPLE 2**   Use synthetic division to find the quotient and the remainder obtained by dividing

$$f(x) = 2x^4 + x^3 - 16x^2 + 18 \qquad \text{by} \qquad x + 2$$

Solution   Since $x - c = x + 2$, we have $c = -2$. After writing the coefficients of $f(x)$ in the first line and supplying zero as the coefficient of the missing x term, we can carry out the steps of synthetic division and get

$$\begin{array}{r|rrrrr} -2 & 2 & +1 & -16 & 0 & +18 \\ & & -4 & +6 & +20 & -40 \\ \hline & 2 & -3 & -10 & +20 & -22 \end{array}$$

From the third row, the quotient is $2x^3 - 3x^2 - 10x + 20$, and the last number is the remainder $R = -22$. Thus

$$f(x) = (x + 2)(2x^3 - 3x^2 - 10x + 20) - 22 \qquad \blacktriangleleft$$

▶ **EXAMPLE 3** Find $f(2)$ and $f(-1)$ if $f(x) = 2x^3 - 5x^2 + 6x - 11$.

Solution By synthetic division

$$
\begin{array}{r|rrrr}
2 & 2 & -5 & 6 & -11 \\
  &   & 4 & -2 & 8 \\
\hline
  & 2 & -1 & 4 & -3
\end{array}
\qquad
\begin{array}{r|rrrr}
-1 & 2 & -5 & 6 & -11 \\
   &   & -2 & 7 & -13 \\
\hline
   & 2 & -7 & 13 & -24
\end{array}
$$

we find that the remainders are -3 and -24. Hence by the remainder theorem, we know that

$$f(2) = -3 \quad \text{and} \quad f(-1) = -24$$

Furthermore the third rows show that

$$f(x) = (x - 2)(2x^2 - x + 4) - 3$$

and

$$f(x) = (x + 1)(2x^2 - 7x + 13) - 24$$ ◀

The Factor Theorem and Its Converse

Our next theorem will help us find factors of a polynomial, and it is based on the remainder theorem. Suppose that c is a zero of $f(x)$, or a root of $f(x) = 0$. Then $f(c) = 0$, and by the remainder theorem, the remainder is $R = f(c) = 0$. Hence

$$f(x) = (x - c) \cdot Q(x) + R = (x - c) \cdot Q(x)$$

Therefore, $x - c$ is a factor of $f(x)$, and we have proved the **factor theorem:**

If $f(x)$ is a polynomial with $f(c) = 0$, then $x - c$ is a factor of $f(x)$

The converse is true also. In fact, if $x - c$ is a factor of $f(x)$, then $f(x) = (x - c) \cdot Q(x)$. Therefore

$$f(c) = (c - c) \cdot Q(c) = 0$$

The factor theorem and its converse may be combined in the following theorem:

$x - c$ is a factor of the polynomial $f(x)$ if and only if $f(c) = 0$.

▶ **EXAMPLE 4** Show that $x - 2$ is a factor of $f(x) = -x^3 + 2x^2 - 2x + 4$.

Solution We have $f(2) = -8 + 8 - 4 + 4 = 0$. By the factor theorem, $x - 2$ is a factor since $f(2) = 0$. ◀

▶ **EXAMPLE 5** Show that $x + 3$ is not a factor of $f(x) = -x^3 + 2x^2 - 2x + 4$.

Solution Since $x + 3 = x - (-3)$, $c = -3$. Now

$$f(-3) = -(-27) + 2(9) - 2(-3) + 4 = 55$$ ◀

▶ **EXAMPLE 6**   For $f(x) = x^4 + 3x^3 + x^2 - 7x - 30$, divide synthetically by

$$x + 3 \qquad x + 1 \qquad x - 2 \qquad \text{and} \qquad x - 4$$

to see if they are factors of $f(x)$.

Solution

$$
\begin{array}{r|rrrrr}
-3 & 1 & 3 & 1 & -7 & -30 \\
   &   & -3 & 0 & -3 & 30 \\
\hline
   & 1 & 0 & 1 & -10 & 0
\end{array}
\qquad
\begin{array}{r|rrrrr}
-1 & 1 & 3 & 1 & -7 & -30 \\
   &   & -1 & -2 & 1 & 6 \\
\hline
   & 1 & 2 & -1 & -6 & -24
\end{array}
$$

$$
\begin{array}{r|rrrrr}
2 & 1 & 3 & 1 & -7 & -30 \\
  &   & 2 & 10 & 22 & 30 \\
\hline
  & 1 & 5 & 11 & 15 & 0
\end{array}
\qquad
\begin{array}{r|rrrrr}
4 & 1 & 3 & 1 & -7 & -30 \\
  &   & 4 & 28 & 116 & 436 \\
\hline
  & 1 & 7 & 29 & 109 & 406
\end{array}
$$

By the remainder theorem, $f(-3) = 0$, $f(-1) = -24$, $f(2) = 0$, and $f(4) = 406$. Thus by the factor theorem and its converse, we know that $x + 3$ and $x - 2$ are factors of $f(x)$, while $x + 1$ and $x - 4$ are not factors.   ◢

Synthetic division can be used not only with real numbers, but also with complex numbers. Real numbers, such as $3 + \sqrt{2}$, may also be used.

▶ **EXAMPLE 7**   Find $f(i)$ and $f(2i)$ by synthetic division if

$$f(x) = 2x^3 + x^2 + 8x + 4$$

Solution

$$
\begin{array}{r|rrrr}
i & 2 & 1 & 8 & 4 \\
  &   & 2i & -2 + i & -1 + 6i \\
\hline
  & 2 & 1 + 2i & 6 + i & 3 + 6i
\end{array}
\qquad
\begin{array}{r|rrrr}
2i & 2 & 1 & 8 & 4 \\
   &   & 4i & -8 + 2i & -4 \\
\hline
   & 2 & 1 + 4i & 2i & 0
\end{array}
$$

Thus $f(i) = 3 + 6i$, $f(2i) = 0$, and $x - 2i$ is a factor of $f(x)$.   ◢

▶ **EXAMPLE 8**   Find k so that $x + 2$ is a factor of $f(x) = x^2 - 2x^2 - 10x + k$.

Solution   Dividing $f(x)$ by $x - c = x + 2$ gives

$$
\begin{array}{r|rrrr}
-2 & 1 & -2 & -10 & k \\
   &   & -2 & 8 & 4 \\
\hline
   & 1 & -4 & -2 & k + 4
\end{array}
$$

Since $f(-2) = k + 4$, we must have $k + 4 = 0$ in order for $x + 2$ to be a factor. Hence $k = -4$.   ◢

▶ **EXAMPLE 9**   Find $f(1.4)$ if $f(x) = x^3 - 1.5x^2 + 0.27x - 0.182$.

Solution   The synthetic division is shown below.

$$
\begin{array}{r|rrrr}
1.4 & 1 & -1.5 & 0.27 & -0.182 \\
    &   & 1.4 & -0.14 & 0.182 \\
\hline
    & 1 & -0.1 & 0.13 & 0
\end{array}
$$

Therefore $f(1.4) = 0$, and so $x - 1.4$ is a factor of $f(x)$.   ◢

EXERCISE 4.3

Use the remainder theorem to find the remainder obtained by dividing the polynomial in each of Probs. 1 to 12 by the binomial which follows it.

1. $x^3 - 3x^2 + 4x - 5,\ x - 2$
2. $x^3 + 5x^2 - 7x + 3,\ x - 1$
3. $x^3 + 3x + 5,\ x + 1$
4. $x^3 - 2x^2 - 3x - 38,\ x + 3$
5. $2x^3 - 7x^2 + 5x + 3,\ x - 1$
6. $3x^3 + 4x^2 - 11x - 13,\ x - 2$
7. $2x^4 + 3x^3 + 7x^2 + 6x + 2,\ x + 1$
8. $3x^4 - 8x^3 - 9x - 7,\ x - 3$
9. $-2x^4 - 3x^3 + 4x^2 + 17x + 7,\ x - 2$
10. $x^5 + x^4 + x^3 + x^2 + x + 22,\ x - 2$
11. $2x^5 - 7x^4 - 5x^3 + 9x^2 - 24x + 17,\ x - 4$
12. $32x^5 - 16x^4 + 8x^3 - 4x^2 + 2x - 1,\ x - \frac{1}{2}$

Use the factor theorem to show that the binomial $x - c$ is a factor of the polynomial in each of Probs. 13 to 36. Use synthetic division as desired.

13. $2x^3 + 3x^2 - 6x + 1,\ x - 1$
14. $3x^3 - 9x^2 - 4x + 12,\ x - 3$
15. $5x^4 + 8x^3 + x^2 + 2x + 4,\ x + 1$
16. $3x^4 + 9x^3 - 4x^2 - 9x + 9,\ x + 3$
17. $-2x^5 + 11x^4 - 12x^3 - 5x^2 + 22x - 8,\ x - 4$
18. $3x^5 + 17x^4 + 17x^3 + 35x^2 - 4x - 20,\ x + 5$
19. $x^6 - x^5 - 7x^4 + x^3 + 8x^2 + 5x + 2,\ x + 2$
20. $2x^6 - 5x^5 + 4x^4 + x^3 - 7x^2 - 7x + 2,\ x - 2$
21. $x^3 - 4ax^2 + 2a^2x + a^3,\ x - a$
22. $x^3 - (2a + b)x^2 + (3a + 2ab)x - 3ab,\ x - b$

In Probs. 23 and 24, n is a positive integer.

23. $x^{2n} - a^{2n},\ x + a$
24. $x^{2n+1} + a^{2n+1},\ x + a$
25. $3x^3 + 2x^2 - 4x + 1,\ x - \frac{1}{3}$
26. $4x^3 + 3x^2 - 5x + 1,\ x - \frac{1}{4}$
27. $4x^5 - 7x^4 - 5x^3 + 2x^2 + 11x - 6,\ x - \frac{3}{4}$
28. $3x^4 - 4x^3 + 5x^2 - 4,\ x + \frac{2}{3}$
29. $x^3 - 3x^2 + x - 3,\ x - i$
30. $x^4 - 2x^2 - 3,\ x + i$
31. $x^3 - 2x^2 + 4x - 8,\ x - 2i$
32. $x^4 + 12x^2 + 27,\ x + 3i$
33. $x^3 - 7x^2 + 25x - 39,\ x - 2 - 3i$
34. $x^3 + x - 10,\ x + 1 - 2i$
35. $2x^3 - 19x^2 + 48x + 29,\ x - 5 + 2i$
36. $3x^3 + 22x^2 + 59x - 50,\ x + 4 + 3i$

In Probs. 37 to 40, find the value of k for which the binomial $x - c$ is a factor of the polynomial.

37. $x^3 + 2x^2 + 4x + k,\ x + 1$
38. $-x^3 + 3x^2 + kx - 4,\ x - 1$
39. $2x^4 - 5x^3 + kx^2 - 6x + 8,\ x - 2$
40. $-3x^4 + kx^3 + 6x^2 - 9x + 3,\ x - 1$

In Probs. 41 to 44, use the converse of the factor theorem to show that $x - c$ is not a factor of the polynomial.

41. $-2x^3 + 4x^2 - 4x + 9,\ x - 2$
42. $-3x^3 - 9x^2 + 5x + 12,\ x + 3$
43. $3x^4 - 8x^3 + 5x^2 + 7x - 3,\ x - 3$
44. $4x^4 + 9x^3 + 3x^2 + x + 4,\ x + 2$

Show that the given value of c is a root of the equation in each of Probs. 45 to 52.

45. $c = 5,\ (x - 5)(x + 2)(x + 1) = 0$
46. $c = -\frac{3}{2},\ (x - 5)(x + 2)(2x + 3) = 0$
47. $c = -\frac{2}{3},\ (x + 3)(3x + 2)(3x + 4) = 0$
48. $c = -\frac{4}{5},\ (2x + 3)(10x + 8)(x - 4) = 0$
49. $c = 1,\ x^3 + 3x^2 - 4x = 0$
50. $c = -1,\ x^3 + 5x^2 - 6x - 10 = 0$
51. $c = -3,\ 5x^4 + 17x^3 + 6x^2 + 9x + 27 = 0$
52. $c = 1,\ 7x^4 - 8x^3 - 9x^2 + 6x + 4 = 0$

In Probs. 53 to 56, show that the polynomial has no factor $x - c$ if c is real.

53. $x^2 + 1$
54. $x^4 + 3x^2 + 2$
55. $x^4 + 5x^2 + 3$
56. $x^6 + 3x^2 + 5$

In Probs. 57 to 64, find the function values by using synthetic division. A calculator is suggested for 57 to 60.

57. $f(1.32)$ if $f(x) = 1.72x^2 - 6.03x + 3.10$
58. $f(2.47)$ if $f(x) = 2.43x^3 - 5.94x - 4.11$
59. $f(3.1)$ if $f(x) = 2.6x^3 + 4.9x^2 - 9.1x - 99$
60. $f(1.7)$ if $f(x) = 0.63x^3 - 4.7x^2 + 11.4x + 5.10081$
61. $f(2 + \sqrt{3})$ if $f(x) = 2x^3 + 5x^2 - 4x - 2$
62. $f(3 - \sqrt{2})$ if $f(x) = x^4 - 5x^2 + 2x - 6$
63. $f(1 + \sqrt{5})$ if $f(x) = 3x^4 + 4x^3 - 5x - 1$
64. $f(4 - \sqrt{3})$ if $f(x) = 2x^4 + 3x^3 - 3x^2 - 5$
65. Find the remainder if $x^{55} + 3x^{47} - 5x^{31} - 8x^{24} + 2x^{18} - 4$ is divided by $x + 1$.
66. Find the remainder if $x^{74} + 5x^{57} + 9x^{29} - 4x^{22} - 6x^6 + 2$ is divided by $x - 1$.

67. Show that $x - c$ is a factor of $x^n - c^n$ for every positive integer n.

68. Show that
$$2 + 4x + 7x^2 - 8x^3 - 5x^4$$
$$= 2 + x\{4 + x[7 + x(-8 - 5x)]\}$$

This special form simplifies the evaluation of polynomial function values by computers and calculators. It is also the basis for synthetic division.

In Probs. 69 to 80, use synthetic division to find the quotient and remainder if the first polynomial is divided by the second.

69. $x^3 + 5x^2 - 2x - 3$, $x - 1$

70. $-x^3 + 7x^2 + 15x - 8$, $x + 2$

71. $-3x^3 - 10x^2 + 5x - 7$, $x - 3$

72. $4x^3 - 18x^2 - 11x + 5$, $x - 5$

73. $x^4 + x^3 - 3x + 6$, $x - 2$

74. $3x^4 - 4x^3 + x^2 - 7$, $x + 1$

75. $-2x^4 + 5x^2 + 3x - 3$, $x + 4$

76. $2x^4 + 2x^3 - 5x^2 - 3x$, $x - 2$

77. $2x^5 - 7x^4 + 10x^3 - 22x^2 - 4x - 1$, $x - 3$

78. $3x^5 + 7x^4 - x^3 - 7x^2 - 2x + 5$, $x + 2$

79. $x^6 + 3x^5 - 11x^4 + 4x^3 - 5x^2 + 7x - 12$, $x - 2$

80. $x^6 - 8x^4 - 10x^2 + 9$, $x - 3$

4.4 Zeros of Polynomials

The Number of Zeros

If $f(c) = 0$, then c is called a **zero of $f(x)$**, or a zero of the function f. The number c is also called a **root,** or a **solution,** of the equation $f(x) = 0$. Recall that the factor theorem and its converse tell us that $x - c$ is a factor of $f(x)$ if and only if c is a zero of f, or in other words, c is a root of $f(x) = 0$. The mathematician Karl F. Gauss proved in 1799 that every polynomial can be factored into linear factors if complex coefficients are used. This is known as

The fundamental theorem of algebra

> Every polynomial function of positive degree with complex coefficients has at least one complex zero.

The proof uses advanced methods and cannot be given here.

We will now use the fundamental theorem of algebra to show that every polynomial function $f(x)$ can be factored. In fact, if

$$f(x) = a_n x^n + a_{n-1} x^{n-1} + \cdots + a_1 x + a_0 \tag{1}$$

and c_1 is a zero, then by the factor theorem,

$$f(x) = Q_1(x)(x - c_1)$$

where $Q_1(x)$ is of degree $n - 1$. The function $Q_1(x)$ also has at least one zero, and we shall let it be c_2. Then $x - c_2$ is a factor of $Q_1(x)$ and $Q_1(x) = Q_2(x)(x - c_2)$, where $Q_2(x)$ is of degree $n - 2$. Thus $f(x) = (x - c_1)(x - c_2)Q_2(x)$. If we continue this process, we can find $n - 2$ additional factors, and we have

$$f(x) = (x - c_1)(x - c_2)(x - c_3) \cdots (x - c_n)Q_n(x) \tag{2}$$

where $Q_n(x)$ is of degree 0 and is therefore a constant. Hence $Q_n(x)$ is the coefficient of

x^n in the right member of (2), and it is thus equal to a_n. Then the factored form of $f(x)$ is

$$f(x) = a_n(x - c_1)(x - c_2)(x - c_3) \cdots (x - c_n)$$

Multiplicity   If a factor $x - c$ occurs k times, then c is called **a zero of multiplicity k.** With this terminology, the equation above shows that every polynomial function of degree n has at least n zeros, counting real and complex zeros and multiplicity.

EXAMPLE 1   If $f(x) = 5(x - 3)^4(x - 1.7)^6$, find the multiplicity of each zero.

Solution   Since $f(x) = 5(x - 3)^4(x - 1.7)^6$, then 3 is a zero of multiplicity 4 and 1.7 is a zero of multiplicity 6.

EXAMPLE 2   Find a third-degree polynomial with zeros 3, 4, and -5 and $f(9) = 840$.

Solution   By the factor theorem,

$$f(x) = a(x - 3)(x - 4)(x + 5)$$

and thus $840 = f(9) = a(9 - 3)(9 - 4)(9 + 5) = a(6)(5)(14) = 420a$

Hence $a = 2$ and $f(x) = 2(x - 3)(x - 4)(x + 5)$.

EXAMPLE 3   Find the zeros of the function

$$f(x) = (x + 1)(x - 3)^2(x + \tfrac{3}{2})^2$$

Solution   Since each factor gives a zero, the zeros of $f(x)$ are -1 with multiplicity 1, 3 with multiplicity 2, and $-\tfrac{3}{2}$ with multiplicity 2.

EXAMPLE 4   Find the four zeros of $f(x) = x^4 - 8x^3 + 20x^2 - 32x + 64$ if 4 is a zero of multiplicity 2.

Solution   Since 4 is a zero of $f(x)$, then $x - 4$ is a factor of $f(x)$. We will find the quotient by synthetic division.

$$\begin{array}{r|rrrrr} 4 & 1 & -8 & 20 & -32 & 64 \\ & & 4 & -16 & 16 & -64 \\ \hline & 1 & -4 & 4 & -16 & 0 \end{array}$$

Thus $f(x) = (x - 4)(x^3 - 4x^2 + 4x - 16)$. Since 4 is a zero of multiplicity 2, we divide synthetically again by $x - 4$.

$$\begin{array}{r|rrrr} 4 & 1 & -4 & 4 & -16 \\ & & 4 & 0 & 16 \\ \hline & 1 & 0 & 4 & 0 \end{array}$$

We now have $f(x) = (x - 4)^2(x^2 + 4)$. The other two zeros of $f(x)$ are found by setting $x^2 + 4 = 0$. The two roots of this equation are $2i$ and $-2i$. Hence the four zeros of $f(x)$ are 4, 4, $2i$, and $-2i$.

Identical Polynomials

One way in which two polynomials $f(x)$ and $g(x)$ may have equal values for all real numbers x is for the coefficients of like powers to be the same. One result of our next theorem is that, in fact, this is the only way. We will use this theorem in Sec. 9.3, where we rewrite a complicated fraction as a sum of simpler fractions.

Theorem

> If a polynomial of degree n with complex coefficients is equal to zero for more than n distinct values, then the polynomial is identically zero.
>
> An equivalent statement is that a polynomial of positive degree n has at most n distinct zeros.

Proof   Let $f(x) = a_n x^n + a_{n-1} x^{n-1} + \cdots + a_1 x + a_0$. The hypothesis says that $f(x_i) = 0$ for $i = 1, 2, \ldots, n, n + 1$. Using the factor theorem with $x_1, x_2, \ldots, x_n$ shows that

$$f(x) = a_n(x - x_1)(x - x_2) \cdots (x - x_n) \tag{3}$$

Furthermore, we know that $f(x_{n+1}) = 0$; so by Eq. (3)

$$0 = f(x_{n+1}) = a_n(x_{n+1} - x_1)(x_{n+1} - x_2) \cdots (x_{n+1} - x_n) \tag{4}$$

Now by hypothesis, $x_1, x_2, \ldots, x_n, x_{n+1}$ are all distinct, and so $x_{n+1} - x_1 \neq 0$ for $i = 1, 2, \ldots, n$. Therefore by Eq. (4) we must have $a_n = 0$. Then from Eq. (3)

$$f(x) = 0(x - x_1)(x - x_2) \cdots (x - x_n) = 0 \qquad \text{for all } x \qquad \blacktriangleleft$$

Corollary   If two polynomials of degree n are equal for all values, then the polynomials are identical.

Proof   If $f(x) = g(x)$ for all values of x, and $h(x) = f(x) - g(x)$, then $h(x) = 0$ for all x. Thus by the theorem above, $f(x) - g(x) = 0$ for all x; this means that $f(x)$ and $g(x)$ are identical. $\qquad \blacktriangleleft$

▶ **EXAMPLE 5**   Under what conditions is it true that

$$2x^3 + 5x^2 - 4x + 1 = Ax^3 + Bx^2 + Cx + D$$

Solution   We will have $2x^3 + 5x^2 - 4x + 1 = Ax^3 + Bx^2 + Cx + D$ for all x if and only if $2 = A, 5 = B, -4 = C$, and $1 = D$. $\qquad \blacktriangleleft$

▶ **EXAMPLE 6**   Find a third-degree polynomial $f(x)$ such that

$$f(2) = 0 \qquad f(5) = 0 \qquad f(-3) = 0 \qquad f(4) = 14$$

Solution   If $f(c) = 0$, then $x - c$ is a factor of $f(x)$. Hence

$$f(x) = k(x - 2)(x - 5)(x + 3)$$

Furthermore, $14 = f(4) = k(4 - 2)(4 - 5)(4 + 3)$, and so $14 = k(2)(-1)(7) = -14k$.

It follows that $k = -1$ and

$$f(x) = (-1)(x - 2)(x - 5)(x + 3)$$

This is the only polynomial satisfying the given conditions. ◢

In this section, we have seen that a polynomial of degree n has at least n zeros, counting multiplicity. We have also seen that there can be at most n distinct zeros. This gives the following result.

> If $f(x)$ is a polynomial of degree n with complex coefficients, then $f(x)$ has exactly n complex zeros, counting a zero of multiplicity k as k zeros. Some of the complex zeros may be real.

Complex Conjugate Zeros

Recall that the conjugate of $a + bi$ is $a - bi$ and that the notation for the conjugate of $a + bi$ is

$$\overline{a + bi} = a - bi$$

It can be readily verified that $x = 2$ is one zero of $x^3 - 4x^2 + 9x - 10 = 0$, and the other two zeros are the conjugates $1 + 2i$ and $1 - 2i$. Furthermore we saw in Example 4 that two of the zeros of $f(x) = x^4 - 8x^3 + 20x^2 - 32x + 64$ were $2i$ and $-2i$, which are complex conjugates. In general the zeros of the quadratic function $g(x) = ax^2 + bx + c$ are

$$x = -\frac{b}{2a} + \frac{1}{2a}\sqrt{b^2 - 4ac} \qquad \text{and} \qquad x = -\frac{b}{2a} - \frac{1}{2a}\sqrt{b^2 - 4ac}$$

Again, if the zeros are complex numbers and a, b, and c are real, then the zeros are conjugates.

These are illustrations of the fact that the complex zeros of a polynomial equation with real coefficients occur in pairs and the complex numbers in each pair are conjugates.

Theorem on Complex Conjugates

> If the complex number $a + bi$, $b \neq 0$, is a zero of the polynomial $f(x)$ with real coefficients, then its conjugate $a - bi$ is also a zero of $f(x)$.

Proof Suppose that

$$f(x) = a_n x^n + a_{n-1} x^{n-1} + \cdots + a_0 = 0 \tag{5}$$

where the coefficients $a_0, a_1, \ldots, a_n$ are real numbers and $z = a + bi$ is a zero of $f(x)$. In Sec. 2.3 on complex numbers, two of the problems were to show that the conjugate of a sum is the sum of the conjugates and that the conjugate of a product is the product of the conjugates. Since a_i is real, then

$$a_i = \overline{a_i} \qquad \text{for } i = 0, 1, 2, \ldots, n$$

Thus, taking the conjugate of each member of (5) gives

$$\overline{f(x)} = \overline{a_n x^n + a_{n-1} x^{n-1} + \cdots + a_0} = \bar{0}$$

or

$$f(\bar{x}) = a_n \bar{x}^n + a_{n-1} \bar{x}^{n-1} + \cdots + a_0 = 0 \tag{6}$$

Equation (6) says that $f(\bar{x}) = 0$; hence the conjugate $\bar{x} = a - bi$ is also a zero of $f(x)$. ◢

▶ **EXAMPLE 7**   Find a third-degree polynomial with real coefficients which has zeros $x = 3$ and $x = 3 - 2i$.

Solution   By the theorem on complex conjugates, we may take $x = 3 + 2i$ as one zero along with $x = 3 - 2i$ and $x = 3$. By the factor theorem the desired polynomial is

$$(x - 3)[x - (3 - 2i)][x - (3 + 2i)] = (x - 3)(x - 3 + 2i)(x - 3 - 2i)$$

$$= (x - 3)[(x - 3)^2 + 4]$$

$$= (x - 3)(x^2 - 6x + 13) = x^3 - 9x^2 + 31x - 39 \tag{7}$$

Any nonzero constant times this polynomial would also be an answer. If real coefficients were not required, then

$$(x - 3)[x - (3 - 2i)](x - c)$$

where c is any complex number, would be an answer. ◢

The discussion above shows that if a polynomial has real coefficients, then its complex zeros occur in conjugate pairs. If the coefficients are rational, however, then certain real zeros occur in pairs. The following theorem may be proved in a similar way, although we will not do so here.

Theorem   If the real number $a + b\sqrt{c}$, $c > 0$ and c not a perfect square, is a zero of a polynomial $f(x)$ which has rational coefficients, then $a - b\sqrt{c}$ is also a zero of $f(x)$.

For instance, if we know that $2 - \sqrt{5}$ is a zero of

$$f(x) = x^4 - 4x^3 + 2x^2 - 12x - 3 = 0$$

then $2 + \sqrt{5}$ is also a zero since the coefficients are rational.

As a consequence of the factorization

$$f(x) = a_n(x - c_1) \cdots (x - c_n)$$

and the theorem on conjugate zeros, we can now state the following corollary.

Corollary   A polynomial with real coefficients can be expressed as the product of linear and irreducible quadratic factors, each factor having real coefficients.

The proof is simply that if $[x - (a + bi)]$ is a factor, then $[x - (a - bi)]$ is another factor. Multiplying these two factors gives

$$[x - (a + bi)][x - (a - bi)] = [(x - a) - bi][(x - a) + bi]$$

$$= x^2 - 2ax + a^2 + b^2$$

which has real coefficients.

EXERCISE 4.4

State the degree of the polynomial function in Probs. 1 to 8, find each zero, and give its multiplicity.

1. $(x + 4)^5(x + 2)^2(x - 3)^3 = f(x)$
2. $(x + 1)^5(x + 2)^4(x + 3)^2 = f(x)$
3. $(x + 16)^3(x - 3)^2(x - 1)^3(x + 5) = f(x)$
4. $(x + 3)^4(x + 12)^2(x + 32)^3(x + 13) = f(x)$
5. $(3x + 17)^3(3x + 12)^4 = f(x)$
6. $(3x + 75)^5(4x + 11)^4 = f(x)$
7. $(3x + 22)^4(x + 23)^2(2x + 37)^3 = f(x)$
8. $(5x + 14)^5(3x + 15)^2(x + 28)^3 = f(x)$

In Probs. 9 to 28, find all zeros of $f(x)$.

9. $f(x) = x^3 - 2x^2 - x + 2$, one zero is -1
10. $f(x) = x^3 - 13x + 12$, one zero is 3
11. $f(x) = x^3 - 3x^2 - 4x + 12$, one zero is -2
12. $f(x) = x^3 + 7x^2 + 16x + 12$, one zero is -2
13. $f(x) = x^4 + x^3 - 3x^2 - x + 2$; 1 is a zero of multiplicity 2
14. $f(x) = x^4 + 2x^3 + 2x^2 + 2x + 1$; -1 is a zero of multiplicity 2
15. $f(x) = x^4 - 3x^3 + 6x^2 - 12x + 8$; two zeros are 1 and 2
16. $f(x) = x^4 - 2x^3 + 6x^2 - 18x - 27$; two zeros are -1 and 3
17. $f(x) = x^3 + x^2 + x + 1$; one zero is i
18. $f(x) = 2x^3 - 3x^2 + 8x - 12$; one zero is $-2i$
19. $f(x) = 3x^3 + 5x^2 + 12x + 20$; one zero is $2i$
20. $f(x) = 4x^3 - 3x^2 + 24x - 18$; one zero is $i\sqrt{6}$
21. $f(x) = 2x^3 - x^2 - 2x + 6$; one zero is $1 + i$
22. $f(x) = 4x^3 + 9x^2 + 22x + 5$; one zero is $-1 + 2i$
23. $f(x) = 4x^3 - 19x^2 + 32x - 15$; one zero is $2 - i$
24. $f(x) = 2x^3 + 7x^2 - 4x - 65$; one zero is $-3 - 2i$
25. $f(x) = x^4 + 2x^3 + 9x^2 + 8x + 20$; $2i$ and $-1 + 2i$ are zeros
26. $f(x) = x^5 + 5x^4 + 2x^3 - 38x^2 - 95x - 75$; $-2 + i$ is a zero of multiplicity 2
27. $f(x) = x^6 + 4x^5 + 15x^4 + 24x^3 + 39x^2 + 20x + 25$; $-1 + 2i$ is a zero of multiplicity 2
28. $f(x) = x^5 - 7x^4 + 24x^3 - 32x^2 + 64$; $2 + 2i$ is a zero of multiplicity 2

Find a polynomial equation of least possible degree with rational (and thus real) coefficients and with the given roots.

29. $1, -1, \frac{2}{3}$
30. $2, 1, \frac{1}{4}$
31. $i, -i, \frac{2}{3}$
32. $2i, -2i, \frac{2}{5}$
33. $-\frac{1}{3}, 1 + 2i$
34. $\frac{7}{2}, -3 + i$
35. $1, 2 + i$
36. $3, 4 - 2i$
37. $-\frac{1}{3}, 1 + \sqrt{2}$
38. $\frac{7}{2}, -3 + \sqrt{5}$
39. $1, 2 - \sqrt{2}$
40. $3, 4 - \sqrt{3}$
41. $-2 - i$, multiplicity 2
42. $-1 + \sqrt{2}$, multiplicity 2
43. $2 - 2i$, multiplicity 2
44. $2i$, multiplicity 3

In Probs. 45 to 56, find a polynomial function of smallest possible degree which satisfies the given conditions.

45. $f(1) = f(3) = f(6) = 0, f(4) = -12$
46. $f(-2) = f(0) = f(3) = 0, f(1) = -18$
47. $f(-3) = f(1) = f(3) = f(4) = 0, f(0) = -36$
48. $f(-2) = f(-1) = f(1) = f(2) = 0, f(0) = 16$
49. $f(-\sqrt{2}) = f(\sqrt{2}) = f(1) = 0, f(-1) = 16$
50. $f(-\sqrt{3}) = f(\sqrt{3}) = f(2) = 0, f(0) = 24$
51. $f(2 + \sqrt{5}) = f(2 - \sqrt{5}) = f(4) = 0, f(3) = 20$
52. $f(1 + \sqrt{5}) = f(1 - \sqrt{5}) = f(3 - \sqrt{3}) = f(3 + \sqrt{3}) = 0, f(2) = 40$
53. $f(2i) = f(-2i) = f(1) = 0, f(4) = 60$
54. $f(3i) = f(-3i) = f(-2) = 0, f(-1) = 30$
55. $f(2 + 3i) = f(2 - 3i) = f(3 + 2i) = f(3 - 2i) = 0, f(1) = 160$
56. $f(5 + i) = f(5 - i) = f(4 + 2i) = f(4 - 2i) = 0, f(3) = 75$

If the roots of $x^3 + ax^2 + bx + c = 0$ are r, s, and t, then

$$x^3 + ax^2 + bx + c = 0 = (x - r)(x - s)(x - t)$$

Multiplying the right member and then equating coefficients leads to the equations

$$r + s + t = -a \quad \text{and} \quad rst = -c \qquad \text{(C)}$$

Use Eqs. (C) in Probs. 57 to 60.

57. Find the sum and product of the roots of $x^3 - 5x^2 + 6x + 7 = 0$.

58. Find the sum and product of the roots of $3x^3 + 4x^2 - 88x + 6 = 0$. *Hint:* Divide each side of the equation by 3.

59. If the sum of two of the roots of $0 = x^3 - 9x^2 + 25x - 25$ is 4, find the other root without solving the equation.

60. Find the roots of $0 = x^3 - 12x^2 + 44x - 48$ using Eqs. (C) if the second root is twice the first and the third root is three times the first.

If the roots of $x^4 + ax^3 + bx^2 + cx + d = 0$ are $r, s, t,$ and $u,$ then

$$x^4 + ax^3 + bx^2 + cx + d = 0$$
$$= (x - r)(x - s)(x - t)(x - u)$$

and therefore (why?)

$$r + s + t + u = -a \quad \text{and} \quad rstu = d \quad \text{(Q)}$$

Use Eqs. (Q) in Probs. 61 to 64.

61. Find the sum and the product of the roots of

$$x^4 - 5x^3 + 22x^2 - 39x + 6 = 0$$

62. Find the sum and the product of the roots of

$$2x^4 + 18x^3 - 51x^2 - 44x + 6 = 0$$

Hint: Divide by 2 first.

63. If 3 is the product of three of the roots of

$$0 = x^4 - 3x^3 - 15x^2 + 49x - 12$$

find the fourth root.

64. Find the other root of

$$0 = x^4 - 3x^3 - 6x^2 + 28x - 24$$

if 2 is a root of multiplicity three.

In Probs. 65 to 68, suppose r and s are the roots of

$$x^2 + bx + c = 0$$

Prove the statements in Probs. 65 to 68, and verify them for $x^2 - 3x - 10 = 0,$ which has roots 5 and -2.

65. $r + s = -b$ and $rs = c$

66. $r^2 + s^2 = b^2 - 2c.$ *Hint:* Use 65 and

$$r^2 + s^2 = (r + s)^2 - 2rs$$

67. $\dfrac{1}{r} + \dfrac{1}{s} = \dfrac{-b}{c}.$ *Hint:* Use Prob. 65 after adding $1/r$ and $1/s$.

68. $r^3 + s^3 = 3bc - b^3.$ *Hint:* Use Probs. 65 and 66 and

$$r^3 + s^3 = (r + s)(r^2 + s^2 - rs)$$

69. Suppose that the cost function is $C(x) = x^3 - 5x^2 + 11x - 3$ and the revenue function is $R(x) = 4x.$ One break-even point is $x = 3$ since $C(3) = R(3).$ Find any other break-even points.

70. The position of a particle after t seconds is $P(t) = 2t^3 - 11t^2 + 13t - 1,$ and its position after 1 second is 3. At what other times is its position 3?

71. Does the theorem on complex conjugate zeros apply to

$$f(x) = x^3 + ix^2 - (3 - i)x + 4$$

4.5 Locating the Real Zeros

It is often useful to be able to determine an interval which contains all the real zeros of a polynomial function. Any number that is larger than or equal to the greatest zero of a polynomial function is called an **upper bound** of the zeros; also, any number that is smaller than or equal to the least zero of a polynomial function is called a **lower bound** of the zeros.

The following theorem employs synthetic division to find upper and lower bounds, and it is called the **theorem on bounds.** Remember that in synthetic division, the numbers in the third row are the coefficients of the quotient, followed by the remainder.

Theorem on Bounds

Suppose that $f(x)$ is a polynomial with real coefficients and its leading coefficient is positive. If we use synthetic division to divide $f(x)$ by $x - c$ and
(a) If $c > 0$ and all terms in the third line of the synthetic division are positive or 0, then c is an upper bound of the real zeros of $f(x)$.
(b) If $c < 0$ and the terms in the third line of the synthetic division alternate in sign, then c is a lower bound of the real zeros of $f(x)$.
The number zero may be given either a plus sign or a minus sign to help the signs alternate.

To prove the first part of the theorem, we begin with

$$f(x) = Q(x)(x - c) + R \qquad (1)$$

In the synthetic division, the coefficients in $Q(x)$ and the value of R are the numbers in the third row. If all of these numbers are positive or zero and $x > c > 0$, then $Q(x)$, $(x - c)$, and R are each positive, and by (1) we know that $f(x) > 0$. Hence there are no real roots of $f(x) = 0$ that are greater than c; this means that c is an upper bound of the real zeros of $f(x)$, as stated in the first part of the theorem. Although we omit the proof of the second part, see Prob. 45 for a hint.

EXAMPLE 1 Find upper and lower bounds for the real roots of the equation

$$x^4 - x^3 - 12x^2 - 2x + 3 = 0$$

Solution If we divide synthetically by $x - 4$ and $x - 5$, we get

```
4| 1  -1  -12  -2   3        5| 1  -1  -12  -2    3
        4   12   0  -8              5   20  40  190
   1   3    0  -2  -5           1   4    8  38 +193
```

In the division by 4, not every sign in the third row is positive or zero; so we cannot say that 4 is an upper bound of the roots. However, in the division by 5 all third-row entries are positive; so 5 is an upper bound of the roots. Division by $x - 1$, $x - 2$, and $x - 3$ all fail to reveal an upper bound.

Dividing by $x + 1 = x - (-1)$ and $x + 2 = x - (-2)$ do not show a lower bound since the third-row signs do not alternate. But if we divide synthetically by -3, then we have

```
-2| 1  -1  -12  -2    3      -3| 1  -1  -12  -2   3
        -2    6  12  -20            -3   12   0   6
   1  -3   -6  10  -17          1  -4    0  -2  +9
```

If we replace the 0 in the middle of the third line by $+$, then the third-row signs alternate. Thus -3 is a lower bound of the roots.

Note that upper bounds are *not unique* since, if 5 for instance is an upper bound of the positive zeros, then so is 6 or 16. The theorem, furthermore, does not always give the smallest upper bound. Similar comments apply to lower bounds. This is illustrated in Example 2.

EXAMPLE 2 Use the theorem on bounds if $f(x) = (x - 4)(x - 5)$.

Solution For $f(x) = (x - 4)(x - 5) = x^2 - 9x + 20$, we know that the zeros are 4 and 5, and it follows that 6 is an upper bound. However, as the synthetic divisions below show,

$$
\begin{array}{r|rrr}
6 & 1 & -9 & 20 \\
  &   & 6 & -18 \\
\hline
  & 1 & -3 & 2
\end{array}
\qquad
\begin{array}{r|rrr}
7 & 1 & -9 & 20 \\
  &   & 7 & -14 \\
\hline
  & 1 & -2 & 6
\end{array}
$$

$$
\begin{array}{r|rrr}
8 & 1 & -9 & 20 \\
  &   & 8 & -8 \\
\hline
  & 1 & -1 & 12
\end{array}
\qquad
\begin{array}{r|rrr}
9 & 1 & -9 & 20 \\
  &   & 9 & 0 \\
\hline
  & 1 & 0 & 20
\end{array}
$$

the theorem on bounds alone does not show that 6 or 7 or even 8 is an upper bound. The number 9 is the smallest integral upper bound that is revealed by the theorem on bounds.   ◢

Descartes' Rule of Signs

The following rule enables us to find the maximum number of positive and negative zeros of a polynomial $f(x)$ with real coefficients. It says nothing about their size, only how many there are.

If the terms of a polynomial are arranged according to descending powers of the variable, we say that a **variation of signs** occurs when the signs of two consecutive terms differ. For example, in the polynomial $2x^4 - 5x^3 - 6x^2 + 7x + 3$, the signs of the terms are $+ - - + +$. Hence there are two variations of sign, since the sign changes from positive to negative and back again to positive. Furthermore, there are three variations of sign in $x^4 - 2x^3 + 3x^2 + 6x - 4$.

We will now state Descartes' rule of signs and then illustrate it. The proof is omitted.

Descartes' rule of signs

> Let $f(x)$ be a polynomial which has real coefficients and a nonzero constant term and is arranged with descending powers of the variable.
> 1. The number of positive roots of $f(x) = 0$ is equal to the number of variations in sign of $f(x)$, or is less than this number by an even integer.
> 2. The number of negative roots of $f(x) = 0$ equals the number of variations in sign of $f(-x)$, or is less than this number by an even integer.

NOTE The only difference between $f(x)$ and $f(-x)$ is in the sign of the odd powers of x. For instance if $f(x) = x^5 + x^4 + x^3 + x^2$, then

$$f(-x) = (-x)^5 + (-x)^4 + (-x)^3 + (-x)^2$$
$$= -x^5 + x^4 - x^3 + x^2$$

◤ **EXAMPLE 3** Find the maximum number of positive roots and the maximum number of negative roots of $x^4 - 3x^3 - 5x^2 + 7x - 3 = 0$.

Solution Since there are three variations of sign in $f(x) = x^4 - 3x^3 - 5x^2 + 7x - 3$, the number of positive zeros of $f(x)$ is either 3 or 1.

Furthermore, $f(-x) = x^4 + 3x^3 - 5x^2 - 7x - 3$, and this polynomial has one variation of sign. Therefore, the number of negative roots of $f(x) = 0$ is one.   ◢

How large and how many

The theorem on bounds supplies information about **upper and lower bounds** for the values of the roots of $f(x) = 0$. Descartes' rule of signs gives information about **the number of positive and negative roots** without saying how large any of them may be.

In the application of either theorem, a 0 may occur. When using the theorem on bounds, a 0 may occur in the third line of the synthetic division. It may be given either a plus sign or a minus sign in the process of determining the bounds of the zeros. With Descartes' rule of signs, if a 0 occurs as a coefficient, it should be ignored.

▶ **EXAMPLE 4** What information can be given about the positive and negative roots of $f(x) = x^3 - 4x^2 + 3x + 2 = 0$?

Solution There are two variations in sign of $f(x)$; so there are either two positive roots or none. Since $f(-x) = -x^3 - 4x^2 - 3x + 2$, there is one variation of sign in $f(-x)$, and so there is exactly one negative root of $f(x) = 0$. Using synthetic division, we obtain

$$
\begin{array}{r|rrrr}
-1 & 1 & -4 & +3 & +2 \\
 & & -1 & +5 & -8 \\
\hline
 & 1 & -5 & +8 & -6
\end{array}
\qquad
\begin{array}{r|rrrr}
4 & 1 & -4 & +3 & +2 \\
 & & 4 & 0 & +12 \\
\hline
 & 1 & 0 & +3 & +14
\end{array}
$$

Thus there is no negative root less than -1 and no positive root greater than 4.

◀

Locating Zeros

When we sketch the graph of a polynomial function by plotting points and then connect them with a smooth curve without gaps, we are using an advanced property of polynomials called **continuity.** Continuity is an important topic which can only be treated fully in a calculus course, but we shall exploit this valuable property freely. If we use substitution or synthetic division to evaluate the polynomial function

$$f(x) = 2x^3 - 3x^2 - 12x + 6 \qquad \text{at } x = 0 \text{ and } x = 1$$

we find that $f(0) = 6$ and $f(1) = -7$. The value of $f(x)$ changes sign, which means its graph is on opposite sides of the x axis for $x = 0$ and $x = 1$. The continuity of the function then forces the graph to cross the x axis somewhere between 0 and 1. See Fig. 4.18.

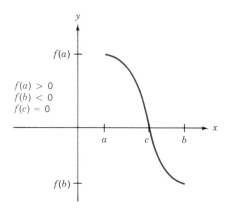

FIGURE 4.18

Intermediate Value Theorem for Polynomials

> If $f(x)$ is a polynomial with real coefficients and $f(a)$ and $f(b)$ have opposite signs, then there is at least one value c between a and b for which $f(c) = 0$.

By the intermediate value theorem, the graph of the polynomial above, namely, $f(x) = 2x^3 - 3x^2 - 12x + 6$, crosses the x axis at three points:

Since $f(-3) = -39$ and $f(-2) = 2$,
   there is a zero between -3 and -2 (approximately -2.1).
Since $f(0) = 6$ and $f(1) = -7$, as above,
   there is a zero between 0 and 1 (approximately 0.5).
Since $f(3) = -3$ and $f(4) = 38$,
   there is a zero between 3 and 4 (approximately 3.1).

▶ **EXAMPLE 5**   Locate the zeros of $f(x) = 2x^3 - x^2 - 6x + 3$.

Solution   We can use substitution or synthetic division to find that $f(-2) = -5$, $f(-1) = 6$, $f(0) = 3$, $f(1) = -2$, and $f(2) = 3$. Hence, there are zeros between -2 and -1, between 0 and 1, and between 1 and 2. Since the degree of the equation is 3, there can be only three zeros.   ◀

▶ **EXAMPLE 6**   Describe the zeros of

$$f(x) = x^5 - 10x^4 + 33x^3 - 38x^2 + 6x + 4 \qquad (2)$$

Solution   Since $f(x)$ has degree 5, there are five zeros, including real and complex ones and multiplicities. Since there are four variations in sign of $f(x)$, there are 4, 2, or 0 positive zeros. In $f(-x) = -x^5 - 10x^4 - 33x^3 - 38x^2 - 6x + 4$, there is one variation in sign. Thus there is precisely one negative zero.

   The following table of values may be found either by calculating function values directly from Eq. (2) or by using synthetic division. The table shows that $x = 2$ is a zero and there are zeros between -1 and 0, between 0 and 1, between 1 and 3, between 3 and 4, and between 4 and 5. This gives a total of four positive zeros, along with the one negative zero.

x	-1	0	1	2	3	4	5
$f(x)$	-84	4	-4	0	4	-4	84

Some of the synthetic divisions are shown below.

```
-1| 1  -10   33  -38    6    4        2| 1  -10   33  -38    6    4
        -1   11  -44   82  -88               2  -16   34   -8   -4
   ─────────────────────────────           ─────────────────────────────
      1  -11   44  -82   88  -84              1   -8   17   -4   -2    0

 5| 1  -10   33  -38    6    4        4| 1  -10   33  -38    6    4
         5  -25   40   10   80               4  -24   36   -8   -8
   ─────────────────────────────           ─────────────────────────────
      1   -5    8    2   16   84              1   -6    9   -2   -2   -4
```

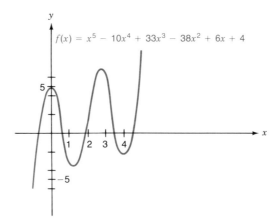

$f(x) = x^5 - 10x^4 + 33x^3 - 38x^2 + 6x + 4$

FIGURE 4.19

In the division by -1, the third-row signs alternate, and hence -1 is a lower bound of the negative zeros. We could also have used the fact that the one negative zero is between -1 and 0. We know that 5 is an upper bound of the positive zeros since we have actually located the four positive zeros between 0 and 5. The third line in synthetic division will not yield an upper bound until we try $x = 10$, since the second number will be negative for $x = 5, 6, 7, 8$, and 9. See Fig. 4.19.

EXERCISE 4.5

Use the theorem on bounds in Probs. 1 to 12 to find upper and lower bounds for the real roots of the given equation.

1. $2x^3 + x^2 + x - 1 = 0$
2. $2x^3 + x^2 + 4x - 15 = 0$
3. $3x^3 - 4x^2 + 3x - 2 = 0$
4. $3x^3 - x^2 + 7x + 6 = 0$
5. $4x^3 - 5x^2 - x - 1 = 0$
6. $4x^3 - 8x^2 - 9x + 18 = 0$
7. $25x^3 + 75x^2 - 4x - 12 = 0$
8. $4x^3 + 9x^2 + 8x - 2 = 0$
9. $x^4 - 6x^3 + 13x^2 - 12x + 4 = 0$
10. $x^4 - 10x^3 + 2x^2 - 60x + 36 = 0$
11. $2x^4 + x^3 - 8x^2 - x + 6 = 0$
12. $3x^4 - 15x^3 - 21x^2 - 17x + 30 = 0$

Determine the number of positive roots and the number of negative roots of the equation in each of Probs. 13 to 24 by Descartes' rule of signs.

13. $x^3 - 4x^2 - 5x + 2 = 0$
14. $-2x^3 - 3x^2 + 5x + 7 = 0$
15. $5x^3 + 3x^2 + 6x + 1 = 0$
16. $2x^3 + 5x^2 - x + 2 = 0$
17. $2x^4 + 5x^3 - 3x^2 + x + 2 = 0$

18. $x^4 - 4x^3 + 12x^2 + 24x + 24 = 0$
19. $-3x^4 - 5x^3 + 8x^2 - 2x + 6 = 0$
20. $3x^4 + 8x^3 - 2x^2 + 5x - 1 = 0$
21. $4x^5 + 3x^4 - 2x^3 + x^2 - x + 4 = 0$
22. $3x^5 - 3x^3 + 2x^2 + 5x - 1 = 0$
23. $3x^5 + 2x^2 + 5x - 1 = 0$
24. $2x^6 - 3x^4 + x^3 - 3 = 0$

In Probs. 25 to 36, use the intermediate value theorem to locate each real root between two consecutive integers.

25. $3x^3 + 10x^2 - 2x - 4 = 0$
26. $3x^3 - 19x^2 + 21x - 4 = 0$
27. $2x^3 - 19x^2 + 50x - 28 = 0$
28. $3x^3 - 28x^2 + 54x + 20 = 0$
29. $x^4 - 8x^3 + 12x^2 + 16x - 16 = 0$
30. $x^4 + 4x^3 - 15x^2 - 66x - 54 = 0$
31. $3x^4 - 12x^3 - 9x^2 + 16x + 4 = 0$
32. $3x^4 - 12x^3 - 6x^2 + 36x - 9 = 0$
33. $2x^3 - 11x^2 + 18x - 14 = 0$
34. $3x^3 - 13x^2 + 19x - 5 = 0$
35. $x^4 - 4x^2 - 8x - 4 = 0$
36. $x^4 - 8x^3 + 21x^2 - 20x - 6 = 0$

The equation in each of Probs. 37 to 40 has two roots between consecutive integers. Locate these roots by use of a value halfway between the consecutive integers. Also locate all other roots between two consecutive integers.

37. $3x^3 - 4x^2 - 7x - 2 = 0$
38. $3x^3 - 5x^2 - 6x + 10 = 0$
39. $9x^3 - 15x^2 - 12x + 20 = 0$
40. $9x^3 - 24x^2 - 48x + 128 = 0$

Use Descartes' rule of signs in Probs. 41 to 44.

41.   Show that $x^6 + 2x^4 + 3x^2 + 4 = 0$ has six imaginary roots.
42.   Show that $5x^5 + 3x^3 + x + 1 = 0$ has four imaginary roots.
43.   Show that $x^5 + 2x - 3 = 0$ has four imaginary roots.
44.   Show that $x^3 + 2x + 3 = 0$ has two imaginary roots.

45.   *Theorem on bounds*   The following example illustrates the method used to prove the theorem on bounds in general for the case $c < 0$. Give reasons for each step. We use $f(x) = x^4 + 3x^3 - 5x^2 - 8x + 4$ and $c = -5$.

(a)

$$\underline{-5|}\ \ \begin{array}{rrrrr} 1 & 3 & -5 & -8 & 4 \\ & -5 & 10 & -25 & 165 \\ \hline 1 & -2 & 5 & -33 & 169 \end{array} \leftarrow \text{signs}$$

alternate

(b) $f(x) = (x + 5)(x^3 - 2x^2 + 5x - 33) + 169$
(c)   If $x < -5$, then

$$f(x) = (\text{negative})(\text{negative}) + 169$$

$$= \text{positive} + \text{positive} = \text{positive}$$

(d)   And thus if $x < -5$, then $f(x) \neq 0$.

46.   Show that if $f(x)$ is a polynomial function of odd degree, then it has at least one real zero. *Hint:* Why does the graph cross the x axis (what is its range)?

4.6   Rational Zeros

If a polynomial function has one or more rational zeros, the work involved in finding any other zeros is greatly reduced if the rational zeros are found first. The process of identifying a rational zero is a matter of trial and error, with the number of trials limited by the next theorem. It gives a set of numbers which includes the rational zeros. We can then use synthetic division and the remainder theorem to identify which of these possible zeros actually are zeros. Remember that c is a rational zero of $f(x)$ if and only if c is a rational root of $f(x) = 0$.

Rational Zeros Theorem

Suppose that the coefficients of

$$f(x) = a_n x^n + a_{n-1} x^{n-1} + \cdots + a_1 x + a_0 \tag{1}$$

are integers and p/q is a rational zero in lowest terms. Then the numerator p is a factor of the constant term a_0, and the denominator q is a factor of the leading coefficient a_n.

Proof   Since we are assuming that p/q is given in lowest terms, we know that p and q do not have a common factor greater than 1. If we substitute p/q for x in $f(x)$, use $f(p/q) = 0$, and multiply both sides by q^n, we obtain

$$a_0 q^n + a_1 q^{n-1} p + \cdots + a_{n-1} q p^{n-1} + a_n p^n = 0 \tag{2}$$

By adding $-a_n p^n$ to each side and then dividing by q, we have

$$a_0q^{n-1} + a_1q^{n-2}p + \cdots + a_{n-1}p^{n-1} = -\frac{a_np^n}{q} \tag{3}$$

The left-hand side of Eq. (3) is an integer since it is made up of the sum, product, and integral powers of integers. Therefore, the right side must be an integer. Since by hypothesis q and p have no common factor greater than 1, q must be a factor of a_n.

Similarly, if we add $-a_0q^n$ to each side of (2) and divide by p, we obtain

$$a_1q^{n-1} + \cdots + a_{n-1}qp^{n-2} + a_np^{n-1} = -\frac{a_0q^n}{p} \tag{4}$$

Hence, p is a factor of a_0, since q and p have no common factor greater than 1 and the left side of (4) is an integer. ◢

If $a_0 = 1$ in (1), we get the following corollary:

If a polynomial function with leading coefficient 1 has integral coefficients,

$$f(x) = x^n + a_{n-1}x^{n-1} + \cdots + a_1x + a_0 \tag{5}$$

then each rational zero of $f(x)$ is an integer which must be a factor of a_0.

NOTE   These theorems only give all of the *possible* rational zeros or all of the *possible* integer zeros.

▶ EXAMPLE 1   Find the possible rational zeros of

$$f(x) = 2x^4 + x^3 - 9x^2 - 4x + 4$$

Solution   The numerators of the rational zeros must be factors of 4 (namely, 1, 2, and 4, each with a + or − sign), and the denominators must be factors of 2. The possibilities for the rational zeros are $\pm\frac{1}{1}$, $\pm\frac{2}{1}$, $\pm\frac{4}{1}$, $\pm\frac{1}{2}$, $\pm\frac{2}{2}$, and $\pm\frac{4}{2}$. If we eliminate repetitions, we are left with the rational numbers

$$-4, \ -2, \ -1, \ -\tfrac{1}{2}, \tfrac{1}{2}, \ 1, \ 2, \ 4$$

We can now use synthetic division and the remainder theorem to determine which of these possibilities are the actual zeros. This will be done in Example 2. ◢

The Depressed Equation

After we locate one zero of a polynomial function, we can simplify further work. If c_1 is a root of $F(x) = 0$, then by the factor theorem,

$$F(x) = F_1(x)(x - c_1) = 0$$

and $F_1(x) = 0$ is called the **depressed equation** corresponding to c_1. Furthermore, the degree of $F_1(x)$ is one less than the degree of $F(x)$. Now if c_2 is a root of $F_1(x) = 0$, then c_2 is also a root of $F(x) = 0$, and we have

$$F(x) = (x - c_1)(x - c_2)F_2(x) = 0$$

We can use $F_2(x) = 0$ to locate the remaining roots of $F(x) = 0$.

This process may be continued after each rational root is found. If we eventually obtain a depressed equation that is quadratic, the remaining roots can be found by factoring or the quadratic formula.

NOTE　The depressed equation $F_1(x) = 0$ is used **only to find roots** of the given equation $F(x) = 0$. The depressed equation may not be used to find function values of $F(x)$ directly since as above $F(x) = (x - c_1) \cdot F_1(x)$.

▶ **EXAMPLE 2**　Find all zeros of the function $2x^4 + x^3 - 9x^2 - 4x + 4$ of Example 1.

Solution　The possible rational zeros were found to be

$$-4, -2, -1, -\tfrac{1}{2}, \tfrac{1}{2}, 1, 2, 4$$

We shall choose 2 first, and use synthetic division to show it is a zero:

$$
\begin{array}{r|rrrrr}
2 & 2 & 1 & -9 & -4 & 4 \\
  &   & 4 & 10 & 2 & -4 \\
\hline
  & 2 & 5 & 1 & -2 & 0
\end{array}
$$

Since the remainder is zero, 2 is a zero. Furthermore, all zeros of the given function $2x^4 + x^3 - 9x^2 - 4x + 4$, except possibly $x = 2$, are roots of the depressed equation $2x^3 + 5x^2 + x - 2 = 0$. If 2 is a multiple root of the given equation, it is also a root of the depressed equation. We next try $x = -2$ in the depressed equation above and obtain

$$
\begin{array}{r|rrrr}
-2 & 2 & 5 & 1 & -2 \\
   &   & -4 & -2 & 2 \\
\hline
   & 2 & 1 & -1 & 0
\end{array}
$$

Since the remainder is zero, -2 is also a zero of $f(x)$. Using the third line of the synthetic division above, the depressed equation corresponding to $x = 2$ and $x = -2$ is the quadratic equation $2x^2 + x - 1 = 0$. We solve it by factoring and find that

$$(2x - 1)(x + 1) = 0$$

$$x = \tfrac{1}{2}, -1$$

We have now found all of the zeros of the given function. They are $2, -2, -1,$ and $\tfrac{1}{2}$. Notice that the degree of the function is 4, and there are four zeros. ◢

Obtaining All Rational Zeros

We can now outline the steps that should be followed to determine all rational zeros of a polynomial function:

1. Use the theorem on rational zeros to find the set of rational numbers that contains the rational zeros, and write them in the order of the magnitude of their numerical values.
2. Use synthetic division or the remainder theorem to test the smallest positive integer in the set, the next larger, and so on, until each integral zero, or a bound of the zeros, is found.
   (a) If an upper bound is found, discard all larger numbers in the set.
   (b) If a zero is found, use the depressed equation in further synthetic divisions; check first for multiplicity.
3. Test the fractions that remain in the set after considering any known upper and lower bounds.
4. Repeat steps 2 and 3 for negative zeros, beginning with the negative integer nearest to 0.

▶ **EXAMPLE 3**   Find all rational zeros of $f(x) = 4x^4 - 4x^3 - 25x^2 + x + 6$.

Solution   The possible numerators of the rational zeros are ± 6, ± 3, ± 2, and ± 1. The possible denominators are ± 4, ± 2, and ± 1. After removing duplicates from the quotients, the possible rational zeros are

$$\pm \tfrac{1}{4}, \ \pm \tfrac{1}{2}, \ \pm \tfrac{3}{4}, \ \pm 1, \ \pm \tfrac{3}{2}, \ \pm 2, \ \pm 3, \ \pm 6$$

We shall test the positive integers first, starting with 1:

$$
\underline{1|} \ \begin{array}{ccccc}
4 & -4 & -25 & +1 & +6 \\
 & +4 & 0 & -25 & -24 \\
\hline
4 & 0 & -25 & -24 & -18
\end{array}
$$

Since the remainder is -18 and not zero, 1 is not a zero. Testing 2, we get

$$
\underline{2|} \ \begin{array}{ccccc}
4 & -4 & -25 & +1 & +6 \\
 & +8 & +8 & -34 & -66 \\
\hline
4 & +4 & -17 & -33 & -60
\end{array}
$$

Therefore, 2 is not a zero, and the theorem on bounds gives no information here. Next we try 3, and obtain

$$
\underline{3|} \ \begin{array}{ccccc}
4 & -4 & -25 & +1 & +6 \\
 & +12 & +24 & -3 & -6 \\
\hline
4 & +8 & -1 & -2 & 0
\end{array}
$$

Since the remainder is zero, 3 must be a zero. The corresponding depressed equation is $4x^3 + 8x^2 - x - 2 = 0$, which has all the roots of the original equation, with the possible exception of 3. Since the constant term in the depressed equation is -2 and the coefficient of x^3 is 4, the possible rational roots of the depressed equation are $\pm \tfrac{1}{4}$, $\pm \tfrac{1}{2}$, ± 1, and ± 2. Not all of these need be considered, since we already know that 1 and 2 are not zeros of the original equation.

   We can use synthetic division to show that $\tfrac{1}{4}$ is not a zero, but $\tfrac{1}{2}$ is a zero:

$$\frac{1}{4} \begin{array}{|rrrr} 4 & 8 & -1 & -2 \\ & 1 & \frac{9}{4} & \frac{5}{16} \\ \hline 4 & 9 & \frac{5}{4} & -\frac{27}{16} \end{array} \qquad \frac{1}{2} \begin{array}{|rrrr} 4 & 8 & -1 & -2 \\ & 2 & 5 & 2 \\ \hline 4 & 10 & 4 & 0 \end{array}$$

We obtain $4x^2 + 10x + 4 = 0$ as the corresponding depressed equation. This is a quadratic equation that can be solved by factoring since

$$4x^2 + 10x + 4 = 2(2x^2 + 5x + 2) = 2(2x + 1)(x + 2)$$

Its roots are $-\frac{1}{2}$ and -2. The zeros of the original function are thus 3, $\frac{1}{2}$, $-\frac{1}{2}$, and -2. ◢

EXAMPLE 4 Show that 3 is a zero of multiplicity 2 of the function

$$f(x) = 2x^3 - 11x^2 + 12x + 9$$

Solution Dividing synthetically by $x - 3$ gives

$$3 \begin{array}{|rrrr} 2 & -11 & 12 & 9 \\ & 6 & -15 & -9 \\ \hline 2 & -5 & -3 & 0 \end{array}$$

The depressed equation is $2x^2 - 5x - 3 = 0$. This is a quadratic equation which can be factored as $(x - 3)(2x + 1) = 0$. This equation also has 3 as a root. Thus 3 is a zero of multiplicity 2 of $f(x)$. ◢

EXAMPLE 5 Show that $f(x) = x^3 + 3x^2 - 4x + 3 = 0$ has no rational zeros.

Solution The possible rational zeros are -3, -1, 1, and 3. None of these values is a zero; this can be checked by substitution or synthetic division. ◢

EXAMPLE 6 Find all zeros of $f(x) = 4x^4 - 12x^3 + 17x^2 - 24x + 18$.

Solution The possible numerators of rational zeros are ± 18, ± 9, ± 6, ± 3, ± 2, and ± 1, and the possible denominators are ± 4, ± 2, and ± 1. Hence the possible rational zeros are the following 24 numbers:

$$\pm \tfrac{1}{4}, \ \pm \tfrac{1}{2}, \ \pm \tfrac{3}{4}, \ \pm 1, \ \pm \tfrac{3}{2}, \ \pm 2, \ \pm \tfrac{9}{4}, \ \pm 3, \ \pm \tfrac{9}{2}, \ \pm 6, \ \pm 9, \ \pm 18$$

The synthetic divisions

$$1 \begin{array}{|rrrrr} 4 & -12 & 17 & -24 & 18 \\ & 4 & -8 & 9 & -15 \\ \hline 4 & -8 & 9 & -15 & 3 \end{array} \qquad 2 \begin{array}{|rrrrr} 4 & -12 & 17 & -24 & 18 \\ & 8 & -8 & 18 & -12 \\ \hline 4 & -4 & 9 & -6 & 6 \end{array}$$

$$3 \begin{array}{|rrrrr} 4 & -12 & 17 & -24 & 18 \\ & 12 & 0 & 51 & 81 \\ \hline 4 & 0 & 17 & 27 & 99 \end{array}$$

show that 3 is an upper bound of the positive zeros and also that $f(1) = 3$ and $f(2) = 6$. One reason to try $x = \frac{3}{2}$ as a zero is that the nearby function values are a lot closer to

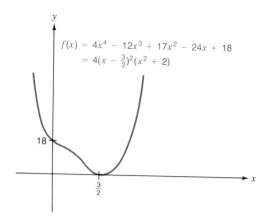

$f(x) = 4x^4 - 12x^3 + 17x^2 - 24x + 18$
$= 4(x - \frac{3}{2})^2(x^2 + 2)$

FIGURE 4.20

zero then are $f(0) = 18$ and $f(3) = 99$. Hence we can at least hope that a nearby number will produce exactly 0. We will try $\frac{3}{2}$ in the original equation and then in the depressed equation:

$$\frac{3}{2}\!\big|\ \ 4 \quad -12 \quad\ \ 17 \quad -24 \quad\ \ 18 \qquad\qquad \frac{3}{2}\!\big|\ \ 4 \quad -6 \quad\ \ 8 \quad -12$$
$$\underline{\qquad\ \ 6 \quad\ -9 \quad\ \ 12 \quad -18} \qquad\qquad\qquad \underline{\qquad\ \ 6 \quad\ \ 0 \quad\ \ 12}$$
$$\ \ \ \ 4 \quad\ -6 \quad\ \ \ 8 \quad -12 \quad\ \ \ 0 \qquad\qquad\qquad \ \ 4 \quad\ \ 0 \quad\ \ 8 \quad\ \ \ 0$$

We see that $\frac{3}{2}$ is a zero of multiplicity two. The resulting depressed equation is the quadratic equation $4x^2 + 8 = 0$. Solving it gives $x^2 = -2$. The four zeros of the original function are thus $\frac{3}{2}$, $\frac{3}{2}$, $i\sqrt{2}$, and $-i\sqrt{2}$. Thus the factorization of the given equation is

$$f(x) = 4(x - \tfrac{3}{2})(x - \tfrac{3}{2})(x - i\sqrt{2})(x + i\sqrt{2})$$

The graph of f is shown in Fig. 4.20.

◢

EXAMPLE 7   Find all roots of the equation

$$(x - 1)^4 + (x - 3)^4 = 16 \tag{6}$$

Solution   In the given form, we can use substitution to show that $x = 1$ and $x = 3$ are roots. Expanding and collecting terms in (1) and then dividing by 2 gives

$$x^4 - 8x^3 + 30x^2 - 56x + 33 = 0 \tag{7}$$

Next, dividing synthetically by the root 1 and then by 3 in the depressed equation gives

$$1\!\big|\ \ 1 \quad -8 \quad\ \ 30 \quad -56 \quad\ \ 33 \qquad\qquad 3\!\big|\ \ 1 \quad -7 \quad\ \ 23 \quad -33$$
$$\underline{\qquad\ \ 1 \quad\ -7 \quad\ \ 23 \quad -33} \qquad\qquad\qquad \underline{\qquad\ \ 3 \quad -12 \quad\ \ 33}$$
$$\ \ \ \ 1 \quad\ -7 \quad\ \ 23 \quad -33 \quad\ \ \ 0 \qquad\qquad\quad 1 \quad\ -4 \quad\ \ 11 \quad\ \ \ 0$$

The resulting depressed equation is the quadratic equation $x^2 - 4x + 11 = 0$. It has the roots $2 \pm i\sqrt{7}$. The four roots of the original equation are 1, 3, $2 + i\sqrt{7}$, and $2 - i\sqrt{7}$. Note that the two complex roots are conjugates.

Alternative Solution   After expanding the given equation, find all possible rational zeros and proceed as in Example 6. ◢

▶ **EXAMPLE 8**   Show that $3 + \sqrt{2}$ is irrational.

Solution   To do this, we will form an equation with $3 + \sqrt{2}$ as a root and show that this equation has no rational root. If $x = 3 + \sqrt{2}$, then

$$x - 3 = \sqrt{2} \qquad \text{subtracting 3 to isolate } \sqrt{2}$$

$$x^2 - 6x + 9 = 2 \qquad \text{squaring}$$

$$x^2 - 6x + 7 = 0 \qquad \text{subtracting 2}$$

The only possible rational roots of this equation are ± 1 and ± 7, and none of these four is in fact a root. It follows that $3 + \sqrt{2}$ is irrational. ◢

EXERCISE 4.6

In Probs. 1 to 8, write all possible rational roots, and then find all roots of the equation.

1. $x^3 - 2x^2 - 5x + 6 = 0$
2. $x^3 - x^2 - 10x - 8 = 0$
3. $x^3 - 4x^2 + x + 6 = 0$
4. $x^3 - 7x - 6 = 0$
5. $2x^3 - x^2 - 7x + 6 = 0$
6. $2x^3 + 3x^2 - 17x - 30 = 0$
7. $3x^3 - 7x^2 - 18x - 8 = 0$
8. $3x^3 + 7x^2 - 18x + 8 = 0$

Find all roots of the equation in each of Probs. 9 to 28.

9. $4x^3 + 16x^2 + 9x - 9 = 0$
10. $4x^3 - 12x^2 + 5x + 6 = 0$
11. $6x^3 - 19x^2 + 19x - 6 = 0$
12. $6x^3 + 19x^2 + 11x - 6 = 0$
13. $x^3 - 3x^2 + 2 = 0$
14. $x^3 + 4x^2 + 3x - 2 = 0$
15. $x^3 - 3x^2 - 2x + 2 = 0$
16. $x^3 - 6x^2 + 9x - 2 = 0$
17. $2x^3 - 5x^2 - 6x + 4 = 0$
18. $2x^3 + 11x^2 + 14x + 3 = 0$
19. $3x^3 + 16x^2 + 9x - 14 = 0$
20. $4x^3 - 19x^2 + 9 = 0$
21. $x^4 - 5x^2 + 4 = 0$
22. $x^4 - 13x^2 + 36 = 0$
23. $6x^4 - 17x^3 + 7x^2 + 8x - 4 = 0$
24. $6x^4 - 35x^3 + 45x^2 - 16 = 0$

25. $2x^4 - 3x^3 - 21x^2 + 17x - 3 = 0$
26. $3x^4 - 22x^3 + 41x^2 - 4x - 28 = 0$
27. $3x^4 + 4x^3 + 6x^2 - 20x - 25 = 0$
28. $2x^4 - 7x^3 + 8x^2 - 2x - 4 = 0$

29. Show that $\frac{1}{3}$ is a root of multiplicity 2 of
$$9x^3 + 12x^2 - 11x + 2 = 0$$

30. Show that $\frac{2}{5}$ is a root of multiplicity 2 of
$$25x^3 + 5x^2 - 16x + 4 = 0$$

31. Show that $-\frac{1}{2}$ is a root of multiplicity 2 of
$$4x^4 + 4x^3 - 3x^2 - 4x - 1 = 0$$

32. Show that $-\frac{1}{3}$ is a root of multiplicity 3 of
$$27x^4 - 27x^3 - 45x^2 - 17x - 2 = 0$$

33. Show that there are no rational roots of
$$x^3 - 7x^2 + 2x - 1 = 0$$

34. Show that there are no rational roots of
$$x^3 + 13x^2 - 6x - 2 = 0$$

35. Show that there are no rational roots of
$$x^4 - 2x^3 + 10x^2 - x + 1 = 0$$

36. Show that there are no rational roots of
$$3x^4 - 9x^3 - 2x^2 - 15x - 5 = 0$$

Show that the number in each of Probs. 37 to 44 is irrational.

37. $\sqrt{6}$

38. $\sqrt[3]{5}$

39. $2 - \sqrt{5}$

40. $1 + \sqrt[3]{6}$

41. $\sqrt{2} + \sqrt{7}$

42. $\sqrt{5} - \sqrt{2}$

43. $6^{2/3}$

44. $1 + \sqrt{2} + \sqrt{3}$

Hint for Prob. 44: Note that if $x = 1 + \sqrt{3} + \sqrt{2}$, then

$$x - 1 = \sqrt{3} + \sqrt{2}$$

45. Solve $(x + 3)^4 + (x - 1)^4 = 82$.

46. Solve $(x^2 + x + 1)(x^2 + x + 3) = 15$.

47. Solve $(x + 1)(x - 1)(x - 2)(x - 4) = -8$.

48. Solve $(x - 2)^4 + (x - 1)^4 = 1$.

49. A right triangle has an area of 60 m², and the hypotenuse is 2 m longer than the longer leg x. Show that

$$x^3 + x^2 - 3600 = 0$$

and solve for x.

50. Suppose that 34 bears are put in a park, and after x years there are $-x^3 + 7x^2 + 60x + 34$ bears there. After how many years will there be 450 bears? Find only the integer solution.

51. Suppose that on a certain day the temperature x hours after midnight is

$$\left(\frac{-x}{16}\right)(x - 6)(x - 18) + 55$$

in degrees F for x between 6 and 18. At what (rational) time is the temperature 75°?

52. Suppose that, in thousands, the number of fruit flies in a laboratory after x days is

$$x^3 + 14x^2 + 53x + 40$$

After how many days will the number of thousands of fruit flies be 352?

53. Suppose that the speed of air moving through the windpipe of a person during a cough is

$$486(1 - r)(r^2)$$

if r is the radius of the windpipe. Which value of r makes the speed 72?

54. If a box with no top is made from a piece of metal, which is 12 by 15, by cutting out a square piece of area x^2 from each corner and turning up the sides, its volume is

$$(x)(15 - 2x)(12 - 2x)$$

Find two values of x between 0 and 6 which make the volume 176. (*Hint:* Find an integer solution, then solve the depressed equation, and use a decimal approximation for the noninteger solution.) Which of these two values of x makes the box have the smaller surface area, including the bottom?

4.7 Approximations and Exact Zeros

There are formulas for solving polynomial equations of degree 1, 2, 3, and 4. The first two have been known at least since the Greeks. Formulas for the solution of cubic and quartic equations were discovered about 1540 by the Italians Ferrari, Tartaglia, and Cardan. Who discovered the formulas, who published them, and the surrounding circumstances make a fascinating story of scientific intrigue. It was not until 1824 that Abel proved that no comparable formulas exist for polynomial equations of degree 5 and higher. Hence we are forced to use approximations in some cases, while in others it is easier to find good approximations than to find exact solutions. If we can find an exact solution, then we can use it to get whatever decimal-place accuracy we may want in a particular situation.

Successive Approximation

If we know that a polynomial function has a zero in an interval (a, b) by using the intermediate value theorem, there are several methods we can use to find a better approximation to that zero.

Bisection

Linear interpolation

Newton's method

Successive approximation

1. We may repeatedly bisect the interval, using the intermediate value theorem.
2. We may find the line through the two points $(a, f(a))$ and $(b, f(b))$ and then find its x intercept.
3. We may use advanced techniques such as Newton's method involving tangent lines.
4. We may use the intermediate value theorem to locate the zero first between consecutive integers, then between consecutive tenths, and then between consecutive hundredths. If more accuracy is needed, we can use some method with the aid of a calculator or computer.

Our choice will be method 4, **successive approximation.**

▶ **EXAMPLE 1**   Approximate the zeros of $f(x) = x^3 - 4x^2 + 7x - 5$.

Solution   The following table of values, found by synthetic division, limits the zero within smaller and smaller intervals. At each stage, we choose two values of x whose function values have opposite signs.

x	1	2	1.5	1.6	1.56	1.57
$f(x)$	-1	1	-0.125	0.056	-0.018	0.003

We will use 1.57 as our *approximation* to the real zero, since $f(1.57)$ is closer to 0 than $f(1.56)$ is. The following synthetic division

$$
\begin{array}{r|rrrr}
1.57 & 1 & -4 & 7 & -5 \\
     &   & 1.57 & -3.8151 & 5.000293 \\
\hline
     & 1 & -2.43 & 3.1849 & 0.000293
\end{array}
$$

gives the *approximate* depressed equation $x^2 - 2.43x + 3.1849 = 0$. The quadratic formula gives us two approximate complex zeros:

$$2x = 2.43 \pm \sqrt{(2.43)^2 - 4(1)(3.1849)}$$

$$= 2.43 \pm \sqrt{5.9049 - 12.7396}$$

$$= 2.43 \pm \sqrt{-6.8347}$$

$$\approx 2.43 \pm 2.614i$$

$$x \approx 1.215 \pm 1.307i$$

Hence there is one real zero and two complex zeros.

> **EXAMPLE 2** Approximate the largest zero of

$$f(x) = x^4 - 8x^3 - 20x^2 - 60x - 25$$

Solution Descartes' rule of signs shows that there is only one positive zero, and it must be between 10 and 11 since $f(10) = -625$ and $f(11) = 888$ have opposite signs. Thus we will use values of x between 10 and 11. The table of values below can be found by substitution or synthetic division, and a calculator helps:

x	10	11	10.4	10.5	10.47	10.48
$f(x)$	-625	888	-112.5	34.1	-10.7	4.1

The table shows that the largest zero is 10.48, to two decimal places. In Example 3, we will show that the exact value is $5 + \sqrt{30}$, which equals 10.47723 to five decimal places.

Quartic Equations

The method for finding the exact solutions of fourth-degree equations, called quartic equations, involves reducing the problem to solving two quadratic equations. We can usually find the **exact** solution of quartic equations by completing the square twice and then finding one rational root of a cubic equation. Occasionally some steps can be skipped, as in Example 3.

> **EXAMPLE 3** Find the exact solutions of $x^4 - 8x^3 - 20x^2 - 60x - 25 = 0$.

Solution This is the same equation as in Example 2. In order to complete the square, we write the terms of degree 4 and 3 on the same side of the equation.

$$x^4 - 8x^3 = 20x^2 + 60x + 25$$

$$x^4 - 8x^3 + 16x^2 = 36x^2 + 60x + 25 \qquad \text{adding } 16x^2 \text{ to complete the square on the left}$$

$$(x^2 - 4x)^2 = (6x + 5)^2 \qquad \text{factoring each side}$$

After we completed the square on the left, the right side happened to be a perfect square also. This will not happen in Example 4. Now if $t^2 = s^2$, then either $t = s$ or $t = -s$. So our next step is to solve these two quadratic equations.

$$x^2 - 4x = 6x + 5 \qquad\qquad\qquad x^2 - 4x = -6x - 5$$

$$x^2 - 10x - 5 = 0 \qquad\qquad\qquad x^2 + 2x + 5 = 0$$

$$x = \frac{10 \pm \sqrt{100 + 20}}{2} \qquad\qquad x = \frac{-2 \pm \sqrt{4 - 20}}{2}$$

$$= 5 \pm \sqrt{30} \qquad\qquad\qquad = -1 \pm 2i$$

The exact solutions are $5 \pm \sqrt{30}$ and $-1 \pm 2i$, two irrational and two complex numbers. Decimal approximations to the two irrational roots are 10.47723 and -0.47723. Any one of the four may be checked by substitution or synthetic division. ◢

► EXAMPLE 4   Solve $x^4 - 2x^3 - 18x^2 + 34x - 7 = 0$.

Solution   Again we begin by leaving only the terms of degree 4 and 3 on one side of the equation.

$$x^4 - 2x^3 = 18x^2 - 34x + 7$$

$$x^4 - 2x^3 + x^2 = x^2 + 18x^2 - 34x + 7 \qquad \text{adding } x^2 \text{ to complete the square on the left}$$

$$(x^2 - x)^2 = 19x^2 - 34x + 7$$

Although the left-hand side is now a perfect square, the right-hand side is not a perfect square. We want to rewrite the equation so that the right-hand side becomes a perfect square, while the left-hand side remains a perfect square. The form of the left-hand side is t^2, where $t = x^2 - x$. For any y, we have

$$t^2 + 2ty + y^2 = (t + y)^2$$

Thus if we now add $2ty + y^2 = t(2y) + y^2 = (x^2 - x)(2y) + y^2$ to both sides, the left-hand side remains a perfect square for any y:

$$(x^2 - x)^2 + 2y(x^2 - x) + y^2 = 19x^2 - 34x + 7 + 2y(x^2 - x) + y^2$$

Factoring the left-hand side and collecting terms on the right-hand side shows that

$$[(x^2 - x) + y]^2 = x^2(19 + 2y) + x(-34 - 2y) + (7 + y^2) \qquad \textbf{(1)}$$

The left-hand side is a perfect square for *every* y. We must now choose a value of y that makes the right-hand side a perfect square also. This requires that its discriminant $b^2 - 4ac$ be 0.

$$(-34 - 2y)^2 - 4(19 + 2y)(7 + y^2) = 0$$

$$1156 + 136y + 4y^2 - 4(133 + 19y^2 + 14y + 2y^3) = 0$$

$$y^3 + 9y^2 - 10y - 78 = 0 \qquad \text{collecting terms} \atop \text{and dividing by } -8$$

We now find **any solution** of this last equation. Using the theorem on rational roots, we try $y = 3$ and find that it is a solution since $27 + 81 - 30 - 78 = 108 - 108 = 0$. Using $y = 3$ on both sides of Eq. (1) gives us a right-hand side which is also a perfect square:

$$(x^2 - x + 3)^2 = 25x^2 - 40x + 16$$

$$(x^2 - x + 3)^2 = (5x - 4)^2$$

Again with $t^2 = s^2$, we have $t = s$ or $t = -s$:

$$x^2 - x + 3 = 5x - 4 \qquad\qquad x^2 - x + 3 = -5x + 4$$

$$x^2 - 6x + 7 = 0 \qquad\qquad\qquad x^2 + 4x - 1 = 0$$

$$x = \frac{6 \pm \sqrt{36 - 28}}{2} \qquad\qquad x = \frac{-4 \pm \sqrt{16 + 4}}{2}$$

$$= 3 \pm \sqrt{2} \qquad\qquad = -2 \pm \sqrt{5} \qquad \blacktriangleleft$$

See Probs. 45 to 48 for the exact solution of cubic equations, which are third-degree equations.

EXERCISE 4.7

Find the least positive irrational root in each of Probs. 1 to 16 to two decimal places.

1. $x^3 - 6x^2 - 6x + 8 = 0$
2. $x^3 - 5x^2 + 5x - 1 = 0$
3. $x^3 - 9x^2 + 21x = 13$
4. $x^3 - 5x - 2 = 0$
5. $x^3 + 9x^2 + 15x - 9 = 0$
6. $x^3 - 6x^2 + 16 = 0$
7. $x^3 - 9x^2 + 54 = 0$
8. $x^3 - x^2 - 9x - 7 = 0$
9. $x^3 + 3x^2 - 2x - 6 = 0$
10. $x^3 + 2x^2 - 3x - 6 = 0$
11. $x^3 - 3x^2 - 2x + 4 = 0$
12. $x^3 - 2x^2 - 7x + 2 = 0$
13. $2x^3 + 3x^2 - 10x + 4 = 0$
14. $3x^3 - 16x^2 + 6x + 12 = 0$
15. $2x^3 - 11x^2 + 8x + 7 = 0$
16. $3x^3 + 8x^2 - 19x + 4 = 0$

In Probs. 17 to 24, find the value of each irrational root to three decimal places by successive approximation.

17. $x^4 - 2x^3 - 4x - 4 = 0$
18. $x^4 - 8x^3 + 12x^2 - 8x + 11 = 0$
19. $x^4 - 6x^3 + 4x^2 - 6x + 3 = 0$
20. $x^4 + 4x^3 - 2x^2 + 4x - 3 = 0$
21. $x^3 + 3x^2 - 3x - 7 = 0$
22. $x^3 + 6x^2 - 28 = 0$
23. $x^3 - 6x^2 + 6x + 2 = 0$
24. $2x^3 - 11x^2 + 12x + 7 = 0$

In Probs. 25 to 36, use the method of Examples 3 and 4 to find all four exact roots of the quartic equation. In each problem, find the largest real root to three decimal places.

25. $x^4 - 4x^3 - 2x^2 + 12x + 8 = 0$

26. $x^4 - 2x^3 - 6x^2 - 14x - 3 = 0$
27. $x^4 - 2x^3 - 16x^2 + 22x + 7 = 0$
28. $x^4 + 2x^3 - 35x^2 - 22x + 36 = 0$
29. $x^4 - 8x^3 + 14x^2 - 8x + 13 = 0$
30. $x^4 - 4x^3 + x^2 - 12x - 6 = 0$
31. $x^4 + 6x^3 + 5x^2 + 24x + 4 = 0$
32. $x^4 + 4x^3 + 2x^2 + 20x - 15 = 0$
33. $x^4 - 10x^3 + 21x^2 + 44x - 121 = 0$
34. $x^4 + 12x^3 + 20x^2 + 24x - 9 = 0$
35. $x^4 + 6x^3 + 24x - 16 = 0$
36. $x^4 - 8x^3 - 8x - 1 = 0$

In Probs. 37 to 44, find the three exact roots of the cubic equation. See Prob. 48 for the formulas and Probs. 45 to 47 for their derivation.

37. $y^3 + 18y + 15 = 0$ 38. $y^3 + 15y - 20 = 0$
39. $y^3 - 6y - 6 = 0$ 40. $y^3 + 12y - 30 = 0$
41. $y^3 + 3y + 6 = 0$ 42. $y^3 + 6y + 4 = 0$
43. $y^3 + 9y + 2 = 0$ 44. $y^3 + 6y + 6 = 0$

The next four problems show how to solve a cubic equation.

45. Show that if we begin with the *general cubic equation*

$$x^3 + ax^2 + bx + c = 0$$

and replace x by $y - a/3$, we get an equation of the form

$$y^3 + py + q = 0$$

Notice that this *reduced cubic equation* has no second-degree term.

46. Show that replacing y by $z - p/3z$ in $y^3 + py + q = 0$ gives

$$z^6 + qz^3 - \frac{p^3}{27} = 0$$

which is a *quadratic in z^3*.

47. Show that the quadratic formula applied to the equation $z^6 + qz^3 - p^3/27 = 0$ gives

$$z^3 = \frac{-q}{2} \pm \sqrt{\frac{q^2}{4} + \frac{p^3}{27}}$$

48. Even though we will not give the details, it can be shown that if $q^2/4 + p^3/27 > 0$ and A and B are real numbers with

$$A = \sqrt[3]{-\frac{q}{2} + \sqrt{\frac{q^2}{4} + \frac{p^3}{27}}}$$

and $$B = \sqrt[3]{-\frac{q}{2} - \sqrt{\frac{q^2}{4} + \frac{p^3}{27}}}$$

and w and w^2 are the complex numbers

$$w = \frac{-1 + i\sqrt{3}}{2} \quad \text{and} \quad w^2 = \frac{-1 - i\sqrt{3}}{2}$$

then the **solutions of $y^3 + py + q = 0$** are

$$y_1 = A + B \qquad y_2 = wA + w^2B$$
$$y_3 = w^2A + wB \quad \text{(C)}$$

Note that y_2 and y_3 are complex conjugates if p and q are real. The solutions of the original cubic equation

$$x^3 + ax^2 + bx + c = 0$$

are thus

$$x_1 = y_1 - \frac{a}{3} \qquad x_2 = y_2 - \frac{a}{3} \qquad x_3 = y_3 - \frac{a}{3}$$

In the case $q^2/4 + p^3/27 > 0$, this gives one real and two complex conjugate roots. In the case $q^2/4 + p^3/27 < 0$, there are three distinct real roots. Here the form given in Eq. (1) on page 244 is still true, but unwieldy, and trigonometry is needed to put the solutions in a manageable form.

4.8 Graphs of Rational Functions

In Chap. 3, we discussed the sum, difference, product, and quotient of two functions. In this section we shall concentrate on quotients of polynomial functions.

If $p(x)$ and $q(x)$ are polynomials, then

$$f(x) = \frac{p(x)}{q(x)}$$

is called a **rational function,** and it is defined for all x for which $q(x) \neq 0$.

We will be especially interested in values of x for which $p(x) = 0$ or $q(x) = 0$ and also in the degrees of $p(x)$ and $q(x)$. We will assume that **$p(x)$ and $q(x)$ have no common factors,** and therefore no common zeros.

Here are some examples of rational functions.

$$f(x) = \frac{1}{x - 4} \qquad g(x) = \frac{x^2 - 9}{x^3 + 8}$$

$$h(x) = \frac{x + 1}{2x - 2} \qquad F(x) = \frac{x^2 + 5x + 8}{4x - 9}$$

Because division by 0 is never allowed, the domain of f is the set of all real numbers such that $q(x) \neq 0$. If, for instance, $q(a) = q(b) = q(c) = 0$, then a, b, and c

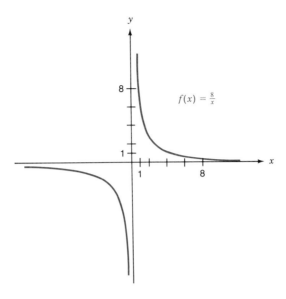

$f(x) = \frac{8}{x}$

FIGURE 4.21

are not in the domain of f. Thus $f(a)$, $f(b)$, and $f(c)$ are not defined. This leads to an important fact about rational functions.

$q(x) = 0$

> The graph of f consists of $k + 1$ separate branches, or pieces, if $q(x) = 0$ has k distinct real roots.

The real numbers where $p(x) = 0$ are also important because $f(x) = 0$ if and only if $p(x) = 0$. This is our second basic fact about rational functions.

$p(x) = 0$

> The x intercepts of f occur precisely where $p(x) = 0$.

The graph of the rational function $f(x) = 8/x$ is a hyperbola, and it is shown in Fig. 4.21. Rational functions can exhibit two types of behavior which are impossible for polynomials of positive degree. We are speaking of

vertical and horizontal asymptotes

which will be formally defined after the next two rational functions and their associated tables of values are given. Let

$$f(x) = \frac{1}{x - 4} \quad \text{and} \quad g(x) = \frac{x + 1}{2x - 2}$$

x	5	4.1	4.01	4.001	3	3.9	3.99	3.999
$f(x)$	1	10	100	1000	-1	-10	-100	-1000

x	5	11	51	101	201	1001	10001
$g(x)$	0.75	0.6	0.52	0.51	0.505	0.501	0.5001

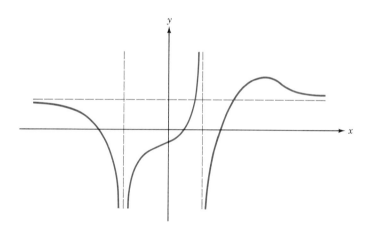

FIGURE 4.22

From the table for $f(x)$, it appears that when x approaches 4 from either the right or left, $|f(x)|$ gets arbitrarily large. The table for $g(x)$ indicates that as x gets larger and larger, $g(x)$ gets closer and closer to $\frac{1}{2}$. We may write these facts as

$$\text{If } x \to 4, \text{ then } |f(x)| \to \infty$$

$$\text{If } x \to \infty, \text{ then } g(x) \to \tfrac{1}{2}$$

because of the following general notation:

"$x \to a$"	means "x approaches a (x gets arbitrarily close to a)."
"$x \to a^{+}$"	means "$x > a$ and x approaches a from the right."
"$x \to a^{-}$"	means "$x < a$ and x approaches a from the left."
"$x \to \infty$"	means "x gets arbitrarily large with x positive."
"$x \to -\infty$"	means "$|x|$ gets arbitrarily large with x negative."

The same notation is used for $f(x) \to a$, $f(x) \to \infty$, and so on. Using this notation, we can now define **asymptotes:**

Asymptotes

> Suppose that $f(x) = p(x)/q(x)$ is a rational function in lowest terms and a is some real number.
> (i) That the vertical line $x = a$ is a vertical asymptote for the graph of f means that if $x \to a$, then $|f(x)| \to \infty$.
> (ii) That the horizontal line $y = a$ is a horizontal asymptote for the graph of f means that if $|x| \to \infty$, then $f(x) \to a$.

In Fig. 4.22, we show a graph that has one horizontal and two vertical asymptotes. The graph never crosses the vertical asymptotes since those x values are not in the domain of the function, but the graph may indeed cross a horizontal asymptote.

We may rewrite rational functions in order to see what happens as $|x| \to \infty$. Merely divide both numerator and denominator by the highest power of x which occurs in the denominator. We of course assume here that $x \neq 0$ since we are now interested in what happens as $x \to \infty$. As $x \to \infty$, clearly $1/x$, $1/x^2$, $1/x^3$, etc., each approach 0. This allows us to find **horizontal asymptotes.** For instance

$$f(x) = \frac{3x + 4}{5x - 6} = \frac{3 + 4/x}{5 - 6/x} \rightarrow \frac{3 + 0}{5 - 0} = \frac{3}{5}$$

Therefore the horizontal line $y = \frac{3}{5}$ is a horizontal asymptote for the graph of f. Similarly the x axis, or $y = 0$, is a horizontal asymptote for the graph of g since

$$g(x) = \frac{14x + 9}{4x^2 + 2x + 5} = \frac{14/x + 9/x^2}{4 + 2/x + 5/x^2} \rightarrow \frac{0 + 0}{4 + 0 + 0} = 0$$

On the other hand, for

$$h(x) = \frac{1}{x - 4}$$

we have a **vertical asymptote.** It is the line $x = 4$ because

$$\text{As } x \rightarrow 4, \text{ then } x - 4 \rightarrow 0 \text{ and } |h(x)| \rightarrow \infty$$

There is also a horizontal asymptote, the x axis, since if

$$|x| \rightarrow \infty, \text{ then } h(x) \rightarrow 0$$

See Fig. 4.23. These examples illustrate the following rules for asymptotes:

Rules for asymptotes

Suppose that the rational function

$$f(x) = \frac{p(x)}{q(x)} = \frac{a_n x^n + \cdots + a_0}{b_m x^m + \cdots + b_0}$$

is in lowest terms.
If $q(a) = 0$, then $x = a$ is a vertical asymptote.
If $n < m$, then the x axis is the horizontal asymptote.
If $n = m$, then the horizontal asymptote is the line $y = a_n/b_m$.
If $n > m$, then the graph has no horizontal asymptote.

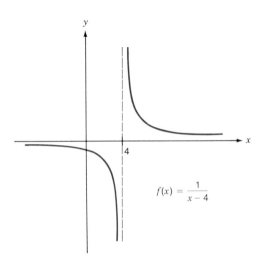

FIGURE 4.23

If there are k vertical asymptotes, then the graph is divided into $k + 1$ branches. Notice that for rational functions there may be several vertical asymptotes, but only one horizontal asymptote.

Sign of f(x)

Knowing the **sign of $f(x)$** is very useful in drawing the graph. If we find all zeros of $p(x) = 0$ and $q(x) = 0$ and indicate the location of each one on the x axis, then in each interval between these zeros of p and q, $f(x)$ will have the same sign. Thus the graph will always be above or below the x axis in each such interval. We may, in these intervals, use test values just as we did when graphing polynomial functions.

▶ **EXAMPLE 1**   Graph $f(x) = 1/(x - 4)$ and $g(x) = 1/(x - 4)^2$.

Solution   Setting each denominator equal to zero shows that:

The line $x = 4$ is a vertical asymptote

Since each function has the degree of the numerator less than the degree of the denominator:

The x axis is the horizontal asymptote

Since there is no x in the numerator of the fraction, $f(x) \neq 0$ and $g(x) \neq 0$. Thus neither graph crosses the x axis. Each denominator is equal to zero at one point, and hence each graph has two separate branches.

We have $g(x) > 0$ for all x in the domain, whereas

$$f(x) > 0 \text{ if } x > 4 \qquad \text{and} \qquad f(x) < 0 \text{ if } x < 4$$

See Figs. 4.23 and 4.24.   ◀

NOTE   Remember that:

For horizontal asymptotes we are interested in $|x| \to \infty$

For vertical asymptotes we need $|f(x)| \to \infty$

▶ **EXAMPLE 2**   Sketch the graphs of

$$f(x) = \frac{x - 2}{x^2 - 2x - 3} \qquad \text{and} \qquad g(x) = \frac{x - 2}{x^2 - 2x + 3}$$

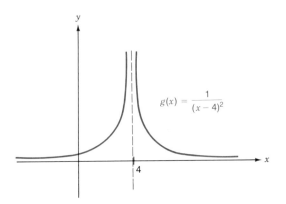

$$g(x) = \frac{1}{(x - 4)^2}$$

FIGURE 4.24

Solution These functions differ only in the $+3$ and -3 in the denominators, but this means that the first one factors while the second one does not. Both graphs have the x axis as a horizontal asymptote since the degree of the denominator is greater than that of the numerator. Both cross the x axis at $x = 2$. For the first function, we can factor the denominator and get

$$f(x) = \frac{x - 2}{x^2 - 2x - 3} = \frac{x - 2}{(x - 3)(x + 1)}$$

The second function requires us to complete the square:

$$g(x) = \frac{x - 2}{x^2 - 2x + 3} = \frac{x - 2}{x^2 - 2x + 1 + 2} = \frac{x - 2}{(x - 1)^2 + 2}$$

Thus the graph of f has two vertical asymptotes, $x = 3$ and $x = -1$. The graph of g has no vertical asymptotes since its denominator is never zero.

It follows that the graph of f has three separate branches, while that of g has only one branch. The tables below give the sign of $f(x)$ and of $g(x)$ in the intervals determined by setting each numerator and denominator equal to zero:

Sign of $f(x)$ $-$ $+$ $-$ $+$

$$\begin{array}{ccccc} & -1 & 2 & 3 & \end{array}$$

Sign of $g(x)$ $-$ $+$

$$\begin{array}{cc} & 2 \end{array}$$

Any number in each interval may be used as a value to calculate the sign of $f(x)$ or of $g(x)$. The y intercepts, found by setting x equal to 0, are $f(0) = \frac{2}{3}$ and $g(0) = -\frac{2}{3}$. The x intercepts are found by setting the numerators equal to 0. For both equations we obtain

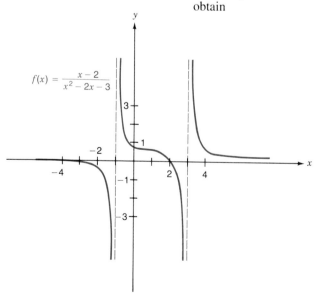

$$f(x) = \frac{x - 2}{x^2 - 2x - 3}$$

FIGURE 4.25

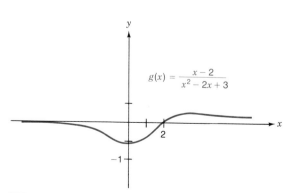

$$g(x) = \frac{x - 2}{x^2 - 2x + 3}$$

FIGURE 4.26

$$x - 2 = 0 \qquad x = 2$$

The results are shown in the following table:

Rational function	y intercept	x intercept
f	$\frac{2}{3}$	2
g	$-\frac{2}{3}$	2

We can use the information about intercepts, asymptotes, branches, and signs to draw sketches of the graphs of these rational functions. See Figs. 4.25 and 4.26. Although additional points can be plotted, our goal is to understand the graphs, not just connect points. ◢

As we saw earlier, if the degree of the numerator is equal to or larger than the degree of the denominator, the x axis is no longer a horizontal asymptote. However we may divide $p(x)$ by $q(x)$ and obtain a quotient $g(x)$ and a remainder $r(x)$:

$$f(x) = \frac{p(x)}{q(x)} = g(x) + \frac{r(x)}{q(x)}$$

Since the degree of $r(x)$ is less than the degree of $q(x)$, $r(x)/q(x) \to 0$ as $|x| \to \infty$. If $g(x)$ is a constant, then f has a **horizontal asymptote**—see Example 3 below. If $g(x)$ is a linear function of the form $mx + b$, then

$$f(x) = mx + b + \frac{r(x)}{q(x)}$$

This means that the graph of f has an asymptote that is a nonvertical straight line since $r(x)/q(x) \to 0$ as $|x| \to \infty$. This straight line is called an **oblique asymptote**—see Example 4 below.

EXAMPLE 3   Draw the graph of $f(x) = (3x - 11)/(x - 4)$.

Solution   Is the degree of the numerator smaller than the degree of the denominator? No. Thus we divide $x - 4$ into $3x - 11$ and get

$$f(x) = 3 + \frac{1}{x - 4}$$

Therefore the graph has the same shape as the graph of $y = 1/(x - 4)$, which was given in Fig. 4.23, but it is translated up 3 units. See Fig. 4.27. ◢

EXAMPLE 4   Draw the graph of $f(x) = (x^2 + 5x + 10)/(2x + 6)$.

Solution   Long division gives

$$f(x) = \frac{x}{2} + 1 + \frac{2}{x + 3}$$

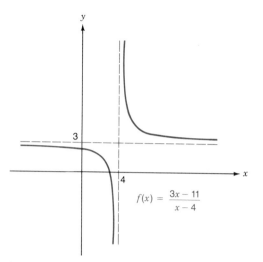

$$f(x) = \frac{3x - 11}{x - 4}$$

FIGURE 4.27

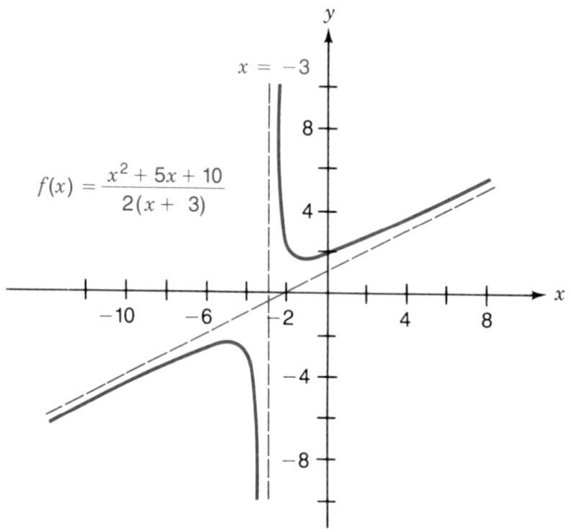

$$f(x) = \frac{x^2 + 5x + 10}{2(x + 3)}$$

$x = -3$

FIGURE 4.28

There is one vertical asymptote, the line $x = -3$, so the graph will have two branches. The y intercept is $f(0) = \frac{10}{6} = \frac{5}{3}$, but there is no x intercept because $x^2 + 5x + 10$ is irreducible. Since $2/(x + 3) \to 0$ as $|x| \to \infty$, the line

$$y = \tfrac{1}{2}x + 1 \quad \text{is an oblique asymptote}$$

for the graph. Since the numerator $x^2 + 5x + 10$ is always positive, the sign of $f(x)$ depends only on $x + 3$, and

$$f(x) > 0 \text{ if } x > -3 \qquad \text{and} \qquad f(x) < 0 \text{ if } x < -3$$

Furthermore

$$\text{If } x > -3, \text{ then } \frac{2}{x + 3} > 0 \qquad \text{and so} \qquad f(x) > \frac{1}{2}x + 1$$

$$\text{If } x < -3, \text{ then } \frac{2}{x + 3} < 0 \qquad \text{and so} \qquad f(x) < \frac{1}{2}x + 1$$

The graph is shown in Fig. 4.28. ◢

We can use Fig. 4.28 to visually solve an **inequality in one variable.** However we must remember that the graph has two branches. The solution of

$$\frac{x^2 + 5x + 10}{2(x + 3)} < 0$$

is the set of all points on the real line for which the graph of f is below the x axis. The solution is $(-\infty, -3)$. See Fig. 4.28.

If $f(x)$ is a polynomial function, it is sometimes an advantage to look at the graphs of $y = f(x)$ and $y = 1/f(x)$ on the same axes. One reason is that $f(x)$ and $1/f(x)$ have the same sign for a given x. Another reason is that where one of them is very small, the other one is very large. Thus information about one graph yields corresponding information about the other one. In Fig. 4.29, we have drawn the graph of $f(x) =$

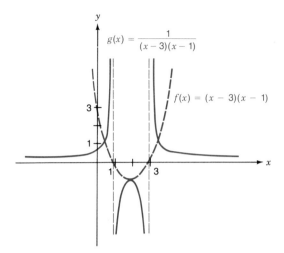

FIGURE 4.29

$(x - 3)(x - 1)$ dashed, and the graph of $g(x) = 1/f(x) = 1/(x - 3)(x - 1)$ solid. The graph of f is a parabola which opens up, and its x intercepts are 1 and 3. Where $x > 3$, for instance, both graphs are above the x axis, and

$$\text{As } x \to \infty, \ f(x) \to \infty \text{ and } g(x) \to 0$$

while $$\text{As } x \to 3 \text{ from the right, } f(x) \to 0 \text{ and } g(x) \to \infty$$

EXERCISE 4.8

Sketch the graph of each function given in Probs. 1 to 24.

1. $f(x) = \dfrac{2}{x - 3}$

2. $f(x) = \dfrac{3}{x + 4}$

3. $f(x) = \dfrac{5}{(x - 1)^2}$

4. $f(x) = \dfrac{4}{(x + 2)^2}$

5. $f(x) = \dfrac{4}{(x - 1)(x + 2)}$

6. $f(x) = \dfrac{3}{(x - 2)(x - 4)}$

7. $f(x) = \dfrac{x - 1}{(x + 1)(x - 2)}$

8. $f(x) = \dfrac{x + 1}{(x - 1)(x + 2)}$

9. $f(x) = \dfrac{12}{(x + 1)(x - 2)(x + 3)}$

10. $f(x) = \dfrac{-8}{(x + 2)(x - 1)(x - 3)}$

11. $f(x) = \dfrac{3}{x^2 + x - 2}$

12. $f(x) = \dfrac{x + 1}{x^2 + x - 6}$

13. $f(x) = \dfrac{12}{x^2 + x + 3}$

14. $f(x) = \dfrac{9}{x^2 + 4x + 6}$

15. $f(x) = \dfrac{1 - x}{x^2 - 2x + 3}$

16. $f(x) = \dfrac{x - 2}{x^2 - 6x + 12}$

17. $f(x) = \dfrac{4x + 1}{2x - 3}$

18. $f(x) = \dfrac{12x - 15}{3x - 5}$

19. $f(x) = \dfrac{3x^2 - 3x - 2}{x^2 - x - 2}$

20. $f(x) = \dfrac{2x^2 - x - 14}{x^2 - x - 6}$

21. $f(x) = \dfrac{2x^2 - 3x + 3}{x}$

22. $f(x) = \dfrac{2x^2 - x - 12}{2x - 5}$

23. $f(x) = \dfrac{3x^2 - x - 1}{3x - 4}$

24. $f(x) = \dfrac{3x^2 + 4x - 3}{3x + 7}$

Solve the inequalities in Probs. 25 to 32. See the stated problem (and its graph in the answer section).

25. (Prob. 5) $\dfrac{4}{(x - 1)(x + 2)} > 0$

26. (Prob. 9) $\dfrac{12}{(x + 1)(x - 2)(x + 3)} > 0$

27. (Prob. 17) $\dfrac{4x + 1}{2x - 3} < 0$

28. (Prob. 21) $\dfrac{2x^2 + x + 2}{x + 1} < 0$

29. (Prob. 7) $\dfrac{x - 1}{(x + 1)(x - 2)} < 0$

30. (Prob. 11) $\dfrac{3}{x^2 + x - 2} > 0$

31. (Prob. 15) $0 < \dfrac{1 - x}{x^2 - 2x + 3}$

32. (Prob. 23) $0 > \dfrac{3x^2 - x - 1}{3x - 4}$

4.9 Key Concepts

Make sure you understand the following important words and ideas.

Quadratic function (p. 198)
Parabola (p. 198)
Vertex (p. 200)
Axis of symmetry is $x = -b/2a$ (p. 200)
Intercepts (p. 201)
Polynomial function (p. 207)
Range when the degree n is even or odd (p. 208)
Factored polynomial (p. 208)
Turning points (p. 208)
Remainder theorem (p. 216)
Synthetic division (p. 217)
Factor theorem and its converse (p. 219)
Fundamental theorem of algebra (p. 222)

Polynomial equation (p. 222)
Multiplicity (p. 223)
Complex conjugate zeros (p. 225)
Upper and lower bounds of the real zeros (p. 229)
Number of positive and negative zeros (p. 230)
Rule for locating real zeros (p. 232)
Rational zeros (p. 234)
Quartic equation (p. 243)
Cubic equation (p. 245)
Rational function (p. 246)
Horizontal asymptote (p. 248)
Vertical asymptote (p. 248)
Oblique asymptote (p. 252)
Inequality in one variable (p. 253)

EXERCISE 4.9   Review

Draw the parabolas in Probs. 1 to 7.

1. $y = 2(x - 3)^2$

2. $y = 2(x + 3)^2$

3. $y - 3 = 2x^2$

4. $y + 2 = 5(x + 3)^2$

5. $x - 2 = -5(y + 3)^2$

6. $y^2 = 4x + 2y + 19$

7. $x^2 + 4x + 8y = 20$

In Probs. 8 to 10, give the coordinates of the vertex, and state whether it is a maximum or a minimum point for the parabola.

8. $y = 4x^2 + 12x + 17$

9. $y = -3x^2 + 12x + 5$

10. $3x + 4y = 3x^2 + 4$

11. Find the remainder if $x^3 + 3x^2 - x - 4$ is divided by $x - 2$.

12. Find the remainder if $-2x^3 + 3x^2 + 7x - 40$ is divided by $x + 3$.

13. What is the remainder when $x^4 - 2x^3 + 5x + 2$ is divided by $x - d$?

14. Show that $x + 4$ is a factor of $x^3 + 4x^2 - x - 4$.

15. Show that $x^3 - 3x^2 - 2x + 6$ is divisible by $x - 3$.

16. Show that $\frac{3}{2}$ is a root of $2x^3 - 3x^2 + 6x - 9 = 0$.

17. Show that $\sqrt{2}$ is a root of $x^3 + 4x^2 - 2x - 8 = 0$.

18. Show that $3i$ is a root of $x^3 - 4x^2 + 9x - 36 = 0$.

19. Find the quotient and remainder if $2x^3 + 5x - 6$ is divided by $x - 2$.

20. Find the quotient and remainder if $3x^4 + 5x^3 + 2x^2 + 6x - 3$ is divided by $x + 2$.

21. Find all roots of $x^3 - x^2 - 8x + 12 = 0$ if 2 is a root of multiplicity 2.

22. Find the other two roots of $x^4 + 6x^3 + 11x^2 + 12x + 18 = 0$ if -3 is a root of multiplicity 2.

23. Find a polynomial of least possible degree with real coefficients whose zeros include 2 and $3 + i$.

24. Find a polynomial of least possible degree with rational coefficients whose zeros include 3 and $1 + \sqrt{3}$.

25. Find a polynomial of degree 4 with real coefficients that has $x - 1 + 2i$ and $x + 2 - i$ as factors.

26. Find a polynomial of degree 4 with real coefficients which has the zeros $2 + \sqrt{3}$ and $2 + i\sqrt{3}$.

27. What is the multiplicity of the root $x = 3$ in $x^4 - 7x^3 + 9x^2 + 27x - 54 = 0$?

28. Find the multiplicity of the root $x = i$ in $x^5 - 2x^4 + 2x^3 - 4x^2 + x - 2 = 0$.

29. What are the sum and the product of the roots of $x^3 - x^2 + x - 1 = 0$?

30. What are the sum and the product of the roots of

$$x^4 - 4x^3 + 8x^2 - 16x + 16 = 0$$

31. Show that all real roots of $2x^3 - x^2 + 4x + 3 = 0$ are between -1 and 1.

32. Show that there is exactly one positive root of $x^4 + 2x^3 + 4x - 5 = 0$.

33. Find the roots of

$$(x - 1)(x - 2)(x - 3)(x + 4)$$
$$= (x - 1)(x - 2)(x - 3)(x + 5)$$

34. Show that $x = \sqrt[3]{4}$ is irrational by checking the

equation $x^3 - 4 = 0$ for rational roots. Show by substitution that the three roots of this equation are

$$x = \sqrt[3]{4} \quad \text{and} \quad x = -\frac{\sqrt[3]{4}}{2}(1 \pm i\sqrt{3})$$

35. Show that the graphs of

$$y = x^3 + 3x^2 - 5x + 4$$

and

$$y = x^3 + 2x^2 - 9x - 3$$

do not intersect each other.

36. Find all roots of the equation $x^3 - 2x^2 + x - 2 = 0$.

37. Find all roots of the equation

$$4x^4 + 12x^3 + 25x^2 + 48x + 36 = 0$$

38. Find all roots of $6x^5 - 17x^4 - 7x^3 + 58x^2 - 78x + 20 = 0$.

39. Use Prob. 58 in this exercise to show that the arithmetic mean of the roots of

$$9x^4 - 24x^3 - 35x^2 - 4x + 4 = 0$$

equals the arithmetic mean of the roots of

$$36x^3 - 72x^2 - 70x - 4 = 0$$

40. Show that $\sqrt[4]{6}$ is irrational.

41. Show that $\sqrt{3} - \sqrt{2}$ is irrational.

42. Is $\sqrt{3} + \sqrt{12} - \sqrt{27}$ irrational?

43. Find the real root of $x^3 + 6x^2 + 12x + 2 = 0$ to two decimal places.

44. Find both real roots of $x^4 + 2x^3 + x^2 + 6x - 6 = 0$ to two decimal places.

45. Find any real root of $x^4 - x^3 - 4x^2 + 3x + 3 = 0$ to three decimal places.

46. Find the exact value of each root of

$$x^4 - x^3 - 4x^2 + 3x + 3 = 0$$

47. Find the three exact roots of $y^3 - 18y - 30 = 0$.

48. Find the three exact roots of $x^3 - 9x^2 - 9x - 15 = 0$.

Graph the functions in Probs. 49 to 57.

49. $f(x) = x^3 - 4x^2 + x + 6$

50. $f(x) = x^3 - 2x^2 - 5x + 6$

51. $f(x) = x^4 + 2x^3 - 7x^2 - 8x + 12$

52. $f(x) = (x + 1)^2(x - 1)^2(x - 3)^3$

53. $f(x) = (x + 2)^3(x - 1)^2(x - 4)^3$

54. $f(x) = \dfrac{4}{x - 2}$

55. $f(x) = \dfrac{2}{(x+1)(x-2)}$ **56.** $f(x) = \dfrac{6x+1}{3x-2}$

57. $f(x) = \dfrac{(x+1)(x-1)}{(x+2)(x-2)}$

58. Show that if

$$x^n + a_{n-1}x^{n-1} + a_{n-2}x^{n-2} + \cdots + a_1x + a_0 = 0$$

and has roots $r_1, r_2, \ldots, r_n$, then the *sum of the roots satisfies*

$$r_1 + r_2 + \cdots + r_n = -a_{n-1} \qquad \text{(S)}$$

and the *product of the roots satisfies*

$$r_1 r_2 \ldots r_n = (-1)^n a_0 \qquad \text{(P)}$$

Hint: Factor the polynomial; then multiply it out using $r_1, r_2, \ldots, r_n$, and compare coefficients with the original polynomial.

59. Find a polynomial equation with real coefficients and roots $2 + 3i$ and $-4 + \sqrt{3}$ and verify Eqs. (S) and (P) in Prob. 58 for this polynomial.

60. Show that a cubic equation with real coefficients has either three real roots or one, counting multiplicity.

61. For $-1 \le x \le 1$, consider all cubic polynomials

$$P(x) = x^3 + ax^2 + bx + c$$

which have real coefficients and leading coefficient 1. The function

$$T(x) = x^3 - \frac{3x}{4}$$

has its maximum distance from the x axis at four points and

$$|T(-1)| = |T(-\tfrac{1}{2})| = |T(\tfrac{1}{2})| = |T(1)| = \tfrac{1}{4}$$

For any other $P(x)$ on $[-1, 1]$, the maximum distance from the x axis is more than $\tfrac{1}{4}$. Graph any such P and verify this property for that P.

62. Solve the inequality using graphs:

$$(x+4)(x+1)(x-3)(x-5) \ge 0$$

63. Solve the inequality using graphs:

$$(x+5)(x+3)(x-1)(x-3) \le 0$$

64. Solve the inequality using graphs:

$$(x+2)(x+1)(x-2)^2(x-3) \ge 0$$

65. Solve the inequality using graphs:

$$(x+1)(x-1)/(x-2)(x-4) < 0$$

5 Exponential and Logarithmic Functions

The polynomial and other functions we have dealt with so far in this book are formed with the four fundamental operations and the extraction of roots. These are called **algebraic functions.** If a function is not algebraic, we refer to it as **transcendental.** In this chapter we introduce two types of transcendental functions, namely, exponential and logarithmic functions. These arise in dealing with equations such as $5^x = 6$. Some other basic transcendental functions occur in trigonometry.

There are a great many applications of exponential and logarithmic functions. In this chapter we include applications in the growth of bacteria, sound intensity, compound interest, atmospheric pressure, population growth, the half-life of radioactive material, advertising effectiveness, the law of cooling, and the Richter scale for earthquakes.

5.1 Exponential Functions

In earlier chapters, we dealt with the following definitions and facts concerning exponential expressions with the base $b > 0$.

Definitions

If m is a positive integer, then

$$b^m = b \cdot b \cdot \cdots \cdot b \qquad \text{where there are } m \text{ factors of } b$$

$$b^{-m} = \frac{1}{b^m} \qquad \text{and} \qquad b^0 = 1$$

Properties or laws of exponents

If m and n are integers (positive, negative, or zero), then

$$b^m \cdot b^n = b^{m+n} \qquad (b^m)^n = b^{mn} \qquad \frac{b^m}{b^n} = b^{m-n}$$

259

We also saw that, for $b > 0$, the above properties apply with rational exponents m/n where by definition

$$b^{m/n} = (b^{1/n})^m = (\sqrt[n]{b})^m = \sqrt[n]{b^m} = (b^m)^{1/n}$$

▶ **EXAMPLE 1**   The definitions above allow us to define a function

$$f(x) = 3^x \qquad \text{for any } rational \text{ value of } x$$

Find the following function values.

Solution   The decimal approximations below came from a calculator, but the exact values merely use the rules for rational exponents.

$$f(-4) = 3^{-4} = (\tfrac{1}{3})^4 = \tfrac{1}{81} \approx 0.0123$$

$$f(-\tfrac{1}{2}) = 3^{-1/2} = \left(\frac{1}{3}\right)^{1/2} = \frac{1}{\sqrt{3}} = \frac{\sqrt{3}}{3} \approx 0.577$$

$$f(\tfrac{1}{2}) = 3^{1/2} = \sqrt{3} \approx 1.732$$

$$f(1.4) = f(\tfrac{7}{5}) = 3^{7/5} = (\sqrt[5]{3})^7 = (1.246)^7 \approx 4.66$$

$$f(1.41) = f(\tfrac{141}{100}) = (\sqrt[100]{3})^{141} \approx 4.71$$
◀

In order to define an exponential function $f(x) = 3^x$ for *all real numbers* x, we need to consider not only rational values of x as above, but irrational values as well. We will start with $3^{\sqrt{2}}$.

When we write $\sqrt{2} = 1.41421 \ldots$, we mean that $\sqrt{2}$ is approximated better and better by the rational numbers

$$1.4, \ 1.41, \ 1.414, \ 1.4142, \ 1.41421, \text{ etc.}$$

Since these numbers are rational, we can use the properties of rational exponents to actually calculate each of the numbers

$$3^{1.4}, \ 3^{1.41}, \ 3^{1.414}, \ 3^{1.4142}, \ 3^{1.41421}, \text{ etc.}$$

in the same manner as in Example 1. It seems reasonable to assume that these numbers approximate some real number better and better, and we call this number $3^{\sqrt{2}}$. In fact, $3^{1.414} \approx 4.728$ and $3^{1.4142} \approx 4.729$ to four significant digits.

We can do a similar thing for any positive base b and any irrational exponent x, although advanced mathematics is required for a proof. Hence we shall simply make the following assumption:

Exponential functions

> For $b > 0$, but $b \neq 1$, the exponential function $f(x) = b^x$ is defined for each real number x.

All the laws of exponents stated at the beginning of the section hold for any real exponents as long as each expression is defined.

If we had allowed $b = 1$ in the definition above of exponential functions, then we would have had $f(x) = 1^x = 1$, which is a constant function whose graph is a horizontal line. For that reason, we will assume that $b \neq 1$.

If $b \neq 1$, then the graph of $f(x) = b^x$ is one of two basic types, depending upon

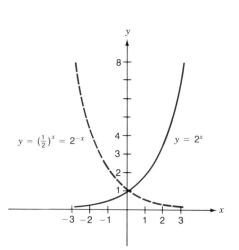

FIGURE 5.1

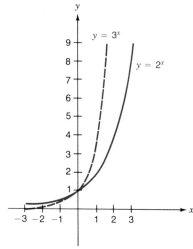

FIGURE 5.2

whether $b > 1$ or $0 < b < 1$. As we move from left to right, the first one increases, while the second one decreases, as in Example 2.

▶ **EXAMPLE 2**   Draw the graphs of $y = 2^x$, $y = (\frac{1}{2})^x$, and $y = 3^x$.

Solution   The following table of values allows us to graph $y = 2^x$ and $y = (\frac{1}{2})^x = 2^{-x}$ in Fig. 5.1, and also $y = 2^x$ and $y = 3^x$ in Fig. 5.2. Notice that each of the graphs in Fig. 5.1 is the reflection of the other one through the x axis. The x axis is a **horizontal asymptote** for all of these graphs.

x	-3	-2	-1	0	1	2	3
2^x	$\frac{1}{8}$	$\frac{1}{4}$	$\frac{1}{2}$	1	2	4	8
$(\frac{1}{2})^x$	8	4	2	1	$\frac{1}{2}$	$\frac{1}{4}$	$\frac{1}{8}$
3^x	$\frac{1}{27}$	$\frac{1}{9}$	$\frac{1}{3}$	1	3	9	27

◢

The graphs in Figs. 5.1 and 5.2, along with the table of values for 2^x, $(\frac{1}{2})^x$, and 3^x, illustrate the following statements. The proofs require advanced mathematics and are omitted.

Properties of $f(x) = b^x$

For every exponential function $f(x) = b^x$ where $b > 0$ and $b \neq 1$,
(1) The domain is the set of all **real numbers.**
(2) The range is the set of all **positive real numbers.**
(3) The graph passes through the point $(0, 1)$ since $f(0) = b^0 = 1$.
(4) If $b > 1$, then $f(x) = b^x$ is increasing.
    If $0 < b < 1$, then $f(x) = b^x$ is decreasing.
(5) $b^x = b^w$ if and only if $x = w$.

Property (1) means that whether x is positive or negative, rational or irrational, b^x

is a well-defined real number. Remember though that b must be positive. Property (2) implies that $b^x > 0$ for all real values of x. Hence the graph of $y = b^x$ is always above the x axis. In fact, the x axis is an asymptote, as in Figs. 5.1 and 5.2. Property (3) tells us that, just as all roads lead to Rome, the graph of $y = b^x$ goes through the point $(0, 1)$ for every $b > 0$.

The meaning of property (4) is that if r and s are real numbers with $r < s$, then the following situations hold:

$$\textit{If } b > 1, \textit{ then } b^r < b^s$$

$$\textit{If } 0 < b < 1, \textit{ then } b^r > b^s$$

For example we can see from Fig. 5.1 that since $2 > 1$

$$2^{0.5} < 2^{1.4} < 2^{1.41} < 2^{1.414} < 2^{3.1} < 2^{\pi}$$

and since $\frac{1}{2} < 1$ we also have

$$(\tfrac{1}{2})^{0.5} > (\tfrac{1}{2})^{1.4} > (\tfrac{1}{2})^{9/4} > (\tfrac{1}{2})^{\pi}$$

Property (5) is commonly called **equating exponents** and it follows directly from property (4) since an increasing (or decreasing) function is also a one-to-one function. As a result of this, the only way that b^x can equal b^w is for x to equal w. For example,

$$\textit{If } 3^x = \tfrac{1}{9} = (\tfrac{1}{3})^2 = 3^{-2}$$

$$\textit{then equating exponents gives } x = -2$$

Property (5) may be restated by saying that:

$$\textit{The function } f(x) = b^x \textit{ is a } 1 - 1 \textit{ function (if } b \neq 1)$$

Two numbers are of particular interest as a base for exponential functions. In Sec. 5.3 we treat the number e, an irrational number which is approximately 2.72. In Sec. 5.4 we consider the other number commonly used as a base, namely, 10.

▶ **EXAMPLE 3**   Graph (a) $f(x) = 2^{x+3}$ and (b) $g(x) = -2^x = -(2^x)$.

Solution   (a) We may graph $f(x) = 2^{x+3}$ by translating the graph of $y = 2^x$ three units to the left, as we have seen in Chap. 3. An alternative method is to write

$$f(x) = 2^{x+3} = 2^x \cdot 2^3 = 8(2^x)$$

which shows that we just multiply each y value in $y = 2^x$ by 8 in order to get $f(x)$. (b) For $g(x) = -2^x$, we multiply each y value in $y = 2^x$ by -1. This is equivalent to reflecting the graph of $y = 2^x$ through the x axis. See Figs. 5.3 and 5.4.   ◀

Exponential growth   It is a fact of considerable social importance that, for sufficiently large values of x, exponential functions become and stay larger than any linear, quadratic, or polynomial function. Thomas Malthus said in 1790 that population growth is exponential while food production is linear, and he concluded from this that after a long enough period of time, the population will overtake the food supply. He was correct, assuming that all other factors remain the same. Even though other things do in fact change (food

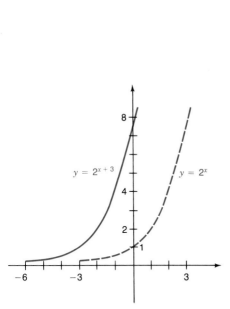

FIGURE 5.3

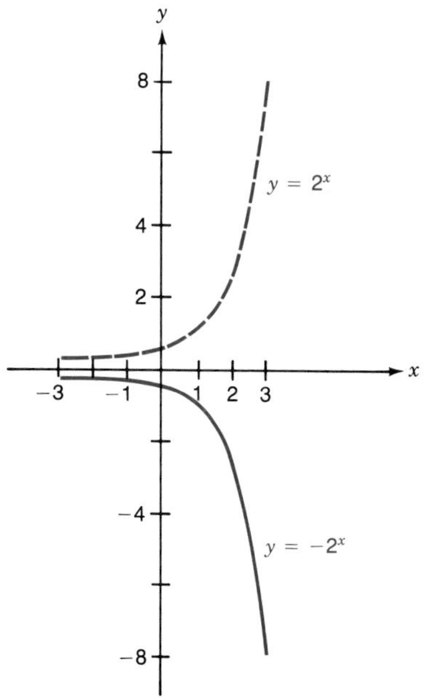

FIGURE 5.4

production has increased dramatically owing to research), his statement has had a profound effect on public policy. See Prob. 55, Exercise 5.6.

EXAMPLE 4   Show that 2^x is larger than x^{100} for $x = 1000$.

Solution   The values of 2^x eventually become and remain larger than those of x^{100}. This is true because x^{100} always has 100 factors, while 2^x has more and more factors of 2 as x increases. Using $x = 1000$, we have

$$2^x = 2^{1000} = (2^{10})^{100} = (1024)^{100} > (1000)^{100} = x^{100}$$

EXAMPLE 5   Solve the equations

(a) $5^x = \frac{1}{625}$ (b) $2^x = 4^{2x-1} \cdot 8^{4-2x}$ (c) $b^{4/3} = 81$

Solution   (a) $5^x = \frac{1}{625} = 5^{-4}$; hence equating exponents gives $x = -4$.
(b) Expressing each term as a power of 2 shows that

$$2^x = (2^2)^{2x-1} \cdot (2^3)^{4-2x}$$

$$2^x = 2^{4x-2} \cdot 2^{12-6x} \qquad \text{multiplying exponents}$$

$$2^x = 2^{10-2x} \qquad \text{adding exponents}$$

$$x = 10 - 2x \qquad \text{equating exponents of 2}$$

$$x = \tfrac{10}{3} \qquad \text{solution}$$

(c) $b^{4/3} = 81$ given

          $(b^{4/3})^{3/4} = 81^{3/4}$ each side raised to the power $\frac{3}{4}$

          $b = (\sqrt[4]{81})^3 = 3^3 = 27$ ◄

In Chap. 11, we will derive the following formula for compound interest, which we use in Example 6 below:

> If P dollars is invested for t years at an annual interest rate of i compounded m times a year, the value will be
>
> $$S = P\left(1 + \frac{i}{m}\right)^{mt}$$
>
> where i is written as a decimal.

EXAMPLE 6   How much will \$35,000 be worth if it is invested at 8 percent compounded quarterly for 10 years? 20 years? 30 years? Consider this when planning for retirement or for children's college education costs.

Solution   Here $P = 35{,}000$, $i = 8$ percent $= 0.08$, $m = 4$, and $i/m = 0.02$. Using a calculator we get

$t = 10$: $35{,}000(1.02)^{40} = 35{,}000(2.2080) \approx 77{,}280$

$t = 20$: $35{,}000(1.02)^{80} = 35{,}000(4.8754) \approx 170{,}639$

$t = 30$: $35{,}000(1.02)^{120} \approx 35{,}000(10.7652) \approx 376{,}782$ ◄

Many situations are governed by exponential functions of the form

$$f(t) = A \cdot b^{kt}$$

where A, b, and k are constants and t represents time. We assume time is measured so that $t \geq 0$. For $t = 0$, we have $f(0) = A \cdot b^0 = A$. Thus A is the initial amount present.

The base b must be positive, and in fact we will assume that $b > 1$. With this assumption, then:

Exponential growth and decay

                    For $k > 0$, we have exponential growth

but   *For $k < 0$, we have exponential decay*

Depending on the situation, various bases may be used. We shall see later in the chapter that we can change from one base to another, if we also change the constant k.

In Example 7 below, we are given the exponential function to work with, while in Example 8 part of the problem is to find the function.

EXAMPLE 7   Suppose that with stable market conditions and no advertising, the sales in the nth month are

$$f(n) = \frac{4500}{1 + 64^{n/12}}$$

What are the sales in the second month? fourth month? sixth month?

Solution We simply find the function values for $n = 2$, 4, and 6:

$$f(2) = \frac{4500}{1 + 64^{2/12}} = \frac{4500}{1 + \sqrt[6]{64}} = \frac{4500}{1 + 2} = 1500$$

$$f(4) = \frac{4500}{1 + 64^{4/12}} = \frac{4500}{1 + \sqrt[3]{64}} = \frac{4500}{1 + 4} = 900$$

$$f(6) = \frac{4500}{1 + 64^{6/12}} = \frac{4500}{1 + \sqrt{64}} = \frac{4500}{1 + 8} = 500$$

Thus in the sixth month with no advertising, sales per month are about 33 percent of what they were in the second month.   ◢

▶ **EXAMPLE 8** The number of bacteria in a certain culture is $f(t) = A \cdot 2^{kt}$ with t measured in hours. After 4 h, the number is $\sqrt[8]{2}$ times as much as at the beginning (about a 9 percent increase). (a) What is the value of k? (b) Find $f(t)$ in terms of A. (c) How long will it take for the number of bacteria to double?

Solution (a) Since we are given $f(4) = A \cdot \sqrt[8]{2}$, then

$$A \cdot \sqrt[8]{2} = A \cdot 2^{4k} \qquad \text{substituting } t = 4$$

$$2^{1/8} = 2^{4k} \qquad \text{dividing by } A$$

Thus $\frac{1}{8} = 4k$, and so $k = \frac{1}{32}$.
(b) Using $k = \frac{1}{32}$ gives $f(t) = A \cdot 2^{t/32}$.
(c) We want to find t so that $f(t) = 2A$, and thus

$$A \cdot 2^{t/32} = 2A$$

Dividing by A and equating exponents gives

$$\frac{t}{32} = 1 \qquad \text{hence} \qquad t = 32$$

It takes 32 h for the number of bacteria to double. The base 2 is especially useful when we are interested in the time it takes for something to double or to halve (half-life).   ◢

EXERCISE 5.1

Graph each of the following equations:

1. $y = 4^x$
2. $y = 5^x$
3. $y = e^x$; use $e = 2.72$
4. $y = 10^x$
5. $y = (\frac{1}{3})^x$
6. $y = (\frac{1}{4})^x$
7. $y = (\frac{5}{6})^x$
8. $y = (\frac{3}{5})^x$
9. $y = 2^{-x}$
10. $y = -(\frac{1}{5})^{-x}$
11. $y = -(\frac{1}{7})^x$
12. $y = (\frac{1}{8})^{-x}$
13. $y = 3^{x+3}$
14. $y = 3^{x-3}$
15. $y = -(\frac{2}{3})^{x-5}$
16. $y = -(\frac{1}{5})^{x+4}$
17. $y = 2^{|x|}$
18. $y = 2^{-(x^2)}$

19. $y = 2^x + 2^{-x}$ **20.** $y = 2^x - 2^{-x}$

Solve the following equations:

21. $16^x = \frac{1}{8}$ **22.** $81^{x/4} = \frac{1}{27}$

23. $(7^{-x})^2 = 343$ **24.** $(9^{3x})^3 = 243$

25. $2^{5x+1} = 8^{2x-3}$ **26.** $4^{4x-3} = 8^{2x+5}$

27. $5^{4x-2} = 25^{x+1}$ **28.** $27^{5x-6} = 9^{7x+3}$

29. $b^{-7/2} = \frac{1}{128}$ **30.** $b^{7/4} = 128$

31. $(2b)^{5/3} = 243$ **32.** $(3b)^{-2/3} = \frac{1}{25}$

Problems 33 to 40 deal with equations of the form $f(t) = A \cdot b^{kt}$. If $k > 0$, we have exponential growth, while if $k < 0$, we have exponential decay.

33. *Biology* The number of bacteria of type T_2 in a certain person's body doubles every 40 min. If 6 are present at 2 A.M., how many will there be at 12 noon? *Hint:* Take $t = 0$ at 2 A.M. Then $6 = f(0) = A \cdot b^{k(0)} = A$, and so $f(t) = 6 \cdot b^{kt}$. We use $b = 2$ since we are given information about doubling; thus $f(t) = 6 \cdot 2^{kt}$. Determine k from the doubling every 40 min. Measure t in hours.

34. *Physics* Under certain conditions, $I = 10^{D/10}$, where D is the number of decibels of a sound and I is its intensity. If he shouts with 30 more decibels than she talks with, what is the ratio of his intensity to hers?

35. *Economics* $A = P(1 + i/m)^m$, where P dollars are invested at interest i compounded m times per year and A is the value of the investment at the end of the year. Is it better to invest \$1000 at $6\frac{1}{4}$ percent simple interest for 1 year ($m = 1$) or to invest it at 6 percent compounded monthly?

36. *Anthropology* The population in thousands of a country is

$$P = 10^8 \cdot (1.5)^{t/20}$$

where t is measured in years. How long will it take for the population to increase 125 percent? *Hint:* If the population increases by 100 percent, it doubles.

37. *Physics* Atmospheric pressure P in pounds per square inch and altitude h in feet are related by $P = (14.7)2^{-0.0000555h}$. What is the approximate pressure at 18,000 ft?

38. *Economics* If we want P dollars n years from now, we must invest $P(1 + i)^{-n}$ dollars now at i per

year compounded annually. On a bond that pays 9 percent per year, about how much should be invested now in order to have \$10,000 in 12 years?

39. *Engineering* The temperature of a rod is 101°C initially, and it cools in air kept at 20°C. After t min, the temperature is $20 + 81(3^{-t})$. How long will it take to get below 23°C?

40. *Physics* The half-life of radioactive material is the time in which half of it will disintegrate. If the amount after t years is $3(4^{-t/120})$ g, what is its half-life?

Problems 41 to 44 are true-false.

41. $2^{1/5} < 3^{1/8}$ *Hint:* Raise each side to the power 40.

42. $3^{1/4} < 5^{1/6}$ *Hint:* Raise each side to the power 12.

43. $(\frac{4}{5})^{1/2} > \frac{4}{5}$ **44.** $(\frac{3}{4})^{3/4} > \frac{3}{4}$

Simplify these exponential expressions.

45. $(7^{\sqrt{2}})^{\sqrt{8}}$ **46.** $(4^{\sqrt{5}})^{-\sqrt{5}}$

47. $(\sqrt{6}^{\sqrt{2}})^{\sqrt{2}}$ **48.** $(\sqrt{5}^{\sqrt{2}/2})^{\sqrt{18}}$

Let $f(x) = 2^x + 2^{-x}$ and $g(x) = 2^x - 2^{-x}$. Find

49. $f(3) + g(3)$ **50.** $f(3) - g(3)$

51. $f(4)g(4)$ **52.** $f^2(5) - g^2(5)$

In general, a^b and b^a are different. In Probs. 53 to 56, however, show that $a^b = b^a$ for the given special values of a and b. You do not need to compute the actual values; just use the properties of exponents carefully.

53. $a = 2, b = 4$ **54.** $a = (\frac{3}{2})^2, b = (\frac{3}{2})^3$

55. $a = (\frac{5}{3})^{3/2}, b = (\frac{5}{3})^{5/2}$ **56.** $a = (\frac{4}{3})^3, b = (\frac{4}{3})^4$

A calculator is useful to solve Probs. 57 to 60. Use three decimal places.

57. Find $5^{1.7}$ and $5^{\sqrt{3}}$.   **58.** Find $3^{2.2}$ and $3^{\sqrt{5}}$.

59. Find $7^{1.4}$ and $7^{\sqrt{2}}$.   **60.** Find $8^{2.6}$ and $8^{\sqrt{7}}$.

61. *Engineering* If

$$T(x) = \frac{3^x - 3^{-x}}{3^x + 3^{-x}}$$

show that $0.5[1 + T(x)]$ can be written in the form $1/(1 + 3^{-2x})$.

62. *Anthropology* The function

$$f(x) = \frac{150{,}000 \cdot 2^{ax}}{1 + 3 \cdot 2^{ax}}$$

occurs in studying population growth, where a is positive. What happens to $f(x)$ as x becomes larger and larger? *Hint:* Divide numerator and denominator by 2^{ax}.

63. *Management* Under certain conditions, the proportion of people informed by advertising after t weeks is

$$P(t) = \frac{25}{40 + 12(6^{-25t})}$$

What value does $P(t)$ approach as t becomes larger and larger?

64. *Cooling* According to Newton's law of cooling, if an object at temperature B is surrounded by a medium (air or water, for instance) at temperature A with $A < B$, then the temperature of the object after t min is

$$f(t) = A + (B - A)10^{-kt}$$

where k is a positive constant. What value does $f(t)$ approach as t becomes larger and larger?

65. Show that $4^{y+2} - 4^y = 15(4^y)$.
66. Show that $5^{t+2} + 3(5^{t+1}) - 40(5^t) = 0$.
67. Show that $2^x + 2^{2x} = 2^x(1 + 2^x)$.
68. Show that $4^n + 4^n = 2^{2n+1}$.
69. It has been shown that the equation $x^2 + 7 = 2^n$ only has integer solutions x for $n = 3, 4, 5, 7,$ and 15. Verify the table below, and check any other value of n to see that it fails.

n	3	4	5	7	15
x	1	3	5	11	181
2^n or $x^2 + 7$	8	16	32	128	32,768

5.2 Logarithmic Functions

We can easily solve the equations

$$2^x = 8 \qquad \text{and} \qquad 2^x = \tfrac{1}{32}$$

because 8 and $\tfrac{1}{32}$ are integer powers of 2. The solutions are 3 and -5, respectively. However $2^x = 6$ does not have a nice integral, or even rational, solution. The graph of $f(x) = 2^x$ shows though that there is a solution, as indicated in Fig. 5.5. This solution is

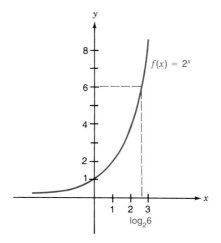

FIGURE 5.5

called $\log_2 6$, and it is read "the logarithm of 6 to the base 2." Notice that the definition of $\log_2 6$ is "the exponent which must be applied to 2 to give 6." We will find out later that its approximate value is 2.585.

Instead of the base 2, we may use any base b if $b > 0$ and $b \neq 1$. Exponential functions $f(x) = b^x$ are increasing if $b > 1$ and decreasing if $0 < b < 1$. In either case, f is a one-to-one function and thus has an inverse function, as we saw in Chap. 3. In other words, $y = b^x$ may be solved for x, and the solution is written $x = \log_b y$. Therefore if $b > 0$ and $b \neq 1$,

Equivalent equations

$$y = b^x \quad \text{means the same as} \quad \log_b y = x \qquad \text{(5.1)}$$

for $y > 0$ and any real x. It is important that you be able to change from either the exponential or logarithmic form to the other one. Substituting either of these forms in the other gives

$$b^{\log_b y} = b^x = y \quad \text{and} \quad \log_b (b^x) = \log_b y = x$$

Consequently, if $f(x) = b^x$ and its inverse function is $g(x) = f^{-1}(x) = \log_b x$, then the equations above show that

$$g(f(x)) = g(b^x) = \log_b (b^x) = x \qquad \text{for all real } x$$

$$f(g(y)) = f(\log_b y) = b^{\log_b y} = y \qquad \text{for any positive } y$$

We thus see that $\log_b y$ is the exponent which must be applied to b to give y. Using b^x for y, we see that the expression $\log_b (b^x)$ is "the exponent which must be applied to b to produce b^x," and you should understand that this is indeed x.

REMEMBER   *A logarithm is an exponent*

◤ **EXAMPLE 1**   Find the following logarithms.

Solution

$$\log_2 16 = 4 \qquad \text{since } 16 = 2^4$$

$$\log_4 8 = \tfrac{3}{2} \qquad \text{since } 8 = 4^{3/2}$$

$$\log_{16} \tfrac{1}{8} = -\tfrac{3}{4} \qquad \text{since } 16^{-3/4} = (2^4)^{-3/4} = 2^{-3} = (\tfrac{1}{2})^3 = \tfrac{1}{8}$$

$$\log_{1/25} 5 = -\tfrac{1}{2} \qquad \text{since } (\tfrac{1}{25})^{-1/2} = (5^{-2})^{-1/2} = 5^1 = 5 \qquad ◀$$

NOTE   Here are some facts which hold for any base $b > 0$, $b \neq 1$,

$$\log_b 1 = 0 \qquad \text{since } b^0 = 1$$

$$\log_b b = 1 \qquad \text{since } b^1 = b$$

$$\log_b 0 \text{ is not defined since } b^x \text{ can never be zero}$$

◤ **EXAMPLE 2**   Verify the properties below.

Solution

$$\log_5(5^7) = 7 \qquad \text{since } 5^7 = 5^7$$

$$3^{\log_3 5} = 5 \qquad \text{since } \log_3 5 \text{ is the exponent which 3 needs to produce 5}$$

Both of these equations are true because exponential and logarithmic functions are inverses of each other.

EXAMPLE 3 Each line below has two equivalent equations, one in exponential form and one in logarithmic form. Be sure you can change from either form to the other.

Solution

Exponential form	**Logarithmic form**
$4^{2x} = 9$	$\log_4 9 = 2x$
$7^{-3/5} = x^2 + 3$	$\log_7 (x^2 + 3) = -\frac{3}{5}$
$x^6 = 23$	$\log_x 23 = 6$
$xy = b^{u+w}$	$\log_b (xy) = u + w$

The properties below of $g(x) = \log_b x$ for $b > 0$ and $b \neq 1$ parallel the properties of exponential functions given in Sec. 5.1. Remember that $f(x) = b^x$, x real, and $g(x) = \log_b x$, $x > 0$, are inverse functions. Since f and g are inverse functions, we know from Chap. 3 that the graph of either of these functions is the reflection of the other one through the line $y = x$. See Fig. 5.6 for the case of $b > 1$. Note that the points $(3, 8)$ and $(-4, \frac{1}{16})$ are on the graph of $f(x) = 2^x$, while $(8, 3)$ and $(\frac{1}{16}, -4)$ are on the graph of the function $g(x) = \log_2 x$.

Properties of $g(x) = \log_b x$

1. The domain is the set of **positive real numbers.**
2. The range is the set of **all real numbers.**
3. The graph goes through $(1, 0)$ since $g(1) = \log_b 1 = 0$.
4. If $b > 1$, then $g(x) = \log_b x$ is increasing.
   If $0 < b < 1$, then $g(x) = \log_b x$ is decreasing.
5. $\log_b x = \log_b w$ if and only if $x = w$.

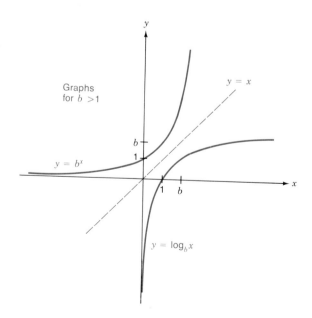

Graphs for $b > 1$

$y = x$

$y = b^x$

$y = \log_b x$

FIGURE 5.6

▶ **EXAMPLE 4**   Solve these equations. (a) $\log_x 32 = \frac{5}{2}$ (b) $\log_9 \frac{1}{27} = 3x$ (c) $\log_7 (x - 2) = 3$

Solution   (a) $\log_x 32 = \frac{5}{2}$ is equivalent to the equation

$$x^{5/2} = 32$$

$$(x^{5/2})^{2/5} = 32^{2/5}$$

$$x = (\sqrt[5]{32})^2 = 2^2 = 4$$

(b) $\log_9 \frac{1}{27} = 3x$ is equivalent to $\frac{1}{27} = 9^{3x}$. Using 3 as a base on both sides gives

$$3^{-3} = (3^2)^{3x}$$

$$3^{-3} = 3^{6x}$$

Since each base is 3, we equate the exponents.

$$-3 = 6x \qquad \text{and thus} \qquad x = -\frac{3}{6} = -\frac{1}{2}$$

(c) $\log_7 (x - 2) = 3$ is equivalent to

$$x - 2 = 7^3 = 343 \qquad \text{and so} \qquad x = 345$$ ◀

Remember that $\log_b x$ is only defined if $x > 0$. For instance, $\log_2 (5x + 8)$ is defined if and only if

$$5x + 8 > 0 \qquad \text{and thus} \qquad x > -\frac{8}{5}$$

The original purpose for logarithms was to help in astronomical calculations, and they did this admirably for centuries because of several properties. These same properties also allow many expressions to be simplified and worked with more easily. The proofs of the properties depend on the laws of exponents since each logarithmic equation has an equivalent exponential form.

Laws of logarithms

Suppose that x and y are positive real numbers, $b > 0$ and $b \neq 1$, and p is any real number. Then

$$\log_b (xy) = \log_b x + \log_b y \tag{5.2}$$

$$\log_b \frac{x}{y} = \log_b x - \log_b y \tag{5.3}$$

$$\log_b (x^p) = p \log_b x \tag{5.4}$$

We shall prove only the first one of these laws. Let $\log_b x = u$ and $\log_b y = w$. The exponential forms of these equations are

$$x = b^u \qquad \text{and} \qquad y = b^w$$

$$xy = b^u \cdot b^w \qquad\qquad \text{multiplying}$$

$$xy = b^{u+w} \qquad\qquad \text{adding exponents}$$

$$\log_b (xy) = u + w \qquad\qquad \text{equivalent equation}$$

$$\log_b (xy) = \log_b x + \log_b y \qquad\qquad \text{definition of } u \text{ and } w$$

We will also give an alternative proof based on inverse functions, one which uses several times the fact that $b^{\log_b N} = N$, for $N > 0$.

$$b^{\log_b (xy)} = xy = b^{\log_b x} \cdot b^{\log_b y} = b^{\log_b x + \log_b y}$$

Now just equate the exponents on b.

It is easier to apply the laws of logarithms if you remember them in words as well as in symbols:

> The logarithm of a product is the sum of the logarithms.
> The logarithm of a quotient is the difference of the logarithms.
> The logarithm of a power of a number is the product of the exponent and the logarithm of the number.

▶ **EXAMPLE 5**   Write $\log_b [x(y + 1)^4/z^3]$ as a sum and difference of logarithms.

Solution
$$\log_b \left[\frac{x(y + 1)^4}{z^3} \right] = \log_b [x(y + 1)^4] - \log_b (z^3)$$

$$= \log_b x + \log_b (y + 1)^4 - \log_b (z^3)$$

$$= \log_b x + 4 \log_b (y + 1) - 3 \log_b z \quad ◀$$

▶ **EXAMPLE 6**   If $\log_{10} 2 \approx 0.30$ and $\log_{10} 3 \approx 0.48$, find a decimal approximation for $\log_{10} 180$.

Solution   Factoring 180 as $10 \cdot 18 = 10 \cdot 2 \cdot 3^2$ gives

$$\log_{10} 180 = \log_{10} (10)(2)(3^2)$$

$$= \log_{10} 10 + \log_{10} 2 + 2 \log_{10} 3$$

$$\approx 1 + 0.30 + 2(0.48) = 2.26 \quad ◀$$

NOTE   Here are some things to watch out for:

$$\log_b (x + y) \neq \log_b x + \log_b y$$

$$(\log_b x)(\log_b y) \neq \log_b (xy)$$

$$\frac{\log_b x}{\log_b y} \neq \log_b \frac{x}{y}$$

On the other hand, it is true that

$$(\log_b x)^2 = (\log_b x)(\log_b x)$$

$$\log_b (x^2) = 2 \log_b x$$

One case of the third law of logarithms deserves special mention. Since $\sqrt[r]{x} = x^{1/r}$, we have

$$\log_b (\sqrt[r]{x}) = \frac{1}{r} \log_b x \tag{5.5}$$

▶ **EXAMPLE 7**   Use $\log_{10} 2 \approx 0.30$ and $\log_{10} 3 \approx 0.48$ to find an approximation for $\log_{10} (\sqrt[3]{6})$.

Solution
$$\log_{10} (\sqrt[3]{6} = \tfrac{1}{3} \log_{10} 6 = \tfrac{1}{3} \log_{10} (2 \cdot 3)$$
$$= \tfrac{1}{3} (\log_{10} 2 + \log_{10} 3)$$
$$\approx \tfrac{1}{3} (0.30 + 0.48) = \tfrac{1}{3}(0.78) = 0.26$$

The exponential form of $\log_{10} (\sqrt[3]{6}) = 0.26$ is $10^{0.26} = \sqrt[3]{6}$.   ◀

▶ **EXAMPLE 8**   Suppose that $\log_7 2 = a$, $\log_7 3 = b$, and $\log_7 5 = c$. Find the following logarithms in terms of a, b, and c.

Solution   (a) $\log_7 63 = \log_7 (9 \cdot 7) = \log_7 (3^2 \cdot 7)$
$$= \log_7 (3^2) + \log_7 7 = 2 \log_7 3 + 1 = 2b + 1$$

(b) $\log_7 \frac{9}{125} = \log_7 9 - \log_7 125 = \log_7 (3^2) - \log_7 (5^3)$
$$= 2 \log_7 3 - 3 \log_7 5 = 2b - 3c$$

(c) $\log_7 \sqrt{48} = \tfrac{1}{2} \log_7 48 = \tfrac{1}{2} \log_7 (2^4 \cdot 3)$
$$= \frac{1}{2}(\log_7 2^4 + \log_7 3) = \frac{1}{2}(4a + b) = 2a + \frac{b}{2}$$

(d) $\log_7 3/\log_7 2 = b/a$, and no further simplification by the present laws is possible. Notice that $\log_7 3/\log_7 2$ and $\log_7 \frac{3}{2} = \log_7 3 - \log_7 2$ are different.   ◀

▶ **EXAMPLE 9**   Sketch the graphs of $f(x) = \log_2 |x|$ and $g(x) = \log_2 (x + 3)$.

Solution   The graph of f is defined only for $|x| > 0$, and thus the domain of f is $\{x | x \neq 0\}$. The graph of f is symmetric with respect to the y axis since $f(-x) = f(x)$. For $x > 0$, $f(x) = \log_2 x$, whose graph we have already seen. See Fig. 5.7.

The graph of g is defined only for $x + 3 > 0$, that is for $x > -3$. It is the graph of $y = \log_2 x$ translated 3 units to the left. See Fig. 5.8.   ◀

Although $\log_b x$ is defined when $0 < b < 1$ and when $b > 1$, **we normally use only bases $b > 1$.** The reason for this is that, for instance,

$$\log_{1/2} 8 = -3 \qquad \text{and} \qquad \log_2 8 = +3$$

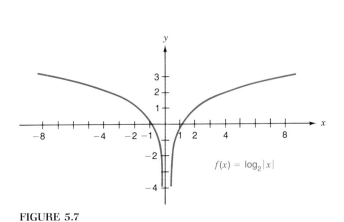

FIGURE 5.7

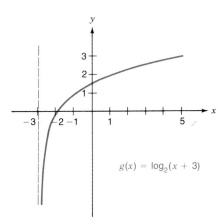

FIGURE 5.8

In Prob. 93, you are asked to show that for $b > 1$ and consequently $0 < 1/b < 1$,

$$\log_{1/b} x = -\log_b x$$

In summary, remember that:

A logarithm is an exponent

$\log_b x$ is the exponent which b must have to produce x

$\log_b x$ is defined only for $x > 0$, with $b > 0$ and $b \neq 1$

The value of $\log_b x$ may be positive, 0, or negative

EXERCISE 5.2

Change the equations in Probs. 1 to 8 to logarithmic form.

1. $3^2 = 9$ **2.** $3^4 = 81$
3. $3^{-3} = \frac{1}{27}$ **4.** $8^{-2} = \frac{1}{64}$
5. $8^{2/3} = 4$ **6.** $36^{3/2} = 216$
7. $(\frac{1}{3})^{-2} = 9$ **8.** $(\frac{1}{5})^{-3} = 125$

Change Probs. 9 to 16 to exponential form.

9. $\log_2 16 = 4$ **10.** $\log_5 125 = 3$
11. $\log_2 \frac{1}{8} = -3$ **12.** $\log_7 \frac{1}{343} = -3$
13. $\log_{36} 216 = \frac{3}{2}$ **14.** $\log_{216} 36 = \frac{2}{3}$
15. $\log_{125} 25 = \frac{2}{3}$ **16.** $\log_{81} 27 = \frac{3}{4}$

Find each of the following logarithms:

17. $\log_3 81$ **18.** $\log_5 125$
19. $\log_4 256$ **20.** $\log_7 2401$
21. $\log_9 \frac{1}{27}$ **22.** $\log_{25} \frac{1}{125}$
23. $\log_4 \frac{1}{128}$ **24.** $\log_4 \frac{1}{32}$
25. $\log_5 (5^{1.3})$ **26.** $\log_{5.5} 5.5$
27. $\log_{4/3} 1$ **28.** $\log_3 (9^{1.2})$

Solve each of the following equations:

29. $\log_5 x = 3$ **30.** $\log_2 x = 4$
31. $\log_3 x = 3$ **32.** $\log_{11} x = 1$
33. $\log_b 125 = 3$ **34.** $\log_b 32 = 5$
35. $\log_b 8 = \frac{3}{2}$ **36.** $\log_b 4 = \frac{2}{3}$

Sketch the graph of the following equations:

37. $y = \log_3 x$ and $y = 3^x$
38. $y = \log_5 x$ and $y = 5^x$
39. $y = \log_2 x$ and $y = \log_3 x$
40. $y = \log_5 x$ and $y = \log_{10} x$
41. $y = \log_5 (x^2)$ **42.** $y = \log_5 (3x)$
43. $y = \log_2 (x - 3)$ **44.** $y = \log_3 (2x + 5)$
45. $x = \log_2 y$ **46.** $y = \log_{1/2} x$
47. $2x = 3^y$ **48.** $3y = 2^{\log_2 x^2}$

In calculus, it is necessary to simplify certain functions before working with them further. In Probs. 49 to 56, use the laws of logarithms (5.2), (5.3), and (5.4) to change the expression to sums and differences of multiples of logarithms, as much as possible.

49. $\log_b \dfrac{x^2 \sqrt{y}}{5z^3}$ **50.** $\log_b \dfrac{8xy^4}{7z}$

51. $\log_b \dfrac{3\sqrt{y}}{x^3 y^7}$ **52.** $\log_b \dfrac{9z}{5\sqrt{xy}}$

53. $\log_4 \dfrac{x(x^3 - 2)}{5x + 3}$ **54.** $\log_5 \dfrac{x^4(x + 1)^{2/3}}{x + 23}$

55. $\log_6 \dfrac{(x - 4)(2x + 7)^5}{x(3x + 8)^3}$

56. $\log_7 \dfrac{(x^2 + 5)(7x - 96)}{3x\sqrt{5x + 37}}$

Write each expression as a single logarithm.

57. $\log_a 3 + 2\log_a x + 3\log_a (y^3)$
58. $2\log_a x - \frac{1}{2}\log_a y + \frac{1}{3}\log_a z$
59. $\log_a (xy^2) + 2\log_a (x/y)$
60. $\log_a (x + y) + 2\log_a y - 3\log_a x$
61. $\log_{10} \dfrac{x^5 y^{12}}{6z} + \log_{10} \dfrac{9x^2 z^7}{y^8}$

62. $\log_9 \dfrac{2x^2 + 5x + 3}{2x - 3} + \log_9 \dfrac{3x - 1}{3x^2 + 2x - 1}$

63. $\log_7 \dfrac{x^5 w^3}{yz} - \log_7 \dfrac{xw}{y^8 z}$

64. $\log_5 \dfrac{2x^2 - 5x - 3}{x^2 + x - 12} - \log_5 \dfrac{6x^2 + 7x + 2}{3x^2 + 10x - 8}$

Use $\log_{10} 2 \approx 0.30$, $\log_{10} 3 \approx 0.48$, and $\log_{10} 7 \approx 0.85$ to estimate the following logarithms:

65. $\log_{10} 28$ **66.** $\log_{10} 630$

67. $\log_{10}\left(\dfrac{27}{\sqrt[4]{3}}\right)$ **68.** $\log_{10}\dfrac{49}{5}$

Is the statement in each of Probs. 69 to 76 true or false?

69. $(\log_2 1)(\log_4 5) = \log_2 8 - \log_3 27$
70. $2 + \log_{16} = 5^{\log_5 3}$
71. $3^{2\log_3 4} = (\log_7 7^8)(\log_7 14)$
72. $\log_6 6^6 = 6\log_6 6$
73. $\log_3 17 < \log_4 17$
74. $\log_9 2 + \log_9 3 > \log_9 5$
75. $\log_3 (3 + 9) < \log_6 6 + \log_3 4$
76. $(\log_{10} 4)(\log_{10} 3) < \log_{10} 12$
77. Show that $\log_b N = \log_{(b^3)} (N^3)$. *Hint:* If $x = \log_b N$, then $b^x = N$ and $(b^x)^3 = N^3$.
78. Show that $x^{\log_2 (\log_2 x)} = (\log_2 x)^{\log_2 x}$. *Hint:* Take the logarithm of both sides.
79. Show that $x^5 = 10^{5\log_{10} x}$. *Hint:* $5\log_{10} x = \log_{10} (x^5)$.
80. Show that $(\log_b a)(\log_a b) = 1$. *Hint:* If $x = \log_b a$, then $b^x = a$ and $b = a^{1/x}$.

Use a calculator, if one is available, to verify each of the following equations. Change the equation from logarithmic to exponential form first.

Calculator
81. $\log_3 46.77 \approx \frac{7}{2}$ **82.** $\log_5 11.18 \approx \frac{3}{2}$
83. $\log_4 13.93 \approx 1.9$ **84.** $\log_6 442.3 \approx 3.4$

85. *Anthropology* Under certain conditions, the kinship coefficient f between two populations is related to their time of separation by

$$f = 1 - 5^{-t/2N}$$

where N is the population size. Solve for the time t.

86. *Anthropology* The formula for measuring information H, developed by Shannon, is

$$H = -p_1 \log_2 p_1 - p_2 \log_2 p_2 - \cdots - p_n \log_2 p_n$$

where $p_1, p_2, \ldots, p_n$ are numbers from 0 to 1 whose sum is 1.
(a) Show $H = p_1 \log_2 (1/p_1) + p_2 \log_2 (1/p_2) + \cdots + p_n \log_2 (1/p_n)$.
(b) Calculate H for $n = 4$, $p_1 = \frac{1}{8}$, $p_2 = \frac{1}{8}$, $p_3 = \frac{1}{4}$, and $p_4 = \frac{1}{2}$.

87. *Anthropology* The equation

$$F = \frac{\log_2 [(N - s)/N]}{\log_2 [(N - 1)/N]}$$

arises in the statistical theory of marriage structures. Solve it for s.

88. *Management* In a department store with sales of S boxes per month, n boxes of each brand, and v the number of brands, we have $nv = c$ ($= $ constant) and want to maximize the sales

$$S = S(v) = k \cdot c^v \cdot v^{c/v} \cdot v^{-c} \qquad \text{as a function of } v$$

(a) Show that S has a maximum, as a function of v, if

$$\log k + v \log c + \left(\frac{c}{v} - c\right) \log v$$

has a maximum.
(b) If $0 < c < 54$, then it has been shown that $v = \sqrt{c}$ makes S a maximum. Find $\log S(\sqrt{c})$.

89. *Psychology* Fechner's law in psychology about a stimulus S is

$$S = S_0(1 + c)^r$$

where S_0 is a standard stimulus, c is a constant, and r is a variable. Solve the equation for r.

90. *Advertising* In a short, intense advertising campaign, the response R and dollars received A are related by

$$R = c \log_{10} A + d$$

where $c > 0$ and $d < 0$.
(a) Find the threshold amount of advertising by solving the following equation for A:

$$0 = c \log_{10} A + d$$

(b) If there are x campaigns with each one getting an equal amount of the total of A dollars, what is the total response from all campaigns?

91. *Anthropology* In the study of agricultural terraces in Ecuador, the following equation arises with $W = $ width and $H = $ height:

$$A = \frac{WH}{2} \log_5 \left(\frac{x^2}{W^2} + 1\right)$$

Solve the equation for x.

92. *Finance* If money is invested at 5 percent per year, it will double in

$$\frac{\log_3 2}{\log_3 1.05} \text{ years}$$

but at 6 percent per year it takes $\log_3 2/\log_3 1.06$ years. Simplify the following difference in years, leaving logarithms in your answer:

$$\frac{\log_3 2}{\log_3 1.05} - \frac{\log_3 2}{\log_3 1.06}$$

93. Show that for $b > 1$,

$$\log_{1/b} x = -\log_b x$$

5.3 The Number e: e^x and $\ln x$

In Secs. 5.1 and 5.2, we introduced first exponential functions and then logarithmic functions. In this section, we shall bind these two ideas together even more closely by working with both types of functions simultaneously and by utilizing one of the two most frequently used bases, namely the number e. The other commonly used base is 10, and it will be treated in Sec. 5.4.

The number e occurs both in theory and in practice. Certain formulas in calculus are made as simple as possible by choosing to work with the base e (see Probs. 69 and 70). In working with compound interest, the number e comes up if we decide to actually compound the interest more and more times per year (see Probs. 71 and 72). In both cases, it happens that we need to investigate the expression

$$\left(1 + \frac{1}{n}\right)^n \qquad \text{as } n \to \infty$$

that is, as n increases without bound. In order to demonstrate what happens, we will use the following table for the expression

$$\left(1 + \frac{1}{n}\right)^n = \left(\frac{n+1}{n}\right)^n$$

n	$(1 + 1/n)^n$ to 7 decimal places
4	2.4414062
52	2.6925969
365	2.7145675
1,000	2.7169239
10,000	2.7181459
100,000	2.7182682
1,000,000	2.7182805
10,000,000	2.7182817
100,000,000	2.7182818

It appears from the table that $(1 + 1/n)^n$ approaches some number as $n \to \infty$. It can in fact be proven that this limit does exist, and the number is called e in honor of the Swiss mathematician Leonhard Euler. It is irrational, and decimal approximations are

$$e \approx 2.7182818285 \qquad \text{or} \qquad e \approx 2.72$$

Because e does occur naturally in so many situations, the functions

$$f(x) = e^x \qquad \text{and} \qquad g(x) = \log_e x$$

are called the **natural exponential function** and the **natural logarithmic function,** respectively. The number e is so important that the abbreviation

$$\ln x = \log_e x$$

is used for the natural logarithmic function. Because exponential and logarithmic functions, with the same base, are by definition inverse functions, we know that $g(x) = f^{-1}(x)$ and thus

$$f(g(x)) = x \qquad \text{or} \qquad e^{\ln x} = x \qquad \text{for all } x > 0$$

and $\qquad g(f(x)) = x \qquad \text{or} \qquad \ln (e^x) = x \qquad \text{for any real } x$

For the same reason, the **graphs** of $f(x) = e^x$ and $g(x) = \ln x$ are reflections of each other with respect to the line $y = x$, as shown in Fig. 5.9. Since $2 < e < 3$, the graph of $y = e^x$ lies between the graphs of $y = 2^x$ and $y = 3^x$ in Fig. 5.2.

Values of e^x and $\ln x$ can be found by using a calculator or by looking in the table in the appendix. The table actually gives decimal approximations to the values of e^x, e^{-x}, and $\ln x$. Of course, the normal properties of exponents and logarithms still apply. In particular

Function values

$$\ln (xy) = \ln x + \ln y \qquad e^x \cdot e^y = e^{x+y}$$

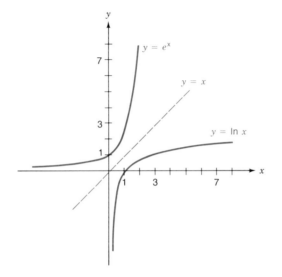

FIGURE 5.9

$$\ln \frac{x}{y} = \ln x - \ln y \qquad \frac{e^x}{e^y} = e^{x-y}$$

$$\ln (x^r) = r \ln x \qquad (e^x)^y = e^{xy}$$

EXAMPLE 1 Find these values involving e^x and $\ln x$.

Solution (a) If $x = 1.6$, then by table or calculator

$$e^{1.6} \approx 4.9530 \qquad e^{-1.6} \approx 0.2019 \qquad \ln 1.6 \approx 0.4700$$

(b) If $x = 0.15$, then by calculator or table

$$e^{0.15} \approx 1.1618 \qquad e^{-0.15} \approx 0.8607 \qquad \ln 0.15 \approx -1.897$$

(c) $\qquad \ln \dfrac{1}{e} = -1 \qquad \ln 1 = 0 \qquad \ln e = 1 \qquad \ln (e^2) = 2$

(d) $\qquad \qquad e^{12} = (e^3)^4 \approx 20^4 = 160,000$ ◢

Almost all scientific calculators have a special key for π, and many have one for e^x or y^x. Using one of these keys, or perhaps a $\ln x$ key along with an inverse key, will allow e^x to be evaluated. Remember that e is irrational, whereas every number on a calculator is a finite decimal and is thus rational.

It is important to be able to switch between **logarithmic and exponential notation** with base e. Just remember that a logarithm is an exponent, and that

$$e^c = d \qquad \text{is equivalent to} \qquad c = \ln d$$

EXAMPLE 2 Solve the equations (a) $\ln (x + 3) = 2$, (b) $e^{4x} = 5$.

Solution (a) $\qquad \ln (x + 3) = 2$ *given*

$\qquad\qquad\qquad x + 3 = e^2$ *equivalent equation*

$\qquad\qquad\qquad x = e^2 - 3$ *the exact solution*

$\qquad\qquad\qquad x \approx 7.3891 - 3 = 4.3891$ *decimal approximation*

(b) $\qquad\qquad\qquad e^{4x} = 5$ *given*

$\qquad\qquad\qquad 4x = \ln 5$ *equivalent equation*

$\qquad\qquad\qquad x = \dfrac{\ln 5}{4}$ *the exact solution*

$\qquad\qquad\qquad x \approx \dfrac{1.6094}{4} = 0.4024$ *decimal approximation* ◢

In Example 3, properties of logarithms are used to simplify a complicated expression.

► **EXAMPLE 3**   Write ln y as a sum and difference of logarithms if

$$y = \frac{(3x + 14)\sqrt{x - 7}}{6x^2}$$

Solution   Using the three basic laws of logarithms shows that

$$\ln y = \ln (3x + 14) + \ln \sqrt{x - 7} - \ln (6x^2)$$
$$= \ln (3x + 14) + \ln (x - 7)^{1/2} - [\ln 6 + \ln (x^2)]$$
$$= \ln (3x + 14) + \tfrac{1}{2}\ln (x - 7) - \ln 6 - 2 \ln x$$ ◄

► **EXAMPLE 4**   Solve the equation $(3x^2 + 4x)(2e^{2x}) + (6x + 4)(e^{2x}) = 0$.

Solution   We begin by factoring.

$$(3x^2 + 4x)(2e^{2x}) + (3x + 2)(2e^{2x}) = 0$$
$$(2e^{2x})(3x^2 + 4x + 3x + 2) = 0$$
$$(2e^{2x})(3x^2 + 7x + 2) = 0$$

Since $e^{2x} > 0$ for all x, we may divide both sides of the equation by $2e^{2x}$, leaving the following equation to solve:

$$3x^2 + 7x + 2 = 0$$
$$(3x + 1)(x + 2) = 0$$
$$3x + 1 = 0 \quad \text{or} \quad x + 2 = 0$$

The solutions are $x = -\tfrac{1}{3}$ and $x = -2$.   ◄

► **EXAMPLE 5**   Draw the graph of

$$f(x) = e^{-x^2}$$

Solution   The graph of this function is the familiar bell-shaped curve, and it is extremely important in probability and statistics. The graph is symmetric with respect to the y axis since the x^2 term causes $f(-x) = f(x)$, and thus f is an even function. We have $f(x) > 0$ for every x since e to any power is positive. These facts plus the table of values allow us to draw the graph. See Fig. 5.10.

x	-2	-1.5	-1	-0.5	0
$f(x)$	0.02	0.11	0.37	0.78	1

◄

The **compound interest formula** is

$$S = P\left(1 + \frac{i}{n}\right)^{nt}$$

where S is the amount that P dollars accumulates to in t years if the yearly interest rate is i and it is compounded n times per year.

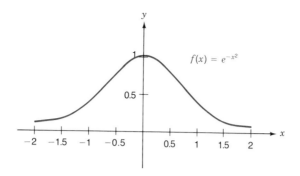

FIGURE 5.10

In the next example, we solve an equation for an exponent by using natural logarithms. *Remember:* A logarithm is an exponent.

EXAMPLE 6 For how long must $75,000 be invested at 8 percent compounded semiannually to have a value of $192,250?

Solution Here $P = 75,000$, $i = 0.08$, $n = 2$, and so, using the compound interest formula, we have to solve the equation

$$75,000(1.04)^{2t} = 192,250$$

$$1.04^{2t} = \frac{192,250}{75,000} = 2.56333$$

Now taking the natural logarithm of each side gives

$$2t \ln 1.04 = \ln 2.56333$$

$$2t = \frac{\ln 2.56333}{\ln 1.04} \qquad \text{solving for } 2t$$

$$2t \approx \frac{0.9413}{0.0392} \approx 24.01 \qquad \text{using table or calculator values}$$

$$t \approx 12 \qquad \text{dividing by 2}$$

It takes 12 years.

The compound interest formula above allows interest to be compounded n times a year. If we let $n \to \infty$, the end result is called **continuous compounding,** and it can be shown that the following statement is true. See Probs. 71 and 72.

Continuous compound interest

If a principal P is invested for n periods at an interest rate of i per period, written as a decimal, and if interest is compounded continuously, then the amount after n periods is $S = P \cdot e^{ni}$.

EXAMPLE 7 Solve the continuous compound interest formula (a) for n and (b) for P.

Solution (a)

$$S = P \cdot e^{ni} \qquad \text{given}$$

$$\frac{S}{P} = e^{ni} \qquad \text{dividing by } P$$

$$\ln \frac{S}{P} = ni \qquad \text{equivalent equation}$$

$$n = \frac{\ln (S/P)}{i} \qquad \text{dividing by } i$$

(b) $\qquad\qquad S = P \cdot e^{ni} \qquad \text{given}$

$$S \cdot e^{-ni} = P \qquad \text{multiplying by } e^{-ni} \qquad \blacktriangleleft$$

EXAMPLE 8   A hospital needs to have 12 units of a radioactive substance at 9 A.M. on Thursday. How much of the substance should they buy at 3 P.M. on the prior Monday if its half-life is 4.95 days?

Solution   The governing equation is $f(t) = A \cdot e^{kt}$ with t in days. Since the half-life is 4.95 days, $f(4.95) = A/2$ and so

$$\frac{A}{2} = A \cdot e^{k(4.95)}$$

$$\tfrac{1}{2} = e^{4.95k} \qquad \text{dividing by } A$$

$$\ln \tfrac{1}{2} = 4.95k \qquad \text{equivalent equation}$$

$$k = \frac{-\ln 2}{4.95}$$

$$\approx \frac{-0.6931}{4.95} \approx -0.14$$

Therefore the amount after t days is $f(t) = A \cdot e^{-0.14t}$, where A is the initial amount. From 3 P.M. Monday to 9 A.M. Thursday is 2.75 days, so we need to determine the value of A for which

$$A \cdot e^{-0.14(2.75)} = 12$$

Since $0.14(2.75) = 0.385$, multiplying both members of the equation by $e^{0.385}$ gives

$$A = 12(e^{0.385}) \approx 12(1.4696) \approx 17.6$$

The hospital must buy 17.6 units at 3 P.M. Monday. $\blacktriangleleft$

In $\log_b x$, we may use any base b as long as $b > 0$ and $b \neq 1$. The next theorem shows how to change the base of a logarithm by simply dividing by a constant.

Change-of-Base Theorem

If a, b, and x are positive numbers with $a \neq 1$, $b \neq 1$, then

$$\log_b x = \frac{\log_a x}{\log_a b}$$

The result may also be written $(\log_b x)(\log_a b) = \log_a x$.

Proof   To begin the proof, let L be the left member above:

$$\log_b x = L \qquad \text{given}$$

$$x = b^L \qquad \text{exponential form}$$

$$\log_a x = \log_a (b^L) \qquad \text{taking the logarithm, base } a, \text{ of each side}$$

$$\log_a x = L \log_a b \qquad \text{by property 3 of logarithms}$$

$$L = \frac{\log_a x}{\log_a b} \qquad \text{solving for } L$$

Equating these two values for L gives the result. ◀

Several significant corollaries are derived below from the change-of-base theorem.

(a) Take $a = e$. Then

$$\log_b x = \frac{\ln x}{\ln b}$$

Thus logarithms to any base can be found using only natural logarithms. For instance,

$$\log_2 17 = \frac{\ln 17}{\ln 2} \approx \frac{2.8332}{0.6931} \approx 4.0877$$

Hence $2^{4.0877} \approx 17$, which is reasonable since $2^4 = 16$.

(b) Take $a = x$. Then $(\log_a b)(\log_b a) = \log_a a = 1$. It follows that $\log_a b = 1/\log_b a$, and hence:

$$\log_a b \text{ is the reciprocal of } \log_b a$$

This was also given in Prob. 80, Exercise 5.2.

(c) Take $a = e$ and $b = 10$. Then

$$\log_{10} x = \frac{\ln x}{\ln 10} \approx \frac{\ln x}{2.3026} \approx 0.4343 \ln x$$

We will discuss common logarithms, that is, $\log_{10} x$, much more fully in Sec. 5.4.

(d) Using the formula in part (a) above shows that

$$(\log_b x)(\log_a y) = \frac{\ln x}{\ln b} \cdot \frac{\ln y}{\ln a} = \frac{\ln x}{\ln a} \cdot \frac{\ln y}{\ln b} = (\log_a x)(\log_b y)$$

In other words, the bases can be interchanged in a product of logarithms. For instance

$$(\log_5 81)(\log_3 25) = (\log_3 81)(\log_5 25) = (4)(2) = 8$$

For any base b and positive number a, we know that $a = b^{\log_b a}$ from the definition of a logarithm. Using $b = e$ gives $a = e^{\ln a}$, and raising both sides to the power x gives

$$a^x = (e^{\ln a})^x = e^{x \ln a}$$

This allows **any exponential function** to be written with base e.

One last comment about natural logarithms. It can be shown that as $n \to \infty$,

$$1 + \frac{1}{2} + \frac{1}{3} + \frac{1}{4} + \cdots + \frac{1}{n} - \ln n \to \text{constant}$$

and that the value of the constant is ≈ 0.5772. Therefore

$$1 + \frac{1}{2} + \frac{1}{3} + \frac{1}{4} + \cdots + \frac{1}{n} \approx \ln n + 0.5772$$

To get a really close approximation requires a fairly large value of n, so this would be ideal for a programmable calculator or a computer.

EXERCISE 5.3

Sketch the graph of the function defined by the equation in each of Probs. 1 to 8.

1. $y = (e^x)^2 = e^{2x}$
2. $y = e^{(x^2)}$
3. $y = e^{x+3}$
4. $y = 2e^{3x}$
5. $y = 2 + e^x$
6. $y = 3 - e^{2x}$
7. $y = (x + 1)e^x$
8. $y = (x + 1)e^{-x}$

Find the values e^x, e^{-x}, and $\ln x$ for the numbers given in Probs. 9 to 12.

9. 3
10. 1
11. 4.2
12. 2.8

Find the value of x in each of Probs. 13 to 20. Give the exact solution, and also a decimal approximation.

13. $e^x = 20.09$
14. $e^x = 37.6$
15. $e^x = 6.73$
16. $e^x = 1.074$
17. $\ln x = 4$
18. $\ln x = 2$
19. $\ln x = 2.303$
20. $\ln x = 0.4343$

Solve the following equations. Give the exact solution, and also a decimal approximation.

21. $\ln (2x + 5) = 3$
22. $\ln (3x - 4) = -1$
23. $\ln (5 - 2x) = -2$
24. $\ln (7x + 6) = 1$
25. $e^{5x} = 2$
26. $e^{2 - 6x} = 4$
27. $e^{6x+5} = 3$
28. $e^{x-7} = 6$

Evaluate the natural logarithm for the number in each of Probs. 29 to 36. In Probs. 33 to 36, give the exact solution.

29. 3.9
30. 6.4
31. 20.1
32. 5.27
33. $e^{\ln 5.9}$
34. $e^{\ln 0.3}$
35. $e^{\ln 3.2}$
36. $e^{\ln 4.9}$

Find $\ln y$ in each of Probs. 37 to 40, and write it as a sum and difference of multiples of logarithms.

37. $y = \dfrac{(2x - 1)\sqrt{x + 1}}{5x^2}$

38. $y = \dfrac{(4x + 7)^3\sqrt{7 - x}}{3x^5}$

39. $y = \dfrac{6\sqrt[5]{2x + 3}}{7x^3}$

40. $y = \dfrac{9(5x + 3)}{x^4\sqrt[3]{3x + 5}}$

Solve each of the equations in Probs. 41 to 44.

41. $(x^2 + 3x)2e^{2x} + (2x + 3)e^{2x} = 0$
42. $(4x^2 - x)3e^{3x} + (8x - 1)e^{3x} = 0$
43. $(x^2 + 5x)3e^{3x} + (2x + 5)e^{3x} = 0$
44. $(3x^2 + 7x)2e^{2x} + (6x + 7)e^{2x} = 0$

45. *Finance* How long will it take \$36,000 to grow to \$53,494 at 2 percent quarterly interest compounded continuously?

46. *Finance* How much time is needed for \$23,257.31 to grow to \$44,139.35 at 12 percent semiannual interest compounded continuously?

47. *Radioactivity* What part of a radioactive substance with a half-life of 75 h remains after 150 h? After 144 h?

48. *Half-life* A radioactive compound has a half-life of 100 h. What part of a given amount remains after 50 h? After 150 h?

49. *Newton's law of cooling* The temperature of a hot ingot upon being immersed in water kept at 20°C is $20 + 670e^{-5t}$ after t min. How long will it take for the temperature to reach 25°C?

50. *Weather* If atmospheric pressure at h ft is $P = 14.7e^{-0.0000555h}$, express P at m mi with base 10.

51. *Population* The population of a city t years after it is P is approximately $Pe^{0.05t}$. Find the population of a city of 100,000 after 5 years, 10 years, and 20 years.

52. *Epidemic* If one person in an urban area gets the flu, the number who will have it after t days is approximately

$$N(t) = \frac{10,000e^t}{e^t + 10,000}$$

About how many will have the disease after 1 day, 4 days, 10 days?

Use the continuous compound interest formula $S = P(e^{ni})$ in Probs. 53 to 56.

53. Find S if $P = 5000$, $n = 4$, and $i = 8$ percent.

54. Find P if $S = 8500$, $n = 6$, and $i = 6$ percent.

55. Find n if $P = 400$, $S = 600$, and $i = 5$ percent.

56. Find i if $S = 2000$, $P = 1200$, and $n = 8$.

Use the change-of-base formula $\log_b x = \ln x / \ln b$ to find the logarithms in Probs. 57 to 60.

57. $\log_3 78$ **58.** $\log_4 40$

59. $\log_5 100$ **60.** $\log_6 38$

Write each of the expressions below as an exponential expression with base e.

61. 2^x **62.** 6^{5x} **63.** 7^{x-2} **64.** 3^{4+x}

65. *Electric circuits* Solve the equation $I = 30e^{-Rt/L}$ for R.

66. *Price and demand* Solve the equation $p = p_0 \cdot e^{-kt}$ for k.

67. *pH in chemistry* Solve the equation $p = -0.43 \ln H$ for H.

68. *Velocity with air resistance* Solve the equation

$$t = -k \ln \frac{kg + v}{kg} \qquad \text{for } v$$

Problems 69 and 70 show one way in which the number e occurs naturally in calculus. Verify the equations by using properties of logarithms.

69. $\dfrac{\log_b (x + h) - \log_b x}{h} = \dfrac{1}{h} \log_b \dfrac{x + h}{x}$

70. $\dfrac{1}{h} \log_b \dfrac{x + h}{x} = \dfrac{1}{x} \log_b \left[\left(1 + \dfrac{h}{x} \right)^{x/h} \right]$; now letting

$\dfrac{h}{x} = \dfrac{1}{n}$ gives $\dfrac{1}{x} \log_b \left[\left(1 + \dfrac{1}{n} \right)^n \right]$.

Problems 71 and 72 show a way in which the number e occurs in actual use of the compound interest formula

$$P\left(1 + \frac{i}{n} \right)^{nt}$$

71. Let $i = 100$ percent for 1 year. Verify that the formula gives

$$P\left(1 + \frac{1}{n} \right)^n$$

72. Let $i = 0.06$ and $t = 1$. Show that the amount at the end of one year is

$$P\left[\left(1 + \frac{0.06}{n} \right)^{n/0.06} \right]^{0.06}$$

Let $1/k = 0.06/n$, and show that this can be written as

$$P\left[\left(1 + \frac{1}{k} \right)^k \right]^{0.06}$$

73. It can be shown that as n increases, the values of $(1 + 1/n)^n$ increase, but the values of $(1 + 1/n)^{n+1}$ decrease. Calculate each of these two expressions for $n = 3$, 6, and 9.

74. It is proved in calculus that

$$f(n) = 1 + \frac{1}{1!} + \frac{1}{2!} + \frac{1}{3!} + \frac{1}{4!} + \cdots + \frac{1}{n!}$$

gets closer and closer to the number $e \approx 2.72$ as n gets larger and larger. Calculate $f(4)$, $f(6)$, and $f(8)$ to five decimal places.

75. For values of x close to 0,

$$e^x \approx 1 + x + \frac{x^2}{2} + \frac{x^3}{6}$$

Calculate both sides above to five decimal places for $x = 0.2$ and $x = 0.1$.

76. For values of x close to 0,

$$\ln (1 + x) \approx x - \frac{x^2}{2} + \frac{x^3}{3}$$

Calculate both sides above to four decimal places for $x = 0.3$ and $x = 0.1$.

77. Stirling's formula for $n!$ says that as n gets larger and larger, the following ratio approaches 1. Evaluate the ratio for $n = 10$.

$$\frac{(n/e)^n \sqrt{2\pi n}}{n!}$$

78. Show that

$$\ln (\sqrt{x^2 + 1} + x) = -\ln (\sqrt{x^2 + 1} - x)$$

79. Storing wine increases its value, but also adds to its cost. One of the equations which must be solved for t, in years, is

$$0.8 = \ln (1 + t) - \frac{t}{t + 1}$$

Which of the numbers 4, 5, 6, or 7 is most nearly a solution?

80. If $0 < x < y$, then

$$\frac{2xy}{x + y} < \sqrt{xy} < \frac{y - x}{\ln y - \ln x} < \frac{x + y}{2}$$

Verify this for $x = 3.8$ and $y = 6.2$.

81. The two approximations below are very accurate and are due to the Indian mathematician Ramanujan.

Verify each one by calculation.

$$e^{(3\pi\sqrt{2})/8} \approx 2\sqrt{7}$$

$$\pi \approx \frac{12}{\sqrt{190}} \ln [(\sqrt{2})(2 + \sqrt{5})(3 + \sqrt{10})]$$

The second of these is said to be accurate to 18 decimal places.

5.4 Common Logarithms and Applications

We have previously defined $\log_b x$ for any base $b > 0$, $b \neq 1$. Since our decimal system of numbers uses the base 10, this is the base for logarithms which was used for centuries, and it is still the standard choice in many situations such as pH values in chemistry, the Richter number of an earthquake, and the intensity of a sound in decibels. Logarithms with base 10 are called **common logarithms** or Briggs logarithms. For the rest of this chapter, $\log x$ with no base written will mean we are using base 10, and thus

$$\log x = \log_{10} x$$

Since exponential and logarithmic functions are inverses of each other, it is true that

$$x = 10^{\log x} \qquad \text{and} \qquad \log (10^x) = x$$

Of course, the normal properties of exponents and logarithms still apply. In particular, if x and y are positive,

$$\log (xy) = \log x + \log y$$

$$\log \frac{x}{y} = \log x - \log y$$

$$\log (x^r) = r \log x$$

The graphs of $f(x) = \log x$ and $g(x) = 10^x$ are reflections of each other through the line $y = x$, as in Fig. 5.6.

We showed in Sec. 5.3 that $\log_{10} x \approx 0.4343 \ln x$. Here we shall develop a standard form for common logarithms based on our number system. Recall that if x is written as a power of 10, say 10^r, then $\log x$ is the exponent on 10, say r, since

$$\log x = \log_{10} x = \log_{10} (10^r) = r \log_{10} 10 = r \cdot 1 = r$$

This is evident also in the following table:

x	$0.01 = 10^{-2}$	$0.1 = 10^{-1}$	$1 = 10^0$	$10 = 10^1$	$100 = 10^2$
$\log x$	-2	-1	0	1	2

Regardless of whether or not x is an integral power of 10, we may write it in scientific notation as $x = m \cdot 10^c$ where $1 \le m < 10$ and c is an integer. Then taking logarithms gives

$$\log x = \log (m \cdot 10^c)$$

$$= \log m + \log (10^c)$$

$$= \log m + c \log 10$$

$$= c + \log m$$

The number c is called the **characteristic** of $\log x$, and $\log m$ is called the **mantissa** of $\log x$. Hence

$$\log x = c + \log m = \text{characteristic} + \text{mantissa}$$

where the characteristic is an integer (. . . , -3, -2, -1, 0, 1, 2, 3, . . .), and the mantissa is in the interval $[0, 1)$. This is true since $f(x)$ is increasing, and thus

If $1 \le m < 10$, then $\log 1 \le \log m < \log 10$

and so $0 \le \text{mantissa} < 1$

SPECIAL NOTE   **The mantissa is positive or 0.**

If your calculator has a LOG key, it should be easy to find $\log x$ for any positive x. See Examples 2 and 3.

The common logarithm table in the appendix gives only the digits in the mantissa of $\log x$. You must supply the decimal point and the characteristic, which is just the exponent from the scientific notation, and then add the mantissa and the characteristic. Using either the table or a calculator gives

$$\log 5.81 = 0.7642$$

$$\log 58.1 = 0.7642 + 1 = 1.7642$$

$$\log 581 = 0.7642 + 2 = 2.7642$$

$$\log 581{,}000 = 0.7642 + 5 = 5.7642$$

$$\log 0.581 = 0.7642 - 1 = -0.2358$$

$$\log 0.0581 = 0.7642 - 2 = -1.2358$$

Position of the decimal point

The characteristic of $\log x$ is determined completely by the **position of the decimal point** in x. For example, if x is any number strictly between 10 and 100, then $\log x$ will have characteristic 1.

Sequence of significant digits

The mantissa of $\log x$ is determined completely by the **sequence of significant digits** in the decimal form of x. As above, the mantissa of $\log x$ is the same whether x is 5.81 or 581,000 or 0.0581.

The number $\log 7$ is the exact solution of $10^x = 7$, and it is irrational. Any decimal value given for it is an approximation, whether by table (0.8451) or calculator (0.84509804). As such, slight differences in calculations using it may appear in the last decimal place depending on roundoff error, order of operations, and other factors. With so many models of calculators available, the best advice is simply to read and understand the owner's manual. This is especially true in a sequence of calculations such as

$$\frac{4 + \log 31.6}{(6 \log 3.8)^{1/2}} \approx 2.9487$$

Generally speaking, a calculator gives more digits than are justified by the situation, so rounding off the answer is essential. Be careful with a negative characteristic. As above,

$$\log 0.0581 = 0.7642 - 2 = -1.2358 = -1 - 0.2358$$

with the characteristic being -2. The mantissa is positive; it is 0.7642, not -0.2358.

EXAMPLE 1   Find (a) log 32.8 and (b) log 328,000.

Solution   (a) By calculator, log 32.8 = 1.51587384. To find log 32.8 by table, find 32 in the left column, then find 8 in the top row. The number at the intersection of this column and row is 5159, and it is the mantissa without its decimal point. Thus log 32.8 = $0.5159 + 1 = 1.5159$.
(b) Similarly, log 328,000 = $0.5159 + 5 = 5.5159$.

EXAMPLE 2   Verify the following common logarithm values.

Solution

x	**Log x by table**	**Log x by calculator**
6.40	0.8062	0.80617997
59.5	1.7745	1.77451697
571	2.7566	2.75663611
6090	3.7846	3.78461729

In Examples 1 and 2, we have had $x > 1$, for which the characteristic is positive or zero. If $0 < x < 1$, then log $x < 0$, and **the characteristic is negative.** To find log 0.0579 by the table, we first find that the mantissa is 0.7627. Since 0.0579 in scientific notation is $5.79(10^{-2})$, then

$$\log 0.0579 = 0.7627 - 2 = -1.2373$$

The number -1.2373 is the correct value, but it is not in standard form since $-1.2373 = -1 - 0.2373$ whereas **the mantissa is always positive or 0.** The standard method is to write -2 as $8 - 10$ or $18 - 20$ or $28 - 30$, etc. Thus we write

$$\log 0.0579 = -2 + 0.7627 = 8.7627 - 10$$

By calculator, log 0.0579 = $-1.23732144 = 8.76267856 - 10$.

EXAMPLE 3 Verify the following common logarithm values.

Solution

x	Characteristic	Log x by table	Log x by calculator
0.576	-1	9.7604 - 10	-0.23957752
0.0551	-2	8.7412 - 10	-1.25884840
0.00622	-3	7.7938 - 10	-2.20620962
0.000646	-4	6.8102 - 10	-3.18976748

Given log x, to find x

If we know log x, we may reverse the steps above to find x by tables. First locate the mantissa in the body of the table, and then read the sequence of digits in x from the left and top of the table. The characteristic of log x will then enable us to place the decimal point properly.

EXAMPLE 4 Find x if log $x = 1.7875$.

Solution Log $x = 1.7875$. Since 7875 occurs at the intersection of 61 and 3, the digits of x are 613. Since the characteristic is 1, $x = 61.3$. Similarly, if log $x = 7.7875 - 10$, then $x = 0.00613$.

Antilog

The number x is sometimes called the **antilog of log x** since

$$x = 10^{\log x}$$

allows us to find x if we are given log x. If your calculator has a y^x key, or a LOG key and some version of an INV key, you should be able to verify the calculation

$$10^{1.7875} = 61.30557921$$

This shows that the antilog of 1.7875 is 61.3, which is consistent with Example 4, which showed that log 61.3 = 1.7875.

EXAMPLE 5 Verify the following values of log x and x.

Solution

Log x	x by table	x by calculator
4.8000	63,100	63,095.734
2.7903	617	617.02108
9.7774 - 10	0.599	0.59896301
7.7574 - 10	0.00572	0.0057200523

In all of the examples so far, we have used numbers x with three significant digits. If we are using a table and working with approximate numbers which have more than three significant digits, we may either

(a) Round off to three significant digits, then proceed as above, or

(b) Round off to four significant digits, if necessary, and then interpolate. This

Interpolation

amounts to replacing a part of the graph of $y = \log x$ with a straight line. **Interpolation** for logarithm tables is explained in the appendix.

If a calculator is used, interpolation is not necessary. The value of log 59.56 by calculator is 1.77495469 to eight places, and also log 87.654321 = 1.94277333. Furthermore,

$$If\ log\ x = 0.13572468$$

$$Then\ x = 10^{0.13572468} = 1.36686203$$

In Sec. 5.3 we presented the change-of-base formula

$$\log_b x = \frac{\log_a x}{\log_a b}$$

and used $a = e$ to give $\log_b x = \ln x/\ln b$. If instead we use $a = 10$, we have the formula

Change of base

$$\log_b x = \frac{\log x}{\log b}$$

valid when x and b are positive and b is not 1. An alternative proof, using the power property of logarithms, is

$$(\log_b x) \log b = \log (b^{\log_b x}) = \log x$$

which, upon dividing by $\log b$, gives the above formula.

EXAMPLE 6 Use the change-of-base formula $\log_b x = \log x/\log b$ to verify the following results.

Solution (a) Consistent with $3^6 = 729$, we have the result

$$\log_3 729 = \frac{\log 729}{\log 3} = \frac{2.8627}{0.4771} \approx 6.0002$$

which is the right value, subject to a slight roundoff error.

(b) $$\log_{16} 1453 = \frac{\log 1453}{\log 16} \approx \frac{3.1623}{1.2041} \approx 2.6262$$

which means that $16^{2.6262} \approx 1453$. Notice that the logarithms are actually divided in the change-of-base formula.

Many laws of **exponential growth or decay** are expressed as powers of 2, e, or 10. These are all similar since

$$\log_2 e = \frac{\log e}{\log 2} \approx \frac{0.4343}{0.3010} \approx 1.443$$

and thus $e = 2^{1.443}$. In fact

$$e^x \approx 2^{1.443x} \approx 10^{0.4343x}$$

$$2^x \approx e^{0.6931x} \approx 10^{0.3010x}$$

$$10^x \approx e^{2.303x} \approx 2^{3.322x}$$

EXAMPLE 7 The Richter scale, which is used in measuring the severity of an earthquake, is defined by

$$R = \log \frac{I}{I_0}$$

where I is the intensity of an earthquake and I_0 is a standard intensity.

(a) What is the magnitude on the Richter scale of an earthquake which is 10,000 times as intense as the standard one?
(b) Of one 1,000,000 times as intense as the standard one?
(c) If two earthquakes have Richter numbers 7.3 and 5.7, what is the ratio of their intensities?

Solution (a) Since $I = 10,000I_0$, we have $R = \log 10,000 = 4$.
(b) Since $I = 1,000,000I_0$, we have $R = \log 1,000,000 = 6$.
(c) Using the exponential form gives $I/I_0 = 10^R$, and so

$$I = I_0(10^R)$$

is the intensity. The ratio of the intensities is

$$\frac{I_0(10^{7.3})}{I_0(10^{5.7})} = 10^{7.3-5.7} = 10^{1.6} = 39.8$$

since 39.8 is the antilog of 1.6000 by table or calculator.

▸ **EXAMPLE 8** Find (a) $\log \left(\frac{843}{302}\right)$ and (b) $\log \left(\sqrt[4]{0.318^3}\right)$.

Solution (a) Using the quotient property gives

$$\log \tfrac{843}{302} = \log 843 - \log 302$$

$$= 2.9258 - 2.4800 = 0.4458$$

(b) Writing the radical using exponents gives

$$\log (0.318^{3/4}) = \tfrac{3}{4} \log 0.318$$

$$= \tfrac{3}{4}(0.5024 - 1)$$

$$= \tfrac{3}{4}(7.5024 - 8) \qquad \text{using } -1 = 7 - 8 \text{ since 8 is divisible by 4}$$

$$= 5.6268 - 6 \qquad \text{multiplying by } \tfrac{3}{4}$$

The value is also -0.3732, but the characteristic is -1, and the mantissa is the positive number 0.6268.

▸ **EXAMPLE 9** It can be shown that, without taking it apart, the number of possible positions of a Rubik's cube is

$$2^{27} \cdot 3^{14} \cdot 5^3 \cdot 7^2 \cdot 11$$

Write this number in scientific notation.

Solution Calling the number x, we have

$$\log x = 27 \log 2 + 14 \log 3 + 3 \log 5 + 2 \log 7 + \log 11$$

$$\approx 27(0.3010) + 14(0.4771) + 3(0.6990) + 2(0.8451) + 1.0414$$

$$= 19.6350$$

Therefore $x \approx 10^{19.6350} = 10^{0.6350} \cdot 10^{19} \approx 4.31(10^{19})$. In the table, 0.6350 is equally far from the entries 0.6345 and 0.6355, and we used the nearest smaller entry. Hence the number of possible positions is more than 43 quintillion.   ◢

EXERCISE 5.4

Find the characteristic of $\log N$ for each value of N given in Probs. 1 to 4.

1. 78.6, 5.31, 0.247   **2.** 9894, 58.37, 2.003
3. $2.13(10^6)$, 0.02009, 497.3
4. $9.73(10^7)$, 0.1007, 7001.0

Find the mantissa of $\log N$ for the given values of N in Probs. 5 to 8.

5. 34.2, 3.42, 0.342   **6.** 42.3, 423, 0.423
7. 8.96, 89.6, 0.0896   **8.** 5793, 57.93, 5.793

Find the logarithm of the number given in each of Probs. 9 to 16 by use of tables or calculator.

9. 8.76   **10.** 34.7   **11.** 598   **12.** 803
13. 0.00903   **14.** 0.0109
15. 0.0632   **16.** 0.494

If the given number is $\log x$, find x in Probs. 17 to 28. If a table is used to find x, use the closest three-digit number in the table. Use scientific notation as needed.

17. 1.6053   **18.** 0.9782
19. 2.8149   **20.** 4.7752
21. $9.3118 - 10$ **22.** $8.6314 - 10$
23. $7.9360 - 10$ **24.** $7.6767 - 10$
25. 3.8777   **26.** 2.7048
27. 0.2488   **28.** 1.8829

Use the change-of-base formula $\log_a x = \log x/\log a$ to evaluate $\log_a x$ in Probs. 29 to 36.

29. $\log_8 76.3$ **30.** $\log_{8.5} 614$
31. $\log_{2.3} 783$ **32.** $\log_{12} 528$
33. $\log_4 512$ **34.** $\log_8 128$
35. $\log_9 243$ **36.** $\log_{25} 125$

Solve each of these equations with common logarithms.

37. $10^{3x-1} = 12.4$ **38.** $100^{x+2} = 65.3$
39. $(0.01)^{2x} = 0.33$ **40.** $(0.1)^{x-3} = 0.042$

In Probs. 41 and 42, use Benford's law, which states that if an extensive collection of numerical data in

decimal form is classified according to the first non-zero significant digit, then the probability that the first significant digit will be p is $\log[(p + 1)/p]$.

41. Find the probability the first significant digit is 1 and the probability it is 6.
42. Show that the sum of all nine probabilities is 1 (for $p = 1, 2, 3, \ldots, 9$).

In Probs. 43 and 44, verify the inequalities by calculation. Similar ones are true for any n positive real numbers (below n is 4 in 43 and 3 in 44).

43. $\dfrac{16.1 + 22.8 + 11.9 + 20.7}{4} > \sqrt[4]{(16.1)(22.8)(11.9)(20.7)}$

44. $\dfrac{196 + 237 + 254}{3} > \sqrt[3]{(196)(237)(254)}$

In Probs. 45 and 46, use Heron's formula for the area A of a triangle with sides a, b, and c where $2s = a + b + c$ and

$$A = \sqrt{s(s - a)(s - b)(s - c)}$$

45. Find the area A of a triangle with sides 20, 21, and 29.
46. Find the area A of a triangle with sides 33, 56, and 65.

In Probs. 47 and 48, use the formula for *decibels*

$$d = 10 \log \frac{I}{I_0}$$

where I is the intensity of the sound being measured and I_0 is the intensity of a standard, faint sound.

47. Find the decibel rating of a sound with
  (a) $I = 125 \cdot I_0$ (a whisper)
  (b) $I = 12,000 \cdot I_0$ (normal voice)
48. If the decibel rating of a sound is as given, find I in terms of I_0.
  (a) $d = 95$ (heavy truck)
  (b) $d = 118$ (heavy metal, as in music)

In Probs. 49 to 52, assume that the growth or decay is governed by a function of the form

$$f(t) = A \cdot 10^{kt}$$

where t is time, $A > 0$, and k may be positive or negative.

49. In a certain week, there are 6800 fruit flies on Monday and 7400 of them on Friday. How many will there be on Sunday?

50. If there are 6 g of a radioactive substance on February 19, and 4 g of it on February 22, how much of it will there be on February 29 of the same year?

51. Suppose the population of a town 10 years after its high school basketball team won the state title is 8810, while 15 years after the title it is 9890. What was its population in the championship year?

52. If the current in an electric circuit is 20.4 after 2 h and 14.8 after 3 h, what was it at the start of timing?

For Probs. 53 to 56, see Example 7 for the Richter scale.

53. What is the relative intensity of an earthquake that reads 8.1 on the Richter scale compared with the one that occurred in 15 states on June 10, 1987, with a Richter number of 5.0?

54. Find the relative intensity of an earthquake with a Richter number of 6.7 compared with one with a Richter number of 8.2.

55. The relative intensity of quake one to quake two is 3258. Find the Richter number of the first if that of the second is 4.4.

56. Find the Richter number of an earthquake that is 4763 times as intense as one with a Richter number of 3.4.

57. *Management* The score on an industrial safety test after t months is

$$67 - 15 \log (1 + t)$$

What is the average monthly score from month 1 to month 6?

58. *Cost analysis* The cost of manufacturing x items is

$$400 + 300 \log (x + 3)$$

What is the cost for (a) 12 items and (b) 24 items?

pH in chemistry

In Probs. 59 and 60, use the fact that the pH of a chemical substance is $\text{pH} = -\log[\text{H}^+]$ where $[\text{H}^+]$ measures the hydrogen ion concentration.

59. Find the pH of milk if its value of $[\text{H}^+]$ is $4[10^{-7}]$.

60. If the pH of wine is 3.3, find its value of $[\text{H}^+]$.

61. *Geology* If the air temperature is 10°C, the temperature of lava is

$$10 + 740(10^{-0.08t})$$

after t hours. How long will it take for the temperature to reach 100°C?

62. *Public health* If five people in an urban area have the flu, the number who will have it after t days is approximately

$$N(t) = \frac{150,000(10^{t/4})}{10^{t/4} + 30,000}$$

About how many will have the flu after 4 days and after 20 days?

63. *Finance* Solve the equation $1.07^n = 2$, which shows how long it takes for money to double if invested at 7 percent compounded annually.

64. *Finance* Solve the equation $1.05^n = 1.08^7$, which shows how many years it would take for money invested at 5 percent compounded annually to equal the value of money invested at 8 percent compounded annually for 7 years.

In Probs. 65 to 66, if the given number is x, use the characteristic of $\log x$ to find the number of digits in x.

65. 17^{76} 　　　　　　　 66. 57^{57}

In Probs. 67 and 68, use the characteristic to decide which number is larger.

67. 65^{66} or 66^{65} 　　　　 68. 84^{87} or 85^{86}

69. Show that $\log a/\log b = \ln a/\ln b$.

70. The graph of $y = mx + b$ is a line. What is the graph of $\ln y = m \ln x + b$?

71. Show that $\log (\log_b x) = \log (\log x) - \log (\log b)$.

72. Show that $\log (x - \sqrt{x^2 - 1}) = -\log (x + \sqrt{x^2 - 1})$.

Using either a table or calculator, evaluate the following:

73. $(237)(4.73)$
74. $(5.94)(38.9)$
75. $(27.3)(0.592)$
76. $(30.7)(0.345)$
77. $257/572$
78. $386/172$
79. $0.597/3.44$
80. $21.9/0.403$
81. $(9.86)(7.07)/3.14$
82. $10.2/(5.87)(1.26)$

83. $(477)(0.00664)/23.6$
84. $6.59/(84.3)(0.0974)$
85. $3.56^{4.2}$
86. $1.87^{5.6}$
87. $83.4^{3/4}$
88. $0.509^{7/3}$
89. $\dfrac{6^{1.8} + \sqrt{29}}{4.2}$
90. $\dfrac{(43)(2.2)^{2.2} + 69}{9.8}$
91. $\dfrac{\sqrt[3]{55}}{1 + 2^{-1.4}}$
92. $\dfrac{\sqrt[5]{0.45}}{3^{2.7} + (7.6)(4.2)}$

5.5 Exponential and Logarithmic Equations

There are several techniques in this chapter which help in solving equations involving exponents or logarithms:

(a) $y = b^x$ if and only if $\log_b y = x$.
(b) $\log_b x = \log_b y$ if and only if $x = y$.
(c) $b^x = b^y$ if and only if $x = y$.
(d) The rules for logarithms of products, quotients, and powers.

EXAMPLE 1 Solve the equations
(a) $3^{(x-1)(x+2)} = 81$ and   (b) $3(9^x) - 28(3^x) + 9 = 0$.

Solution (a) Since $81 = 3^4$, equating exponents gives

$$(x - 1)(x + 2) = 4$$

$$x^2 + x - 6 = 0 \qquad \text{multiplying and collecting terms}$$

$$(x - 2)(x + 3) = 0 \qquad \text{factoring}$$

$$x = 2 \quad \text{and} \quad x = -3 \qquad \text{solutions}$$

(b) Since $9^x = (3^2)^x = (3^x)^2$, we may let $y = 3^x$ and have

$$0 = 3y^2 - 28y + 9 = (y - 9)(3y - 1)$$

whose solutions are $y = 9$ and $y = \frac{1}{3}$. Thus

$$3^x = 9 \qquad \text{gives} \qquad x = 2$$

and

$$3^x = \tfrac{1}{3} = 3^{-1} \qquad \text{gives} \qquad x = -1 \qquad \blacktriangleleft$$

In Sec. 5.1 and in Example 1 above, we solved equations by equating exponents of the same base. In Example 2 below, 15 is not an integer power of 5, and so the same method will not work. However the variable x is again in the exponent, and, since a logarithm is an exponent, we should expect that the solution involves logarithms.

EXAMPLE 2 Solve $5^{2x-1} = 15$.

Solution Writing the given exponential equation in logarithmic form gives

First solution
$$2x - 1 = \log_5 15$$

Using the change-of-base formula for $\log_5 15$, we have

$$2x - 1 = \frac{\log 15}{\log 5}$$

$$2x - 1 \approx \frac{1.1761}{0.6990} \approx 1.68 \qquad \text{by table or calculator}$$

$$2x = 2.68 \qquad \text{and so} \qquad x = 1.34$$

Alternative Solution   Taking the natural logarithm of both sides of the given equation gives

$$(2x - 1) \ln 5 = \ln 15$$

$$2x - 1 = \frac{\ln 15}{\ln 5} \approx \frac{2.708}{1.609} = 1.68$$

and as above we now see that $x = 1.34$.

▶ EXAMPLE 3   Solve $5^{2x} = 7^{x+1}$.

Solution   Since the variable is in the exponent, we take logarithms of both sides. Either base 10 or base e may be used.

$$2x \ln 5 = (x + 1) \ln 7$$

$$2x \ln 5 - x \ln 7 = \ln 7$$

$$x(2 \ln 5 - \ln 7) = \ln 7$$

$$x(\ln 25 - \ln 7) = \ln 7$$

$$x = \frac{\ln 7}{\ln 25 - \ln 7}$$

This is the exact solution, which can also be written as $x = (\ln 7)/(\ln \frac{25}{7})$, and a decimal approximation is

$$\frac{1.9459}{3.2189 - 1.9459} = \frac{1.9459}{1.2730} \approx 1.53$$

A decimal approximation using common logarithms will of course produce the same value.

$$x = \frac{\log 7}{\log 25 - \log 7} \approx \frac{0.8451}{1.3979 - 0.8451} = \frac{0.8451}{0.5528} \approx 1.53$$

▶ EXAMPLE 4   Solve $\log_3 (2x - 3) + \log_3 (x + 6) = 3$.

Solution   By the property of logarithms for products, we see that

$$\log_3 [(2x - 3)(x + 6)] = 3$$

$$(2x - 3)(x + 6) = 3^3 \qquad \text{exponential form}$$

$$2x^2 + 9x - 18 = 27 \qquad \text{multiplying}$$

$$2x^2 + 9x - 45 = 0 \qquad \text{combining terms}$$

$$(2x + 15)(x - 3) = 0 \qquad \text{factoring}$$

The solutions of the last equation are $-\frac{15}{2}$ and 3. However $x = -\frac{15}{2}$ makes the first term in the problem $\log_3 (-18)$, and since $-18 < 0$, this is not defined and thus $-\frac{15}{2}$ is not a solution. You should verify that $x = 3$ is indeed a solution. ◢

▶ **EXAMPLE 5**   Solve $\log (x + 6) - \log (x - 9) = \log 4$.

Solution   The logarithm of a quotient rule shows that

$$\log \frac{x + 6}{x - 9} = \log 4$$

Now if $\log a = \log b$, then $a = b$, and so

$$\frac{x + 6}{x - 9} = 4$$

$$x + 6 = 4(x - 9) = 4x - 36$$

$$3x = 42$$

and thus $\qquad\qquad\qquad x = 14$

This satisfies the original common logarithm equation. ◢

▶ **EXAMPLE 6**   The graph of the equation $y = (a/2)(e^{x/a} + e^{-x/a})$ is called a **catenary,** and it describes the shape of a uniform flexible cable whose ends are at the same height. Taking $a = 1$ and $y = 10$ above, solve the equation

$$10 = \frac{e^x + e^{-x}}{2}$$

Solution   We begin by multiplying both sides by 2.

$$e^x + e^{-x} = 20$$

$$(e^x)^2 + 1 = 20(e^x) \qquad \text{multiplying by } e^x$$

$$(e^x)^2 - 20(e^x) + 1 = 0 \qquad \text{subtracting } 20(e^x)$$

This is a quadratic equation in e^x, so using the quadratic formula with $a = 1$, $b = -20$, and $c = 1$ shows that

$$e^x = \frac{20 \pm \sqrt{396}}{2} = 10 \pm \sqrt{99}$$

$$x = \ln (10 \pm \sqrt{99}) \qquad \text{equivalent equation}$$

For decimal approximations, using $\sqrt{99} \approx 9.9499$ gives

$$x \approx \ln (10 + 9.9499) = \ln 19.9499 \approx 2.99$$

or $\qquad x \approx \ln (10 - 9.9499) = \ln 0.0501 \approx -2.99$ ◄

► **EXAMPLE 7**   Solve the inequality $3^x > 13$.

Solution   Since the natural logarithm function is increasing, the given inequality is equivalent to

$$\ln (3^x) > \ln 13$$

$$x \ln 3 > \ln 13 \qquad \text{logarithm of a power}$$

$$x > \frac{\ln 13}{\ln 3} \qquad \text{since } \ln 3 > 0$$

This is the exact solution. A decimal approximation is

$$x > \frac{2.565}{1.099} = 2.33$$

We could also have used common logarithms. ◄

EXERCISE 5.5

Solve the equations in Probs. 1 to 12 by using a common base.
1. $3^x = 243$
2. $5^x = 125$
3. $2^{x^2 - 2x + 3} = 4$
4. $7^{x^4 - 1} = 1$
5. $5^{(-2x+1)x} = \frac{1}{5}$
6. $3^{3(x+2)} \cdot 27 = 3$
7. $2^{3(x+2)} \cdot 8 = 2^{2x+1} 8^{2/3}$
8. $7^{3(x-1)} \cdot 343 = 7^{x+1} \cdot 49^{3/2}$
9. $(2^x)^2 - 20(2^x) - 64 = 0$
10. $(3^x)^2 - 10(3^x) + 9 = 0$
11. $25^x - 6(5^x) + 5 = 0$
12. $49^x - 50(7^x) + 49 = 0$

Solve the equation for x in Probs. 13 to 32.
13. $5^{3x-1} = 22$
14. $7^{4-x} = 47$
15. $9^{2x+3} = 8$
16. $12^{5-3x} = 5$
17. $3^{2x} = 5^{x+1}$
18. $5^{x-1} = 3^x$
19. $2^{3x+1} = 5^{2x-1}$
20. $7^{2x-3} = 5^x$
21. $18.7^x = 8.4^{3x-1}$
22. $2.97^x = 2.71^{x+2}$
23. $7.63^{2x} = 9.18^{x+1}$
24. $21.5^x = 13.2^{x+1}$
25. $\log_5 (2x - 1) + \log_5 (x + 2) = 2$
26. $\log_3 (2x + 1) - \log_3 (x - 1) = 1$
27. $\log_7 (9x + 4) + \log_7 (x + 2) = 3$
28. $\log_5 (3x - 4) + \log_5 (7x + 4) = 3$
29. $\log_2 (x^2 + 3x + 3) - \log_2 (2x - 3) = \log_2 (2x + 1)$
30. $\log_3 (x + 4) + \log_3 (x + 2) = \log_3 (x^2 + 3x + 11)$
31. $\log_5 (x^2 + 3x - 5) - \log_5 (x - 1) = \log_5 (x + 3)$
32. $\log_7 (x + 2) + \log_7 (x + 3) = \log_7 (2x^2 + 10)$

Solve each equation in Probs. 33 to 40 for x in terms of y.
33. $y = 10^x$
34. $y = 10^{-x}$
35. $y = 5(10^{-2x})$
36. $y = 3(10^{2x})$
37. $y = \dfrac{e^x + e^{-x}}{2}$
38. $y = \dfrac{e^x - e^{-x}}{2}$
39. $y = \dfrac{e^x + e^{-x}}{e^x - e^{-x}}$
40. $y = \dfrac{e^x - e^{-x}}{e^x + e^{-x}}$

Solve the following inequalities:
41. $3.1^x < 5.5$
42. $6.7^{2x} < 4.4$
43. $(0.7)^{3x} < 3.5$
44. $(0.84)^x < 12$
45. $x^{4.3} < 6.6$
46. $(3x)^{3.8} < 88$
47. $(5x)^{0.55} < 14$
48. $(4x)^{0.18} < 2.1$

Solve these equations.
49. $\log_2 (\log_3 x) = 4$
50. $x^{\log_3 x} = 81$
51. $x^{\log x} = 10,000x$
52. $\log (x^2) = (\log x)^2$
53. $\log (x^3) = (\log x)^3$
54. $\log \sqrt{x} = \sqrt{\log x}$

55. Show that for all $x > e$,

$$x^{\ln (\ln x)} = (\ln x)^{\ln x}$$

Hint: Take the natural logarithm of both sides.

56. *Theory* Show that if $f(x) = x/\ln x$, then

$$f(2x) - f(x) = \frac{x \ln (x/2)}{\ln x \ln 2x}$$

5.6   Key Concepts

Be sure you understand each of the following important words and ideas.

b^x for x rational and irrational (p. 260)
Graphing exponential functions (p. 261)
Properties of exponential functions (p. 261)
Exponential growth and decay (p. 264)
Half-life (p. 265)
Definition of $\log_b x$ for $x > 0$, $b > 0$, and $b \neq 1$ (p. 268)
Exponential and logarithmic functions as inverses (p. 268)

Graphing logarithmic functions (p. 269)
Properties of logarithmic functions (p. 270)
e as the limit of $(1 + 1/n)^n$ (p. 275)
e^x and $\ln x$ (p. 276)
Change of base (p. 280)
Common logarithm = characteristic + mantissa (p. 285)
Exponential and logarithmic equations (p. 292)

(5.1) $y = \log_b x$ if and only if $b^y = x$
        $\log_b (b^y) = y$ and $b^{\log_b x} = x$ for $x > 0$, y real

(5.2) $\log_b (xy) = \log_b x + \log_b y$

(5.3) $\log_b (x/y) = \log_b x - \log_b y$

(5.4) $\log_b (x^p) = p \cdot \log_b x$

(5.5) $\log_b \sqrt[r]{x} = \dfrac{1}{r} \log_b x$

        $(\log_a x)(\log_b a) = \log_b x$

EXERCISE 5.6   Review

Graph the following:

1. $y = \log_7 x$, $y = 7^x$

2. $y = \log_5 (x + 3)$, $y + 3 = \log_5 x$

3. $y = \log |x|$, $y = |\log x|$

4. $2y = \log x$, $2x = \log y$

Verify the following equations and inequalities:

5. $3^{1/5} > 5^{1/8}$ **6.** $\sqrt{0.7} > 0.7$

7. $a^b = b^a$ if $a = \left(\frac{6}{5}\right)^5$, $b = \left(\frac{6}{5}\right)^6$

8. $2^{\sqrt{2}} > (\sqrt{2})^2$ **9.** $\log_3 (3^5) = 5$

10. $6^{\log_6 8} = 2^3$ **11.** $\log_{101} 1 = 0$

12. $\log_{2/5} \left(\frac{8}{125}\right) = 3$ **13.** $\log_9 243 = \frac{5}{2}$

14. $\log_4 \frac{1}{128} = -\frac{7}{2}$

15. $\log_2 30 = 1 + \log_2 3 + \log_2 5$

Use $\log_7 2 = x$, $\log_7 3 = y$, and $\log_7 5 = z$ to find these logarithms.

16. $\log_7 8$ **17.** $\log_7 \left(\frac{21}{20}\right)$ **18.** $\log_7 \sqrt{45}$

Find the following common logarithms:

19. $\log 485$ **20.** $\log 67.2$

21. $\log 0.974$ **22.** $\log 10^{0.3347}$

If $\log x$ is the given number, find x.

23. 4.7419 **24.** $4.9269 - 10$

25. $8.9050 - 10$ **26.** $14.3345 - 15$

Solve the following equations:

27. $7^x = 343$ **28.** $4^{x^2 + 3x} = 256$

29. $7^x = 243$

30. $\log_5 (x - 3) + \log_5 (3x + 1) = 3$
31. $\log_5 (x^2 - 5x + 10) - \log_5 (2x^2 - 3) = -1$
32. $3^{2x+1} = 5^{x-1}$
33. $\log_4 (\log_3 x) = 2$ 34. $4^{(x^2)} = (4^x)^2$

Solve the following inequalities:
35. $4^{3x} < 6.1$ 36. $(3x)^{0.71} < 2$
37. $5^x < 2 - x$
38. Find ln y and write it as a sum and difference of multiples of logarithms.

$$y = \frac{(12x + 31)\sqrt{x^2 + 17}}{5x^2 + 6}$$

39. Solve the equation below.

$$(x^2 - 5x)3e^{3x} + (2x - 5)e^{3x} = 0$$

40. *Law of cooling*   The Celsius temperature of a glass vase made at Jamestown, VA, is

$$15 + (740)e^{-0.2t}$$

after t min. How long will it take to cool down to 35°C?

41. *Secrets*   If 3 people in a group of 600 know a secret, the number who will know it after t days is approximately

$$N(t) = \frac{600e^t}{e^t + 200}$$

About how many will know it after 5 days?

42. *Different bases*   Use the change-of-base formulas

$$\log_b x = \frac{\ln x}{\ln b} = \frac{\log x}{\log b}$$

to find $\log_3 246$ and $\log_{5/2} \frac{8}{125}$.

43. *Value of π*   The approximation below, due to the Indian mathematician Ramanujan, is very accurate. Verify it by calculation.

$$\pi \approx \frac{12}{\sqrt{130}} \ln \frac{(2 + \sqrt{5})(3 + \sqrt{13})}{\sqrt{2}}$$

44. *Average values*   Verify the inequality by calculation.

$$\frac{56.5 + 42.8 + 35.6 + 20.4}{4}$$

$$> \sqrt[4]{(56.5)(42.8)(35.6)(20.4)}$$

45. *Intensity of sound*   Using the formula for *decibels*

$$d = 10 \cdot \log \frac{I}{I_0}$$

find I in terms of I_0 if $d = 125$ (this level can cause pain).

46. *Growth of bacteria*   In a certain culture, there are 62,000 bacteria on Monday and 72,000 on Wednesday. How many will there be on Friday?

47. *Radioactivity*   If there is 8 g of a radioactive substance on May 10, and 4 g of it on May 15, how much of it will there be on May 20?

48. *Management*   The cost of manufacturing x items is

$$600 + 250 \log (x + 4)$$

What is the cost for (a) 6 items and (b) 46 items?

49. *pH value*   Use the fact that the pH of a substance is pH $= -\log [H^+]$, where $[H^+]$ measures the hydrogen ion concentration. If the pH of sea water is 8.5, find its value of $[H^+]$.

50. *Pick a number*   Use the characteristic to decide which number is larger.

$$36^{63} \quad \text{or} \quad 60^{55}$$

51. *Biology*   The number of bacteria after t hours is $4.8(10^4) \cdot 2^{t/3}$. How long will it take for the number to double? How long to triple?

52. *Earth science*   A mild earthquake has a Richter number of 4.5, while a severe one has a Richter number of 8.2. What is the ratio of their intensities? See Example 7, Sec. 5.4.

53. *Chemistry*   Carbon 14 occurs in organic objects in a fixed percentage Q. When the organism dies, the carbon 14 decays in such a way that after t years the percentage of carbon 14 is $P = (Q)2^{-t/5600}$. If a dead organism is found to have $P = 0.76Q$, approximately how long has it been dead?

54. *Terminal velocity*   If we take into account air resistance and initial velocity, the velocity in feet per second of a falling body after t seconds is $v = 120 - 180 e^{-t/4}$. For which values of t is $v \geq 115$? What happens to v as t becomes larger and larger (that is, what is the terminal velocity)?

55. *Economics*   With appropriate units and constants, Thomas Malthus in 1790 said that population grows exponentially, while food production grows linearly. He concluded that after a long enough period of time, the population will overtake the available food (assuming all other factors do not change). For the case

$$f(t) = 25t + 2000 - (3)2^{t/30}$$

show that $f(90) > 0$, $f(180) > 0$, $f(270) > 0$, $f(300) > 0$, $f(354) > 0$, $f(355) < 0$, and $f(390) < 0$.

56. *Theory*   Let $f(p) = [(4^p + 5^p)/2]^{1/p}$. Show by calculation that $f(2) < f(3) < f(4)$. Show that

$$f(p) = (5)\left[\frac{(\frac{4}{5})^p + 1}{2}\right]^{1/p}$$

What value does $f(p)$ seem to approach as $p \to \infty$?

57. *Area formula*   The area of a triangle with sides a, b, and c and $s = (a + b + c)/2$ is given by Heron's formula $K = \sqrt{s(s - a)(s - b)(s - c)}$. Find the area of a triangle with sides $a = 64.3$, $b = 47.9$, and $c = 38.4$.

58. *Probability*   The definition of $n!$, read n factorial, is $n(n - 1)(n - 2) \cdots (4)(3)(2)(1)$, the product of all integers between 1 and n inclusive. Since this involves n factors, a handy approximation for large n is Stirling's formula $n! \approx (n/e)^n \cdot \sqrt{2\pi n}$. Use Stirling's formula to approximate the probability

$$\frac{100!}{50! \cdot 50! \cdot 2^{100}}$$

59. *Management*   New equipment should be installed every x years where

$$e^{-dx} = \frac{1}{1 + da/mb + xd}$$

Show that $x = 3.75$ is an approximate solution for the situation where $a = 10,000 = b$, $d = 0.06$, and $m = 2$.

60. *Anthropology*   One equation governing population growth in thousands is

$$y = \frac{2.91}{e^{-0.03x} + 0.015}$$

Calculate y for $x = 28$ years.

61. *Physics*   The pressure and volume of a certain gas are related by $pv^{1.4} = 14{,}720$. Find v if $p = 115$.

62. *Inequalities*   For $0 < y < x$, it is true that

$$\frac{2(x - y)}{x + y} < \ln x - \ln y$$

$$< (\sqrt{x} - \sqrt{y})\left(\frac{1}{\sqrt{x}} + \frac{1}{\sqrt{y}}\right)$$

Verify this by calculation for $x = 8$ and $y = 7$.

63. Show that $3^x + 3^{x+1} = 4(3^x)$.

Calculate the following numbers. If you use logarithms, some problems require that parts be calculated first. If you use a calculator, be careful of the order of operations.

64. $(48.3)(6.44)(0.555)$

65. $64.2/(9.87)(11.3)$

66. $\sqrt{41.8/(1.35)^5}$

67. $10^{4.4440}$

68. $(\log 3)(\log 5)$

69. $\log_6 12$

70. $\dfrac{8.31 + \sqrt{46.4}}{(\log 74.3)^2}$

71. $\dfrac{18.3 - \sqrt[3]{500}}{(\log 51)^3}$

72. $\dfrac{5.62}{3.48 + (6.55)(0.392)}$

73. $\dfrac{2^{0.6} + 3^{0.7}}{4^{0.8}}$

6

Trigonometric Functions

The word "trigonometry" means literally "triangle measurement" since that is what the Babylonians, Egyptians, and Greeks invented and used it for over 2000 years ago. Trigonometry today deals not only with triangles, but also with the relationships between six basic trigonometric functions. These functions may be treated with the domains being either sets of angles or sets of real numbers. One of our main goals in this chapter will be to present both approaches early, and show that they are closely tied to each other. We may then use whichever one is more convenient for the purpose at hand.

Applications of trigonometry to right triangles are given as soon as practical, in Sec. 6.4, in order that you may quickly perceive the power of trigonometry. Trigonometry is used not only for triangle measurement, but for many repeating or periodic phenomena. We will see how it is used in radio, TV, sound waves, ocean waves, electricity, seasonal sales, navigation, electrocardiograms, engineering, optics, and many other ways.

6.1 Angles and Circles

An angle is determined by two sides (line segments) which intersect at a common point. To deal with many applications, however, we must give a more precise definition of an angle.

Whereas a line extends infinitely far in opposite directions, the **line segment** AB is only the part of the line between points A and B on the line. The **ray,** or half-line, AB

is the part of the line which starts at A and extends through and beyond B. The point A is called the **endpoint** of the ray, as in Fig. 6.1(a). An angle may be defined using either line segments or rays.

An **angle** is formed if a ray is rotated in a plane about its endpoint from a given position, called the **initial side,** to a second position, called the **terminal side** of the angle. The endpoint is called the **vertex** of the angle. The angle in Fig. 6.1(b) may be called angle A, angle BAC, or angle θ (theta). Other Greek letters which are commonly used for angles are α (alpha), β (beta), and ϕ (phi).

The ray may be rotated in either direction and by any amount. In particular, the rotation may be more than one complete revolution. The angle is said to be **positive** if the rotation is counterclockwise and **negative** if the rotation is clockwise. In Fig. 6.2, α is a positive angle and β is a negative angle.

The amount of rotation needed to move the initial side of an angle to the terminal side is called the **measure,** or **magnitude,** or **size** of the angle. It is convenient for future work to place the angle in **standard position,** which means that the vertex of the angle is placed at the origin of a rectangular coordinate system, and its initial side is along the positive x axis. In Fig. 6.3, the positive angle θ and the negative angle β are
NOTE   shown in standard position. If an angle is in standard position, it is said to be **in the quadrant** in which its terminal side lies. Thus in Fig. 6.3, θ is in quadrant II, while β is in quadrant III.

Degrees

Angles have been measured in degrees since the Babylonians, who believed that there were 360 days in a year. For this reason, they assigned 360 degrees, or 360°, to a complete circle or revolution.

> One **degree** is the measure of an angle which is formed by $\frac{1}{360}$ of one complete counterclockwise revolution.

NOTE   In Fig. 6.4, we show several angles with various degree measures. Instead of referring to "the angle θ whose degree measure is 70°," it is common practice to just say an angle of 70°, or a 70° angle, or $\theta = 70°$. Notice that the angle of 495° has more than one revolution and is in the second quadrant, while the $-150°$ angle is negative and is in the third quadrant.

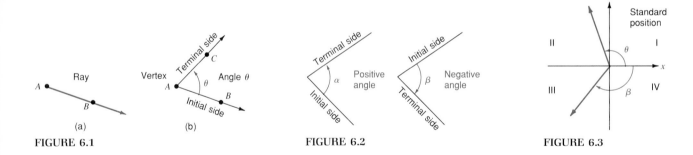

FIGURE 6.1   FIGURE 6.2   FIGURE 6.3

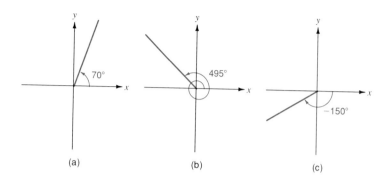

FIGURE 6.4

If $0° < \theta < 90°$, then θ is called **acute.** A $90°$ angle is called a **right angle.** Furthermore, θ is **obtuse** if $90° < \theta < 180°$. If $\theta = 180°$, then θ is a **straight angle.** Two acute angles α and β are **complementary** if $\alpha + \beta = 90°$. Thus $33°$ and $57°$ are complementary angles, as are the two angles

$$\alpha \text{ and } 90° - \alpha \text{ for any acute angle } \alpha$$

Complementary angles will be very important for us when we define and study the trigonometric functions.

If the terminal side of an angle in standard position coincides with the x axis or the y axis, the angle is called a **quadrantal angle.** Hence $0°$, $\pm 90°$, $\pm 180°$, $\pm 270°$, or any integral multiple of $90°$ is a quadrantal angle.

An angle of $1°$ can be divided still further. One way is to use **decimal degrees** such as $47.3°$, $281.55°$, and $0.756631°$. Most calculators use degrees in decimal form for actual calculation, and Table A.5 gives trigonometric function values for every tenth of a degree.

One degree may also be divided into **minutes and seconds** by defining

$$1° = 60 \text{ minutes} = 60' \qquad \text{and} \qquad 1' = 60 \text{ seconds} = 60''$$

It follows that $1° = 60' = 3600''$. For instance the angle $28°44'13''$ has $28°$, $44'$, and $13''$. The next example shows how to change from degrees in decimal form to degrees, minutes, and seconds, and vice versa.

▶ **EXAMPLE 1** Put $18°24'45''$ in decimal form, and $68.47°$ in degrees, minutes, and seconds.

Solution (a)
$$\begin{aligned} 18°24'45'' &= 18° + \left(\tfrac{24}{60}\right)° + \left(\tfrac{45}{3600}\right)° \\ &= 18° + 0.4° + 0.0125° = 18.4125° \end{aligned}$$

(b)
$$\begin{aligned} 68.47° &= 68° + (0.47)(60') && \text{since } 1° = 60' \\ &= 68° + 28.2' && \text{multiplying} \\ &= 68° + 28' + (0.2)(60'') && \text{since } 1' = 60'' \\ &= 68°28'12'' \end{aligned}$$

◀

Two angles which have the same initial side and also the same terminal side are called **coterminal angles.** If two angles are coterminal, then they differ by an integral multiple of $360°$. Hence if all these angles are in standard position,

$$100° \qquad 460° \qquad 3700° \qquad -260° \qquad -1340°$$

then they are all coterminal. For instance,

$$3700° - 100° = 3600° = 10(360°)$$
$$-1340° - 100° = -1440° = -4(360°)$$

Radian Measure

The most common unit used to measure angles in scientific work is the **radian,** which we shall presently define. In Fig. 6.5, we show an angle placed with its vertex at the center of a circle of radius r. The angle θ intercepts an arc of length s on the circumference.

From plane geometry, the arc length s is proportional to the measure of the angle θ. For instance, if the angle is doubled (or tripled), then the arc length is also doubled (or tripled). We shall use this fact to define the number of radians in the angle θ.

Radians

> If a central angle in a circle of radius r cuts off an arc of length s, then the number of radians θ in the angle is s/r.

In particular, an angle of **1 radian** cuts off an arc (on the circumference) whose length equals the radius since $1 = r/r$. In Fig. 6.6, there are angles of 1, 2, and 3 radians.

Since the circumference of a circle is $2\pi r$, it follows that the number of radians in one complete revolution is $s/r = 2\pi r/r = 2\pi$. We also know that there are 360° in one revolution. Consequently, 2π radians $= 360°$, and dividing by 2 gives the fundamental fact that

$$\pi \text{ radians} = 180°$$

This allows us to change from radians to degrees, or from degrees to radians. In fact,

$$1 \text{ radian} = \left(\frac{180}{\pi}\right)° \qquad \text{and} \qquad 1° = \frac{\pi}{180} \text{ radians}$$

Therefore we have the following basic rule:

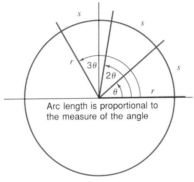

Arc length is proportional to
the measure of the angle

FIGURE 6.5

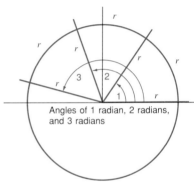

Angles of 1 radian, 2 radians,
and 3 radians

FIGURE 6.6

$$\pi \text{ radians} = 180° \qquad \qquad \text{(6.1)}$$

To change from radians to degrees, multiply by $180/\pi$.
To change from degrees to radians, multiply by $\pi/180$.

We shall follow the usual custom, which is to

IMPORTANT NOTE   *Omit the word "radian"*

if an angle is expressed in terms of radians. Thus $\theta = 3$ means that θ has 3 radians, and $\theta = \pi/6$ means that θ has $\pi/6$ radian. If θ has 24 degrees, we must write the degree symbol: $\theta = 24°$.

► EXAMPLE 2   Change from radians to degrees in parts (a) and (b), and from degrees to radians in parts (c) and (d).

Solution   (a) $\dfrac{\pi}{9} = \dfrac{\pi \cdot 180°}{9 \cdot \pi} = \dfrac{180°}{9} = 20°$ radians to degrees

(b) $2.35 = 2.35(180/\pi)°$ multiply by $180/\pi$
        $= (423/\pi)°$ exact number of degrees
        $= 134.6°$ decimal approximation

(c) $315° = 315(\pi/180) = 7\pi/4$ degrees to radians
(d) $25° = 25(\pi/180)$ multiply by $\pi/180$
        $= 5\pi/36$ exact number of radians
        $= 0.43633$ decimal approximation ◄

► EXAMPLE 3   Write 1 radian in degrees in exact form, as a decimal approximation, and as an approximation in degrees, minutes, and seconds.

Solution   1 radian $= (180/\pi)°$ exact form
            $\approx 57.2958°$ decimal approximation in degrees
            $= 57° + 0.2958(60') = 57°17.748'$ degrees and minutes
            $= 57°17' + 0.748(60'')$
            $= 57°17'45''$ degrees, minutes, and seconds

As a result of this we may approximate 1 radian by either

$$57.2958° \text{ or by } 57°17'45'' \qquad \qquad ◄$$

Most calculators use decimal form for both radians and degrees. Example 4 shows how to change between radians in decimal form and degrees in both forms.

► EXAMPLE 4   Express (a) 3.2 radians in terms of degrees; (b) $33°10'54''$ in radians.

Solution   (a) $3.2 = 3.2(180/\pi)°$ radians to degrees
            $\approx 183.3465°$ degrees in decimals
            $= 183° + (0.3465)(60') = 183° + 20.79'$
            $= 183°20' + (0.79)(60'')$
            $\approx 183°20'47''$ degrees, minutes, and seconds

(b) $\qquad 33°10'54'' = 33° + (10/60)° + (54/3600)°$

$\qquad\qquad\qquad \approx 33° + 0.16667° + 0.015°$

$\qquad\qquad\qquad = 33.18167°$ degrees in decimals

$\qquad\qquad\qquad = 33.18167(\pi/180)$ degrees to radians

$\qquad\qquad\qquad = 0.57913$ radians in decimals ◢

The mil and the grad are commonly used units of angular measure. The mil is used by the U.S. Army in artillery fire, and is the angle subtended by an arc that is $\frac{1}{6400}$ of the circumference. The mil is important because a central angle of 1 mil intercepts an arc almost exactly 1 m in length on a circle of radius 1 km. The grad is used on some calculators, and is $\frac{1}{100}$ of a right angle.

NOTE   All scientific calculators have a key, often called the *DRG key*, which changes the mode of the calculator from degrees to radians to grads and back to degrees. However, using this key changes only the units used, not the number of units. For instance, if 3 is on the display and the mode is degrees, we are working with 3°, a first quadrant angle. If the mode is now changed to radians, we will then be working with 3 radians, a second quadrant angle.

The angles $3\pi/4$ and $-5\pi/4$ are **coterminal** because they have the same terminal side. They differ by one revolution. Other angles which are coterminal with $3\pi/4$ are $11\pi/4$, $19\pi/4$, and

$$\frac{3\pi}{4} + n(2\pi) \qquad \text{and} \qquad \frac{3\pi}{4} - n(2\pi)$$

where n is a positive integer. In fact, for any given angle there are an infinite number of angles coterminal with it, some positive and some negative.

Coterminal angles in radians:	θ and $\theta \pm n \cdot 2\pi$
Coterminal angles in degrees:	θ and $\theta \pm n \cdot 360°$
where n is a positive integer.	

EXAMPLE 5   Name several angles which are coterminal with $5\pi/3$, or $300°$.

Solution   The following angles in radians

$$\frac{-13\pi}{3} \qquad \frac{-7\pi}{3} \qquad \frac{-\pi}{3} \qquad \frac{5\pi}{3} \qquad \frac{11\pi}{3} \qquad \frac{17\pi}{3}$$

are all coterminal since the difference between any two of them is an integral multiple of 2π. In degrees these same angles are

$$-780° \qquad -420° \qquad -60° \qquad 300° \qquad 660° \qquad 1020° \quad ◢$$

The chart below gives the radian and degree measure of some angles which will be used frequently later in the book.

Common angles

Angle in radians	0	$\pi/6$	$\pi/4$	$\pi/3$	$\pi/2$	π	$3\pi/2$	2π
Angle in degrees	0°	30°	45°	60°	90°	180°	270°	360°

Some other convenient angles are $\pi/5 = 36°$, $\pi/8 = 22.5°$, $\pi/9 = 20°$, $\pi/10 = 18°$, and $\pi/12 = 15°$.

Arc Length

The relation $\theta = s/r$ that was used in defining the number of radians in a central angle may easily be solved for s, giving the next result.

Arc length formula

> Suppose that in a circle of radius r, a central angle θ is measured in radians. The arc length s cut off on the circumference by the initial and terminal sides of the angle satisfies
>
> $$s = r\theta \tag{6.2}$$

IMPORTANT   The angle must be measured in *radians*, not degrees.

EXAMPLE 6   What arc length is subtended, or cut off, by a central angle of 105° on a circle of radius 8.3 cm?

Solution   The angle must be in radians and $105° = 105(\pi/180) = 7\pi/12$. Therefore, the arc length is

$$s = 8.3\left(\frac{7\pi}{12}\right) \approx 15.2 \text{ cm}$$

EXAMPLE 7   Hobart, Tasmania is 43°S latitude and Mertz Glacier, Antarctica, is 68°S latitude. About how far apart are they if both have the same longitude? Assume the Earth's radius is 4000 mi.

Solution   Since they have the same longitude, the angle determined by Hobart, the center of the earth, and Mertz Glacier is

$$68° - 43° = 25° = \frac{25\pi}{180} = \frac{5\pi}{36}$$

See Fig. 6.7. Consequently, the required distance is

$$s = r\theta = 4000\left(\frac{5\pi}{36}\right) \text{ mi}$$

$$= \frac{5000\pi}{9} \text{ mi}$$

$$\approx 1745 \text{ mi} \qquad \text{to 4 digits}$$

Later in this chapter we will often use a unit circle, meaning that the radius is $r = 1$.

Angular Velocity

Suppose that a point on a circle is rotating about the center at a constant velocity. If we divide $s = r\theta$ by the time t, we get

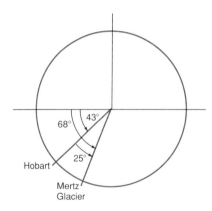

FIGURE 6.7

$$\frac{s}{t} = r\frac{\theta}{t} \tag{1}$$

Since s/t is "distance divided by time," it is velocity and we will write it as v. The quantity θ/t is called **angular velocity** since it measures the angular change per unit of time, and we will write it as ω. Remember that with θ in radians, θ is just a number and has no units. Thus θ/t has the units "radians per time," and $r(\theta/t)$ has the units "distance divided by time." Hence by Eq. (1)

$$v = r\omega$$

or in words: "linear velocity is the product of the radius and angular velocity."

▶ **EXAMPLE 8**   A flywheel has a diameter of 81.2 cm and is revolving at 1743 r/min (revolutions per minute). Find the linear speed of a point on the rim of the flywheel. How far does it go in 12 s?

Solution   We have $r = 81.2/2 = 40.6$ and $\omega = 1743$ r/min $= 1743(2\pi)$ radians/min since one revolution is 2π radians. Hence

$$
\begin{aligned}
v = r\omega &= (40.6)(1743)(2\pi) \\
&= 444{,}635 &&\text{cm/min to 6 digits} \\
&= 444{,}635(60) &&\text{cm/h} \\
&\approx 2.67(10^7) &&\text{cm/h} \\
&= 267 &&\text{km/h}
\end{aligned}
$$

The point goes 444,635 cm in 1 min = 60 s, so in 12 s it goes 444,635/5 cm = 88,927 cm $\approx$ 889 m $\approx$ 972 yards $\approx$ 0.55 mi.   ◢

EXERCISE 6.1

Construct the angles given in each of Probs. 1 to 8. Indicate the direction of rotation.

1. $120°$, $-80°$
2. $300°$, $-135°$
3. $-90°$, $230°$
4. $-240°$, $270°$
5. 4 radians, $-\pi/3$ radians
6. -2.2 radians, $4\pi/3$ radians
7. -1.7 radians, π radians
8. 5.1 radians, $-7\pi/4$ radians

Express each angle in Probs. 9 to 24 as a constant times π radians.

9. 36°   **10.** 30°   **11.** 9°
12. 12°   **13.** 12°15′   **14.** 20°40′
15. 11°15′   **16.** 6°15′   **17.** 2°5′10″
18. 16°8′24″   **19.** 1°5′42″   **20.** 10°7′30″
21. 3.1 right angles   **22.** 1.7 right angles
23. 1.7 revolutions   **24.** 5.4 revolutions

Express the angle in each of Probs. 25 to 32 in terms of radians correct to three decimal places.

25. 31°   **26.** −12°   **27.** 49°
28. 165°   **29.** −9°10′   **30.** 11°9′
31. 27°14′6″   **32.** 74°31′27″

Express the angle in each of Probs. 33 to 44 in terms of degrees, minutes, and seconds. In Probs. 41 to 44, use 1 radian equals $(180/\pi)°$.

33. $\pi/4$ **34.** $\pi/12$ **35.** $\pi/15$ **36.** $\pi/36$
37. $5\pi/32$ **38.** $4\pi/27$ **39.** $7\pi/36$ **40.** $9\pi/64$
41. 2.6 radians   **42.** 3.7 radians
43. 1.5 radians   **44.** 5.9 radians

In Probs. 45 to 52, find a positive and a negative angle, each of which is coterminal with the given angle. In each case, find the angles closest to 0 or 0°.

45. $5\pi/6$ **46.** $-\pi/4$ **47.** $5\pi/2$
48. $-7\pi/3$ **49.** 330°   **50.** 480°
51. −540°   **52.** −45°

In Probs. 53 to 64, use the arc length formula to find the missing quantities of s, r, and θ.

53. If $\theta = 0.234$ and $r = 6.37$ cm, find s.
54. If $\theta = 2.07$ and $r = 4.31$ in, find s.
55. If $\theta = 3.71$ and $r = 8.63$ cm, find s.
56. If $\theta = 0.763$ and $r = 87.3$ in, find s.
57. If $\theta = 106°25′$ and $s = 6.029$ cm, find r.
58. If $\theta = 82°33′$ and $s = 38.09$ ft, find r.
59. If $\theta = 115°32′$ and $s = 198.5$ ft, find r.
60. If $\theta = 57°42′$ and $s = 11.84$ ft, find r.
61. If $s = 3.75$ and $r = 5.04$, find θ in radians.
62. If $s = 28.3$ and $r = 78.7$, find θ in radians.
63. If $s = 0.926$ and $r = 0.489$, find θ in radians.
64. If $s = 0.858$ and $r = 1.73$, find θ in radians.

65. *Physics*   A bucket is drawn from a well by pulling a rope over a pulley. Find the radius of the pulley if the bucket is raised 63.4 in while the pulley turns through 3.47 revolutions.

66. *Civil engineering*   A curve on a highway subtends an angle of 34° on a circle of radius 1700 ft. How long will it take a car traveling at 45 mi/h to round the curve?

67. *Physics*   A vehicle has wheels 5 ft in diameter, and it is traveling at 60 mi/h. Find the angular velocity of the wheels in radians per second.

68. *Navigation*   Find the latitude and longitude of a point that is 3000 mi south of the equator and 3229 mi east of the meridian through Greenwich, England. The longitude of Greenwich is 0°. Use 4000 mi as the radius of the earth.

69. *Geometry*   An isosceles triangle whose equal sides meet at an angle of 50° is inscribed in a circle. Find the radius of the circle if the base of the triangle intercepts an arc of 6.6 cm on the circle.

70. *Geometry*   Tangents are drawn from each end of a 36-in arc on a circle of radius 18 in and produced until they meet. Find, to the nearest degree, the angle α between them. (See the figure.) *Hint:* The tangent to a circle is perpendicular to the radius drawn to the point of tangency.

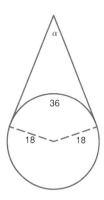

71. *Space*   Find the angular velocity in radians per hour of an earth satellite which travels in a circular orbit with radius 4800 mi at a speed of 19,200 mi/h.

72. *Astronomy*   Find the linear velocity in miles per hour of the earth as it moves about the sun. Assume that it completes one circular orbit every 365 days and that the distance from the earth to the sun is 93,000,000 mi.

The area of a **sector** of a circle is

$$\frac{r^2\theta}{2}$$

where θ is the central angle in **radians** and r is the radius of the circle. Note that when $\theta = 2\pi$, the formula above gives πr^2 for the area of a circle. Find the area of the indicated sector in Probs. 73 to 76.

73. $r = 6.1$, $\theta = 0.53$ **74.** $r = 1.7$, $\theta = 1.2$
75. $r = 3.3$, $\theta = 2.7$ **76.** $r = 4.9$, $\theta = 0.78$

In Probs. 77 to 80, find the distance between the two places in each problem under the assumption that they have the same longitude and that the radius of the earth is 4000 mi.

77. Addis Ababa, Ethiopia, is 7°N and Rostov, Russia, is 52°N.
78. Agra, India, is 27°N and Bangalore, India, is 13°N.
79. Sydney, Australia, is 33°S and Simushirce, Kuril Islands, is 47°N.
80. Cape Town, South Africa, is 33°S and Stockholm, Sweden, is 58°N.

81. Show that the sum of the angles in a triangle is 180°. (See the figure.) *Hint:* Draw a line through one vertex parallel to the opposite side. Use the fact that if two lines are parallel, and a third line crosses them, then alternate angles are equal.

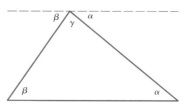

82. Find the radian and degree measure of the smaller angle between the hands of a clock at 3:45. *Hint:* The big hand has made $\frac{45}{60}$ of a revolution from the vertical, while the small hand has moved from the vertical by the amount $(3 + \frac{3}{4})(\frac{1}{12})$ of a revolution.

83. Find the linear speed in inches per minute of a point on the tip of the long hand of a famous clock whose long hand is 8 ft long.

84. Assume that the earth revolves on its axis once every 24 h, and that its radius is 4000 mi. Find the angular speed in radians per hour of Singapore (on the equator), and its linear speed in miles per hour.

6.2 Trigonometric Functions of an Angle

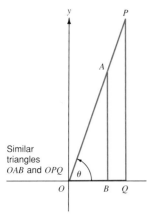

Similar triangles *OAB* and *OPQ*

FIGURE 6.8

In Fig. 6.8, we show an angle θ in standard position with the points A and P on the terminal side, A and P being different from the origin O. The angle may be in any of the four quadrants, but quadrantal angles will be treated separately.

We draw a perpendicular line from each of the points A and P to the x axis, intersecting it at points B and Q, respectively. We thus have the **right triangles** OAB and OPQ. Then OB, BA, and OA are the abscissa, ordinate, and radius vector of A; similarly, OQ, QP, and OP are the abscissa, ordinate, and radius vector of P. The six ratios

$$BA/OA, \ OB/OA, \ BA/OB, \ OB/BA, \ OA/OB, \ and \ OA/BA$$

can be formed from the sides of the triangle OAB. Furthermore, the corresponding ratios formed from the triangle OPQ are equal to these ratios because the two triangles are similar, and in similar triangles.

The ratios of corresponding sides are equal

For instance, $BA/OA = QP/OP$, and $BA/OB = QP/OQ$. Consequently, we know that

the values of these ratios depend only on the angle

and not on the point chosen on its terminal side. These ratios are called the **trigonometric function values** of the angle, and each one is assigned a name.

Definition of the trigonometric functions

> If θ is any angle in standard position, $P(x, y)$ is any point on its terminal side, and r is the distance from P to the origin, as in Fig. 6.9, then the six trigonometric functions are defined by
>
> $$\text{sine } \theta = \frac{y}{r} = \sin \theta \qquad\qquad \text{cosecant } \theta = \frac{r}{y} = \csc \theta$$
>
> $$\text{cosine } \theta = \frac{x}{r} = \cos \theta \qquad\qquad \text{secant } \theta = \frac{r}{x} = \sec \theta \qquad\qquad (6.3)$$
>
> $$\text{tangent } \theta = \frac{y}{x} = \tan \theta \qquad\qquad \text{cotangent } \theta = \frac{x}{y} = \cot \theta$$

Notice that the abbreviations for the trigonometric functions are written without periods.

Quadrantal angles may be treated by using the ratio definitions above, except we have to remember that either x or y is zero for each quadrantal angle. Then use the fact that for any nonzero real number d

$$\frac{0}{d} = 0 \qquad \text{and} \qquad \frac{d}{0} \text{ is not defined}$$

NOTE   As stated in the definition, the angle may be any angle as long as it is in standard position. We merely have to remember that x and y may be positive, negative, or zero, and that r is the positive number $\sqrt{x^2 + y^2}$.

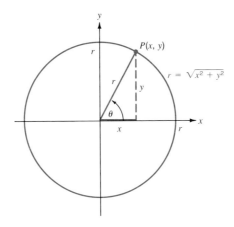

FIGURE 6.9

Finding Function Values

The signs of the function values are determined by the signs of x, y, and r along with the usual laws of signs for quotients. The values for x and y may be positive, negative, or zero, but r is always positive. Since $|x|$, $|y|$, and r are the sides of a right triangle, we always have

Pythagorean Theorem $x^2 + y^2 = r^2$

 **EXAMPLE 1**   If $(3, -4)$ is on the terminal side of an angle θ in standard position, find the six trigonometric function values of θ?

Solution   See Fig. 6.10, where we show the angle θ in the fourth quadrant with $x = 3$ and $y = -4$. Then $r^2 = 9 + 16 = 25$, and so $r = 5$. The function values are therefore

$$\sin \theta = \frac{-4}{5} = -0.8 \qquad\qquad \csc \theta = \frac{5}{-4} = -1.25$$

$$\cos \theta = \frac{3}{5} = 0.6 \qquad\qquad \sec \theta = \frac{5}{3} \approx 1.667$$

$$\tan \theta = \frac{-4}{3} \approx -1.333 \qquad \cot \theta = \frac{3}{-4} = -0.75$$

Although we used $x = 3$ and $y = -4$, we could have used the coordinates of *any point* on the terminal side of θ, say $(6, -8)$ or $(15, -20)$. ◀

Since two numbers are reciprocals of one another if their product is 1, and since

$$\sin \theta \csc \theta = \frac{y}{r} \cdot \frac{r}{y} = 1 \qquad \text{if } y \neq 0$$

$$\cos \theta \sec \theta = \frac{x}{r} \cdot \frac{r}{x} = 1 \qquad \text{if } x \neq 0 \qquad\qquad \textbf{(6.4)}$$

$$\tan \theta \cot \theta = \frac{y}{x} \cdot \frac{x}{y} = 1 \qquad \text{if } x \neq 0, y \neq 0$$

it follows that $\sin \theta$ and $\csc \theta$ are **reciprocals,** $\cos \theta$ and $\sec \theta$ are reciprocals, and $\tan \theta$ and $\cot \theta$ are also reciprocals. For instance, with the angle θ in Example 1

$$\sin \theta \csc \theta = \frac{-4}{5} \cdot \frac{5}{-4} = 1$$

$$\cos \theta \sec \theta = \frac{3}{5} \cdot \frac{5}{3} = 1$$

$$\tan \theta \cot \theta = \frac{-4}{3} \cdot \frac{3}{-4} = 1$$

In order to be able to find the values of the other five functions if one is given, we use the Pythagorean relation $x^2 + y^2 = r^2$. If any two of these three quantities are known, the other one can be found except possibly for its sign. Only one value can be

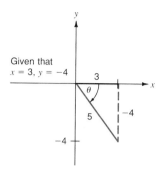

FIGURE 6.10

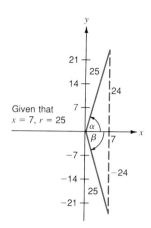

FIGURE 6.11

found for r since it is always positive. However, two values can be found for x, and two for y also, since each one can be either positive or negative.

EXAMPLE 2 If the x and r values of a point on the terminal side of an angle are 7 and 25, find the ordinate y and all six trigonometric function values of the angle.

Solution We have

$$7^2 + y^2 = 25^2$$
$$y^2 = 25^2 - 7^2 = 625 - 49 = 576$$
$$y = \pm 24$$

In finding the function values, we must use both of these values of y. In Fig. 6.11, we show the two angles which satisfy the given conditions, α in quadrant I and β in quadrant IV. Using $x = 7$, $y = 24$, and $r = 25$ for α gives the function values

$$\sin \alpha = \frac{24}{25} \qquad \cos \alpha = \frac{7}{25} \qquad \tan \alpha = \frac{24}{7}$$

$$\csc \alpha = \frac{25}{24} \qquad \sec \alpha = \frac{25}{7} \qquad \cot \alpha = \frac{7}{24}$$

Using $x = 7$, $y = -24$, and $r = 25$ for β gives

$$\sin \beta = \frac{-24}{25} \qquad \cos \beta = \frac{7}{25} \qquad \tan \beta = \frac{-24}{7}$$

$$\csc \beta = \frac{25}{-24} \qquad \sec \beta = \frac{25}{7} \qquad \cot \beta = \frac{7}{-24}$$

In Example 1, we were given x and y, and then we found the value of r. In Example 2, we were given x and r, and then found the two values of y. If we are given one of the six function values of an angle, we do not know the values of x, y, and r

for a specific point on the terminal side of the angle, but do know the ratio of two of them. That and the Pythagorean theorem are enough, as we see in Example 3.

EXAMPLE 3   Find the other function values if csc $\theta = 2.6$.

Solution   Since csc $\theta = r/y = 2.6 = \frac{26}{10} = \frac{13}{5}$, we may use $r = 13$ and $y = 5$. We now have

$$x^2 + 5^2 = 13^2$$
$$x^2 = 13^2 - 5^2 = (13 - 5)(13 + 5) = 8(18) = 144$$
$$x = \pm 12$$

See Fig. 6.12. Consequently, we have two angles, one in the first quadrant and one in the second. The other five function values are

$$\sin \theta = \frac{5}{13} \qquad \cos \theta = \frac{\pm 12}{13} \qquad \tan \theta = \frac{5}{\pm 12}$$
$$\sec \theta = \frac{13}{\pm 12} \qquad \cot \theta = \frac{\pm 12}{5}$$

If we are given the quadrant in which the angle lies in addition to one of its function values, there is only one value for each of the other functions.

EXAMPLE 4   Find the other function values if tan $\theta = \frac{8}{15}$ and the angle is in the third quadrant.

Solution   Since the angle is in the third quadrant, both of the coordinates of a point on the terminal side are negative, as in Fig. 6.13. We may therefore take $x = -15$ and $y = -8$, giving

$$r^2 = (-15)^2 + (-8)^2 = 225 + 64 = 289 = 17^2$$

Since we now have $r = 17$, the function values are

$$\sin \theta = \frac{-8}{17} \qquad \cos \theta = \frac{-15}{17} \qquad \tan \theta = \frac{-8}{-15} = \frac{8}{15}$$
$$\csc \theta = \frac{17}{-8} \qquad \sec \theta = \frac{17}{-15} \qquad \cot \theta = \frac{-15}{-8} = \frac{15}{8}$$

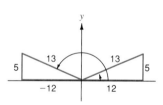

FIGURE 6.12

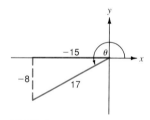

FIGURE 6.13

Terminal side on a line

In Example 4, the information could also have been given by saying that the angle is a third quadrant angle whose terminal side lies on the line whose equation is $y = 8x/15$. Then letting $x = -15$ would show that $y = (8)(-15)/15 = -8$, and hence $\tan \theta = (-8)/(-15) = \frac{8}{15}$. The problem is now completed as above.

The information for Example 4 could also have been given by saying that the angle is in quadrant III and the terminal side of θ is parallel to the line $15y = 8x + 91$. It would follow that the terminal side lies on the line whose equation is $15y = 8x$, or $y = 8x/15$. Hence, as above, we could take $x = -15$, giving $y = (8)(-15)/15 = -8$, and thus $\tan \theta = (-8)/(-15) = \frac{8}{15}$. Again the problem is completed as in Example 4.

Each of the examples in this section so far has had integral values for x, y, and r. However, the same methods apply if for instance angle α has $x = 2$ and $r = 3$ with $y > 0$. Then

$$y^2 = r^2 - x^2 = 9 - 4 = 5$$

and so $y = \sqrt{5}$, giving the values

$$\sin \alpha = \frac{\sqrt{5}}{3} \qquad\qquad \cos \alpha = \frac{2}{3} \qquad \tan \alpha = \frac{\sqrt{5}}{2}$$

$$\csc \alpha = \frac{3}{\sqrt{5}} = \frac{3\sqrt{5}}{5} \qquad \sec \alpha = \frac{3}{2} \qquad \cot \alpha = \frac{2}{\sqrt{5}} = \frac{2\sqrt{5}}{5}$$

We have found all of the function values in this section without finding the angles. In Sec. 6.3 we will see how to use tables or a calculator to find function values.

Since right triangles with integral sides are often used as examples, here is a list of the lengths of the sides of the most commonly used right triangles:

$$3,4,5 \qquad 5,12,13 \qquad 8,15,17 \qquad 7,24,25 \qquad 20,21,29$$

EXERCISE 6.2

In Probs. 1 to 8, verify that $x^2 + y^2 = r^2$. Then find the values of the six trigonometric functions of the angle in standard position whose terminal side goes through the point (x, y).

1. $x = 3$, $y = 4$, $r = 5$
2. $x = 8$, $y = 15$, $r = 17$
3. $x = 12$, $y = 5$, $r = 13$
4. $x = 21$, $y = 20$, $r = 29$
5. $x = 2$, $y = 3$, $r = \sqrt{13}$
6. $x = 5$, $y = \sqrt{11}$, $r = 6$
7. $x = \sqrt{11}$, $y = \sqrt{38}$, $r = 7$
8. $x = \sqrt{13}$, $y = 2\sqrt{3}$, $r = 5$

For an angle in standard position that satisfies the conditions in each of Probs. 9 to 16, find the values of the trigonometric functions of the angle. Use $x^2 + y^2 = r^2$.

9. $(3, -4)$ is on the terminal side
10. $(-8, 15)$ is on the terminal side
11. $(6, 8)$ is on the terminal side
12. $(-24, -7)$ is on the terminal side
13. $(3, y)$ is 5 units out on the terminal side, $y < 0$
14. $(x, -15)$ is 17 units out on the terminal side, $x > 0$
15. $(7, y)$, $y > 0$, is 25 units out on the terminal side
16. $(x, -15)$, $x < 0$, is 17 units out on the terminal side

For an angle in standard position that satisfies the conditions in each of Probs. 17 to 28, find the other function values of the angle.

17. $\sin \theta = 4/5$, θ in the first quadrant
18. $\cos \theta = 5/13$, θ in the fourth quadrant
19. $\tan \theta = 8/15$, θ in the third quadrant
20. $\csc \theta = 25/7$, θ in the second quadrant
21. $\cot \theta = -5/12$, θ in the fourth quadrant

22. sec $\theta = -13/12$, θ in the second quadrant
23. cos $\theta = -3/5$, θ in the third quadrant
24. sin $\theta = -8/17$, θ in the fourth quadrant
25. sec $\theta = 1.5$, θ in the fourth quadrant
26. tan $\theta = 1.5$, θ in the third quadrant
27. sin $\theta = 0.7$, θ in the second quadrant
28. cos $\theta = -0.3$, θ in the third quadrant

There are two positive angles less than 2π or $360°$ in standard position that satisfy the condition in each of Probs. 29 to 32. Find all six function values for each of the two angles.

29. sin $\theta = 0.96 = 24/25$
30. cot $\theta = -1.875 = -15/8$
31. sec $\theta = -2.6 = -13/5$ 32. tan $\theta = 0.75 = 3/4$
33. Find the value of sin θ if θ is in quadrant I and the terminal side of θ lies on the line whose equation is $y = 20x/21$.
34. Find the value of cot α if α is in quadrant II and the terminal side of α lies on the line whose equation is $y = -5x/12$.
35. Find the value of sec β if β is in quadrant III and the terminal side of β lies on the line whose equation is $y = 6x/7$.
36. Find the value of cos ϕ if ϕ is in quadrant IV and the terminal side of ϕ lies on the line whose equation is $y = -2x/25$.
37. Find the value of tan θ if θ is in quadrant III and the terminal side of θ is parallel to the line $7y = 24x + 13$.
38. Find the value of sin β if β is in quadrant I and the terminal side of β is parallel to the line $9y = 12x - 7$.
39. Find the value of csc ϕ if ϕ is in quadrant IV and the terminal side of ϕ is parallel to the line $12y + 5x = 13$.
40. Find the value of sec α if α is in quadrant II and the terminal side of α is parallel to the line $24y + 10x = 13$.
41. Find csc θ if sin $\theta = 3/8$.
42. Find tan β if cot $\beta = -7/11$.
43. Find cos θ if sec $\theta = -19/14$.
44. Find sec α if cos $\alpha = 18/45$.

6.3 Values of the Trigonometric Functions

In this section we begin by working with the acute angles of a right triangle. Then we express functions of general angles in terms of functions of acute angles, and also as functions of an angle between 0 and $\pi/4$ radian, or $0°$ and $45°$. Next, we find the values of the functions of integral multiples of $\pi/3$ and $\pi/4$, or $30°$ and $45°$. Finally, we will use calculators and tables to find function values for any angle.

Functions of Acute Angles

In Fig. 6.14, we draw a right triangle with one of its acute angles in standard position. The x coordinate of the endpoint on the terminal side of the angle is the length of the **side adjacent** to the angle, and the y coordinate of the point is the length of the **side opposite** the angle. The longest side of the right triangle is the hypotenuse. If we make these substitutions in the definitions of the six trigonometric functions, we find that **for an acute angle of a triangle**

An acute angle of a triangle

$$\sin \theta = \frac{\text{opposite side}}{\text{hypotenuse}} = \frac{\text{opp}}{\text{hyp}}$$

$$\cos \theta = \frac{\text{adjacent side}}{\text{hypotenuse}} = \frac{\text{adj}}{\text{hyp}}$$

(6.5)

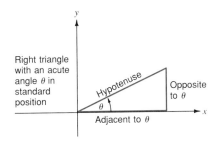

FIGURE 6.14

$$\tan \theta = \frac{\text{opposite side}}{\text{adjacent side}} = \frac{\text{opp}}{\text{adj}}$$

$$\cot \theta = \frac{\text{adjacent side}}{\text{opposite side}} = \frac{\text{adj}}{\text{opp}}$$

$$\sec \theta = \frac{\text{hypotenuse}}{\text{adjacent side}} = \frac{\text{hyp}}{\text{adj}}$$

$$\csc \theta = \frac{\text{hypotenuse}}{\text{opposite side}} = \frac{\text{hyp}}{\text{opp}}$$

(6.5)

NOTE   Since angles and ratios of the sides of a triangle are not dependent on the position of the figure, it follows that these definitions can be used without having the acute angle in standard position, and even without the use of a coordinate system.

EXAMPLE 1   Find the function values of the smallest angle θ of the right triangle with sides 8, 15, and 17.

Solution   The Pythagorean theorem shows that the given numbers are indeed the sides of a right triangle. Now in any triangle

The smallest angle is opposite the smallest side

and so opp = 8, adj = 15, and hyp = 17. Applying the definitions above to this triangle, we have

$$\sin \theta = \frac{8}{17} \qquad \cos \theta = \frac{15}{17} \qquad \tan \theta = \frac{8}{15}$$

$$\csc \theta = \frac{17}{8} \qquad \sec \theta = \frac{17}{15} \qquad \cot \theta = \frac{15}{8}$$

The Cofunction Theorem

The two acute angles of a right triangle are complements since their sum is 90° or $\pi/2$. Figure 6.15 shows a right triangle with side a opposite angle A, side b opposite angle B, and the hypotenuse c opposite the right angle C. From the figure we also see that side a is adjacent to angle B, and side b is adjacent to angle A. By the definition above of the functions of an acute angle of a right triangle, we have

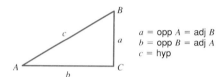

FIGURE 6.15

$$a = \text{opp } A = \text{adj } B$$
$$b = \text{opp } B = \text{adj } A$$
$$c = \text{hyp}$$

$$\sin A = \frac{a}{c} = \cos B$$

$$\cos A = \frac{b}{c} = \sin B$$

$$\tan A = \frac{a}{b} = \cot B$$

$$\cot A = \frac{b}{a} = \tan B$$

$$\sec A = \frac{c}{b} = \csc B$$

$$\csc A = \frac{c}{a} = \sec B$$

Two functions are called **cofunctions** if their names differ only in that one has *co* as part of its name, and the other does not. Now recalling that A and B are complementary angles, and noting that the two functions in each of the six equations above are cofunctions, we have established the cofunction theorem.

Cofunction Theorem   Any trigonometric function of an acute angle is equal to the corresponding cofunction of the complementary angle.

In Examples 2 and 3 we work with trigonometric functions without actually finding their values. At the end of this section, we will see how to find the function values.

▶ **EXAMPLE 2**   Use the cofunction theorem to rewrite the given function values.

Solution

$$\sec \frac{\pi}{3} = \csc \frac{\pi}{6} \qquad \sin 37° = \cos 53°$$

$$\sin \frac{\pi}{8} = \cos \frac{3\pi}{8} \qquad \cot 81° = \tan 9°$$

$$\tan \frac{\pi}{4} = \cot \frac{\pi}{4} \qquad \csc 22° = \sec 68°$$

◀

▶ **EXAMPLE 3**   Solve $\tan(A + 58°) = \cot(3A + 12°)$ for A if each angle in parentheses is acute.

Solution   Since the functions above are cofunctions, and the angles are acute, then the angles are complementary. Therefore

$$A + 58° + 3A + 12° = 90°$$
$$4A = 90° - 70° = 20° \qquad \text{and} \qquad A = 5°$$ ◢

We have just discussed cofunctions, and in Sec. 6.2 we discussed functions which are reciprocals. This gives two different ways of pairing functions, and these are summarized below:

Reciprocals	Cofunctions
$\sin \theta$ and $\csc \theta$	$\sin \theta$ and $\cos \theta$
$\cos \theta$ and $\sec \theta$	$\sec \theta$ and $\csc \theta$
$\tan \theta$ and $\cot \theta$	$\tan \theta$ and $\cot \theta$

Functions of $\pi/6$ or 30°, $\pi/4$ or 45°, and $\pi/3$ or 60°

We shall discuss function values obtained from calculators and from tables later in this section. These values will usually be **decimal approximations** since $\sin \theta$, for instance, is irrational for most values of θ. Here we shall find the exact values of all six functions of $\pi/6$ radians or 30°, $\pi/4$ radians or 45°, and $\pi/3$ radians or 60°.

In Fig. 6.16, we have an equilateral triangle with each side of length 2. The second triangle in the figure is half of the first one, formed by drawing a perpendicular line from one vertex to the opposite side, resulting in a triangle with angles 30°, 60°, and 90° and sides 1, h, and 2. The height h satisfies $1^2 + h^2 = 2^2$, and so $h = \sqrt{3}$. Thus the sides are 1, $\sqrt{3}$, and 2, and using the definition of functions of an acute angle for the 30° angle in the figure, we get

30° or $\pi/6$ radians

$$\sin 30° = \frac{1}{2} \qquad \cos 30° = \frac{\sqrt{3}}{2} \qquad \tan 30° = \frac{1}{\sqrt{3}} = \frac{\sqrt{3}}{3}$$

$$\csc 30° = 2 \qquad \sec 30° = \frac{2}{\sqrt{3}} = \frac{2\sqrt{3}}{3} \qquad \cot 30° = \sqrt{3}$$

The values of the trigonometric functions of $\pi/3$ or 60° can be found from the definitions and Fig. 6.16, or they can be found from the values of the functions of $\pi/6$ or 30° and the cofunction theorem. In either case we find that

60° or $\pi/3$ radians

$$\sin 60° = \frac{\sqrt{3}}{2} \qquad \cos 60° = \frac{1}{2} \qquad \tan 60° = \sqrt{3}$$

$$\csc 60° = \frac{2}{\sqrt{3}} = \frac{2\sqrt{3}}{3} \qquad \sec 60° = 2 \qquad \cot 60° = \frac{1}{\sqrt{3}} = \frac{\sqrt{3}}{3}$$

FIGURE 6.16

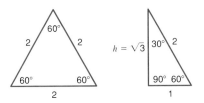

▶ **EXAMPLE 4** Verify that $\tan 60° = \dfrac{\sin 60°}{\cos 60°}$ and $\tan 30° = \dfrac{\sin 60°}{1 + \cos 60°}$.

Solution

$$\frac{\sin 60°}{\cos 60°} = \frac{\sqrt{3}/2}{\tfrac{1}{2}} = \sqrt{3} = \tan 60°$$

and

$$\frac{\sin 60°}{1 + \cos 60°} = \frac{\sqrt{3}/2}{1 + \tfrac{1}{2}} = \frac{\sqrt{3}/2}{\tfrac{3}{2}} = \frac{\sqrt{3}}{3} = \tan 30° \qquad ◀$$

Our next task will be finding the six function values of $\pi/4$ or $45°$, and it will be done by the definition and Fig. 6.17. A $45°$-$45°$-$90°$ triangle is an isosceles right triangle, and consequently two of its sides are equal. If we take each of them to be 1, and use the Pythagorean theorem, we find that the hypotenuse is $\sqrt{1^2 + 1^2} = \sqrt{2}$. Now applying the definition to either one of the $45°$ angles gives

π/4 radians or 45°

$$\sin 45° = \cos 45° = \frac{1}{\sqrt{2}} = \frac{\sqrt{2}}{2}$$
$$\tan 45° = \cot 45° = 1$$
$$\sec 45° = \csc 45° = \sqrt{2}$$

For **quadrantal angles,** either x or y is zero. If $\theta = 0°$ or 0 radians, we may take $x = r$ and $y = 0$, giving

$$\sin 0° = \frac{0}{r} = 0 \qquad\qquad \csc 0° \text{ is not defined}$$

$$\cos 0° = \frac{x}{r} = \frac{r}{r} = 1 \qquad \sec 0° = \frac{r}{x} = \frac{r}{r} = 1$$

$$\tan 0° = \frac{0}{r} = 0 \qquad\qquad \cot 0° \text{ is not defined}$$

Similarly, for instance, if $\theta = 270°$ or $3\pi/2$ radians, then $x = 0$ and $y = -r$, and hence

$$\sin 270° = \frac{-r}{r} = -1 \qquad \csc 270° = \frac{r}{-r} = -1$$

$$\cos 270° = \frac{0}{r} = 0 \qquad\qquad \sec 270° \text{ is not defined}$$

$$\tan 270° \text{ is not defined} \qquad \cot 270° = \frac{0}{-r} = 0$$

Other quadrantal angles can be handled in the same fashion.

The Reference Angle Theorem

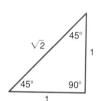

FIGURE 6.17

Suppose now that θ is in standard position, but is not a quadrantal angle. The reference angle of θ is an acute angle which can be used to find the function values of θ.

> The **reference angle** of θ is the (positive) acute angle θ' between the x axis and the terminal side of the given angle θ.

The following chart gives reference angles for each quadrant:

If θ is in quadrant	I	II	III	IV
Then θ' in radians is	θ	$\pi - \theta$	$\theta - \pi$	$2\pi - \theta$
And θ' in degrees is	θ	$180° - \theta$	$\theta - 180°$	$360° - \theta$

EXAMPLE 5 Find the reference angles for the following angles. See Fig. 6.18.

Solution

(a) In radians, if $\theta = \dfrac{2\pi}{3}$, then $\theta' = \pi - \dfrac{2\pi}{3} = \dfrac{\pi}{3}$

In degrees, if $\theta = 120°$, then $\theta' = 180° - 120° = 60°$

(b) In radians, if $\theta = \dfrac{5\pi}{4}$, then $\theta' = \dfrac{5\pi}{4} - \pi = \dfrac{\pi}{4}$

In degrees, if $\theta = 225°$, then $\theta' = 225° - 180° = 45°$

(c) In radians, if $\theta = 5.60$, then $\theta' = 2\pi - 5.60 \approx 0.68$

In degrees, if $\theta = 5.6\left(\dfrac{180}{\pi}\right)° \approx 321°$, then $\theta' \approx 39°$

We shall now show how to express a trigonometric function of an angle θ in terms of the same function of the reference angle θ'. Each part of Fig. 6.19 consists of an angle θ in standard position, the reference angle θ', and the right triangles formed by drawing a perpendicular from the terminal side of the angle to the x axis. Each point P on the terminal side of θ is chosen to be the same distance r from the origin.

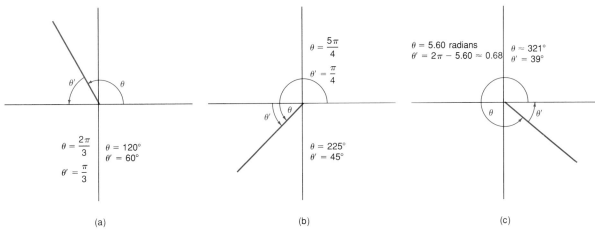

(a)   (b)   (c)

FIGURE 6.18

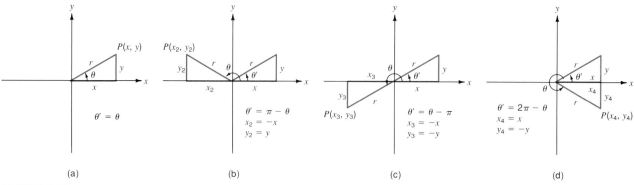

(a)   (b)   (c)   (d)

FIGURE 6.19

Look at Fig. 6.19(b), for instance. The two right triangles are congruent since they each have an acute angle θ', and each hypotenuse was chosen to have length r. It follows that $x_2 = -x$, and $y_2 = y$. Now the function values of θ are defined to be

$$\sin \theta = \frac{y_2}{r} \qquad \cos \theta = \frac{x_2}{r} \qquad \tan \theta = \frac{y_2}{x_2}$$

the other three being the reciprocals of these. Moreover the corresponding function values of θ' are

$$\sin \theta' = \frac{y}{r} \qquad \cos \theta' = \frac{-x}{r} \qquad \tan \theta' = \frac{y}{-x}$$

If we now compare these function values of θ and θ', and use $x_2 = -x$, and $y_2 = y$, we see that they are the same except for a change in sign in some of them. A similar approach may be used in quadrants III and IV. This proves the reference angle theorem below.

Reference Angle Theorem

The trigonometric function value of any angle θ is that same function value of the reference angle θ', except possibly for the sign. The sign is determined by the quadrant in which the angle θ lies. Either radians or degrees may be used.

The **signs of the trigonometric functions** are determined by the quadrant in which the angle lies. Remember that r **is always positive.** For instance, since $\cos \theta = x/r$, then $\cos \theta$ is positive when x is positive—namely, in quadrants I and IV.

Positive function values

Quadrant I:	all six are positive
Quadrant II:	$y > 0$, $\sin \theta = y/r > 0$, $\csc \theta = r/y > 0$
Quadrant III:	$x < 0$, $y < 0$, $\tan \theta = y/x > 0$, $\cot \theta = x/y > 0$
Quadrant IV:	$x > 0$, $\cos \theta = x/r > 0$, $\sec \theta = r/x > 0$

It may help to remember that sine and second both start with s, and tangent and third with t. However, a firm grasp of the geometry and definitions involved will be invaluable.

▶ EXAMPLE 6   Write $f(\theta)$ as $\pm f(\theta')$ using the reference angle θ' and the reference angle theorem.

Solution   (a) $\sin 154° = \sin 26°$ since $26° = \theta'$ and θ is in quadrant II
(b) $\cos 147° = -\cos 33°$ since $33° = \theta'$ and θ is in quadrant II
(c) $\tan 246° = \tan 66°$ since $66° = \theta'$ and θ is in quadrant III
(d) $\sec 246° = -\sec 66°$ since $66° = \theta'$ and θ is in quadrant III
(e) $\cot 5\pi/6 = -\cot \pi/6$ since $\pi/6 = \theta'$ and θ is in quadrant II
(f) $\csc 7\pi/4 = -\csc \pi/4$ since $\pi/4 = \theta'$ and θ is in quadrant IV ◀

▶ EXAMPLE 7   Find the following function values using the reference angle theorem.

Solution   (a)
$$\tan \frac{3\pi}{4} = -\tan \frac{\pi}{4} = -1$$

(b)
$$\sec \frac{11\pi}{6} = \sec \frac{\pi}{6} = \frac{2}{\sqrt{3}} = \frac{2\sqrt{3}}{3}$$

(c)
$$\cos \frac{2\pi}{3} = -\cos \frac{\pi}{3} = -\frac{1}{2}$$

(d)
$$\sin 240° = -\sin 60° = \frac{-\sqrt{3}}{2}$$

(e)
$$\cos 315° = \cos 45° = \frac{\sqrt{2}}{2}$$
◀

The reference angle theorem, which deals with functions of an *angle and its reference angle,* must not be confused with the cofunction theorem, which deals with the functions of an *angle and its complement.* They can be stated symbolically as

$$f(\theta) = \pm f(\theta') \qquad \text{reference angle theorem}$$
and
$$f(\theta) = \text{cof}(90° - \theta) \qquad \text{cofunction theorem}$$

These two theorems can be used to express any trigonometric function of any angle in terms of that function or its cofunction of an acute angle from $0°$ to $45°$, or 0 to $\pi/4$. This is what allows the compact format of the **trigonometric tables** in the appendix, which we will use at the end of this section.

▶ EXAMPLE 8   Write $\tan 308°$, $\cos 308°$, and $\sin 221°$ in terms of angles between $0°$ and $45°$.

Solution   By the reference angle theorem, we have

$$\tan 308° = -\tan 52°$$

since the reference angle of $308°$ is $52°$, and the tangent of a fourth quadrant angle is negative. Now by the cofunction theorem

$$\tan 52° = \cot 38° \qquad \text{hence} \qquad \tan 308° = -\cot 38°$$

Similarly we see that

$$\cos 308° = +\cos 52° = \sin 38°$$
$$\sin 221° = -\sin 41°$$
◀

Variation of Trigonometric Function Values

We shall now investigate the variation of each of the trigonometric function values as the angle increases through the first, second, third, and fourth quadrants. In constructing the following table, we assume that θ is an angle in standard position, and $P(x, y)$ is a point on the terminal side of θ, a distance of r units from the origin $(0, 0)$.

θ, radians	θ, deg	x	y	$\sin \theta = y/r$	$\cos \theta = x/r$	$\tan \theta = y/x$
0 to $\pi/2$	0° to 90°	r to 0	0 to r	0 to 1	1 to 0	0 to ∞
$\pi/2$ to π	90° to 180°	0 to $-r$	r to 0	1 to 0	0 to -1	$-\infty$ to 0
π to $3\pi/2$	180° to 270°	$-r$ to 0	0 to $-r$	0 to -1	-1 to 0	0 to ∞
$3\pi/2$ to 2π	270° to 360°	0 to r	$-r$ to 0	-1 to 0	0 to 1	$-\infty$ to 0

An examination of the table above shows that

$$-1 \leq \sin \theta \leq 1 \qquad \text{and} \qquad -1 \leq \cos \theta \leq 1$$

while the values of tan θ include all real numbers. Since the other three function values are the reciprocals of the three considered above, it follows that cot θ may be any real number, while

$$|\sec \theta| \geq 1 \qquad \text{and} \qquad |\csc \theta| \geq 1$$

Thus for instance, sin θ is never $\frac{5}{3}$, sec θ is never $\frac{2}{29}$, but tan θ may have either value.

The values of sin θ and cos θ are defined for all values of θ. However since tan $\theta = y/x$, then tan θ is not defined when $x = 0$, which occurs when $\theta = \pi/2$ or $\theta = 90°$, for instance. Similar reasoning shows that

tan θ and sec θ are not defined if θ is

$$\frac{\pi}{2} \pm k\pi \qquad \text{or} \qquad 90° \pm k \cdot 180° \qquad \text{\small k a positive integer}$$

cot θ and csc θ are not defined if θ is

$$k\pi \qquad \text{or} \qquad k \cdot 180° \qquad \text{\small k a positive integer.}$$

Use of Tables and Calculators

So far we have actually found the values of only those angles that are multiples of 30° and 45°. It is beyond the scope of this book to show how to calculate function values in general, but there are two sources we can use to get them, **calculators** and **tables.** Since they were introduced in the 1970s, most of us own and use calculators for a variety of purposes, and scientific calculators include the values of trigonometric functions. Calculators are not all alike, so we cannot give detailed suggestions for carrying out calculations.

To begin, we must be certain that the calculator is in the proper mode, i.e., set for either degrees or radians. Most calculators use both radians and degrees in decimal form, but some models can also use the degree, minute, second form. The display often shows 8 or more digits, whether or not such accuracy is warranted. Only sin θ, cos θ, and tan θ are normally given directly. For the other three, use the $1/x$ key along with the reciprocal identities in the form

$$\csc \theta = \frac{1}{\sin \theta} \qquad \sec \theta = \frac{1}{\cos \theta} \qquad \cot \theta = \frac{1}{\tan \theta}$$

Reference angles are not necessary if a calculator is used. Sometimes an ERROR message occurs, indicating any number of things including an angle out of the calculator's capability, or perhaps an undefined function value.

▶ **EXAMPLE 9**   Find the values

(a) cos 58.3°   (b) tan 76°54′32″   (c) sin 210°

Solution   Be sure the calculator is in the degree mode.

(a) Since 58.3° is in decimal form already, put the angle on the display and depress the cos key, the order of these two things depending on the type of calculator. Your result should be 0.52547165 with a possibly different last digit due to roundoff or your calculator chip.

(b) Your calculator might be able to handle the angle in this form directly. If not, change to decimal form.

$$\tan 76°54′32″ = \tan(76 + 54/60 + 32/3600)°$$
$$= \tan 76.908889 = 4.3002660$$

(c) sin 210° = −0.5, in keeping with the exact result since the reference angle of 210° is 30°.   ◣
      The *exact* value of sin 60° is $\sqrt{3}/2$. However, a calculator gives a good decimal approximation, say 0.86602540.

▶ **EXAMPLE 10**   Find the values

(a) tan 1.28   (b) sin($\pi/5$)   (c) cos 2.3456

Solution   Be sure that your calculator is in the radian mode.

(a) Since 1.28 is already in decimal form, put it on the display, use the tan key, and read the value 3.34134998.

(b) Putting $\pi/5$ in decimal form gives

$$\sin(\pi/5) = \sin 0.62831853 = 0.58778525$$

(c) $\cos 2.3456 = -0.69957580$ ◣

▶ **EXAMPLE 11**   Find (a) sec 4.96°; (b) cot 4.96.

Solution   (a) The angle is in degrees. Use the $1/x$ key after first finding cos 4.96°, giving

$$\sec 4.96° = \frac{1}{\cos 4.96°} = \frac{1}{0.99625530} = 1.00375877$$

(b) The angle is in radians. First find tan 4.96, then use the $1/x$ key to write

$$\cot 4.96 = \frac{1}{\tan 4.96} = \frac{1}{-3.95571612} = -0.25279873 \quad \blacktriangleleft$$

There are **tables** that give decimal approximations to the trigonometric function values, and such a table is included in the appendix (Table A.5). The angles are listed every **tenth of a degree,** which means every 6 minutes, and also given are the corresponding number of radians. Doing it this way has several advantages:

(i) It makes it easy to compare answers with calculator values, which are usually given as decimals.
(ii) There are more entries than if angles were listed every 10′.
(iii) Interpolation is more accurate since there are more entries. Note that interpolation may be helpful with other tables one may encounter whose values may not be on a calculator.
(iv) Having radians and degrees together helps to reinforce their relationship with each other.

Table A.5 of trigonometric values is constructed with the angles from 0° to 45°, or 0 to $\pi/4 \approx 0.7854$ radian, on the left of the page, and the complements of these angles on the right. The function names are at the top of the page for the angles on the left, and the cofunction of each function at the top is listed below it at the bottom of the page. This arrangement is possible because of the cofunction theorem. Thus

$$\sin 35.6° = \cos 54.4°$$

and they are the same entry in the table. One of them is across from 35.6° on the left and under sin, whereas the other is across from 54.4° on the right and above cos. Similarly, each entry in Table A.5 is in fact two function values:

1. A function of an angle
2. The cofunction of the complementary angle

Remember, when using the trigonometric table, the function names to be used with

Left and top

Angles on the left are at the top of the page

and function names to be used with

Right and bottom

Angles on the right are at the bottom of the page

EXAMPLE 12   Use Table A.5 in the appendix to find (a) tan 38.3° and (b) cos 54.7°.

Solution   (a) Since 38.3° is on the left of the page in the table, look across from 38.3° and under tan. The value of tan 38.3° is 0.7898. Notice that tan 38.3° = tan 38°18′ = tan 0.6685, so either of the last two could have been found in the same way.

(b) Since 54.7° is on the right of the page in the table, look across from 54.7° and above cos. The value of cos 54.7° is 0.5779. In a similar way we would find the same value for cos 54°42′ or cos 0.9547.

Finding the angle

To **find the angle** if one of its function values is given, either tables or a calculator can be used. Doing this with a calculator usually requires either one or two keys. Some calculators have one key called *arcsin* or *invsin,* for instance. For others, you must use a key usually called *INV* along with the regular function key. Names other than INV are sometimes used. We will treat inverse trigonometric functions in detail in Sec. 7.6.

EXAMPLE 13 Use a calculator to find θ if sin $\theta = 0.2487$ and θ is between 0° and 360°, or between 0 and 2π.

Solution There are angles in quadrants I and II with sin $\theta = 0.2487$, but the calculator will only give the one in quadrant I. We put 0.2487 on the display, use the appropriate inverse key, and find that **in degrees** the angle is $\theta = 14.400598°$, or 14.4° to the nearest tenth of a degree. Using 14.4° as the reference angle, the quadrant II angle is $180° - 14.4° = 165.6°$. In **radians** the angle is $\theta = 0.2513378$, and the angle in quadrant II is $\pi - 0.2513378 \approx 2.8902548$.

Finding angles by table

If a function of an angle is given, the angle can also be found by tables. If the function value is in the table, we look on the left for the angle if the function name is on the top of the page, and on the right if the function name is on the bottom of the page. If the function value is not in the table, we use the entry that is at least as near the desired number as any other entry.

EXAMPLE 14 If tan $A = 0.3899$, find A from Table A.5 where $0° < A < 360°$ or $0 < A < 2\pi$.

Solution We look in Table A.5 above and below tan, and find 0.3899 below tan and across from 21.3°, or 0.3718, on the left. Therefore, $A = 21.3°$, or 0.3718. There is a third-quadrant angle also, and it is $180° + 21.3° = 201.3°$, or $\pi + 0.3718 \approx 3.1416 + 0.3718 = 3.5134$.

EXAMPLE 15 Find A from Table A.5 if sin $A = 0.6789$ and $0° < A < 360°$ or $0 < A < 2\pi$.

Solution We look above and below sin for .6789 and discover it is not there. The nearest entry is 0.6794, and the corresponding angle is 42.8°, or 0.7470. Hence $A = 42.8°$, or 0.7470 is in the first quadrant, and $180° - 42.8° = 137.2°$, or $\pi - 0.7470 \approx 2.3946$, is in the second quadrant.

We shall now give one more example, done with both a calculator and by Table A.5.

EXAMPLE 16 Find the acute angle B if sec $B = 1.2345$.

Solution   *By calculator* we have

$$\sec B = 1.2345 \qquad \text{given}$$

$$\cos B = \frac{1}{1.2345} = 0.8100445 \qquad \text{reciprocal values}$$

$$B = 35.899715° \text{ or } 0.6265682 \qquad \text{use inverse key}$$

By table, the nearest entry above or below sec is 1.235, which is below sec and opposite 35.9°, or 0.6266, on the left.   ◀

If a value is not in a trigonometric table, we may use interpolation, which is also presented in the appendix. Interpolation is not needed if a calculator is used because we rarely need 8-digit accuracy.

EXERCISE 6.3

Find the function values of the largest acute angle in Probs. 1 to 4 and of the smallest angle in Probs. 5 to 8 if the sides are as given.

1. $a = 8$, $b = 15$, $c = 17$
2. $a = 4$, $b = 3$, $c = 5$
3. $a = 7$, $b = 24$, $c = 25$
4. $a = 7\sqrt{2}$, $b = 7\sqrt{2}$, $c = 14$
5. $a = 3\sqrt{2}$, $b = 3\sqrt{2}$, $c = 6$
6. $a = 24$, $b = 7$, $c = 25$
7. $a = 3$, $b = 4$, $c = 5$
8. $a = 8$, $b = 15$, $c = 17$

Use the cofunction theorem to express each of the following values in terms of another function of another acute angle. Use 1.5708 for $\pi/2$ in Probs. 13 to 16.

9. $\sin 29°$
10. $\cos 47°$
11. $\tan 87°$
12. $\cot 36°$
13. $\sec 0.9774$
14. $\csc 1.0297$
15. $\cos 0.2094$
16. $\tan 1.2566$

Use the reference angle theorem to express each of the following values in terms of a function of an acute angle.

17. $\cos 147°$
18. $\tan 327°$
19. $\sec 169°$
20. $\cos 348°$

Use the cofunction theorem and the reference angle theorem to express each of the following in terms of a function of a positive angle less than 45°.

21. $\tan 127°$
22. $\sec 306°$
23. $\cos 253°$
24. $\sin 432°$

Use the function values of multiples of 30° and 45°, or $\pi/6$ and $\pi/4$, to verify each of the following statements.

25. $\sin^2 120° + \cos^2 240° = 1$
26. $1 + \tan^2 240° = \sec^2 300°$
27. $1 + \cot^2 300° = \csc^2 120°$
28. $\sec^2 210° - \tan^2 330° = 1$
29. $\sin (4\pi/3) = -2 \sin (2\pi/3) \sin (7\pi/6)$
30. $\sec (5\pi/6) = \csc (2\pi/3) \tan (3\pi/4)$
31. $\cos (\pi/2) + \cot (4\pi/3) = \cot (\pi/3)$
32. $\cot (5\pi/4) = \cot (\pi/2) - \csc (3\pi/2)$

In Probs. 33 to 36, tell what quadrant θ is in.

33. $\sin \theta > 0$ and $\tan \theta < 0$
34. $\cot \theta > 0$ and $\sec \theta < 0$
35. $\cos \theta > 0$ and $\csc \theta < 0$
36. $\sin \theta > 0$ and $\cos \theta < 0$

Problems 37 to 48 are true or false.

37. $\sin 30° + \sin 90° = \sin 120°$
38. $2 \cos 45° = \cos 90°$
39. $\sin 3\pi/4 + \sin 7\pi/4 = \cot \pi/2$
40. $\cos 5(\pi/2) = 5 \cos \pi/2$
41. $\sin 37° = \cos 53°$
42. $\sec 41° = \csc 49°$
43. $\tan 64° = \cot 36°$
44. $\sin 77° = \cos 13°$
45. $\sec A = 0.5768$ has a solution
46. $\sin A = -0.6262$ has a solution
47. $\tan B = -1234$ has a solution
48. $\csc C = -\frac{64}{65}$ has a solution

Solve the equations in Probs. 49 to 52 under the assumption that all angles in parentheses are acute.

49. $\tan(4A + 10°) = \cot(2A + 8°)$
50. $\sin(3A + 8°) = \cos(2A + 7°)$
51. $\csc(3A + 8°) = \sec A$
52. $\cos(A + 21°) = \sin(2A + 12°)$

Find the value in each of Probs. 53 to 60.

53. $\tan 1.3648 = \tan 78.2°$
54. $\cot 1.2758 = \cot 73.1°$
55. $\sin 0.4102 = \sin 23.5°$
56. $\cos 0.6772 = \cos 38.8°$
57. $\cos 0.8692 = \cos 49.8°$
58. $\sin 1.3334 = \sin 76.4°$
59. $\tan 1.1449 = \tan 65.6°$
60. $\cot 0.3019 = \cot 17.3°$

Use a calculator or table to find the acute angle in Probs. 61 to 68. Use either radians or degrees.

61. $\sin A = 0.4555$ **62.** $\cos A = 0.9252$
63. $\tan A = 0.5384$ **64.** $\cos A = 0.9907$
65. $\sin A = 0.4879$ **66.** $\sin A = 0.9681$
67. $\tan A = 2.145$ **68.** $\cos A = 0.4726$

Use a calculator or table to find two positive angles in Probs. 69 to 72. Use either radians or degrees.

69. $\sec A = 1.877$ **70.** $\csc A = 2.226$
71. $\cot A = 1.594$ **72.** $\csc A = 1.135$

In Probs. 73 to 76, use the reference angle theorem and a calculator or table to show that each sum is zero, except possibly for roundoff errors.

73. $\sin 27° + \sin 147° + \sin 267°$
74. $\sin 96° + \sin 216° + \sin 336°$
75. $\cos 73° + \cos 163° + \cos 253° + \cos 343°$
76. $\cos 39° + \cos 111° + \cos 183° + \cos 255° + \cos 327°$

In Probs. 77 to 80, verify the inequality below for the given value of θ, where $\boldsymbol{\theta}$ **is in radians.** It is true for $0 < \theta < \pi/2$.

$$\cos \theta < \frac{\sin \theta}{\theta} < 1$$

77. $\theta = 0.0541$ **78.** $\theta = 0.1326$

79. $\theta = 0.1257$ **80.** $\theta = 0.1728$

In Probs. 81 to 84, verify the following inequality if θ is in radians:

$$\sin \theta < \theta < \tan \theta \text{ for } 0 < \theta < \pi/2$$

81. $\theta = 0.1623$ **82.** $\theta = 0.1326$
83. $\theta = 0.0925$ **84.** $\theta = 0.0454$

Verify the statements in Probs. 85 to 88, except possibly for roundoff errors.

85. If $\tan x = \frac{1}{2}$ and $\tan y = \frac{1}{3}$, then $x + y = 45°$ or $\pi/4$.
86. If $\tan x = \frac{2}{3}$ and $\tan y = \frac{1}{5}$, then $x + y = 45°$ or $\pi/4$.
87. If $\tan x = \frac{1}{3}$, $\tan y = \frac{1}{4}$, and $\tan z = \frac{2}{9}$, then $x + y + z = 45°$ or $\pi/4$.
88. If $\tan x = \frac{2}{5}$ and $\tan y = \frac{5}{2}$, then $x + y = 90°$ or $\pi/2$.

Verify the calculations in Probs. 89 to 100.

89. $\tan (\pi/7) \tan (2\pi/7) \tan (3\pi/7) = \sqrt{7}$
90. $\cos^4 (\pi/7) + \cos^4 (2\pi/7) + \cos^4 (3\pi/7) = \frac{13}{16}$
91. $\sec^4 (\pi/7) + \sec^4 (2\pi/7) + \sec^4 (3\pi/7) = 416$
92. $\csc^4 (\pi/7) + \csc^4 (2\pi/7) + \csc^4 (3\pi/7) = 32$
93. $\dfrac{\sin 9°}{\sin 48°} = \dfrac{\sin 12°}{\sin 81°}$
94. $\sin 18° + \cos 18° = \sqrt{2} \cos 27°$
95. $\cos 6° \cos 42° \cos 66° \cos 78° = \frac{1}{16}$
96. $\dfrac{\sin 23° + \sin 46°}{1 + \cos 23° + \cos 46°} = \tan 23°$
97. $\cos (\pi/11) \cos (2\pi/11) \cos (3\pi/11) \cos (4\pi/11) \times \cos (5\pi/11) = \frac{1}{32}$
98. $\cos (\pi/15) \cos (2\pi/15) \cos (3\pi/15) \cos (4\pi/15) \times \cos (5\pi/15) \cos (6\pi/15) \cos (7\pi/15) = \frac{1}{128}$
99. $4 \cos (\pi/10) = 3(\sec \pi/10) + 2(\tan \pi/10)$
100. If $\theta = \pi/19$, then $\dfrac{\sin 23\theta - \sin 3\theta}{\sin 16\theta + \sin 4\theta} = -1$
101. The average value of $\cos x$ on the interval $[\pi/8, 3\pi/8]$ is approximately 0.689. Calculate the value of the average below:

$$\frac{\cos (\pi/6) + \cos (\pi/4) + \cos (\pi/3)}{3}$$

6.4 **Applications to Right Triangles**

In this section we will see how to find all of the sides and angles of a right triangle if appropriate parts are given. This was one of the original purposes of trigonometry, and it is still used every day in a wide variety of situations. A right triangle can be solved if we know the length of one side and two other parts.

Digits in Sides and Accuracy of Angles

We need to know how many digits to use in the length of the sides for specified degrees of accuracy for the angles. Thus we will briefly consider corresponding degrees of accuracy of sides and angles. If $\sin \theta = 0.38$ to 2 digits, then by table or calculator

$$0.375 < \sin \theta \le 0.385 \qquad \text{and} \qquad \text{hence } 22.0° < \theta < 22.6°$$

This does not determine the angle even to within 0.5°. Furthermore, if we know that $\cos \theta = 0.246$ to 3 digits, then

$$0.2455 < \cos \theta \le 0.2465 \qquad \text{and hence} \qquad 75.79° > \theta \ge 75.73°$$

Consequently, we do not know the angle even to the nearest tenth of a degree. A similar study of other functions of other angles will show why we follow the commonly used table of accuracy given below. Even it should be modified for angles near 0° and 90°, or 0 and $\pi/2$ radians.

Significant digits in sides	Angle to the nearest
2	Degree
3	Tenth of a degree
4	Hundredth of a degree

The number of significant digits in a product or quotient should not exceed the least number of significant digits in any of the factors.

Solving Right Triangles

As we saw in Sec. 6.3, the definition of each function value of an acute angle of a right triangle involves an angle and two sides. Consequently, we can find any one of these three if we know the other two, provided that we

NOTE   *Select a function value and an angle such that the two*
known parts and the desired unknown are involved

Recall the definitions of trigonometric functions for any right triangle with side a opposite angle A, side b opposite angle B, and the hypotenuse c opposite the right angle C, as was shown in Fig. 6.15:

$$\sin A = \frac{\text{side opposite } A}{\text{hypotenuse}} = \frac{a}{c} = \cos B$$

$$\cos A = \frac{\text{side adjacent to } A}{\text{hypotenuse}} = \frac{b}{c} = \sin B$$

$$\tan A = \frac{\text{side opposite to } A}{\text{side adjacent to } A} = \frac{a}{b} \qquad \text{and} \qquad \tan B = \frac{b}{a}$$

Use the given information whenever possible to avoid building up roundoff errors. The sum of the angles in any triangle is $180°$ or π, and since $C = 90°$ or $\pi/2$ in a right triangle, we have

Angles

$$A + B = 90° \qquad \text{or} \qquad A + B = \frac{\pi}{2}$$

The Pythagorean theorem holds in any right triangle, and so

Sides

$$a^2 + b^2 = c^2$$

These two basic relationships for right triangles will be used to help find unknown parts, and also to check solutions.

▶ **EXAMPLE 1** Solve the right triangle with $a = 7$ and $B = 60°$.

Solution Since we know one of the acute angles, the other one is

$$A = 90° - B = 90° - 60° = 30° \qquad \text{solving for } A$$

We will use $\cos B = a/c$, since it has the two given parts:

$$\cos 60° = \frac{7}{c}$$

$$c = \frac{7}{\cos 60°} = \frac{7}{\frac{1}{2}} = 14 \qquad \text{solving for } c$$

$$\tan 60° = \frac{b}{7} \qquad \text{given information}$$

$$b = 7 \tan 60° = 7\sqrt{3} \qquad \text{solving for } B \qquad ◀$$

In Example 2, we will solve a triangle given an acute angle and an adjacent side.

▶ **EXAMPLE 2** Solve the right triangle in which $A = 27.5°$ and $b = 27.3$.

Solution We shall begin by drawing a figure reasonably near to scale, as in Fig. 6.20. We can find B readily since $B = 90° - 27.5° = 62.5°$. If we use $\tan A = a/b$, we have

$$\tan 27.5° = \frac{a}{27.3} \qquad \text{given information}$$

$$a = 27.3 \tan 27.5° \qquad \text{solving for } a$$

$$= 27.3 \, (0.5206) \qquad \text{by calculator or Table A.5}$$

$$= 14.2 \qquad \text{to 3 digits}$$

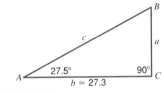

FIGURE 6.20

We shall now find c using $\cos A = a/c$:

$$\cos 27.5° = \frac{27.3}{c} \qquad \text{given information}$$

$$c = \frac{27.3}{\cos 27.5°} \qquad \text{solving for } c$$

$$= \frac{27.3}{0.8870} \qquad \text{by calculator or Table A.5}$$

$$= 30.8 \qquad \text{to 3 digits}$$

Check

$$\sqrt{a^2 + b^2} = \sqrt{14.2^2 + 27.3^2} = \sqrt{201.64 + 745.29}$$
$$= \sqrt{946.93} \approx 30.77 \approx 30.8 = c$$

In Example 3, we will solve a triangle where the given information is a side and the hypotenuse.

EXAMPLE 3   Solve the right triangle in which $a = 27.4$ and $c = 38.4$.

Solution   A sketch is shown in Fig. 6.21. To find A, we use $\sin A = a/c$ and have

$$\sin A = \frac{27.4}{38.4}$$

$$= 0.7135 \qquad \text{to 4 digits}$$

Hence to the nearest tenth, using a calculator or Table A.5

$$A = 45.5° \text{ or } 45°30'$$

Consequently, since A and B are complementary:

$$B = 90° - 45.5° = 44.5° \text{ or } 44°30'$$

Finally, using $\tan B = b/a$ gives

$$\tan 44.5° = \frac{b}{27.4}$$

$$b = 27.4 \tan 44.5° \qquad \text{solving for } b$$

$$= 27.4(0.9827) \qquad \text{by calculator or Table A.5}$$

$$= 26.9 \qquad \text{to 3 digits}$$

Another way to find b, which uses the given data, is to use the Pythagorean theorem and a calculator:

$$b^2 = c^2 - a^2 = 38.4^2 - 27.4^2 \approx 1475 - 751 = 724$$
$$b = \sqrt{724} \approx 26.9$$

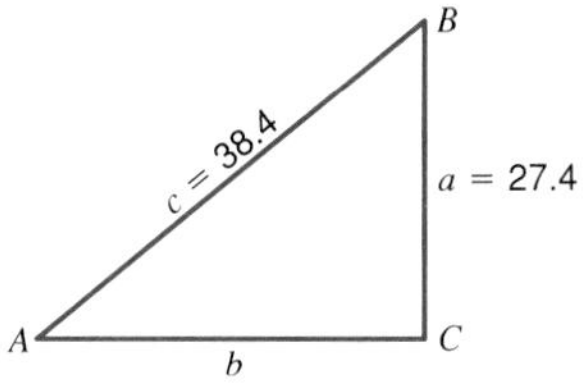

FIGURE 6.21

Line of Sight

The ray from an observer to an object is called the **line of sight.** The angle made by the line of sight and a horizontal line through the observer is called the **angle of depression** or **angle of elevation** of P according to whether the object is below or above the observer. We show an angle of depression in Example 4, Fig. 6.22, and two angles of elevation in Example 5, Fig. 6.23.

EXAMPLE 4   An observer in a balloon finds that the angle of depression from the balloon to a car is $51°18'$. How high is the balloon if the point on the ground directly under it is 237 ft horizontally from the car?

Solution   A sketch of the situation is shown in Fig. 6.22. To find the height h, we solve $\tan 51°18' = h/237$ for h and have

$$h = 237 \tan 51°18' = 237 \tan 51.3° = 237(1.248) \approx 296$$

EXAMPLE 5   A surveying team measures the angle of elevation to the top of a cliff as $18°$. From a point 180 m closer on horizontal ground, the angle of elevation is $33°$. How high is the cliff?

Solution   Figure 6.23 shows the situation with the first measurement taken at A, and the second at B. We let the height of the cliff be h, and the distance from the base of the cliff to B be called x. There is a right angle at the base of the cliff at point C, and point D is at the top of the cliff. From triangles ADC and BCD,

$$\tan 18° = \frac{h}{x + 180} \qquad \text{and} \qquad \tan 33° = \frac{h}{x}$$

These equations give

$$x + 180 = h \cot 18° \qquad \text{and} \qquad x = h \cot 33°$$

Substituting the value of x from the second equation into the first equation shows that

$$h \cot 33° + 180 = h \cot 18°$$
$$180 = h(\cot 18° - \cot 33°)$$
$$h = \frac{180}{\cot 18° - \cot 33°}$$
$$= \frac{180}{3.078 - 1.540} = \frac{180}{1.538} \approx 117$$

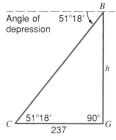

FIGURE 6.22

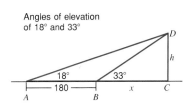

FIGURE 6.23

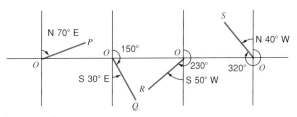

FIGURE 6.24

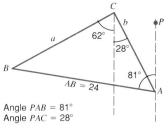

Angle PAB = 81°
Angle PAC = 28°

FIGURE 6.25

Bearing

The bearing or direction of a ray, or the course of flight, in **air navigation,** is expressed as the clockwise angle less than 360° that the ray makes with the *due north direction*. In Fig. 6.24, the directions of OP, OQ, OR, and OS are 70°, 150°, 230°, and 320°, respectively. Each of these directions is measured clockwise from due north.

On the other hand, the direction or bearing of a ray in **marine navigation** and in **surveying** is given by the acute angle that the given ray makes with a due north or due south direction, and whether it is to the east or west of that direction. Thus, if the direction or bearing is 22° east of a due south direction, it is written as S22°E. The directions N70°E, S30°E, S50°W, and N40°W are also shown in Fig. 6.24.

�----- **EXAMPLE 6**   Two freighters at A and B are 24 mi apart. The bearing from a cruise ship to A is S28°E, while the bearing to B is S62°W. How far is the cruise ship from each freighter if the bearing from A to B is N81°W?

Solution   In Fig. 6.25, the cruise ship is at C, and we let $b = AC$ and $a = BC$. The angle BCA is 90° since 62° + 28° = 90°. Draw a vertical line through A, and choose any point P above A. Then angle PAC is 28° by corresponding angles. Since angle PAB is 81°, then angle CAB is 81° − 28° = 53°. Thus the right triangle ABC has C = 90°, $AB = c = $ 24, and A = 53°. Hence

$$\sin 53° = \frac{a}{24} \qquad \text{and} \qquad a = 24 \sin 53° \approx 24(0.7986) \approx 19.2$$

$$\cos 53° = \frac{b}{24} \qquad \text{and} \qquad b = 24 \cos 53° \approx 24(0.6018) \approx 14.4$$

EXERCISE 6.4

Solve the right triangles in Probs. 1 to 8 without using a calculator or a table.

1. B = 30°, c = 12
2. A = 60°, c = 36
3. A = 60°, b = 16
4. A = 30°, a = 20
5. B = 45°, a = 20
6. B = 45°, b = $7\sqrt{2}$
7. b = 17, c = $17\sqrt{2}$
8. a = 48, c = $48\sqrt{2}$

Solve the right triangles with the parts given in Probs. 9 to 28. Obtain each result to the degree of accuracy justified by the given parts.

9. A = 73.7°, b = 73.4
10. A = 68.8°, b = 42.7
11. B = 37.5°, a = 644
12. B = 25.3°, a = 5.68
13. A = 41.2°, c = 921
14. A = 32.5°, c = 8.13
15. B = 63.7°, c = 98.6
16. B = 58.6°, c = 8.72
17. A = 42.9°, a = 31.3
18. A = 69.6°, a = 4.97
19. B = 76.3°, b = 402
20. B = 28.7°, b = 1.23
21. a = 56.78, b = 67.89
22. a = 0.3726, b = 0.5375
23. a = 3.724, b = 2.637
24. a = 4.523, b = 5.127

25. $b = 7.117$, $c = 9.876$
26. $a = 2.013$, $c = 3.748$
27. $a = 8.976$, $c = 12.34$
28. $b = 9.147$, $c = 13.29$

29. *Tree* How tall is a tree standing on horizontal ground if its shadow is 7.5 m, and the tip of its shadow is 15 m from the top of the tree, measured in a line through the air? (See the figure.)

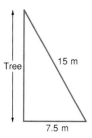

30. *Tree* How tall is a tree if the angle of elevation to its top is 74.5° from a point 39.3 ft from its base?

31. *Civil engineering* A sewer pipe was to be placed under a level lot at an angle of 2.2° with the horizontal. At one point the trench for the pipe is 2.75 ft below the surface. How deep should the trench be at a point 250 ft away measured along the pipe, if it is deeper at this point?

32. *Construction* A brace runs from a lower corner of a rectangular wall to the diagonally opposite upper corner. If the wall is 10.8 by 16.5 ft, find the length of the brace and the angle it makes with the longest side.

33. *Mining* The entrance of a mine is 3242 ft above sea level. The shaft is straight and has an angle of depression of 20.3°. Find the elevation of the lower end if the shaft is 216 ft long.

34. *Landscaping* Find the height of a retaining wall built to level a lot that is 73.2 ft wide measured along the ground and slopes at 2.2° with the horizontal. (See the figure.)

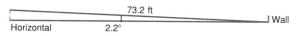

35. *Safety lights* Strings of lights are to reach from the top of a 250-ft pole and make an angle of elevation of 60.6° with the horizontal ground. How far from the pole are they fastened to the ground?

36. *Crane safety* The boom of a crane is 28.6 ft long and the operating manual says that it is not to be lowered so as to make an angle of less than 45.8° with the horizontal. What is the greatest horizontal distance from the crane that can be reached by the boom?

37. *Transportation* A train traveled at 55 mi/h on a straight track that headed N68.8°E from Center Point to Centerville. A car left Center Point as the train did and went 45.8 mi due east and then north to Centerville at 65 mi/h. Which reached Centerville first and by how long?

38. *Surveying* A wall that runs S48.2°W for 135 ft is one side of a triangular lot. What is the area of the lot if the other sides run north-south and east-west? The area is one-half the base times the altitude.

39. *Highways* Mason is due north of Dickson and due west of Kerr. Dickson and Kerr are connected by a straight highway that runs N29.3°E and is 59.8 mi long. How many miles out of her way did Hannah go in going from Dickson to Kerr by way of Mason? (See the figure.)

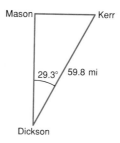

40. *Transportation* A pilot headed due east at an airspeed of 324 mi/h in a south wind. If the ground speed of the plane was 325 mi/h, find the direction of the flight and the velocity of the wind.

41. *Navigation* Larry flew his plane 505 mi at 22.2° in going from A to B. In returning by car, he followed roads due west and due south. How much further did he travel by car than by plane? (See the figure.)

42. *Fire* During a fire in a refinery on Zeitung Street, it was decided that everyone within 800 ft of the plant should be evacuated. Akron Avenue intersects Zeitung Street at right angles 250 ft from the plant. Was it necessary to evacuate a house on Akron Avenue that is 740 ft from the intersection?

43. *Docking* The gangplank of a ship is 28.6 ft long and makes an angle of 10.3° with the horizontal. If the lower end of the gangplank is 3.00 ft from the dock's edge, how far is the ship from the dock?

44. *Navigation* Ramona is flying at an airspeed of 200 mi/h in a west wind blowing at 30.6 mi/h. In what direction must she head in order to fly due south? What is her ground speed?

45. *Geometry* How long is a chord that subtends a central angle of 26.20° in a circle of radius 16.45 ft?

46. *Hiking* Janice walked 510 m N15°E and then S75°E for 630 m. Find the direction and distance from her destination to her starting point. (See the figure.)

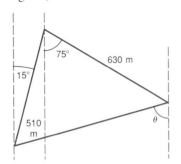

47. *Biking* Two bikers on an east-west highway find that the angles of elevation of a helicopter are 22.52° and 24.70°. If the helicopter is 2500 ft directly above a point on the highway east of both observers, how far apart are they?

48. *Hilltop* At a point on a horizontal line, the angle of elevation of a hilltop is 23.62°. At a point, on the same line, 1225 ft nearer the hill, the angle of elevation of the hilltop is 30.37°. How high is the hill?

49. *Tunnel* A tunnel must be cut through a mountain which sits on level ground. From a point 340 m from the base of the mountain, the angle of elevation to the peak is 34°. From a point 420 m from the opposite side of the base of the mountain, the angle of elevation to the peak is 42°. Assume that a line through these two observation points passes directly under the mountain peak. How wide is the base of the mountain on this line if the peak is 680 m high?

50. *Cliff divers* Two cliffs at Acapulco face each other and have their bases at the same level. The angle of elevation from the top of the lower cliff to the top of the higher cliff is 57°, while it is 70° from the base of the lower cliff to the top of the higher cliff. If the lower cliff is 85 ft high, how high is the higher cliff, and how far apart are their bases?

51. *Satellite dish* A satellite dish is on top of a building which is 38 ft tall. Suppose we go straight down from the dish to level ground, and then out 140 ft to an observer. How tall is the dish if it cuts off an angle of 7° from the observer? (See the figure.)

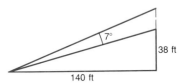

52. *Buildings* A person who is 28 ft up in one building finds that the angle of elevation to the top of a second building is 38°, while the angle of depression to the bottom of the second building is 19°. How far apart are the two buildings, and how tall is the second one?

53. *Baseball* What is the angle of depression of the path of a ball which is released by a pitcher from a height of 7 ft 9 in to a batter whose bat contacts the ball a horizontal distance away of 57 ft 4 in at a height of 3 ft 7 in?

54. *Football* A football field is 100 yards long and $\frac{160}{3}$

yards wide. What is the angle made by the diagonal and the goal line (the shorter side)?

55. *Basketball* What is the angle of elevation from the eyes of a basketball player at the free throw line to the rim 10 ft above the floor if the eyes are 6 ft 5 in above the floor, and it is 15 ft horizontally between the line and the basket?

56. *Track and field* Two sighting positions on the same side of the pole vault bar are each 1.7 m above ground, and they are 2.2 m apart. The angle of elevation to the pole vault bar is 53.8° from the closer position, and it is 42.6° from the further position. How high is the bar above ground?

The right triangles in Probs. 57 to 60 have integral side lengths. Find both of the acute angles in each problem to the nearest tenth of a degree.

Nice triangles
57. $a = 3$, $b = 4$, $c = 5$
58. $a = 5$, $b = 12$, $c = 13$

59. $a = 20$, $b = 21$, $c = 29$
60. $a = 33$, $b = 56$, $c = 65$

61. Show that in any right triangle $c = \dfrac{a}{\sin A} = \dfrac{b}{\sin B}$.

62. Show that in any right triangle $\dfrac{\tan A}{\tan B} = \left(\dfrac{a}{b}\right)^2$.

63. Prove that for any right triangle $a \cos A = b \cos B$.

64. Prove that the area of any right triangle is

$$\tfrac{1}{2}a^2 \tan B = \tfrac{1}{2}b^2 \tan A = \tfrac{1}{2}c^2 \sin A \sin B$$

65. In any right triangle

$$\frac{a - b}{c\sqrt{2}} = \sin \frac{A - B}{2}$$

Verify this by calculation for the right triangle with

$$a = 33 \qquad b = 56 \qquad \text{and} \qquad c = 65$$

66. A room is 16 by 28 by 9. Two diagonals are drawn from one corner, one along the floor and one to the furthest point on the ceiling. Find the angle between these two diagonals. *Hint:* The length of the longer diagonal is $\sqrt{16^2 + 28^2 + 9^2}$.

6.5 Trigonometric Functions of a Real Number

We shall now define the six trigonometric functions with the set of real numbers as the domain. This form of the definition is preferable for developing many properties of the trigonometric functions, whereas the definition in terms of angles is desirable for some other applications.

Trigonometric functions of real numbers

We define sin s, where s is a real number, to be sin θ, where θ is an angle whose radian measure is s. Similarly we define

$$\cos s = \cos \theta \qquad \tan s = \tan \theta \qquad \cos s = \cot \theta$$
$$\sec s = \sec \theta \qquad \text{and} \qquad \csc s = \csc \theta \tag{6.7}$$

for any real number s.

There is a fundamental relationship between circles and the definitions of trigonometric functions of a real number. Suppose we take the circle with center at the origin whose equation is $x^2 + y^2 = 1$, as in Fig. 6.26. It is called the **unit circle** since its radius is 1.

Next, place an angle θ in standard position, and let (x, y) be the point of intersection of the terminal side of θ and the unit circle. If we measure θ in radians, then by the arc length formula

$$s = r\theta = 1 \cdot \theta = \theta$$

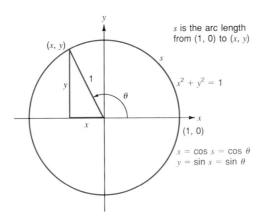

FIGURE 6.26

Consequently, the number of radians in the angle θ is the real number s. Furthermore

$$\cos s = \cos \theta = \frac{x}{r} = \frac{x}{1} = x$$

$$\sin s = \sin \theta = \frac{y}{r} = \frac{y}{1} = y$$

which shows that for any real number s,

$$(\cos s, \sin s) = (x, y)$$

NOTE   Hence **(cos s, sin s) is always a point on the unit circle.** It is found by starting at the point $(1, 0)$, and then going a distance of $|s|$ on the circle. The direction is counterclockwise if $s > 0$, and clockwise if $s < 0$. For this reason the trigonometric functions are sometimes called the **circular functions.**

Thus for the real number 2, sin 2 is defined to have the same value as the sine of the angle whose measure is 2 radians. Similarly tan $(\pi/6)$ is defined to have the same value as the tangent of the angle whose measure is $\pi/6$ radian.

▶ **EXAMPLE 1**   Find the following trigonometric function values.

Solution   (a)

$$\sin \frac{\pi}{4} = \sin \left(\frac{\pi}{4} \text{ radian} \right) = \frac{\sqrt{2}}{2}$$

(b)

$$\cos \frac{\pi}{3} = \cos \left(\frac{\pi}{3} \text{ radians} \right) = \frac{1}{2}$$

(c)

$$\tan \frac{\pi}{6} = \tan \left(\frac{\pi}{6} \text{ radian} \right) = \frac{\sqrt{3}}{3}$$ ◢

Recall that if θ is an angle measured in radians and $0 < \theta < 2\pi$, and θ not a quadrantal angle, there is a reference angle θ'. Similarly, we define a **reference number** for any real number s in the interval $(0, 2\pi)$:

Reference numbers

If $0 < s < \dfrac{\pi}{2}$, it is s (recall $\theta' = \theta$ in quadrant I)

If $\dfrac{\pi}{2} < s < \pi$, it is $\pi - s$ (recall $\theta' = \pi - \theta$ in quadrant II)

If $\pi < s < \dfrac{3\pi}{2}$, it is $s - \pi$ (recall $\theta' = \theta - \pi$ in quadrant III)

If $\dfrac{3\pi}{2} < s < 2\pi$, it is $2\pi - s$ (recall $\theta' = 2\pi - \theta$ in quadrant IV)

Algebraic signs

If s is a real number, the sign of each of the trigonometric functions is determined by the following chart. The chart is due to the definitions, for instance, $\sin s = \sin \theta$, where θ is an angle whose radian measure is s.

Positive values

Interval	Positive values	Approximate interval
$0 < s < \pi/2$	All six	$(0, 1.57)$
$\pi/2 < s < \pi$	$\sin s$ and $\csc s$	$(1.57, 3.14)$
$\pi < s < 3\pi/2$	$\tan s$ and $\cot s$	$(3.14, 4.71)$
$3\pi/2 < s < 2\pi$	$\cos s$ and $\sec s$	$(4.71, 6.28)$

EXAMPLE 2   Use the reference number to find these values.

Solution   (a) $\sin \dfrac{7\pi}{6} = -\sin\left(\dfrac{7\pi}{6} - \pi\right) = -\sin \dfrac{\pi}{6} = -\dfrac{1}{2}$ since $\pi < \dfrac{7\pi}{6} < \dfrac{3\pi}{2}$

(b) $\sec \dfrac{3\pi}{4} = -\sec\left(\pi - \dfrac{3\pi}{4}\right) = -\sec \dfrac{\pi}{4} = -\sqrt{2}$ since $\dfrac{\pi}{2} < \dfrac{3\pi}{4} < \pi$

(c) $\cot \dfrac{5\pi}{3} = -\cot\left(2\pi - \dfrac{5\pi}{3}\right) = -\cot \dfrac{\pi}{3} = -\dfrac{\sqrt{3}}{3}$ since $\dfrac{3\pi}{2} < \dfrac{5\pi}{3} < 2\pi$

Use $\pi \approx 3.14$ in the remaining parts.

(d) $\cos 2.76 = -\cos(\pi - 2.76) \approx -\cos 0.38$ since $1.57 < 2.76 < 3.14$

(e) $\tan 3.5 = \tan(3.5 - \pi) \approx \tan 0.36$ since $3.14 < 3.5 < 4.71$

(f) $\csc 6.05 = -\csc(2\pi - 6.05) \approx -\csc 0.23$ since $4.71 < 6.05 < 6.28$ ◢

Periodic Functions

We shall now study a basic property of the trigonometric functions which simplifies the work of finding their values and graphs. It is called **periodicity** and is defined as follows:

A nonconstant function f is **periodic** if there is a positive number p for which

$$f(x + p) = f(x)$$

for every x in the domain of f. The smallest such value of p is called **the period of f.**

It follows from the definition that

$$f(x - p) = f(x)$$

since $f(x - p) = f[(x - p) + p] = f(x)$. Similarly,

$$f(x) = f(x + 2p) = f(x - 2p), \text{ etc.}$$

The values of a periodic function are repeated every time x changes by p, whether it be an increase or a decrease. We now show that each of the six trigonometric functions is periodic.

In Fig. 6.27, we show an angle θ intersecting the unit circle $x^2 + y^2 = 1$ at the point P on the terminal side. Since the circumference of the unit circle is 2π, if we start at the point $(1, 0)$ and then go a distance of either s or $s + 2\pi$ on the circle, we will arrive at the same point on the unit circle. The coordinates of this point are either

$$(\cos s, \sin s) \qquad \text{or} \qquad (\cos (s + 2\pi), \sin (s + 2\pi))$$

Since these are the same point, the coordinates are equal and

$$\cos s = \cos (s + 2\pi) \qquad \text{and} \qquad \sin s = \sin (s + 2\pi)$$

In Probs. 69 and 70, you are asked to show that 2π is the smallest such value. Hence

2π is the period of the sine and cosine functions

Since $\sec s = 1/\cos s$ and $\csc s = 1/\sin s$, these two functions have period 2π also. Both $\tan s$ and $\cot s$ have period π, as we will show below. Using periodicity repeatedly shows that any trigonometric function of $s + k2\pi$ is the same as that function of s. Symbolically,

$$f(s + k2\pi) = f(s)$$

for all s in the domain of the trigonometric function f and any integer k. In degrees this becomes $f(\theta + k \cdot 360°) = f(\theta)$.

For $\tan s$ and $\cot s$, the period is π, or $180°$, as we will see now. Figure 6.28 shows $(\cos s, \sin s)$ on the terminal side of θ. Since $(\cos s, \sin s)$ and $(-\cos s, -\sin s)$ are symmetric with respect to the origin, then $(-\cos s, -\sin s)$ is on the terminal side of $\theta + \pi$. Now

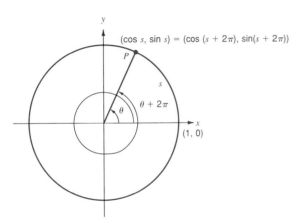

FIGURE 6.27

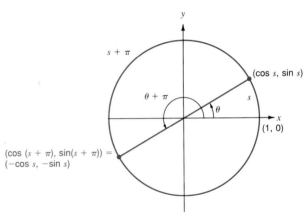

FIGURE 6.28

$$\tan (s + \pi) = \frac{-\sin s}{-\cos s} = \frac{\sin s}{\cos s} = \tan s$$

and therefore **tan s and cot s have period π.**

> The sine, cosine, secant, and cosecant functions have period 2π, or $360°$. The tangent and cotangent functions have period π, or $180°$.   **(6.8)**

▶ **EXAMPLE 3**   Using periodicity, find these function values.

Solution   (a)

$$\tan \frac{31\pi}{6} = \tan \left(\frac{31\pi}{6} - 5\pi \right) \qquad \text{period } \pi$$

$$= \tan \frac{\pi}{6} = \frac{\sqrt{3}}{3}$$

(b)

$$\cos \frac{19\pi}{4} = \cos \left(\frac{19\pi}{4} - 4\pi \right) \qquad \text{period } 2\pi$$

$$= \cos \left(\frac{3\pi}{4} \right) = -\cos \frac{\pi}{4} = -\frac{\sqrt{2}}{2}$$

(c) To find sec 21.13, use period $2\pi \approx 6.28$:

$$\sec 21.13 \approx \sec [21.13 - 3(6.28)] = \sec 2.29$$
$$= -\sec (3.14 - 2.29) \qquad \text{reference number}$$
$$= -\sec 0.85 \approx -1.5152 \qquad\blacktriangleleft$$

▶ **EXAMPLE 4**   Using periodicity, write each of these function values as the same function value of an angle between $0°$ and $90°$.

Solution   (a)

$$\sin 438° = \sin (360° + 78°) \qquad\qquad \text{period } 360°$$
$$= \sin 78°$$

(b)

$$\cos 823° = \cos (2 \cdot 360° + 103°) = \cos 103° \qquad \text{period } 360°$$
$$= -\cos (180° - 103°) = -\cos 77° \qquad \text{reference angle}$$

(c)

$$\cot 1489° = \cot (7 \cdot 180° + 229°) = \cot 229° \qquad \text{period } 180°$$
$$= \cot (229° - 180°) = \cot 49° \qquad \text{reference angle} \quad\blacktriangleleft$$

The discussion in the last few paragraphs along with the related examples can be summarized as follows:

> To find the value of any trigonometric function of any real number (or angle in degrees):
>
> 1. Add or subtract an integral multiple of 2π (or $360°$), if necessary, giving a number in $[0, 2\pi)$ {or in $[0°, 360°)$}.
> 2. Find the reference number of the real number in step 1 (or the reference angle).
> 3. Attach the correct sign to the function value of the reference number (or reference angle) from step 2.

The steps above show that the value $f(s)$ of any of the six trigonometric functions may be found by using only real numbers between 0 and $\pi/2$. Similarly for angles between 0° and 90°. By using the cofunction theorem, if necessary, we only need to use numbers between 0 and $\pi/4$, or angles between 0° and 45°.

▶ EXAMPLE 5   Write each of the values below in terms of a number from 0 to $\pi/4$, or an angle from 0° to 45°.

Solution   (a) $$\tan \frac{7\pi}{3} = \tan \frac{\pi}{3} = \cot \frac{\pi}{6} = \sqrt{3}$$

(b) $$\sec \frac{20\pi}{3} = \sec \left(6\pi + \frac{2\pi}{3}\right) = \sec \frac{2\pi}{3}$$
$$= -\sec \left(\pi - \frac{2\pi}{3}\right) = -\sec \frac{\pi}{3} = -\csc \frac{\pi}{6} = -2$$

(c) $$\cos 410° = \cos (360° + 50°) = \cos 50° = \sin 40°$$

(d) $$\sin 980° = \sin (2 \cdot 360° + 260°) = \sin 260°$$
$$= -\sin 80° = -\cos 10°$$ ◀

Negative numbers or angles   In Exercise 6.5, Prob. 62 and its figure, you are asked to show that

$$\sin (-s) = -\sin s \qquad \text{hence, the sine function is odd}$$
$$\cos (-s) = \cos s \qquad \text{hence the cosine function is even}$$

Odd and even functions   The tangent function is also odd since

$$\tan (-s) = \frac{\sin (-s)}{\cos (-s)} = \frac{-\sin s}{\cos s} = -\tan s$$

Function values of negative numbers or angles may be handled using either odd and even functions, or using periodicity as for positive angles.

▶ EXAMPLE 6   Find the exact values of (a) $\sin (-7\pi/4)$ and (b) $\cos (-200°)$.

Solution   (a) Since the sine function is odd

$$\sin \frac{-7\pi}{4} = -\sin \frac{7\pi}{4}$$
$$= -\left[-\sin \left(2\pi - \frac{7\pi}{4}\right)\right] \qquad \text{reference number}$$
$$= \sin \frac{\pi}{4} = \frac{\sqrt{2}}{2} \qquad \text{exact value}$$

However, using periodicity first gives

$$\sin \frac{-7\pi}{4} = \sin \left(\frac{-7\pi}{4} + 2\pi\right) = \sin \frac{\pi}{4} = \frac{\sqrt{2}}{2}$$

(b) $$\cos (-200°) = \cos 200° \qquad \text{even function}$$
$$= -\cos (200° - 180°) = -\cos 20°$$

Using periodicity initially shows that

$$\cos(-200°) = \cos(-200° + 360°) = \cos 160°$$
$$= -\cos(180° - 160°) = -\cos 20°$$

EXERCISE 6.5

Find the values in Probs. 1 to 12.

1. $\cos \pi/6$ **2.** $\tan \pi/4$ **3.** $\sin \pi/3$

4. $\sec \pi/4$ **5.** $\cot 2\pi/3$ **6.** $\sin 4\pi/3$

7. $\sec 7\pi/4$ **8.** $\cos 5\pi/3$ **9.** $\csc 11\pi/6$

10. $\sec 3\pi/4$ **11.** $\cot 3\pi/2$ **12.** $\tan 5\pi/6$

Express the function value in each of Probs. 13 to 28 in terms of that same function value of a number between 0 and $\pi/2 \approx 1.57$, or an angle between 0° and 90°.

13. $\tan 7.13$ **14.** $\cot(-9.87)$

15. $\sec 11.43$ **16.** $\csc 5.38$

17. $\sin 15\pi/4$ **18.** $\cos(-17\pi/6)$

19. $\tan(-13\pi/5)$ **20.** $\cot 16\pi/9$

21. $\sec 204°$ **22.** $\csc(-330°)$

23. $\sin(-370°)$ **24.** $\cos 615°$

25. $\tan 2001°$ **26.** $\sin(-1492°)$

27. $\cot(-1984°)$ **28.** $\cos 1812°$

Express each function value in Probs. 29 to 40 in terms of a function of a number between 0 and $\pi/4 \approx 0.785$, or an angle between 0° and 45°.

29. $\cos 14.73$ **30.** $\sec(-8.41)$

31. $\csc 12.58$ **32.** $\sin(-11.79)$

33. $\cos 12\pi/5$ **34.** $\tan 22\pi/3$

35. $\cot 37\pi/6$ **36.** $\sec 49\pi/9$

37. $\csc 1184°$ **38.** $\sin(-804°)$

39. $\cos 1027°$ **40.** $\tan(-937°)$

If Probs. 41 to 44, write each value as $\pm\sin \theta$ for some value of θ where $0 \leq \theta < \pi/2 \approx 1.57$.

41. $\sin 1.62$ **42.** $\cos 3.07$ **43.** $\sin 4.56$ **44.** $\cos 5.79$

Find all six trigonometric function values in Probs. 45 to 52.

45. $-5\pi/6$ **46.** $-\pi$ **47.** $-4\pi/3$ **48.** $-\pi/4$

49. $17\pi/6$ **50.** $9\pi/2$ **51.** $9\pi/4$ **52.** $13\pi/6$

In Probs. 53 to 60, verify by calculation that

$$\sin^2 s + \cos^2 s = 1$$

53. $\sin s = 9/41$, $\cos s = 40/41$

54. $\sin s = 11/61$, $\cos s = 60/61$

55. $\sin s = 33/65$, $\cos s = 56/65$

56. $\sin s = 39/89$, $\cos s = 80/89$

57. $\sin 22.5° = \frac{1}{2}\sqrt{2-\sqrt{2}}$, $\cos 22.5° = \frac{1}{2}\sqrt{2+\sqrt{2}}$

58. $\sin 15° = \dfrac{\sqrt{6}-\sqrt{2}}{4}$, $\cos 15° = \dfrac{\sqrt{6}+\sqrt{2}}{4}$

59. $\sin 18° = \dfrac{\sqrt{5}-1}{4}$, $\cos 18° = \dfrac{\sqrt{10+2\sqrt{5}}}{4}$

60. $\sin 36° = \dfrac{\sqrt{10-2\sqrt{5}}}{4}$, $\cos 36° = \dfrac{\sqrt{5}+1}{4}$

61. Use the figure to prove the cofunction theorem

$$\sin\left(\frac{\pi}{2} - \theta\right) = \cos \theta \quad \text{and}$$

$$\cos\left(\frac{\pi}{2} - \theta\right) = \sin \theta$$

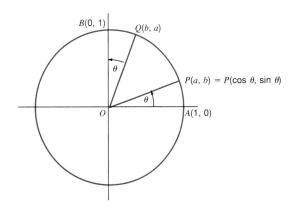

62. Use the figure to show that

$$\sin(-\theta) = -\sin \theta \quad \text{and} \quad \cos(-\theta) = \cos \theta$$

This shows that the sine function is **odd** and the cosine function is **even.**

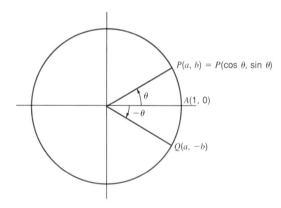

63. Use the figure to show that

$$\sin (\theta + \pi) = -\sin \theta \quad \text{and}$$
$$\cos (\theta + \pi) = -\cos \theta$$

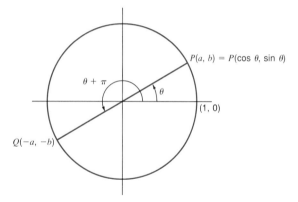

64. Use the figure to show that

$$\sin \left(\theta + \frac{\pi}{2}\right) = \cos \theta \quad \text{and}$$
$$\cos \left(\theta + \frac{\pi}{2}\right) = -\sin \theta$$

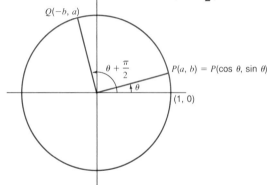

65. Let $f(x) = x - [x]$, where $[x]$ is the greatest integer $\leq x$. What is the period of f?

66. Let $g(n) =$ "the remainder if the integer n is divided by 3." What is the period of g?

67. For $a \neq 0$ and $b \neq 0$, let $f(1) = a$, $f(2) = b$, and

$$f(n) = \frac{1 + f(n - 1)}{f(n - 2)}$$

for $n = 3, 4, 5, 6$, etc. Show that $f(1) = f(6)$ and $f(2) = f(7)$. What is the period of f?

68. Let $f(1) = 2$, $f(2) = 5$, and for $n = 3, 4, 5$, etc., define $f(n) = |f(n - 1)| - f(n - 2)$. Show that $f(1) = f(10)$, and $f(2) = f(11)$. What is the period of f?

69. Try to verify each step in the following proof that the sine function has period 2π. Suppose there is a p, $0 < p < 2\pi$, such that $\sin (s + p) = \sin s$ for all s. Using $s = 0$ gives $\sin p = 0$. Thus $p = \pi$, which implies that $\sin (s + \pi) = \sin s$ for all s. However using $s = \pi/2$ gives a contradiction.

70. Prove that the cosine function has period 2π. *Hint:* Imitate the proof in Prob. 69.

71. Prove that if r is any real number, there is an s so that $\tan s = r$. *Hint:* Show that

$$\left(\frac{1}{\sqrt{1 + r^2}}, \frac{r}{\sqrt{1 + r^2}}\right)$$

is on the unit circle $x^2 + y^2 = 1$. Why is there an s such that $\cos s = 1/\sqrt{1 + r^2}$ and $\sin s = r/\sqrt{1 + r^2}$. Show that $\tan s = r$.

72. Let $f(x) = 2x + \cos x$ and $g(x) = 2 - \sin x$. Find a solution in the interval $(0, \pi/2)$ to the equation

$$\frac{f(\pi/2) - f(0)}{\pi/2} = g(x)$$

In Probs. 73 to 75, find the following values for $n = 1$, 2, 3, and 4.

73. $\cos n\pi$ \qquad\qquad **74.** $\cos [n(n + 1)\pi/2]$

75. $\dfrac{1 - \cos n\pi}{2} + \cos \dfrac{n\pi}{2}$

76. Calculate the value of the average below:

$$\frac{\sec 0.1 + \sec 0.3 + \sec 0.5 + \sec 0.7}{4}$$

6.6 Graphs of the Trigonometric Functions

In earlier sections, we have used the notation

$$\cos \theta = \frac{x}{r} \qquad \text{and} \qquad \sin \theta = \frac{y}{r}$$

when working with triangles as well as

$$\cos s = x \qquad \text{and} \qquad \sin s = y$$

when working with the unit circle. In each case we used notation consistent with an xy coordinate system. We now want to draw the graphs of the trigonometric functions on an xy coordinate system, and so we will write

$$y = \sin x \qquad \text{and} \qquad y = \cos x$$

and similarly for the other four trigonometric functions. Here x is a real number, and it may also be interpreted as the radian measure of an angle.

The graph of $f(x) = \sin x$ consists of

All the points (x, y) for which $y = \sin x$

Recall that the sine function has period 2π. We will make a table of values using for x the multiples of $\pi/6$ and $\pi/4$ between 0 and 2π. The values are given to 1 decimal place in the following table since more accuracy in graphing is difficult. Exact values are $\sin \pi/6 = \frac{1}{2} = 0.50$, $\sin \pi/4 = \sqrt{2}/2 \approx 0.71$, $\sin \pi/3 = \sqrt{3}/2 \approx 0.87$. Since $\pi/6 \approx 0.52$, the graph of $y = \sin x$ passes through $(0, 0)$ and nearly through $(0.52, 0.50)$, and thus the graph is not much different from the graph of $y = x$ for $0 \le x \le \pi/6$.

x	0	$\pi/6$	$\pi/4$	$\pi/3$	$\pi/2$	$2\pi/3$	$3\pi/4$	$5\pi/6$	π
$y = \sin x$	0	0.5	0.7	0.9	1	0.9	0.7	0.5	0

$7\pi/6$	$5\pi/4$	$4\pi/3$	$3\pi/2$	$5\pi/3$	$7\pi/4$	$11\pi/6$	2π
-0.5	-0.7	-0.9	-1	-0.9	-0.7	-0.5	0

We now draw a pair of coordinate axes, locate the points (x, y) from the table, and draw a smooth curve through them. For the sine function, the most convenient points to mark on the x axis are the integral multiples of $\pi/2$, but of course the numbers 1, 2, 3, and so on are still there. We thereby get the part of the graph for $0 \le x \le 2\pi$, as in Fig. 6.29. More of the curve can be obtained from the fact that it has a period of 2π. Since the sine function is odd, $\sin x = -\sin (-x)$, and the graph of $y = \sin x$ is symmetric about the origin. The range is $[-1, 1]$.

The **graph of $y = \cos x$** can be drawn in a manner similar to that used in sketching $y = \sin x$, using the table of values below. Again the domain is the set of all real numbers, the range is $[-1, 1]$, and the period is 2π. The portion of the graph with

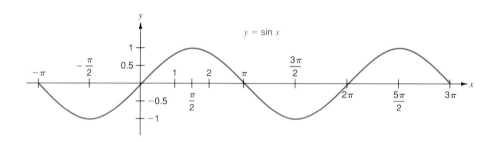

$0 \le x \le 2\pi$ is called a **cycle,** as is any portion whose horizontal length is equal to one period. Since the cosine function is even, $\cos x = \cos (-x)$, and the graph of $y = \cos x$ is symmetric about the y axis. See Fig. 6.30.

x	0	$\pi/6$	$\pi/4$	$\pi/3$	$\pi/2$	$2\pi/3$	$3\pi/4$	$5\pi/6$	π
$y = \cos x$	1	0.9	0.7	0.5	0	-0.5	-0.7	-0.9	-1

$7\pi/6$	$5\pi/4$	$4\pi/3$	$3\pi/2$	$5\pi/3$	$7\pi/4$	$11\pi/6$	2π
-0.9	-0.7	-0.5	0	0.5	0.7	0.9	1

Horizontal translation

The graph of $y = \cos x$ can be found by translating the graph of $y = \sin x$ to the left by $\pi/2$. In fact,

$$\sin \left(x + \frac{\pi}{2} \right) = \sin \left[\frac{\pi}{2} - (-x) \right] \qquad \text{by algebra}$$

$$= \cos (-x) \qquad \text{by cofunction theorem}$$

$$= \cos x \qquad \text{even function}$$

From Sec. 3.4, we know that the graph of $y = \sin (x + \pi/2)$ is the same as the graph of $y = \sin x$ translated $\pi/2$ units to the left since $x + \pi/2 = 0$ if $x = -\pi/2$.

Graph of $y = \tan x$

We shall use the following table in sketching the graph of $y = \tan x$. Some decimal approximations of tangent values below are $\sqrt{3} \approx 1.73$ and $\sqrt{3}/3 \approx 0.58$. The table is not carried further because the tangent function has period π, and the distance from $-\pi/2$ to $\pi/2$ is π.

x	$-\pi/2$	$-\pi/3$	$-\pi/4$	$-\pi/6$	0	$\pi/6$	$\pi/4$	$\pi/3$	$\pi/2$
$y = \tan x$		$-\sqrt{3}$	-1	$-\sqrt{3}/3$	0	$\sqrt{3}/3$	1	$\sqrt{3}$	

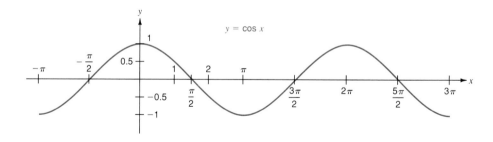

FIGURE 6.30

The entries for $-\pi/2$ and $\pi/2$ are left blank since $\tan x$ is not defined for these values. On the interval $(0, \pi/2)$, the tangent function is increasing since $\tan x = \sin x/\cos x$, and on this interval $\sin x$ increases while $\cos x$ decreases. See Fig. 6.31. Since the tangent function is odd, $\tan(-x) = -\tan x$. Thus the graph of $y = \tan x$ is symmetric about the origin, and it is increasing on $(-\pi/2, \pi/2)$. The other cycles were drawn using the periodicity.

Notice that $\tan x$ does not exist if $x = \pi/2 \pm k\pi$, where k is an integer. The closer x approaches $\pi/2$ from the left, the greater the value of $\tan x$ becomes. In fact since $\pi/2 \approx 1.570796$, we can use a calculator to find these values:

$$\tan 1.56 \approx 93 \qquad \tan 1.57 \approx 1256 \qquad \tan 1.5707 \approx 10{,}381$$

Similarly, we can see from the graph that the closer x comes to $\pi/2$ from the right, the greater $|\tan x|$ becomes, with $\tan x$ being negative. The vertical line

$$x = \pi/2 \text{ is a } \textbf{vertical asymptote}$$

as is each of the lines through a value of x where $\tan x$ is not defined, namely, $x = \pi/2 \pm k\pi$, where k is an integer.

The graphs of $y = \cot x$, $y = \sec x$, and $y = \csc x$ can be drawn by using the reciprocal identities $(\tan x)(\cot x) = 1$, $(\cos x)(\sec x) = 1$, and $(\sin x)(\csc x) = 1$, which show that

$$\cot x = \frac{1}{\tan x} \qquad \sec x = \frac{1}{\cos x} \qquad \csc x = \frac{1}{\sin x}$$

Graph of $y = \csc x$

Since $\csc x = 1/\sin x$, we know that $\csc x$ and $\sin x$ have the same sign, and the value of $\csc x$ is the reciprocal of the value of $\sin x$. Also, $\csc x$ is not defined when $\sin x = 0$, namely, when $x = k\pi$ where k is an integer. Each of the lines $x = k\pi$ is a vertical asymptote for the graph of $y = \csc x$. The cosecant function has period 2π, and

The values of $\csc x$ satisfy $|\csc x| \geq 1$

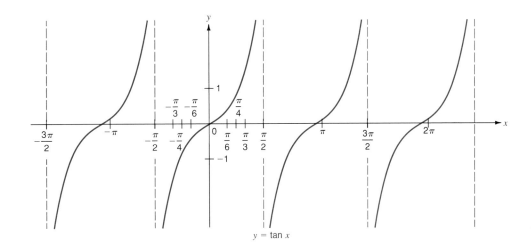

FIGURE 6.31 $y = \tan x$

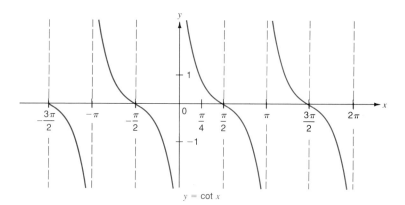

FIGURE 6.32

The cosecant function is odd. The cycle of its graph defined on $(0, \pi) \cup (\pi, 2\pi)$ consists of two separate pieces. Figure 6.34 has the graphs of both the cosecant and sine functions.

The graphs of $y = \cot x$ and of $y = \sec x$ can also be treated as we did the graph of $y = \csc x$ above using properties of the reciprocal function. See Figs. 6.32 and 6.33. We give a short table of values below, where a blank space indicates that the function value is not defined:

x	0	$\pi/4$	$\pi/2$	$3\pi/4$	π	$5\pi/4$	$3\pi/2$	$7\pi/4$	2π
$\cot x$		1	0	-1		1	0	-1	
$\sec x$	1	$\sqrt{2}$		$-\sqrt{2}$	-1	$-\sqrt{2}$		$\sqrt{2}$	1
$\csc x$		$\sqrt{2}$	1	$\sqrt{2}$		$-\sqrt{2}$	-1	$-\sqrt{2}$	

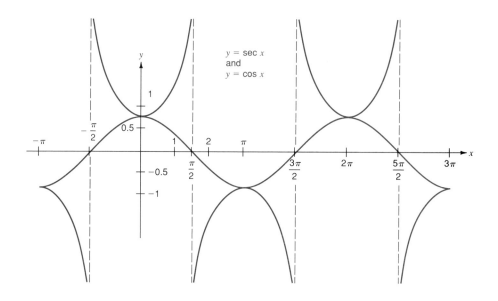

FIGURE 6.33

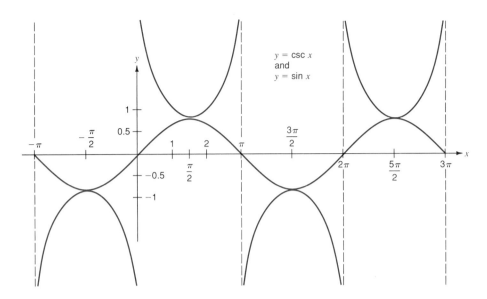

FIGURE 6.34

Notice that we have a connected cycle of the graph of $y = \cot x$ for $0 < x < \pi$, whereas the interval $-\pi/2 < x < \pi/2$ gives a connected cycle for the graph of $y = \tan x$.

The table below gives the **period and range** of each of the six trigonometric functions, and also one **part of the domain** which produces one complete cycle of the graph of the function. Other parts of the domain could also have been used.

Period, domain, and range

Function	Period	Domain for 1 cycle	Range
$\sin x$	2π	$[0, 2\pi]$	$[-1, 1]$
$\cos x$	2π	$[0, 2\pi]$	$[-1, 1]$
$\tan x$	π	$(-\pi/2, \pi/2)$	$(-\infty, \infty)$
$\cot x$	π	$(0, \pi)$	$(-\infty, \infty)$
$\sec x$	2π	$(-\pi/2, \pi/2) \cup (\pi/2, 3\pi/2)$	$(-\infty, -1] \cup [1, \infty)$
$\csc x$	2π	$(0, \pi) \cup (\pi, 2\pi)$	$(-\infty, -1] \cup [1, \infty)$

Now that we know the graphs of the six trigonometric functions, we can look at some closely related graphs. We learned in Chap. 3 that the graph of $y = -f(x)$ is found by reflecting the graph of $y = f(x)$ through the x axis. This also allows us to graph $y = |f(x)|$ if we recall that $|f(x)| = f(x)$ if $f(x) \geq 0$, whereas $|f(x)| = -f(x)$ when $f(x) < 0$.

▶ **EXAMPLE 1** Sketch the graph of $y = |\cos x|$ for $0 \leq x \leq 2\pi$.

Solution In this interval we see that the graph of $y = \cos x$ is below the x axis for $\pi/2 \leq x \leq 3\pi/2$. Thus we reflect this portion of the graph of $y = \cos x$ through the x axis, and leave the other part alone. See Fig. 6.35. ◀

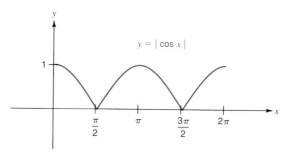

FIGURE 6.35

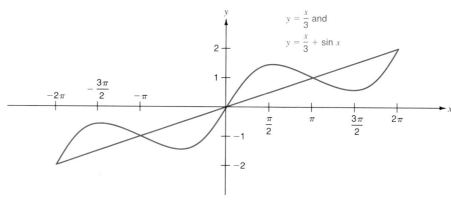

FIGURE 6.36

       Knowing where $\sin x$, or $\cos x$, is zero, positive, and negative allows us to combine them easily with straight lines and other basic curves.

 **EXAMPLE 2**   Draw the graph of $f(x) = x/3 + \sin x$ for $-2\pi \le x \le 2\pi$.

Solution   Since $f(-x) = -f(x)$, the graph of f is symmetric about the origin, and so we will first consider $x \ge 0$. Note that $\sin x = 0$ in $[0, 2\pi]$ for $x = 0$, π, and 2π. Now if $0 \le x \le \pi$, then $\sin x \ge 0$ and so the graph of f is above the graph of $y = x/3$. Similarly the graph of f is below the straight line for $\pi \le x \le 2\pi$. For reference we include the graph of $y = x/3$ for $-2\pi \le x \le 2\pi$ in Fig. 6.36. The short table of decimal approximations below has no negative values of x since they are not needed due to the symmetry about the origin.

x	0	$\pi/2$	π	$3\pi/2$	2π
$f(x)$	0	1.52	1.05	0.57	2.1

In Probs. 1 to 12, draw 1 cycle of the graph which satisfies the given conditions. Choose an interval from -2π to 2π; more than one interval may be possible.

1. $y = \sin x$, cycle starts at a maximum point
2. $y = \cos x$, cycle starts at a minimum point
3. $y = \cos x$, cycle starts on the x axis

4. $y = \sin x$, cycle starts on the x axis with function decreasing
5. $y = \tan x$, cycle starts at a point on the negative x axis
6. $y = \cot x$, connected cycle with all values of x negative

7. $y = \tan x$, connected cycle with all values of x positive

8. $y = \cot x$, cycle starts at a point on the positive x axis

9. $y = \sec x$, function increasing at the start of the cycle, decreasing at the end of the cycle

10. $y = \sec x$, function increasing both at the start and at the end of the cycle

11. $y = \csc x$, the cycle has two separate pieces

12. $y = \csc x$, the cycle has three separate pieces

Problems 13 to 16 are true-false.

13. If $\sin x$ has a maximum value, then $\tan x$ is not defined.

14. If $\cot x$ is not defined, then $\cos x$ has a maximum value.

15. If $\sin x$ has a maximum value at $x = c$, then $\cos c = 0$.

16. If $\sec b \le \sec x$ for all x with $-1 \le x \le 1$, then $\tan b = 0$.

In Probs. 17 to 20, give the largest interval or intervals in $[0, 2\pi]$ satisfying the conditions.

17. The cosine function is decreasing.

18. The tangent function is increasing.

19. The cosecant function is decreasing.

20. The sine function is increasing.

Draw the graphs in Probs. 21 to 32.

21. $y = |\tan x|$ for $0 \le x \le 2\pi$.

22. $y = |\sec x|$ for $-\pi/2 \le x \le 3\pi/2$.

23. $y = -\cos x$ for $-\pi \le x \le \pi$.

24. $y = -\csc x$ for $-2\pi \le x \le 0$.

25. $y = 1 + \sin x$ on $[-\pi, \pi]$.

26. $y = -2 + \tan x$ on $(-\pi/2, \pi/2)$.

27. $y = -3 + \sec x$ on $(-\pi/2, \pi/2) \cup (\pi/2, 3\pi/2)$.

28. $y = 4 + \cos x$ on $[0, 2\pi]$.

29. $y = x$ and $y = x + \cos x$, on $[-2\pi, 2\pi]$. Note that where $\cos x > 0$, the second graph is above the first one.

30. $y = x$ and $y = x - \sin x$, on $[-2\pi, 2\pi]$. Note that if $\sin x > 0$, then the second graph is below the first one.

31. $y = x/2$ and $y = (x/2) + \sin x$, on $[-2\pi, 2\pi]$. Note that where $\sin x > 0$, the second graph is above the first one.

32. $y = x/2$ and $y = x/2 - \cos x$, on $[-2\pi, 2\pi]$. Note that where $\cos x > 0$, the second graph is below the first one.

33. It is true that $\sin x < x < \tan x$ for $0 < x < \pi/2$. Draw the graphs of $y = \sin x$, $y = x$, and $y = \tan x$ for $0 < x < \pi/2$ on one coordinate system.

6.7 Trigonometric Graphs of $y = a \cdot f(bx + c)$

After having learned how to sketch the graph of $y = f(x)$ for each of the six trigonometric functions f, we will next see how to sketch the graph of $y = a \cdot f(bx + c)$ where a, b, and c are constants. The results below will show that if a and b are **positive,** then

1. The maximum value, if any, is multiplied by a.
2. The period is divided by b.
3. The graph is translated left or right by c/b.

One cycle of either $y = a \sin (bx + c)$ or $y = a \cos (bx + c)$ is called a **sine wave** or a **sinusoidal curve** or a **simple harmonic curve.**

Amplitude

The simplest situation is that of

$$y = a \sin x \qquad \text{or} \qquad y = a \cos x \qquad \text{(1)}$$

where the sine and cosine values are simply multiplied by a. In both cases, the range is from $-|a|$ to $|a|$, instead of -1 to 1. The number a may be positive or negative, and

$| a |$ is called the **amplitude** of the function or of its graph. In each case in (1), the period is 2π. If a sine wave is translated up or down, the amplitude is

$$\frac{\text{Maximum value} - \text{minimum value}}{2}$$

► **EXAMPLE 1**   Find the amplitude of the graph of each of these equations.

Solution   The amplitude of $y = 4 \sin x$ is 4.
The amplitude of $y = -2 \cos x$ is $| -2 | = 2$.
The amplitude of $y = 14.7 \cos x$ is 14.7.
The amplitude of $y = 5 + 3 \sin x$ is 3.   ◄

No amplitude   Although the sine and cosine functions are bounded, the other four trigonometric functions are not bounded and **do not have an amplitude.** Suppose that $a \neq 0$. For both $f(x) = a \tan x$ and $g(x) = a \cot x$, the range is $(-\infty, \infty)$. However,

If $h(x) = sec\ x$ and $H(x) = a\ sec\ x$, then the range of h is $(-\infty, -1] \cup [1, \infty)$, whereas the range of H is $(-\infty, -a] \cup [a, \infty)$.

Period   Suppose now that $y = a \sin bx$ or $y = a \cos bx$, where a is not zero and $b > 0$. The amplitude is $| a |$, and we want to look at the period, which is the same for $a \sin bx$ as it is for $\sin bx$. We will have 1 cycle of the graph if bx increases by 2π. Using $[0, 2\pi]$ requires solving the inequality

$$0 \leq bx \leq 2\pi$$

Dividing by b, $b > 0$, shows that the solution is

$$0 \leq x \leq \frac{2\pi}{b} \qquad \text{since } b > 0$$

This interval is of length $2\pi/b$, which is the period. Another way to show that the period is $2\pi/b$ is to let $f(x) = \sin bx$ and write

$$f\left(x + \frac{2\pi}{b}\right) = \sin\left[b\left(x + \frac{2\pi}{b}\right)\right]$$
$$= \sin (bx + 2\pi) = \sin bx = f(x)$$

Similarly,

$$\tan b\left(x + \frac{\pi}{b}\right) = \tan (bx + \pi) = \tan bx$$

shows that the period of $\tan bx$ is π/b. The other trigonometric functions may be handled in the same way.

Period

> If f is any one of the six trigonometric functions, then multiplying the number or angle by the positive number b divides the period by b. Specifically,
>
> *The period of sin bx, of cos bx, of sec bx, and of csc bx is $2\pi/b$*
> *The period of tan bx and cot bx is π/b*

The graph of $y = -f(x)$ is the graph of $y = f(x)$ reflected through the x axis. We may use this to help graph $y = f(bx)$, where f is one of the six trigonometric functions and b may be *positive or negative*. Recall that $\sin(-x) = -\sin x$ since $\sin x$ is odd, $\cos(-x) = \cos x$ since $\cos x$ is even, and $\tan(-x) = -\tan x$ since $\tan x$ is odd. We may thus write

$$\sin(-5x) = -\sin 5x$$
$$\cos(-12x) = \cos 12x$$
$$\tan(-4x) = -\tan 4x$$

EXAMPLE 2 Find the period of each of the following.

Solution The period of $f(x) = \cos 3x$ is $2\pi/3$.
The period of $f(x) = 9 \tan 5x$ is $\pi/5$.

The period of $f(x) = 7 \sec \dfrac{x}{4}$ is $\dfrac{2\pi}{\frac{1}{4}} = 8\pi$.

The period of $f(x) = \sin(-2x) = -\sin 2x$ is $2\pi/2 = \pi$.
The period of $f(x) = \cot \pi x$ is $\pi/\pi = 1$.

Now that we know how to find the period and amplitude, if any, of $y = a \cdot f(bx)$, we will draw some graphs.

EXAMPLE 3 Draw the graphs of these functions on the interval $[0, 2\pi]$:

$$f(x) = 3 \cos x \qquad \text{and} \qquad g(x) = \cos 3x$$

Solution The amplitude of f is 3 and its period is 2π. For g, the amplitude is 1 and the period is $2\pi/3 \approx 2.1$. We can now draw the graph of f on the interval $[0, 2\pi]$ by drawing one cosine cycle with amplitude 3, while the graph of g on the interval $[0, 2\pi]$ has three

NOTE cycles with amplitude 1. **When drawing each cycle,** divide that part of the x axis into four parts of equal length, and then locate the maximum and minimum points as well as the x intercepts. See Fig. 6.37.

EXAMPLE 4 Draw one cycle of the graph of $y = -\frac{1}{2} \sec 4x$.

Solution There is no amplitude, and the range is $(-\infty, -\frac{1}{2}] \cup [\frac{1}{2}, \infty)$. The period is $2\pi/4 = \pi/2 \approx 1.57$. In order to have only two parts to the graph, as $y = \sec x$ does for $-\pi/2 < x < 3\pi/2$, we solve the inequality

$$\frac{-\pi}{2} < 4x < \frac{3\pi}{2} \qquad \text{since we are given } -\frac{1}{2}\sec 4x$$

$$\frac{-\pi}{8} < x < \frac{3\pi}{8} \qquad \text{dividing by 4}$$

Notice that $3\pi/8 - (-\pi/8) = 4\pi/8 = \pi/2$, which is one period. Due to the minus sign in $-\frac{1}{2} \sec 4x$, the left half of the cycle is below the x axis. See Fig. 6.38, which has asymptotes at

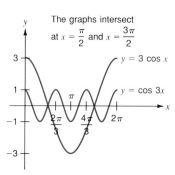

The graphs intersect at $x = \dfrac{\pi}{2}$ and $x = \dfrac{3\pi}{2}$

$y = 3 \cos x$

$y = \cos 3x$

FIGURE 6.37

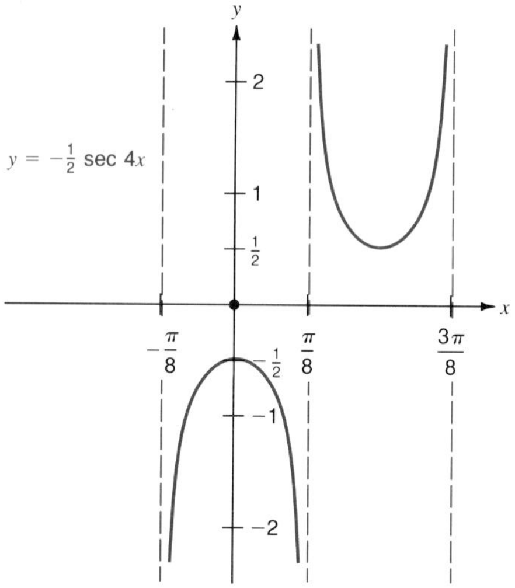

$y = -\dfrac{1}{2} \sec 4x$

FIGURE 6.38

$$x = \frac{-\pi}{8} \approx -0.39 \quad x = \frac{\pi}{8} \approx 0.39 \quad \text{and} \quad x = \frac{3\pi}{8} \approx 1.18$$

$y = a \cdot f(bx + c)$

The graphs of $y = a \cdot f(bx + c)$ and $y = a \cdot f(bx)$ are very similar. Their periods are the same, as are their amplitudes, if any. And since $f(bx + c) = f[b(x + c/b)]$, the graph of $y = a \cdot f(bx + c)$ is merely a **horizontal translation** of the graph of $y = a \cdot f(bx)$. The distance and direction of the translation may be found by solving

$$bx + c = 0 \qquad \text{which gives } x = \frac{-c}{b}$$

The graph of $y = a \cdot f(bx)$ is translated

to the right if $-c/b > 0$, *and to the left if* $-c/b < 0$

For instance, the sine function has period 2π, and we will have one complete cycle of the graph of $y = a \cdot \sin(bx + c)$ if $bx + c$ goes through any interval of length 2π. If we choose the interval $[0, 2\pi]$, for instance, this may be done by *either*

NOTE

Solving the inequality $0 \le bx + c \le 2\pi$ *or by*
Solving the equations $bx + c = 0$ *and* $bx + c = 2\pi$.

Also $y = a \cdot \sin(bx + c)$ has amplitude $|a|$ and period $2\pi/|b|$.

EXAMPLE 5   Draw the graph of $y = \sin(5x + 4)$.

Solution   The amplitude is 1 and the period is $2\pi/5$. Since the equation is $y = \sin(5x + 4)$, we will solve the inequality

$$
\begin{aligned}
0 &\le 5x + 4 \le 2\pi && \text{sine has period } 2\pi \\
-4 &\le 5x \le -4 + 2\pi && \text{subtracting 4} \\
-\frac{4}{5} &\le x \le -\frac{4}{5} + \frac{2\pi}{5} && \text{dividing by 5}
\end{aligned}
$$

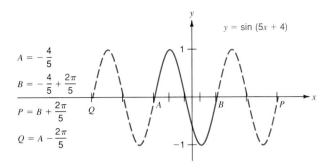

$A = -\dfrac{4}{5}$

$B = -\dfrac{4}{5} + \dfrac{2\pi}{5}$

$P = B + \dfrac{2\pi}{5}$

$Q = A - \dfrac{2\pi}{5}$

$y = \sin(5x + 4)$

FIGURE 6.39

If you prefer to work with **equations instead of inequalities,** you may find the end-points of this interval by solving the two equations $5x + 4 = 0$ and $5x + 4 = 2\pi$. The solutions are $x = -\frac{4}{5}$ and $x = (-4 + 2\pi)/5$. Either way shows that **one complete cycle** of the graph of $y = \sin(5x + 4)$

$$\text{begins at } -\tfrac{4}{5} = -0.80 \text{ and ends at } -\tfrac{4}{5} + 2\pi/5 \approx 0.46$$

The graph in Fig. 6.39 can be drawn easily by dividing the interval from $A = -\frac{4}{5}$ to $B = -\frac{4}{5} + 2\pi/5$ into four equal parts, and then drawing 1 sine cycle there. Now other cycles can be drawn using the period $2\pi/5$.

EXAMPLE 6 Draw the graph of $y = \tan(4x - 3)$.

Solution There is no amplitude, and the period is $\pi/4$. To graph 1 cycle of $y = \tan(4x - 3)$, we may begin with the interval $(-\pi/2, \pi/2)$ since it has one unbroken cycle of the tangent function. Now either (a) solve the inequality

$$\frac{-\pi}{2} < 4x - 3 < \frac{\pi}{2} \qquad \text{tangent has period } \pi$$

$$3 - \frac{\pi}{2} < 4x < 3 + \frac{\pi}{2} \qquad \text{adding 3}$$

$$\frac{3}{4} - \frac{\pi}{8} < x < \frac{3}{4} + \frac{\pi}{8} \qquad \text{dividing by 4}$$

or (b) solve the equations

$$4x - 3 = \frac{-\pi}{2} \qquad \text{and} \qquad 4x - 3 = \frac{\pi}{2}$$

$$4x = 3 - \frac{\pi}{2} \qquad\qquad\qquad 4x = 3 + \frac{\pi}{2}$$

$$x = \frac{3}{4} - \frac{\pi}{8} \qquad\qquad\qquad x = \frac{3}{4} + \frac{\pi}{8}$$

Therefore we start one cycle at $A = \frac{3}{4} - \pi/8 \approx 0.36$, and we end it at $B = \frac{3}{4} + \pi/8 \approx 1.14$. The graph crosses the x axis at $\frac{3}{4} = 0.75$. See Fig. 6.40.

Since the graph of $y = f(bx + c)$ is just the graph of $y = f(bx)$ translated by $-c/b$ units, we sometimes say that the graphs of two functions **differ in phase,** or that there is a **phase shift.** This is just another terminology for a horizontal translation.

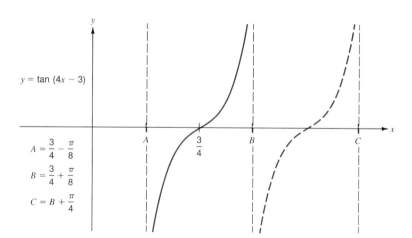

$y = \tan (4x - 3)$

$A = \dfrac{3}{4} - \dfrac{\pi}{8}$

$B = \dfrac{3}{4} + \dfrac{\pi}{8}$

$C = B + \dfrac{\pi}{4}$

FIGURE 6.40

▶ **EXAMPLE 7**   Without graphing, give the period, amplitude, and phase shift.

Solution   (a) The period of $y = 5 \cos (3x + 8)$ is $2\pi/3$, the amplitude is 5, and by solving $3x + 8 = 0$ we find that the phase shift is $-\frac{8}{3}$.
(b) The period of $y = 17 \cot (5x - \pi/2)$ is $\pi/5$, it has no amplitude, and by solving $5x - \pi/2 = 0$, the phase shift is $\pi/10$.
(c) The period of $y = -\csc (\pi x/7)$ is $2\pi/(\pi/7) = 14$, there is no amplitude and no phase shift.
(d) The period of $y = 9 \sin (-6x + 1) = (-9) \sin (6x - 1)$ is $2\pi/6 = \pi/3$, the amplitude is 9, and by solving either $-6x + 1 = 0$ or $6x - 1 = 0$ we find that the phase shift is $\frac{1}{6}$. ◀

▶ **EXAMPLE 8**   Find b so that the period of $\sec bx$ is 4π.

Solution   In order for the period of $\sec bx$ to be 4π, we solve $2\pi/b = 4\pi$, getting $b = \frac{1}{2}$.

▶ **EXAMPLE 9**   Draw these graphs on the same set of axes:

$$y = \sin x \qquad y = \sin 3x \qquad \text{and} \qquad y = 2 \sin \left(3x - \frac{\pi}{2}\right)$$

Solution   The graph of $y = \sin x$ is drawn for $0 \le x \le 2\pi$.
    The graph of $y = \sin 3x$ has amplitude 1 and period $2\pi/3$, and it is drawn for $0 \le x \le 2\pi/3$.
    The graph of $y = 2 \sin (3x - \pi/2)$ has amplitude 2 and period $2\pi/3$. Since $3x - \pi/2 = 0$ if $x = \pi/6$, it is translated $\pi/6$ units to the right from the graph of $y = 2 \sin 3x$. The graph of $y = 2 \sin (3x - \pi/2)$ is drawn for $\pi/6 \le x \le \pi/6 + 2\pi/3 = 5\pi/6$. See Fig. 6.41 for 1 cycle of each graph. ◀
    The graph of $y = a \cdot f(bx + c) + d$ is a **vertical translation** of the graph of $y = a \cdot f(bx + c)$. In Probs. 57 to 60, there are some functions of this form dealing with blood pressure and the number of hours of daylight, for instance.

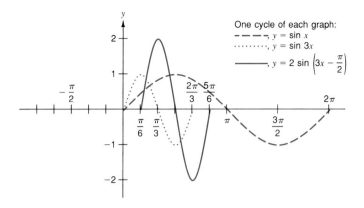

FIGURE 6.41

If a particle is in **simple harmonic motion** with

$$y = a \cdot \sin(bt + c) + d$$

where $b > 0$, t in seconds, then the period is $2\pi/b$, which tells the number of seconds required for 1 cycle. The number $b/(2\pi)$ is called the **frequency,** and it tells the number of cycles per second. Thus if $y = \sin 120\pi t$ then the period is $2\pi/(120\pi) = \frac{1}{60}$, and the frequency is 60 cycles/s.

    Electromagnetic waves are phenomena such as x-rays, visible light, microwaves, radar, television, and radio waves. They all obey equations of the form

$$y = A \sin(2\pi ft - B)$$

where A is the amplitude and $f =$ frequency $= 1/\text{period}$.

    FM radio stations operate by **frequency modulation** (changing the frequency or period), while AM radio stations operate by **amplitude modulation.**

EXAMPLE 10   One of the most important uses of trigonometric functions is in **Fourier series.** These are infinite series which can be used to study functions that arise in heat flow, electric fields, and sound waves, for instance. For $0 < x < 2\pi$, we have

$$\frac{\pi - x}{2} = \sin x + \frac{\sin 2x}{2} + \frac{\sin 3x}{3} + \frac{\sin 4x}{4} + \cdots$$

by which we mean that the graphs of

$$y = \sin x \qquad y = \sin x + \frac{\sin 2x}{2}$$

$$y = \sin x + \frac{\sin 2x}{2} + \frac{\sin 3x}{3}$$

and so on, look more and more like the graph of $y = (\pi - x)/2$, for $0 < x < 2\pi$. Draw the graphs of

$$f(x) = \sin x + \frac{\sin 2x}{2} + \frac{\sin 3x}{3} \qquad \text{and} \qquad g(x) = \frac{\pi - x}{2}$$

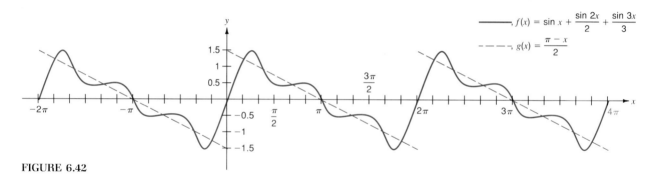

FIGURE 6.42

Solution   In Fig. 6.42 we graph both

$$f(x) = \sin x + \frac{\sin 2x}{2} + \frac{\sin 3x}{3} \qquad \text{and} \qquad g(x) = \frac{\pi - x}{2}$$

for $0 < x < 2\pi$ by using the table below. The graphs are extended by periodicity to $-2\pi < x < 4\pi$ in the figure.

x	0.1	$\pi/6$	$\pi/3$	$\pi/2$	$2\pi/3$	$5\pi/6$	π	$7\pi/6$	$4\pi/3$	$3\pi/2$	$5\pi/3$	$11\pi/6$	6.2
$f(x)$	0.30	1.27	1.30	0.67	0.43	0.40	0	-0.40	-0.43	-0.67	-1.30	-1.27	-0.25
$g(x)$	1.52	1.31	1.05	0.79	0.52	0.26	0	-0.26	-0.52	-0.79	-1.05	-1.31	-1.53

EXERCISE 6.7

Find the amplitude (if any), the period, and the phase shift in Probs. 1 to 16.

1. $y = 3 \tan 2x$
2. $y = 5 \cot 3x$
3. $y = 2 \sec 5x$
4. $y = 4 \sec 7x$
5. $y = -2 \sin 0.5x$
6. $y = 3 \cos 2.5x$
7. $y = 0.2 \sin \pi x$
8. $y = 5 \cos 0.5\pi x$
9. $y = 3 \tan (2x + \pi)$
10. $y = -2 \cot (5x + 9)$
11. $y = 4 \sec (-3x - 7)$
12. $y = 4 \csc (6x + \pi/2)$
13. $y = 7 \sin (-6x + 9)$
14. $y = 2 \cos (2x - \pi/3)$
15. $y = -5 \tan (0.5x - 6)$
16. $y = 3 \cot (3x - \pi/2)$

Find the value of b so that the graph of the equation in Probs. 17 to 20 has the number after the comma as its period.

17. $y = \sec bx$, π
18. $y = \sin bx$, π
19. $y = \cos bx$, 3
20. $y = \tan bx$, 2π

Sketch the graphs of the functions defined by the equations in Probs. 21 to 40.

21. $y = 4 \sin x$
22. $y = -\frac{3}{2} \cos x$
23. $y = 2 \tan x$
24. $y = \frac{2}{3} \sec x$
25. $y = \cot 3x$
26. $y = \sec \pi x$
27. $y = \cos(-x/2)$
28. $y = \sin (-\pi x/3)$
29. $y = 2 \sin 3x$
30. $y = -3 \cos 2x$
31. $y = -\tan 2x$
32. $y = 0.5 \sec (x/2)$
33. $y = \pi \cos (x - \pi/3)$
34. $y = -2 \tan (x + 1)$
35. $y = 0.75 \csc (x - \pi/2)$
36. $y = 2.5 \sin (x + \pi/4)$
37. $y = -\frac{1}{2} \csc (2x + \pi)$
38. $y = 3 \cot (0.5x - \pi/3)$
39. $y = 4 \cos (\pi x + 2)$
40. $y = 3 \sin (3x - \pi/4)$

If the position of a particle at time t is $y = A \sin (Bt + C)$ or $y = D \cos (Et + F)$, we say that it is in **simple harmonic motion.** In Probs. 41 to 44 find the amplitude, period, and phase shift of the particle.

41. $y = 4 \sin (3t + 1.5)$
42. $y = 3 \cos (2t + 1.6)$
43. $y = 3.1 \cos (3t - \pi/3)$
44. $y = 2.3 \sin (8t - 5\pi)$

If a particle is in simple harmonic motion with $y = A \sin (Bt + C)$, then its velocity is $V = AB \cos (Bt + C)$.

In Probs. 45 to 48 find the amplitude, period, and phase shift of the velocity.

45. $y = 3 \sin (2t + 6.7)$ **46.** $y = 2.1 \sin (3t + 2.4)$

47. $y = 5.6 \sin (8t - 7)$ **48.** $y = 1.4 \sin (7t - 5)$

In Chap. 7 we will show that the graph of $y = a \sin x + b \cos x$ is a sine wave with period 2π and amplitude $\sqrt{a^2 + b^2}$. There is also a phase shift which occurs, but we will not calculate it here. Use these facts along with a table of values to draw the graphs for $0 \le x \le 2\pi$ in Probs. 49 to 52.

49. $y = \sin x + \cos x$

50. $y = 3 \sin x + 4 \cos x$

51. $y = 15 \sin x - 8 \cos x$

52. $y = -5 \sin x + 12 \cos x$

53. Draw the graph of $y = e^{-x} \cos x$ for $0 \le x \le 4\pi$. *Hint:* The graph lies between the graphs of $y = e^{-x}$ and $y = -e^{-x}$, and touches them whenever $\cos x = \pm 1$. This is an example of a **damped sine wave,** which occurs when a spring is compressed and released.

54. It is true that $1 - (x^2/2) < \cos x$ for all real numbers x. On one set of axes, draw the graphs of

$$y = 1 - \frac{x^2}{2} \quad \text{and} \quad y = \cos x \quad \text{for } 0 \le x \le \frac{\pi}{2}$$

55. The graphs of

$$y = \sin \left(x + \frac{\pi}{4} \right) \quad \text{and} \quad y = \frac{\sqrt{2}}{2} (\sin x + \cos x)$$

are the same, which can be shown with the methods of Chap. 7. Draw either one over 1 cycle.

56. Draw the graph of $y = (\sin x)^2$ on $[0, 2\pi]$. This graph is the same as the graph of $y = (1 - \cos 2x)/2$ since it is true, as we will see in Chap. 7, that $(\sin x)^2 = (1 - \cos 2x)/2$.

Problems 57 to 60 deal with equations of the form $y = a \cdot \sin (bx + c) + d$ or $y = a \cdot \cos(bx + c) + d$

57. *Blood pressure* Suppose that the blood pressure of a person is

$$y = 110 + 30 \cos \frac{12\pi t}{5}$$

where t is in seconds. Draw the graph for $0 \le t \le \frac{5}{2}$. What is the systolic (maximum) pressure and the diastolic (minimum) pressure?

58. *Hours of daylight* Suppose that the number of hours of daylight in a city is

$$y = 12 + 4 \sin \frac{2\pi t}{365}$$

where t is in days with $t = 0$ corresponding to March 21. Draw the graph for $0 \le t \le 365$. What is the amplitude? What are the maximum and minimum number of hours of daylight?

59. *Mass on a spring* Suppose that the height of a mass attached to a spring is

$$y = 20 + 5 \sin \left(2t - \frac{\pi}{2} \right)$$

where t is in seconds. Draw the graph for $0 \le t \le 2\pi$.

60. *Magnitude of a star* Suppose that the magnitude or brightness of a star is

$$y = 6.5 + 2.5 \cos \left(\frac{\pi t}{25} + 10 \right)$$

where t is in days. Draw the graph for $0 \le t \le 100$.

61. Draw the graph of $y = 3 \cos x + \cos 3x$ for $0 \le x \le 2\pi$. *Hint:* The only x intercepts are $\pi/2$ and $3\pi/2$.

62. Draw the graph of $y = 3 \sin 2x + 2 \sin 3x$ for $0 \le x \le 2\pi$. *Hint:* There are two maximum values and two minimum values.

63. Show that $f(x) = \sin 6x + \cos 9x$ has period $2\pi/3$. *Hint:* Find $f(x + 2\pi/3)$.

64. Show that $g(x) = \sin 25x + \cos 15x$ has period $2\pi/5$. *Hint:* Find $g(x + 2\pi/5)$.

65. The graphs of $y = \sin (x + \pi)$ and $y = -\sin x$ are the same. Draw 1 cycle of either one.

66. The graphs of $y = \tan (x + \pi/2)$ and $y = -\cot x$ are the same. Draw 1 cycle of either one.

Predator-prey model

The functions $f(t) = a \cdot \cos (bt) + d$ and $g(t) = A \cdot \cos (bt + c) + D$, with t in years, differ in amplitude and phase shift, but have the same period. As the predators (g below) eat the prey (f below), there are fewer prey. This means less food for the predators, and consequently fewer predators later. Fewer predators leads to more prey, and so on. Draw 2 cycles of each graph on one coordinate system in Probs. 67 and 68.

67. $f(t) = 8000 + 3000 \cos t$ = number of rabbits

$g(t) = 500 + 200 \cos \left(t + \dfrac{\pi}{2}\right)$ = number of foxes

68. $f(t) = 1200 + 700 \cos \dfrac{\pi t}{4}$ = number of reeboks

$g(t) = 80 + 50 \cos \left(\dfrac{\pi t}{4} + \dfrac{\pi}{2}\right)$

= number of cheetahs

6.8 Key Concepts

Be sure that you understand and can use each of the following terms and formulas.

Positive angle (p. 300)
Negative angle (p. 300)
Degree (p. 300)
Radian (p. 302)
Sine (p. 309)
Cosine (p. 309)
Tangent (p. 309)
Cotangent (p. 309)
Secant (p. 309)
Cosecant (p. 309)
Quadrantal angle (pp. 309, 318)
Trigonometric functions (pp. 309, 314, 335)
Cofunction theorem (p. 316)
Function values of 30° and 45°, or
   $\pi/6$ and $\pi/4$, and their multiples
   (p. 317)
Reference angle or number (pp. 321, 336)
Function values by tables and
   calculator (p. 322)

Right triangles (p. 328)
Opposite side, adjacent side, and
   hypotenuse (p. 329)
Angle of depression (p. 330)
Angle of elevation (p. 331)
Bearing (p. 332)
Periodic function (p. 337)
Period (pp. 337, 350)
Functions of negative angles (p. 340)
Graphs of the trigonometric functions
   (p. 343)
Vertical asymptotes (p. 345)
Domain (p. 347)
Range (p. 347)
Amplitude (p. 350)
Phase shift (p. 353)
Simple harmonic motion (p. 355)
Frequency (p. 355)

(6.1) π radians $= 180°$

(6.2) $s = r\theta$

(6.3) $\dfrac{y}{r} = \sin \theta \qquad \dfrac{x}{r} = \cos \theta \qquad \dfrac{y}{x} = \tan \theta$

$\dfrac{r}{y} = \csc \theta \qquad \dfrac{r}{x} = \sec \theta \qquad \dfrac{x}{y} = \cot \theta$

(6.4) $\sin \theta \csc \theta = 1 \qquad \cos \theta \sec \theta = 1 \qquad \tan \theta \cot \theta = 1$

(6.5) $\sin \theta = \dfrac{\text{opp}}{\text{hyp}} \qquad \cos \theta = \dfrac{\text{adj}}{\text{hyp}} \qquad \tan \theta = \dfrac{\text{opp}}{\text{adj}}$

$\cot \theta = \dfrac{\text{adj}}{\text{opp}} \qquad \sec \theta = \dfrac{\text{hyp}}{\text{adj}} \qquad \csc \theta = \dfrac{\text{hyp}}{\text{opp}}$

(6.6) Any trigonometric function of an acute angle is equal to the corresponding cofunction of the complementary angle.

We define sin s, where s is a real number, to be sin θ, where θ is an angle whose radian measure is s. Similarly we define

(6.7) cos s = cos θ, tan s = tan θ, cot s = cot θ, sec s = sec θ, and csc s = csc θ for any real number s.

(6.8) The sine, cosine, secant, and cosecant functions have period 2π, or 360°. The tangent and cotangent functions have period π, or 180°.

EXERCISE 6.8   Review

Express each angle in Probs. 1 to 6 as a constant times π radians, and those in 7 to 9 in radians to three decimal places.

1. 72°
2. 126°
3. 375°
4. 10°20'
5. 11°15'
6. 3.9 revolutions
7. 47°
8. 17°23'
9. 34°18'29"

Express the angle, given in radians, in each of Probs. 10 to 12 in degrees, minutes, and seconds.
10. $\pi/24$
11. $7\pi/54$
12. 3.7

In Probs. 13 and 14, use the arc length formula $s = r\theta$.
13. If $\theta = 0.149$ and $r = 2.47$, find s.
14. If $s = 8.72$, and $r = 5.23$, find θ.
15. If $r = 36$, and $\theta = 10°$, find the area of the sector. Recall that the area is $0.5r^2\theta$, where θ is in radians.
16. If Eskimo Point, Canada, is 61°N latitude and Center Point, Texas, is 30°N, find the distance between them if both have the same longitude.
17. Find the values of the functions of the largest acute angle of a right triangle with $\sqrt{17}$, $4\sqrt{2}$, and 7 as lengths of sides.
18. If the coordinates of a point on the terminal side of an angle in standard position are $x = -15$ and $y = -8$, evaluate the functions of the angle.
19. Find the values of the other functions of θ if sin $\theta = 21/29$.
20. Show that sin 150° = $\sqrt{2}$ sin 45° cos 60° + cos 90° sin 77°.
21. Use tables or a calculator to show that

cos 23° + cos 95° + cos 167°
          + cos 239° + cos 311° = 0

22. Express sin 312° as $\pm$ sin α where α is a positive acute angle, and as $\pm$ cos β where β is a positive angle less than 45°.

Find these trigonometric function values.
23. sin $5\pi/4$, cot $2\pi/3$, and sec 0
24. cos $(-5\pi/3)$, tan $(-\pi/4)$, and csc $(-\pi/2)$
25. sin $21\pi/4$, cos $23\pi/4$, and tan $(-44\pi/3)$

Find the amplitude, period, and phase shift in these problems.
26. $y = 7 \sin 5x$
27. $y = \tan 9x$
28. $y = 3 \cos 2.5\pi x$
29. $y = \csc 4x/3$
30. $y = 0.4 \sec (x - \pi/2)$
31. $y = \sin (2x + \pi/4)$

Sketch these graphs on $[0, 2\pi]$.
32. $y = -3 \sin x$
33. $y = \cos 2x$
34. $y = \tan (2x - \pi/4)$
35. $y = 2 \cos (3x + \pi/2)$
36. $y = \sin 2x + \cos 2x$
37. Packaging 5 by 9 boxes efficiently requires the value of $5 \cos x + 9 \sin x$. Evaluate it for $x = 49.7°$ or 0.8674 radian.
38. If x is a real number close to 0, cos x is approximately $1 - \dfrac{x^2}{2} + \dfrac{x^4}{24}$. Calculate both for $x = 0.6$.
39. If x is a real number close to 0, sin x is approximately $x - \dfrac{x^3}{6} + \dfrac{x^5}{120}$. Calculate both for $x = 1$.
40. Verify by calculation that $\tan \dfrac{3\pi}{11} + 4 \sin \dfrac{2\pi}{11} = \sqrt{11}$.
41. Show by calculation that

$$\sec^2 \frac{\pi}{7} \sec^2 \frac{2\pi}{7} \sec^2 \frac{3\pi}{7}$$

$$\times \csc^2 \frac{\pi}{7} \csc^2 \frac{2\pi}{7} \csc^2 \frac{3\pi}{7} = 585$$

42. Show that the sign of sin 85° sin 185° sin 285° is the opposite of the sign of cos 111° × cot 222° sec 333°.

43. Prove that if $0 < x < \pi/2$, then sin x + cos $x > 1$. *Hint:* Square both sides and use $\sin^2 x + \cos^2 x = 1$.

44. (a) Which trigonometric functions can attain the value $-\frac{3}{4}$?
(b) Which ones can attain the value 5678?

45. (a) Find the maximum value of 4 + 3 sin x.
(b) Find the maximum value of 4 cos x + 3 sin x.

46. (a) Show that sin (sin x) = 0.9 has no solution.
(b) Show that sin (sin x) = 0.8 does have a solution.

47. Find the value of sin θ if θ is in quadrant IV and the terminal side of θ lies on the line whose equation is $y = -7x/24$.

48. Find the linear velocity in feet per second of a seat on a Ferris wheel if the seat is 120 ft from the center and the Ferris wheel makes one revolution every 3 min.

49. Find the radian and degree measure of the smaller angle between the hands of a clock at 2:30.

50. What quadrant is θ in if sin θ tan $\theta > 0$ and cos $\theta < 0$.

51. If sin θ = tan 36°, find the value of cos θ sec θ.

52. Show that if tan $x = \frac{4}{9}$ and tan $y = \frac{5}{13}$, then $x + y = \pi/4$.

53. Draw 1 cycle of the graph of $y = \sin(x + 3\pi/2)$. Note that it is the same as the graph of $y = -\cos x$.

54. Let $f(x) = x + \sin x$ and $g(x) = 1 + \cos x$. Find a solution in the interval $(\pi/6, \pi/2)$ of the equation
$$\frac{f(\pi/2) - f(\pi/6)}{\pi/2 - \pi/6} = g(x)$$

55. In a sense which can be made precise using more advanced mathematics, the average value of tan x on the interval [0, $\pi/4$] is ≈ 0.44. Calculate the value of the average below; note $\pi/4 ≈ 0.785$.
$$\frac{\tan 0.13 + \tan 0.39 + \tan 0.65}{3}$$

56. Let ABC be a right triangle with $C = \pi/2$ and $AB = 1$. Extend the line segment AC to D with $AD = 1$.

Let θ be angle CAB, and justify these statements. (See the figure.)

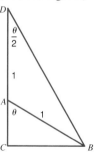

(a) Angle ADB equals angle ABD.
(b) Use triangle BAD and show angle ADB is $\theta/2$.
(c) Use triangle ABC and show sin $\theta = BC$ and cos $\theta = AC$.
(d) Use triangle BCD and show
$$\tan \frac{\theta}{2} = \frac{\sin \theta}{1 + \cos \theta}$$

Solve the right triangles in Probs. 57 to 61. Use the degree of accuracy justified by the given parts.

57. $A = 33.7°$, $b = 28.2$ **58.** $A = 61.2°$, $c = 652$

59. $A = 48.3°$, $a = 50.4$ **60.** $a = 33.7$, $b = 61.2$

61. $b = 6.178$, $c = 8.016$

62. How tall is a telephone pole if the angle of elevation to its top is 54.7° from a point 29.5 ft from its base?

63. A brook that runs S25.8°W for 404 ft is one side of a triangular lot. What is the area of the lot if the other sides run north-south and east-west?

64. Joey flew her plane 135 mi at 17.2°. In returning by bicycle, she followed roads due west and due south. How much further did she travel by bicycle than by plane?

65. Merritt jogged 3000 m N34°E and then S56°E for 2000 m. Find the direction and distance from the destination to the starting point.

66. At a point on a horizontal line, the angle of elevation of a hilltop is 18.7°. At a point, on the same line, 850 ft nearer the hill, the angle of elevation of the hilltop is 38.7°. How high is the hill?

67. Find both of the acute angles to the nearest tenth of a degree in the right triangle with $a = 8$, $b = 15$, $c = 17$.

7 Trigonometric Identities and Equations

We have dealt with algebraic identities such as $x^2 - y^2 = (x - y)(x + y)$ earlier in the book, and we made passing reference to trigonometric identities in Chap. 6, but mostly from a numerical standpoint. The ability to handle trigonometric identities easily is vital in order to be able to simplify trigonometric expressions, and to change the form of complicated expressions. This inevitably involves using good techniques in algebraic manipulation. The eight fundamental identities of Sec. 7.1 deal with just one angle in each identity: e.g., $\tan \theta = \sin \theta / \cos \theta$. From Sec. 7.2 on, we base our identities on two angles, such as $\cos(A + B) = \cos A \cos B - \sin A \sin B$. From these we will develop many other identities as well.

Applications of these ideas are given in areas such as art appreciation, conic sections, three-dimensional spherical coordinates, hanging cables, rotation of axes, a geometrical interpretation of each of the six trigonometric function values, and the fact that it is possible, though not preferable, to get by with only the sine function.

7.1 Fundamental Identities

If an equation involves at least one trigonometric function of a variable, it is called a **trigonometric equation.** An **identity** is an equation which is true for every value of the variable in its domain.

From the ratio definitions of the trigonometric functions in Eq. (6.4), we see that for all values of θ for which both functions are defined

$$\sin\theta\,\csc\theta = \frac{y}{r}\cdot\frac{r}{y} = 1$$

Consequently, we get identity (7.1) below. The other **reciprocal identities** (7.2) and (7.3) are proved similarly.

Reciprocal identities

$\sin\theta\,\csc\theta = 1$	(7.1)
$\cos\theta\,\sec\theta = 1$	(7.2)
$\tan\theta\,\cot\theta = 1$	(7.3)

These equations allow us, for instance, to replace a **factor** of $\csc\theta$ in the numerator by a **factor** of $\sin\theta$ in the denominator. Therefore,

$$\csc\theta(1 + \cos\theta) = \frac{1 + \cos\theta}{\sin\theta}$$

It is important to be able to use each identity in several forms. For instance you should become very familiar with the equivalent forms

$$\sin\theta\,\csc\theta = 1 \qquad \sin\theta = \frac{1}{\csc\theta} \qquad \csc\theta = \frac{1}{\sin\theta}$$

By using the definitions of the functions again, we get the identities

$$\frac{\sin\theta}{\cos\theta} = \frac{y/r}{x/r} = \frac{y}{x} = \tan\theta$$

and also

$$\frac{\cos\theta}{\sin\theta} = \frac{x/r}{y/r} = \frac{x}{y} = \cot\theta$$

Consequently we have the **ratio identities** below.

Ratio identities

$\tan\theta = \dfrac{\sin\theta}{\cos\theta}$	(7.4)
$\cot\theta = \dfrac{\cos\theta}{\sin\theta}$	(7.5)

In order to obtain the third set of fundamental identities, we begin with the Pythagorean relation

$$x^2 + y^2 = r^2 \tag{1}$$

If we divide each side by r^2, we have

$$\left(\frac{x}{r}\right)^2 + \left(\frac{y}{r}\right)^2 = \left(\frac{r}{r}\right)^2 = 1$$

Thus using the definitions $\cos\theta = x/r$ and $\sin\theta = y/r$, we have (7.6) below:

Pythagorean identities

$$\cos^2 \theta + \sin^2 \theta = 1 \qquad \text{(7.6)}$$

$$1 + \tan^2 \theta = \sec^2 \theta \qquad \text{(7.7)}$$

$$1 + \cot^2 \theta = \csc^2 \theta \qquad \text{(7.8)}$$

The identity (7.7) can be derived by dividing each side of (1) by x^2, giving

$$1 + \left(\frac{y}{x}\right)^2 = \left(\frac{r}{x}\right)^2$$

The identity (7.8) may be proved similarly, dividing (1) by y^2.

Alternative proof   Another proof of (7.6) relies on the fact that, by definition, $(\cos \theta, \sin \theta)$ is a point on the unit circle. Thus the coordinates must satisfy the equation $x^2 + y^2 = 1$, and hence

$$\cos^2 \theta + \sin^2 \theta = 1$$

Of the eight fundamental identities, only (7.6) is true for **every** real value of θ. Each of the others involves a function which is not defined somewhere, such as $\tan \theta$ at $\theta = 90°$ or $\pi/2$.

As a numerical illustration, we shall now calculate $\tan \theta$ and $\sin \theta/\cos \theta$ to 4 digits for $\theta = 57°$ or 0.9948:

$$\tan 57° \approx 1.540 \qquad \text{and} \qquad \frac{\sin 57°}{\cos 57°} \approx \frac{0.8387}{0.5446} \approx 1.540$$

In a similar manner if we use $21°$ or 0.3665, we get, accurate to 4 digits,

$$(\cos 21°)(\sec 21°) \approx (0.9336)(1.071) \approx 0.9999 \; (\approx 1)$$

Also to 4 digits, using $73°$ or 1.274:

$$1 + \cot^2 73° \approx 1 + (0.3057)^2 \approx 1 + 0.0935 = 1.0935$$

and $$\csc^2 73° \approx (1.046)^2 \approx 1.094$$

Once again we remind you that table and calculator values are **decimal approximations,** and calculations with them may unavoidably lead to **small** discrepancies.

On the other hand, the exact value of $\cos 21°$ multiplied by the **exact** value of $\sec 21°$ gives the product 1 **exactly,** due to the fact that $\cos \theta \sec \theta = 1$ is an **identity.** Also, **exact** values give

$$\tan 0.3579 \cdot \cot 0.3579 = 1$$

The most desirable form for a trigonometric expression depends on how the expression will be used, and there are usually several procedures available for changing the form. A considerable amount of practice is required to become adept at problems of this type. Frequently, the required process involves performing the indicated algebraic operations before using one or more of the fundamental trigonometric identities.

▶ **EXAMPLE 1**   Change $4 + (\tan \theta - \cot \theta)^2$ to $\sec^2 \theta + \csc^2 \theta$.

Solution   If we square the binomial in the first expression, we have

$$4 + (\tan \theta - \cot \theta)^2$$

$$= 4 + \tan^2 \theta - 2 \tan \theta \cot \theta + \cot^2 \theta$$

$$= 4 + \tan^2 \theta - 2 + \cot^2 \theta \qquad \text{since } \tan \theta \cot \theta = 1$$

$$= 2 + \tan^2 \theta + \cot^2 \theta$$

$$= 1 + \tan^2 \theta + 1 + \cot^2 \theta \qquad 2 = 1 + 1$$

$$= \sec^2 \theta + \csc^2 \theta \qquad \text{using (7.7) and (7.8)}$$

EXAMPLE 2   Change $\tan \theta(\sin \theta + \cot \theta \cos \theta)$ to $\sec \theta$.

Solution

$$\tan \theta(\sin \theta + \cot \theta \cos \theta) \qquad \text{given}$$

$$= \tan \theta \sin \theta + \tan \theta \cot \theta \cos \theta \qquad \text{multiplying}$$

$$= \tan \theta \sin \theta + \cos \theta \qquad \text{using } \tan \theta \cot \theta = 1$$

$$= \frac{\sin \theta}{\cos \theta} \sin \theta + \cos \theta \qquad \text{using (7.4)}$$

$$= \frac{\sin^2 \theta + \cos^2 \theta}{\cos \theta} \qquad \text{add with common denominator}$$

$$= \frac{1}{\cos \theta} \qquad \text{using (7.6)}$$

$$= \sec \theta \qquad \text{using (7.2)}$$

There is no procedure that is always the desirable one for proving that an equation is an identity. There are, however, procedures that are usually worth trying.

Proving identities

1. In most cases, work with the more complicated side of the equation.
2. Perform the indicated algebraic operations.
3. Factor either side, if possible.
4. If the denominator of one side contains only one term and the numerator is the sum or difference of several terms, do the indicated division: use $(a + b)/c = a/c + b/c$.
5. Multiply the numerator and denominator of a term by the same factor. This just multiplies that term by 1.
6. If no procedure above seems to be applicable, express the function values in the more complicated side in terms of sines and cosines, or else in terms of the function (if there is only one) that appears in the other side.

EXAMPLE 3   Prove that

$$\frac{\cos A}{\csc A - 1} + \frac{\cos A}{\csc A + 1} = 2 \tan A$$

is an identity.

Solution   The left-hand side is the more complicated; hence, we shall begin by performing the indicated addition. The common denominator is $\csc^2 A - 1$, and by using it we have

$$\frac{\cos A}{\csc A - 1} + \frac{\cos A}{\csc A + 1} = \frac{\cos A(\csc A + 1) + \cos A(\csc A - 1)}{\csc^2 A - 1}$$

$$= \frac{\cos A \csc A + \cos A + \cos A \csc A - \cos A}{\csc^2 A - 1}$$

$$= \frac{2 \cos A \csc A}{\cot^2 A} \qquad \text{combining terms in numerator and using (7.8) in denominator}$$

$$= \frac{2 \cos A}{\sin A \cdot \cot^2 A} \qquad \text{using (7.1)}$$

$$= \frac{2 \cot A}{\cot^2 A} \qquad \text{using (7.5)}$$

$$= \frac{2}{\cot A} \qquad \text{removing factor of } \cot A$$

$$= 2 \tan A \qquad \text{using (7.3)}$$

◢

▶ **EXAMPLE 4**   Prove that $\cos^4 B - \sin^4 B = \cos^2 B - \sin^2 B$ is an identity.

Solution   If we factor the left-hand side using $x^4 - y^4 = (x^2 + y^2)(x^2 - y^2)$, we have

$$\cos^4 B - \sin^4 B = (\cos^2 B + \sin^2 B)(\cos^2 B - \sin^2 B)$$

$$= \cos^2 B - \sin^2 B \qquad \text{since } \cos^2 B + \sin^2 B = 1$$

◢

▶ **EXAMPLE 5**   Show that

$$\frac{\cos \theta}{1 - \sin \theta} - \tan \theta = \sec \theta$$

is an identity.

Solution   We shall work with the left-hand side since it is the more complicated:

$$\frac{\cos \theta}{1 - \sin \theta} - \tan \theta = \frac{\cos \theta}{1 - \sin \theta} - \frac{\sin \theta}{\cos \theta} \qquad \text{by (7.4)}$$

$$= \frac{\cos^2 \theta - \sin \theta + \sin^2 \theta}{(1 - \sin \theta) \cos \theta} \qquad \text{adding fractions}$$

$$= \frac{1 - \sin \theta}{(1 - \sin \theta) \cos \theta} \qquad \text{by (7.6)}$$

$$= \frac{1}{\cos \theta} \qquad \text{removing common factor}$$

$$= \sec \theta$$

◢

Another way to verify the identity in Example 5 is to multiply the numerator and denominator of the first quantity by the same nonzero expression:

$$\frac{\cos \theta}{1 - \sin \theta} - \tan \theta = \frac{\cos \theta(1 + \sin \theta)}{(1 - \sin \theta)(1 + \sin \theta)} - \tan \theta$$

$$= \frac{\cos \theta(1 + \sin \theta)}{\cos^2 \theta} - \tan \theta$$

$$= \frac{1 + \sin \theta}{\cos \theta} - \tan \theta$$

$$= \frac{1}{\cos \theta} + \frac{\sin \theta}{\cos \theta} - \tan \theta$$

$$= \sec \theta$$

▶ **EXAMPLE 6**   Verify the identity

$$\frac{\cos \theta + \sin \theta \cot \theta}{\sin \theta} = 2 \cot \theta$$

Solution   Since the denominator of the left-hand side is a single term and the numerator is a sum, we begin by writing the expression as the sum of separate fractions:

$$\frac{\cos \theta + \sin \theta \cot \theta}{\sin \theta} = \frac{\cos \theta}{\sin \theta} + \frac{\sin \theta \cot \theta}{\sin \theta}$$

$$= \cot \theta + \cot \theta \qquad \text{by (7.5)}$$

$$= 2 \cot \theta \qquad \blacktriangleleft$$

NOTE   In proving identities, the best procedure is to work with one side by itself and change it into the same form as the other side. Alternatively, we may work with each side **separately** in an attempt to get both to the same form. Sometimes it helps to rewrite $f(\theta) = g(\theta)$ as $f(\theta) - g(\theta) = 0$.

In addition to the eight fundamental identities already given in this section, we shall restate several basic identities given in Chap. 6, along with a few counterparts based on this section. In the cofunction theorem, we may of course use $\pi/2$ or $90°$.

Even and odd functions

$$\sin (-\theta) = -\sin \theta \qquad \cos (-\theta) = \cos \theta \qquad \tan (-\theta) = -\tan \theta$$

$$\csc (-\theta) = -\csc \theta \qquad \sec (-\theta) = \sec \theta \qquad \cot (-\theta) = -\cot \theta$$

Cofunction theorem ($\pi/2$ or $90°$)

$$\sin \left(\frac{\pi}{2} - \theta\right) = \cos \theta \qquad \tan \left(\frac{\pi}{2} - \theta\right) = \cot \theta \qquad \sec \left(\frac{\pi}{2} - \theta\right) = \csc \theta$$

$$\cos \left(\frac{\pi}{2} - \theta\right) = \sin \theta \qquad \cot \left(\frac{\pi}{2} - \theta\right) = \tan \theta \qquad \csc \left(\frac{\pi}{2} - \theta\right) = \sec \theta$$

Double your pleasure

Given one identity in $\sin x$, $\cos x$, $\tan x$, $\cot x$, $\sec x$, and $\csc x$, we can **get another identity** by replacing each function value by the corresponding cofunction value. Just replace

$$\text{sin } x \text{ by cos } x \qquad \text{cos } x \text{ by sin } x \qquad \text{tan } x \text{ by cot } x$$

$$\text{cot } x \text{ by tan } x \qquad \text{sec } x \text{ by csc } x \qquad \text{csc } x \text{ by sec } x$$

For example, the identity

$$\tan x \sin x + \cos x = \sec x \qquad \text{given}$$

becomes, upon using the cofunction theorem

$$\cot (90° - x) \cos (90° - x) + \sin (90° - x) = \csc (90° - x)$$

Now, using θ for $90° - x$ gives the new identity

$$\cot \theta \cos \theta + \sin \theta = \csc \theta$$

which, except for the name of the variable, is clearly the same identity as

$$\cot x \cos x + \sin x = \csc x$$

Fundamental identities

$$\sin \theta \csc \theta = 1 \qquad \cos \theta \sec \theta = 1 \qquad \tan \theta \cot \theta = 1$$

$$\tan \theta = \frac{\sin \theta}{\cos \theta} \qquad \cot \theta = \frac{\cos \theta}{\sin \theta}$$

$$\sin^2 \theta + \cos^2 \theta = 1 \qquad 1 + \tan^2 \theta = \sec^2 \theta \qquad 1 + \cot^2 \theta = \csc^2 \theta$$

EXERCISE 7.1

Reduce the first expression to the second in each of Probs. 1 to 12.

1. $\cos A/\sec A$, $1 - \sin^2 A$ 2. $\cot A \sin A$, $1/\sec A$
3. $\sin^2 A$, $(1 - \cos A)(1 + \cos A)$
4. $\tan A \cot A$, $\sec^2 A - \tan^2 A$
5. $\sec \theta \cos \theta$, $\csc^2 \theta - \cot^2 \theta$
6. $\cos \theta \tan \theta \csc \theta$, $\sin \theta \cot \theta \sec \theta$
7. $\cos \theta \tan \theta$, $\sin \theta$ 8. $\sin \theta \sec \theta$, $\tan \theta$
9. $\sin B \cot B$, $\cos B$ 10. $\cos B \csc B$, $\cot B$
11. $\sec B/\csc B$, $\tan B$ 12. $\cot B/\csc B$, $\cos B$

Prove the identities in Probs. 13 to 68.
13. $\tan x + \cot x = \sec x \csc x$
14. $\sin x + \cos x \cot x = \csc x$
15. $\sec x - \cos x = \sin x \tan x$
16. $\tan x + \sec x = \sec x(1 + \sin x)$
17. $\sin \beta(\csc \beta + \sin \beta \sec^2 \beta) = \sec^2 \beta$
18. $(1 + \sin \beta)(1 - \sin \beta) = \cos^2 \beta$
19. $(\csc \beta + 1)(\csc \beta - 1) = \cot^2 \beta$
20. $\sec^2 \beta - \csc^2 \beta = \tan^2 \beta - \cot^2 \beta$
21. $1 - \cos^4 A = 2 \sin^2 A - \sin^4 A$
22. $\csc^4 A = \cot^4 A + 2 \cot^2 A + 1$
23. $\tan^2 A \sec^2 A = \sec^4 A - \sec^2 A$
24. $\cos^2 A - \sin^2 A \cos^2 A = \cos^4 A$

25. $\dfrac{\sec t}{\sin t} - \dfrac{\sin t}{\cos t} = \cot t$

26. $\dfrac{\csc t}{\cos t} - \dfrac{\cos t}{\sin t} = \tan t$

27. $\dfrac{\tan t}{\csc t} + \dfrac{\sin t}{\tan t} = \sec t$

28. $\dfrac{\cos t}{\cot t} + \dfrac{\cot t}{\sec t} = \csc t$

29. $\dfrac{1}{1 + \sin u} + \dfrac{1}{1 - \sin u} = 2 \sec^2 u$

30. $\dfrac{1 + \csc u}{\cot u} = \dfrac{\cos u}{1 - \sin u}$

31. $\dfrac{\cos u}{\sec u - \tan u} = \dfrac{\cos^2 u}{1 - \sin u}$

32. $\dfrac{1 - \sec u}{1 + \sec u} = \dfrac{\cos u - 1}{\cos u + 1}$

33. $\tan (-\theta) \sin (-\theta) + \cos (-\theta) = \sec (-\theta)$
34. $\sin (-\theta) \tan (-\theta) \sec (-\theta) + 1 = \sec^2 \theta$
35. $\sin (-\theta) - \csc (-\theta) = \cot \theta \cos (-\theta)$
36. $\cot \theta - \tan (-\theta) = \csc \theta \sec (-\theta)$
37. $\cos (\pi/2 - A) + \cos A \tan (\pi/2 - A) = \csc A$
38. $\cot (\pi/2 - A) + \tan A = 2 \sin A \csc (\pi/2 - A)$

39. $\csc A - \cos(A - \pi/2) = \tan(\pi/2 - A)\cos(-A)$

40. $\sin(\pi/2 - A)[\tan(-A) + \cot(-A)] = \csc(-A)$

41. $(\sin y + \cos y)(\tan y + \cot y) = \sec y + \csc y$

42. $(\sec y + \csc y)(\cos y - \sin y) = \cot y - \tan y$

43. $\dfrac{\cos y + \sin y}{\cos y - \sin y} = \dfrac{\cot y + 1}{\cot y - 1}$

44. $\dfrac{1 + \sec y}{1 - \sec y} = \dfrac{\cos y + 1}{\cos y - 1}$

45. $\dfrac{1}{1 - \cos B} + \dfrac{1}{1 + \cos B} = 2\csc^2 B$

46. $\dfrac{\tan B}{1 - \cot B} + \dfrac{\cot B}{1 - \tan B} = 1 + \tan B + \cot B$

47. $\dfrac{\cos B}{\tan B} + \dfrac{\sin B}{\cot B} = \sec B + \csc B - \sin B - \cos B$

48. $\dfrac{\cos B}{1 - \tan B} + \dfrac{\sin B}{1 - \cot B} = \cos B + \sin B$

49. $\dfrac{1 - \sin s}{1 + \sin s} = (\sec s - \tan s)^2$

50. $\dfrac{1 - \tan^2 s}{1 + \tan^2 s} = 1 - 2\sin^2 s$

51. $\dfrac{\cos^2 s - \cot s}{\sin^2 s - \tan s} = \cot^2 s$

52. $\dfrac{\csc s + \cot s}{\tan s + \sin s} = \cot s\csc s$

53. $\dfrac{\tan \alpha}{1 + \cos \alpha} + \dfrac{\sin \alpha}{1 - \cos \alpha} = \cot \alpha + \sec \alpha \csc \alpha$

54. $\dfrac{\sec \alpha + \tan \alpha}{\cos \alpha - \tan \alpha - \sec \alpha} = -\csc \alpha$

55. $\dfrac{\cot \alpha}{\sec \alpha - \tan \alpha} - \dfrac{\cos \alpha}{\sec \alpha + \tan \alpha} = \sin \alpha + \csc \alpha$

56. $\dfrac{1 + \cos \alpha}{1 - \cos \alpha} - \dfrac{1 - \cos \alpha}{1 + \cos \alpha} = 4\cot \alpha \csc \alpha$

57. $\sin x + \cos x + \dfrac{\sin x}{\cot x} = \sec x + \csc x - \dfrac{\cos x}{\tan x}$

58. $\dfrac{\tan x - \tan^2 x + \sec^2 x}{\sec x} = \sin x + \cos x$

59. $\dfrac{2\sin^2 x - 1}{\sin x \cos x} = \tan x - \cot x$

60. $\dfrac{1 + \cos x}{1 - \cos x} - \dfrac{\csc x - \cot x}{\csc x + \cot x} = 4\cot x \csc x$

61. $\dfrac{1 + \sin y}{1 - \sin y} - \dfrac{\sec y - \tan y}{\sec y + \tan y} = 4\tan y \sec y$

62. $\dfrac{1 - 2\sin y}{\cos^2 y} - \dfrac{1 - 3\sin y}{1 - \sin y} = 3\tan^2 y$

63. $\dfrac{\cos y + \sin y}{\cos y - \sin y} + \dfrac{\cot y - 1}{\cot y + 1} = \dfrac{-2}{\sin^2 y - \cos^2 y}$

64. $\dfrac{1}{\sin y + \cos y} + \dfrac{1}{\sin y - \cos y} = \dfrac{2\sin y}{2\sin^2 y - 1}$

In identities 65 to 68, remember that $\ln x = \log_e x$.

Useful in calculus

65. $\ln|\sec t| = -\ln|\cos t|$

66. $\ln|\sin t| + \ln|\csc t| = 0$

67. $\ln|\sec t + \tan t| = -\ln|\sec t - \tan t|$

68. $\ln|\csc t + \cot t| + \ln|\csc t - \cot t| = 0$

In Probs. 69 to 72, write the given function value using only $\sin A$. For instance,

$$\cos A = \pm\sqrt{1 - \sin^2 A}$$

Only need $\sin A$

69. $\tan A$ **70.** $\cot A$ **71.** $\sec A$ **72.** $\csc A$

In Probs. 73 to 76, show that the equation is **not an identity** by finding a value of θ with $0 \le \theta < 2\pi$ or $0° \le \theta < 360°$ for which the equation fails.

73. $(\sin \theta + \cos \theta)^2 = 1$ **74.** $\sin(2\theta) = 2\sin \theta$

75. $(1 + \tan \theta)^2 = \sec^2 \theta$

76. $\tan(\theta + 45°) = \tan \theta + \tan 45°$

77. *Circle* Let $x = 2 + \sin t$ and $y = 3 - \cos t$. Show that for every value of t, the point (x, y) lies on the circle with radius 1 and center $(2, 3)$, which has the equation $(x - 2)^2 + (y - 3)^2 = 1$.

78. *Ellipse* Let $x = 3 + 4\cos t$ and $y = -9 + 7\sin t$. Show that for every value of t, the point (x, y) lies on the ellipse

$$\frac{(x - 3)^2}{16} + \frac{(y + 9)^2}{49} = 1$$

79. *Hyperbola* Let $x = -5 - 3\tan t$ and $y = 8 + 8\sec t$. Show that for every value of t, the point (x, y) lies on the hyperbola

$$\frac{(y - 8)^2}{64} - \frac{(x + 5)^2}{9} = 1$$

80. *Spherical coordinates* For three-dimensional **spherical coordinates** (ρ, ϕ, θ) and rectangular coordinates (x, y, z), we have the relations

$$x = \rho \sin \phi \cos \theta \qquad y = \rho \sin \phi \sin \theta$$
$$z = \rho \cos \phi$$

Show that (1) $x^2 + y^2 + z^2 = \rho^2$, and (2) $y/x = \tan\theta$.

81. *Hyperbolic functions* The **circular functions** are $\sin\theta$ and $\cos\theta$, so called because $(\cos\theta, \sin\theta)$ is on the unit circle $x^2 + y^2 = 1$. The **hyperbolic functions** are defined by

$$\cosh t = \frac{e^t + e^t}{2} \quad \text{and} \quad \sinh t = \frac{e^t - e^{-t}}{2}$$

Show that $(\cosh t, \sinh t)$ satisfies $x^2 - y^2 = 1$. The hyperbolic cosine $\cosh t$ can be used to describe the position of a cable hanging between two points—the curve is called a **catenary.**

82. *Rotation of axes* Show that if $t = x\cos\theta + y\sin\theta$ and $u = y\cos\theta - x\sin\theta$, then $t^2 + u^2 = x^2 + y^2$.

83. *tan θ and sec θ as line segments* Use Fig. 7.1 and the similar triangles *ODB* and *OAC* to show that $\tan\theta = AC$. Now use triangle *OAC* and $1 + \tan^2\theta = \sec^2\theta$ to show that $\sec\theta = OC$.

84. In Fig. 7.1, why is angle *FEO* equal to θ? Now use triangle *OFE* and $1 + \cot^2\theta = \csc^2\theta$ to show that

$$\cot\theta = FE \quad \text{and} \quad \csc\theta = OE$$

Prove the identities in Probs. 85 to 88.

85. $\dfrac{\sin A \cos B + \cos A \sin B}{\cos A \cos B - \sin A \sin B} = \dfrac{\tan A + \tan B}{1 - \tan A \tan B}$

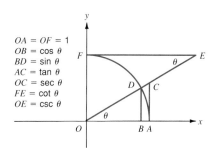

$OA = OF = 1$
$OB = \cos\theta$
$BD = \sin\theta$
$AC = \tan\theta$
$OC = \sec\theta$
$FE = \cot\theta$
$OE = \csc\theta$

FIGURE 7.1

Hint: Divide each term in the left-hand side by $\cos A \cos B$. This is used later to derive Eq. (7.19).

86. $\dfrac{\tan A - \tan B}{1 + \tan A \tan B} = \dfrac{\cot B - \cot A}{1 + \cot A \cot B}$

Hint: Multiply the left-hand side by $\cot A \cot B / \cot A \cot B$.

87. $\dfrac{(\sin A + \cos B)^2 + (\cos A + \sin B)(\cos A - \sin B)}{\sin A + \cos B}$

$= 2\cos B$

Hint: Use $\cos^2\theta + \sin^2\theta = 1$.

88. $\dfrac{\tan A + \tan B}{\cot A + \cot B} = \tan A \tan B$

Hint: Change the left-hand side to sines and cosines, then add the numerator and denominator separately.

89. Simplify $\sqrt{36 - x^2}$ after replacing x by $6\sin\theta$.
90. Simplify $\sqrt{49 + x^2}$ after replacing x by $7\tan\theta$.
91. Simplify $\sqrt{4 - x^2}$ after replacing x by $2\cos\theta$.
92. Simplify $\sqrt{x^2 - 16}$ after replacing x by $4\sec\theta$.

7.2 The Identities cos $(A \pm B)$ and sin $(A \pm B)$

So far we have only looked at function values of one angle, such as $\cos\theta$ or $\sin x$ or $\tan A$. We will in this section see how to evaluate $\cos(A - B)$ if we know the function values of A and of B. It is usually true that

$$\cos(A - B) \neq \cos A - \cos B$$

In fact, if $A = \pi/3$ and $B = \pi/4$, then to four decimals

$$\cos A - \cos B = \cos\frac{\pi}{3} - \cos\frac{\pi}{4} = \frac{1}{2} - \frac{\sqrt{2}}{2} = -0.2071$$

$$\cos(A - B) = \cos\left(\frac{\pi}{3} - \frac{\pi}{4}\right) = \cos\frac{\pi}{12} = \cos 0.2618 = 0.9659$$

We will now derive the formula for $\cos(A - B)$.

In Fig. 7.2, we have angles A, B, and $A - B$ in standard position with their terminal sides intersecting the **unit circle** at P_2, P_3, and P_4. The following argument works for any angles A and B, but in the figure we have $0 < A - B < B < A$. The points on the unit circle are

$$P_1 = (1, 0) \qquad\qquad P_4 = (\cos (A - B), \sin (A - B))$$

$$P_2 = (\cos A, \sin A) \qquad P_3 = (\cos B, \sin B)$$

The arc length from P_1 to P_4 is the same as the arc length from P_3 to P_2; hence the chords P_2P_3 and P_4P_1 are of equal length. If we apply the distance formula, we find that

$$\begin{aligned}
(P_2P_3)^2 &= (\cos A - \cos B)^2 + (\sin A - \sin B)^2 \\
&= \cos^2 A - 2 \cos A \cos B + \cos^2 B \\
&\quad + \sin^2 A - 2 \sin A \sin B + \sin^2 B \\
&= 2 - 2(\cos A \cos B + \sin A \sin B) \qquad \text{by (7.6)}
\end{aligned}$$

and
$$\begin{aligned}
(P_4P_1)^2 &= [\cos (A - B) - 1]^2 + [\sin (A - B) - 0]^2 \\
&= \cos^2 (A - B) - 2 \cos (A - B) + 1 + \sin^2 (A - B) \\
&= 2 - 2 \cos (A - B) \qquad \text{since } \cos^2 (A - B) + \sin^2 (A - B) = 1
\end{aligned}$$

We now equate the values of $(P_2P_3)^2$ and $(P_4P_1)^2$ and find that

$$\cos (A - B) = \cos A \cos B + \sin A \sin B \qquad\qquad \textbf{(7.9)}$$

This equations is known as the identity for the **cosine of a difference,** and it should be remembered in words:

*The cosine of a difference is the product of
the cosines plus the product of the sines*

The quantities A and B may be angles expressed in degrees or radians, or they may be real numbers. Equation (7.9) may be used for changing the form of a trigono-

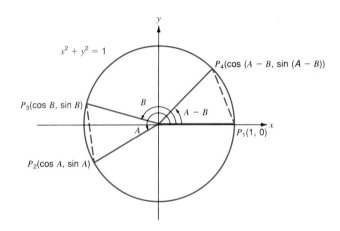

FIGURE 7.2

metric equation, or for the numerical calculation of exact function values. We shall also use it to derive several other identities.

EXAMPLE 1   Find the exact value of $\cos 15° = \cos \pi/12$.

Solution   We shall think of 15° as 45° − 30°, or $\pi/4 - \pi/6$, so as to be able to use (7.9). If this is done, we have

$$\cos 15° = \cos (45° - 30°)$$

$$= \cos 45° \cos 30° + \sin 45° \sin 30°$$

$$= \frac{\sqrt{2}}{2} \frac{\sqrt{3}}{2} + \frac{\sqrt{2}}{2} \frac{1}{2}$$

$$= \frac{\sqrt{6} + \sqrt{2}}{4}$$

This is the **exact value,** and an **approximation** can be obtained by calculator or by using $\sqrt{2}$ and $\sqrt{6}$ in decimal form. Thus $\cos 15° = \cos \pi/12 \approx 0.9659$.   ◄

EXAMPLE 2   Just as a check for consistency, find cos 30° using (7.9).

Solution
$$\cos 30° = \cos (150° - 120°)$$

$$= \cos 150° \cos 120° + \sin 150° \sin 120°$$

$$= \frac{-\sqrt{3}}{2} \frac{-1}{2} + \frac{1}{2} \frac{\sqrt{3}}{2}$$

$$= 2\left(\frac{\sqrt{3}}{4}\right) = \frac{\sqrt{3}}{2}$$ ◄

If we replace A in (7.9) by $\pi/2$, we get

$$\cos \left(\frac{\pi}{2} - B\right) = \cos \frac{\pi}{2} \cos B + \sin \frac{\pi}{2} \sin B = \sin B$$

since $\cos \pi/2 = 0$ and $\sin \pi/2 = 1$. Therefore,

$$\cos \left(\frac{\pi}{2} - B\right) = \sin B \qquad (7.10)$$

for any angle or real number B. Also $\cos (90° - B) = \sin B$.

If, in (7.10), B is replaced by $\pi/2 - B$, we get

$$\cos \left[\frac{\pi}{2} - \left(\frac{\pi}{2} - B\right)\right] = \sin \left(\frac{\pi}{2} - B\right)$$

Therefore
$$\sin \left(\frac{\pi}{2} - B\right) = \cos B \qquad (7.11)$$

since $\pi/2 - (\pi/2 - B) = B$. Also $\sin (90° - B) = \cos B$.

The identities for the other functions of $\pi/2 - B$ or $90° - B$ can be formed readily by using the relations between these functions and sine and cosine. If this is done using (7.10) and (7.11), we have another proof of the **cofunction theorem.**

Cofunction Theorem   Any trigonometric function of any angle or number is equal to the cofunction of the complementary angle or number.

▶ **EXAMPLE 3**   Verify the use of the cofunction theorem in these calculations.

Solution   (a) $\cos 59° = \sin (90° - 59°) = \sin 31° = 0.5150$

(b) $\tan 161° = \tan [90° - (-71°)]$
                                              $= \cot (-71°) = -\cot 71° = -0.3443$

Using $\pi/2 \approx 1.5708$ gives

(c) $\sin 0.6448 = \cos (1.5708 - 0.6448)$
                                              $= \cos 0.9260 = 0.6010$

(d) $\sec \dfrac{\pi}{15} = \csc \left(\dfrac{\pi}{2} - \dfrac{\pi}{15} \right)$

                                              $= \csc \dfrac{13\pi}{30} = \csc 1.3614 = 1.0223$ ◀

Using $A = 0$ in (7.9) gives

$$\cos (-B) = \cos (0 - B) = \cos 0 \cos B + \sin 0 \sin B = \cos B$$

showing again that the cosine function is even.

Since (7.9) is true for all angles and all real numbers, it is true if we replace B by $-B$. If that is done, we get

$$\cos (A + B) = \cos [A - (-B)]$$
$$= \cos A \cos (-B) + \sin A \sin (-B)$$
$$= \cos A \cos B - \sin A \sin B$$

since $\cos (-B) = \cos B$ and $\sin (-B) = -\sin B$. Consequently we have the formula for the **cosine of a sum:**

$$\cos (A + B) = \cos A \cos B - \sin A \sin B \qquad\qquad \textbf{(7.12)}$$

▶ **EXAMPLE 4**   Find the exact value of $\cos 75° = \cos 5\pi/12$.

Solution $\cos 75° = \cos (45° + 30°)$

                $= \cos 45° \cos 30° - \sin 45° \sin 30°$ by (7.12)

                $= \dfrac{\sqrt{2}}{2} \dfrac{\sqrt{3}}{2} - \dfrac{\sqrt{2}}{2} \dfrac{1}{2} = \dfrac{\sqrt{6} - \sqrt{2}}{4}$ exact value

                ≈ 0.2588 approximation to 4 digits   ◀

▶ **EXAMPLE 5**   Find cos $(x - y)$ if sin $x = \frac{24}{25}$, cos $y = \frac{4}{5}$, x is in quadrant II, and y is in quadrant IV.

Solution   With the given values and quadrants, we may use right triangles to find

$$\cos x = \frac{-7}{25} \quad \text{and} \quad \sin y = \frac{-3}{5}$$

and thus

$$\cos (x - y) = \cos x \cos y + \sin x \sin y$$

$$= \frac{-7}{25} \cdot \frac{4}{5} + \frac{24}{25} \cdot \frac{-3}{5} = \frac{-28 - 72}{125} = \frac{-100}{125} = \frac{-4}{5} \qquad ◢$$

We will now derive formulas for sin $(A \pm B)$ to go with the ones we already have for cos $(A \pm B)$. We begin by using the cosine formulas (7.9), (7.10), and (7.11). If we use the cofunction theorem (7.10) with B replaced by $A + B$, we have

$$\sin (A + B) = \cos \left[\frac{\pi}{2} - (A + B) \right]$$

$$= \cos \left[\left(\frac{\pi}{2} - A \right) - B \right] \qquad \text{by algebra}$$

$$= \cos \left(\frac{\pi}{2} - A \right) \cos B + \sin \left(\frac{\pi}{2} - A \right) \sin B \qquad \text{cosine of a difference}$$

$$= \sin A \cos B + \cos A \sin B \qquad \text{by (7.10) and (7.11)}$$

Thus we get the formula for the **sine of a sum:**

$$\sin (A + B) = \sin A \cos B + \cos A \sin B \qquad \textbf{(7.13)}$$

To obtain a formula for the sine of a difference, say $A - B$, we use (7.13) by writing

$$\sin (A - B) = \sin [A + (-B)] \qquad \text{by algebra}$$

$$= \sin A \cos (-B) + \cos A \sin (-B) \qquad \text{sine of a sum}$$

$$= \sin A \cos B - \cos A \sin B \qquad \text{even and odd functions}$$

Here is the formula for the **sine of a difference:**

$$\sin (A - B) = \sin A \cos B - \cos A \sin B \qquad \textbf{(7.14)}$$

▶ **EXAMPLE 6**   Find sin $105° = \sin 7\pi/12$ by using the formula for the sine of a sum.

Solution $\sin 105° = \sin (60° + 45°)$

$$= \sin 60° \cos 45° + \cos 60° \sin 45°$$

$$= \left(\frac{\sqrt{3}}{2} \right) \left(\frac{\sqrt{2}}{2} \right) + \left(\frac{1}{2} \right) \left(\frac{\sqrt{2}}{2} \right)$$

$$\sin 105° = \frac{\sqrt{6} + \sqrt{2}}{4} \qquad \text{exact value}$$

$$\approx 0.9659 \qquad \text{approximation to 4 digits}$$

This is consistent with Example 1 since

$$\sin 105° = \sin 75° = \cos 15°$$ ◀

▶ **EXAMPLE 7**   Use the formula for $\sin(A - B)$ to evaluate

$$\sin 55° \cos 25° - \cos 55° \sin 25°$$

Solution   Using $A = 55°$ and $B = 25°$ gives

$$\sin 55° \cos 25° - \cos 55° \sin 25° = \sin(55° - 25°) = \sin 30° = 0.5$$

which is the exact value. Calculator or table values give

$$(0.8192)(0.9063) - (0.5736)(0.4226) \approx 0.7424 - 0.2424 = 0.5$$ ◀

▶ **EXAMPLE 8**   Find the exact value of $\sin(\theta + \phi)$ if θ and ϕ are in quadrant I with $\cos \theta = \frac{3}{5}$ and $\tan \phi = \frac{15}{8}$.

Solution   Using right triangles shows that $\sin \theta = \frac{4}{5}$, $\sin \phi = \frac{15}{17}$, and $\cos \phi = \frac{8}{17}$. Hence the given expression is

$$\sin(\theta + \phi) = \sin \theta \cos \phi + \cos \theta \sin \phi$$
$$= \left(\frac{4}{5}\right)\left(\frac{8}{17}\right) + \left(\frac{3}{5}\right)\left(\frac{15}{17}\right) = \frac{32 + 45}{85} = \frac{77}{85}$$ ◀

▶ **EXAMPLE 9**   Prove that $\cos(\alpha - \beta) - \cos(\alpha + \beta) = 2 \sin \alpha \sin \beta$.

Solution   If we use (7.9) and (7.12) we get

$$\cos(\alpha - \beta) - \cos(\alpha + \beta)$$
$$= \cos \alpha \cos \beta + \sin \alpha \sin \beta - (\cos \alpha \cos \beta - \sin \alpha \sin \beta)$$
$$= 2 \sin \alpha \sin \beta$$ ◀

▶ **EXAMPLE 10**   Simplify $\sin(30° + \theta) + \sin(30° - \theta)$.

Solution   The given expression equals

$$\sin 30° \cos \theta + \cos 30° \sin \theta + \sin 30° \cos \theta - \cos 30° \sin \theta$$
$$= \tfrac{1}{2} \cos \theta + \tfrac{1}{2} \cos \theta = \cos \theta$$ ◀

Summary

$\cos(x - y) = \cos x \cos y + \sin x \sin y$	**(7.9)**
$\cos(x + y) = \cos x \cos y - \sin x \sin y$	**(7.12)**
$\sin(x + y) = \sin x \cos y + \cos x \sin y$	**(7.13)**
$\sin(x - y) = \sin x \cos y - \cos x \sin y$	**(7.14)**

EXERCISE 7.2

Find the exact function value in Probs. 1 to 12.
1. $\cos 195°$, use $195° = 240° - 45°$
2. $\cos 165°$, use $165° = 120° + 45°$
3. $\cos 255°$, use $255° = 135° + 120°$
4. $\cos 285°$, use $285° = 330° - 45°$
5. $\sin 15°$ 6. $\sin 165°$
7. $\sin 195°$ 8. $\sin 345°$
9. $\sin 195° + \sin 105°$ 10. $\sin 105° - \sin 15°$
11. $\cos 195° - \cos 75°$ 12. $\cos 255° + \cos 165°$

Find $\cos (A + B)$ and $\cos (A - B)$ if A, B, and their function values are as given in Probs. 13 to 16.
13. $\cos A = \frac{3}{5}$, A acute; $\cos B = \frac{7}{25}$, B acute
14. $\sin A = \frac{4}{5}$, $\pi/2 < A < \pi$; $\cos B = -\frac{5}{13}$, $\pi < B < 3\pi/2$
15. $\cos A = \frac{3}{5}$, $3\pi/2 < A < 2\pi$; $\sin B = -\frac{4}{5}$, $\pi < B < 3\pi/2$
16. $\sin A = -\frac{7}{25}$, $3\pi/2 < A < 2\pi$; $\sin B = \frac{24}{25}$, $\pi/2 < B < \pi$

Find $\sin (A + B)$ and $\sin (A - B)$ if A, B, and their function values are as given in Probs. 17 to 20.
17. $\cos A = \frac{3}{5}$, $0 < A < \pi/2$; $\cos B = -\frac{4}{5}$, $\pi/2 < B < \pi$
18. $\cos A = -\frac{5}{13}$, $\pi < A < 3\pi/2$; $\sin B = \frac{3}{5}$, $\pi/2 < B < \pi$
19. $\sin A = -\frac{8}{17}$, $3\pi/2 < A < 2\pi$; $\cos B = \frac{12}{13}$, $0 < B < \pi/2$
20. $\sin A = \frac{4}{5}$, $\pi/2 < A < \pi$; $\sin B = -\frac{7}{25}$, $3\pi/2 < B < 2\pi$

In Probs. 21 to 24, let x and y be first-quadrant angles with $\tan x = \frac{3}{4}$ and $\sec y = \frac{25}{24}$. Find the exact values below.
21. $\sin (x + y) + \sin (x - y)$
22. $\cos (x + y) - \cos (x - y)$
23. $\sin (x + y) \cdot \sin (x - y)$
24. $\cos (x + y) \cdot \cos (x - y)$

Prove the statements in Probs. 25 to 32.
25. $\cos (\pi/2 + \theta) = -\sin \theta$
26. $\cos (\pi - \theta) = -\cos \theta$
27. $\cos (\pi + \theta) = -\cos \theta$
28. $\cos (3\pi/2 + \theta) = \sin \theta$
29. $\sin (\pi - \theta) = \sin \theta$ 30. $\sin (\pi + \theta) = -\sin \theta$
31. $\sin (3\pi/2 + \theta) = -\cos \theta$
32. $\sin (\pi/2 + \theta) = \cos \theta$

In Probs. 33 to 40, write the expression as one function value of one angle.
33. $\cos 37° \cos 83° - \sin 37° \sin 83°$
34. $\cos 178° \cos 133° + \sin 178° \sin 133°$
35. $\sin 239° \cos 179° - \cos 239° \sin 179°$
36. $\sin 193° \cos 167° + \cos 193° \sin 167°$
37. $\sin 134° \cos (-63°) - \cos 134° \sin (-63)°$
38. $\cos 222° \sin (-129°) + \sin 222° \cos (-129°)$
39. $\sin 45° \sin (-32°) + \cos 45° \cos (-32°)$
40. $\sin 141° \sin (-56°) - \cos 141° \cos (-56°)$

Prove each of the following identities.
41. $\cos (A + B) + \cos (A - B) = 2 \cos A \cos B$
42. $\sin (A + B) + \sin (A - B) = 2 \sin A \cos B$
43. $\sin (A + B) - \sin (A - B) = 2 \cos A \sin B$
44. $\cos (A + B) - \cos (A - B) = -2 \sin A \sin B$
45. $\cos 3x \cos 5x + \sin 3x \sin 5x = \cos 2x$
46. $\cos 8x \cos 4x - \sin 8x \sin 4x = \cos 12x$
47. $\sin 9y \cos 4y - \cos 9y \sin 4y = \sin 5y$
48. $\sin 5y \cos 8y + \cos 5y \sin 8y = \sin 13y$
49. $\sin 5x + \sin 3x = 2 \sin 4x \cos x$. *Hint:* Use $4x \pm x$.
50. $\sin 3x + \sin x = 2 \cos x \sin 2x$. *Hint:* Use $2x \pm x$.
51. $\sin 10x - \sin 2x = 2 \cos 6x \sin 4x$.   *Hint:*   Use $6x \pm 4x$.
52. $\cos 11x + \cos 5x = 2 \cos 8x \cos 3x$.   *Hint:*   Use $8x \pm 3x$.
53. $\dfrac{\sin 2x}{\sin x} - \dfrac{\cos 2x}{\cos x} = \sec x$
54. $\dfrac{\sin 4x}{\cos 2x} + \dfrac{\cos 4x}{\sin 2x} = \csc 2x$
55. $\dfrac{\sin 6x}{\sin 3x} - \dfrac{\cos 6x}{\cos 3x} = \sec 3x$
56. $\dfrac{\cos 3x}{\sin 6x} - \dfrac{\sin 3x}{\cos 6x} = \cos 9x \sec 6x \csc 6x$
57. $\tan x + \cot x = \sec x \csc x$
58. $\tan 3x - \tan x = \sin 2x \sec x \sec 3x$
59. $\tan 4x + \cot 2x = \sec 4x \cot 2x$
60. $\cot 4x + \tan 2x = \csc 4x$
61. $\sin \left(x + \dfrac{\pi}{4} \right) = \dfrac{\sqrt{2}}{2} (\sin x + \cos x)$
62. $\cos \left(x - \dfrac{\pi}{4} \right) = \dfrac{\sqrt{2}}{2} (\sin x + \cos x)$
63. $\sin \left(x - \dfrac{\pi}{6} \right) = \dfrac{\sqrt{3}}{2} \sin x - \dfrac{1}{2} \cos x$

64. $\cos\left(x - \dfrac{\pi}{3}\right) = \dfrac{1}{2}\cos x + \dfrac{\sqrt{3}}{2}\sin x$

65. $\cos x - \tan y \sin x = \sec y \cos(x + y)$

66. $\tan x \cos y + \sin y = \sec x \sin(x + y)$

67. $\cos x + \cot y \sin x = \csc y \sin(x + y)$

68. $\sin x (\cot x - \tan y) = \sec y \cos(x + y)$

69. $\dfrac{\tan A + \tan B}{\tan A - \tan B} = \dfrac{\sin(A + B)}{\sin(A - B)}$

70. $\dfrac{\cot A - \tan B}{\cot A + \tan B} = \dfrac{\cos(A + B)}{\cos(A - B)}$

71. $\dfrac{\tan A + \tan B}{1 + \tan A \tan B} = \dfrac{\sin(A + B)}{\cos(A - B)}$

72. $\tan A + \tan B = \dfrac{\sin(A + B)}{\cos A \cos B}$

73. Prove that for any real number x and any $h \neq 0$

$$\frac{\cos(x + h) - \cos x}{h} = \frac{\cos x (\cos h - 1)}{h}$$
$$- \frac{\sin x \sin h}{h}$$

74. Prove that for any real number x and any real $h \neq 0$

$$\frac{\sin(x + h) - \sin x}{h} = \frac{\sin x (\cos h - 1)}{h}$$
$$+ \frac{\cos x \sin h}{h}$$

75. In the last problem of Sec. 7.3, we will show that the exact value of $\sin 18°$ is $(-1 + \sqrt{5})/4$.

The exact value of $\cos 18°$ can be found from $\sin^2 18° + \cos^2 18° = 1$. We also found the exact values of $\sin 15° = \dfrac{\sqrt{6} - \sqrt{2}}{4}$ and $\cos 15° = \dfrac{\sqrt{6} + \sqrt{2}}{4}$. Write the exact value of $\sin 3°$ by using $3° = 18° - 15°$.

76. Verify by table, calculator, or otherwise that if $A = 2\pi/7$, then

$$\sin A + \sin 2A + \sin 4A = \frac{\sqrt{7}}{2}$$

77. Show that $\sin(x + y + z) = \sin x \cos y \cos z + \sin y \cos x \cos z + \sin z \cos x \cos y - \sin x \sin y \sin z$.

78. Use Prob. 77 to show that $\sin(x + y + z) = (\cos x \cos y \cos z)(\tan x + \tan y + \tan z - \tan x \tan y \tan z)$.

79. Use Prob. 78 to show that if $x + y + z = \pi$, and each angle is acute, then $\tan x + \tan y + \tan z = \tan x \tan y \tan z$.

80. Show that if $x + y + z = \pi$, then

$$\cos^2 x + \cos^2 y + \cos^2 z$$
$$+ 2 \cos x \cos y \cos z = 1$$

81. Prove that

$$\sec(x + y) = \frac{\sec x \sec y}{1 - \tan x \tan y}$$

7.3 Multiple-Angle Identities

In this section we will present several consequences of the four basic identities for $\cos(A \pm B)$ and $\sin(A \pm B)$ given in Sec. 7.2. We again work only with sine and cosine identities in this section so as to have a manageable number of identities in any one section.

Double-Angle Formulas

If we replace B by A in the formula for $\cos(A + B)$, it becomes $\cos(A + A) = \cos A \cos A - \sin A \sin A$. Hence

$$\cos 2A = \cos^2 A - \sin^2 A \tag{7.15a}$$

The form of this equation can be changed by using the identity $\sin^2 A + \cos^2 A = 1$ to replace first $\sin^2 A$, and then $\cos^2 A$:

$$\cos 2A = 2 \cos^2 A - 1 \qquad \text{(7.15b)}$$

$$\cos 2A = 1 - 2 \sin^2 A \qquad \text{(7.15c)}$$

In order to find a formula for the sine of twice an angle, we replace B by A in the formula for $\sin (A + B)$:

$$\sin(A + A) = \sin A \cos A + \cos A \sin A$$

$$\sin 2A = 2 \sin A \cos A \qquad \text{(7.16)}$$

▶ **EXAMPLE 1** If θ is in quadrant III with $\sin \theta = -\frac{20}{29}$, find $\sin 2\theta$ and $\cos 2\theta$.

Solution Both $\sin \theta$ and $\cos \theta$ are negative in the third quadrant, and $\cos \theta = -\frac{21}{29}$ since 20, 21, and 29 are the sides of a right triangle. Thus

$$\sin 2\theta = 2 \sin \theta \cos \theta = 2 \left(\frac{-20}{29} \right) \left(\frac{-21}{29} \right) = \frac{840}{841}$$

$$\cos 2\theta = 1 - 2(\sin^2 \theta) = 1 - 2 \left(\frac{400}{841} \right) = \frac{41}{841}$$

These values are consistent with each other since

$$\sin^2 2\theta + \cos^2 2\theta = \frac{705,600}{707,281} + \frac{1681}{707,281} = \frac{707,281}{707,281} = 1$$

Notice that in this case, $\sin 2\theta \neq 2 \sin \theta$ since $\sin 2\theta = \frac{840}{841}$, but $2 \sin \theta = 2(-\frac{20}{29}) = -\frac{40}{29}$. ◀

▶ **EXAMPLE 2** Prove the identity

$$\frac{\cos 2\theta + \cos \theta + 1}{\sin 2\theta + \sin \theta} = \cot \theta$$

Solution By the double-angle formulas, the left-hand side is

$$\frac{2 \cos^2 \theta - 1 + \cos \theta + 1}{2 \sin \theta \cos \theta + \sin \theta} = \frac{\cos \theta (2 \cos \theta + 1)}{\sin \theta (2 \cos \theta + 1)}$$

$$= \frac{\cos \theta}{\sin \theta} = \cot \theta \qquad ◀$$

▶ **EXAMPLE 3** Verify that $\sec x \cos 2x = 2 \cos x - \sec x$.

Solution $\quad \sec x \cos 2x = \sec x(2 \cos^2 x - 1)$
$$= 2(\sec x \cos x) \cos x - \sec x = 2 \cos x - \sec x \qquad ◀$$

▶ **EXAMPLE 4** Prove that $(1 - \tan^2 A)/(1 + \tan^2 A) = \cos 2A$ is an identity.

Solution   We prove that the equation above is an identity by reducing the left-hand side to the right:

$$\frac{1 - \tan^2 A}{1 + \tan^2 A} = \frac{1 - \dfrac{\sin^2 A}{\cos^2 A}}{1 + \dfrac{\sin^2 A}{\cos^2 A}} \qquad \text{by } \tan A = \frac{\sin A}{\cos A}$$

$$= \frac{\cos^2 A - \sin^2 A}{\cos^2 A + \sin^2 A} \qquad \text{multiplying by } \frac{\cos^2 A}{\cos^2 A} = 1$$

$$= \cos^2 A - \sin^2 A \qquad \text{since } \cos^2 A + \sin^2 A = 1$$

$$= \cos 2A \qquad \text{by (7.15a)}$$

EXAMPLE 5   Write $\cos 3\theta$ in terms of $\cos \theta$.

Solution

$$\cos 3\theta = \cos (2\theta + \theta) = \cos 2\theta \cos \theta - \sin 2\theta \sin \theta$$

$$= (2 \cos^2 \theta - 1)(\cos \theta) - (2 \cos \theta \sin \theta)(\sin \theta)$$

$$= 2 \cos^3 \theta - \cos \theta - (2 \cos \theta)(1 - \cos^2 \theta)$$

$$= 2 \cos^3 \theta - \cos \theta - 2 \cos \theta + 2 \cos^3 \theta$$

$$= 4 \cos^3 \theta - 3 \cos \theta$$

If we now wanted $\cos 4\theta$, we could use Example 5, or other identities, and begin with any of these forms:

$$\cos (3\theta + \theta) \qquad \text{or} \qquad \cos (2\theta + 2\theta) \qquad \text{or} \qquad \cos 2(2\theta)$$

We may use identities when working with inequalities as well as with equations, as in Examples 6 and 7.

EXAMPLE 6   Prove that $\cos 2x \leq \cos^2 x$ for every real number x.

Solution   The given inequality is equivalent to each of these:

$$2 \cos^2 x - 1 \leq \cos^2 x \qquad \text{by (7.15b)}$$

$$\cos^2 x \leq 1 \qquad \text{adding } 1 - \cos^2 x$$

The last one is true for all x since $|\cos x| \leq 1$, and thus the given inequality is proven.

EXAMPLE 7   Show that $|\sin 2x| \leq 2 |\sin x|$, for all real numbers x.

Solution

$$|\sin 2x| = |2 \sin x \cos x| \qquad \text{by (7.16)}$$

$$= 2 \cdot |\sin x| \cdot |\cos x|$$

$$\leq 2 \cdot |\sin x| \qquad \text{since } |\cos x| \leq 1$$

It is also true that $|\sin nx| \leq n \cdot |\sin x|$ for $n = 1, 2, 3, 4, 5, \ldots$, but a complete proof requires mathematical induction (Chap. 12). Try to prove it yourself for $n = 3$. ◢

▶ **EXAMPLE 8**   Simplify the expression $\sin A/\sin B - \cos A/\cos B$.

Solution

$$\frac{\sin A}{\sin B} - \frac{\cos A}{\cos B} = \frac{\sin A \cos B - \cos A \sin B}{\sin B \cos B}$$

$$= \frac{2 \sin (A - B)}{2 \sin B \cos B} = \frac{2 \sin (A - B)}{\sin 2B}$$ ◢

Half-Angle Identities

If we solve $\cos 2x = 2 \cos^2 x - 1$ for $\cos^2 x$, and also solve $\cos 2x = 1 - 2 \sin^2 x$ for $\sin^2 x$, we see that

$$\cos^2 x = \frac{1 + \cos 2x}{2} \qquad \text{and} \qquad \sin^2 x = \frac{1 - \cos 2x}{2}$$

Using $\theta = 2x$, and thus $\theta/2 = x$, gives (7.17) and (7.18) below:

$$\cos^2 \left(\frac{\theta}{2}\right) = \frac{1 + \cos \theta}{2} \qquad\qquad \textbf{(7.17)}$$

$$\sin^2 \left(\frac{\theta}{2}\right) = \frac{1 - \cos \theta}{2} \qquad\qquad \textbf{(7.18)}$$

These are called **half-angle identities.** The sign of $\cos (\theta/2)$ and of $\sin (\theta/2)$ must be determined by the quadrant in which the angle $\theta/2$ lies. These identities could also be solved for $\cos (\theta/2)$ and $\sin (\theta/2)$ by simply taking square roots, but then we would have to deal with $\pm$ signs, as in the expression

$$\sin \left(\frac{\theta}{2}\right) = \pm \sqrt{\frac{1 - \cos \theta}{2}}$$

▶ **EXAMPLE 9**   Use the half-angle identity (7.18) to find $\sin 15°$.

Solution   Since $\sin 15° > 0$, we have

$$\sin^2 15° = \sin^2 \left(\frac{30°}{2}\right) = \frac{1 - \cos 30°}{2}$$

$$= \frac{1 - \sqrt{3}/2}{2} \cdot \frac{2}{2} = \frac{2 - \sqrt{3}}{4}$$

and so

$$\sin 15° = \tfrac{1}{2} \sqrt{2 - \sqrt{3}} \qquad \text{exact value}$$

$$\approx 0.2588 \qquad \text{four decimal places}$$

Had we used $\sin 15° = \sin(45° - 30°)$, the result would have been

$$\sin 15° = \frac{\sqrt{6} - \sqrt{2}}{4} \approx 0.2588$$

You should show that these radical expressions have *exactly* the same value by squaring and simplifying each side of the equation

$$\frac{\sqrt{2 - \sqrt{3}}}{2} = \frac{\sqrt{6} - \sqrt{2}}{4}$$

EXAMPLE 10 If $\cot \theta = \frac{7}{24}$ and $\pi < \theta < 3\pi/2$, find $\cos \theta/2$.

Solution We have $\cos \theta = -\frac{7}{25}$ since θ is in quadrant III, and so

$$\cos^2 \left(\frac{\theta}{2}\right) = \frac{1 + (-\frac{7}{25})}{2} = \frac{\frac{18}{25}}{2} = \frac{9}{25}$$

Since $\pi/2 < \theta/2 < 3\pi/4$, then $\cos \theta/2 < 0$ and

$$\cos \frac{\theta}{2} = -\frac{3}{5}$$

Summary

$\cos 2A = \cos^2 A - \sin^2 A$	(7.15a)
$\cos 2A = 2\cos^2 A - 1$	(7.15b)
$\cos 2A = 1 - 2\sin^2 A$	(7.15c)
$\sin 2A = 2\sin A \cos A$	(7.16)
$\cos^2 \dfrac{\theta}{2} = \dfrac{1 + \cos \theta}{2}$	(7.17)
$\sin^2 \dfrac{\theta}{2} = \dfrac{1 - \cos \theta}{2}$	(7.18)

EXERCISE 7.3

Find the function values in Probs. 1 to 8.
1. $\cos 15°$, use $15° = 30°/2$
2. $\sin 15°$, use $15° = 30°/2$
3. Show that $\cos 22.5° = \cos 45°/2 = \frac{1}{2}\sqrt{2 + \sqrt{2}}$
4. Show that $\cos \dfrac{22.5°}{2} = \frac{1}{2}\sqrt{2 + \sqrt{2 + \sqrt{2}}}$
5. $\cos 60°$, use $60° = 2(30°)$
6. $\sin 60°$, use $60° = 2(30°)$
7. $\cos 300°$, use $300° = 2(150°)$
8. $\sin 120°$, use $120° = 2(60°)$

Find the exact values of $\cos 2A$ and $\cos A/2$ in Probs. 9 to 20.
9. $\cos A = \frac{4}{5}$, A in quadrant I
10. $\cos A = \frac{7}{25}$, A in quadrant IV
11. $\sin A = -\frac{5}{13}$, A in quadrant III
12. $\sin A = \frac{24}{25}$, A in quadrant II
13. $\cos A = -\frac{4}{5}$, $\pi/2 < A < \pi$
14. $\sin A = \frac{12}{13}$, $\pi/2 < A < \pi$
15. $\cos A = \frac{5}{13}$, $3\pi/2 < A < 2\pi$
16. $\sin A = -\frac{15}{17}$, $\pi < A < 3\pi/2$

17. $\tan A = \frac{5}{12}$, $\pi < A < 3\pi/2$
18. $\sec A = \frac{5}{3}$, $0 < A < \pi/2$
19. $\cot A = \frac{24}{7}$, $\pi < A < 3\pi/2$
20. $\csc A = -\frac{5}{4}$, $3\pi/2 < A < 2\pi$

Find the exact values of $\sin 2A$ and $\sin A/2$ in Probs. 21 to 32.
21. $\sin A = -\frac{5}{13}$, $\pi < A < 3\pi/2$
22. $\cos A = \frac{12}{13}$, $3\pi/2 < A < 2\pi$
23. $\cot A = -\frac{24}{7}$, $\pi/2 < A < \pi$
24. $\tan A = \frac{5}{12}$, $\pi < A < 3\pi/2$
25. $\cos A = \frac{3}{5}$, $3\pi/2 < A < 2\pi$
26. $\sin A = \frac{5}{13}$, $\pi/2 < A < \pi$
27. $\tan A = -\frac{12}{5}$, $3\pi/2 < A < 2\pi$
28. $\cot A = \frac{7}{24}$, $\pi < A < 3\pi/2$
29. $\sec A = \frac{13}{5}$, $3\pi/2 < A < 2\pi$
30. $\csc A = \frac{5}{3}$, $\pi/2 < A < \pi$
31. $\sin A = \frac{5}{13}$, $0 < A < \pi/2$
32. $\cos A = -\frac{5}{13}$, $\pi < A < 3\pi/2$

Prove the following identities.
33. $\sin 12x = 2 \sin 6x \cos 6x$
34. $\cos 10x = \cos^2 5x - \sin^2 5x$
35. $\sin x = 2 \sin \dfrac{x}{2} \cos \dfrac{x}{2}$
36. $\cos x = 2 \cos^2 \dfrac{x}{2} - 1$
37. $2 \cos^2 4x - \cos 8x = 1$
38. $2 \sin^2 3x + \cos 6x = 1$
39. $\dfrac{\sin 2x}{2 \sin x} = \cos x$ **40.** $2 \csc 2x = \sec x \csc x$
41. $\tan x + \cot x = 2 \csc 2x$
42. $\cos^4 x - \sin^4 x = \cos 2x$
43. $\cos 4x = 2 \cos^2 2x - \cos 2x \sec 2x$
44. $\sin 2x = \dfrac{2 \tan x}{1 + \tan^2 x}$
45. $\cos 2x + \sin x = (1 + 2 \sin x)(1 - \sin x)$
46. $\cos 2x + \cos x = (2 \cos x - 1)(\cos x + 1)$
47. $\sin 4x + \cos 2x = (4 \sin x \cos x + 1)(2 \cos^2 x - 1)$
48. $2 \sin 2x = (1 + \cos 2x)^2 \sec^2 x \tan x$
49. $\sin 3x = 3 \sin x - 4 \sin^3 x$
50. $\sin 4x = 4 \sin x \cos x (1 - 2 \sin^2 x)$
51. $\cos 3x = \cos x(1 - 4 \sin^2 x)$
52. $\cos 4x = 8 \cos^4 x - 8 \cos^2 x + 1$
53. $8 \cos^4 x = \cos 4x + 4 \cos 2x + 3$
54. $8 \sin^4 x = \cos 4x - 4 \cos 2x + 3$
55. $\sin 4x = 4 \sin x \cos x(2 \cos^2 x - 1)$

56. $4 \sin^2 x \cos^2 x + (\cos 3x \cos x + \sin 3x \sin x)^2 = 1$
57. $\dfrac{\sin 3x}{\sin x} - \dfrac{\cos 3x}{\cos x} = 2$
58. $\dfrac{\cos 3x}{\sin x} + \dfrac{\sin 3x}{\cos x} = 2 \cot 2x$
59. $\dfrac{\sin 3x}{\sin x} + \dfrac{\cos 3x}{\cos x} = 4 \cos 2x$
60. $\dfrac{\sin 7x}{\sin x} + \dfrac{\cos 7x}{\cos x} = 8 \cos 4x \cos 2x$
61. $\dfrac{1 - \sin 2x}{1 + \sin 2x} = \dfrac{\sec x - 2 \sin x}{\sec x + 2 \sin x}$
62. $\dfrac{1 + \sin 2x}{\cos 2x} = \dfrac{\cos x + \sin x}{\cos x - \sin x}$
63. Use a right triangle to show that if $\tan (x/2) = z$, then $\sin (x/2) = z/\sqrt{1 + z^2}$ and $\cos (x/2) = 1/\sqrt{1 + z^2}$.
64. Use Prob. 63, and $x = 2(x/2)$, to show that
$$\sin x = \frac{2z}{1 + z^2} \qquad \cos x = \frac{1 - z^2}{1 + z^2}$$
$$\tan x = \frac{2z}{1 - z^2}$$
65. $\sec^2 x = \dfrac{2}{1 + \cos 2x}$
66. $\csc^2 x = \dfrac{2 \sec 2x}{\sec 2x - 1}$
67. $\sec 2x = \dfrac{\sec^2 x}{2 - \sec^2 x}$
68. $\cos 2x = \dfrac{\csc^2 x - 2}{\csc^2 x}$

Prove each of the inequalities in Probs. 69 to 72.
69. $2 \mid \csc 2x \mid \geq \mid \sec x \mid$
70. $\tan 2x > 2 \tan x$ for $0 < x < \pi/4$
71. $\sin (x + y) > \sin x \cos y$ for x and y in quadrant I
72. $\cos (x + y) < \cos x \cos y$ for x and y in quadrant I
73. The following argument shows that $\sin 18° = (-1 + \sqrt{5})/4$. Justify each step, and fill in the details. If $A = 18°$, then $2A = 36°$, and $3A = 54°$.

$$\sin 2A = \cos 3A$$
$$2 \sin A \cos A = 4 \cos^3 A - 3 \cos A$$
$$2 \sin A = 4 \cos^2 A - 3$$
$$4 \sin^2 A + 2 \sin A - 1 = 0$$

Now use the quadratic formula.

74. Show that $y = \sin 50°$ satisfies the equation $8y^3 - 6y + 1 = 0$. *Hint:* Use the identity from Prob. 49, $\sin 3x = 3 \sin x - 4 \sin^3 x$ with $x = 50°$.

75. Show that $y = \cos 20°$ satisfies the equation $8y^3 - 6y - 1 = 0$. *Hint:* Use the identity from Example 5, $\cos 3x = 4 \cos^3 x - 3 \cos x$ with $x = 20°$.

76. Show that $y = \sin 15°$ satisfies the equation $8y^3 - 6y + \sqrt{2} = 0$. *Hint:* Use the identity from Prob. 49, $\sin 3x = 3 \sin x - 4 \sin^3 x$ with $x = 15°$.

77. If a projectile is fired at an angle θ with level ground and it has initial velocity V, then it will go a horizontal distance of

$$V \cos \theta \; \frac{2V \sin \theta}{g}$$

before it hits the ground, where g is a constant. Show that this distance is $(V^2/g) \sin 2\theta$. Which value of θ makes this largest?

78. Use $\sin 18° = (\sqrt{5} - 1)/4$, which was shown in Prob. 73, and $\sin 3x = 3 \sin x - 4 \sin^3 x$, which was shown in Prob. 49, to show that $\sin 54° = (\sqrt{5} + 1)/4$. Notice that it then follows that $\sin 54° - \sin 18° = \frac{1}{2}$.

7.4 Tangent Identities

In this section, we use the sine and cosine identities to prove tangent identities. Applications in Probs. 41 to 52 include a technique needed in rotation of axes, an identity useful in calculus, a problem in art appreciation, and an inequality. Problem 13 shows that the tangent function has period π or $180°$, which is true also for the cotangent.

In order to derive an identity for the tangent of the sum of two angles, we use the fact that the tangent of an angle is equal to its sine divided by its cosine, and get

$$\tan (A + B) = \frac{\sin (A + B)}{\cos (A + B)}$$

$$= \frac{\sin A \cos B + \cos A \sin B}{\cos A \cos B - \sin A \sin B} \qquad \text{by (7.13) and (7.12)}$$

$$= \frac{\dfrac{\sin A \cos B}{\cos A \cos B} + \dfrac{\cos A \sin B}{\cos A \cos B}}{\dfrac{\cos A \cos B}{\cos A \cos B} - \dfrac{\sin A \sin B}{\cos A \cos B}} \qquad \begin{array}{l}\text{dividing numerator}\\\text{and denominator}\\\text{by } \cos A \cos B\end{array}$$

Now, removing common factors, and replacing $\sin A/\cos A$ by $\tan A$ and $\sin B/\cos B$ by $\tan B$, we have

Tangent of a sum
$$\tan (A + B) = \frac{\tan A + \tan B}{1 - \tan A \tan B} \qquad \textbf{(7.19)}$$

▶ **EXAMPLE 1**   Find a formula for $\tan (\theta + \phi)$ if $\tan \theta = x$ and $\tan \phi = y$.

Solution   Using the formula for the tangent of a sum gives

$$\tan (\theta + \phi) = \frac{\tan \theta + \tan \phi}{1 - \tan \theta \tan \phi} = \frac{x + y}{1 - xy}$$

For instance if $\tan \theta = \frac{3}{8}$ and $\tan \phi = \frac{5}{11}$, then

$$\tan (\theta + \phi) = \frac{\frac{3}{8} + \frac{5}{11}}{1 - (\frac{3}{8})(\frac{5}{11})} \cdot \frac{88}{88}$$

$$= \frac{33 + 40}{88 - 15} = \frac{73}{73} = 1$$

This shows that $\theta + \phi = \pi/4$ or $45°$.

If, in (7.19), we replace B by A, we get

$$\tan (A + A) = \frac{\tan A + \tan A}{1 - \tan A \tan A}$$

This proves the **tangent double-angle formula:**

$$\tan 2A = \frac{2 \tan A}{1 - \tan^2 A} \qquad (7.20)$$

EXAMPLE 2   If $\tan \theta = \frac{1}{5}$ and $\tan \phi = \frac{4}{5}$, find both

$$\tan (\theta + \phi) \qquad \text{and} \qquad \tan 2\theta$$

Solution

$$\tan (\theta + \phi) = \frac{\frac{1}{5} + \frac{4}{5}}{1 - \frac{1}{5} \cdot \frac{4}{5}} = \frac{1}{\frac{21}{25}} = \frac{25}{21}$$

$$\tan 2\theta = \frac{2\frac{1}{5}}{1 - \frac{1}{25}} = \frac{\frac{2}{5}}{\frac{24}{25}} = \frac{5}{12}$$

Notice that $\tan 2\theta = \frac{5}{12}$ and $2 \tan \theta = \frac{2}{5}$ are different.

Since the tangent of an angle is its sine divided by its cosine, we have

$$\tan (\theta/2) = \frac{\sin (\theta/2)}{\cos (\theta/2)} = \frac{2 \sin (\theta/2) \cdot \sin (\theta/2)}{2 \sin (\theta/2) \cdot \cos (\theta/2)}$$

$$= \frac{2 \sin^2 (\theta/2)}{\sin 2(\theta/2)} \qquad \text{double-angle formula for sine}$$

$$= \frac{1 - \cos \theta}{\sin \theta} \qquad \text{double-angle formula for cosine}$$

This proves the **tangent half-angle formula:**

$$\tan \frac{\theta}{2} = \frac{1 - \cos \theta}{\sin \theta} \qquad (7.21a)$$

Another form of this tangent half-angle formula can be obtained by multiplying the numerator and denominator of (7.21a) by $1 + \cos \theta$:

$$\frac{(1 - \cos\theta)(1 + \cos\theta)}{(\sin\theta)(1 + \cos\theta)} = \frac{1 - \cos^2\theta}{\sin\theta(1 + \cos\theta)}$$

$$= \frac{\sin\theta\sin\theta}{\sin\theta(1 + \cos\theta)} = \frac{\sin\theta}{1 + \cos\theta}$$

Thus
$$\tan\frac{\theta}{2} = \frac{\sin\theta}{1 + \cos\theta} \qquad (7.21b)$$

Another version of the tangent half-angle formula comes by using (7.17) and (7.18) along with $\tan^2(\theta/2) = \sin^2(\theta/2)/\cos^2(\theta/2)$:

$$\tan^2\frac{\theta}{2} = \frac{1 - \cos\theta}{1 + \cos\theta} \qquad (7.21c)$$

EXAMPLE 3   Find tan 15° by using 15° = 30°/2.

Solution   Using (7.21a) with $\theta/2 = 15°$ and $\theta = 30°$, we have

$$\tan 15° = \frac{1 - \cos 30°}{\sin 30°} = \frac{1 - \sqrt{3}/2}{\frac{1}{2}}\cdot\frac{2}{2} = 2 - \sqrt{3}$$

EXAMPLE 4   Use Eq. (7.21b) to find tan ($\pi/8$) or tan (22.5°).

Solution
$$\tan\frac{\pi}{8} = \tan\frac{1}{2}\left(\frac{\pi}{4}\right) = \frac{\sin(\pi/4)}{1 + \cos(\pi/4)} = \frac{1/\sqrt{2}}{1 + 1/\sqrt{2}}\cdot\frac{\sqrt{2}}{\sqrt{2}}$$

$$= \frac{1}{\sqrt{2} + 1}\cdot\frac{\sqrt{2} - 1}{\sqrt{2} - 1} = \frac{\sqrt{2} - 1}{2 - 1} = \sqrt{2} - 1$$

The exact value of tan $\pi/8$ is $\sqrt{2} - 1$, and an approximate decimal value is 0.4142.

EXAMPLE 5   Verify the steps used in proving the two identities below.

Solution   (a)
$$\frac{\sin 2\theta}{1 + \cos 2\theta} = \tan\left(\frac{1}{2}\right)(2\theta) = \tan\theta$$

(b)
$$\frac{\sin 2\theta}{1 + \cos 2\theta + 2\cos\theta} = \frac{2\sin\theta\cos\theta}{1 + (2\cos^2\theta - 1) + 2\cos\theta}$$

$$= \frac{2\cos\theta\cdot\sin\theta}{2\cos\theta(\cos\theta + 1)} = \frac{\sin\theta}{\cos\theta + 1} = \tan\frac{\theta}{2}$$

We may use the formula for the tangent of a sum to derive a formula for the tangent of a difference by writing

$$A - B = A + (-B)$$

Then
$$\tan(A - B) = \frac{\tan A + \tan(-B)}{1 - \tan A\tan(-B)}$$

Now, replacing tan $(-B)$, by $-\tan B$, we have the following formula:

Tangent of a difference $$\tan (A - B) = \frac{\tan A - \tan B}{1 + \tan A \tan B}$$ **(7.22)**

EXAMPLE 6   Prove that

$$\tan (\theta + 45°) + \tan (\theta - 45°) = 2 \tan 2\theta$$

Solution   If we use the identities (7.19) and (7.22) for the tangent of a sum and of a difference, we get

$$\tan (\theta + 45°) + \tan (\theta - 45°)$$

$$= \frac{\tan \theta + \tan 45°}{1 - \tan \theta \tan 45°} + \frac{\tan \theta - \tan 45°}{1 + \tan \theta \tan 45°}$$

$$= \frac{\tan \theta + 1}{1 - \tan \theta} + \frac{\tan \theta - 1}{1 + \tan \theta} \qquad \text{since } \tan 45° = 1$$

$$= \frac{(1 + \tan \theta)^2 - (1 - \tan \theta)^2}{1 - \tan^2 \theta} \qquad \begin{array}{l}\text{adding with the common}\\ \text{denominator } 1 - \tan^2 \theta\end{array}$$

$$= \frac{(1 + 2 \tan \theta + \tan^2 \theta) - (1 - 2 \tan \theta + \tan^2 \theta)}{1 - \tan^2 \theta}$$

$$= \frac{4 \tan \theta}{1 - \tan^2 \theta} = (2) \frac{2 \tan \theta}{1 - \tan^2 \theta} = 2 \tan 2\theta \qquad \blacktriangleleft$$

EXAMPLE 7   Use the formula for the tangent of a difference to prove the identity below.

Solution $$\frac{\tan 8A - \tan 5A}{1 + \tan 8A \tan 5A} = \tan (8A - 5A) = \tan 3A \qquad \blacktriangleleft$$

EXAMPLE 8   Simplify $[f(x + h) - f(x)]/h$ for $f(x) = \tan x$.

Solution $$\frac{\tan(x + h) - \tan x}{h} = \left(\frac{\tan x + \tan h}{1 - \tan x \tan h} - \tan x \right) / h$$

$$= \frac{\tan x + \tan h - \tan x + \tan^2 x \tan h}{h(1 - \tan x \tan h)} \qquad \text{adding fractions}$$

$$= \frac{\tan h(1 + \tan^2 x)}{h(1 - \tan x \tan h)} \qquad \text{common factor of } \tan h$$

$$= \frac{\tan h(\sec^2 x)}{h(1 - \tan x \tan h)} \cdot \frac{\cos x \cos h}{\cos x \cos h} \qquad \begin{array}{l}\text{a Pythagorean}\\ \text{identity}\end{array}$$

$$= \frac{(\tan h \cdot \cos h)(\sec^2 x \cdot \cos x)}{h(\cos x \cos h - \sin x \sin h)} \qquad \cos \theta \tan \theta = \sin \theta$$

$$= \frac{\sin h}{h} \cdot \frac{\sec x}{\cos (x + h)} \qquad \text{cosine of a sum} \qquad \blacktriangleleft$$

$$\tan (A + B) = \frac{\tan A + \tan B}{1 - \tan A \tan B}$$

$$\tan 2A = \frac{2 \tan A}{1 - \tan^2 A}$$

$$\tan \frac{\theta}{2} = \frac{1 - \cos \theta}{\sin \theta} = \frac{\sin \theta}{1 + \cos \theta}$$

$$\tan (A - B) = \frac{\tan A - \tan B}{1 + \tan A \tan B}$$

EXERCISE 7.4

Find the exact function values in Probs. 1 to 4.

1. tan 15°, with 15° = 60° − 45°
2. tan 240°, with 240° = 2(120°)
3. tan 75°, with 75° = 150°/2
4. tan 75°, with 75° = 30° + 45°

Find $\tan (A + B)$ and $\tan (A - B)$ if A, B, and their function values are as given in Probs. 5 to 8.

5. $\tan A = \frac{3}{4}$, $0 < A < \pi/2$; $\tan B = -\frac{5}{12}$, $\pi/2 < B < \pi$
6. $\tan A = \frac{8}{15}$, $\pi < A < 3\pi/2$; $\sin B = -\frac{3}{5}$, $\pi < B < 3\pi/2$
7. $\cos A = \frac{15}{17}$, $3\pi/2 < A < 2\pi$; $\sin B = \frac{8}{17}$, $\pi/2 < B < \pi$
8. $\sin A = -\frac{7}{25}$; $\pi < A < 3\pi/2$; $\cot B = -\frac{12}{5}$, $\pi/2 < B < \pi$

If A and one of its function values are as given in Probs. 9 to 12, find $\tan 2A$ and $\tan A/2$.

9. $\tan A = \frac{15}{8}$, $0 < A < \pi/2$
10. $\cot A = -\frac{7}{24}$, $\pi/2 < A < \pi$
11. $\sec A = \frac{5}{3}$, $3\pi/2 < A < 2\pi$
12. $\sin A = -\frac{5}{13}$, $\pi < A < 3\pi/2$

Prove that the statements in Probs. 13 to 16 are identities. The first one shows that π is a period of the tangent function.

13. $\tan (\pi + \theta) = \tan \theta$ **14.** $\tan (\pi - \theta) = -\tan \theta$
15. $\tan (2\pi - \theta) = -\tan \theta$
16. $\tan (3\pi/2 + \theta) = -\cot \theta$

Change the first expression to the second in Probs. 17 to 24.

17. $\tan (\theta + 60°)$, $\dfrac{\tan \theta + \sqrt{3}}{1 - \sqrt{3} \tan \theta}$
18. $\tan (\theta + 45°) - \tan (\theta - 45°)$, $2 \sec 2\theta$
19. $\cot 4\theta + \tan 2\theta$, $\csc 4\theta$
20. $\tan 4\theta - \tan 2\theta$, $\tan 2\theta \sec 4\theta$
21. $\tan \theta \tan \theta/2$, $\sec \theta - 1$
22. $\cot \theta - \tan \theta$, $2 \cot 2\theta$
23. $\cot 2\theta + \tan \theta$, $\csc 2\theta$
24. $\cot \theta - \cot 3\theta$, $2 \cos \theta \csc 3\theta$

Prove that the statement in each of Probs. 25 to 40 is an identity.

25. $\dfrac{\tan 4\theta - \tan 2\theta}{1 + \tan 4\theta \tan 2\theta} = \dfrac{2 \tan \theta}{1 - \tan^2 \theta}$

26. $\dfrac{\tan 3\theta + \tan \theta}{1 - \tan 3\theta \tan \theta} = \dfrac{2 \tan 2\theta}{1 - \tan^2 2\theta}$

27. $\tan 3\theta = \dfrac{3 \tan \theta - \tan^3 \theta}{1 - 3 \tan^2 \theta}$

28. $\tan 4\theta = \dfrac{4 \tan \theta - 4 \tan^3 \theta}{1 - 6 \tan^2 \theta + \tan^4 \theta}$

29. $\tan 2\theta = \dfrac{2}{\cot \theta - \tan \theta}$

30. $\tan \left(\dfrac{\theta}{2} + \dfrac{\pi}{4} \right) = \dfrac{1 + \sin \theta}{\cos \theta}$

31. $\tan \left(\dfrac{\pi}{4} - \theta \right) = \dfrac{1 - \tan \theta}{1 + \tan \theta}$

32. $\tan \left(\dfrac{\pi}{4} + \theta \right) = \dfrac{1 + \tan \theta}{1 - \tan \theta}$

33. $\tan (\theta + 60°) + \tan (\theta - 60°) = \dfrac{8 \tan \theta}{1 - 3 \tan^2 \theta}$

34. $\tan(\theta + 30°) + \tan(\theta - 30°) = \dfrac{8 \tan \theta}{3 - \tan^2 \theta}$

35. $\tan\left(\dfrac{\theta}{2} - \dfrac{\pi}{4}\right) = \dfrac{\sin \theta - 1}{\cos \theta}$

36. $\cot \theta + \tan \theta = 2 \csc 2\theta$

37. $\dfrac{2 \tan \theta}{\sin 2\theta} = 1 + \tan^2 \theta$

38. $1 - 2 \cot 2\theta \tan \theta = \tan^2 \theta$

39. $\dfrac{2 \tan (\theta/2)}{1 + \tan^2 (\theta/2)} = \sin \theta$

40. $\tan(A + B + C) =$
$$\dfrac{\tan A + \tan B + \tan C - \tan A \tan B \tan C}{1 - \tan A \tan B - \tan A \tan C - \tan B \tan C}$$

In Probs. 41 to 48, first find the positive value of $\tan A$. Then find $\sin A$ and $\cos A$ by using right triangles. This is used in rotation of axes to simplify equations.

41. $\tan 2A = \frac{3}{4}$ **42.** $\tan 2A = \frac{12}{5}$

43. $\tan 2A = -\frac{8}{15}$ **44.** $\tan 2A = -\frac{24}{7}$

45. $\cot 2A = -\frac{8}{15}$ **46.** $\cot 2A = -\frac{4}{3}$

47. $\cot 2A = \frac{12}{5}$ **48.** $\cot 2A = \frac{24}{7}$

Prove the cotangent identities in Probs. 49 to 52.

49. $\cot(A + B) = \dfrac{\cot A \cot B - 1}{\cot A + \cot B}$

50. $\cot(A - B) = \dfrac{\cot A \cot B + 1}{\cot B - \cot A}$

51. $\cot 2A = \dfrac{\cot^2 A - 1}{2 \cot A}$

52. $\cot A/2 = \csc A + \cot A$

53. *Art appreciation* A picture on the wall of a museum is 5 ft high and has its base 9 ft above the floor. A patron whose eyes are 6 ft high is x feet from the wall, directly opposite the picture. Show that the angle the picture makes, with the eye at the vertex, is $\alpha - \beta$ where $\tan \alpha = 8/x$ and $\tan \beta = 3/x$. Show also that

$$\tan(\alpha - \beta) = \dfrac{5x}{x^2 + 24}$$

54. Use the double-angle formula to show that if $0 < A < \pi/4$, then $\tan 2A > 2 \tan A$.

7.5 Product and Sum Formulas

We give several formulas below which allow a product of sines and cosines to be written as a sum, and also a sum as a product. They can be used in solving trigonometric equations, in graphing, in calculus, and in proving identities.

The first four formulas are proved by expanding the right-hand side and collecting terms. We proved the fourth one in Example 9, Sec. 7.2.

Product-to-sum formulas

$$\sin A \cos B = \tfrac{1}{2}[\sin(A + B) + \sin(A - B)] \tag{7.23}$$

$$\cos A \sin B = \tfrac{1}{2}[\sin(A + B) - \sin(A - B)] \tag{7.24}$$

$$\cos A \cos B = \tfrac{1}{2}[\cos(A + B) + \cos(A - B)] \tag{7.25}$$

$$\sin A \sin B = \tfrac{1}{2}[-\cos(A + B) + \cos(A - B)] \tag{7.26}$$

▶ **EXAMPLE 1** Use the first equation, (7.23), to rewrite $\sin 47° \cos 19°$ as a sum.

Solution Using $A = 47°$ and $B = 19°$ gives

$$\sin 47° \cos 19° = (0.5)[\sin(47° + 19°) + \sin(47° - 19°)]$$
$$= (0.5)(\sin 66° + \sin 28°)$$

This is the exact value. Decimal approximations show that

$$\sin 47° \cos 19° \approx (0.7314)(0.9455) \approx 0.6915$$

and also

$$(0.5)(\sin 66° + \sin 28°) \approx (0.5)(.9135 + .4695)$$
$$= .5(1.383) \approx 0.6915$$

◄

EXAMPLE 2   Write each product as a sum or difference.

Solution   (a) Using (7.23) shows that

$$2 \sin 5x \cos 3x = \sin (5x + 3x) + \sin (5x - 3x)$$
$$= \sin 8x + \sin 2x$$

(b) The identity (7.26) yields

$$2 \sin 3x \sin x = -\cos (3x + x) + \cos (3x - x)$$
$$= -\cos 4x + \cos 2x$$

◄

EXAMPLE 3   Find the exact value of $\cos 15° \cdot \cos 75°$.

Solution   By (7.25) we have

$$\cos 15° \cdot \cos 75° = \tfrac{1}{2}[\cos 90° + \cos (-60°)]$$
$$= \tfrac{1}{2}(0 + \tfrac{1}{2}) = \tfrac{1}{4}$$

◄

If we let

$$A + B = x \qquad \text{and} \qquad A - B = y$$

then adding these equations gives $x + y = A + B + A - B = 2A$, while subtracting shows that $x - y = A + B - (A - B) = 2B$. Thus

$$A = \frac{x + y}{2} \qquad \text{and} \qquad B = \frac{x - y}{2}$$

Substituting these values of A and B in (7.23), we have

$$\sin \frac{x + y}{2} \cos \frac{x - y}{2} = \tfrac{1}{2}(\sin x + \sin y)$$

Multiplying by 2 and interchanging the sides of this equation gives the first formula below. The others are proved similarly.

Sum-to-product formulas

$$\sin x + \sin y = 2 \sin \frac{x + y}{2} \cos \frac{x - y}{2} \qquad (7.27)$$

$$\sin x - \sin y = 2 \cos \frac{x + y}{2} \sin \frac{x - y}{2} \qquad (7.28)$$

$$\cos x + \cos y = 2 \cos \frac{x + y}{2} \cos \frac{x - y}{2} \qquad (7.29)$$

$$\cos x - \cos y = -2 \sin \frac{x + y}{2} \sin \frac{x - y}{2} \qquad (7.30)$$

These last four formulas are also sometimes called **factoring formulas** since each one expresses a sum as a product.

▶ **EXAMPLE 4**   Use the second formula, (7.28), to rewrite $\sin 64° - \sin 48°$.

Solution   Letting $x = 64°$ and $y = 48°$ shows that

$$\sin 64° - \sin 48° = 2 \cos \frac{64° + 48°}{2} \sin \frac{64° - 48°}{2}$$

$$= 2 \cos 56° \sin 8°$$

◀

▶ **EXAMPLE 5**   Prove the identity $(\sin 7x - \sin 5x)/(\cos 7x + \cos 5x) = \tan x$.

Solution   We have first of all that $(7x + 5x)/2 = 6x$ and $(7x - 5x)/2 = x$. Then by the second and third formulas above, (7.28) and (7.29):

$$\frac{\sin 7x - \sin 5x}{\cos 7x + \cos 5x} = \frac{2 \cos 6x \sin x}{2 \cos 6x \cos x} = \frac{\sin x}{\cos x} = \tan x$$

◀

▶ **EXAMPLE 6**   Factor the expression $\sin x + \sin 2x + \sin 3x$.

Solution

$\sin x + \sin 2x + \sin 3x$	given
$= (\sin x + \sin 3x) + \sin 2x$	grouping terms
$= 2 \sin \dfrac{x + 3x}{2} \cos \dfrac{x - 3x}{2} + \sin 2x$	by (7.27)
$= 2 \sin 2x \cos x + \sin 2x$	$\cos(-x) = \cos x$
$= \sin 2x \cdot (2 \cos x + 1)$	common factor of $\sin 2x$
$= 2 \sin x \cos x (2 \cos x + 1)$	

◀

EXERCISE 7.5

In Probs. 1 to 12, write each product as a sum or difference.

1. $4 \sin 38° \cos 77°$
2. $2 \sin 46° \sin 41°$
3. $6 \cos 136° \cos 85°$
4. $2 \cos 231° \sin 155°$
5. $\sin 5x \sin 7x$
6. $\sin 18x \cos 4x$
7. $\cos 13x \sin 6x$
8. $\cos 11x \cos 4x$
9. $2 \cos(-3x) \cdot \sin 4x$
10. $2 \cos(-6x) \cdot \cos 9x$
11. $2 \sin x \sin (-5x)$
12. $2 \sin (-x) \cos 4x$

In Probs. 13 to 24, write each sum or difference as a product.

13. $\sin 15° + \sin 27°$
14. $\sin 38° - \sin 12°$
15. $\cos 49° + \cos 39°$
16. $\cos 88° - \cos 32°$
17. $\sin 3x - \sin 7x$
18. $\cos 9x + \cos 5x$
19. $\cos 14x - \cos 4x$
20. $\sin 8x - \sin 12x$
21. $\cos 7x + \cos (-5x)$
22. $\cos 16x - \cos (-4x)$
23. $\sin 10x + \sin (-4x)$
24. $\sin 2x - \sin (-6x)$

Prove the identities in Probs. 25 to 36.

25. $\dfrac{\sin x + \sin y}{\cos x + \cos y} = \tan \dfrac{x + y}{2}$

26. $\dfrac{\sin x - \sin y}{\cos x - \cos y} = -\cot \dfrac{x + y}{2}$

27. $\dfrac{\sin x + \sin y}{\sin x - \sin y} = \tan \dfrac{x + y}{2} \cot \dfrac{x - y}{2}$

28. $\dfrac{\cos x - \cos y}{\cos x + \cos y} = \tan \dfrac{x+y}{2} \tan \dfrac{y-x}{2}$

29. $2 \sin kx \cos nx = \sin (k+n)x + \sin (k-n)x$

30. $2 \cos kx \cos nx = \cos (k+n)x + \cos (k-n)x$

31. $\sin (x+y) \cdot \sin (x-y) = \sin^2 x - \sin^2 y$

32. $\sin (x+y) \cdot \sin (x-y) = \cos^2 y - \cos^2 x$

33. $2 \sin \left(x + \dfrac{\pi}{4}\right) \sin \left(x - \dfrac{\pi}{4}\right) = -\cos 2x$

34. $\dfrac{\sin 2x + \sin 5x + \sin 8x}{\cos 2x + \cos 5x + \cos 8x} = \tan 5x$

35. $\dfrac{\sin (x+h) - \sin x}{h} = \cos \left(x + \dfrac{h}{2}\right) \dfrac{\sin (h/2)}{h/2}$

36. $\dfrac{\cos (x+h) - \cos x}{h} = -\sin \left(x + \dfrac{h}{2}\right) \dfrac{\sin (h/2)}{h/2}$

In Probs. 37 to 40, factor the expression.

37. $\sin 4x + \sin 6x + \sin 8x$

38. $\sin 2x + \cos 5x - \sin 8x$

39. $\cos x + \cos 6x + \cos 11x$

40. $\cos 3x + \sin 7x - \cos 11x$

Suppose that $f(x)$ and $g(x)$ are periodic functions of the type

$$a \sin sx \qquad \text{or} \qquad b \cos tx$$

where s and t are nonzero. It can be shown that $f(x) + g(x)$ is periodic if and only if the periods $2\pi/s$ and $2\pi/t$ have a rational quotient. Note that $(2\pi/s)/(2\pi/t) = t/s$, and furthermore that if $t/s = m/n$ where m and n are positive integers with no common factor, then the period of $f(x) + g(x)$ is $2\pi n/s$, which also equals $2\pi m/t$. Use this to find the periods in Probs. 41 to 44.

41. $3 \sin 8x + 4 \sin 6x$

42. $5 \sin 9x - 3 \cos 15x$

43. $7 \cos 12x + 9 \sin 8x$

44. $\cos 15x - 2 \cos 20x$

7.6 Inverse Functions

The definition of an inverse function was given in Sec. 3.7. We found out there that in order for a function defined by $y = f(x)$ to have an inverse, the function must be 1 to 1, and thus

Algebraic condition

$$\text{if } a \neq b \text{ then } f(a) \neq f(b)$$

This may be stated geometrically by saying

Graphical condition

every horizontal line intersects the graph at most once

Since $\pi/6 \neq 5\pi/6$, yet $\sin \pi/6 = \sin (5\pi/6) = \tfrac{1}{2}$, we see that if we use the set of **all real numbers** as the domain for $f(x) = \sin x$, then f is not 1 to 1, and thus has no inverse.

We can, however, **restrict the domain** in a variety of ways so that the sine function with the new, smaller domain does have an inverse. The restricted domain used for the sine function is $[-\pi/2, \pi/2]$. The reason for this choice is apparent if we look at the graph of $y = \sin x$ for $-\pi/2 \leq x \leq \pi/2$. It includes each value of y in the interval $[-1, 1]$ exactly once. See Fig. 7.3.

For emphasis, let us temporarily consider the two functions

$$f(x) = \text{Sin } x \text{ defined on } [-\pi/2, \pi/2]$$

and $\qquad\qquad g(x) = \sin x$ defined for all real numbers

where for $-\pi/2 \leq x \leq \pi/2$, we define Sin $x = \sin x$. Now f and g are different functions since they have different domains. Notice that f is 1 to 1, and hence f **has an inverse.** However g is not 1 to 1 and so g **does not have an inverse.** The notation used

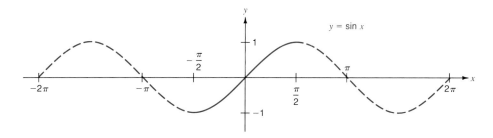

FIGURE 7.3

for the value of an inverse function is $f^{-1}(x)$, and so by definition we have

$$y = \text{Sin}^{-1} x \qquad \text{if and only if} \qquad \text{Sin } y = x$$

However due to tradition and despite the paragraph above, the standard notation for the inverse sine function is $\sin^{-1}$, with a small "s," and we will follow it. Therefore we make the following definition:

> The inverse sine function $\sin^{-1}$ is defined by
>
> $$y = \sin^{-1} x \qquad \text{if and only if} \qquad \sin y = x$$
>
> where $-1 \le x \le 1$ and $-\pi/2 \le \sin^{-1} x \le \pi/2$.

Other notations commonly used are $y = \arcsin x$ and $y = \text{invsin } x$. Hence we have

$$\arcsin x = \sin^{-1} x$$

The reason for the notation $y = \arcsin x$ is that we then have $\sin y = x$, i.e., y is the number or *arc length* whose sine is equal to x. Also, $\sin^{-1} x$ is "the angle whose sine is x." Notice the difference in

$$\sin^{-1} x \text{ or } \arcsin x$$

which is defined above, and

$$(\sin x)^{-1} = \frac{1}{\sin x} = \csc x$$

where -1 is an exponent.

EXAMPLE 1 Find the following values, remembering that

$$\frac{-\pi}{2} \le \arcsin x \le \frac{\pi}{2}.$$

Solution (a) $\qquad \sin^{-1} \dfrac{1}{2} = \dfrac{\pi}{6} \qquad$ since $\sin \dfrac{\pi}{6} = \dfrac{1}{2}$ and $\dfrac{-\pi}{2} \le \dfrac{\pi}{6} \le \dfrac{\pi}{2}$

(b) $\quad \arcsin \dfrac{-\sqrt{3}}{2} = \dfrac{-\pi}{3} \qquad$ since $\sin \dfrac{-\pi}{3} = \dfrac{-\sqrt{3}}{2}$ and $\dfrac{-\pi}{2} \le \dfrac{-\pi}{3} \le \dfrac{\pi}{2}$

(c) $\sin^{-1} 0.5678 = 0.6038 \qquad$ since by table or calculator $\sin 0.6038 = 0.5678$ and

$\dfrac{-\pi}{2} \le 0.6038 \le \dfrac{\pi}{2}$

We find the inverse of $y = \sin x$, $-\pi/2 \le x \le \pi/2$, by interchanging x and y, then solving for y. The domain and range of $y = \sin^{-1} x$ are the range and domain of $y = \sin x$, respectively.

$y = \sin^{-1} x$ means $\sin y = x$

$$y = \sin x \qquad \text{given}$$

$$\sin y = x \qquad \text{interchanging } x \text{ and } y$$

$$y = \sin^{-1} x \qquad \text{solving for } y$$

Furthermore since sin and $\sin^{-1}$ are inverse functions, we have

$$\sin (\sin^{-1} x) = x \qquad \text{for } -1 \le x \le 1$$

$$\sin^{-1} (\sin x) = x \qquad \text{for } \frac{-\pi}{2} \le x \le \frac{\pi}{2}$$

This may also be written in the form

$$\sin (\arcsin x) = x \qquad \text{for } -1 \le x \le 1$$

$$\arcsin (\sin x) = x \qquad \text{for } \frac{-\pi}{2} \le x \le \frac{\pi}{2}$$

◢ **EXAMPLE 2**   Find these function values.

Solution   (a) $\sin (\arcsin 0.1357) = 0.1357$ since 0.1357 is in $[-1, 1]$.

(b) $\sin^{-1} (\sin 3) = \pi - 3$ since $\pi - 3$ is in $[-\pi/2, \pi/2]$ and $\sin 3 = \sin (\pi - 3)$.

In particular, $\sin^{-1} (\sin 3)$ cannot be 3 since 3 is not in the interval $[-\pi/2, \pi/2]$.

◢

If a calculator is in degree mode and the $\sin^{-1}$ key or keys are used, the calculator will give, for instance, $\sin^{-1} \frac{1}{2} = 30°$. A definition using degrees may be given for the inverse sine function, and it parallels the definition above except that

$$-90° \le \sin^{-1} x \le 90°$$

In words, $\sin^{-1} x$ or $\arcsin x$ is "the angle between $-90°$ and $90°$ whose sine is x."

◢ **EXAMPLE 3**   Find these values in degrees.

Solution   (a) $\arcsin \dfrac{-\sqrt{2}}{2} = -45°$ since $-90° \le -45° \le 90°$ and $\sin (-45°) = \dfrac{-\sqrt{2}}{2}$

(b) $\sin^{-1} (\sin 130°) = \sin^{-1} (\sin 50°) = 50°$ since $-90° \le 50° \le 90°$ and $\sin 130° = \sin 50°$

◢

To find an inverse for the function defined by $y = \cos x$, we examine its graph and find a portion that contains each value in the range exactly once. From Fig. 7.4, we see that the solid portion with $0 \le x \le \pi$ will suffice, and so we will restrict the

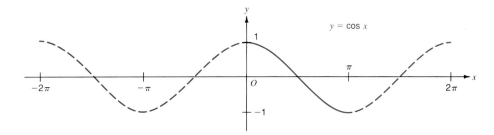

FIGURE 7.4

domain of the cosine function to $0 \leq x \leq \pi$ in order to define $\cos^{-1} x$. There are other portions that would be acceptable, but the one specified is the standard one used.

$$y = \cos^{-1} x \qquad \text{if and only if} \qquad \cos y = x$$

where $-1 \leq x \leq 1$ and $0 \leq \cos^{-1} x \leq \pi$.

To define the inverse tangent function, we use the open interval from $-\pi/2$ to $\pi/2$ since $\tan \pi/2$ and $\tan (-\pi/2)$ are not defined. This gives a connected portion of the graph of $y = \tan x$ which uses each value of y exactly once. See Fig. 7.5.

$$y = \tan^{-1} x \qquad \text{if and only if} \qquad \tan y = x$$

where x is any real number and $-\pi/2 < \tan^{-1} x < \pi/2$.

As with the notations $\sin^{-1} x$ and $\arcsin x$, we may write

Notation

$$\cos^{-1} x = \arccos x \qquad \text{and} \qquad \tan^{-1} x = \arctan x$$

Although we could define inverse functions for $y = \cot x$, $y = \sec x$, and $y = \csc x$, we will not do so since they are not used as often as the others.

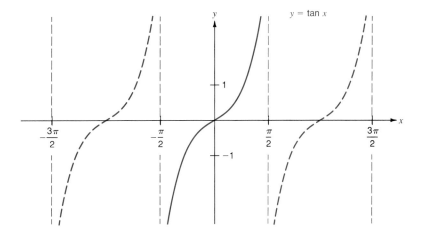

FIGURE 7.5

▶ **EXAMPLE 4**   Find the following inverse function values in radians.

Solution (a) $\arccos \dfrac{\sqrt{2}}{2} = \dfrac{\pi}{4}$ since $\cos \dfrac{\pi}{4} = \dfrac{\sqrt{2}}{2}$ and $0 \leq \dfrac{\pi}{4} \leq \pi$

(b) $\arcsin \dfrac{\sqrt{3}}{2} = \dfrac{\pi}{3}$ since $\sin \dfrac{\pi}{3} = \dfrac{\sqrt{3}}{2}$ and $-\dfrac{\pi}{2} \leq \dfrac{\pi}{3} \leq \dfrac{\pi}{2}$

(c) $\arctan 1 = \dfrac{\pi}{4}$ since $\tan \dfrac{\pi}{4} = 1$ and $-\dfrac{\pi}{2} < \dfrac{\pi}{4} < \dfrac{\pi}{2}$

(d) $\tan^{-1}\left(\dfrac{-1}{\sqrt{3}}\right) = \dfrac{-\pi}{6}$ since $\tan \dfrac{-\pi}{6} = \dfrac{-1}{\sqrt{3}}$ and $-\dfrac{\pi}{2} < \dfrac{-\pi}{6} < \dfrac{\pi}{2}$

(e) $\cos^{-1} \dfrac{-1}{2} = \dfrac{2\pi}{3}$ since $\cos \dfrac{2\pi}{3} = \dfrac{-1}{2}$ and $0 \leq \dfrac{2\pi}{3} \leq \pi$ ◢

Degrees may be used in the definitions of arccos x and arctan x if we require that

$$0° \leq \arccos x \leq 180° \qquad \text{and} \qquad -90° < \arctan x < 90°$$

▶ **EXAMPLE 5**   Find the following inverse function values in degrees.

Solution (a) $\arccos 0.432 = 64.4°$ since $\cos 64.4° \approx 0.432$ and $0° \leq 64.4° \leq 180°$

(b) $\arctan (\tan 211°) = 31°$ since $-90° < 31° < 90°$ and $\tan 211° = \tan 31°$

(c) $\tan (\arctan 3.8) = 3.8$

(d) $\cos (\cos^{-1} 0.718) = 0.718$

(e) $\sec (\arcsin 0.8765) \approx \sec 61.2° \approx 2.076$ ◢

Since $y = \arcsin x$ and $\sin y = x$, for $-\pi/2 \leq y \leq \pi/2$ and $-1 \leq x \leq 1$, express the same relationship between x and y, they have the same graph. It is the reflection of the graph of $y = \sin x$, $-\pi/2 \leq x \leq \pi/2$, through the line $y = x$. Recall Sec. 3.7 on the graph of an inverse function. The graph of $y = \arcsin x$ is shown in Fig. 7.6, and that of $y = \cos^{-1} x$ in Fig. 7.7.

We can use the formula for $\cos (\alpha + \beta)$ to find the exact value of certain expressions, and these may then be approximated to any desired degree of accuracy.

▶ **EXAMPLE 6**   Find the exact value of $\cos [\arcsin (\tfrac{3}{5}) + \arctan (\tfrac{24}{7})]$.

Solution   If we let $\alpha = \arcsin (\tfrac{3}{5})$ and $\beta = \arctan (\tfrac{24}{7})$, then $\sin \alpha = \tfrac{3}{5}$ and $\tan \beta = \tfrac{24}{7}$, as shown in Fig. 7.8. It follows that $\cos \alpha = \tfrac{4}{5}$, $\sin \beta = \tfrac{24}{25}$, and $\cos \beta = \tfrac{7}{25}$. Therefore the formula for the cosine of a sum shows that

$$\cos [\arcsin (\tfrac{3}{5}) + \arctan (\tfrac{24}{7})]$$
$$= \cos (\alpha + \beta) = \cos \alpha \cos \beta - \sin \alpha \sin \beta$$
$$= \frac{4}{5} \cdot \frac{7}{25} - \frac{3}{5} \cdot \frac{24}{25} = \frac{28 - 72}{125} = \frac{-44}{125} \approx -0.352$$ ◢

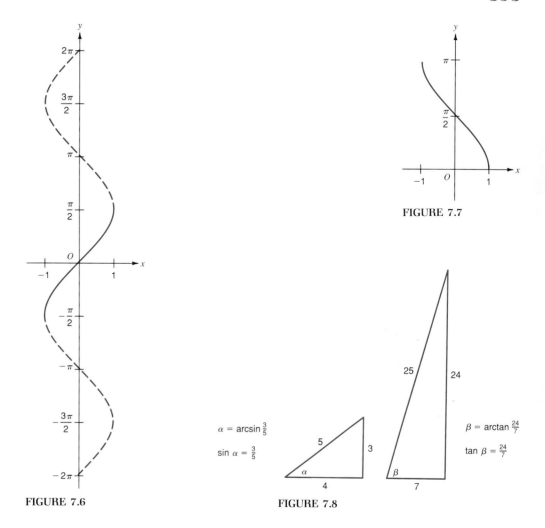

FIGURE 7.6

FIGURE 7.7

$\alpha = \arcsin \frac{3}{5}$

$\sin \alpha = \frac{3}{5}$

$\beta = \arctan \frac{24}{7}$

$\tan \beta = \frac{24}{7}$

FIGURE 7.8

A decimal approximation to $\cos [\arcsin (\frac{3}{5}) + \arctan (\frac{24}{7})]$ can also be found by evaluating the two angles, adding them, and then finding the cosine of the sum. This yields

$$\cos (36.8699° + 73.7398°) = \cos 110.6097° = -0.3520$$

which is the same value found in Example 6.

In Sec. 6.3, we saw how to find the other function values if one is given. Here is a related example.

EXAMPLE 7 If u is a positive number, evaluate $\cos (\arctan u)$.

Solution We begin by letting $\theta = \arctan u$, as shown in Fig. 7.9. Then $\tan \theta = u$, and by the Pythagorean theorem, the hypotenuse is $\sqrt{1 + u^2}$, and hence

$$\cos (\arctan u) = \cos \theta = \frac{1}{\sqrt{1 + u^2}}$$

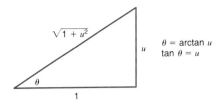

FIGURE 7.9

▶ **EXAMPLE 8**   Solve the equation below for x if

$$-3 \leq y \leq 3 \qquad \text{and} \qquad \frac{-3\pi}{8} \leq x \leq \frac{\pi}{8}$$

Solution

$$y = 3 \sin \left(2x + \frac{\pi}{4} \right) \qquad \text{given}$$

$$\frac{y}{3} = \sin \left(2x + \frac{\pi}{4} \right) \qquad \text{dividing by 3}$$

This equation and the next one are equivalent if $-1 \leq y/3 \leq 1$ and $-\pi/2 \leq 2x + (\pi/4) \leq \pi/2$. These are equivalent to the conditions stated in the problem.

$$\arcsin \left(\frac{y}{3} \right) = 2x + \frac{\pi}{4} \qquad \text{equivalent equations}$$

$$\arcsin \left(\frac{y}{3} \right) - \frac{\pi}{4} = 2x \qquad \text{subtracting } \frac{\pi}{4}$$

$$x = \frac{1}{2} \left(\arcsin \frac{y}{3} - \frac{\pi}{4} \right) \qquad \text{dividing by 2} \qquad ◀$$

▶ **EXAMPLE 9**   Prove the identity $\sin (2 \sin^{-1} x) = 2x \sqrt{1 - x^2}$.

Solution   Let $\theta = \sin^{-1} x$, as in Fig. 7.10. Since $-\pi/2 \leq \sin^{-1} x \leq \pi/2$, then $\cos \theta \geq 0$, and from the figure, $\cos \theta = \sqrt{1 - x^2}$. Also $\sin \theta = x$. Using the double-angle identity gives

$$\sin (2 \sin^{-1} x) = \sin (2\theta) = 2 \sin \theta \cos \theta = 2x \sqrt{1 - x^2} \qquad ◀$$

When light waves go from one medium to another, say from air to water, they **bend** or **refract.** The speed of light is greatest in a vacuum, about $3(10^8)$ m/s. The

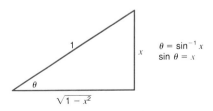

FIGURE 7.10

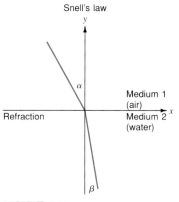

FIGURE 7.11

speed of light in any other medium is less than that, and the ratio

$$n = \frac{\text{speed of light in a vacuum}}{\text{speed of light in another medium}}$$

is called the **index of refraction** of the medium. By definition $n > 1$ for any medium other than a vacuum. For example,

$$n = 1.0003 \text{ for air} \qquad \text{and} \qquad n = 1.331 \text{ for water}$$

Snell's law states that

$$n_1 \sin \alpha = n_2 \sin \beta$$

where n_1 is the index of refraction in medium 1, n_2 is the index of refraction in medium 2, and α and β are the angles made by the light waves with the vertical. See Fig. 7.11. The controlled refraction, or bending, of light is what makes it possible to have microscopes, telescopes, cameras, and eye glasses.

▶ **EXAMPLE 10**   If light goes from air to water with $\alpha = 26.6°$ as in Fig. 7.11, find β.

Solution   Using Snell's law gives

$$1.003 \sin 26.6° = 1.331 \sin \beta$$

$$\sin \beta = \frac{1.003 \sin 26.6°}{1.331} = 0.3374 \qquad \text{by Table A.2 or calculator}$$

Thus $\beta = \sin^{-1} (0.3374) \approx 19.7°$ using a calculator or Table A.5 to the nearest tenth of a degree.   ◢

EXERCISE 7.6

Problems 1 to 4 are true-false.
1. arcsin 3.33 is defined.
2. arctan (-5678) is defined.
3. cos (arccos 0.12345) = 0.12345
4. arccos (-0.2468) is negative.

Find the exact values in radians in Probs. 5 to 16.
5. arcsin $\frac{1}{2}$
6. arccos $\frac{1}{2}$
7. arctan 1
8. arccos $(\sqrt{3}/2)$
9. $\tan^{-1} (\sqrt{3}/3)$
10. $\sin^{-1} 0$
11. $\cos^{-1} 1$
12. $\tan^{-1} \sqrt{3}$
13. arccos $(-\frac{1}{2})$
14. arctan (-1)
15. arcsin $(-\sqrt{3}/2)$
16. arcsin $(-\sqrt{2}/2)$

In Probs. 17 to 24, find the exact values in degrees.
17. $\tan^{-1} (-\sqrt{3})$
18. $\sin^{-1} (\sqrt{3}/2)$
19. $\cos^{-1} (-\sqrt{3}/2)$
20. $\tan^{-1} 0$

21. $\cos^{-1} (\cos 201°)$ and $\cos^{-1} (\cos 46°)$
22. $\sin^{-1} (\sin 103°)$ and $\sin^{-1} [\sin (-37°)]$
23. $\tan^{-1} (\tan 164°)$ and $\tan^{-1} (\tan 40°)$
24. $\tan^{-1} (\tan 308°)$ and $\tan^{-1} (\tan 1°)$

Find the value in Probs. 25 to 28 by using either a table or calculator. Use either radians or degrees.
25. $\tan^{-1} 1.428$
26. $\cos^{-1} 0.3551$
27. $\sin^{-1} (-1.2386)$
28. $\tan^{-1} (-0.4727)$

Find the exact values in Probs. 29 to 36.
29. tan (arctan 2) and arctan (tan 2)
30. cos (arccos 0.99) and arccos (cos 0.99)
31. sin [arcsin (-0.2)] and arcsin [sin (-0.2)]
32. tan (arctan 0.7) and arctan (tan 0.7)
33. cos $[\cos^{-1} (\frac{3}{5}) + \sin^{-1} (\frac{5}{13})]$
34. sin $[\sin^{-1} (\frac{15}{17}) + \tan^{-1} (\frac{3}{4})]$

35. $\cos [\tan^{-1} (\frac{5}{12}) + \sin^{-1} (\frac{7}{25})]$
36. $\tan [\sin^{-1} (\frac{20}{29}) + \cos^{-1} (\frac{4}{5})]$

If $u > 0$, find the function value in each of Probs. 37 to 40.

37. $\sin (\arctan u)$ **38.** $\cos (\arcsin u)$
39. $\sec (\arccos u)$ **40.** $\cot (\arctan u)$

Find the values in Probs. 41 to 44.
41. $\sin^{-1} 0.1236 + \cos^{-1} 0.1236$
42. $\tan^{-1} 4 + \tan^{-1} (\frac{1}{4})$
43. $\sin^{-1} 0.1444 + \sin^{-1} (-0.1444)$
44. $\cos^{-1} 0.2181 + \cos^{-1} (-0.2181)$

In Probs. 45 to 52, show that the equation is an identity.
45. $\sin^{-1} x + \cos^{-1} x = \pi/2$
46. $\tan^{-1} x + \tan^{-1} (1/x) = \pi/2$, if $x > 0$
47. $\sin^{-1} x + \sin^{-1} (-x) = 0$
48. $\cos^{-1} x + \cos^{-1} (-x) = \pi$
49. $\arcsin \dfrac{2x}{1 + x^2} = 2 \arctan x$, if $-1 < x < 1$
50. $\arctan x + \arctan y = \arctan \dfrac{x + y}{1 - xy}$, if $0 < x < 1$, $0 < y < 1$, and $xy < 1$
51. $2 \arccos x = \arccos (2x^2 - 1)$ for $0 \le x \le 1$
52. $2 \arcsin \sqrt{x} - \arcsin (2x - 1) = \pi/2$ if $0 \le x \le 1$
53. Show that $(\arcsin x)^2 + (\arccos x)^2$ is not identically equal to 1 by calculating it for $x = \frac{1}{2}$.
54. Show that $\arctan x$ is not the same as $\dfrac{\arcsin x}{\arccos x}$ by calculating both for $x = 0.2334$.
55. Define $\cot^{-1}$ by restricting the domain of $f(x) = \cot x$ to the interval $[0, \pi]$.
56. Define $\sec^{-1}$ by restricting the domain of $f(x) = \sec x$ to the union $[0, \pi/2) \cup [\pi, 3\pi/2)$.

Find the exact value of each expression in Probs. 57 to 60.
57. $\sin^{-1} (\cos 0.3821)$ **58.** $\cos^{-1} (\sin 0.3821)$

59. $\sin^{-1} (\cos 38°)$ **60.** $\cos^{-1} (\sin 162°)$

Show that each sum in Probs. 61 to 64 is $\pi/4$. *Hint:* Show that the tangent of each expression is 1.
61. $\arctan (\frac{3}{7}) + \arctan (\frac{2}{5})$
62. $\arctan (\frac{5}{3}) - \arctan (\frac{1}{4})$
63. $2 \arctan (\frac{1}{3}) + \arctan (\frac{1}{7})$
64. $\arctan (\frac{2}{3}) + \arctan (\frac{1}{7}) + \arctan (\frac{1}{18})$

The **Mach number M** of an airplane is the ratio of its speed to the speed of sound. Suppose that a plane is flying faster than the speed of sound, and so $M > 1$. The sound waves, which create a sonic boom as they cross a point, form a cone behind the plane with vertex angle θ. For speeds with $M > 1$, it is true that $\sin \theta/2 = 1/M$. Use this in Probs. 65 and 66.
65. If $M = 1.3$, find a decimal approximation to θ.
66. If $M > 1$, find the exact value of θ.

For two points in the northern (or southern) hemisphere on the earth's surface, the shortest distance between them is the shorter arc of the **great circle** through them—that is, the circle on the earth's surface through the two points with its center at the center of the earth. If two points are at latitudes α and β (the equator has latitude 0°), and if the **difference** in their longitudes is θ, then the shortest distance in miles between them is

$$4000 \arccos (\sin \alpha \sin \beta + \cos \alpha \cos \beta \cos \theta)$$

where the arccos is in radians. Find this distance for the cities in Probs. 67 and 68.
67. New Orleans: 30°N latitude, 90°W longitude
London: 51.5°N latitude, 0° longitude
68. Auckland, New Zealand: 37°S latitude, 175°E longitude
Alice Springs, Australia: 23.7°S latitude, 134°E longitude

7.7 Trigonometric Equations

Most of our attention so far in this chapter has been on identities. In this section we will solve conditional trigonometric equations, those which are true for some but not all values of the variable in the domain. Factoring, quadratic equations, and other standard algebraic methods will be used along with any of the trigonometric identities from this chapter. We will normally have to solve first for $\sin x$ or $\tan \theta$, for instance, instead of x or θ. The solutions for x or θ may then be given in either angles or real numbers. Sometimes we will ask for all solutions, and sometimes only for those in a certain interval such as $[0, 2\pi]$.

▶ **EXAMPLE 1**   Solve the equation $2 \cos x = \sqrt{3}$.

Solution   Here we have to find all solutions, and we will begin by finding those in the interval $[0°, 360°)$:

$$2 \cos x = \sqrt{3} \qquad \text{given}$$

$$\cos x = \frac{\sqrt{3}}{2} \qquad \text{dividing by 2}$$

The values of $\cos x$ are positive in the first and fourth quadrants, and so the solutions for x in the interval $[0°, 360°)$ are $30°$ and $330°$. Note that if we had written $x = \cos^{-1}(\sqrt{3}/2)$, we would have had only the solution $30°$. Using periodicity, the solutions are

$$30° + n \cdot 360° \qquad \text{and} \qquad 330° + n \cdot 360° \qquad \text{where } n \text{ is an integer} \qquad \blacktriangleleft$$

▶ **EXAMPLE 2**   Solve the equation $\tan^2 \theta = 3$ for $0 \le \theta < 2\pi$.

Solution

$$\tan^2 \theta = 3 \qquad \text{given}$$

$$\tan \theta = \pm\sqrt{3} \qquad \text{solving for } \tan \theta$$

There is one solution in each quadrant, and they are $\pi/3$, $2\pi/3$, $4\pi/3$, and $5\pi/3$. $\blacktriangleleft$

We will normally find the solutions

In the interval $[0, 2\pi)$ or $[0°, 360°)$

However, θ is in the interval $[0, 2\pi)$ if and only if 2θ is in the interval $[0, 4\pi)$. Thus when the angle in the original equation is, say, 2θ, we must find the solutions first for $0 \le 2\theta \le 4\pi$, or $0° \le 2\theta \le 720°$.

▶ **EXAMPLE 3**   Solve the equation $\sin x \cos x = \frac{1}{4}$ for $0 \le x < 2\pi$.

Solution

$$\sin x \cos x = \tfrac{1}{4} \qquad \text{given}$$

$$2 \sin x \cos x = \tfrac{1}{2} \qquad \text{multiplying by 2}$$

$$\sin 2x = \tfrac{1}{2} \qquad \text{double-angle identity}$$

Hence the sine of $2x$ is $\frac{1}{2}$, and so the solutions with $0 \le 2x < 4\pi$ are

$$2x = \frac{\pi}{6} \qquad \frac{5\pi}{6} \qquad \frac{13\pi}{6} \qquad \frac{17\pi}{6}$$

and thus

$$x = \frac{\pi}{12} \qquad \frac{5\pi}{12} \qquad \frac{13\pi}{12} \qquad \frac{17\pi}{12} \qquad \blacktriangleleft$$

▶ **EXAMPLE 4**   Solve the equation $3 \cos 2\theta - \cos \theta + 1 = 0$.

Solution   We will first find the solutions for $0° \leq \theta < 360°$, and we use the identity $\cos 2\theta = 2 \cos^2 \theta - 1$ to get an equation that contains only $\cos \theta$:

$$3(2 \cos^2 \theta - 1) - \cos \theta + 1 = 0 \qquad \text{by the identity}$$

$$6 \cos^2 \theta - \cos \theta - 2 = 0 \qquad \text{combining similar terms}$$

$$(2 \cos \theta + 1)(3 \cos \theta - 2) = 0 \qquad \text{factoring}$$

$$\cos \theta = -\tfrac{1}{2} \text{ and } \tfrac{2}{3} \qquad \text{solving for } \cos \theta$$

Now if $\cos \theta = -\tfrac{1}{2}$, then $\theta = 120°$ or $240°$ ($2\pi/3$ or $4\pi/3$). As a check of $\theta = 120°$ in the original equation,

$$3 \cos 240° - \cos 120° + 1 = -\tfrac{3}{2} - (-\tfrac{1}{2}) + 1 = 0$$

The value $\theta = 240°$ also works in the original equation. Moreover if $\cos \theta = \tfrac{2}{3} \approx 0.6667$, then to the nearest tenth of a degree, $\theta = 48.2°$ or $311.8°$ (0.8412 or 5.4420), each of which also checks in the original equation. Using periodicity, all of the solutions are

$$120° + n \cdot 360° \qquad 240° + n \cdot 360° \qquad 48.2° + n \cdot 360° \qquad 311.8° + n \cdot 360°$$

where n is an integer.   ◢

Each solution should be checked in the original equation. This is especially important in Example 5.

▶ **EXAMPLE 5**   Solve the equation $\sin x \tan x = \tan x$ for $0 \leq x < 2\pi$.

Solution   Resist the temptation to divide by $\tan x$; it might be 0.

$$\sin x \tan x - \tan x = 0 \qquad \text{subtracting } \tan x$$

$$\tan x (\sin x - 1) = 0 \qquad \text{common factor of } \tan x$$

Since the product is equal to zero, we set each factor equal to zero. This gives

$$\tan x = 0 \qquad x = 0, \pi$$

$$\sin x = 1 \qquad x = \frac{\pi}{2}$$

Remember that each solution should be checked in the original equation. Both 0 and π check in the original equation. However $\tan (\pi/2)$ is not defined, and so $\pi/2$ is not a solution.   ◢

Squaring both sides of an equation can lead to extraneous solutions, as in Example 6.

▶ **EXAMPLE 6**   Solve the equation $\sec \theta + \tan \theta = 4$ for $0° \leq \theta < 360°$.

Solution

$$\sec \theta + \tan \theta = 4 \qquad \text{given}$$

$$\sec \theta = 4 - \tan \theta \qquad \text{subtracting } \tan \theta$$

$$\sec^2 \theta = 16 - 8 \tan \theta + \tan^2 \theta \qquad \text{squaring}$$

$$\sec^2 \theta - \tan^2 \theta - 16 = -8 \tan \theta \qquad \text{combining terms}$$

$$-15 = -8 \tan \theta \qquad \sec^2 \theta - \tan^2 \theta = 1$$

$$\tan \theta = \tfrac{15}{8} = 1.875$$

Since $\tan \theta$ is positive in the first and third quadrants, using a calculator or a table yields

$$\theta \approx 61.9° \qquad \text{or} \qquad \theta \approx 241.9°$$

The first value $\theta = 61.9°$ works since

$$\sec 61.9° + \tan 61.9° \approx 2.123 + 1.873 \approx 3.996 \approx 4$$

except for reasonable roundoff error. The second value $\theta = 241.9°$ does not check in the equation since

$$\sec 241.9° + \tan 241.9° \approx -2.123 + 1.873 = -0.25$$

The only solution is $\theta = \arctan \tfrac{15}{8} \approx 62.9°$. ◢

EXAMPLE 7 Solve $\cos \theta - \cos 5\theta = 2 \sin 3\theta$, for $0° \le \theta < 360°$.

Solution The formula (7.30), $\cos x - \cos y = -2[\sin (x + y)/2][\sin (x - y)/2]$, applied to the terms $\cos \theta - \cos 5\theta$, allows the given equation to be written as

$$2 \sin 3\theta \sin 2\theta - 2 \sin 3\theta = 0$$

$$2 \sin 3\theta(\sin 2\theta - 1) = 0 \qquad \text{common factor}$$

Setting each factor equal to zero yields (a) $2 \sin 3\theta = 0$ or (b) $\sin 2\theta = 1$. The solutions of (a) for 3θ from $0°$ to $3(360°) = 1080°$ are

$$3\theta = 0° \qquad 180° \qquad 360° \qquad 540° \qquad 720° \qquad \text{or} \qquad 900°$$

whereas the solutions of (b) for 2θ from $0°$ to $2(360°) = 720°$ are

$$2\theta = 90° \qquad \text{or} \qquad 450°$$

Consequently, the values of θ from $0°$ to $360°$ are

$$0° \qquad 60° \qquad 120° \qquad 180° \qquad 240° \qquad 300° \qquad \text{and} \qquad 45° \qquad 225°$$

In radians these values are

$$0 \qquad \frac{\pi}{3} \qquad \frac{2\pi}{3} \qquad \pi \qquad \frac{4\pi}{3} \qquad \frac{5\pi}{3} \qquad \text{and} \qquad \frac{\pi}{4} \qquad \frac{5\pi}{4} \qquad ◢$$

Equations of the Form $A \sin \theta + B \cos \theta = C$

An equation of the form

$$A \sin \theta + B \cos \theta = C$$

can be solved by first dividing by $\sqrt{A^2 + B^2}$:

$$\frac{A}{\sqrt{A^2 + B^2}} \sin \theta + \frac{B}{\sqrt{A^2 + B^2}} \cos \theta = \frac{C}{\sqrt{A^2 + B^2}} \tag{1}$$

Now the point $\left(\dfrac{A}{\sqrt{A^2 + B^2}}, \dfrac{B}{\sqrt{A^2 + B^2}} \right)$ is a point on the unit circle $x^2 + y^2 = 1$ because

$$\left(\frac{A}{\sqrt{A^2 + B^2}} \right)^2 + \left(\frac{B}{\sqrt{A^2 + B^2}} \right)^2 = \frac{A^2 + B^2}{A^2 + B^2} = 1$$

But every point on the unit circle has the form $(\cos \alpha, \sin \alpha)$, and so we may choose α to satisfy

$$\cos \alpha = \frac{A}{\sqrt{A^2 + B^2}} \qquad \text{and} \qquad \sin \alpha = \frac{B}{\sqrt{A^2 + B^2}}$$

This allows us to rewrite Eq. (1) as

$$\cos \alpha \sin \theta + \sin \alpha \cos \theta = \frac{C}{\sqrt{A^2 + B^2}}$$

Using the identity for the sine of a sum gives

$$\sin (\theta + \alpha) = \frac{C}{\sqrt{A^2 + B^2}} \tag{7.31}$$

Remember that we started with $A \sin \theta + B \cos \theta = C$, and thus we may rewrite Eq. (7.31) as

$$\sqrt{A^2 + B^2} \cdot \sin (\theta + \alpha) = A \sin \theta + B \cos \theta \tag{2}$$

We may find α by using

$$\tan \alpha = \frac{\sin \alpha}{\cos \alpha} = \frac{B/\sqrt{A^2 + B^2}}{A/\sqrt{A^2 + B^2}} = \frac{B}{A}$$

The quadrant that α is in may be determined by the signs of $\cos \alpha$ and $\sin \alpha$.

▶ **EXAMPLE 8**   Solve the equation $\sqrt{3} \sin \theta - \cos \theta = 1$.

Solution   This is of the form $A \sin \theta + B \cos \theta = C$ with $A = \sqrt{3}$, $B = -1$, and $C = 1$. Therefore by Eq. (7.23) we get

$$\sin (\theta + \alpha) = \frac{1}{\sqrt{(\sqrt{3})^2 + (-1)^2}} = \frac{1}{2}$$

Also, from Eq. (2), $\cos \alpha = \sqrt{3}/2$ and $\sin \alpha = -\frac{1}{2}$; thus α is in the fourth quadrant, and we may take $\alpha = -30°$ or $-\pi/6$. Consequently the original equation is equivalent to

Degrees	**Radians**
$\sin (\theta - 30°) = \frac{1}{2}$	$\sin (\theta - \pi/6) = \frac{1}{2}$
$\theta - 30° = 30°$ or $150°$	$\theta - \pi/6 = \pi/6$ or $5\pi/6$
$\theta = 60°$ or $180°$	$\theta = \pi/3$ or π

EXAMPLE 9   Solve the equation $8 \sin \theta + 15 \cos \theta = 12$.

Solution   With $A = 8$ and $B = 15$, we get

$$\sqrt{A^2 + B^2} = \sqrt{64 + 225} = 17$$

and dividing the original equation by 17 gives

$$\frac{8 \sin \theta}{17} + \frac{15 \cos \theta}{17} = \frac{12}{17}$$

Now by Eq. (2), we may choose α so that

$$\cos \alpha = \tfrac{8}{17} \qquad \text{and} \qquad \sin \alpha = \tfrac{15}{17}$$

Thus α is in the first quadrant, and since $\tfrac{8}{17} \approx 0.4706$ we have $\alpha \approx 61.9°$ or 1.0808. Then from (7.31) we have

$$\sin (\theta + \alpha) = \tfrac{12}{17}$$

Now using $\tfrac{12}{17} = 0.7059$ gives either

Degrees	**Radians**
$\sin (\theta + 61.9°) = 0.7059$	$\sin (\theta + 1.0808) = 0.7059$
$\theta + 61.9° = 44.9°$ or $135.1°$	$\theta + 1.0808 = 0.7837$ or 2.3579
$\theta = -17°$ or $73.2°$	$\theta = -0.2971$ or 1.2771
or else $343°$ or $73.2°$	or else 5.9861 or 1.2771

These solutions can be checked by substitution in the given equation.

EXAMPLE 10   Show that there is no solution to

$$8 \sin \theta + 15 \cos \theta = 18 \tag{3}$$

Solution   Since $A = 8$ and $B = 15$, as in Example 9, we can proceed just as above, Eq. (3) becoming

$$\sin (\theta + \alpha) = \tfrac{18}{17}$$

This equation has no solution since $\left| \sin (\theta + \alpha) \right| \le 1$ whereas $\tfrac{18}{17} > 1$.

EXERCISE 7.7

Find all solutions in Probs. 1 to 8. The answers are given in both radians and degrees.

1. $2 \cos \theta = -1$
2. $\tan \theta = \sqrt{3}$
3. $\sec \theta = 1$
4. $2 \sin \theta = -\sqrt{3}$
5. $\cot^2 x = 1$
6. $\cos^2 x = \frac{1}{2}$
7. $\sin^2 x = \frac{3}{4}$
8. $\csc^2 x = 2$

Solve the equations in Probs. 9 to 36 for values of the variable in the interval $[0, 2\pi)$, or $[0°, 360°)$. The answers will be given both ways.

9. $\sin t \cos t = \frac{1}{2}$
10. $\sec 2t = 2$
11. $\tan 3t = \sqrt{3}$
12. $\cos 3t = -\frac{1}{2}$
13. $2 \sin^2 \theta + 3 \sin \theta - 2 = 0$
14. $2 \sec^2 \theta - 3 \sec \theta + 1 = 0$
15. $4 \tan^2 \theta - 3 \sec^2 \theta = 0$
16. $2 \sin^2 \theta + 5 \cos \theta + 1 = 0$
17. $\tan^2 \beta + (1 - \sqrt{3}) \tan \beta - \sqrt{3} = 0$
18. $2 \cos^2 \beta + (1 + 2\sqrt{3}) \cos \beta + \sqrt{3} = 0$
19. $2 \sin \beta \tan \beta - \sqrt{3} \tan \beta - 4 \sin \beta + 2\sqrt{3} = 0$
20. $\cos \beta \tan \beta - \cos \beta - \tan \beta + 1 = 0$

Hint: In Probs. 21 to 24, first use one of the identities

$$\tan \frac{\theta}{2} = \frac{\sin \theta}{1 + \cos \theta} \quad \text{or} \quad \tan \frac{\theta}{2} = \frac{1 - \cos \theta}{\sin \theta}$$

21. $\cot \theta + \tan \dfrac{\theta}{2} = 0$

22. $\cot \dfrac{\theta}{2} + 1 + \cos \theta = 0$

23. $\tan \frac{1}{2}\theta + \sin 2\theta = \csc \theta$ **24.** $\cos \theta + \tan \frac{1}{2}\theta = 1$
25. $\sin 2y \cos 3y - \sin 3y \cos 2y = 0$
26. $\sin 3y \cos y - \cos 3y \sin y = 0$
27. $\cos 3y \cos 2y + \sin 3y \sin 2y = \sin 2y$
28. $\sin 3y \cos 2y - \cos 3y \sin 2y = \sin 2y$

Hint: In Probs. 29 to 36, use one of the sum-to-product identities.

29. $\sin u + \sin 3u = 0$
30. $\cos 4u + \cos 2u = 0$
31. $\cos 3u - \cos u = 0$
32. $\sin 4u - \sin 2u = 0$
33. $\sin 5\alpha + \sin \alpha = \sin 3\alpha$
34. $\sin 4\alpha - \sin 2\alpha = 2 \cos 3\alpha$
35. $\cos 5\alpha + \cos \alpha = \cos 2\alpha$
36. $\cos 5\alpha - \cos 3\alpha = 2 \sin 4\alpha$

In Probs. 37 to 40, use the quadratic formula and then either tables or a calculator to find the solutions to the nearest tenth of a degree.

37. $9 \cos^2 x - 6 \cos x - 1 = 0$
38. $16 \tan^2 x - 16 \tan x - 1 = 0$
39. $8 \sin x - 8 = \csc x$
40. $4 \tan x + 13 \cot x = 16$

In Probs. 41 to 44, use either tables or a calculator to find the solutions to the nearest tenth of a degree.

41. $\sec y + \tan y = 4$ **42.** $\csc y + \cot y = -5$
43. $1 + \sin y = -3 \cos y$ **44.** $1 + \cos y = 6 \sin y$

In Probs. 45 to 52, use Eq. (7.31).

45. $3 \sin \theta + 4 \cos \theta = 4.5$
46. $\sin \theta + \cos \theta = \sqrt{2}/2$
47. $5 \sin \theta + 12 \cos \theta = 9.1026$
48. $\sin \theta + \sqrt{3} \cos \theta = 2$
49. $\sin \theta - \sqrt{3} \cos \theta = 1$
50. $\sqrt{3} \sin \theta - \cos \theta = 1$
51. $-12 \sin \theta + 5 \cos \theta = 6.5$
52. $-5 \sin \theta + 12 \cos \theta = 6.5\sqrt{3}$
53. Use Eq. (3) to show that

the maximum value of $A \sin x + B \cos x$ is $\sqrt{A^2 + B^2}$

In Probs. 54 to 56, use Prob. 53 to show that there is no solution to the given equation.

54. $5 \sin x + 6 \cos x = 8$
55. $7 \sin x - 8 \cos x = 11$
56. $3 \sin x + 9 \cos x = 10$
57. The number of hours of daylight in certain northern latitudes is approximately $12 + 3 \sin (2\pi x/365)$, where x is the number of days after March 21. What is the first day after March 21 when there are 13 h of daylight?
58. The voltage in an electrical signal is $90 \cos (120\pi t - 0.785)$. For which value of t is the voltage equal to 40?
59. The graph of $y = e^{-x} \cos 2x$ is an example of damped oscillation. (See the figure.) It can be shown by calculus that at the maximum point A and the minimum point B the x value must satisfy the equation

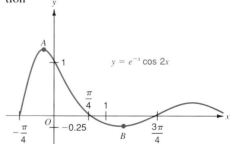

$$-e^{-x}(2 \sin 2x + \cos 2x) = 0$$

Solve this equation for the values of x corresponding to A and B.

60. Some equations cannot be solved easily, and numerical analysis is helpful. A Roman aqueduct was built in the shape of a trapezoid with base a, slant b, and angle θ. (See the figure.) The area of a cross section is

$$(a + b \cos \theta)(b \sin \theta)$$

which you should be able to prove. To the nearest degree, find the two angles which make the area 60 m^2 if a is 9 m and b is 6 m. *Hint:* First calculate

$$(9 + 6 \cos \theta)(6 \sin \theta)$$

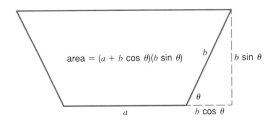

every 10°; then for those angles which give an area near 60, calculate it for every degree. This is ideal for a computer, a programmable calculator, or a graphing calculator.

7.8 Key Concepts

Be sure that you understand and can use the following formulas.

(7.1) $\sin \theta \csc \theta = 1$

(7.2) $\cos \theta \sec \theta = 1$

(7.3) $\tan \theta \cot \theta = 1$

(7.4) $\tan \theta = \dfrac{\sin \theta}{\cos \theta}$

(7.5) $\cot \theta = \dfrac{\cos \theta}{\sin \theta}$

(7.6) $\cos^2 \theta + \sin^2 \theta = 1$

(7.7) $1 + \tan^2 \theta = \sec^2 \theta$

(7.8) $1 + \cot^2 \theta = \csc^2 \theta$

(7.9) $\cos (A - B) = \cos A \cos B + \sin A \sin B$

(7.10) $\cos \left(\dfrac{\pi}{2} - B \right) = \sin B$

(7.11) $\sin \left(\dfrac{\pi}{2} - B \right) = \cos B$

(7.12) $\cos (A + B) = \cos A \cos B - \sin A \sin B$

(7.13) $\sin (A + B) = \sin A \cos B + \cos A \sin B$

(7.14) $\sin (A - B) = \sin A \cos B - \cos A \sin B$

(7.15a) $\cos 2\theta = \cos^2 \theta - \sin^2 \theta$

(7.15b) $\cos 2\theta = 2 \cos^2 \theta - 1$

(7.15c) $\cos 2\theta = 1 - 2 \sin^2 \theta$

(7.16) $\sin 2\theta = 2 \sin \theta \cos \theta$

(7.17) $\sin^2 \dfrac{\theta}{2} = \dfrac{1 - \cos \theta}{2}$

(7.18) $\cos^2 \dfrac{\theta}{2} = \dfrac{1 + \cos \theta}{2}$

(7.19) $\tan (A + B) = \dfrac{\tan A + \tan B}{1 - \tan A \tan B}$

(7.20) $\tan 2\theta = \dfrac{2 \tan \theta}{1 - \tan^2 \theta}$

(7.21a) $\tan \dfrac{\theta}{2} = \dfrac{1 - \cos \theta}{\sin \theta}$

(7.21b) $\tan \dfrac{\theta}{2} = \dfrac{\sin \theta}{1 + \cos \theta}$

(7.22) $\tan (A - B) = \dfrac{\tan A - \tan B}{1 + \tan A \tan B}$

Product-to-Sum Formulas

(7.23) $\sin A \cos B = \frac{1}{2}[\sin(A + B) + \sin (A - B)]$
(7.24) $\cos A \sin B = \frac{1}{2}[\sin (A + B) - \sin (A - B)]$
(7.25) $\cos A \cos B = \frac{1}{2}[\cos (A + B) + \cos (A - B)]$
(7.26) $-\sin A \sin B = \frac{1}{2}[\cos (A + B) - \cos (A - B)]$

Sum-to-Product Formulas

(7.27) $\sin x + \sin y = 2 \sin \dfrac{x + y}{2} \cos \dfrac{x - y}{2}$

(7.28) $\sin x - \sin y = 2 \cos \dfrac{x + y}{2} \sin \dfrac{x - y}{2}$

(7.29) $\cos x + \cos y = 2 \cos \dfrac{x + y}{2} \cos \dfrac{x - y}{2}$

(7.30) $\cos x - \cos y = -2 \sin \dfrac{x + y}{2} \sin \dfrac{x - y}{2}$

(7.31) $\sin (\theta + \alpha) = \dfrac{C}{\sqrt{A^2 + B^2}}$ is $A \sin \theta + B \cos \theta = C$

with $\cos \alpha = \dfrac{A}{\sqrt{A^2 + B^2}}$ and $\sin \alpha = \dfrac{B}{\sqrt{A^2 + B^2}}$

EXERCISE 7.8   Review

In Probs. 1 to 9, find the exact values if $\sin x = \frac{5}{13}$ with x in the first quadrant, and $\tan y = -\frac{15}{8}$ with y in the second quadrant.

1. $\cos (x + y)$ **2.** $\cos 2x$ **3.** $\sin (y - x)$
4. $\sin 2y$ **5.** $\tan (x + y)$ **6.** $\tan x/2$
7. $\sin^2 y/2$ **8.** $\sin (x + 2y)$ **9.** $\sin 4x$
10. Find the exact value of $\cos 255°$.
11. Find the exact value of $\tan 67.5°$.
12. Write $\cos 47° \cos 36° - \sin 133° \sin 36°$ as one function value of one angle.

Prove the identities in Probs. 13 to 43.
13. $\cos 10\theta = \cos^2 5\theta - \sin^2 5\theta$
14. $\sec^2 3t - \tan^2 3t = \sin^2 5t + \cos^2 5t$
15. $(1 + \tan^2 \alpha)(1 - \sin^2 \alpha) = 1$
16. $\sin 2x \sec x = 2 \sin x$
17. $1 + \tan^2 \theta = 2 \tan \theta \csc 2\theta$
18. $1 + \csc^2 x \cos 2x = \cot^2 x$
19. $\csc 2x - \cot 2x = \tan x$
20. $\dfrac{1 + \sin 2x}{\cos 2x} = \dfrac{1 + \tan x}{1 - \tan x}$

21. $1 + \dfrac{\cos 3x}{\cos x} = 2 \cos 2x$

22. $\cot 2x = \dfrac{\csc x - 2 \sin x}{2 \cos x}$

23. $\dfrac{1}{\sec x - \tan x} - \dfrac{1}{\sec x + \tan x} = 2 \tan x$

24. $\dfrac{(1 + \cot x)^2}{1 + \cot^2 x} = 1 + \sin 2x$

25. $\dfrac{1 + 2 \sin 2x + \cos 2x}{2 + \sin 2x - 2 \cos 2x} = \cot x$

26. $\dfrac{\sin x - \sin 3x + \sin 2x}{2(1 - \cos x)} = \sin x + \sin 2x$

27. $\dfrac{\cos 3x}{\sin x} + \dfrac{\sin 3x}{\cos x} = 2 \cos 2x \csc 2x$

28. $\dfrac{\sin 5x}{\sin x} - \dfrac{\cos 5x}{\cos x} = 4 \cos 2x$

29. $\cot \dfrac{x}{2} = \dfrac{\sin x + \sin 2x}{\cos x - \cos 2x}$

30. $\sin \theta = \dfrac{\sin 2\theta \cos \theta}{1 + \cos 2\theta}$

31. $\csc y - 2 \sin y = 2 \cos y \cot 2y$

32. $\tan x + \cot x = \sec x \csc x$

33. $\dfrac{\sin^3 x - \cos^3 x}{\sin x - \cos x} = \dfrac{2 + \sin 2x}{2}$

34. $\sin^6 A + \cos^6 A = 1 - \frac{3}{4}(\sin 2A)^2$

35. $\tan(x - y) + \tan y = \sec (x - y) \sin x \sec y$

36. $\cot x - \cot (x - y) = \csc (y - x) \sin y \csc x$

37. $\cos x + \sin x \tan y = \sec y \cos (x - y)$

38. $\sin x - \cos x \cot y = -\csc y \cos (x + y)$

39. $\cot y - \cot x = \dfrac{\sin (x - y)}{\sin x \sin y}$

40. $\sin y(\cot y - \tan x) = \cos (x + y) \sec x$

41. $\dfrac{\sin 4x}{4} = \sin x \cos^3 x - \cos x \sin^3 x$

42. $2 \tan^{-1} x = \tan^{-1} \dfrac{2x}{1 - x^2}$

43. $2 \sin (\alpha + \beta) \cos (\alpha + \beta) = \sin 2\alpha \cos 2\beta + \cos 2\alpha \sin 2\beta$

44. Simplify $\sqrt{9 - x^2}$ after replacing x by $3 \sin \theta$.

45. Simplify $\sqrt{16 + x^2}$ after replacing x by $4 \tan \theta$.

46. Factor the expression $\cos 5y + \cos 7y + \cos 9y$.

In Probs. 47 and 48, write each product as a sum or difference.

47. $\sin 6x \sin 14x$ **48.** $\sin 16x \cos 6x$

In Probs. 49 and 50, write each sum or difference as a product.

49. $\cos 9x - \cos 3x$ **50.** $\sin 4x - \sin 10x$

51. Let $x = 4 - \sin t$ and $y = -2 + \cos t$. Show that for every value of t, the point (x, y) lies on the circle with radius 1 and center $(4, -2)$, whose equation is $(x - 4)^2 + (y + 2)^2 = 1$.

52. Evaluate each of the following expressions:
(a) $\arcsin (-\sqrt{3}/2) + \arccos (-\sqrt{3}/2)$
(b) $\tan [\sin^{-1} (\frac{2}{5}) + \cos^{-1} (\frac{3}{4})]$
(c) $\csc (\arcsin u)$

Find the exact values in Probs. 53 and 54.

53. (a) $\arctan (\tan \frac{1}{4})$; (b) $\tan (\arctan 0.3)$

54. (a) $\arctan (\cot 58°)$; (b) $\cot (\arctan 7)$

55. Verify that $\cos (2 \arctan \frac{1}{7}) = \sin (4 \arctan \frac{1}{3})$.

56. Show that $\cos^{-1} x = 2 \tan^{-1} \sqrt{\dfrac{1 - x}{1 + x}}$ if $|x| < 1$.

The result in Prob. 56 is useful since many versions of the programming language BASIC include $\arctan x$, but neither $\arcsin x$ nor $\arccos x$. Verify the calculations in Probs. 57 to 60.

57. $\sin^{-1} \dfrac{3}{\sqrt{73}} + \cos^{-1} \dfrac{11}{\sqrt{146}} = \dfrac{\pi}{4}$

58. $4 \tan^{-1} \dfrac{1}{5} - \tan^{-1} \dfrac{1}{239} = \dfrac{\pi}{4}$

59. $\arctan \frac{1}{7} + \arctan \frac{1}{8} = \arctan \frac{1}{3} - \arctan \frac{1}{18}$

60. $\arcsin \dfrac{1}{3} + \arcsin \dfrac{1}{3\sqrt{11}} = \dfrac{\pi}{2} - \arcsin \dfrac{3}{\sqrt{11}}$

Solve the equation in each of Probs. 61 to 85 for values of x such that $0 \le x < 360°$, or $0 \le x < 2\pi$.

61. $\csc x = -1$ **62.** $\cos^2 x = \frac{3}{4}$

63. $\tan 2t = -\sqrt{3}$

64. $2 \cos^2 x + \cos x - 1 = 0$

65. $\sqrt{3} \tan^2 x + 2 \tan x - \sqrt{3} = 0$

66. $2 \tan^2 x - 3 \tan x = 0$

67. $5 \sin x + 4 - 2 \cos^2 x = 0$

68. $\sec^2 x + \tan x - 1 = 0$

69. $2 \cos x + 1 - \sec x = 0$

70. $\cos^2 x - \cos 2x = 0$

71. $\sin 3x \cos x - \cos 3x \sin x = 0$

72. $2 \sin^2 x - (1 + 2\sqrt{3}) \sin x + \sqrt{3} = 0$

73. $2 \sin x \cos x + 4 \sin x - \cos x - 2 = 0$

74. $2 \sec x \tan x + 6 \tan x - \sec x - 3 = 0$

75. $\cos 2x \sin x + \sin x = 0$

76. $\sin 3x + 4 \sin^3 x = 0$

77. $\sin 2x + \sin x = 0$ **78.** $\cos 4x + \cos x = 0$

79. $\sin 3x - \sin x = 0$ **80.** $\cos 5x + \cos 3x = 0$

81. $\sec x = 5 - \tan x$

82. $\sqrt{3} \sin x + \cos x = 2$

83. $3 \sin x - 4 \cos x = 5$

84. $5 \sin x + 12 \cos x = 6.5\sqrt{3}$

85. $24 \sin x - 7 \cos x = 12.5\sqrt{2}$

86. Show that $5 \sin x + 8 \cos x = 9$ **has** a solution (do not find it), but that $5 \sin x + 8 \cos x = 10$ has no solution.

Prove each of the following inequalities.

87. $\cos (x - y) > \sin x \sin y$ for x and y in quadrant I

88. Show that $| \sin (x + y) | \le | \sin x | + | \sin y |$.

89. Show that $| \sin (x + y + z) | \le | \sin x | + | \sin y | + | \sin z |$.

90. Prove that $\tan 2\theta > 2 \tan \theta$ for $0 < \theta < \pi/4$.

91. It is true that $3 \tan 5A > 5 \tan 3A$ for $0° < A < 18°$. Check this for $A = 13°$, or 0.2269.

92. Verify that if $A = 49°$, $B = 61°$, and $C = 70°$, then

$$\cos^2 A + \cos^2 B + \cos^2 C + 2 \cos A \cos B \cos C = 1$$

This is true whenever $A + B + C = 180°$.

93. Verify that if $A = 12°$, $B = 46°$, and $C = 32°$, then

$$\sin^2 A + \sin^2 B + \sin^2 C + 2 \sin A \sin B \sin C = 1$$

This is true whenever $A + B + C = 90°$.

94. Verify that if $A = 12°$, $B = 15°$, and $C = 18°$, then

$$(\sin A + \cos A)(\sin B + \cos B)(\sin C + \cos C)$$
$$= 2(\sin A \sin B \sin C + \cos A \cos B \cos C)$$

This is true whenever $A + B + C = 45°$.

95. Show that if $\tan x = \frac{1}{2}$, then

$$\tan 2x = \frac{4}{3} \qquad \text{and} \qquad \tan 3x = \frac{11}{2}$$

96. Show that if $\tan y = \frac{1}{3}$, then

$$\tan 2y = \frac{3}{4} \qquad \text{and} \qquad \tan 3y = \frac{13}{9}$$

and hence

$$\tan (\tfrac{1}{3} \arctan \tfrac{13}{9}) = \tfrac{1}{3}$$

8 Triangles and Applications

One of the original uses of trigonometry was finding the sides and angles of a triangle when certain parts were given. We have already done this for right triangles in Sec. 6.4, and we will do it for oblique triangles here, as well as develop several formulas for the area of a triangle. A triangle can be solved if we know three parts including the length of a side. In order to find a specified part of a triangle, we have to select a formula which involves this part as the only unknown value. We also need to know how many digits to use in the lengths of the sides for angles of specific accuracy.

This chapter is especially rich in applications. They include landscaping, mining, the heights of objects, construction, crane safety, highways, airplanes, geometry, physics, surveying, navigation, hiking, and biking.

8.1 Law of Sines

An **oblique triangle** is a triangle with no right angle. Since the sum of the angles in any triangle is 180°, there is at most one obtuse angle (larger than 90°), and there may be two or three acute angles. In every triangle

The shortest side is opposite the smallest angle
The longest side is opposite the largest angle

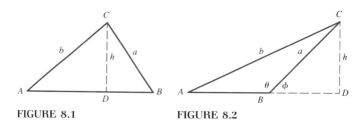

FIGURE 8.1   FIGURE 8.2

There are several formulas that can be used in solving oblique triangles, and we shall now develop one of the most basic of them. In so doing, we use Figs. 8.1 and 8.2, which are obtained by drawing two oblique triangles and dropping a perpendicular to the opposite side in one, and to the opposite side extended in the other. We call h the length of the perpendicular to the opposite side in each figure. From Fig. 8.1, we have $\sin A = h/b$ and $\sin B = h/a$. In Fig. 8.2, let B denote the angle inside the triangle formed by sides AB and BC. Then we get $\sin A = h/b$ and $\sin B = \sin \theta = \sin \phi = h/a$, the values $\sin \theta$ and $\sin \phi$ being equal since the angles θ and ϕ are supplementary, and $\sin \phi = \sin (180° - \phi) = \sin \theta$. Consequently, from each figure

$$h = a \sin B = b \sin A$$

If we divide each member of the last equation by $\sin A \sin B$, we get $a/\sin A = b/\sin B$. We can prove in a similar manner that $c/\sin C = a/\sin A$.

Law of sines

> In any triangle ABC with sides a, b, and c
>
> $$\frac{a}{\sin A} = \frac{b}{\sin B} = \frac{c}{\sin C} \qquad (8.1)$$

This equation (8.1) is known as the **law of sines,** and it can be put in words in the following manner:

Law of sines

> The three ratios obtained by dividing the length of a side of a triangle by the sine of the opposite angle are equal.

In Probs. 61 to 64 of Exercise 8.2, it is pointed out that each of the ratios $a/\sin A$, $b/\sin B$, and $c/\sin C$ equals the diameter of the circle circumscribed about the triangle.
    The law of sines may also be written

$$\frac{\sin A}{a} = \frac{\sin B}{b} = \frac{\sin C}{c} \qquad (8.1a)$$

We can use either (8.1) or (8.1a) if three of the four quantities involved in any two of the ratios are known. Thus it can be used if we know:

Any two angles and a side (this is called *AAS*)
Two sides and an angle opposite one of them (called *SSA*)

The case AAS is equivalent to knowing *three angles and any side*. We shall illustrate these cases in the following examples.

Remember that you should round your answer to conform with the least accurate data given, and that

2 *digits in the sides corresponds to the nearest degree*
3 *digits corresponds to the nearest tenth of a degree*

EXAMPLE 1 (AAS) Find the other angle and sides of a triangle in which

$$b = 309 \qquad A = 62.7° \qquad \text{and} \qquad B = 73.3°$$

Solution We begin by drawing Fig. 8.3, reasonably close to scale. Since the sum of the angles of a triangle is 180°, we know that

$$C = 180° - 62.7° - 73.3° = 44.0°$$

The angles are $A = 62.7° = 62°42'$, $B = 73.3° = 73°18'$, and $C = 44.0° = 44°$. Since the angles satisfy $B > A > C$, then the sides satisfy $b > a > c$. From the law of sines, we have

$$\frac{a}{\sin 62.7°} = \frac{309}{\sin 73.3°}$$

$$a = \frac{309 \sin 62.7°}{\sin 73.3°} \qquad \text{solving for } a$$

This can be evaluated by a calculator or Table A.5. In either case, we have

$$a = \frac{309(0.8886)}{0.9578} \approx 287 \qquad \text{to 3 digits}$$

Now using the law of sines with b and c, we have

$$\frac{c}{\sin 44.0°} = \frac{309}{\sin 73.3°}$$

$$c = \frac{309 \sin 44.0°}{\sin 73.3°} \qquad \text{solving for } c$$

$$= \frac{309(0.6947)}{0.9578} \qquad \begin{matrix} \text{by calculator} \\ \text{or Table A.2} \end{matrix}$$

$$\approx 224$$

We shall now consider **the case SSA** of the law of sines, in which we know two sides and an angle opposite one of them. If the known parts are a, b, and A, we may solve for $\sin B$ and get

$$\sin B = \frac{b \sin A}{a} \tag{1}$$

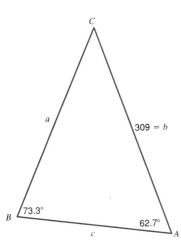

FIGURE 8.3

For any angle B in a triangle, $0 < \sin B \leq 1$. However, $(b \sin A)/a$ may be greater than 1, equal to 1, or less than 1. We now consider these situations separately.

(i) **If (b sin A)/a > 1,** there is no angle B which satisfies Eq. (1) and hence no triangle. See Fig. 8.4.

(ii) **If (b sin A)/a = 1,** then sin B = 1 and hence B = 90°. We thus have a *right angle,* and

> *there is a triangle containing A and B if A is acute*
> *there is no triangle containing A and B if A is not acute*

See Fig. 8.5 if A is acute.

(iii) **If (b sin A)/a < 1,** then Eq. (1) has a solution and an acute angle B can be found from a calculator or Table A.5. There is also an obtuse angle $B' = 180 - B$ with sin $B' = \sin(180 - B) = \sin B$. For instance, sin 60° = sin 120°. Therefore there are

> *Two triangles if B + A < 180° and B' + A < 180°*
> *One triangle if B + A < 180° and B' + A ≥ 180°*
> *No triangles if both B + A and B' + A ≥ 180°*

Fortunately, it is not necessary to memorize the various situations discussed above. Instead, find all possible angles B from the law of sines that can be angles of a triangle, and then use the ones that fit into a triangle with the given angle.

Figures 8.4, 8.5, 8.6, and 8.7 show the situations when the given angle A is acute, and b is a fixed length. In the four figures, we see what happens as a increases.

If the given angle A is obtuse, then A is certainly the largest angle and so a must be the longest side.

Because the different situations above may arise, the case SSA of two sides and an angle opposite one of them is called the **ambiguous case.** In Example 6, Sec. 8.2, we solve a physical situation involving two possible distances from the Earth to Venus. The ambiguous case is handled there by the law of cosines; it could also be done in this section by the law of sines. We give below several straightforward, complete examples resulting in two, one, and no triangles.

EXAMPLE 2   Find the number of possible triangles if $a = 176$, $b = 189$, and $A = 48.2° = 48°12'$, and solve each one.

Solution   If we substitute the given values in the law of sines, we get

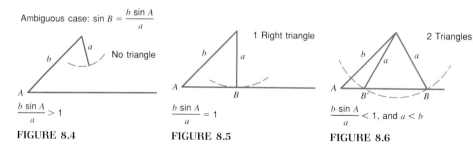

Ambiguous case: sin $B = \dfrac{b \sin A}{a}$

No triangle   1 Right triangle   2 Triangles

$\dfrac{b \sin A}{a} > 1$ $\dfrac{b \sin A}{a} = 1$ $\dfrac{b \sin A}{a} < 1$, and $a < b$

FIGURE 8.4   **FIGURE 8.5**   **FIGURE 8.6**

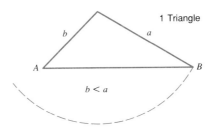

1 Triangle

$b < a$

FIGURE 8.7

$$\sin B = \frac{b \sin A}{a} = \frac{189 \sin 48.2°}{176}$$

$$\approx \frac{189(0.7455)}{176} \approx 0.8005 \qquad \text{by calculator} \atop \text{or Table A.5}$$

Therefore, $B \approx 53.2° = 53°12'$ and $B' \approx 180° - 53.2° = 126.8° = 126°48'$. Now

$$A + B \approx 48.2° + 53.2° = 101.4° < 180°$$

and $$A + B' \approx 48.2° + 126.8° = 175.0° < 180°$$

Consequently, both B and B' fit into a triangle with the given angle, and there are **two triangles.** See Fig. 8.8.

The triangle in Fig. 8.8a has $a = 176$, $b = 189$, $A = 48.2° = 48°12'$, $B = 53.2° = 53°12'$, $C = 180° - A - B = 78.6° = 78°36'$, and

$$c = \frac{(\sin C)\, a}{\sin A} = \frac{(\sin 78.6°)(176)}{\sin 48.2°} \approx 231 \qquad \text{to 3 digits}$$

The triangle in Fig. 8.8b has $a = 176$, $b = 189$, $A = 48.2° = 48°12'$, $B' = 126.8° = 126°48'$, $C' = 180° - A - B' = 5°$, and

$$c' = \frac{(\sin C')(a)}{\sin A} = \frac{(\sin 5°)(176)}{\sin 48.2°} \approx 20.6 \qquad \text{to 3 digits}$$

◢

EXAMPLE 3   Find the number of possible triangles if $a = 176$, $b = 167$, and $a = 48.2° = 48°12'$.

Solution   If we substitute the given values in the law of sines, we have

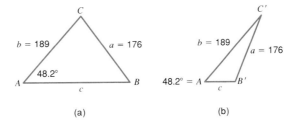

(a)   (b)

FIGURE 8.8

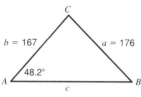

FIGURE 8.9

$$\sin B = \frac{b \sin A}{a} = \frac{167 \sin 48.2°}{176}$$

$$= 0.7074 \qquad \text{by calculator or Table A.5}$$

Therefore, $B = 45.0°$ and $B' = 180° - B = 135.0°$. Now

$$A + B = 48.2° + 45.0° = 93.2° < 180°$$

and $$A + B' = 48.2° + 135.0° = 183.2° > 180°$$

Consequently, $B = 45.0°$ fits into a triangle with $A = 48.2°$ whereas $B' = 135.0°$ does not fit into a triangle with $A = 48.2°$, and there is one solution. See Fig. 8.9.

The triangle has $a = 176$, $b = 167$, $A = 48.2° = 48°12'$, $B = 45.0° = 45°$, $C = 180° - A - B = 86.8° = 86°48'$, and

$$c = \frac{(\sin C)(a)}{\sin A} = \frac{(\sin 86.8°)(176)}{\sin 48.2°} \approx 236 \qquad \text{to 3 digits}$$

◢

▶ **EXAMPLE 4**   Find the number of possible triangles if $a = 176$, $b = 189$, and $A = 76.4° = 76°24'$.

Solution   If we substitute the given values in the law of sines, we get

$$\sin B = \frac{189 \sin 76.4°}{176}$$

$$\approx 1.044 \qquad \text{by calculator or Table A.5}$$

There is no solution to this equation since $\sin B \leq 1$ for all angles B. Consequently, there are **no solutions.**   ◢

When flying in an airplane, the pilot usually gives you the height of the plane above the ground. Using this height and measuring the two angles A and D in Fig. 8.10 allows you to find several interesting distances. Suppose that L and K are points on the edge of a lake, and Q is a point directly below the plane and on a line with L and K. If the ground distance from K to Q is a, then

$$\tan A = \frac{a}{h}$$

$$a = h \tan A \tag{2}$$

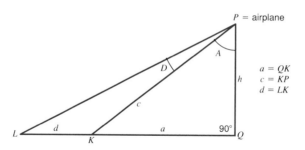

FIGURE 8.10

The distance from the plane P to the edge of the lake K is c, and

$$\cos A = \frac{h}{c}$$

$$c = \frac{h}{\cos A} = h \sec A \tag{3}$$

The distance d across the lake can be found by using the law of sines in triangle *PKL:*

$$\frac{d}{\sin D} = \frac{c}{\sin L}$$

$$d = \frac{c \sin D}{\sin L} \tag{4}$$

However, from the right triangle *PQL,* we know that

$$(A + D) + L = 90°$$
$$L = 90° - (A + D)$$
$$\sin L = \sin [90° - (A + D)]$$
$$= \cos (A + D) \qquad \text{by cofunction theorem} \tag{5}$$

Substituting in Eq. (4) gives
$$d = \frac{c \sin D}{\cos (A + D)}$$

$$= \frac{h \sin D}{\cos A \cos (A + D)} \qquad \text{by Eq. (3)} \tag{6}$$

Equations (2), (3), and (6) allow us to find a, c, and d if we know h, A, and D. Furthermore, Eq. (6), for instance, can be solved for the height h if the distance d across the lake is known, as in Example 5.

▶ **EXAMPLE 5**   Find the height h of an airplane as shown in Fig. 8.10 if $d = 3750$ ft, $A = 40.3°$, and $D = 12.8°$, respectively.

Solution   Substituting the given values in Eq. (6) solved for h gives

$$h = \frac{d \cos 40.3° \cos 53.1°}{\sin 12.8°}$$

$$= \frac{3750(0.7627)(0.6004)}{0.2215}$$

$$\approx 7750 \qquad \text{to 3 digits} \qquad ◀$$

▶ **EXAMPLE 6**   Two pine trees at A and B on one side of a gorge are 254 ft apart. Point Contentment is at C on the other side of the gorge. Find the distance from each tree to Point Contentment if angle A is $73.4°$ and angle B is $65.7°$.

Solution   Since the sum of the angles is $180°$, then

$$C = 180° - 73.4° - 65.7° = 40.9°$$

By the law of sines, the distances to three digits are

$$a = \frac{c \sin A}{\sin C} = \frac{254 \sin 73.4°}{\sin 40.9} \approx \frac{254(0.9583)}{0.6547} \approx 372$$

$$b = \frac{c \sin B}{\sin C} = \frac{254 \sin 65.7°}{\sin 40.9} \approx \frac{254(0.9114)}{0.6547} \approx 354$$

EXERCISE 8.1

Solve the following triangles by use of the law of sines. Carry each result to the degree of accuracy justified by the given data.

1. $A = 37.4°$, $B = 76.3°$, $a = 312$
2. $B = 42.7°$, $C = 81.4°$, $b = 187$
3. $C = 81.6°$, $A = 63.3°$, $c = 20.7$
4. $A = 57.1°$, $B = 68.7°$, $a = 30.1$
5. $B = 72.2°$, $C = 53.4°$, $b = 5.13$
6. $C = 67.6°$, $A = 49.8°$, $c = 7.12$
7. $A = 110.3°$, $B = 41.8°$, $a = 83.6$
8. $B = 96.3°$, $C = 57.4°$, $b = 96.3$
9. $C = 72.37°$, $A = 57.72°$, $c = 28.73$
10. $A = 81.18°$, $B = 78.87°$, $a = 90.32$
11. $B = 21.32°$, $C = 38.83°$, $b = 41.11$
12. $C = 118.83°$, $A = 47.74°$, $c = 22.73$
13. $A = 127.81°$, $B = 29.76°$, $a = 97.73$
14. $B = 131.42°$, $C = 27.22°$, $b = 98.89$
15. $C = 62.37°$, $A = 54.46°$, $c = 49.96$
16. $A = 39.93°$, $B = 82.26°$, $a = 103.7$

Find only the number of solutions in Probs. 17 to 20.
17. $a = 193$, $b = 143$, $A = 55.8°$
18. $a = 54.1$, $b = 77.2$, $A = 40.5°$
19. $a = 725$, $b = 453$, $B = 23.2°$
20. $a = 2.47$, $b = 3.02$, $A = 69.7°$

Find not only the number of solutions in Probs. 21 to 24, but also solve the triangles.
21. $b = 183$, $c = 81.3$, $C = 32.6°$
22. $b = 247$, $c = 231$, $C = 38.7°$
23. $a = 217$, $c = 204$, $A = 45.1°$
24. $a = 12.3$, $c = 23.6$, $C = 28.3°$
25. The points A and B are on one side of a canyon and are 168 m apart. Point C is on the other side of the canyon. Find AC if angle A is 58.4° and angle B is 47.8°.

26. An airplane in the air at C is seen simultaneously from two places A and B on the ground which are 17.5 km apart. Suppose that A, B, and C form a plane which is perpendicular to the ground, and that the plane is between A and B. If the angle of elevation from A to C is 21.3°, and the angle of elevation from B to C is 28.2°, find the distance from the plane to A.

27. A person traveling N42°E on a highway had planned to turn off on a road that went N54°E to a small town 24 mi from the intersection. He missed the turn and took a second road that ran S59°E to the town. How much longer was the actual trip than the planned trip?

28. A room 14 ft on a side is to be added to the side of a house. The angle of elevation of the present roof is 28.5°, and the angle of elevation of the new roof is to be 17.5°. How far along the old roof will the two roofs intersect? (See the figure.)

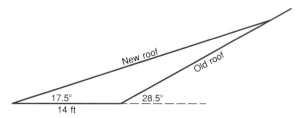

29. If one side of a triangle is 32.6 ft and the angles adjacent to it are 29.7° and 70.5°, by how much do the other sides differ?

30. Two surveyors are known to be 1.76 km apart and both observe a cathedral spire. The spire is N21.3°E of one surveyor and N28.8°W of the other. How far is each surveyor from the cathedral? (See the figure.)

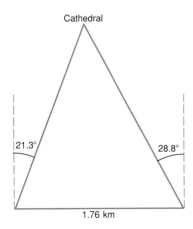

Cathedral

21.3° 28.8°

1.76 km

31. One diagonal of a parallelogram is 38.4 cm long and makes angles of 49.3° and 34.2° with the sides. How long is each side?

32. A pilot flew for 183 mi on a course that was in error by 19.3° and then reached her destination by turning through an acute angle and flying 112 mi. Find the delay in arriving at her destination if she flew at a ground speed of 450 mi/h for the entire journey and the air was calm.

In Probs. 33 through 36, use Eqs. (2), (3), and (6) to find the distances. See Fig. 8.10.

33. Find d if $h = 34,100$ ft, $A = 34°$, $D = 7°$.
34. Find a and c if $h = 32,600$ ft, $A = 21°$.
35. Find d if $h = 18,800$ ft, $A = 53°$, $D = 3°$.
36. Find h if $d = 4390$ ft, $A = 44°$, $D = 9°$.
37. Suppose that a, b, and c form a triangle with angles A, B, and C. In Chap. 11, we will give the following definition: The three numbers x, y, and z form an **arithmetic progression** if $y - x = z - y$. Furthermore, they form a **geometric progression** if $y/x = z/y$. Use the law of sines to prove

  (i) If a, b, and c form an arithmetic progression, so do $\sin A$, $\sin B$, and $\sin C$.
  (ii) If a, b, and c form a geometric progression, so do $\sin A$, $\sin B$, and $\sin C$.

Hint: Set $a/\sin A = b/\sin B = c/\sin C = k$, where k is a constant.

38. If A, B, and C are the angles of a triangle, then

$$1 < \sin \frac{A}{2} + \sin \frac{B}{2} + \sin \frac{C}{2} \le \frac{3}{2}$$

with the upper inequality only for an equilateral triangle. Choose any three angles you wish which are the angles in a triangle, and verify the inequality above. Try it with degrees and also radians.

8.2 Law of Cosines

The law of sines requires that we know at least one angle, and thus it cannot be used in **the case SSS,** where all three sides are given. The law of cosines, to be given below, can be used for the SSS case, as well as giving an alternative tool for the ambiguous case SSA (see Examples 1 and 2). It can be applied in other situations also. Remember, as stated before,

The shortest side is always opposite the smallest angle

Problems 29 to 36 give a variety of applications. Problems 37 to 40 and 25 to 28 deal with the special angles 60° or $\pi/3$, and 120° or $2\pi/3$.

   We shall now derive our second formula for solving oblique triangles, using Fig. 8.11. The triangles there are constructed by starting with an oblique triangle and dropping a perpendicular from the vertex C to the opposite side, or to the opposite side extended at D. We then have the right triangle ACD which contains angle A or the

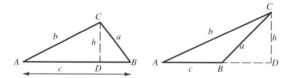

FIGURE 8.11

supplement of it. Now we apply the Pythagorean theorem to the triangle BCD in either part of Fig. 8.11, and thus have

$$a^2 = h^2 + (DB)^2 \tag{1}$$

Next we express the right-hand side in terms of b, c, A, B, and C. In doing this, we use $\sin A = h/b$ in each case since the sine of an angle and of its supplement are equal; hence

$$h = b \sin A$$

Furthermore,

$$
\begin{aligned}
DB &= |c - AD| \\
   &= |c - b \cos A| \qquad \text{since } \cos A = AD/b
\end{aligned}
$$

Substituting these values of h and DB in (1) gives

$$
\begin{aligned}
a^2 &= (b \sin A)^2 + (c - b \cos A)^2 \\
    &= b^2 \sin^2 A + c^2 - 2bc \cos A + b^2 \cos^2 A \\
    &= b^2 (\sin^2 A + \cos^2 A) + c^2 - 2bc \cos A
\end{aligned}
$$

Finally, we use the fact that $\sin^2 A + \cos^2 A = 1$ and have

$$a^2 = b^2 + c^2 - 2bc \cos A \tag{8.2a}$$

This is known as the **law of cosines,** and it can be put in words as follows:

Law of cosines

> The square of any side of a triangle is equal to the sum of the squares of the other two sides decreased by twice the product of these two sides and the cosine of the angle between them.

There are three ways to write Eq. (8.2a) by interchanging a and b, or a and c:

> If ABC is a triangle with sides a, b, and c, then
>
> $$a^2 = b^2 + c^2 - 2bc \cos A \tag{8.2a}$$
> $$b^2 = a^2 + c^2 - 2ac \cos B \tag{8.2b}$$
> $$c^2 = a^2 + b^2 - 2ab \cos C \tag{8.2c}$$

In Prob. 43, you are asked to show that the law of cosines includes the *Pythagorean theorem* as a special case. The law of cosines may be rewritten, by solving for $\cos A$, as

$$\cos A = \frac{b^2 + c^2 - a^2}{2bc} \tag{8.2d}$$

The law of cosines involves all three sides and one angle; hence, it can be used to obtain the fourth of these parts if three of them are given. Three parts can be chosen as

1. Two sides and the angle opposite one of them (SSA)
2. Two sides and the included angle (SAS)
3. Three sides (SSS)

Case 1 was handled as **the ambiguous case** of the law of sines in Sec. 8.1. Even so, we shall illustrate its use here by two examples. In doing this, we must bear in mind that the sides of a triangle are represented by positive real numbers.

▶ EXAMPLE 1   (SSA) Find the number of possible triangles if

$$a = 11 \qquad b = 13 \qquad \text{and} \qquad A = 60°$$

Solution   Since angle A is known, we use the law of cosines in the form $a^2 = b^2 + c^2 - 2bc \cos A$ and have

$$11^2 = 13^2 + c^2 - 2(13)c \cos 60°$$

$$121 = 169 + c^2 - 13c \qquad \text{since } 2 \cos 60° = 2(\tfrac{1}{2}) = 1$$

$$0 = c^2 - 13c + 48 \qquad \text{quadratic equation}$$

$$c = \frac{13 \pm \sqrt{169 - 192}}{2}$$

Consequently, there are no real solutions since $\sqrt{-23}$ is not a real number.   ◢

▶ EXAMPLE 2   (SSA) Find the numbers of possible triangles if

$$a = 17 \qquad b = 11 \qquad \text{and} \qquad A = 60°$$

Solution   Using the law of cosines in the form of Eq. (8.2a) gives

$$17^2 = 11^2 + c^2 - 2(11)c \cos 60° \qquad \text{law of cosines}$$

$$289 = 121 + c^2 - 11c$$

$$0 = c^2 - 11c - 168$$

$$c = \frac{11 \pm \sqrt{121 + 672}}{2} \qquad \text{quadratic formula}$$

$$= \frac{11 \pm \sqrt{793}}{2}$$

$$= \text{a positive and a negative number}$$

Therefore, there is **one solution.** Using 2 digits, the triangle has

$$a = 17 \qquad b = 11 \quad A = 60° \qquad c = \frac{11 + \sqrt{793}}{2} \approx 20$$

and using the **given information:**

$$\sin B = \frac{b \sin A}{a} = \frac{(11)(\sin 60°)}{17} = 0.5604 \quad \text{and} \quad b \approx 34°$$

Finally, $C = 180° - A - B = 180° - 60° - 34° = 86°$.

EXAMPLE 3   (SAS) Find c if $a = 17$, $b = 22$, and $C = 47°$.

Solution   Since the known angle is C, we must use the law of cosines in the form

$$c^2 = a^2 + b^2 - 2ab \cos C$$

Substituting in this gives

$$c^2 = 17^2 + 22^2 - 2(17)(22) \cos 47°$$
$$= 289 + 484 - 748(0.6820) \qquad \text{by calculator or Table A.2}$$
$$= 262.864 \qquad \text{do not round off yet to 2 digits}$$
$$c = \sqrt{262.864} \approx 16 \qquad \text{to 2 digits}$$

Since all three sides are now known, the unknown angles A and B can be found by using the law of sines as in Example 2, or by the law of cosines as in Example 4 below.

EXAMPLE 4   Find the largest angle of the triangle that has

$$a = 36 \qquad b = 47 \qquad \text{and} \qquad c = 41$$

Solution   Since the largest angle is opposite the longest side b, we use

$$b^2 = a^2 + c^2 - 2ac \cos B \qquad \text{law of cosines}$$
$$47^2 = 36^2 + 41^2 - 2(36)(41) \cos B$$
$$2209 = 1296 + 1681 - 2952 \cos B \qquad \text{multiplying}$$
$$\cos B = \frac{1296 + 1681 - 2209}{2952} \qquad \text{solving for } \cos B$$
$$= 0.2602 \qquad \text{to 4 digits}$$
$$B = 75°$$

to the nearest degree by calculator or Table A.5.

EXAMPLE 5   A golfer drives her ball 27° from the line between the tee and the hole that is 360 yards away. How far is she from the hole if her shot was 170 yards?

Solution   The situation is shown in Fig. 8.12. Applying the law of cosines gives

$$d^2 = 170^2 + 360^2 - 2(170)(360) \cos 27°$$
$$= 28{,}900 + 129{,}600 - 122{,}400(0.8910)$$
$$= 158{,}500 - 109{,}058.4 = 49{,}441.6$$

Hence, $d \approx 222$

FIGURE 8.12

EXAMPLE 6 The planet Venus (V) is observed from the Earth (E) with $\theta = 17°30'$, as in Fig. 8.13. What are the two possible distances from the Earth to Venus? Assume that the two orbits are circles with the sun (S) at the center, the distance from the sun to Earth (SE) is 93,000,000 mi, and the distance from the sun to Venus (SV) is 67,500,000 mi.

Solution   We will use the law of cosines in the form

$$a^2 = b^2 + c^2 - 2bc \cos \theta$$

and we will let a, b, and c be the distances in *millions of miles,* where

$$a = SV = 67.5 \qquad b = SE = 93$$
$$\theta = 17°30' \quad \text{and} \quad c = EV = \text{distance from Earth to Venus}$$

The equation becomes (using decimal approximations throughout)

$$67.5^2 = 93^2 + c^2 - 2(93)(c) \cos 17°30'$$
$$4556 = 8649 + c^2 - 186(c)(0.9537)$$
$$0 = c^2 - 177c + 4093$$

By the quadratic formula, the possible distances c satisfy

$$2c = 177 \pm \sqrt{177^2 - 4(4093)}$$
$$= 177 \pm \sqrt{31,329 - 16,372}$$
$$= 177 \pm \sqrt{14,957}$$
$$\approx 177 \pm 122$$
$$= 299 \text{ or } 55$$

Remember that these values for $2c$ are in millions of miles. Thus the distance from the Earth to Venus is about 150,000,000 mi or 28,000,000 mi, rounding up in both cases. ◢

Area of a Triangle

It is a familiar fact from plane geometry that the area K of a triangle is one-half the product of the base and the altitude. In proving both the law of sines and the law of

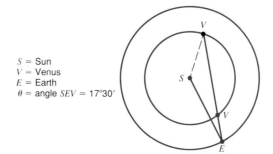

S = Sun
V = Venus
E = Earth
θ = angle SEV = 17°30'

FIGURE 8.13

cosines, we showed that $\sin A = h/b$, where h is an altitude. Recall Fig. 8.11, for instance. Using c as the base gives

$$K = \tfrac{1}{2}c \cdot b \sin A$$

Since the lettering of the triangle is immaterial, we also have

$$K = \tfrac{1}{2}ac \sin B \qquad \text{and} \qquad K = \tfrac{1}{2}ab \sin C \qquad\qquad \textbf{(8.3)}$$

These give the area in **the case SAS.**

> The area of any triangle is equal to half the product of any two sides and the sine of the included angle.

▶ **EXAMPLE 7**   Find the area of a triangular parcel of land which has sides 337 m and 421 m if the angle between them is 67.8°.

Solution   Using the formula gives

$$\begin{aligned}
K &= \tfrac{1}{2}(337)(421)(\sin 67.8°) \\
&= 70{,}938.5(0.9259) \\
&= 6.57(10^4) \text{ m}^2 \qquad \text{to three digits}
\end{aligned}$$ ◢

If we replace a by $c \sin A/\sin C$ from the law of sines, and use it above in $K = \tfrac{1}{2}ac \sin B$, we have

$$K = \frac{c^2 \sin A \sin B}{2 \sin C} \qquad\qquad \textbf{(8.4)}$$

as a formula for the area in **the case AAS.** This may be used if a side and any two angles are known since the third angle can be found immediately. Since $C = 180° - (A + B)$, the area formula (8.4) may be written as $K = c^2 \sin A \sin B/[2 \sin (A + B)]$.

We shall now state another area formula, called *Heron's formula,* for **the case SSS.** Its proof uses the law of cosines, and is outlined in Prob. 73. The semiperimeter s is defined by

$$s = \frac{a + b + c}{2} \qquad\qquad \textbf{(8.5)}$$

Heron's formula

> If $s = (a + b + c)/2$ = half the perimeter, then the area is
>
> $$K = \sqrt{s(s - a)(s - b)(s - c)} \qquad\qquad \textbf{(8.6)}$$

▶ **EXAMPLE 8**   Find the area of a triangle with

$$a = 32.7 \qquad b = 21.6 \qquad \text{and} \qquad c = 18.3$$

Solution   We have $s = (32.7 + 21.6 + 18.3)/2 = 36.3$, and so

$$\begin{aligned}
K &= \sqrt{(36.3)(36.3 - 32.7)(36.3 - 21.6)(36.3 - 18.3)} \\
&= \sqrt{(36.3)(3.6)(14.7)(18)} \\
&\approx \sqrt{34{,}578} \approx 186 \qquad \text{to three digits}
\end{aligned}$$ ◢

Checking Answers

Since these two sections have given formulas to solve triangles, we will now give three formulas which hold for any triangle. They may be used to check solutions.

Mollweide's equation

$$\frac{a - b}{c} = \frac{\sin [(A - B)/2]}{\cos (C/2)} \tag{8.7}$$

$$a = b \cos C + c \cos B \tag{8.8}$$

Law of tangents

$$\frac{a - b}{a + b} = \frac{\tan [(A - B)/2]}{\tan [(A + B)/2]} \tag{8.9}$$

The simplest and most obvious checks, which work for any triangle, are

$$A + B + C = 180°$$

$$a < b + c \qquad b < a + c \qquad c < a + b$$

EXERCISE 8.2

Find the third side in Probs. 1 to 8 to the justified degree of accuracy.
1. $a = 31$, $b = 13$, $C = 60°$
2. $a = 73$, $c = 89$, $B = 120°$
3. $a = 13\sqrt{2}$, $b = 23$, $C = 45°$
4. $c = 13\sqrt{3}$, $a = 29$, $B = 30°$
5. $a = 113$, $c = 137$, $B = 46°$
6. $b = 211$, $c = 277$, $A = 93°$
7. $a = 307$, $c = 345$, $B = 51°$
8. $b = 376$, $c = 403$, $A = 109°$

In Probs. 9 to 16, find the specified angle.
9. If $a = 13$, $b = 17$, and $c = 19$, find A.
10. If $a = 47$, $b = 53$, and $c = 71$, find C.
11. If $a = 33$, $b = 39$, and $c = 31$, find B.
12. If $a = 14$, $b = 37$, and $c = 53$, find A.
13. If $a = 124$, $b = 321$, and $c = 214$, find B.
14. If $a = 211$, $b = 123$, and $c = 187$, find C.
15. If $a = 379$, $b = 425$, and $c = 522$, find B.
16. If $a = 911$, $b = 723$, and $c = 517$, find A.

In Probs. 17 to 24, find each possible value of the third side, and also the number of triangles.
17. $a = 13$, $b = 17$, $A = 60°$
18. $a = 33$, $c = 30$, $C = 120°$
19. $b = 17\sqrt{2}$, $c = 21$, $C = 45°$
20. $b = 17$, $c = 8\sqrt{3}$, $B = 30°$
21. $a = 9\sqrt{2}$, $c = 19$, $C = 135°$
22. $b = 27$, $c = 18\sqrt{3}$, $B = 150°$
23. $b = 27$, $c = 18\sqrt{3}$, $B = 30°$
24. $a = 25$, $b = 33$, $B = 60°$

Show that the largest angle in each of Probs. 25 to 28 is 120°.
25. $a = 13$, $b = 35$, $c = 43$
26. $a = 77$, $b = 103$, $c = 40$
27. $a = 387$, $b = 523$, $c = 208$
28. $a = 403$, $b = 115$, $c = 333$

29. *Geometry* Find the shorter diagonal of a parallelogram if its sides are 39 and 59 ft and meet at an angle of 61°.

30. *Navigation* Find the ground speed and direction of flight of a plane with a heading of 231° at 325 mi/h in a wind of 27 mi/h from the east. (See the figure.)

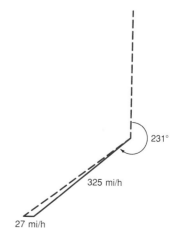

231°

325 mi/h

27 mi/h

31. *Nature*   Each of three elephants has a circular region where he is dominant. The regions are tangent externally with radii of 370 m, 410 m, and 300 m and have a "no man's land" in between. If each animal stands at the center of his region, what is the angle made by the two lines going from the third elephant to each of the other two? (See the figure.)

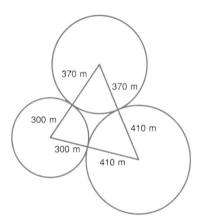

32. *Hiking*   Johannes should have gone 5.13 km N23.6°E but instead went 4.61 km N20.7°E. How far was he from his intended destination?

33. *Golf*   A golfer drives the ball 16° from the line between the tee and the hole that is 425 yards away. How far is the ball from the hole if the shot was 240 yards?

34. *Maps*   If *A* can be reached from *B* by going 37 mi west and then 28 mi N34°W, how far is *A* from *B*?

35. *Geometry*   If the sides of a triangle are 313 m, 277 m, and 244 m, what is the largest angle?

36. *Surveying*   A 37-ft vertical pole is on a hillside that makes an angle of 2° with the horizontal. How far is it from the top of the pole to a point 69 ft downhill from the base of the pole?

Show that the middle angle in Probs. 37 to 40 is 60°.
37. $a = 3$, $b = 7$, $c = 8$
38. $a = 5$, $b = 19$, $c = 21$
39. $a = 13$, $b = 43$, $c = 48$
40. $a = 40$, $b = 79$, $c = 91$

41. *Chord length*   Prove that the length of a chord in a circle of radius *r* is

$$s = r\sqrt{2 - 2\cos\theta}$$

where θ is the central angle made by the two radii to the ends of the chord. Show also that

$$s = 2r\sin\frac{\theta}{2}$$

42. *Logarithms*   The law of cosines may be adapted to logarithmic computation as outlined below. Justify each step.

$$1 + \cos C = 1 + \frac{a^2 + b^2 - c^2}{2ab}$$

$$= \frac{(a + b)^2 - c^2}{2ab}$$

$$= \frac{(a + b + c)(a + b - c)}{2ab}$$

Thus

$$\log(1 + \cos C) = \log(a + b + c) + \\ \log(a + b - c) - \log 2 - \log a - \log b$$

Then find successively $1 + \cos C$, $\cos C$, and finally C.

43. Show that the Pythagorean theorem is a special case of the law of cosines.

44. If *a*, *b*, and *c* form a triangle, what is the value of

$$\arccos\frac{a^2 + b^2 - c^2}{2ab} + \arccos\frac{b^2 + c^2 - a^2}{2bc} + \\ \arccos\frac{c^2 + a^2 - b^2}{2ca}$$

Find the area of the triangle whose parts are given in Probs. 45 to 60.
45. $a = 14$, $b = 23$, $C = 71°$
46. $b = 29$, $c = 37$, $A = 48°$
47. $a = 509$, $c = 387$, $B = 59.7°$
48. $a = 813$, $b = 677$, $C = 103.4°$
49. $a = 53$, $A = 37°$, $B = 82°$
50. $b = 47$, $A = 53°$, $C = 74°$
51. $c = 917$, $A = 62.3°$, $B = 51.1°$
52. $b = 857$, $A = 83.7°$, $C = 53.3°$
53. $a = 28$, $b = 31$, $c = 53$

54. $a = 34, b = 37, c = 43$
55. $a = 92, b = 84, c = 70$
56. $a = 13, b = 15, c = 22$
57. $a = 707, b = 606, c = 505$
58. $a = 838, b = 644, c = 572$
59. $a = 416, b = 213, c = 347$
60. $a = 103, b = 171, c = 144$

If a circle is inscribed in a triangle with sides $a, b,$ and $c,$ then its radius is

$$r = \sqrt{\frac{(s - a)(s - b)(s - c)}{s}}$$

If a circle is circumscribed about the triangle with sides $a, b,$ and $c,$ its radius R satisfies

$$2R = \frac{a}{\sin A} = \frac{b}{\sin B} = \frac{c}{\sin C}$$

Find the radii r and R of the inscribed and circumscribed circles for the triangles with sides as given in Probs. 61 to 64.

61. $a = 31, b = 47, c = 44$
62. $a = 107, b = 188, c = 149$
63. $a = 208, b = 317, c = 291$
64. $a = 2731, b = 3721, c = 4768$

65. *Engineering* What is the radius of the largest circular water tank that can be placed inside a level triangular area that is 10.2 ft by 11.8 ft by 14.0 ft?

66. *Navigation* The distances from Santa Fe to Amarillo and to El Paso are 286 mi and 333 mi, respectively, and Amarillo is 423 mi from El Paso. Find the directions from Santa Fe and Amarillo to El Paso if Amarillo is S80°E of Santa Fe.

67. *Geometry* Two sides of a triangle are 325 mm and 465 mm. What is the angle between these sides if the third side is 512 mm?

68. *Surveying* A tract of land is in the form of a quadrilateral $ABCD$ with $AB = 1200$ yards, $BC = 1500$ yards, $CD = 1600$ yards, $DA = 1400$ yards, and diagonal $BD = 2000$ yards. Find the number of acres in the tract if 1 acre is 4840 square yards. *Hint:* Use two triangles.

69. Starting from the law of cosines, in the form

$$\cos A = \frac{b^2 + c^2 - a^2}{2bc}$$

use $\sin^2 A + \cos^2 A = 1$ to show that

$$\sin^2 A =$$
$$\frac{(a + b + c)(b + c - a)(c + a - b)(a + b - c)}{4b^2c^2} \quad (*)$$

Hint: Use $x^2 - y^2 = (x - y)(x + y)$ several times.

70. Using Eq. (*) from Prob. 69, and symmetry, show that

$$\frac{\sin^2 A}{a^2} = \frac{\sin^2 B}{b^2} = \frac{\sin^2 C}{c^2}$$

Note: This provides another proof of the law of sines.

71. For any $k > 2,$ the triangle with sides

$$\frac{5k^2 - 4k + 4}{k^2 - 4} \quad \text{and} \quad \frac{k(k^2 - 4k + 20)}{2(k^2 - 4)}$$

and $\quad \dfrac{k + 2}{2}$

has area $k.$ Either prove this for k arbitrary, or verify it for the particular value $k = 5.$

72. For the right triangle with $a = 20, b = 21,$ and $c = 29,$ show that the formula $\frac{1}{2}$(base)(height) gives the same area as Heron's formula

$$\sqrt{s(s - a)(s - b)(s - c)}$$

73. Prove Heron's formula, Eq. (8.6), by starting with

$$\text{Area} = \tfrac{1}{2}bc \sin A$$

and using next the result of Prob. 69.

74. Another check for the solutions of a triangle with acute angles $A, B,$ and C is

$$\tan A + \tan B + \tan C = \tan A \tan B \tan C$$

Verify this equation for a triangle with $A = 35°, B = 65°,$ and $C = 80°.$

75. If $A, B,$ and C are the angles of a triangle, then

$$2 < \cos \frac{A}{2} + \cos \frac{B}{2} + \cos \frac{C}{2} \leq \frac{3\sqrt{3}}{2}$$

with the upper inequality only for an equilateral triangle. Choose any three angles you wish which are the angles in a triangle, and verify the inequality above. Try it with degrees and then radians.

8.3 Vectors

In this section, we will deal only with vectors in a plane. Vectors in three dimensions, and higher, are not treated here.

If a quantity has only magnitude, it is called a **scalar** and can be described by a single number. This is the situation with weight, temperature, height, and many other quantities. There are, however, other quantities that have both magnitude and direction. Such quantities are called **vectors,** and they require two numbers to describe them. Displacement, velocity, acceleration, and force are vectors.

A vector can be represented by a line segment pointing in a specified direction. Such a directed line segment is also called a *two-dimensional geometric vector,* and it can be written in two ways. One way is to give it a single letter, such as **V** or **W**, which will be printed in boldface in the book. The other common way, often used when writing a vector by hand, is to write its initial point *A* followed by its terminal point *B*, with an arrow over them. See Fig. 8.14. Thus we may write

$$\mathbf{V} = \overrightarrow{AB}$$

The number that represents the length of a vector **V** is called its *magnitude* or *norm* and is designated by $|\mathbf{V}|$. The direction of **V** can be written as an angle the vector makes with the *x* axis or a line parallel to it, as in Fig. 8.15.

Examples of Vectors

Displacement   A person walks 143 m to the southeast. The magnitude is 143 and the direction is $-\pi/4$.

Velocity   An airplane travels at 408 mi/h in the direction 250°. The magnitude is 408 and the direction is 250° (measured clockwise from the north).

Acceleration   If an airplane on its takeoff goes from a dead stop to 140 mi/h in 35 s in a runway heading at 157°, then its direction is 157°, and the magnitude of its acceleration is

$$\frac{140 \text{ mi/h}}{35 \text{ s}} = \frac{4 \text{ mi}}{\text{s(h)}} = \frac{(4)(5280 \text{ ft})}{(1 \text{ s})[(60)(60 \text{ s})]} = 5.87 \ \frac{\text{ft}}{\text{s}^2}$$

Note that 15 mi/h = 22 ft/s.

Force   A loaded cart pulled up an incline of 27° requires an effort of 135 newtons.

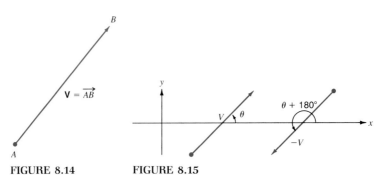

FIGURE 8.14   FIGURE 8.15

For any vector $\mathbf{V}$, there is a vector $-\mathbf{V}$ that has the same magnitude as $\mathbf{V}$, and an angle that differs from that of $\mathbf{V}$ by $180°$ or π. See Fig. 8.15. Therefore

$$\text{if } \mathbf{V} = \overrightarrow{AB}, \text{ then } -\mathbf{V} = \overrightarrow{BA}$$

A vector may be translated from one position in the plane to another position provided that it has the same magnitude and direction in both positions. Two vectors are equal if they have the same magnitude and the same direction. In Fig. 8.16, $\mathbf{V}_1$ and $\mathbf{V}_2$ are equal, but $\mathbf{V}_1$ and $\mathbf{V}_3$ are not equal since they do not have the same direction. The vectors $\mathbf{V}_1$ and $\mathbf{V}_4$ are not equal because they have different magnitudes. Furthermore, $\mathbf{V}_1$ and $\mathbf{V}_5$ are not equal because they have different magnitudes and different directions.

Scalar × vector

The product of a vector $\mathbf{V}$ and a scalar or real number c is a vector which is written $c\mathbf{V}$. Its magnitude is $|c\mathbf{V}| = |c| \cdot |\mathbf{V}|$, and it has the same direction as $\mathbf{V}$ if $c > 0$ and the same direction as $-\mathbf{V}$ if $c < 0$.

If $\mathbf{V}$ and $\mathbf{W}$ are vectors, as in Fig. 8.17, then we may find $\mathbf{V} + \mathbf{W}$ in two ways. One way is to draw $\mathbf{V}$, and then draw $\mathbf{W}$ with its initial point at the terminal point of $\mathbf{V}$. The sum $\mathbf{V} + \mathbf{W}$ then is the vector with the same initial point as $\mathbf{V}$ and the same terminal point as $\mathbf{W}$. See Fig. 8.17(a).

Another way to find $\mathbf{V} + \mathbf{W}$ is to use the **parallelogram rule.** Draw $\mathbf{V}$ and $\mathbf{W}$ with the same initial point, and then complete a parallelogram with two more vectors in this manner. Place the initial point of $\mathbf{W}$ at the terminal point of $\mathbf{V}$, and also the initial point of $\mathbf{V}$ at the terminal point of $\mathbf{W}$. The sum $\mathbf{V} + \mathbf{W}$ then lies along the diagonal which includes the common initial point of $\mathbf{V}$ and $\mathbf{W}$. See Fig. 8.17(b). **(8.10)**

We call $\mathbf{V} + \mathbf{W}$ the **sum or resultant of V and W,** and $\mathbf{V}$ and $\mathbf{W}$ are called the **components of V + W.**

We can resolve any vector $\mathbf{V}$ into two components which are perpendicular, one horizontal and one vertical. In Fig. 8.18, we have by definition of $\cos \theta$ and $\sin \theta$ that $\cos \theta = OA/OP$ and $\sin \theta = AP/OP = OB/OP$. Since $OP = |\mathbf{V}|$, we have

$$OA = |\mathbf{V}| \cos \theta \qquad \text{and} \qquad OB = |\mathbf{V}| \sin \theta \qquad \text{(1)}$$

*Unit vectors **i** and **j***

We use $\mathbf{i}$ for a vector of length 1 whose direction is from the origin along the positive x axis, and similarly for $\mathbf{j}$ and the positive y axis. Then from Eq. (1) we have

$$\mathbf{V} = (|\mathbf{V}| \cos \theta)\mathbf{i} + (|\mathbf{V}| \sin \theta)\mathbf{j} \qquad \text{(2)}$$

From Eq. (2), if we know the magnitude and direction of the vector $\mathbf{V}$, we can then write its horizontal and vertical components $(|\mathbf{V}| \cos \theta)\mathbf{i}$ and $(|\mathbf{V}| \sin \theta)\mathbf{j}$.

Conversely if we start with the horizontal and vertical components $a\mathbf{i}$ and $b\mathbf{j}$, then

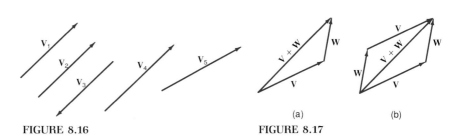

FIGURE 8.16

(a)   (b)

FIGURE 8.17

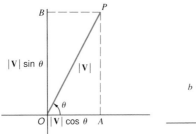

FIGURE 8.18

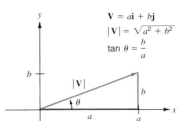

FIGURE 8.19

the magnitude and direction of

$$\mathbf{V} = a\mathbf{i} + b\mathbf{j}$$

satisfy the equations below. See Fig. 8.19.

$$|\mathbf{V}| = \sqrt{a^2 + b^2} \qquad (8.10)$$

$$\tan \theta = \frac{b}{a} \qquad (8.11)$$

To determine θ, except for an integral multiple of 2π or $360°$, Eq. (8.11) is not enough. We also must decide what quadrant θ is in from the signs of a and b.

EXAMPLE 1   Find the magnitude and direction for these vectors.

Solution   (a) If $\mathbf{V} = 2\mathbf{i} + 2\sqrt{3}\mathbf{j}$, then

$$|\mathbf{V}| = \sqrt{2^2 + (2\sqrt{3})^2} = \sqrt{4 + 12} = \sqrt{16} = 4$$

$$\tan \theta = \frac{2\sqrt{3}}{2} = \sqrt{3}$$

and so the magnitude is 4 and the direction may be chosen as $\pi/3$ or $60°$ because $(2, 2\sqrt{3})$ is in the first quadrant.

(b) If $\mathbf{V} = -3\mathbf{i} + 4\mathbf{j}$, then the magnitude is

$$|\mathbf{V}| = \sqrt{9 + 16} = \sqrt{25} = 5$$

Also $\tan \theta = 4/(-3)$, and θ is in quadrant II, so

$$\theta = 180° - \tan^{-1} \tfrac{4}{3}$$

$$\approx 180° - 53.1° = 126.9°$$

Vectors may also be **added algebraically,** and the definition is

Sum of two vectors $$(a\mathbf{i} + b\mathbf{j}) + (c\mathbf{i} + d\mathbf{j}) = (a + c)\mathbf{i} + (b + d)\mathbf{j}$$

while the definition of scalar multiplication is

Scalar multiplication $$c(a\mathbf{i} + b\mathbf{j}) = (ca)\mathbf{i} + (cb)\mathbf{j}$$

► **EXAMPLE 2** Find the value of each expression below.

Solution (a) $(3\mathbf{i} + 12\mathbf{j}) + (-5\mathbf{i} + 3\mathbf{j}) = (3 - 5)\mathbf{i} + (12 + 3)\mathbf{j} = -2\mathbf{i} + 15\mathbf{j}$
(b) $4(3\mathbf{i} + 14\mathbf{j}) = 12\mathbf{i} + 56\mathbf{j}$
(c) $2(7\mathbf{i} - 6\mathbf{j}) - 5(4\mathbf{i} - \mathbf{j}) = 14\mathbf{i} - 12\mathbf{j} - (20\mathbf{i} - 5\mathbf{j})$
                                $= 14\mathbf{i} - 12\mathbf{j} - 20\mathbf{i} + 5\mathbf{j} = -6\mathbf{i} - 7\mathbf{j}$ ◄

The vector $a\mathbf{i} + b\mathbf{j}$ may also be written as $\langle a, b \rangle$. This avoids any possible confusion with (a, b), which is used for open intervals and for points. Thus

$$2\mathbf{i} - 5\mathbf{j} = \langle 2, -5 \rangle \qquad 13\mathbf{i} + 9\mathbf{j} = \langle 13, 9 \rangle$$
$$\mathbf{i} = 1 \cdot \mathbf{i} + 0 \cdot \mathbf{j} = \langle 1, 0 \rangle \qquad \text{and} \qquad \mathbf{j} = \langle 0, 1 \rangle$$

Sections 8.4 and 8.5 on complex numbers also deal with geometric, algebraic, and trigonometric ways of writing and interpreting symbols representing two quantities.

► **EXAMPLE 3** Write the vector **V** in the form $a\mathbf{i} + b\mathbf{j}$ if

$$|\mathbf{V}| = 13 \text{ and the direction of } \mathbf{V} \text{ is } 58°$$

Solution The vector **V** is shown in Fig. 8.20. We only need to find a and b, and since the direction is 58° we have

$$a = 13 \cos 58° \approx 6.9 \qquad \text{and} \qquad b = 13 \sin 58° \approx 11$$

Therefore $\mathbf{V} \approx 6.9\mathbf{i} + 11\mathbf{j}$.   ◄

In Example 4 below, two forces (i.e., two vectors) $\overrightarrow{AB}$ and $\overrightarrow{AD}$ are given and we are to find $\overrightarrow{AC}$. Since the vectors $\overrightarrow{AD}$ and $\overrightarrow{BC}$ are equal, this figure could also represent these diverse situations.

Displacement   (a) If a boat or a car goes due east 37 mi, then changes direction and goes along $\overrightarrow{BC}$ for 29 mi, what is its distance and direction from the starting point?

Velocity   (b) If a glider heads due east at 37 knots (1 knot $\approx$ 1.16 mi/h) while a wind of 29 knots is blowing in the direction of $\overrightarrow{BC}$, what is the ground speed and bearing of the glider—in other words, what is the magnitude and direction of the velocity vector?

► **EXAMPLE 4** Two forces, whose magnitudes are 29 and 37 lb, act at the same point with an angle of 33° between them. Find their resultant if the larger force is 37**i**.

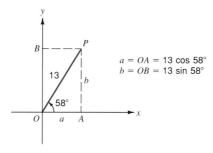

$a = OA = 13 \cos 58°$
$b = OB = 13 \sin 58°$

FIGURE 8.20

Angle *DAB* + angle *ABC* = 180°

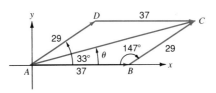

FIGURE 8.21

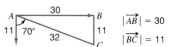

FIGURE 8.22

Solution   The forces and their resultant are shown in Fig. 8.21. We know two sides, 29 and 37, of the triangle *ABC,* and the angle at *B* is $180° - 33° = 147°$. Consequently we may find the magnitude of the resultant from the law of cosines:

$$b^2 = 37^2 + 29^2 - 2(37)(29) \cos 147° \qquad \text{using } b = |\overrightarrow{AC}|$$
$$\approx 1369 + 841 + (2146)(0.8387) \approx 4010$$

Hence, $b = 63$ to 2 digits. By the law of sines

$$\frac{\sin \theta}{29} = \frac{\sin 147°}{63}$$
$$\sin \theta \approx 0.2507$$
$$\theta \approx 15° \qquad \text{from calculator or table}$$

EXAMPLE 5   A boat is headed due east at 30 mi/h across a stream that is flowing due south at 11 mi/h. Find the speed and course of the boat.

Solution   The situation is shown in Fig. 8.22 with

$$|\overrightarrow{AB}| = 30 \qquad \text{and} \qquad |\overrightarrow{BC}| = 11$$

The angle *A*, or angle *BAC*, is given by

$$\tan A = \tfrac{11}{30} = 0.3667$$

and so $A = 20°$ to the nearest degree. Moreover, the Pythagorean theorem gives

$$b^2 = 30^2 + 11^2 = 1021$$

Therefore, to 2 digits, $b \approx 32$; hence, the boat travels S70°E at 32 mi/h.

EXAMPLE 6   Find the angle between vectors of magnitudes 209 and 287 if their resultant, or sum, has magnitude 465.

Solution   A sketch of the situation is shown in Fig. 8.23. We find angle *B*, using the law of cosines, and subtract it from 180° to get angle *BAC*:

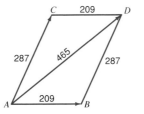

FIGURE 8.23

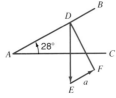

$|\overrightarrow{DE}| = 184$
Angle $EDF = 28°$

$\overrightarrow{DE}$ parallel to $\overrightarrow{DE}$
Angle ADE = angle E

FIGURE 8.24

$$\cos B = \frac{209^2 + 287^2 - 465^2}{2(209)(287)}$$

$$\approx -0.7517 \qquad \text{by calculator}$$

$$B \approx 138.7°$$

$$\text{angle } BAC = 180° - B = 41.3°$$

EXAMPLE 7   What force is needed to keep a loaded box that weighs 184 lb from sliding down an inclined plane if the angle of inclination is 28°?

Solution   A sketch of the situation is shown in Fig. 8.24. AB is perpendicular to DF, and AB is parallel to EF, angle EDF is 28°, and the vector from D to E represents the force of gravity, its magnitude being 184. Letting a be the magnitude of the vector from E to F, then from triangle DEF

$$\sin 28° = \frac{a}{184}$$
$$a = 184 \sin 28° \approx 86.4$$

Thus the force needed has magnitude 86.4 and is parallel to either EF or AD.

EXAMPLE 8   Find the ground speed and course of a plane with a heading of 170° at 320 mi/h in an 18-mi/h wind from the west.

Solution   The situation is shown pictorially in Fig. 8.25. Since the heading is 170°, then angle SPA is 10°, angle PAS is 80°, and thus angle PAB is 100°. In triangle PAB, $PA = 320$ and $AB = 18$; hence we know two sides and the included angle. Thus we use the law of cosines with $g = PB$ and have

$$g^2 = 320^2 + 18^2 - 2(320)(18) \cos 100°$$
$$\approx 104,724$$
$$g \approx 324 \qquad \text{to 3 digits}$$

The ground speed is 324 mi/h. To find the course, we first find $\theta = $ angle APB of the triangle. By the law of sines

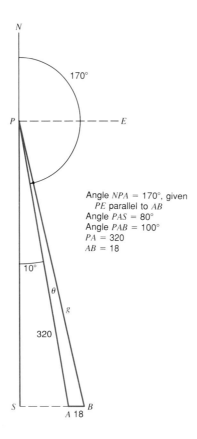

Angle $NPA = 170°$, given
PE parallel to AB
Angle $PAS = 80°$
Angle $PAB = 100°$
$PA = 320$
$AB = 18$

FIGURE 8.25

$$\frac{\sin \theta}{18} = \frac{\sin 100°}{324}$$

$$\sin \theta = \frac{18 \sin 100°}{324}$$

$$\approx 0.0547$$

$$\theta \approx 3.1°$$

Consequently, the course is $180° - 10° - 3.1° = 166.9°$.

EXERCISE 8.3

Sketch the vectors in Probs. 1 to 4 using the vectors below.

1. $2\mathbf{V}$ and $2\mathbf{V} + \mathbf{W}$
3. $-3\mathbf{V}$ and $\mathbf{W} - 3\mathbf{V}$
2. $-\mathbf{W}$ and $\mathbf{V} - \mathbf{W}$
4. $2\mathbf{W}$ and $2\mathbf{W} + 3\mathbf{V}$

In Probs. 5 to 12, find the magnitude and direction of the given vectors.

5. $12\mathbf{i} + 5\mathbf{j}$
6. $7\mathbf{i} - 24\mathbf{j}$
7. $-3\mathbf{i} - 4\mathbf{j}$
8. $-20\mathbf{i} + 21\mathbf{j}$
9. $(-2\mathbf{i} + 7\mathbf{j}) + (5\mathbf{i} - 4\mathbf{j})$
10. $(-6\mathbf{i} + 3\mathbf{j}) + (13\mathbf{i} - 3\mathbf{j})$
11. $(5\mathbf{i} + \sqrt{3}\mathbf{j}) - (4\mathbf{i} + 2\sqrt{3}\mathbf{j})$
12. $(2\sqrt{3}\mathbf{i} + \mathbf{j}) - (\sqrt{3}\mathbf{i} - 2\mathbf{j})$

In Probs. 13 to 20, the magnitude and direction of a vector are given. Write the vectors in the form $a\mathbf{i} + b\mathbf{j}$.

13. $|\mathbf{V}| = 4$, $\theta = 35°$ **14.** $|\mathbf{V}| = 7$, $\theta = 122°$
15. $|\mathbf{V}| = 5$, $\theta = 222°$ **16.** $|\mathbf{V}| = 2$, $\theta = 161°$
17. $|\mathbf{V}| = 8$, $\theta = 60°$ **18.** $|\mathbf{V}| = 5\sqrt{3}$, $\theta = 30°$
19. $|\mathbf{V}| = 7\sqrt{2}$, $\theta = 45°$ **20.** $|\mathbf{V}| = 13$, $\theta = 90°$

In Probs. 21 to 24, magnitudes of two forces are given along with the angle α between them. Find the magnitude of the resultant, and the angle it makes with the component whose magnitude is larger.

21. $|\mathbf{F}_1| = 38$ lb, $|\mathbf{F}_2| = 51$ lb, $\alpha = 42°$
22. $|\mathbf{F}_1| = 47$ lb, $|\mathbf{F}_2| = 78$ lb, $\alpha = 73°$
23. $|\mathbf{F}_1| = 140$ mi/h, $|\mathbf{F}_2| = 185$ mi/h, $\alpha = 60.6°$
24. $|\mathbf{F}_1| = 239$ mi/h, $|\mathbf{F}_2| = 283$ mi/h, $\alpha = 93.7°$

In Probs. 25 to 28, the magnitudes of two forces and of their resultant are given. Find the angle between the forces if the last number is the magnitude of the resultant.

25. 327 g, 403 g, 586 g
26. 507 g, 615 g, 718 g
27. 234 lb, 343 lb, 423 lb
28. 176 lb, 219 lb, 329 lb

What force is necessary to keep a box of the given weight from slipping down a ramp with the specified inclination?

29. 100 g, 12.3°   **30.** 217 g, 17.6°
31. 428 lb, 21.5°   **32.** 528 lb, 23.8°

Find the inclination of a plane if a force equal to the first number is required to hold a weight equal to the second number in Probs. 33 to 36.

33. 27 lb, 68 lb   **34.** 39 lb, 86 lb
35. 41 kg, 99 kg   **36.** 13 kg, 51 kg

The first two numbers give the heading of an airplane and the magnitude of its velocity. The second two numbers give the direction the wind is from and its velocity. Find the ground speed and course of the airplane.

37. 180°, 310 mi/h, 125°, 23 mi/h
38. 75°, 290 mi/h; 40°, 20 mi/h
39. 203°, 370 mi/h; from the west, 18 mi/h
40. 320°, 320 mi/h; from the east, 15 mi/h

8.4 **Trigonometric Form of Complex Numbers**

We have already studied complex numbers in Sec. 2.3,

$$x + yi \qquad \text{where } i^2 = -1$$

and seen how to add, subtract, multiply, and divide them. In this section we shall develop a new way to write complex numbers which makes their multiplication and division much easier.

To graph the complex number $x + yi$, we use a horizontal axis called the **real axis** and a vertical axis called the **imaginary axis.** We measure x on the real axis, and y on the imaginary axis. There is clearly a parallel development with previously discussed ideas. See Fig. 8.26. Of course, i is used in two different ways below in the vector and complex number notation:

Point: (x, y) in rectangular coordinates
Vector: $\langle x, y \rangle = x\mathbf{i} + y\mathbf{j}$, where $\mathbf{i}$ and $\mathbf{j}$ are unit vectors
Complex number: $x + yi$, where $i^2 = -1$

We will pursue this even further in Sec. 8.6 when we write $(x, y) = (r \cos \theta, r \sin \theta)$ when treating polar coordinates.

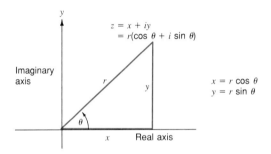

FIGURE 8.26

From Fig. 8.26, we have $x = r \cos \theta$ and $y = r \sin \theta$, and so we may write the complex number $x + yi$ in the form

$$x + yi = r \cos \theta + (r \sin \theta)i$$
$$= r(\cos \theta + i \sin \theta) \tag{8.12}$$

This is called the **trigonometric** or **polar form** of the complex number, and we use the following equations to change from the $x + yi$ form to polar form, and vice versa:

$x = r \cos \theta$	$y = r \sin \theta$	(8.13)
$r^2 = x^2 + y^2$	$\tan \theta = \dfrac{y}{x}$	(8.14)

The number $|z|$ is called the **absolute value** of the complex number $z = x + yi$, where by definition

$$|z| = |x + yi| = \sqrt{x^2 + y^2} = r$$

This is just the distance from the origin to the point (x, y).

If z and w are complex numbers, then

$$|z + w| \le |z| + |w|$$

This is called the **triangle inequality**—see Probs. 41 to 44. All points z with $|z| = 1$ lie on the unit circle with center at the origin.

The angle θ is called an **argument** or **amplitude** of z. If θ is an argument of z, so is $\theta + 360°$, or $\theta + 2\pi$. In fact, there are an infinite number of angles. In particular, the angle θ is not necessarily arctan (y/x) since θ need not be between $-\pi/2$ and $\pi/2$, or from $-90°$ to $90°$. The values of x and y will show which quadrant θ is in. Each complex number has

more than one trigonometric form

NOTE   For a specific complex number z, $|z|$ is unique, but θ is not.
Sometimes the notation cis θ is used for $\cos \theta + i \sin \theta$.

EXAMPLE 1   Express the complex number $-1 - i\sqrt{3}$ in trigonometric form.

Solution   We shall first find values of r and θ:
$$r = \sqrt{(-1)^2 + (-\sqrt{3})^2} = \sqrt{1 + 3} = 2 \qquad \text{by (8.14)}$$

Since the point corresponding to $-1 - i\sqrt{3}$ is in the third quadrant, and $\tan\theta = (-\sqrt{3})/(-1) = \sqrt{3}$, we may take $\theta = 240°$ or $4\pi/3$. Two other possible values for θ are $240° \pm 360°$. Consequently

$$-1 - i\sqrt{3} = 2(\cos 240° + i \sin 240°) = 2 \text{ cis } 240°$$ ◢

EXAMPLE 2 Express $4 - 5i$ in trigonometric form.

Solution The absolute value of $4 - 5i$ is

$$r = \sqrt{4^2 + (-5)^2} = \sqrt{16 + 25} = \sqrt{41} \qquad \text{by (8.14)}$$

Since the point corresponding to $4 - 5i$ is in the fourth quadrant, we may use $\theta = \arctan(-5/4)$. Consequently,

$$4 - 5i = \sqrt{41} \{\cos [\arctan (-5/4)] + i \sin [\arctan (-5/4)]\}$$
$$= \sqrt{41} \text{ cis } [\arctan (-5/4)]$$

This is the exact value. Using a table or a calculator, we find that $\arctan (-5/4) = -\arctan 1.25 \approx -51°$, or -0.89, and thus

$$4 - 5i \approx \sqrt{41} [\cos (-51°) + i \sin (-51°)]$$
$$\approx \sqrt{41} [\cos (-0.89) + i \sin (-0.89)]$$ ◢

If $z = a + bi = r(\cos\theta + i \sin\theta)$, then the **conjugate of** z is defined to be $\bar{z} = a - bi$. We then have

$$\bar{z} = a - bi = r[\cos (-\theta) + i \sin (-\theta)]$$
$$= r[\cos\theta - i \sin\theta]$$

Also, the **negative of** z is

$$-z = -a - bi = r[\cos (\pi + \theta) + i \sin (\pi + \theta)]$$

Finally, we have $z \cdot \bar{z} = (a + bi)(a - bi) = a^2 + b^2 = |z|^2$, and so

$$\frac{1}{z} = \frac{1 \cdot \bar{z}}{z \cdot \bar{z}} = \frac{\bar{z}}{|z|^2} = \frac{r[\cos (-\theta) + i \sin (-\theta)]}{r^2}$$

Reciprocal

$$= \frac{1}{r} [\cos (-\theta) + i \sin (-\theta)] = \frac{1}{r} [\cos\theta - i \sin\theta] \qquad \textbf{(1)}$$

If $r > 1$, then $1/r < 1$, and $1/z$ will be closer to the origin than z is, as in Fig. 8.27.

Figure 8.27 shows z, $\bar{z}$, $-z$, and $1/z$ geometrically.

Multiplication and Division

We shall consider two complex numbers

$$z = x + yi = r(\cos\theta + i \sin\theta)$$
and
$$w = u + vi = R(\cos\phi + i \sin\phi)$$

By multiplying them, we have

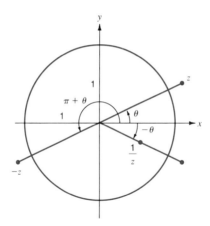

FIGURE 8.27

$$zw = (x + yi)(u + vi) = xu + xvi + yui + yvi^2$$
$$= (xu - yv) + (xv + yu)i$$

Now, if we replace x, y, u, and v by $r \cos \theta$, $r \sin \theta$, $R \cos \phi$, and $R \sin \phi$, respectively, and simplify, we have

$$zw = rR(\cos \theta \cos \phi - \sin \theta \sin \phi) + i(\cos \theta \sin \phi + \sin \theta \cos \phi)$$

We may simplify this by using the identities

$$\cos \theta \cos \phi - \sin \theta \sin \phi = \cos (\theta + \phi)$$
and $\qquad \cos \theta \sin \phi + \sin \theta \cos \phi = \sin (\theta + \phi)$

Therefore, since $zw = r(\cos \theta + i \sin \theta) \cdot R(\cos \phi + i \sin \phi)$, we have the following formula:

> The product of two complex numbers in trigonometric form is
> $$r(\cos \theta + i \sin \theta) \cdot R(\cos \phi + i \sin \phi)$$
> $$= rR[\cos (\theta + \phi) + i \sin (\theta + \phi)] \qquad (8.15)$$

Thus we multiply two complex numbers by multiplying their absolute values and adding their angles or arguments.

▶ **EXAMPLE 3** Find the product of $1 - i$ and $-2 + 2i$.

Solution Trigonometric forms of these complex numbers are

$$1 - i = \sqrt{2}(\cos 315° + i \sin 315°)$$
$$-2 + 2i = 2\sqrt{2}(\cos 135° + i \sin 135°)$$

By Eq. (8.15), their product is

$$(\sqrt{2})(2\sqrt{2})[\cos (315° + 135°) + i \sin (315° + 135°)]$$
$$= 4(\cos 450° + i \sin 450°)$$
$$= 4(\cos 90° + i \sin 90°) = 4(0 + i) = 4i$$

As a check, direct multiplication gives

$$(1 - i)(-2 + 2i) = -2 + 2i + 2i - 2i^2 = -2 + 4i + 2 = 4i$$

Although this direct multiplication is certainly quicker with just two factors, the point is to understand formula (8.15), and this can only be done by using it. ◢

Since the product of two complex numbers is itself a complex number, we can obtain the product of three or more complex numbers by a repeated application of Eq. (8.15).

▶ **EXAMPLE 4**   Find the product of $1 + i$, $-1 + i\sqrt{3}$, and $\sqrt{3} - i$.

Solution   We first express each of these numbers in trigonometric form. Since $1 + i$ is in the first quadrant and $\tan 45° = 1$, then

$$1 + i = \sqrt{2}(\cos 45° + i \sin 45°)$$

Since $-1 + i\sqrt{3}$ is in the second quadrant and $\tan 120° = -\sqrt{3}$, then

$$-1 + i\sqrt{3} = 2(\cos 120° + i \sin 120°)$$

Since $\sqrt{3} - i$ is in the fourth quadrant and $\tan 330° = -1/\sqrt{3}$:

$$\sqrt{3} - i = 2(\cos 330° + i \sin 330°)$$

Therefore, the product is

$$
\begin{aligned}
(1 + i)&(-1 + i\sqrt{3})(\sqrt{3} - i) \\
&= \sqrt{2} \, (\cos 45° + i \sin 45°) \cdot 2 \, (\cos 120° + i \sin 120°) \cdot 2 \, (\cos 330° + i \sin 330°) \\
&= 4\sqrt{2} \, [\cos (45° + 120° + 330°) + i \sin (45° + 120° + 330°)] \\
&= 4\sqrt{2} \, (\cos 495° + i \sin 495°) \\
&= 4\sqrt{2} \, (\cos 135° + i \sin 135°) \\
&= 4\sqrt{2}\left(-\frac{\sqrt{2}}{2} + i\frac{\sqrt{2}}{2}\right) = -4 + 4i
\end{aligned}
$$

◢

We can divide two complex numbers by using Eq. (1), which stated that

$$\frac{1}{z} = \frac{1}{r} \, [\cos (-\theta) + i \sin (-\theta)]$$

To divide w by z, we multiply w and $1/z$:

$$
\begin{aligned}
\frac{w}{z} &= w\frac{1}{z} \\
&= [R(\cos \phi + i \sin \phi)] \cdot \left[\frac{1}{r} \cos (-\theta) + i \sin (-\theta))\right] \\
&= \frac{R}{r} \, [\cos (\phi - \theta) + i \sin (\phi - \theta)]
\end{aligned}
\tag{8.16}
$$

Therefore, we have the following rule for quotients:

Division of two complex numbers

> The absolute value of the quotient of two complex numbers is equal to the absolute value of the numerator divided by the absolute value of the denominator. An argument of the quotient is equal to the argument of the numerator minus the argument of the denominator.

Thus we may divide two complex numbers by dividing their absolute values and subtracting their angles or arguments.

EXAMPLE 5 Find the quotient $(-3 + 3i)/(1 + i)$.

Solution Since $-3 + 3i$ is in the second quadrant and $1 + i$ is in the first quadrant, we may write each of the given complex numbers in the trigonometric forms below and have

$$\frac{-3 + 3i}{1 + i} = \frac{3\sqrt{2}(\cos 135° + i \sin 135°)}{\sqrt{2}(\cos 45° + i \sin 45°)}$$
$$= 3[\cos (135° - 45°) + i \sin (135° - 45°)]$$
$$= 3(\cos 90° + i \sin 90°)$$
$$= 3(0 + i) = 3i$$

As a check, $3i(1 + i) = 3i + 3i^2 = 3i - 3 = -3 + 3i$.

EXERCISE 8.4

Express the complex numbers in Probs. 1 to 8 in polar or trigonometric form. Give the exact angle in Probs. 1 to 4, and in the others to the nearest tenth of a degree.

1. $-1 + i\sqrt{3}$
2. $4\sqrt{3} - 12i$
3. $5 + 5i$
4. $-1 + i$
5. $7 - 6i$
6. $-2i$
7. $-5 + 12i$
8. $-15 - 8i$

In Probs. 9 to 20, evaluate the given expression.

9. $2(\cos 139° + i \sin 139°) \cdot 3(\cos 71° + i \sin 71°)$
10. $5(\cos 178° + i \sin 178°) \cdot 2(\cos 47° + i \sin 47°)$
11. $7(\cos 197° + i \sin 197°) \cdot 5(\cos 43° + i \sin 43°)$
12. $6(\cos 119° + i \sin 119°) \cdot 3(\cos 151° + i \sin 151°)$
13. $\dfrac{12(\cos 64° + i \sin 64°)}{3(\cos 34° + i \sin 34°)}$
14. $\dfrac{15(\cos 72° + i \sin 72°)}{3(\cos 27° + i \sin 27°)}$
15. $\dfrac{22(\cos 85° + i \sin 85°)}{2(\cos 25° + i \sin 25°)}$
16. $\dfrac{18(\cos 103° + i \sin 103°)}{9(\cos 13° + i \sin 13°)}$

17. $\dfrac{18(\cos 187° + i \sin 187°) \cdot 2(\cos 58° + i \sin 58°)}{9(\cos 20° + i \sin 20°)}$
18. $\dfrac{4(\cos 237° + i \sin 237°) \cdot 3(\cos 44° + i \sin 44°)}{6(\cos 41° + i \sin 41°)}$
19. $\dfrac{6(\cos 198° + i \sin 198°) \cdot 4(\cos 146° + i \sin 146°)}{12(\cos 44° + i \sin 44°)}$
20. $\dfrac{10(\cos 249° + i \sin 249°) \cdot 21(\cos 170° + i \sin 170°)}{42(\cos 104° + i \sin 104°)}$

In Probs. 21 to 28, find both zw and z/w. Write the answers in either form.

21. $z = -2 + 2i$, $w = \sqrt{3} + i$
22. $z = -1 - i\sqrt{3}$, $w = i$
23. $z = 1 - i\sqrt{3}$, $w = -\sqrt{3} - i$
24. $z = 4 - 4i$, $w = 1 + i\sqrt{3}$
25. $z = 3 + 3i$, $w = -2i$
26. $z = -1 + i\sqrt{3}$, $w = -\sqrt{3} + i$
27. $z = -4 - 4i$, $w = \sqrt{3} - i$
28. $z = -1 + i$, $w = -2 + 2i$
29. Show that $A + B$, $A + Bi$, $A - B$, and $A - Bi$ are the vertices of a square if A and B are complex numbers with $B \neq 0$.

30. Show that $A + B$, $Aw + B$, and $Aw^2 + B$ are the vertices of an equilateral triangle if A and B are complex numbers with $w \neq 1$ and $w^3 = 1$.

31. Show that $(\cos \theta + i \sin \theta)^2 = \cos 2\theta + i \sin 2\theta$.

32. Show that $(\cos \theta + i \sin \theta)^{-1} = \cos \theta - i \sin \theta$.

Find the trigonometric form of the complex number in Probs. 33 to 36.

33. $\cos 30° + i \sin 60°$ **34.** $\cos 45° + i \sin 30°$

35. $\cos 40° - i \sin 40°$ **36.** $-\cos 65° - i \sin 65°$

In Probs. 37 to 40, prove the given property for the complex numbers $z = a + bi$ and $w = c + di$.

37. $|zw| = |z| \cdot |w|$ **38.** $|z/w| = |z|/|w|$

39. $|6z| = 6|z|$ **40.** $|\bar{z}| = |z|$

It is true for all complex numbers z and w that

$$|z + w| \le |z| + |w|$$

This is called the **triangle inequality.** Verify it in the following cases.

41. $z = 3 + i$, $w = 5$

42. $z = -2 + 5i$, $w = 4 - 10i$

43. $z = 3 + 5i$, $w = 9 + 14i$

44. $z = 4i$, $w = -2 + 7i$

45. Find the two square roots of $3 + 4i$ by solving the equation

$$(a + bi)^2 = 3 + 4i$$

Square the left member, equate real parts and imaginary parts, and solve the resulting two equations in two unknowns.

46. Show that $\overline{-z} = -(\bar{z})$. Which quadrant is it in if z is in the first quadrant, as in Fig. 8.27?

47. If z is in the second quadrant, what quadrant is iz in? Describe how to go from z to iz in general.

48. Suppose the alternating current in an electric inductor is E/Z, where E is the voltage and Z is the impedance. Find the current for

$$E = 10(\cos 25° + i \sin 25°) \quad \text{and} \quad Z = 6 + 4i$$

8.5 De Moivre's Theorem and *n*th Roots

We shall now discuss a theorem proved by Abraham De Moivre (1667–1754) that is very useful for finding powers and roots of a complex number. If we square the complex number $z = r \cos \theta + i \sin \theta$ by using the product theorem, we get

$$\begin{aligned}
z^2 &= [r(\cos \theta + i \sin \theta][r(\cos \theta + i \sin \theta)] \\
&= r^2[\cos (\theta + \theta) + i \sin (\theta + \theta)] \qquad \text{by (8.15)} \\
&= r^2(\cos 2\theta + i \sin 2\theta)
\end{aligned}$$

Furthermore, multiplying z and z^2 gives

$$\begin{aligned}
z^3 = z^2(z) &= [r^2(\cos 2\theta + i \sin 2\theta)][r(\cos \theta + i \sin \theta)] \\
&= r^3[\cos (2\theta + \theta) + i \sin (2\theta + \theta)] \qquad \text{by (8.15)} \\
&= r^3(\cos 3\theta + i \sin 3\theta)
\end{aligned}$$

A repeated application of this procedure leads to the statement known as **De Moivre's theorem:**

De Moivre's Theorem

If $r(\cos \theta + i \sin \theta)$ is a complex number, and n is an integer, then

$$[r(\cos \theta + i \sin \theta)]^n = r^n(\cos n\theta + i \sin n\theta) \qquad (8.17)$$

De Moivre's theorem is actually true for any real number n. The complete proof of this theorem for positive integral values of n requires the use of mathematical induction, as in Chap. 12.

EXAMPLE 1   Use De Moivre's theorem to find the fifth power of $\sqrt{3} + i$.

Solution

$$
\begin{aligned}
(\sqrt{3} + i)^5 &= [2(\cos 30° + i \sin 30°)]^5 \\
&= 2^5[\cos 5(30°) + i \sin 5(30°)] \\
&= 32(\cos 150° + i \sin 150°) \\
&= 32\left(-\frac{\sqrt{3}}{2} + \frac{1}{2}i\right) \\
&= -16\sqrt{3} + 16i
\end{aligned}
$$

Roots of Complex Numbers

The complex number z is called an nth root of w if and only if

$$z^n = w$$

For instance i is a cube root of $-i$ since $i^3 = -i$, and $2 + 3i$ is a square root of $-5 + 12i$ since $(2 + 3i)^2 = -5 + 12i$.

EXAMPLE 2   Show that $\cos 45° + i \sin 45°$ and $\cos 90° + i \sin 90°$ are both eighth roots of unity (i.e., of 1).

Solution

$$
\begin{aligned}
(\cos 45° + i \sin 45°)^8 &= \cos 8(45°) + i \sin 8(45°) \\
&= \cos 360° + i \sin 360° = 1 + 0i = 1
\end{aligned}
$$

$$
\begin{aligned}
(\cos 90° + i \sin 90°)^8 &= \cos 8(90°) + i \sin 8(90°) \\
&= \cos 720° + i \sin 720° \\
&= \cos 0° + i \sin 0° = 1 + 0i = 1
\end{aligned}
$$

Both i and $-i$ are square roots of -1 since $i^2 = -1$, and also $(-i)^2 = -1$. All three of the complex numbers

$$-1 \qquad \cos 60° + i \sin 60° \qquad \text{and} \qquad \cos 300° + i \sin 300°$$

are cube roots of -1, which can be checked using De Moivre's theorem. If we use **complex numbers,** we can find n nth roots of any nonzero complex number with the help of De Moivre's theorem. We shall illustrate the method in Examples 3 and 4.

EXAMPLE 3   Find the three cube roots of 64.

Solution   We first express 64 in the form $r(\cos \theta + i \sin \theta)$, and get

$$
\begin{aligned}
64 &= 64(\cos 0° + i \sin 0°) \\
&= 64[\cos (0° + n360°) + i \sin (0° + n360°)] \qquad \textbf{(1)}
\end{aligned}
$$

for any integral value of n, since sine and cosine have period 360° or 2π. Now if we let $s(\cos \alpha + i \sin \alpha)$ be a cube root of 64, then by definition

$$64[\cos{(0° + n360°)} + i \sin{(0° + n360°)}]$$
$$= [s(\cos{\alpha} + i \sin{\alpha})]^3$$
$$= s^3(\cos{3\alpha} + i \sin{3\alpha}) \qquad \text{by De Moivre's theorem} \qquad \text{(2)}$$

We next use the fact that if two complex numbers are equal, such as the ones in Eqs. (1) and (2), then their absolute values are equal, and their arguments are either equal or differ by an integral multiple of 360°. Thus

$$s^3 = 64 \qquad \text{remember that } s \text{ is real}$$
$$s = 4 \qquad \text{since } 4^3 = 64$$

Furthermore, for the angles we have

$$3\alpha = 0° + n360° = n360°$$
$$\alpha = n120°$$

Thus $\alpha = 0°$ for $n = 0$, $\alpha = 120°$ for $n = 1$, and $\alpha = 240°$ for $n = 2$. Consequently, the three cube roots of 64 are

$$4(\cos{0°} + i \sin{0°}) = 4 \qquad \text{for } n = 0$$
$$4(\cos{120°} + i \sin{120°}) = -2 + 2i\sqrt{3} \qquad \text{for } n = 1$$
$$4(\cos{240°} + i \sin{240°}) = -2 - 2i\sqrt{3} \qquad \text{for } n = 2$$

There is no need to assign additional values to n, since to do so would yield angles that differ from those above by integral multiples of 360°; consequently, the cube root so determined would be one of those already obtained. For instance, letting $n = 4$ gives $\alpha = 4(120°) = 480°$, and the cube root is

$$4(\cos{480°} + i \sin{480°})$$
$$= 4(\cos{120°} + i \sin{120°}) = -2 - 2i\sqrt{3}$$

which is the same root we found earlier for $n = 1$. ◢

The same method used in Example 3 may be used for any nonzero complex number $r(\cos{\theta} + i \sin{\theta})$ and any positive integer n, giving the result below:

n complex nth roots

If n is any positive integer, and $z = r(\cos{\theta} + i \sin{\theta})$ is any nonzero complex number in trigonometric form, then z has exactly n distinct complex nth roots, and they are

$$\sqrt[n]{r}\left[\cos{\left(\frac{\theta + k \cdot 360°}{n}\right)} + i \sin{\left(\frac{\theta + k \cdot 360°}{n}\right)}\right]$$

for $k = 0, 1, 2, \ldots, n - 1$.

The value $k = n$ gives the same root that $k = 0$ does. The n nth roots of $a + bi = r(\cos{\theta} + i \sin{\theta})$ are equally spaced about the circle whose center is the origin and whose radius is

$$\sqrt[n]{r} = r^{1/n} = (\sqrt{a^2 + b^2})^{1/n}$$

with one angle being θ/n. The n angles, for $k = 0, 1, 2, \ldots, n - 1$, may be written either

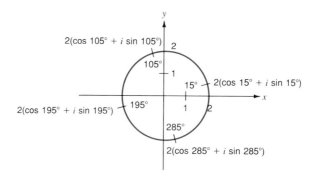

FIGURE 8.28

in degrees

$$\frac{\theta}{n} + k \cdot \frac{360°}{n}$$

or in radians

$$\frac{\theta}{n} + k \cdot \frac{2\pi}{n}$$

EXAMPLE 4   Find the four fourth roots of $1 + i\sqrt{3}$.

Solution   If we express $1 + i\sqrt{3}$ in trigonometric form, we have

$$r = \sqrt{(1)^2 + (\sqrt{3})^2} = 2$$

and we may choose $\theta = 60°$ or $\pi/3$, giving

$$1 + i\sqrt{3} = 2[\cos(60° + k360°) + i \sin(60° + k360°)]$$

Using $n = 4$, the angles of the four fourth roots are

$$\frac{60° + k \cdot 360°}{4} = 15° + k \cdot 90°$$

and the absolute value of each fourth root is $2^{1/4} = \sqrt[4]{2}$. Hence we have $\theta = 15°$ for $k = 0$, $\theta = 105°$ for $k = 1$, $\theta = 195°$ for $k = 2$, and $\theta = 285°$ for $k = 3$. The corresponding values of the four fourth roots of $1 + i\sqrt{3}$ are

$$\sqrt[4]{2}[\cos 15° + i \sin 15°] \qquad \sqrt[4]{2}[\cos 105° + i \sin 105°]$$
$$\sqrt[4]{2}[\cos 195° + i \sin 195°] \qquad \sqrt[4]{2}[\cos 285° + i \sin 285°]$$

Approximate decimal values in $a + bi$ form can be found for each root by using a calculator or tables. For instance

$$\sqrt[4]{2}(\cos 105° + i \sin 105°) \approx -0.3078 + 1.149i$$

The four fourth roots of $1 + i\sqrt{3}$ are equally spaced about the circle with center the origin and radius $\sqrt[4]{2}$, the smallest angle being 15°. See Fig. 8.28.   ◢

EXERCISE 8.5

Use De Moivre's theorem to find the indicated powers in Probs. 1 to 12. Write the answer in exact form, simplified if possible.

1. $[3(\cos 27° + i \sin 27°)]^4$
2. $[2(\cos 44° + i \sin 44°)]^6$
3. $[\sqrt{5}(\cos 16° + i \sin 16°)]^8$

4. $[\sqrt{3}(\cos 38° + i \sin 38°)]^5$

5. $\left[\sqrt{6}\left(\cos \dfrac{\pi}{7} + i \sin \dfrac{\pi}{7}\right)\right]^5$

6. $\left[4\left(\cos \dfrac{\pi}{5} + i \sin \dfrac{\pi}{5}\right)\right]^4$

7. $\left[\sqrt{3}\left(\cos \dfrac{\pi}{8} + i \sin \dfrac{\pi}{8}\right)\right]^3$

8. $\left[3\left(\cos \dfrac{\pi}{5} + i \sin \dfrac{\pi}{5}\right)\right]^6$

9. $(2 + 2i)^5$ **10.** $(-\sqrt{3} + i)^6$

11. $(1 - i\sqrt{3})^4$ **12.** $(-3 - 3i)^3$

In Probs. 13 to 20, find the indicated powers by De Moivre's theorem. Write the answers in the $a + bi$ form, using decimal approximations.

13. $(\cos 12° + i \sin 12°)^9$ **14.** $(\cos 27° + i \sin 27°)^7$

15. $\left(\cos \dfrac{\pi}{5} + i \sin \dfrac{\pi}{5}\right)^4$

16. $\left(\cos \dfrac{\pi}{12} + i \sin \dfrac{\pi}{12}\right)^7$

17. $(\tfrac{5}{13} + \tfrac{12}{13}i)^5$ **18.** $(\tfrac{24}{25} + \tfrac{7}{25}i)^6$

19. $\left(\dfrac{1 + 2i}{\sqrt{5}}\right)^4$ **20.** $\left(\dfrac{3 + 5i}{\sqrt{34}}\right)^6$

In Probs. 21 to 32, write the roots in trigonometric form.

21. The fourth roots of $8\sqrt{2} - 8i\sqrt{2}$
22. The fifth roots of $243i$
23. The sixth roots of $-32 - 32i\sqrt{3}$
24. The cube roots of $-4\sqrt{2} + 4i\sqrt{2}$
25. The cube roots of $27(\cos 126° + i \sin 126°)$
26. The fourth roots of $81(\cos 232° + i \sin 232°)$
27. The cube roots of $125(\cos 330° + i \sin 330°)$
28. The fourth roots of $16(\cos 248° + i \sin 248°)$
29. The cube roots of 1
30. The fourth roots of i

31. The fifth roots of -1
32. The sixth roots of $-i$

In Probs. 33 to 36, find all complex solutions to the equation. Write the answers in trigonometric form.

33. $z^3 = -64$ **34.** $z^4 = 81$
35. $z^4 = -8 + 8i\sqrt{3}$ **36.** $z^3 = 4 + 4i\sqrt{3}$
37. Show that if $z \neq 1$ and z is an nth root of 1, then

$$1 + z + z^2 + z^3 + \cdots + z^{n-1} = 0$$

Hint: $0 = z^n - 1$. Now divide by $z - 1$.

38. Show by calculation or otherwise that

$$\cos 20° + \cos 92° + \cos 164° +$$
$$\cos 236° + \cos 308° = 0$$

and

$$\sin 20° + \sin 92° + \sin 164° +$$
$$\sin 236° + \sin 308° = 0$$

Note: these are the real and imaginary parts of the sum of the five fifth roots of $\cos 100° + i \sin 100°$.

39. Replace z by $\cos A + i \sin A$ in

$$1 + z + z^2 + z^3 + z^4 = \dfrac{1 - z^5}{1 - z}$$

and equate real parts to show that

$$1 + \cos A + \cos 2A + \cos 3A + \cos 4A$$
$$= \dfrac{(1 - \cos A)(1 - \cos 5A) + \sin A \sin 5A}{2 - 2 \cos A}$$

and equate imaginary parts to also show that

$$\sin A + \sin 2A + \sin 3A + \sin 4A$$
$$= \dfrac{(1 - \cos 5A) \sin A - (1 - \cos A) \sin 5A}{2 - 2 \cos A}$$

40. Show that $(\cos \theta + i \sin \theta)^{-2} = \cos(-2\theta) + i \sin(-2\theta)$.

8.6 Polar Coordinates

Up until now, we have located points in the plane by using the rectangular coordinate system. To use it, we locate a point by giving its distance and direction from each of two perpendicular lines. There are other coordinate systems, and one of them is called

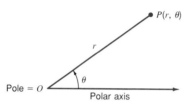

FIGURE 8.29

the **polar coordinate system.** It is based on a point O called the **pole,** and on a ray whose endpoint is the pole. The ray is called the **polar axis.**

Suppose that P is any point in the plane except the pole. First choose any angle θ whose initial side is the polar axis and whose terminal side is the line segment from O to P. The angle θ can be positive or negative or 0, and it may be measured in degrees or radians. Let r be the distance from the pole O to the point P, as in Fig. 8.29, where $r > 0$. Then

(r, θ) are polar coordinates of the point P

We shall agree that $(0, \theta)$ are the polar coordinates of the pole, whatever the angle θ may be.

If the polar coordinates of a point are (r, θ), with $r > 0$, the distance r is measured along the terminal side of the angle θ. However if the polar coordinates of a point are (r, θ), with $r < 0$, the distance $|r|$ is measured on the extension of the terminal side of the angle, that is, on the terminal side of the angle $\theta + 180°$ or $\theta + \pi$.

EXAMPLE 1   Verify the polar coordinates of the points shown in Fig. 8.30.

Solution   The point P with polar coordinates $(2, 60°)$ is found by measuring an angle of $60°$ from the polar axis, then locating the point which is 2 units from the pole and on the terminal side of the angle. Since -2 is negative, the point $Q(-2, 60°)$ is found by going along the extension of the terminal side of a $60°$ angle, that is, along a $240°$ angle. The point P also has polar coordinates $(-2, 240°)$. The points R and S are found similarly.

In rectangular coordinates, each point has exactly one pair of coordinates. This is not true for polar coordinates. Each point in the plane has an **infinite number** of pairs of polar coordinates. In addition to (r, θ), we may use

$$(r, \theta + k \cdot 360°) \qquad \text{or} \qquad (r, \theta + 2k\pi) \qquad \text{for } k = \pm1, \pm2, \pm3, \dots$$

FIGURE 8.30   (a)   (b)

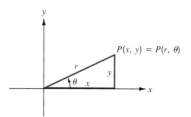

FIGURE 8.31

Furthermore, $(-r, \theta + 180°)$ is the same point, as is $(-r, \theta + \pi)$, and we may use

$$(-r, \theta + 180° + k \cdot 360°) \qquad \text{or} \qquad (-r, \theta + \pi + 2k\pi)$$

for $k = \pm1, \pm2, \ldots$, which are also polar coordinates for the given point (r, θ).

NOTE   The **pole** and **polar axis** are often placed so that the pole corresponds to the origin in rectangular coordinates, and the polar axis to the positive x axis. There are simple relations between the rectangular and polar coordinates of a point, which can be deduced from Fig. 8.31.

By using the definition of trigonometric functions, we have

$$\cos \theta = \frac{x}{r} \qquad \text{and} \qquad \sin \theta = \frac{y}{r}$$

Thus, to change from polar to rectangular coordinates, use

$$x = r \cos \theta \qquad \text{and} \qquad y = r \sin \theta \qquad \text{(8.13)}$$

By the Pythagorean theorem and the definition of the tangent of an angle, we get the following equations which relate rectangular coordinates to polar coordinates:

$$r^2 = x^2 + y^2 \qquad \text{and} \qquad \tan \theta = \frac{y}{x} \qquad \text{(8.14)}$$

These equations do not define r and θ uniquely for a given (x, y). Knowing which quadrant (x, y) is in determines θ except for an integral multiple of 2π or of $360°$. This situation is inevitable since each point has infinitely many pairs of polar coordinates.

▶ **EXAMPLE 2**   Express $(3, -5)$ in polar coordinates.

Solution   By using the transformation equations (8.14), we get

$$r = \sqrt{3^2 + (-5)^2} = \sqrt{34} \qquad \text{and} \qquad \tan \theta = \frac{-5}{3} \approx -1.6667$$

Now since $(3, -5)$ is in the fourth quadrant, we may use

$$\theta = \arctan (-1.6667) \approx -59°$$

Therefore, $(\sqrt{34}, -59°)$ are polar coordinates for the point whose rectangular coordinates are $(3, -5)$. Some of the other polar coordinates for this point are

$$(\sqrt{34}, -59° + 360°) \qquad \text{and} \qquad (-\sqrt{34}, -59° + 180°) \qquad ◢$$

▶ EXAMPLE 3   Find the rectangular coordinates of $(2, 120°)$ or $(2, 2\pi/3)$.

Solution   Using Eqs. (8.13) gives

$$x = r \cos \theta = 2 \cos \frac{2\pi}{3} = 2 \cos 120° = -1$$

and

$$y = r \sin \theta = 2 \sin \frac{2\pi}{3} = 2 \sin 120° = \sqrt{3}$$

Therefore, $(-1, \sqrt{3})$ are the rectangular coordinates of the point whose polar coordinates are $(2, 120°)$ or $(2, 2\pi/3)$.   ◀

Certain graphs have simpler equations in one coordinate system or the other. An equation in rectangular coordinates can be changed to polar coordinates by the transformation equations, and vice versa.

▶ EXAMPLE 4   Change $x^2 + (y - 3)^2 = 9$ to polar coordinates.

Solution   If we replace x by $r \cos \theta$ and y by $r \sin \theta$, as in (8.13), we have

$$
\begin{aligned}
&(r \cos \theta)^2 + (r \sin \theta - 3)^2 = 9 \\
&r^2 \cos^2 \theta + r^2 \sin^2 \theta - 6r \sin \theta + 9 = 9 \qquad \text{squaring} \\
&r^2(\cos^2 \theta + \sin^2 \theta) - 6r \sin \theta = 0 \qquad \text{common factor of } r^2 \\
&r^2 - 6r \sin \theta = 0 \qquad \cos^2 \theta + \sin^2 \theta = 1 \\
&r(r - 6 \sin \theta) = 0 \qquad \text{common factor of } r \\
&r = 6 \sin \theta \qquad \text{dividing by } r
\end{aligned}
$$

No part of the curve was lost in dividing by r since $(0, 180°)$ satisfies the equation $r = 6 \sin \theta$, and $(0, 180°)$ is one pair of polar coordinates for the pole.   ◀

▶ EXAMPLE 5   Express

$$r = \frac{3}{1 - \cos \theta}$$

in terms of rectangular coordinates.

Solution   We begin by multiplying by $1 - \cos \theta$:

$$
\begin{aligned}
r - r \cos \theta &= 3 \\
r &= r \cos \theta + 3
\end{aligned}
$$

Next we square both sides:

$$r^2 = (r \cos \theta)^2 + 6(r \cos \theta) + 9$$

We now replace r^2 by $x^2 + y^2$ and $r \cos \theta$ by x, giving

$$
\begin{aligned}
x^2 + y^2 &= x^2 + 6x + 9 \\
y^2 &= 9 + 6x
\end{aligned}
$$

This is the rectangular form of the equation. The graph is a parabola, which we will study in detail in Chap. 13.   ◀

In order to **sketch the graph** of an equation given in polar coordinates, we make a table of values of θ and r, then plot enough points (r, θ) to draw the graph. It often helps to decide which values of θ make $r > 0$, and which ones make $r < 0$.

NOTE A point belongs to the graph of a polar equation if **any pair of its polar coordinates** satisfies the equation. For example, the point with polar coordinates $(2, \pi/2)$ belongs to the graph of the equation $r = 2 \cos 2\theta$ even though these coordinates do not satisfy the equation. But $(-2, 3\pi/2)$ is a pair of polar coordinates for the same point, and these coordinates do satisfy the equation.

▶ **EXAMPLE 6** Describe the graphs of $r = 5$ and $\theta = 4$.

Solution (a) The graph of $r = 5$ is the set of all points $(5, \theta)$, which is a circle with center at the pole and radius 5.
(b) The graph of $\theta = 4$ is the set of all points $(r, 4)$, which is the line through the pole making an angle of 4 radians with the polar axis. We get the whole line since r may be any real number. See Fig. 8.32. ◀

The amount of labor required for sketching a curve whose equation is known is often decreased if we use intercepts and symmetry. We can find the **intercepts** by putting $\theta = 0°$, $90°$, $180°$, and $270°$ in $f(r, \theta) = 0$, then solving for r. We also find it helpful to extend the polar axis through the pole and to draw a line perpendicular to the polar axis through the pole. This perpendicular is called the **normal axis.**

We are mainly interested in seeing whether the graph is symmetric with respect to the pole, the polar axis, or the normal axis. These correspond to the origin, the x axis, and the y axis in rectangular coordinates.

Symmetry

> If an equation $f(r, \theta) = 0$ in polar coordinates is not changed, or if an equivalent equation results, when (r, θ), is replaced by
>
> 1. Either $(r, \theta + 180°)$ or by $(-r, \theta)$, then the curve is symmetric with respect to the pole
> 2. Either $(r, -\theta)$ or by $(-r, 180° - \theta)$, then the curve is symmetric with respect to the polar axis and/or its extension through the pole
> 3. Either $(r, 180° - \theta)$ or by $(-r, -\theta)$, then the curve is symmetric with respect to the normal axis and/or its extension through the pole

See Fig. 8.33 to justify these facts. We may of course use π instead of $180°$.

The tests above for symmetry are **positive tests:** That is, if a test works, then there is symmetry. There may be symmetry even if one of the tests fails. For instance, in Example 7 below we show that $r = 1 + \sin \theta$ is symmetric with respect to the normal axis by using test 3 in the version $(r, 180° - \theta)$. However if we use test 3 in the version $(-r, -\theta)$, we get

$$-r = 1 + \sin (-\theta)$$

which is equivalent to

$$-r = 1 - \sin \theta \qquad \text{or} \qquad r = -1 + \sin \theta$$

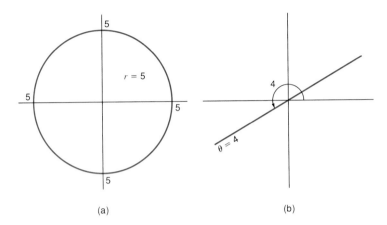

FIGURE 8.32

(a)   (b)

The last equation is not equivalent to the given equation $r = 1 + \sin \theta$, and so the test in the $(-r, -\theta)$ version fails to reveal the symmetry. Nevertheless, there is symmetry with respect to the normal axis.

EXAMPLE 7   Sketch the graph of $r = 1 + \sin \theta$.

Solution   If θ is replaced by $180° - \theta$, we have by test 3

$$r = 1 + \sin (180° - \theta) = 1 + \sin \theta$$

Since the equation is not changed by this substitution, the graph is symmetric with respect to the normal axis. The other two tests 1 and 2 do not show any symmetry. Note that $r \geq 0$ for every θ, and so for example angles in the second quadrant give points in the second quadrant. Also, $r = 0$ only for $\theta = 270°$.

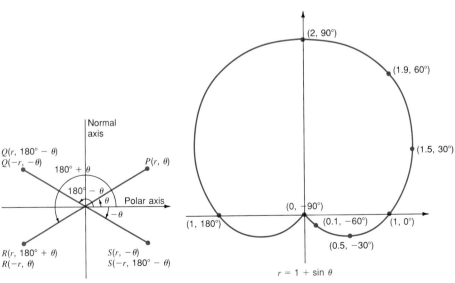

FIGURE 8.33   FIGURE 8.34

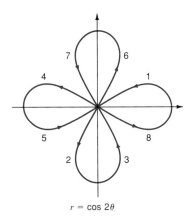

FIGURE 8.35

$r = \cos 2\theta$

We now assign values to θ, compute r to one decimal place, and have the following table:

θ	$-\pi/2$ $-90°$	$-\pi/3$ $-60°$	$-\pi/6$ $-30°$	0 0	$\pi/6$ $30°$	$\pi/3$ $60°$	$\pi/2$ $90°$
$r = 1 + \sin \theta$	0	0.1	0.5	1	1.5	1.9	2

After plotting these points and drawing a smooth curve through them, we obtain the curve to the right of the normal axis in Fig. 8.34. Since the normal axis is an axis of symmetry, the left half of the curve will be a reflection of the right half with respect to the normal axis and can be sketched as indicated. ◣

EXAMPLE 8 Sketch the graph of the equation $r = \cos 2\theta$.

Solution The tests for symmetry show that the curve is symmetric with respect to the polar axis, normal axis, and the pole. We will find the intercepts as we proceed with the following argument.

As θ varies from 0 to 45° or $\pi/4$, 2θ varies from 0 to 90° or $\pi/2$, and $r = \cos 2\theta$ decreases from 1 to 0. Hence this portion of the curve is the curve numbered 1 in Fig. 8.35. Similarly, the information tabulated below enables us to sketch the other portions of the curve indicated. The graph of $r = \cos 2\theta$ is called a *four-leaf rose*.

Angle	Value of r	The part of the curve in Fig. 8.35
$45° \le \theta \le 90°$	r decreases from 0 to -1	2
$90° \le \theta \le 135°$	r increases from -1 to 0	3
$135° \le \theta \le 180°$	r increases from 0 to 1	4

Furthermore, by considering the variation of r as θ passes through the four intervals $180° \le \theta \le 225°$, $225° \le \theta \le 270°$, $270° \le \theta \le 315°$, and $315° \le \theta \le 360°$, we obtain the portions of the graph numbered 5, 6, 7, and 8 in Fig. 8.35. Again, using the symmetry fully would allow the complete graph to be drawn based only on the parts of the graph labeled 1 and 2. ◣

EXERCISE 8.6

Give two other pairs of polar coordinates for each point in Probs. 1 to 4.
 1. $(3, 160°)$, $(4, -25°)$
 2. $(-4, -40°)$, $(-5, 220°)$
 3. $(5, -82°)$, $(-3, 167°)$
 4. $(-6, 99°)$, $(6, -99°)$

Convert from rectangular to polar coordinates in Probs. 5 to 8.
 5. $(1, -\sqrt{3})$ 6. $(-\sqrt{5}, -\sqrt{5})$ 7. $(-1, 2)$
 8. $(-\sqrt{2}, -3)$

Change from polar to rectangular coordinates in Probs. 9 to 12.
 9. $(3, 60°)$ 10. $(-2, 135°)$ 11. $(\sqrt{3}, 240°)$
 12. $(4, -330°)$

In Probs. 13 to 20, express the equation in terms of polar coordinates.
 13. $x + 3y = 2$
 14. $9x^2 + 16y^2 = 144$
 15. $y^2 = ax^3$
 16. $(x^2 + y^2)^{3/2} - x^2 + y^2 - 2xy = 0$
 17. $x(x^2 + y^2) = a(3x^2 - y^2)$
 18. $(x^2 + y^2)^2 = 2a^2xy$
 19. $x^2 - 4y^2 = 4$
 20. $(x - a)^2 + (y - b)^2 = a^2 + b^2$

In Probs. 21 to 28, write the equation in terms of rectangular coordinates.
 21. $r = 2/(\cos \theta + 3 \sin \theta)$
 22. $9r^2 + 7r^2 \sin^2 \theta = 144$
 23. $ar = \sec \theta \tan^2 \theta$ 24. $r = \cos 2\theta + \sin 2\theta$
 25. $r \cos \theta = a(3 \cos^2 \theta - \sin^2 \theta)$
 26. $r^2 = a^2 \sin 2\theta$
 27. $r^2 = 4/(\cos^2 \theta - 4 \sin^2 \theta)$
 28. $r = 2(a \cos \theta + b \sin \theta)$
 29. Show that the graph of $r = 8 \cos \theta$ is symmetric with respect to the polar axis.
 30. Show that the graph of $r = \sin 3\theta$ is symmetric with respect to the normal axis.
 31. Show that the graph of $r = 3$ is symmetric with respect to the pole, the polar axis, and the normal axis.
 32. Show that the graph of $r = 2 + \sec \theta$ is symmetric with respect to the polar axis.

Sketch the graphs of the equations in Probs. 33 to 44.
 33. $r = 5 \csc \theta$ 34. $r = 3 \sin \theta$
 35. $r = 6 \cos \theta$ 36. $r(2 \cos \theta + 3 \sin \theta) = 6$
 37. $r = \sin 2\theta$ 38. $r = \sin 3\theta$
 39. $r = 3 + 2 \sin \theta$ 40. $r = 2 + 3 \sin \theta$
 41. $r = 4$ 42. $\theta = \pi/6$
 43. $r = 6 \cos \theta + 8 \sin \theta$ 44. $r = \theta$

8.7 Key Concepts

Be certain that you understand and can use the following concepts and formulas.

Law of sines (p. 410)
Ambiguous case (pp. 412, 419)
Law of cosines (p. 418)
Vector (p. 426)
Magnitude (pp. 426, 428)
Direction (pp. 426, 428)
Sum or resultant (p. 427)
Unit vectors **i** and **j** (p. 427)

Trigonometric form (p. 434)
Multiplication and division
  (pp. 436, 438)
De Moivre's theorem (p. 439)
Roots of complex numbers (p. 440)
Polar coordinates (p. 444)
Symmetry (p. 447)

(8.1) $\dfrac{a}{\sin A} = \dfrac{b}{\sin B} = \dfrac{c}{\sin C}$ or $\dfrac{\sin A}{a} = \dfrac{\sin B}{b} = \dfrac{\sin C}{c}$

(8.2) $a^2 = b^2 + c^2 - 2bc \cos A$ or $\cos A = \dfrac{b^2 + c^2 - a^2}{2bc}$

(8.3) $K = \frac{1}{2}ab \sin C = \frac{1}{2}ac \sin B = \frac{1}{2}bc \sin A$

(8.4) $K = \dfrac{c^2 \sin A \sin B}{2 \sin C} = \dfrac{b^2 \sin A \sin C}{2 \sin B} = \dfrac{a^2 \sin B \sin C}{2 \sin A}$

(8.5) $s = \dfrac{a + b + c}{2}$

(8.6) $K = \sqrt{s(s - a)(s - b)(s - c)}$

(8.7) $\dfrac{a - b}{c} = \dfrac{\sin (A - B)/2}{\cos C/2}$ Mollweide's equation

(8.8) $a = b \cos C + c \cos B$

(8.9) $\dfrac{a - b}{a + b} = \dfrac{\tan [(A - B)/2]}{\tan [(A + B)/2]}$ law of tangents

(8.10) $|\mathbf{V}| = \sqrt{a^2 + b^2}$

(8.11) $\tan \theta = \dfrac{b}{a}$

(8.12) $z = x + yi = r(\cos \theta + i \sin \theta)$

(8.13) $x = r \cos \theta, \, y = r \sin \theta$

(8.14) $r^2 = x^2 + y^2, \, \tan \theta = \dfrac{y}{x}$

(8.15) $[r(\cos \theta + i \sin \theta)][R(\cos \phi + i \sin \phi)]$
$= rR[\cos (\theta + \phi) + i \sin (\theta + \phi)]$

(8.16) $\dfrac{r(\cos \theta + i \sin \theta)}{s(\cos \phi + i \sin \phi)} = \dfrac{r}{s} [\cos (\theta - \phi) + i \sin (\theta - \phi)]$

(8.17) $[r(\cos \theta + i \sin \theta)]^n = r^n(\cos n\theta + i \sin n\theta)$

EXERCISE 8.7   Review

Find these complex numbers in trigonometric form.
1. $6(\cos 42° + i \sin 42°) \cdot 5(\cos 35° + i \sin 35°)$
2. $(2 + 2i)(-1 + i\sqrt{3})$
3. $(6 - 6i\sqrt{3})/(-2\sqrt{3} - 2i)$
4. $(\cos 56° + i \sin 56°)^7$ 5. $[(-1 + i\sqrt{3})/2]^6$
6. Find the three cube roots of $27(\cos 111° + i \sin 111°)$.
7. Find all solutions of the equation $z^4 + 8 + 8i\sqrt{3} = 0$.

Find the third side of the triangle to the justified degree of accuracy in Probs. 8 to 12.
8. $a = 31, b = 47, C = 60°$
9. $a = 41, c = 54, B = 120°$
10. $b = 17\sqrt{3}, c = 25, A = 150°$
11. $a = 231, c = 312, B = 47.3°$
12. $b = 501, c = 415, A = 97.7°$
13. If $a = 21, b = 23$, and $c = 29$, find A to the nearest tenth of a degree.

14. If $a = 38, b = 47$, and $c = 69$, find C to the nearest tenth of a degree.
15. If $a = 437, b = 743$, and $c = 396$, find B to the nearest tenth of a degree.
16. Show that $B = 60°$ if $a = 13, b = 43$, and $c = 48$.

Show that the largest angle is $120°$ in Probs. 17 and 18.
17. $a = 40, b = 77, c = 103$
18. $a = 523, b = 208, c = 387$

How many solutions are there in each of Probs. 19 to 22?
19. $a = 13, b = 22, A = 40°$
20. $a = 29, b = 44, A = 43°$
21. $a = 87, b = 83, A = 58°$
22. $a = 38, b = 56, A = 37°$
23. How far apart are A and B if Stan goes 31 mi east and then 23 mi N31°E in going from A to B?

24. Find the ground speed of the plane and the direction of flight if a pilot is heading at 186° with an airspeed of 327 mi/h in a 11.6-mi/h wind from the west.
25. Lynn should have gone 6.71 mi N33°E but went 5.94 mi N37°E. How far was she from her intended destination?
26. Show that the length of a chord in a circle of radius r is $s = r\sqrt{2 - 2\cos\theta}$ where θ is the central angle made by the two radii to the ends of the chord. Show that s may be written as

$$2r \sin (\theta/2)$$

27. Find the ratio r/R for a triangle with $a = 187$, $b = 218$, and $c = 371$. (See Exercise 8.2, instructions for Probs. 61 to 64.)
28. If forces of magnitude 217 g and 308 g act at the same point, find their resultant provided that their directions differ by 24.3°.
29. If two forces and their resultant have magnitudes 183, 216, and 301, respectively, find the angle between the forces.
30. Find the angle of inclination of a plane, if a force of magnitude 27.6 lb is needed to hold a weight of 83.7 lb.
31. Find the rectangular coordinates of $(4\sqrt{2}, 135°)$, and a set of polar coordinates for $(\sqrt{6}, -2)$.
32. Express $r = 5/(2\cos\theta - 3\sin\theta)$ in terms of rectangular coordinates, and also $x^2 = 4y$ in terms of polar coordinates.
33. Sketch the graph of $r = 2 + 3\cos\theta$.
34. The graph of $r = 6\sin\theta$ is a circle. What is its radius?
35. If $z = a + bi = r(\cos\theta + i\sin\theta)$, show that

$$|z| = |-z| = |\bar{z}| = |iz|$$

Prove that the statements in Probs. 36 and 37 are true for any triangle.

36. $a^2 + b^2 + c^2 = 2(bc \cos A + ac \cos B + ab \cos C)$
37. $\dfrac{\cos A}{a} + \dfrac{\cos B}{b} + \dfrac{\cos C}{c} = \dfrac{a^2 + b^2 + c^2}{2abc}$
38. Use the law of cosines to show that there is no triangle with sides a, b, and c if $a + b < c$.
39. Show that if the sides of a triangle are 2, $\sqrt{6}$, and $\sqrt{3} - 1$, then the angles are 45°, 120°, and 15°.

40. Show that if the sides of a triangle are 2, $\sqrt{6}$, and $\sqrt{3} + 1$, then the angles are 45°, 60°, and 75°.

In Probs. 41 through 43, show that the largest angle is 120°.

41. $a = 16$, $b = 39$, $c = 49$
42. $a = 13$, $b = 120$, $c = 127$
43. $a = 384$, $b = 805$, $c = 1051$
44. Show by the law of cosines that a, b, and c are the sides of a triangle in which the angle opposite c is 120° if and only if

$$c^2 = a^2 + b^2 + ab$$

45. Show that if $m > n$ and $a = m^2 - n^2$, $b = 2mn + n^2$, and $c = m^2 + mn + n^2$, then

$$c^2 = a^2 + b^2 + ab$$

46. Use the law of cosines to show that p, q, and r are the sides of a triangle with r opposite a 60° angle if and only if

$$r^2 = p^2 + q^2 - pq$$

47. Suppose that a, b, and c are the sides of a triangle in which the angle opposite c is 120°. Show that the triangle with sides a, $a + b$, and c has a 60° angle opposite side c. (Use Probs. 44 and 46.)

In Probs. 48 to 50, show that the angle opposite r is 60°. *Note:* The triangles below came via Probs. 41, 42, 43, and 47.

48. $p = 16$, $q = 55$, $r = 49$
49. $p = 13$, $q = 133$, $r = 127$
50. $p = 384$, $q = 1189$, $r = 1051$
51. Find a and b if $a\mathbf{i} + b\mathbf{j}$ is a vector with magnitude 4 and direction angle 135°.

In Probs. 52 to 54, let $\mathbf{V} = 3\mathbf{i} + 5\mathbf{j}$ and $\mathbf{W} = 2\mathbf{i} - 3\mathbf{j}$.
52. Find $3\mathbf{V} + 5\mathbf{W}$.   53.   Find $|\mathbf{V} - 2\mathbf{W}|$.
54. Find $|2\mathbf{V}| + |3\mathbf{W}|$.
55. Suppose that the magnitudes and directions of two forces are 56 kg, S34°E and 38 kg, N18°E. Find the magnitude and direction of their resultant.
56. Find the angle between the vectors $6\mathbf{i} + 8\mathbf{j}$ and $7\mathbf{i} + 24\mathbf{j}$.
57. Find the resultant of $7\mathbf{i} - 5\mathbf{j}$ and $2\mathbf{i} + 5\mathbf{j}$.

9 Systems of Equations and Inequalities

Many problems that we encounter in applications involve more than one variable. When the relations between the variables involve several equations or inequalities, then we must solve the equations or inequalities of the resulting system *simultaneously*.

Often the variables are called x, y, and z, and we encounter linear equations such as

$$12x - 7y = 9 \qquad \text{or} \qquad 6x + 5y + 1.5z = -4$$

An equation of the form

$$a_1 x_1 + a_2 x_2 + \cdots + a_n x_n = b$$

is called a **linear equation** in the n variables $x_1, x_2, \ldots, x_n$ if at least one coefficient a_i is nonzero. If all of the equations in the system are linear, the system is called a **linear system.** Otherwise it is a **nonlinear system.** In this chapter, we use elimination and substitution as methods for solving systems of equations and of inequalities. In Chap. 10 we will treat matrix and determinant methods.

9.1 Systems of Linear Equations

We have studied equations and inequalities in earlier chapters of this book and will now work with systems of linear equations in several variables. We will introduce the topic by considering two linear equations in two variables; similar methods will be used later in more complicated situations.

Two Linear Equations in Two Variables

We say that $(2, 3)$ is a solution of the equation $5x + 4y = 22$ if its coordinates satisfy the equation. It is true in this case since $5(2) + 4(3) = 10 + 12 = 22$. The ordered pair

453

of numbers (p, q) is called a **solution,** or a simultaneous solution, of the two linear equations

$$ax + by = e$$
$$cx + dy = f$$

if its coordinates satisfy each equation. In this section, we will discuss three methods of solution:

1. Elimination by addition and subtraction
2. Substitution
3. Graphs

NOTE   The phrase "add two equations" means to add the corresponding sides of the equations. Similarly "to multiply an equation by k" means to multiply both sides of the equation by k.

 **EXAMPLE 1**   Find the solution of the linear system of equations

$$2x - 3y = 3 \tag{1}$$
$$3x + 5y = 14 \tag{2}$$

Solution   This method of solution requires that each equation be multiplied by a nonzero number, which is chosen so that the resulting coefficients of one of the variables are either equal or different only in their signs. We can then eliminate that variable by addition or

The elimination method   subtraction of the equations. To do that with the equations above, we will multiply Eq. (1) by 3 and Eq. (2) by 2, in order to eliminate the variable x by subtraction:

$$6x - 9y = 9 \tag{3}$$
$$\underline{6x + 10y = 28} \tag{4}$$
$$-19y = -19 \qquad \text{subtracting (4) from (3)}$$

Therefore $y = 1$. To find x, substitute $y = 1$ in either of the given equations (1) or (2). Using $y = 1$ in (1) gives

$$2x - 3 = 3 \qquad 2x = 6 \qquad x = 3$$

Consequently, (3, 1) is the solution of the given pair of equations. The solution may be checked by substituting in each original equation. Using $x = 3$ and $y = 1$, we get

CHECK $2(3) - 3(1) = 3$ from (1)

and $3(3) + 5(1) = 14$ from (2)

See Fig. 9.1 for the graphs of the two linear equations and their point of intersection (3, 1). We will look at graphing more closely after Example 2.   ◢

NOTE   In Example 1, we chose to eliminate x by **subtraction.** We could have eliminated x by **addition** if we had multiplied Eq. (1) by 3 and Eq. (2) by -2. Multiplying the equations by 5 and 3 respectively would allow *eliminating y by addition,* while multiplying the equations by -5 and 3 would allow *eliminating y by subtraction.* Try one of these alternative methods, and make sure you get the solution above, namely (3, 1).

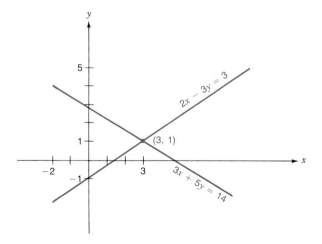

FIGURE 9.1

The substitution method

Our second method for solving a system of equations is called the **substitution method.** To use this method in the present situation of two equations in two variables, solve one of the equations for one of the variables, say y. Substitute this expression for y into the other equation, and solve it for x. Of course, the roles of x and y may be interchanged in the substitution method.

If this procedure gives any corresponding values for x and y, then the ordered pair (x, y) is a **possible solution** of the system, and each ordered pair should be checked in each of the original equations. In this section, the check should be done to guard against arithmetic mistakes and to develop the habit of checking. Checking is especially important in the next section when dealing with nonlinear systems.

NOTE   It is easiest to use the method of substitution when:

One of the coefficients in an equation is 1

EXAMPLE 2   Solve the system of equations

$$x + 2y = 9 \tag{5}$$

$$4x + 3y = 1 \tag{6}$$

Solution   Since in the first equation, the coefficient of x is 1, we will solve it for x:

$$x = 9 - 2y \qquad \text{solving (5) for } x$$

$$4(9 - 2y) + 3y = 1 \qquad \text{substituting for } x \text{ in (6)}$$

$$36 - 8y + 3y = 1 \qquad \text{multiplying}$$

$$35 = 5y \qquad \text{collecting terms}$$

$$7 = y \qquad \text{dividing by 5}$$

$$x = 9 - 2(7) = -5 \qquad \text{using (5) solved for } x$$

The solution may be checked by substituting in each original equation. Using $x = -5$ and $y = 7$ gives

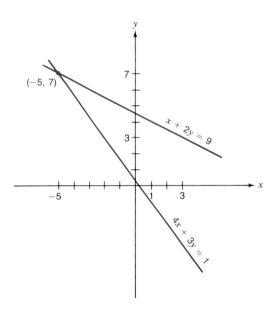

FIGURE 9.2

CHECK

$$-5 + 2(7) = -5 + 14 = 9 \qquad \text{from (5)}$$

and

$$4(-5) + 3(7) = -20 + 21 = 1 \qquad \text{from (6)}$$

Figure 9.2 shows the graphs of the two linear equations and their point of intersection $(-5, 7)$.

Graphs

The **graph** of one linear equation in two variables is a straight line. Consequently, two linear equations in two variables may represent two intersecting lines, two parallel lines, or two coincident lines (in effect, one line).

If the two lines **intersect** in exactly one point, the solution is one ordered pair of numbers and the system of equations is said to be **consistent** or **independent.** This has already been seen in Examples 1 and 2, Figs. 9.1 and 9.2. If the two lines are **parallel and distinct,** there is no point of intersection and therefore no solution, and in this case the system of equations is called **inconsistent.** See Fig. 9.3. If the two lines **coincide** and are thus actually the same line, then every solution of either equation is a solution of the other and the system of equations is called **dependent.**

Recall that two nonvertical lines are parallel if and only if their slopes are equal. Using the slope-intercept form, $y = mx + b$, of the equation of a line enables us to decide whether a system of two linear equations in two variables is consistent, inconsistent, or dependent. Figure 9.3 shows the three systems which are in Example 3.

EXAMPLE 3 Decide whether each system below is consistent, inconsistent, or dependent. See Fig. 9.3.

Solution (a) The system of equations

$$2x - 3y = 4$$

$$5x + 2y = 8$$

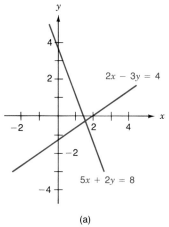

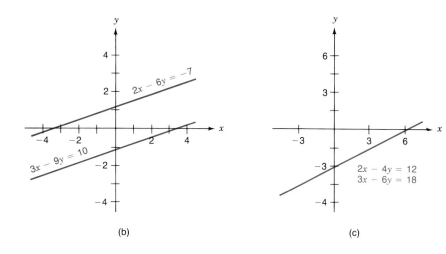

(a)   (b)   (c)

FIGURE 9.3

is consistent since the slope-intercept forms

$$y = \tfrac{2}{3}x - \tfrac{4}{3} \qquad \text{and} \qquad y = -\tfrac{5}{2}x + 4$$

show that the lines are not parallel. See Fig. 9.3(a). There is one solution, and we will find it using elimination. Multiply the first equation by 2 and the second one by 3:

$$
\begin{array}{rl}
4x - 6y = & 8 \\
15x + 6y = & 24 \\
\hline
19x \qquad = & 32 \qquad \text{adding the equations}
\end{array}
$$

Thus $x = \tfrac{32}{19}$. Using this in the first equation $2x - 3y = 4$ gives $2(\tfrac{32}{19}) - 3y = 4$. Thus $3y = \tfrac{64}{19} - 4 = (64 - 76)/19 = -\tfrac{12}{19}$, and so $y = -\tfrac{4}{19}$. The solution is $(\tfrac{32}{19}, -\tfrac{4}{19})$, and it should be checked in each of the given equations.

(b) The system of equations

$$
\begin{aligned}
3x - 9y &= 10 \\
2x - 6y &= -7
\end{aligned}
$$

is inconsistent. The slope-intercept forms are

$$y = \tfrac{1}{3}x - \tfrac{10}{9} \qquad \text{and} \qquad y = \tfrac{1}{3}x + \tfrac{7}{6}$$

Since the slopes are the same, the lines are parallel. Since the y intercepts are different, the lines are distinct, and hence there are no solutions. See Fig. 9.3(b). If we were to use the method of elimination for these two equations, we could multiply the first equation by 2 and the second one by 3:

$$
\begin{array}{rl}
6x - 18y = & 20 \\
6x - 18y = & -21 \\
\hline
0 = & 41 \qquad \text{subtracting}
\end{array}
$$

The equation $0 = 41$ is satisfied by no values of x and y, and thus again we see that there are no solutions.

(c) The system of equations

$$2x - 4y = 12$$

$$3x - 6y = 18$$

is dependent. The slope-intercept forms are

$$y = \tfrac{1}{2}x - 3 \qquad \text{and} \qquad y = \tfrac{1}{2}x - 3$$

and since these are identical, the lines are in fact the same. See Fig. 9.3(c). If we use the method of elimination, we may multiply the first equation by 3 and the second one by 2:

$$
\begin{array}{r}
6x - 12y = 36 \\
\underline{6x - 12y = 36} \\
0 = 0 \qquad \text{subtracting}
\end{array}
$$

The number of solutions is infinite since the equation $0 = 0$ is satisfied by all values of x and y. The graphs of the equations are coincident lines. ◢

Graphical solution   A pair of linear equations in two variables can be solved graphically by sketching the graphs of the lines and then estimating the coordinates of the point of intersection. In general this method is not accurate enough for us to be able to completely depend on it. Even though this gives only approximate solutions and methods for exact solutions have already been given, it is worthwhile studying the graphical method in the present simple situation because the same method can be used with nonlinear systems in the next section to determine whether there are any solutions and, if so, how many. It can also serve as a rough check for an algebraic solution.

▶ **EXAMPLE 4**   Sketch the graphs of

$$4x + 6y = 11$$

$$x - 3y = -1$$

and estimate the coordinates of their point of intersection.

Solution   Two standard methods for graphing are to use the slope-intercept form $y = mx + b$, and to find the intercepts of each line. The two lines in slope-intercept form are

$$y = \frac{-2}{3}x + \frac{11}{6} \qquad \text{and} \qquad y = \frac{1}{3}x + \frac{1}{3}$$

The lines appear to intersect near $(1.5, 1)$, as shown in Fig. 9.4. The exact solution is in fact $(\tfrac{3}{2}, \tfrac{5}{6})$, which may be checked in the original equations. ◢

An application, or word problem, can frequently be expressed with equations most directly by using more than one variable. In such cases we need more than one equation also. The equations can be set up and the answers interpreted most easily if we

Let the variables represent the quantities which are called for in the problem

In order to solve the system of equations:

The number of equations formed must be equal to the number of variables introduced

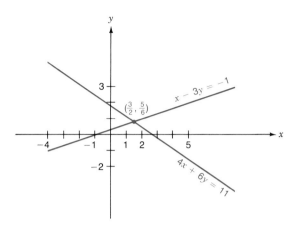

FIGURE 9.4

▶ **EXAMPLE 5**   A real estate broker, Kreutziger, received $4800 in rents on two country cottages in 1988, and one of the dwellings brought $40 per month more than the other. How much did she receive per month for each cottage if the more expensive cottage was vacant for 2 months?

Solution   Since the problem asks for the monthly rentals, we let

$$x = \text{the monthly rental on the more expensive house in dollars}$$

$$y = \text{the monthly rental on the other house in dollars}$$

In the problem, there are two basic relations: the connection between the separate rentals and the total income per year. Since one house rented for $40 more than the other, then

$$x - y = 40 \tag{7}$$

Furthermore, since the first house was rented for 10 months and the other was rented for 12 months, we know that $10x + 12y$ is the total amount received in rentals. Hence,

$$10x + 12y = 4800 \tag{8}$$

We now have the two equations (7) and (8) in the variables x and y, and we will solve them simultaneously by eliminating y:

$$
\begin{array}{lll}
12x - 12y = & 480 & \text{(7) multiplied by 12} \\
\underline{10x + 12y = 4800} & & \text{(8) recopied} \\
22x \quad\quad = & 5280 & \text{adding the equations} \\
x \quad\quad = & 240 & \text{dividing by 22}
\end{array}
$$

By substituting 240 for x in (7), we get $y = x - 40 = 200$. The monthly rentals were $240 and $200, respectively.

CHECK   Total income $= 10(240) + 12(200) = 2400 + 2400 = 4800$.   ◢

▶ **EXAMPLE 6**   Two airfields, A and B, are 720 mi apart, and B is due east of A. A plane flew from A to B in 1.8 h and then returned to A in 2 h. If the wind blew with a constant velocity from the west during the entire trip, find the speed of the plane in still air and the speed of the wind.

Solution   We let

$$x = \text{the speed of the plane in still air, mi/h}$$

$$y = \text{the speed of the wind, mi/h}$$

The essential point in solving such a problem is that the wind helps the plane in one direction and hinders it in the other. We therefore have the basis for two equations that involve the speed of the plane, the speed of the wind, and the time for the trip. Then, since the wind blew constantly from the west,

$$x + y = \text{the speed of the plane eastward from } A \text{ to } B \text{ (wind helping)}$$

$$x - y = \text{the speed of the plane westward from } B \text{ to } A \text{ (wind hindering)}$$

The distance traveled each way was 720 mi, and we set up two equations using distance = (speed)(time) in each case:

$$720 = 1.8(x + y) \qquad \text{for trip from } A \text{ to } B \tag{9}$$

$$720 = 2(x - y) \qquad \text{for trip from } B \text{ to } A \tag{10}$$

Now divide (9) by 1.8 and (10) by 2 to get

$$
\begin{aligned}
400 &= x + y \\
\underline{360} &= x - y \\
760 &= 2x \qquad \text{adding the equations} \\
380 &= x \qquad \text{dividing by 2}
\end{aligned}
$$

On substituting 380 for x in (10), we have

$$720 = 2(380 - y)$$

$$360 = 380 - y \qquad \text{dividing by 2}$$

$$y = 20 \qquad \text{adding } y - 360$$

Hence, the speed of the plane in still air was 380 mi/h, and the speed of the wind was 20 mi/h. We check in the original problem.

$$(1.8)(380 + 20) = 1.8(400) = 720 \qquad \text{from } A \text{ to } B$$

$$(2)(380 - 20) = 2(360) = 720 \qquad \text{from } B \text{ to } A \qquad \blacktriangleleft$$

Three Equations in Three Variables

Systems of three linear equations in three variables will be treated with matrices and determinants in Chap. 10, but here we will solve such a system by **elimination** and by **substitution**. The procedures used are essentially the same as those used in solving a pair of linear equations in two variables. We will illustrate the elimination method first.

▶ **EXAMPLE 7**   Solve the following system of equations by elimination:

$$2x + 3y + 3z = 10 \tag{11}$$

$$3x - 2y - 3z = -1 \tag{12}$$

$$2x + 5y + 2z = 5 \tag{13}$$

Solution   We must eliminate the **same variable** from two different pairs of equations. We will first eliminate z between the pair of equations (11) and (12) by adding these equations.

$$2x + 3y + 3z = 10 \qquad \text{Eq. (11) copied}$$
$$\underline{3x - 2y - 3z = -1} \qquad \text{Eq. (12) copied}$$
$$5x + y = 9 \qquad \text{adding} \tag{14}$$

We now **eliminate z again,** this time between (11) and (13).

$$4x + 6y + 6z = 20 \qquad \text{Eq. (11) times 2}$$
$$\underline{6x + 15y + 6z = 15} \qquad \text{Eq. (13) times 3}$$
$$-2x - 9y = 5 \qquad \text{subtracting} \tag{15}$$

We now have the system (14) and (15) of **two equations in two variables,** and it may be solved by either elimination or by substitution. We will use substitution since it is easy to solve (14) for y. This gives $y = 9 - 5x$, and substituting in (15) gives one equation in one variable.

$$-2x - 9(9 - 5x) = 5 \qquad \text{substituting in (15)}$$
$$-2x - 81 + 45x = 5 \qquad \text{removing parentheses}$$
$$43x = 86 \qquad \text{collecting similar terms}$$
$$x = 2 \qquad \text{dividing by 43}$$

We can use $x = 2$ in (14) and have

$$y = 9 - 5x = 9 - 5(2) = 9 - 10 = -1$$

We find z by substituting $x = 2$ and $y = -1$ in any one of the three original equations. Using (11) gives

$$2(2) + 3(-1) + 3z = 10$$
$$3z = 10 - 4 + 3$$
$$z = \tfrac{9}{3} = 3$$

Therefore the solution is $(2, -1, 3)$, and it satisfies all three of the given equations. ◀

To use **substitution** with three equations in three variables, solve one of the equations for either variable, and then substitute this expression into each of the other two equations. This will give two equations in two variables, and they may be solved by any method.

▶ **EXAMPLE 8**   Solve the following system of equations by substitution:

$$3x - 4y - 2z = -4 \tag{16}$$
$$-5x + 2y - 4z = -14 \tag{17}$$
$$x + 3y + 3z = -1 \tag{18}$$

Solution　　We will solve Eq. (18) for x since its coefficient is 1. This gives $x = -1 - 3y - 3z$. Substituting this in Eqs. (16) and (17) shows that

$$3(-1 - 3y - 3z) - 4y - 2z = -4$$

$$-5(-1 - 3y - 3z) + 2y - 4z = -14$$

Combining terms in each equation gives this system of **two equations in two variables:**

$$-13y - 11z = -1$$

$$17y + 11z = -19$$

If we add these two equations, we get

$$4y = -20 \qquad \text{and so} \qquad y = -5$$

Using this in the last equation, we have

$$17(-5) + 11z = -19$$

and hence　　　　　　　　　　　　　$$11z = 85 - 19 = 66$$

$$z = 6$$

Thus $x = -1 - 3y - 3z = -1 - 3(-5) - 3(6) = -1 + 15 - 18 = -4$. The solution $(-4, -5, 6)$ checks in each original equation.　　◢

It can be shown that, just as with two equations in two variables, a system of three equations in three variables may have one solution, no solutions, or an infinity of solutions. Examples of the last two cases will be given in Sec. 10.2.

A system of n linear equations, where $n > 3$, in n variables can be solved similarly by either elimination or by substitution. The elimination method is more efficient in general, and it will be studied further in Chap. 10 when we study matrix methods.

EXERCISE 9.1

Solve the systems of equations in Probs. 1 to 12 by either elimination or substitution.

1. $3x + 2y = 7$
$2x + 5y = 12$

2. $3x + y = 7$
$2x + 3y = 7$

3. $x + 2y = 5$
$3x + 2y = 11$

4. $3x + 2y = 12$
$2x + 3y = 13$

5. $2x + y = 3$
$3x + 5y = 1$

6. $2x + 3y = 0$
$x + 2y = 1$

7. $2x + y = -1$
$3x + 2y = 0$

8. $x - y = 3$
$3x + 2y = 4$

Hint: In Probs. 9 to 12, let $x = 1/r$ and $y = 1/t$.

9. $1/r - 4/t = 3$
$2/r - 5/t = 3$

10. $3/r - 1/t = -3$
$2/r - 7/t = 17$

11. $2/r - 5/t = 0$
$3/r + 1/t = -17$

12. $4/r - 3/t = 1$
$5/r - 2/t = -4$

Solve the systems of equations in Probs. 13 to 24 by either elimination or substitution.

13. $3x - 2y - z = 3$
$2x - y + z = 4$
$x - 2y + 3z = 3$

14. $3x + 2y + 2z = -1$
$5x - 3y + 4z = -3$
$2x + y + 2z = -2$

15. $x + 3y + 3z = -1$
$2x - y + z = -3$
$3x + 5y + 7z = -1$

16. $5x + 4y + 7z = 2$
$3x - 2y + z = 0$
$x + 5y + 8z = -2$

17. $2x - y - z = 0$
$6x - 7y + 2z = 11$
$-17y + 8z = 7$

18. $3x + 2y - 5z = 1$
$-13y - 24z = 11$
$x + 5y + 8z = -5$

19. $3x + 4y \quad\quad = 1$
$\quad\, 2x + 3y - z = 1$
$\quad\, 3x + 4y - 3z = 4$

20. $x \quad\quad - z = 3$
$\quad\, 3x + 2y - 3z = 3$
$\quad\, 2x + 3y + 2z = 1$

21. $x + y + 2z + w = 3$
$\quad\, 2x + 3y \quad\quad - 2w = -6$
$\quad\, 3x - 2y + z \quad\quad = -2$
$\quad\quad\quad 3y - z + 3w = 5$

22. $x + y + z + w = 1$
$\quad\, 2x \quad\quad + 3z + 2w = 5$
$\quad\, 3x - y \quad\quad + w = -2$
$\quad\quad\quad 2y + 5z + 3w = 12$

23. $x + y + z + w = 6$
$\quad\, 2x \quad\quad + 3z - 2w = 8$
$\quad\quad\quad 3y - z + 3w = 7$
$\quad\, x - y + 2z + w = 6$

24. $x + y + z + w = 6$
$\quad\, x - y - z \quad\quad = 1$
$\quad\, 2x + y - z - w = 7$
$\quad\, 2x - 2y \quad\quad + 3w = 5$

Determine whether the system in each of Probs. 25 to 32 is consistent, inconsistent, or dependent, and solve each consistent system.

25. $3x - 2y = 4$
$\quad\, 2x - 3y = 1$

26. $x - 2y = 3$
$\quad\, 3x - 6y = 8$

27. $2x + y = 4$
$\quad\, 4x + 2y = 8$

28. $3x - 2y = 9$
$\quad\, 6x - 4y = 16$

29. $2x + 6y = 4$
$\quad\, 3x + 9y = 6$

30. $3x + y = 1$
$\quad\, 2x + 4y = -6$

31. $x - 2y = -1$
$\quad\, 3x - 6y = -3$

32. $x - 2y = -1$
$\quad\, 3x + 4y = 17$

Solve each system graphically to the nearest half-unit.

33. $5x + 3y = 11$
$\quad\, 3x + y = 5$

34. $5x + 2y = 10$
$\quad\, 2x + y = 4$

35. $3x + 2y = 2$
$\quad\, x + 4y = 4$

36. $x + y = 1$
$\quad\, 4x + 3y = 2$

37. At a basketball game, a high school club earned a net profit of $45.80 selling team rosters and suckers, which cost them $0.08 apiece. If they sold 480 team rosters and 610 suckers, what was the selling price of each one if the combined price of a team roster and a sucker was $0.25?

38. Karen spent $5.98 for $2\frac{1}{2}$ qt of cream to make ice cream. If whipping cream cost $0.66 per half-pint and the half-and-half cost $0.70 per pint, how much of each type was used? *Note:* There are 2 pt in 1 qt.

39. Tickets for a banquet at St. Martins were $8 for a single ticket or $15 for a couple. If 144 people attended the banquet and $1098 was collected from ticket sales, how many couples and how many singles attended?

40. A ranger inspecting a forest trail walked at a rate of 3.5 mi/h. A second ranger inspecting another portion of the trail walked at a rate of 3 mi/h. If the trail was 42 mi long and the whole inspection required 13 h, how far did each ranger walk?

41. Janice has 6 gal of paint to cover 2380 ft^2 of fencing. One gal will cover 470 ft^2 with one coat and 250 ft^2 with two coats. If she used all the paint, how many square feet received one coat and how many received two coats?

42. Two different routes between two cities differ by 20 mi. Two people made the trip between the cities in exactly the same time. One traveled the shorter route at 50 mi/h, and the other traveled the longer route at 55 mi/h. Find the length of each route.

43. A biology class of 35 students took a field trip that included a hike of 8 mi. Part of the class also investigated a side trail, which added 3 mi to their hike. If the students in the class walked a total of 331 mi, how many students took each hike?

44. One year Juan worked at a part-time job for some of the 9 months he was in school. In the months he worked, he was able to save $65 per month, but in the months he was idle he had to dip into his savings at the rate of $150 per month. If at the end of the school year (9 months), he had $60 less in his savings account than he had at the beginning, how many months did he work and how many months was he idle?

45. Ivan, Isabella, and Ian assembled 741 newsletters for bulk mailing. Ivan could assemble 124/h, Isabella 118/h, and Ian 132/h. One morning the three volunteers worked a total of 6 h. If Ivan worked 2 h, how long did Isabella and Ian work?

46. A class of 32 students was made up of people who were all 18, 19, and 20 years old. The average of their ages was 18.5. How many of each age were in the class if the number of 18-year-olds was 6 more than the combined number of 19- and 20-year-olds?

47. The perimeter of a triangle is 54 cm. Find the lengths of the three sides if the longest one is twice as long as the shortest one and the other one is 6 cm more than the shortest one.

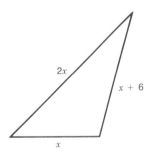

48. Three cities form a triangle. The distance from Arlington to Burlington is 6 km more than the distance from Burlington to Lexington. The distance from Arlington to Lexington is 6 km less than the distance from Burlington to Lexington. Find the distance from Arlington to Lexington if the distance from Arlington to Burlington plus the distance from Burlington to Lexington is 50 km.

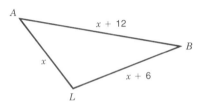

In Probs. 49 and 50, use this form for the equation of a circle.

$$x^2 + y^2 + Dx + Ey + F = 0$$

49. Find an equation of the circle which passes through the points $(5, 1)$, $(-1, 1)$, and $(7, -3)$.

50. Find an equation of the circle which passes through the points $(9, 7)$, $(4, 8)$, and $(-9, -5)$.

In Probs. 51 and 52, assume that the height of a particle after t seconds is

$$s(t) = at^2 + bt + c$$

51. Find $s(3)$ if $s(0) = 20$, $s(1) = 84$, and $s(2) = 116$.
52. Find $s(6)$ if $s(1) = 112$, $s(4) = 256$, and $s(8) = 0$.

9.2 Nonlinear Systems

If a system of equations includes at least one nonlinear equation, we call it a **nonlinear system.** Although a linear system of equations always has either zero, one, or an infinite number of solutions, a nonlinear system is not so simple. It may have, for instance, zero, one, two, three, or four solutions. Try to draw for yourself a parabola and a circle which illustrate each of these five cases. *Hint:* See Prob. 65 in Exercise 9.2.

There may be complex solutions to some of the equations, but they are not on the graphs, and we will not use them.

We may often solve a nonlinear system using elimination, substitution, or graphing. Sometimes a combination of substitution and elimination by addition or subtraction is useful. **Check all solutions** in each of the given equations.

In this section each equation in each system is a special case of the general second-degree equation

$$Ax^2 + Bxy + Cy^2 + Dx + Ey = F$$

We will see how to solve certain types of such systems.

An accurate graph helps to determine how many solutions there are, if any, and approximately what they are. It will help to recall the following standard forms for graphs:

$$Ax^2 + Cy^2 = F \qquad \text{Ellipse if } A > 0,\ C > 0,\ \text{and } F > 0$$
$$Ax^2 - Cy^2 = F \qquad \text{Hyperbola if } A > 0,\ C > 0,\ \text{and } F \neq 0$$
$$xy = F \qquad \text{Hyperbola if } F \neq 0$$
$$y = ax^2 + bx + c \qquad \text{Parabola if } a \neq 0$$
$$x = ay^2 + by + c \qquad \text{Parabola if } a \neq 0$$
$$ax + by + c = 0 \qquad \text{Line unless } a = b = 0$$

Translation to the left, right, up, or down may add or subtract linear terms to or from the standard forms above.

Elimination by Addition and Subtraction

Two equations of the type $Ax^2 + Cy^2 = F$

In Sec. 9.1, we used elimination to solve a pair of linear equations. The same procedure is applicable to two equations of the form $Ax^2 + Cy^2 = F$, where A and C may each be positive or negative.

 EXAMPLE 1 Find the solution of the system of equations

Ellipse
$$2x^2 + 3y^2 = 21 \tag{1}$$

Hyperbola
$$3x^2 - 4y^2 = 23 \tag{2}$$

Solution We arbitrarily select y as the variable to be eliminated, and proceed as follows:

$$8x^2 + 12y^2 = 84 \qquad \text{multiplying (1) by 4} \tag{3}$$

$$9x^2 - 12y^2 = 69 \qquad \text{multiplying (2) by 3} \tag{4}$$

Now we add Eqs. (3) and (4):

$$17x^2 = 153 \qquad \text{adding (3) and (4)}$$

$$x^2 = 9 \qquad \text{dividing by 17}$$

$$x = \pm 3 \qquad \text{solving for } x$$

Now replace x by 3 or -3 in (1) to solve for y:

$$18 + 3y^2 = 21$$

$$3y^2 = 3 \qquad \text{adding } -18 \text{ to each side}$$

$$y^2 = 1 \qquad \text{and hence} \qquad y = \pm 1$$

Thus the solutions are $(3, 1)$, $(3, -1)$, $(-3, 1)$, and $(-3, -1)$.

CHECK   If we replace x and y in the two given equations by 3 and 1, respectively, we get

$$18 + 3 = 21 \qquad \text{from (1)}$$

$$27 - 4 = 23 \qquad \text{from (2)}$$

The other solutions can be checked in a similar manner. Figure 9.5 shows the graphs of the two equations and the coordinates of their points of intersection. The graph of

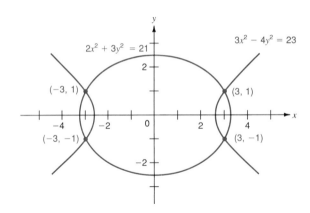

FIGURE 9.5

$2x^2 + 3y^2 = 21$ is an ellipse, and the graph of $3x^2 - 4y^2 = 23$ is a hyperbola, with the center of each one being the origin.   ◄

Two equations of the form $Ax^2 + Cy^2 + Dx = F$

We may solve two equations of the type $Ax^2 + Cy^2 + Dx = F$ by using the method of elimination to eliminate the y^2 term. This will give a quadratic equation in x, whose real solutions can be found easily. The values of y can then be found from either original equation.

► **EXAMPLE 2**   Solve the system of equations

Ellipse

$$x^2 + 2y^2 - 8x = 2 \qquad \textbf{(5)}$$

Hyperbola

$$2x^2 - 5y^2 + 4x = 3 \qquad \textbf{(6)}$$

Solution   We will eliminate the y^2 terms.

$$5x^2 + 10y^2 - 40x = 10 \qquad \text{multiplying (5) by 5}$$

$$4x^2 - 10y^2 + 8x = 6 \qquad \text{multiplying (6) by 2}$$

Adding these equations gives

$$9x^2 - 32x = 16$$

$$9x^2 - 32x - 16 = 0 \qquad \text{subtracting 16 from each side}$$

$$(x - 4)(9x + 4) = 0 \qquad \text{factoring}$$

$$x = 4 \qquad \text{and} \qquad x = -\tfrac{4}{9} \qquad \text{solutions for } x$$

If we now replace x in Eq. (5) by 4, we get

$$16 + 2y^2 - 32 = 2 \qquad 2y^2 = 18 \qquad y^2 = 9 \qquad y = \pm 3$$

However replacing x by $-\tfrac{4}{9}$ in Eq. (5) gives

$$\tfrac{16}{81} + 2y^2 - 8(-\tfrac{4}{9}) = 2 \qquad \text{which gives} \qquad y^2 = -\tfrac{71}{81}$$

which has no real solutions for y. Thus the solutions are

$$(4, 3) \qquad \text{and} \qquad (4, -3)$$

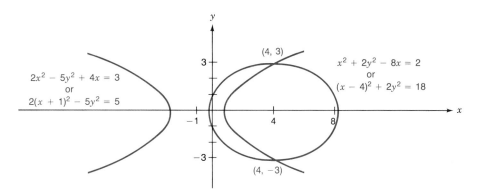

FIGURE 9.6

and each one satisfies both original equations. The graphs of Eqs. (5) and (6), together with the coordinates of their points of intersection, are shown in Fig. 9.6. Note that by completing the square, Eq. (5) may be rewritten as $(x - 4)^2 + 2y^2 = 18$, and Eq. (6) may be rewritten as $2(x + 1)^2 - 5y^2 = 5$. These forms help to find the centers and intercepts.

Eliminating one of the variables   In Example 2, we solved two equations of the type $Ax^2 + Cy^2 + Dx = F$ by eliminating the y^2 term and solving a quadratic equation in x. To solve two equations of the type $Ax^2 + Cy^2 + Ey = F$, we proceed in a manner similar to that of Example 2; namely, we eliminate the x^2 term to get a quadratic equation in y. If we have two equations of the form $Ax^2 + Bxy + Dx = F$, we may obtain a quadratic equation in x by eliminating the xy term. For two equations of the type $Bxy + Cy^2 + Ey = F$, eliminating the xy term gives a quadratic equation in y. In all four cases we use addition or subtraction to eliminate either x and y, then

> *Solve the resulting equation in one variable*

and   *Use each real solution in either original equation*

Elimination by Substitution

In a system of two equations in two variables, if one equation can be solved for one variable, say y, in terms of the other variable, say x, then y can be eliminated by substituting in the other equation. This gives one equation, in the variable x, which we try to solve. With each solution for x, we then find the corresponding values of y from the substitution.

EXAMPLE 3   Solve the system of equations

Ellipse

$$x^2 + 2y^2 = 54 \tag{7}$$

Line

$$2x - y = -9 \tag{8}$$

by the method of substitution.

Solution   The graph of $x^2 + 2y^2 = 54$ is an ellipse with center at the origin and intercepts $(\pm 3\sqrt{6}, 0)$ and $(0, \pm 3\sqrt{3})$, while the graph of $2x - y = -9$ is a straight line with

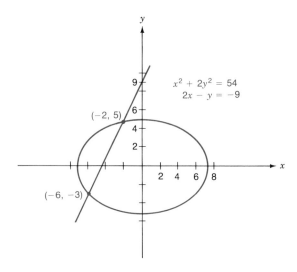

FIGURE 9.7

slope 2 and y intercept 9. From Fig. 9.7, there seem to be two solutions. It is easy to solve Eq. (8) for y and get

$$y = 2x + 9 \tag{9}$$

Substituting this in Eq. (7) gives

$$x^2 + 2(2x + 9)^2 = 54$$

$$x^2 + 2(4x^2 + 36x + 81) = 54 \qquad \text{squaring } 2x + 9$$

$$x^2 + 8x^2 + 72x + 162 = 54 \qquad \text{multiplying by 2}$$

$$9x^2 + 72x + 108 = 0 \qquad \text{combining similar terms}$$

$$x^2 + 8x + 12 = 0 \qquad \text{dividing by 9}$$

$$(x + 6)(x + 2) = 0 \qquad \text{factoring}$$

$$x = -6 \qquad \text{or} \qquad x = -2$$

We now use $y = 2x + 9$ with $x = -6$ and then $x = -2$:

$$y = 2(-6) + 9 = -12 + 9 = -3 \qquad \text{for } x = -6$$

$$y = 2(-2) + 9 = -4 + 9 = 5 \qquad \text{for } x = -2$$

Therefore, the solutions of the system are $(-6, -3)$ and $(-2, 5)$. These solutions should be checked in the original equations.   ◢

▶ **EXAMPLE 4**   Solve this system of equations by substitution:

Hyperbola
$$xy = 6 \tag{10}$$

Line
$$5x - 6y = 3 \tag{11}$$

Solution   Either equation may be solved easily for either variable, and we arbitrarily choose to solve Eq. (10) for y. Also, by Eq. (10), neither x nor y is 0.

$$y = \frac{6}{x} \tag{12}$$

$$5x - 6\left(\frac{6}{x}\right) = 3 \qquad \text{substituting in (11)}$$

$$5x^2 - 36 = 3x \qquad \text{multiplying both sides by } x$$

$$5x^2 - 3x - 36 = 0 \qquad \text{subtracting } 3x$$

$$(x - 3)(5x + 12) = 0 \qquad \text{factoring}$$

$$x = 3 \qquad x = -\tfrac{12}{5} \qquad \text{solutions for } x$$

Now using $x = 3$ in Eq. (12) gives

$$y = \frac{6}{3} = 2$$

while using $x = -\tfrac{12}{5}$ in Eq. (12) shows that

$$y = \frac{6}{x} = \frac{6}{-\tfrac{12}{5}} = 6\left(\frac{-5}{12}\right) = \frac{-5}{2}$$

The solutions to the original equations are

$$(3, 2) \qquad \text{and} \qquad (-\tfrac{12}{5}, -\tfrac{5}{2})$$

and these satisfy each equation. See Fig. 9.8. The graph of (10) is a hyperbola with the x axis and y axis as asymptotes. The graph of (11) is a straight line with x intercept $\tfrac{3}{5}$ and y intercept $-\tfrac{1}{2}$.

Equations of the type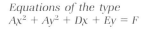
$Ax^2 + Ay^2 + Dx + Ey = F$

If each of the given equations is of the type $Ax^2 + Ay^2 + Dx + Ey = F$, we can **eliminate both of the second-degree terms** by addition or subtraction and obtain a linear equation in x and y. We can then solve this equation with one of the given

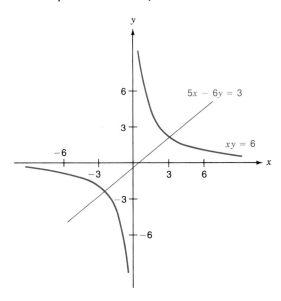

FIGURE 9.8

equations by substitution, as illustrated in Example 5 below. The graphs are circles since the coefficients of x^2 and y^2 are the same.

EXAMPLE 5   Solve the system of equations

Circle
$$3x^2 + 3y^2 + x - 2y = 20 \tag{13}$$

Circle
$$2x^2 + 2y^2 + 5x + 3y = 9 \tag{14}$$

Solution

$$
\begin{aligned}
6x^2 + 6y^2 + 2x - 4y &= 40 && \text{multiplying (13) by 2} \\
\underline{6x^2 + 6y^2 + 15x + 9y = 27} && \text{multiplying (14) by 3} \\
-13x - 13y &= 13 && \text{subtracting} \\
y &= -x - 1 && \text{solving for } y \tag{15}
\end{aligned}
$$

Substituting this in Eq. (14) gives

$$2x^2 + 2(-x - 1)^2 + 5x + 3(-x - 1) = 9$$

$$2x^2 + 2x^2 + 4x + 2 + 5x - 3x - 3 = 9 \qquad \text{multiplying}$$

$$4x^2 + 6x - 10 = 0 \qquad \text{combining similar terms}$$

$$2x^2 + 3x - 5 = 0 \qquad \text{dividing by 2}$$

$$(2x + 5)(x - 1) = 0 \qquad \text{factoring}$$

From the last equation, we have either $x = -\frac{5}{2}$ or $x = 1$. We find the corresponding y values from (15), $y = -x - 1$:

$$y = -1 - 1 = -2 \qquad \text{replacing } x \text{ by } 1$$

$$y = -(-\tfrac{5}{2}) - 1 = \tfrac{3}{2} \qquad \text{replacing } x \text{ by } -\tfrac{5}{2}$$

Consequently the solutions are $(1, -2)$ and $(-\frac{5}{2}, \frac{3}{2})$, which can and should be checked in the original equations. The graphs of the two circles are shown in Fig. 9.9. If we had used $x = 1$ in Eq. (13) instead of (15), we would have gotten

$$3 + 3y^2 + 1 - 2y = 20 \qquad \text{or} \qquad 3y^2 - 2y - 16 = 0$$

Thus $0 = (3y - 8)(y + 2)$, and so $y = \frac{8}{3}$ or $y = -2$. This emphasizes that we must

Check each solution in both given equations

since $(1, \frac{8}{3})$ satisfies Eq. (13), but not Eq. (14).   ◀

    Sometimes a graph will show that there is **no solution.** Using the standard forms of the graphs will make this easier.

EXAMPLE 6   Show by graphing that there is no solution to the system

$$x^2 + y^2 = 4 \qquad \text{and} \qquad x^2 + y = 6$$

Solution   The graph of the first equation is a circle of radius 2 with its center at the origin. The second equation, $y = 6 - x^2$, is a parabola which opens down, its maximum point being at $(0, 6)$. We see in Fig. 9.10 that they do not intersect. A solution by substitution would lead to complex values for x.   ◀

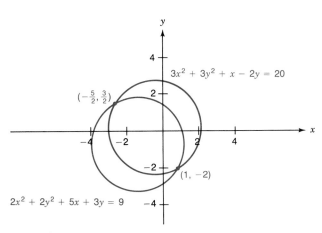

$(-\frac{5}{2}, \frac{3}{2})$

$3x^2 + 3y^2 + x - 2y = 20$

$(1, -2)$

$2x^2 + 2y^2 + 5x + 3y = 9$

FIGURE 9.9

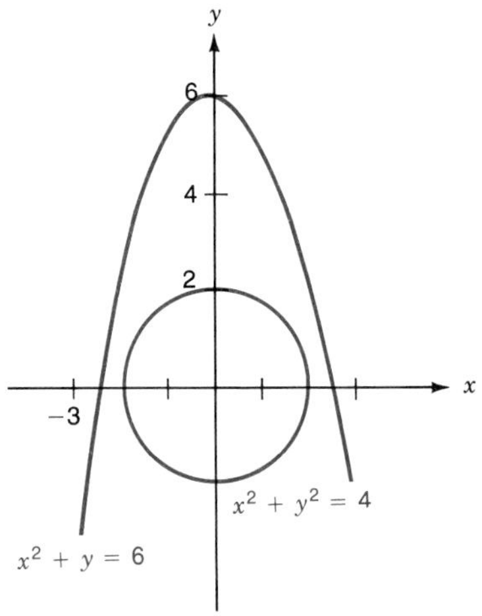

$x^2 + y^2 = 4$

$x^2 + y = 6$

FIGURE 9.10

▶ **EXAMPLE 7** The yearly income from a certain investment is \$480. If the principal were increased by \$2000 and the interest rate decreased by $\frac{1}{2}$ percent, the annual income would increase by \$70. Find the principal and the interest rate.

Solution If the principal is P and the interest rate is r, then

$$Pr = 480 \qquad \text{given}$$

$$(P + 2000)(r - 0.005) = 550 \qquad \text{given}$$

We could solve the first equation for either variable and substitute, but this would lead to fractions. Instead, multiplying the factors in the second equation gives

$$Pr + 2000r - 0.005P - 10 = 550$$

Replacing Pr by 480 from the first equation gives

$$480 + 2000r - 0.005P - 10 = 550$$

$$2000r - 0.005P = 80 \qquad \text{combining terms}$$

$$400{,}000r - P = 16{,}000 \qquad \text{multiplying by 200}$$

$$P = 400{,}000r - 16{,}000 \qquad \text{solving for } P$$

Substituting this in $Pr = 480$ shows that

$$(400{,}000r - 16{,}000)r = 480$$

$$400{,}000r^2 - 16{,}000r - 480 = 0 \qquad \text{equivalent equation}$$

$$10{,}000r^2 - 400r - 12 = 0 \qquad \text{dividing by 40}$$

$$2500r^2 - 100r - 3 = 0 \qquad \text{dividing by 4}$$

Using the quadratic formula gives

$$r = \frac{-(-100) \pm \sqrt{(-100)^2 - 4(2500)(-3)}}{2(2500)}$$

$$= \frac{100 \pm \sqrt{10{,}000 + 30{,}000}}{5000} = \frac{100 \pm 200}{5000}$$

The positive value is $r = 300/5000 = 0.06$, and the principal is $P = 480/0.06 = 8000$. ◀

EXERCISE 9.2

Solve Probs. 1 to 12 by the method of elimination.

1. $x^2 + y^2 = 1$
$2x^2 + 3y^2 = 2$

2. $x^2 + y^2 = 2$
$3x^2 + 4y^2 = 7$

3. $x^2 + 4y^2 = 5$
$9x^2 - y^2 = 8$

4. $9x^2 + 4y^2 = 72$
$x^2 - 9y^2 = -77$

5. $x^2 + y^2 + 2x = 9$
$x^2 + 4y^2 + 3x = 14$

6. $x^2 + y^2 - 4x = -2$
$9x^2 + y^2 + 18x = 136$

7. $9x^2 + 4y^2 - 17y = 21$
$4x^2 - y^2 - 2y = 1$

8. $16x^2 - 9y^2 - 10y = 0$
$9x^2 + 4y^2 + 12y = 1$

Hint: In Probs. 9 to 12, use elimination on the xy terms.

9. $x^2 + xy + 4x = -4$
$3x^2 - 2xy + x = 4$

10. $x^2 - xy + 5x = 4$
$2x^2 - 3xy + 10x = -2$

11. $2x^2 + 3xy + x = -2$
$3x^2 - 2xy + 4x = 1$

12. $x^2 + 4xy - 7x = 10$
$x^2 + 3xy - 6x = 7$

Use substitution to find the real solutions of the following systems of equations.

13. $x - 2y = -5$
$x^2 - 2y^2 = -23$

14. $9x^2 + 5y^2 = 1$
$3x - 2y = 1$

15. $y^2 - 2x = -2$
$x + 2y = 7$

16. $x^2 - 6y = 13$
$x - 2y = 5$

17. $x^2 - 6xy = -20$
$x - 2y^2 - 3y = -4$

18. $x^2 - 2xy + y^2 = 9$
$x^2 + x - y = 4$

19. $x^2 - 12xy + 2y^2 = -72$
$x = 2y^2 + 6y$

20. $2x^2 - 12xy + y^2 = -36$
$x = y^2 + 3y$

21. $2x^2 + y^2 = 9$
$xy = 2$

22. $2x^2 + 3y^2 = 29$
$xy = 3$

23. $x^2 + 2xy + 2y^2 = 17$
$xy = -5$

24. $x^2 - 6xy + 4y^2 = 1$
$2xy = 3$

In Probs. 25 to 32, show that there is no real solution. This may be done either algebraically or graphically.

25. $x^2/4 + y^2 = 1$
$3x + 5y = 15$

26. $x^2/4 + y^2/9 = 1$
$2y = x - 12$

27. $x^2 - 4y^2 = 1$
$y = 3x$

28. $4y^2 - 25x^2 = 100$
$y = x + 1$

29. $(x - 3)^2 + (y - 1)^2 = 4$
$(x + 1)^2 + (y + 1)^2 = 4$

30. $x^2 + y^2 + x + y - 0.5 = 0$
$x^2 + y^2 - 2x - 2y + 1 = 0$

31. $x^2/16 - y^2/4 = 1$
$x^2/9 + y^2/24 = 1$

32. $y^2/4 - x^2/24 = 1$
$x^2/81 + y^2 = 1$

Find the real solutions of the systems of equations in Probs. 33 to 48.

33. $6x^2 + 6y^2 - 5x + 3y = -1$
$9x^2 + 9y^2 - 7x + 4y = -1$

34. $x^2 + y^2 - x + 3y = 0$
$2x^2 + 2y^2 + 3x + 5y = -3$

35. $3x^2 + 3y^2 - 13x - y = -2$
$5x^2 + 5y^2 - 16x + 4y = 25$

36. $x^2 + y^2 + 2x + 2y = 6$
$2x^2 + 2y^2 + 3x + 3y = 10$

37. $x^2 + y^2 = 29$
$x^2 + y = 27$

38. $x^2 - y^2 = 7$
$x^2 - y = 13$

39. $xy = -8$
$3x - 2y = 14$

40. $xy = -9$
$2x + 3y = 3$

Hint: In Probs. 41 to 44, use elimination on the constant term first. Next solve the resulting equation for y in terms of x, then substitute.

41. $3x^2 + 3xy - 2y^2 = 1$
$5x^2 + xy - 2y^2 = -1$

42. $2x^2 - 5xy + 3y^2 = 5$
$x^2 + 2xy - 2y^2 = -2$

43. $3x^2 + 2xy - 3y^2 = 3$
$4x^2 - 2xy - y^2 = -4$

44. $x^2 - 3xy + y^2 = -4$
$2x^2 - 4xy + y^2 = 4$

Hint: In Probs. 45 to 48 eliminate the xy term, and then substitute from the resulting linear equation.

45. $xy + x + y = 11$
$2xy - 3x - 3y = -3$

46. $xy - x - y = 0$
$3xy - 2x - 2y = 4$

47. $2xy + 2x - y = 7$
$3xy - 2x + 3y = 5$

48. $4xy + 3x - 2y = 1$
$5xy + 4x - 3y = 2$

In Probs. 49 to 52, use the fact that there is exactly one solution to $ax^2 + bx + c = 0$ if and only if $b^2 - 4ac = 0$.

49. The point (2, 4) is on the parabola $y = x^2$. For every m, the line $y - 4 = m(x - 2)$ passes through the point (2, 4). Find the value of m for which the line and the parabola intersect in exactly one point.

50. The point (1, −1) is on the parabola $y = 2x^2 - 3$. For every m, the line $y + 1 = m(x - 1)$ passes through the point (1, −1). Find the value of m for which the line and the parabola intersect in exactly one point.

51. Find the values of b for which the line $y = 2x + b$ and the circle $x^2 + y^2 = 5$ intersect in exactly one point.

52. Find the values of b for which the line $y = x + b$ and the ellipse $2x^2 + 3y^2 = 6$ intersect in exactly one point.

53. Find two numbers whose sum is 15 and whose product is 56.

54. Find two numbers such that the sum of their squares is 113 and the difference of their squares is 15.

55. Does the line $x + y = 5$ intersect the hyperbola $xy = 5$?

56. Does the line $x + y = 4$ intersect the ellipse $4x^2 + 9y^2 = 36$?

57. Loewe sold a square carpet, and also a rectangular carpet whose length was $\frac{5}{4}$ the width. The combined area of the two carpets was 405 ft². The price of the first carpet was $10 per square yard, and of the second $12 per square yard. If $10 more was received for the square piece than for the other, find the dimensions of each.

58. The cost of the paint for a rectangular box with a square base and an open top was $0.24 per square yard for the base and $0.16 per square yard for the sides. The total paint cost was $27.84. Find the dimensions of the box if the combined area of the base and sides was 156 yd².

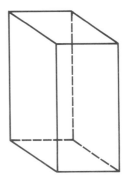

59. A rectangle of area 48 ft² is inscribed in a circle of area $78\frac{4}{7}$ ft². Find the dimensions of the rectangle. (Use $\frac{22}{7}$ for π.)

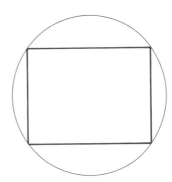

60. A rectangular pasture with an area of 6400 rods² (1 rod = 16.5 ft) is divided into three smaller pastures by two fences parallel to the shorter sides. The widths of two of the smaller pastures are the same and the width of the third is twice that of the others. Find the dimensions of the original pasture if the perimeter of the larger of the subdivisions is 240 rods.

61. A civic club adopted a project that would cost $960. Before the project was completed, 16 new members joined the club and agreed to pay their share of the cost of the project. The cost per member was thereby reduced by $2. Find the original number of members and the original cost per member.

62. Lynda worked for 90 days during the summer. She worked 570 h in the first 60 days and earned $1920 in the daytime and $450 at night. During the last 30 days, she worked 8 h each day and 3 h each night and earned $1410. Find the hourly wage in the daytime and at night.

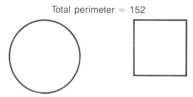

Total perimeter = 152

63. A piece of wire 152 in long is cut into two parts. One piece is bent into a circle and the other into a square. If the combined areas are 872 in^2, find the side of the square and the radius of the circle.

64. A swimming pool is in the shape of a rectangle with a semicircle on each end. The area of the pool is $\frac{1248}{7}$ yd^2 and the perimeter is $\frac{400}{7}$ yd. Find the width and overall length of the pool.

65. Draw the graphs of the parabola and the circle

$$y = 4(x - 2)^2 - 2 \qquad \text{and} \qquad x^2 + y^2 = 1$$

and see that they do not intersect. Show graphically that by gradually translating the circle more and more to the right, until its center moves from $(0, 0)$ to $(2, 0)$, the number of points of intersection may be 0, 1, 2, 3, or 4.

9.3 Partial Fractions

In earlier chapters, we worked with fractions and saw how to add and subtract them. For instance

$$\frac{3}{x + 1} + \frac{2x + 7}{x^2 - 3x + 5} = \frac{5x^2 + 22}{(x + 1)(x^2 - 3x + 5)}$$

The terms on the left side above are called the **partial-fraction decomposition** of the fraction on the right side. In this section, we will look at the reverse problem, namely, how to write a rational function as the sum of several fractions. This allows a complicated expression to be written in a simpler form.

Partial-fraction decomposition

In order to decompose a fraction into partial fractions, we must have

The degree of the numerator < the degree of the denominator

If this is not the case, then begin with long division.

Second, factor the denominator into a product where each factor of the denominator is

$$(dx + e)^m \quad \text{or} \quad (ax^2 + bx + c)^n$$

with m and n positive integers. It was shown in Chap. 4 that this can always be done. We also require that $ax^2 + bx + c$ be an **irreducible quadratic,** which means that it has no real zeros. In other words, it cannot be factored with real coefficients. Remember that the quadratic $ax^2 + bx + c$ is irreducible if and only if $b^2 - 4ac < 0$.

Third, use the following rules. For each factor $(dx + e)^m$, the partial-fraction decomposition includes the terms

$$\frac{A_1}{dx + e} + \frac{A_2}{(dx + e)^2} + \cdots + \frac{A_m}{(dx + e)^m}$$

where each A_i is a real number. For each factor $(ax^2 + bx + c)^n$, the partial-fraction decomposition includes the terms

$$\frac{B_1x + C_1}{ax^2 + bx + c} + \frac{B_2x + C_2}{(ax^2 + bx + c)^2} + \cdots + \frac{B_nx + C_n}{(ax^2 + bx + c)^n}$$

where all of the coefficients B_i and C_i are real numbers.

Fourth and finally, **use algebraic methods** to find the constants A_i, B_i, and C_i.

The algebraic methods referred to above include multiplying by the lcd, replacing x by the root of each linear factor $dx + e$, and solving systems of linear equations. We will illustrate these methods in the following examples.

If the numerator is of the same or higher degree than the denominator, we divide first. Make sure to get **a remainder of lower degree than the denominator.**

▶ **EXAMPLE 1**   Write the fraction

$$f(x) = \frac{x^4 - 3x^3 + 5x^2 + 6x - 6}{(x + 2)(x^2 - 3x + 4)}$$

as a sum of partial fractions, but do not find the constants.

Solution   Since the numerator is of higher degree than the denominator, we begin by dividing by the denominator $(x + 2)(x^2 - 3x + 4) = x^3 - x^2 - 2x + 8$. The long division gives

$$\frac{x^4 - 3x^3 + 5x^2 + 6x - 6}{(x + 2)(x^2 - 3x + 4)} = x - 2 + \frac{5x^2 - 6x + 10}{(x + 2)(x^2 - 3x + 4)}$$

Now $x^2 - 3x + 4$ is irreducible because

$$b^2 - 4ac = (-3)^2 - 4(1)(4) = 9 - 16 < 0$$

Thus we can write $f(x)$ as

$$f(x) = x - 2 + \frac{A}{x + 2} + \frac{Bx + C}{x^2 - 3x + 4} \tag{1}$$

In Example 4, we will find A, B, and C.   ◀

Finding the constants

We will now learn how to evaluate the constants that go in the numerators of the partial fractions. There are two procedures that can be used, as well as a combination of them.

Substitute for x

One method for evaluating the constants in the numerators is to use the fact that:

*If two polynomials are identical, then they are
equal for any value assigned to the variable*

To make the equations as simple as possible, we select values of x that make one of the linear factors equal to zero.

Equate coefficients

Another procedure is to use the fact that:

*Two polynomials are identical if and only if the coefficient
of each power of the variable in one polynomial is equal
to the corresponding coefficient in the other polynomial*

For instance

$$Ax^3 + Bx^2 + Cx + D = -3x^2 + 7$$

if and only if $A = 0$, $B = -3$, $C = 0$, and $D = 7$.

▶ **EXAMPLE 2**   Find the partial-fraction decomposition of

$$\frac{6x^2 - 28x - 18}{x^3 + x^2 - 6x}$$

Solution   The denominator can be factored as

$$x(x^2 + x - 6) = x(x - 2)(x + 3)$$

Since we have only linear factors to the first power, then

$$\frac{6x^2 - 28x - 18}{x^3 + x^2 - 6x} = \frac{A}{x} + \frac{B}{x - 2} + \frac{C}{x + 3}$$

Now we multiply both sides of this equation by $x(x - 2)(x + 3)$.

$$6x^2 - 28x - 18 = A(x - 2)(x + 3) + Bx(x + 3) + Cx(x - 2)$$

This is a polynomial identity, and we may substitute any three values of x to determine the three constants A, B, and C. It can be shown by advanced mathematics (continuous functions) that we may use the values 0, 2, and -3 even though the original fraction is not defined for them. We will use 0, 2, and -3 since these values give simple equations to solve.

$$x = 0 \qquad -18 = A(-2)(3) \qquad \text{and hence} \qquad A = -18/(-6) = 3$$
$$x = 2 \qquad 24 - 56 - 18 = B(2)(5) \qquad \text{and hence} \qquad B = -50/10 = -5$$
$$x = -3 \qquad 54 + 84 - 18 = C(-3)(-5) \qquad \text{and hence} \qquad C = 120/15 = 8$$

Therefore $\qquad \dfrac{6x^2 - 28x - 18}{x^3 + x^2 - 6x} = \dfrac{3}{x} - \dfrac{5}{x - 2} + \dfrac{8}{x + 3}$ ◢

In Example 2, all linear factors were to the first power. In Example 3 we will see how to treat a linear factor which is to the second power.

EXAMPLE 3 Find the partial-fraction decomposition of

$$\frac{1}{(x - 1)^2(x - 3)}$$

Solution Since $x - 1$ occurs to the power 2 and $x - 3$ is to the power 1,

$$\frac{1}{(x - 1)^2(x - 3)} = \frac{A}{x - 1} + \frac{B}{(x - 1)^2} + \frac{C}{x - 3}$$

Multiplying by $(x - 1)^2(x - 3)$ gives the polynomial identity

$$1 = A(x - 1)(x - 3) + B(x - 3) + C(x - 1)^2 \qquad (2)$$

We may use any three values of x in Eq. (2), and we choose $x = 1$ because then $x - 1 = 0$, $x = 3$ because then $x - 3 = 0$, and $x = 0$ just for a third value:

$$x = 1 \qquad 1 = B(-2) \qquad \text{and hence} \qquad B = -\tfrac{1}{2}$$
$$x = 3 \qquad 1 = C(4) \qquad \text{and hence} \qquad C = \tfrac{1}{4}$$
$$x = 0 \qquad 1 = A(-1)(-3) + B(-3) + C(1)$$
$$\qquad\qquad 1 = 3A - 3(-\tfrac{1}{2}) + \tfrac{1}{4}$$
$$\qquad\qquad 1 - \tfrac{3}{2} - \tfrac{1}{4} = 3A \qquad \text{and hence} \qquad 3A = -\tfrac{3}{4} \qquad A = -\tfrac{1}{4}$$

Therefore $\qquad \dfrac{1}{(x - 1)^2(x - 3)} = \dfrac{-\tfrac{1}{4}}{x - 1} - \dfrac{\tfrac{1}{2}}{(x - 1)^2} + \dfrac{\tfrac{1}{4}}{x - 3}$

$$= -\frac{1}{4(x - 1)} - \frac{1}{2(x - 1)^2} + \frac{1}{4(x - 3)}$$ ◢

NOTE In Example 3 we got the equation $1 = 3A - 3B + C$ by using $x = 0$. We would get exactly the same equation by equating the constant terms in the polynomial identity. In the remaining examples we will use the technique of equating coefficients of like powers of x extensively.

EXAMPLE 4 Determine the constants A, B, and C in Eq. (1) of Example 1.

Solution The fraction is

$$\frac{5x^2 - 6x + 10}{(x + 2)(x^2 - 3x + 4)} = \frac{A}{x + 2} + \frac{Bx + C}{x^2 - 3x + 4}$$

The general form of the numerators on the right, namely, A and $Bx + C$, would be the same no matter what the numerator is on the left as long as its degree is at most 2. After multiplying by the lcd $(x + 2)(x^2 - 3x + 4)$, we have

$$5x^2 - 6x + 10 = A(x^2 - 3x + 4) + (Bx + C)(x + 2) \tag{3}$$

and after collecting terms

$$5x^2 - 6x + 10 = x^2(A + B) + x(-3A + 2B + C) + 4A + 2C \tag{3'}$$

First we will use $x = -2$ in (3), since then $x + 2 = 0$:

$$5(-2)^2 - 6(-2) + 10 = A[(-2)^2 - 3(-2) + 4] + 0$$

$$20 + 12 + 10 = A(4 + 6 + 4)$$

$$42 = 14A \qquad \text{and hence} \qquad A = 3$$

Since no other real value of x will make a factor zero in (3), we now equate coefficients of like powers of x in (3'):

$$5 = A + B \qquad \text{from coefficients of } x^2 \tag{4}$$

$$-6 = -3A + 2B + C \qquad \text{from coefficients of } x \tag{5}$$

$$10 = 4A + 2C \qquad \text{from constant terms} \tag{6}$$

Since we know that $A = 3$, we use (4) and get $B = 2$ and then use (6) and get $C = -1$. This avoids having to solve the system made up of (4), (5), and (6) from scratch. Consequently,

$$\frac{5x^2 - 6x + 10}{(x + 2)(x^2 - 3x + 4)} = \frac{3}{x + 2} + \frac{2x - 1}{x^2 - 3x + 4}$$

This can be verified by adding the fractions on the right.   ◢

▶ **EXAMPLE 5**   Find the partial-fraction decomposition for the fraction

$$\frac{10x^3 + 3x^2 - 7x - 6}{(2x - 1)^2(x^2 + x + 3)}$$

Solution   The denominator is completely factored because $x^2 + x + 3$ is irreducible since $b^2 - 4ac = (1)^2 - 4(1)(3) = 1 - 12 < 0$. Thus

$$\frac{10x^3 + 3x^3 - 7x - 6}{(2x - 1)^2(x^2 + x + 3)} = \frac{A}{2x - 1} + \frac{B}{(2x - 1)^2} + \frac{Cx + D}{x^2 + x + 3}$$

We clear of fractions by multiplying by the lcd, which is the given denominator. Accordingly, we get

$$10x^3 + 3x^2 - 7x - 6$$

$$= A(2x - 1)(x^2 + x + 3) + B(x^2 + x + 3) + (Cx + D)(2x - 1)^2 \tag{7}$$

$$= x^3(2A + 4C) + x^2(A + B - 4C + 4D) + x(5A + B + C - 4D) - 3A + 3B + D$$

If we use $x = \frac{1}{2}$ in (7), then $2x - 1 = 0$ and we get

$$\tfrac{10}{8} + \tfrac{3}{4} - \tfrac{7}{2} - 6 = A(0) + B(\tfrac{1}{4} + \tfrac{1}{2} + 3) + (\tfrac{1}{2}C + D)(0)$$

$$-\frac{15}{2} = \frac{15B}{4}$$

$$B = -2$$

Since there are no other real values of x that make a coefficient in (7) equal to zero, we resort to equating coefficients of like powers and get

$$10 = 2A + 4C \qquad \text{from coefficients of } x^3$$

$$3 = A + B - 4C + 4D \qquad \text{from coefficients of } x^2$$

$$-7 = 5A + B + C - 4D \qquad \text{from coefficients of } x$$

$$-6 = -3A + 3B + D \qquad \text{from constant terms}$$

Since $B = -2$, these four equations reduce to

$$10 = 2A + 4C \tag{8}$$

$$5 = A - 4C + 4D \tag{9}$$

$$-5 = 5A + C - 4D \tag{10}$$

$$0 = -3A + D \tag{11}$$

We still have four equations but only three variables. We can use **any three of the equations,** for instance (9), (10), and (11). From (11), $D = 3A$, and substituting this in the other two gives

$$5 = A - 4C + 4(3A) = 13A - 4C \tag{12}$$

$$-5 = 5A + C - 4(3A) = -7A + C \tag{13}$$

By (13), $C = 7A - 5$. Therefore from (12)

$$5 = 13A - 4(7A - 5) = -15A + 20$$

$$15A = 15 \quad \text{and thus} \quad A = 1$$

By (13), $C = 7A - 5 = 7 - 5 = 2$. And from (11), $D = 3A = 3$. Thus

$$A = 1 \quad B = -2 \quad C = 2 \quad D = 3$$

and consequently

$$\frac{10x^3 + 3x^2 - 7x - 6}{(2x - 1)^2(x^2 + x + 3)} = \frac{1}{2x - 1} - \frac{2}{(2x - 1)^2} + \frac{2x + 3}{x^2 + x + 3}$$

◢

EXAMPLE 6 Find the partial-fraction decomposition of

$$\frac{2x^2 + 3x}{(x^2 + 4)^2}$$

Solution   Since $x^2 + 4$ has degree two and is irreducible

$$\frac{2x^2 + 3x}{(x^2 + 4)^2} = \frac{Ax + B}{x^2 + 4} + \frac{Cx + D}{(x^2 + 4)^2}$$

Multiplying by $(x^2 + 4)^2$ shows that

$$2x^2 + 3x = (Ax + B)(x^2 + 4) + Cx + D$$

$$2x^2 + 3x = Ax^3 + Bx^2 + (4A + C)x + (4B + D)$$

The coefficients of x^3 and x^2 show that $A = 0$ and $B = 2$. Also

Coefficient of x: $3 = 4A + C = C$
Constant term: $0 = 4B + D = 8 + D$ and so $D = -8$

The partial-fraction decomposition is

$$\frac{2x^2 + 3x}{(x^2 + 4)^2} = \frac{2}{x^2 + 4} + \frac{3x - 8}{(x^2 + 4)^2}$$ ◀

Sometimes using partial fractions can simplify a problem a lot. For instance instead of subtracting these fractions directly

$$\frac{12x^2 + 22x + 34}{(x + 4)(x - 3)(x + 2)} - \frac{10x^2 + 42x + 38}{(x + 4)(x + 1)(x + 2)}$$

we can find the partial-fraction decompositions

$$\left(\frac{5}{x + 4} + \frac{4}{x - 3} + \frac{3}{x + 2}\right) - \left(\frac{5}{x + 4} + \frac{2}{x + 1} + \frac{3}{x + 2}\right)$$

and combine similar terms to get

$$\frac{4}{x - 3} - \frac{2}{x + 1} = \frac{4(x + 1) - 2(x - 3)}{(x - 3)(x + 1)} = \frac{2x + 10}{(x - 3)(x + 1)}$$

EXERCISE 9.3

Find the partial-fraction decomposition of each of the following fractions.

1. $\dfrac{5x + 7}{(x + 1)(2x + 3)}$

2. $\dfrac{6x + 2}{(x + 2)(3x - 4)}$

3. $\dfrac{-6x + 7}{(3x - 1)(2x + 1)}$

4. $\dfrac{3}{(2x + 1)(x + 2)}$

5. $\dfrac{3x^2 - 6x + 6}{(x + 1)(x - 2)(2x - 3)}$

6. $\dfrac{10x^2 + 13x - 69}{(3x - 5)(x + 2)(x - 3)}$

7. $\dfrac{6x^2 - 40x - 14}{(5x - 2)(2x - 3)(x + 4)}$

8. $\dfrac{-64x^2 - 111x - 50}{(4x + 3)(2x + 1)(3x + 5)}$

9. $\dfrac{-8x^2 + 33x + 10}{(2x - 1)(x - 4)^2}$

10. $\dfrac{12x^2 - 9x + 20}{(2x + 3)(3x - 1)^2}$

11. $\dfrac{-22x^2 + 32x + 138}{(5x + 2)(2x - 7)^2}$

12. $\dfrac{24x^2 - 94x + 88}{(2x - 3)(3x - 5)^2}$

13. $\dfrac{-2x + 5}{(x - 1)(x^2 + 2)}$

14. $\dfrac{5x^2 + x + 2}{(x + 1)(x^2 + 1)}$

15. $\dfrac{3x^2 - 10x + 16}{(x - 3)(x^2 + x + 1)}$

16. $\dfrac{2x^2 + 4}{(x + 1)(x^2 + 5)}$

17. $\dfrac{5x^3 - 6x^2 + 12x + 13}{(x - 1)(2x + 1)(x^2 + 3)}$

18. $\dfrac{5x^3 + 14x^2 + 71x + 14}{(x + 5)(2x - 1)(x^2 + 3)}$

19. $\dfrac{x^3 + 11x^2 + 13x - 5}{(x - 3)(3x + 1)(x^2 - x + 2)}$

20. $\dfrac{-9x^3 + 19x^2 + 2x + 3}{(2x - 3)(x + 2)(x^2 + 3)}$

21. $\dfrac{3x^3 - 10x^2 + 9x - 6}{(x - 1)^2(x^2 + 1)}$

22. $\dfrac{-x^3 + 8x^2 + 2x - 19}{(x - 2)^2(x^2 + 5)}$

23. $\dfrac{4x^3 - 11x^2 + 12x - 19}{(x - 2)^2(x^2 + x + 1)}$

24. $\dfrac{8x^2 + 19x + 12}{(x + 1)^2(x^2 + 3x - 3)}$

25. $\dfrac{2x^3 + 7x - 1}{(x^2 + 2)(x^2 + 3)}$

26. $\dfrac{3x^3 - 10x^2 + 7x - 3}{(x^2 + 1)(x^2 - 3x - 1)}$

27. $\dfrac{3x^3 - 3x^2 - 4x - 14}{(x^2 - 5)(x^2 - x + 3)}$

28. $\dfrac{-x^3 - 13x^2 + 9}{(x^2 + 3)(x^2 - 3x - 3)}$

29. $\dfrac{x^3 + 2x^2 + 4x + 5}{(x^2 + 2)^2}$

30. $\dfrac{2x^3 - 3x^2 + 3x - 10}{(x^2 + 3)^2}$

31. $\dfrac{2x^3 - x^2 - 6x - 8}{(x^2 - x + 3)^2}$

32. $\dfrac{3x^3 + 4x - 5}{(x^2 + 2)^2}$

33. $\dfrac{2x^4 + 13x^3 + 13x^2 - 12x + 2}{x^2(x^2 + 3x - 1)^2}$

34. $\dfrac{x^5 + x^4 - 4x + 4}{x^2(x^2 - x + 2)^2}$

35. $\dfrac{x^4 - x^3 + 1}{x^2(x^2 + 1)^2}$

36. $\dfrac{-2x^5 - 4x^4 + 12x^3 + 9x^2 - 24x - 16}{x^2(x^2 + 3x + 4)^2}$

In Probs. 37 to 44, use long division first and then find the partial-fraction decomposition of the proper fractions.

37. $\dfrac{2x^3 - 9x^2 + 10x + 11}{(x + 1)(2x - 3)}$

38. $\dfrac{6x^4 - 35x^3 + 55x^2 + 11x - 50}{(x - 2)^2(3x + 2)}$

39. $\dfrac{2x^4 - 9x^3 + 7x^2 + 14x + 18}{(x - 3)(x^2 + x + 2)}$

40. $\dfrac{2x^5 + 7x^4 + 27x^3 + 17x^2 + 14x + 1}{(x^2 + x + 1)(2x^2 + x + 1)}$

41. $\dfrac{6x^3 + 31x^2 + 63x + 35}{6x^2 + 13x + 6}$

42. $\dfrac{-40x^3 + 34x^2 + 2x + 19}{20x^2 - 7x - 3}$

43. $\dfrac{24x^3 - 34x^2 + x + 20}{8x^2 + 2x - 3}$

44. $\dfrac{-18x^3 + 27x^2 + 45x - 35}{6x^2 - x - 15}$

45. Find A and B so that

$$\frac{cx + d}{(x - r)(x - s)} = \frac{A}{x - r} + \frac{B}{x - s}$$

9.4 Systems of Inequalities

In Chap. 2, we studied inequalities in one variable such as $5x + 1 \le 3x - 7$. In this section we will study inequalities in two variables, and also systems of inequalities, such as

$$y \ge 2x - 5$$
$$y < 3x^2 + 1$$

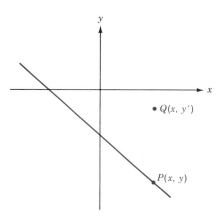

FIGURE 9.11

We need to use inequalities because, for instance, a company might know only that it must produce at least 550 items or that it can employ at most 10 people.

In most of our discussion, we will be concerned with finding the solution of an inequality such as $y \geq 3x + 1$ or $y < x^2$. As in previous sections, $P(x, y)$ stands for the point with coordinates x and y. A **solution of an inequality** is an ordered pair (a, b) whose coordinates satisfy the inequality. The **graph of an inequality** is the graph of all of the solutions.

To solve $y \geq ax + b$, for instance, we begin with the graph of $y = ax + b$, as in Fig. 9.11. If $P(x, y)$ is on the graph of $y = ax + b$ and $y' \geq y$, then $Q(x, y')$ is on or above the graph. Moreover, since $y' \geq y$, it follows that $y' \geq ax + b$. In other words, points above the line $y = ax + b$ have greater y coordinates than points on the line itself. Therefore:

The solutions of $y \geq ax + b$ are

$$\{(x, y)|(x, y) \text{ is on or above the graph of } y = ax + b\}$$

For similar reasons, the following statements are true. Graphs for some of these cases appear in Figs. 9.12 to 9.14.

Let f and g be functions.
(a) The graph of $y < f(x)$ is the set of all points below the graph of $y = f(x)$.
(b) The graph of $y > f(x)$ is the set of all points above the graph of $y = f(x)$.
(c) The graph of $x < g(y)$ is the set of all points to the left of the graph of $x = g(y)$.
(d) The graph of $x > g(y)$ is the set of all points to the right of the graph of $x = g(y)$.

The graph of $y \leq f(x)$ is the set of all points on or below the graph of $y = f(x)$, with similar comments for (b), (c), and (d).

The rules in the box above make it easy to see the solution to an inequality when it is (or can be) solved for x or y. If the inequality is not (or cannot easily be) solved for x or y, the graph of the equation will usually divide the plane into two or three or more

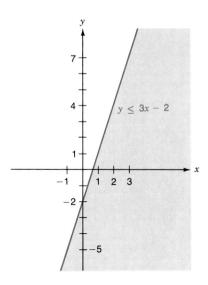

FIGURE 9.12

Note

regions. To see if a particular region is part of the solution to the graph of the inequality, choose **any point** which is in the region, but not on the boundary, and see if its coordinates satisfy the inequality.

When drawing the graph of an inequality, we will shade the graph of the solution. If the inequality sign is $\leq$ or $\geq$, we will use a **solid** line or curve to indicate that the line or curve *is* part of the graph of the solution. If the inequality sign is $<$ or $>$, it is called a **strict inequality** and we will use a **dashed** line or curve to indicate that the line or curve *is not* part of the graph of the solution.

EXAMPLE 1   Draw the graph of the inequality $y \leq 3x - 2$.

Solution   The graph of $y \leq 3x - 2$ is the set of all points on or below the graph of $y = 3x - 2$. This region is shaded in Fig. 9.12, and the line is solid. Since the inequality is equivalent to

$$y + 2 \leq 3x \qquad \text{or} \qquad x \geq \frac{y + 2}{3}$$

the graph of the inequality may also be thought of as all points on, or to the right of, the line.

CHECK   The point $(3, 0)$ is below, or to the right of, the line, and its coordinates satisfy the given inequality.   ◀

EXAMPLE 2   Draw the graph of the inequality

$$y > (x + 2)(x - 1)(2x - 7)$$

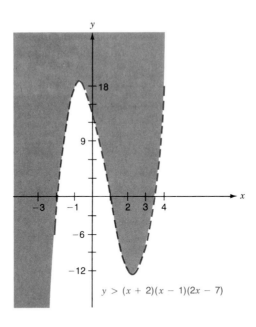

FIGURE 9.13

Solution   The graph of the cubic $y = (x + 2)(x - 1)(2x - 7)$ is dashed in Fig. 9.13. By (b), the graph of the given inequality is the shaded region above the graph of

$$y = (x + 2)(x - 1)(2x - 7).$$

CHECK   The point $(2, 0)$ is above the graph of the polynomial, and its coordinates satisfy the given inequality.

▶ **EXAMPLE 3**   Draw the graph of the inequality $x \geq 2y^2$.

Solution   The graph of the parabola $x = 2y^2$ is solid in Fig. 9.14. Similar to (d) above, the graph of the inequality is the shaded region on, or to the right of, the parabola.

CHECK   The point $(4, 0)$ is to the right of the parabola, and its coordinates satisfy the given inequality.

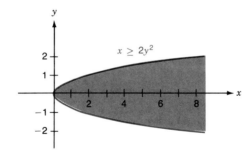

FIGURE 9.14

Systems of Inequalities

In the remainder of this section, we will be concerned with **systems of inequalities.** The graph of a system of inequalities is the intersection of all of the graphs of the inequalities in the system, and we shade the common region. Thus solving a system of inequalities begins by first drawing the graph of each corresponding equation.

The graph of the equation $ax + by + c = 0$ is a line. The regions on either side of the line, but not including the line, are called **open half-planes.** However if the line is included in a region, then the region is called a **closed half-plane.** See Fig. 9.12.

▶ EXAMPLE 4   Draw the graph of the system of inequalities

$$x \geq 0 \qquad y \geq 0 \qquad y \geq 3x - 3 \qquad \text{and} \qquad y \leq 0.5x + 2$$

Solution   We begin by sketching the graphs of the equations

$$x = 0 \qquad y = 0 \qquad y = 3x - 3 \qquad \text{and} \qquad y = 0.5x + 2$$

The first one is the y axis, the second is the x axis, and the third and fourth lines intersect at $(2, 3)$. All four lines are shown in Fig. 9.15, and the graph of the system is the intersection of the four closed half-planes:

To the right of the line $x = 0$, which is the y axis
Above the line $y = 0$, which is the x axis
Above the line $y = 3x - 3$
Below the line $y = 0.5x + 2$

The region determined by the inequalities is the boundary and interior of the quadrilateral with vertices at

$$O(0, 0) \qquad Q(1, 0) \qquad I(2, 3) \qquad \text{and} \qquad R(0, 2) \qquad ◢$$

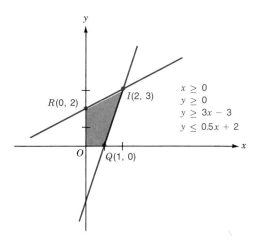

FIGURE 9.15

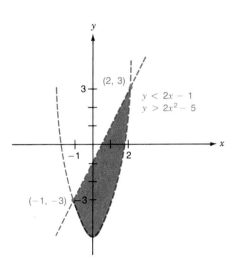

FIGURE 9.16

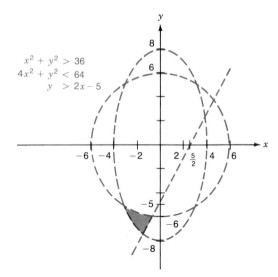

FIGURE 9.17

▶ **EXAMPLE 5** Draw the graph of the system

$$y > 2x^2 - 5 \quad \text{and} \quad y < 2x - 1$$

Solution We want the part above the parabola $y = 2x^2 - 5$, and also below the line $y = 2x - 1$. They intersect at the points $(-1, -3)$ and $(2, 3)$. Since both inequalities are strict, the graphs of the equations are drawn with dashed lines. The graph of the system is the shaded region between the dashed lines in Fig. 9.16.

CHECK The point $(0, -3)$ is above the parabola, below the line, and its coordinates satisfy both of the given inequalities. ◀

▶ **EXAMPLE 6** Draw the graph of the system

$$x^2 + y^2 > 36 \qquad 4x^2 + y^2 < 64 \qquad y > 2x - 5$$

Solution See Fig. 9.17, where we have drawn the graphs of the corresponding equations. The first one is the circle whose center is at the origin and radius is 6. Since $(0, 0)$ does not satisfy $x^2 + y^2 > 36$ and $(0, 0)$ is within the circle, we want the part **outside** the circle. The second is an ellipse with center at the origin and crossing the x axis at $(\pm 4, 0)$ and the y axis at $(0, \pm 8)$. Since $(0, 0)$ does satisfy $4x^2 + y^2 < 64$ and $(0, 0)$ is within the ellipse, we want the part **inside** the ellipse. The third one is of course a line, and we want the part **above** the line since the inequality is written in the form $y > f(x)$. The shaded solution is outside the circle, inside the ellipse, and above the line. Each graph is dashed since each inequality is strict.

CHECK The point $(-2, -6)$ is outside the circle, inside the ellipse, and above the line, and its coordinates satisfy each of the given inequalities. ◀

EXERCISE 9.4

In Probs. 1 to 12, draw the graph of the inequality.

1. $y < 3x - 2$
2. $y \geq -2x + 1$
3. $x > y + 1$
4. $x \leq 2y - 4$
5. $y \leq 2 - x^2$
6. $x \geq y^2 - 1$
7. $3x > (y - 3)(y)(y - 2)$
8. $2y < (x + 2)(x - 1)(x - 3)$
9. $x^2 + 4y^2 \leq 16$
10. $x^2 + y^2 \leq 2$
11. $x^2 + 9y^2 > 9$
12. $x^2 + y^2 > 1$

Draw the graph of each system of linear inequalities in Probs. 13 to 24.

13. $x \leq 1, y \geq -1, y - x \leq 0$
14. $x \leq 2, y \geq -1, -x + y \leq -2$
15. $2x - y \geq 6, 4x + y \geq 4$
16. $5x - 2y \leq 10, 3x + 2y \geq 6$
17. $x \leq 0, y \leq 0, y \leq 3x + 2, y \geq x - 3$
18. $x \leq 1, y \geq -1, x - 3y + 7 \geq 0, 4x + y + 6 \geq 0$
19. $x \leq 2, y \geq 1, x - 3y + 2 \geq 0, 3x + 2y \geq 6$
20. $2x - y + 4 \geq 0, x + y + 2 \leq 0, x \leq 1, y \geq -3$
21. $y \leq 2x - 1, y \geq -x + 5, x \leq 12 - 2y$
22. $5x + y \leq 25, x \leq 3y, x + y \geq -1$
23. $2x + y \leq 2, y - 3x \geq -3, 3x + 2y \geq -6$
24. $4y \geq x, 4y - 3x \leq 12, 3x - 2y \geq 0$

Draw the graph of the system of inequalities in each of Probs. 25 to 36.

25. $x^2 + y^2 \leq 16$
   $y \geq 2$
26. $3x^2 + y^2 \geq 6$
   $y \leq 3$
27. $y \geq x^2 - 1$
   $y \geq x$
28. $4x^2 - y^2 \leq 4$
   $2x + y \leq 3$
29. $y \geq x^2 - 2$
   $y \leq x + 1$
30. $x^2 - 16y^2 \leq 16$
   $y \leq x/3 - 1$
31. $x^2 + y^2 \geq 3$
   $y \leq 3$
32. $x^2 + 4y^2 \leq 4$
   $y \leq x$
33. $x^2 + y^2 \leq 13$
   $7x^2 + y^2 \leq 37$
   $y \geq 2x - 1$
34. $x^2 + y^2 \leq 17$
   $18x^2 + 3y^2 \leq 66$
   $2y \geq x + 7$
35. $3x^2 + y^2 \leq 28$
   $y \geq x^2$
   $y \leq x + 2$
36. $10x^2 + 3y^2 \leq 37$
   $y \geq 3x^2$
   $y \leq 2x + 1$

Draw the graph of each inequality in Probs. 37 to 40.

37. $|x| + |y| \leq 1$
38. $\sqrt{x} + \sqrt{y} \leq 1$
39. $x^4 + y^4 \leq 1$
40. $x^{1/4} + y^{1/4} \leq 1$

9.5 Linear Programming

In this section, we will see how to find the maximum and minimum values of some types of functions when certain conditions are placed on the variables. For instance we may want to minimize cost, maximize profit, minimize calories, or maximize storage capacity. The **maximum** and **minimum** values are also referred to as the **extrema.**

If a problem involves **constraints,** which are given by a set of linear inequalities, and $f(x, y) = ax + by + c$ is to be an extremum subject to the constraints, then the determination of the extremum and the point or points where it occurs is called **linear programming.** The region S determined by the constraints is called the set of **feasible solutions,** and the linear function f is called the **objective function.**

If S is a set of points in the plane and all points of the line segment PQ are in S *whenever P* and *Q* are in S, we call S a **convex set.** For instance a half-plane is convex, as is the interior of a circle. The interior of a regular five-pointed-star-shaped region is not convex. See Fig. 9.18. Furthermore, the intersection of two convex sets is also convex. Our main reason for looking at convex sets is that the solution of a finite system of linear inequalities is convex since it is the intersection of half-planes.

We will now state without proof a basic theorem on linear programming. A

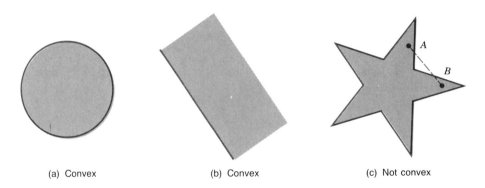

FIGURE 9.18   (a) Convex   (b) Convex   (c) Not convex

region is **bounded** if it lies inside some circle whose center is at the origin and radius is sufficiently large.

Theorem   If S is a bounded region determined by a system of linear inequalities, $f(x, y) = ax + by + c$ has domain S, and B is the boundary of S, then f has a maximum and a minimum in S and each one occurs at a vertex of B.

Although we will not prove this theorem, it is made plausible by Fig. 9.20 and the chart that follows Example 2.

▶ **EXAMPLE 1**   Find the maximum and minimum values of $f(x, y) = 2x - 3y + 4$ in the region S with vertices at

$$(0, 5) \qquad (6, 4) \qquad (7, 1) \qquad \text{and} \qquad (-3, -2)$$

Assume that the convex region is in fact formed from a system of linear inequalities. See Fig. 9.19.

Solution   The assumption about the region is made simply to avoid solving in this example for the four vertices; each one would require solving two equations in two variables. Since f is a linear function in two variables, we know that the extrema of f are attained at vertices of the boundary. Therefore, we only need to evaluate f at each vertex. The values are

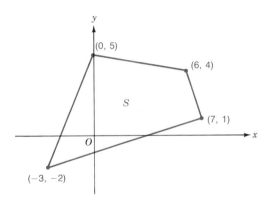

FIGURE 9.19

$$f(0, 5) = 2(0) - 3(5) + 4 = -11$$
$$f(6, 4) = 2(6) - 3(4) + 4 = 4$$
$$f(7, 1) = 2(7) - 3(1) + 4 = 15$$
$$f(-3, -2) = 2(-3) - 3(-2) + 4 = 4$$

Consequently, the maximum value of f in S is $f(7, 1) = 15$ and the minimum value is $f(0, 5) = -11$. Note that, for instance, the point $(1, 4)$ is in S and $f(1, 4) = 2(1) - 3(4) + 4 = 2 - 12 + 4 = -6$, which is indeed between -11 and 15. The same will be true for any point in S not a vertex. ◢

NOTE   In Example 1 we began with several vertices joined by straight lines and stated that the region was determined by a system of linear inequalities. In Example 2, we actually begin with a system of linear inequalities.

▶ EXAMPLE 2   For the region determined by

$$x \geq 0 \qquad y \geq 0 \qquad y \geq 3x - 3 \qquad \text{and} \qquad y \leq 0.5x + 2$$

find the maximum and minimum values of the function

$$f(x, y) = 5x + 6y$$

Solution   The region R is the same as the one in Example 4, Sec. 9.4. See Figs. 9.15 and 9.20. The vertices are

$$(0, 0) \qquad (1, 0) \qquad (0, 2) \qquad \text{and} \qquad (2, 3)$$

the last one being the solution of $y = 3x - 3$ and $y = 0.5x + 2$. The conditions of the theorem are satisfied, and the values of $f(x, y)$ at the vertex points of R are

$$f(0, 0) = 0 \qquad f(1, 0) = 5 \qquad f(2, 3) = 28 \qquad f(0, 2) = 12$$

Therefore the maximum is 28 and the minimum is 0. ◢

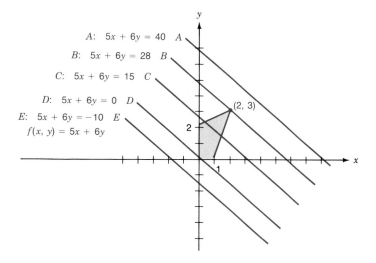

FIGURE 9.20

Figure 9.20 and the chart below are not a proof, but they should strongly suggest why the extreme values of $f(x, y)$ occur at vertex points of the feasible region R. The region R is shown in Fig. 9.20, along with the five extra lines called $A, B, C, D,$ and E which are related to the function f. We want to find the points (x, y) which are in the **feasible region** R that produce the maximum and minimum values of f. For instance,

$$f(x, y) = 40 \qquad \text{means that} \qquad 5x + 6y = 40$$

The graph of $5x + 6y = 40$ is the top line, A, in the figure, and line A does not intersect the feasible region R. This means there are *no points in the feasible region with* $f(x, y) = 40$. Also

$$f(x, y) = 15 \qquad \text{means that} \qquad 5x + 6y = 15$$

Thus line C, which is the graph of $5x + 6y = 15$, intersects the feasible region R in infinitely many points, and at each one of them we have $f(x, y) = 15$. Similar comments apply to the other three lines.

Line	Value of f	Number of intersection points of line and R
A	$f(x, y) = 40$	0
B	$f(x, y) = 28$	1
C	$f(x, y) = 15$	Infinite
D	$f(x, y) = 0$	1
E	$f(x, y) = -10$	0

▶ EXAMPLE 3   A maker of animal shoes specializes in horseshoes, mule shoes, and ox shoes and can produce 200 sets of shoes per unit of time. He has standing orders for 60 sets of horseshoes and 20 sets of ox shoes and can sell at most 150 sets of horseshoes and 50 sets of mule shoes. How many sets of each type should he produce to make a maximum profit if his profit on a set of shoes is \$0.40 for horseshoes, \$0.50 for mule shoes, and \$0.30 for ox shoes?

Solution   If we represent the number of sets of horseshoes produced by x and of mule shoes by y, then $200 - x - y$ is the number of ox shoes. Consequently, his profit in dollars is

$$f(x, y) = 0.4x + 0.5y + 0.3(200 - x - y)$$

$$= 0.1x + 0.2y + 60$$

This objective function is subject to the constraints imposed by the problem. They are

$$x \geq 60 \qquad \text{since he has a standing order for 60 sets of horseshoes}$$

$$200 - x - y \geq 20 \qquad \text{since he has a standing order for 20 sets of ox shoes}$$

$$x \leq 150 \qquad \text{since he cannot sell more than 150 sets of horseshoes}$$

$$y \leq 50 \qquad \text{since he cannot sell more than 50 sets of mule shoes}$$

$$\left. \begin{array}{ll} x \geq 0 & y \geq 0 \\ 200 - x - y \geq 0 & \end{array} \right\} \qquad \text{since he cannot sell a negative number of any type of shoe}$$

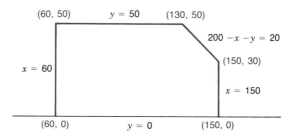

FIGURE 9.21

Figure 9.21 shows these constraints graphically, along with the vertices of the polygonal boundary of the set of feasible solutions as obtained by solving the equations of the pair of lines that meet at each vertex. We now evaluate

$$f(x, y) = 0.1x + 0.2y + 60$$

at each vertex and find that

$$f(60, 0) = 66 \qquad f(150, 0) = 75 \qquad f(150, 30) = 81$$

$$f(130, 50) = 83 \qquad \text{and} \qquad f(60, 50) = 76$$

Consequently, the shoemaker has the greatest profit, $83, if he makes 130 sets of horseshoes, 50 sets of mule shoes, and 20 sets of ox shoes. ◢

EXERCISE 9.5

Find the maximum and minimum values of the linear function $f(x, y)$ on the convex polygon determined by the given points as vertices in each of Probs. 1 to 16. Also give the coordinates of the vertex at which each extreme value occurs.

1. $(-1, 2)$, $(2, 3)$, $(1, 0)$, $f(x, y) = 2x - y + 2$
2. $(-1, 1)$, $(2, 2)$, $(0, 0)$, $f(x, y) = 7x + 6y - 5$
3. $(3, 1)$, $(0, 2)$, $(-2, 1)$, $f(x, y) = 2x - y + 1$
4. $(2, 0)$, $(3, 2)$, $(1, 4)$, $f(x, y) = x + 2y - 3$
5. $(0, 1)$, $(4, 2)$, $(5, 5)$, $(3, 6)$, $f(x, y) = x + 5y - 1$
6. $(1, 4)$, $(9, 1)$, $(3, 6)$, $(-2, -3)$, $f(x, y) = 3x - y + 2$
7. $(2, -1)$, $(7, 1)$, $(2, 7)$, $(-1, 1)$, $f(x, y) = 4x + 3y - 7$
8. $(2, 3)$, $(7, -2)$, $(4, 3)$, $(-1, 0)$, $f(x, y) = -2x + 3y + 4$
9. $(1, 0)$, $(2, 4)$, $(-2, 3)$, $(-3, -2)$, $f(x, y) = 7x - 6y + 3$
10. $(0, 1)$, $(3, 0)$, $(2, 2)$, $(-1, 3)$, $f(x, y) = 5x + 2y - 1$
11. $(0, -1)$, $(2, 4)$, $(-5, -1)$, $(6, -2)$, $f(x, y) = 6x + 4y - 7$

12. $(1, 0)$, $(3, 5)$, $(-5, 4)$, $(-6, 0)$, $f(x, y) = -3x + 2y + 6$
13. $(-1, -2)$, $(1, 2)$, $(0, 6)$, $(-2, 5)$, $(-5, 3)$, $f(x, y) = 4x - y - 1$
14. $(-1, -1)$, $(0, 4)$, $(-1, 6)$, $(-3, 5)$, $(-4, 3)$, $f(x, y) = -5x + 3y - 2$
15. $(1, 2)$, $(4, 5)$, $(2, 6)$, $(0, 6)$, $(-2, 4)$, $f(x, y) = -4x + 5y - 1$
16. $(0, 0)$, $(2, 3)$, $(1, 5)$, $(-3, 4)$, $(-4, 1)$, $f(x, y) = 6x - 2y + 5$

For each system of constraints in Probs. 17 to 32, find the maximum and minimum values of the objective function f and the coordinates of the vertices at which they are attained.

17. $x \geq 0$, $y \geq 0$, $2x + 3y \leq 6$, $f(x, y) = 4x + 7y + 1$
18. $x \geq 0$, $y \geq 0$, $2x + 3y \leq 6$, $f(x, y) = 5x + y - 2$
19. $x \geq 0$, $y \leq 2$, $y \geq x$, $f(x, y) = 3x + 5y + 2$
20. $x + y \leq 4$, $3y \geq x$, $y \leq 3x$, $f(x, y) = 6x - y + 5$
21. $-x + y \leq 1$, $x + y \geq -1$, $x - y \leq 1$, $x + y \leq 1$, $f(x, y) = x + y + 1$

22. $3x - y - 7 \leq 0$, $x - 4y + 5 \geq 0$,
    $2x + 3y - 1 \geq 0$, $f(x, y) = 3x + y + 2$
23. $3x - 2y - 5 \leq 0$, $4x - y + 2 \geq 0$,
    $3x + y - 2 \leq 0$, $f(x, y) = 4x - 2y - 1$
24. $3x - y - 7 \leq 0$, $x - 4y + 5 \geq 0$,
    $2x + 3y - 1 \geq 0$, $f(x, y) = 7x + 6y - 13$
25. $x \geq 0$, $y \leq 0$, $x + y + 1 \geq 0$, $x - y - 3 \leq 0$,
    $f(x, y) = 3x - 4y + 8$
26. $x \leq 0$, $y \geq 0$, $2x + y + 2 \geq 0$, $x - 2y + 6 \geq 0$,
    $f(x, y) = 5x - y - 1$
27. $x \leq 2$, $y \leq 1$, $2x - y + 1 \geq 0$, $x + 3y + 4 \geq 0$,
    $f(x, y) = 3x - 2y + 7$
28. $x \leq 2$, $y \geq -1$, $2x - y + 1 \geq 0$, $x - 2y + 2 \geq 0$,
    $f(x, y) = x + 4y + 9$
29. $x - y + 1 \geq 0$, $4x - y - 2 \geq 0$, $x - 2y - 4 \leq 0$,
    $x \leq 2$, $f(x, y) = 2x + 5y - 3$
30. $x \leq 3$, $2x - 3y - 9 \leq 0$, $4x + y + 3 \geq 0$,
    $x - 4y + 5 \geq 0$, $f(x, y) = x - y - 2$
31. $2x - 3y + 2 \geq 0$, $4x + y - 10 \leq 0$,
    $x - 3y - 9 \leq 0$, $3x + y + 3 \geq 0$, $f(x, y) = x + 3y - 4$
32. $x + 3y - 3 \leq 0$, $3x - y - 9 \leq 0$,
    $x + 4y + 10 \geq 0$, $3x - 2y + 2 \geq 0$, $f(x, y) = 2x - 7y - 5$

33. A manufacturer produces three types of products in 930 h. Product X requires 5 h/unit, product Y requires 7 h/unit, and product Z requires 3 h/unit. The profits per unit are $60 on X, $85 on Y, and $35 on Z. She has orders for 38 X units, 45 Y units, and 100 Z units. If she can sell all she can produce, what combination should she produce to make a maximum profit under the assumption that she can not produce more than 150 X units or more than 60 Y units?

34. Repeat Prob. 33 with profit on an X unit changed to $65.

35. Feed for animals is to be a mixture of products X and Y. The cost and content of 1 kg of each product is

	X	Y
Cost	$0.80	$0.42
Protein, g	680	85
Fat, g	5	15
Carbohydrates, g	520	364

How much of each product should be used to make

cost a minimum if each bag must contain a minimum 2890 g of protein and 50 g of fat and not more than 5200 g of carbohydrates? What is the minimum cost of a bag?

36. Repeat Prob. 35 with the cost of 1 kg of product X reduced to $0.75.

37. A shoe manufacturer makes oxfords, sandals, and boots and can produce 500 pairs per unit of time. There are standing orders for 200 pairs of oxfords and 70 pairs of boots, and the company can sell at most 300 pairs of oxfords and 120 pairs of sandals. How many pairs of each type should be produced to make a maximum profit provided the profit on a pair of footwear is $3.50 for oxfords, $4.25 for sandals, and $6 for boots? What is that profit?

38. Repeat Prob. 37 if the profit on a pair of oxfords is increased to $4.50 and on a pair of boots decreased to $5.50.

39. A farmer raises corn and wheat. The corn requires 8 units of fertilizer and 11 units of labor, whereas the wheat needs 10 units of fertilizer and 8 units of labor. To maximize his profit, how many acres of each should he plant if the profit per acre on corn is $90 and on wheat $80. Assume he has 7000 units of fertilizer, 7440 units of labor, and 800 acres.

40. Repeat Prob. 39 with the profit on corn at $100 per acre and on wheat at $110 per acre.

41. A farmer has 600 acres available for planting corn, wheat, and soybeans. He thinks that he can make a profit of $90 per acre on corn, $80 per acre on wheat, and $70 per acre on soybeans. He can not take care of more than 200 acres of corn, 400 acres of wheat, or 300 acres of soybeans. How many acres of each should he plant to make a maximum profit? What is that profit?

42. Repeat Prob. 41 with 800 acres available, but the farmer not able to care for more than 300 acres of corn, 500 acres of wheat, or 100 acres of soybeans.

43. A floriculturist raises day lilies and amaryllis. For a unit of each she uses labor, fertilizer, and insecticide. To produce 1 unit of day lilies she uses 2 units of labor, 5 of fertilizer, and 1 of insecticide. For 1 unit of amaryllis, she uses 3 units of labor, 4 of fertilizer, and 2 of insecticide. The profit on a unit of each flower is $300 for day lilies and $250 for amaryllis. She has 400 units of labor, 650 units of fertilizer, and 200 units of insecticide. How many units

of each flower should be produced to maximize profit? What is that profit?

44. Repeat Prob. 43 with the profit per unit $400 on day lilies and $200 on amaryllis.

45. An importer sells boxes of Belgian chocolates and designer jeans. The Belgian chocolates cost $18 to import and sell for $25, while the jeans cost $28 to import and sell for $45. The company can import between 400 and 500 boxes of chocolates and between 150 and 200 pair of jeans, but not more than 650 items altogether. How many boxes of chocolate and pairs of jeans should the company import to make a maximum profit?

46. Repeat Prob. 45 with the selling price of jeans $40 and the ability to import being between 450 and 550 boxes of chocolates and 200 to 250 pairs of jeans.

47. Janice Gotthoeld has a ranch of 3216 acres and raises cattle and sheep. Cattle require 24 acres per animal, and sheep need 2 acres each. How many of each type of animal should she have to make the largest profit if her per-head profit is $130 on cattle and $11 on sheep? Assume that she cannot care for more than 120 cattle or 1500 sheep.

48. Repeat Prob. 47 with the profit per head $132 on cattle and $10.50 on sheep.

9.6 Key Concepts

Be certain that you understand and can use each of the following words and concepts:

Linear system of equations (p. 453)
Solution of a system of equations (p. 454)
Elimination by addition or subtraction (p. 454)
Substitution method (p. 455)
Consistent, inconsistent, and dependent equations (p. 456)
Graphical solution (p. 458)
Nonlinear system of equations (p. 464)

Partial-fraction decomposition (p. 475)
System of inequalities (p. 481)
Half-plane (p. 485)
Linear programming (p. 487)
Maximum, minimum (p. 487)
Constraint (p. 487)
Objective function (p. 487)
Feasible region (p. 487)

EXERCISE 9.6   Review

State whether the pair of equations in each of Probs. 1, 2, and 3 is consistent, inconsistent, or dependent, and solve each consistent pair.

1. $\begin{aligned}3x + 5y &= 11\\ 6x + 10y &= 22\end{aligned}$

2. $\begin{aligned}3x + 5y &= 11\\ 6x + 10y &= 21\end{aligned}$

3. $\begin{aligned}3x + 5y &= 11\\ 6x + 3y &= 15\end{aligned}$

Solve the systems of equations in Probs. 4 to 6 by either elimination or substitution.

4. $\begin{aligned}4x - y - 2z &= -2\\ x - 4y + 3z &= 2\\ 2x - y + 3z &= 17\end{aligned}$

5. $\begin{aligned}3x + 2y &= 28\\ 5x + 4z &= 46\\ y + 2z &= 13\end{aligned}$

6. $\begin{aligned}2/(x + 4) + 5/(y - 4) &= 29\\ 4/(x + 4) - 3/(y - 4) &= 19\end{aligned}$

7. Use this form for the equation of a circle

$$x^2 + y^2 + Dx + Ey + F = 0$$

to find an equation of the circle which passes through the points $(7, 1)$, $(6, 4)$, and $(5, 5)$.

Solve the systems in Probs. 8 to 11 for x and y.

8. $\begin{aligned}3x^2 + 5y^2 &= 17\\ 2x - y &= 3\end{aligned}$

9. $\begin{aligned}x^2 + 2y^2 - 3y &= 8\\ 2x^2 - 5y^2 + 2y &= 15\end{aligned}$

10. $3x^2 - 2xy + 4y^2 = 23$
$3x^2 \qquad + 4y^2 = 19$

11. $3x^2 + 5y^2 = 47$
$xy = 6$

12. Use elimination of the xy terms to solve the system:

$$x^2 + 2xy + 3x = 6$$

$$3x^2 - xy + 4x = 6$$

13. Use elimination on the constant term first. Next solve the resulting equation for y in terms of x, and then substitute.

$$2x^2 + xy + 3y^2 = 12$$

$$4x^2 - xy - y^2 = 2$$

14. Show that there is no real solution. This may be done either algebraically or graphically.

$$2x^2 - y^2 = -18$$

$$x^2 + 3y = 4$$

15. The point $(3, 9)$ is on the parabola $y = x^2$. For every m, the line $y - 9 = m(x - 3)$ passes through the point $(3, 9)$. Find the value of m for which the line and the parabola intersect in exactly one point. *Hint:* Use the fact that there is exactly one solution to $ax^2 + bx + c = 0$ if and only if $b^2 - 4ac = 0$.

In Probs. 16 to 21, draw the graph of the inequality.
16. $y < 4x - 3$ **17.** $x > 2y + 1$
18. $y \le 9 - x^2$ **19.** $x \ge 3y^2 - 12$
20. $2x > (y + 2)(y)(y - 3)$
21. $x^2 + 9y^2 \le 36$

Draw the graph of each system of inequalities.
22. $x^2 + y^2 \le 9$ **23.** $y \ge x^2 - 2$
     $y \ge 1$ $y \ge x/2$

Draw the graph of each system of linear inequalities in Probs. 24 to 25.
24. $x \le 2, \ y \ge -1, \ y - 2x \le 1$
25. $3x - y \ge 6, \ 2x + y \ge 4, \ x + 3y \le 3$
26. Show graphically the convex region determined by

$$x \ge 0 \qquad 3x + 2y \le 6 \qquad 4x - 3y \le 12$$

27. Find the vertices of the polygonal region determined by

$$x - 4y + 3 \ge 0 \qquad 3x + 2y - 5 \ge 0$$

$$y - 2x \ge -8$$

28. Find the extrema of $f(x, y) = 4x - 5y + 7$ in the convex region with vertices at

$$(3, -2) \qquad (4, 1) \qquad (-1, 2) \qquad \text{and} \qquad (-2, -1)$$

29. Find the extrema of $f(x, y) = 2x + 3y - 4$ in the region

$$y \ge 0 \qquad -2x + y + 6 \ge 0$$

$$x + 3y \le 10 \qquad 3x - y \ge 0$$

30. A ranger inspecting a forest trail walked at a rate of 4.5 mi/h. A second ranger inspecting another portion of the trail walked at a rate of 4 mi/h. If the trail was 36 mi long and the whole inspection required 8.5 h, how far did each ranger walk?

31. Find two positive numbers whose difference is 1 and whose product is 56.

32. A farmer has 700 acres for growing corn, soybeans, and wheat. He thinks he can make a profit of $30 per acre on corn, $18 per acre on soybeans, and $35 per acre on wheat. He must plant 200 acres or less of corn, 250 acres or less of soybeans, and 400 acres or less of wheat. How many acres of each should he plant to make a maximum profit? What is that profit?

Decompose the following fractions into partial fractions:

33. $\dfrac{4x + 2}{x(4x + 5)}$ **34.** $\dfrac{2x - 1}{(x - 3)^2}$

35. $\dfrac{9x^2 + 34x + 29}{(x + 1)(x + 2)(x + 3)}$

36. $\dfrac{4x^2 + 25x + 37}{x^2 + 5x + 6}$

37. $\dfrac{5x^2 + 4x + 5}{(x + 1)(x^2 + x + 3)}$

38. $\dfrac{3x^4 - 9x^3 + 23x^2 - 27x + 11}{(x - 2)(x^2 - x + 3)^2}$

10 Matrices and Determinants

A **matrix** is a rectangular array of numbers. If a matrix is square, it can be assigned a real number called its **determinant.** The concepts of a matrix and a determinant have been extremely important in mathematics and have become even more so with the widespread use of computers. Determinants were invented independently by Kiowa, a Japanese, in 1683 and Leibnitz, a German and one of the inventors of calculus, in 1693. They were rediscovered in 1750 by Cramer, a Swiss, who used them for solving systems of linear equations. Matrices were invented by Cayley, an Englishman, during the nineteenth century, and they provide the most efficient ways of solving systems of linear equations, especially when there are a large number of variables.

10.1 Properties of Matrices

The two systems of equations

$$3x + 8y = -1 \quad \text{and} \quad 3E + 8Z = -1$$
$$x - 2y = 23 \qquad\qquad E - 2Z = 23$$

clearly have the same solution, namely $(13, -5)$. In fact, the essential information in either system is conveyed by the coefficients and constant terms 3, 8, −1, and 1, −2,

23. These numbers are usually written in the form

$$\begin{bmatrix} 3 & 8 & -1 \\ 1 & -2 & 23 \end{bmatrix}$$

which is an example of a matrix. We will see how to use matrices to solve systems of equations in the next section. A rectangular array of numbers with m rows and n columns

$$\begin{bmatrix} a_{11} & a_{12} & \cdots & a_{1j} & \cdots & a_{1n} \\ a_{21} & a_{22} & \cdots & a_{2j} & \cdots & a_{2n} \\ \cdots\cdots\cdots\cdots\cdots\cdots\cdots \\ a_{i1} & a_{i2} & \cdots & a_{ij} & \cdots & a_{in} \\ \cdots\cdots\cdots\cdots\cdots\cdots\cdots \\ a_{m1} & a_{m2} & \cdots & a_{mj} & \cdots & a_{mn} \end{bmatrix}$$

is called an $m \times n$ **matrix.** If $m = n$, it is called a **square matrix.** As seen from the array, an $m \times n$ matrix consists of m rows (horizontal) and n columns (vertical). Each number a_{ij} in the matrix is called an **element** of the matrix. In the above array, a_{ij} is the element in the ith row and jth column. Sometimes

$$A = (a_{ij})$$

is used to designate the matrix. The numbers i and j satisfy $1 \le i \le m$ and $1 \le j \le n$. The symbol $A_{m \times n}$ is used to indicate that A is an $m \times n$ matrix, and the **order or dimension** of a is $m \times n$. A matrix with $n = 1$ has just one column and is called a **column matrix,** while a matrix with $m = 1$ has only one row and is called a **row matrix.** For instance $[-3 \quad 14 \quad 6]$ is a row matrix.

Equality of matrices   Two m by n matrices are **equal** if and only if each element of one is equal to the corresponding element of the other. Symbolically, if $A = (a_{ij})$ and $B = (b_{ij})$ and both A and B are $m \times n$ matrices, then

$$A = B \text{ means } a_{ij} = b_{ij}$$

for all possible subscripts i and j.

▶ **EXAMPLE 1**   Verify these examples of matrix equality and inequality.

Solution   (a)

$$\begin{bmatrix} 3 & 2 & 1 \\ 2 & \sqrt{9} & 7 \end{bmatrix} = \begin{bmatrix} 3 & \sqrt{4} & 1 \\ \sqrt[3]{8} & 3 & 7 \end{bmatrix}$$

since all corresponding elements are the same.

(b)

$$\begin{bmatrix} 5 & -3 \\ 4 & -2 \end{bmatrix} = \begin{bmatrix} 2x + 1 & y \\ z + 2 & w - 1 \end{bmatrix}$$

if and only if $5 = 2x + 1$, $-3 = y$, $4 = z + 2$, and $-2 = w - 1$. Hence the matrices are equal if and only if

$$x = 2 \qquad y = -3 \qquad z = 2 \qquad \text{and} \qquad w = -1$$

(c)
$$\begin{bmatrix} 1 & 4 \\ 2 & 5 \end{bmatrix} \neq \begin{bmatrix} 2 & 1 \\ 5 & 4 \end{bmatrix}$$

Even though the sets of elements are the same, their positions are different. ◄

The matrix obtained by interchanging the rows and columns of a matrix A is called the **transpose** of A, and it is written A^T. If A is an $m \times n$ matrix, then A^T will be $n \times m$. For a row matrix A, the transpose A^T is a column matrix.

► **EXAMPLE 2** Find the transpose of

$$A = \begin{bmatrix} 3 & 1 & 2 \\ 4 & 0 & -5 \end{bmatrix}$$

Solution The first row of A becomes the first column of A^T, and the second row of A is the second column of the transpose.

$$A = \begin{bmatrix} 3 & 1 & 2 \\ 4 & 0 & -5 \end{bmatrix} \qquad A^T = \begin{bmatrix} 3 & 4 \\ 1 & 0 \\ 2 & -5 \end{bmatrix}$$ ◄

The **sum** of two $m \times n$ matrices A and B is the $m \times n$ matrix obtained by adding corresponding elements of A and B. Symbolically,

$$(a_{ij}) + (b_{ij}) = (a_{ij} + b_{ij})$$

The sum is defined if and only if both matrices have the same order. For instance two 3×3 matrices can be added, and two 2×5 matrices can be added, but we cannot add a 3×4 matrix and a 4×3 matrix.

► **EXAMPLE 3** Find the sum of the two 2×3 matrices below.

Solution The sum of

$$A = \begin{bmatrix} 1 & 3 & 5 \\ 2 & 4 & 6 \end{bmatrix} \quad \text{and} \quad B = \begin{bmatrix} -2 & 7 & 8 \\ 9 & -5 & -6 \end{bmatrix}$$

is
$$A + B = \begin{bmatrix} 1 + (-2) & 3 + 7 & 5 + 8 \\ 2 + 9 & 4 + (-5) & 6 + (-6) \end{bmatrix} = \begin{bmatrix} -1 & 10 & 13 \\ 11 & -1 & 0 \end{bmatrix}$$ ◄

The **product of a number k and the matrix A** is written kA, and it is the matrix obtained by multiplying each element of A by the constant k. Symbolically

$$kA = k(a_{ij}) = (k \cdot a_{ij})$$

When working with matrices, a real number is often called a **scalar,** and thus when working with kA, we are dealing with **scalar multiplication.** For example if

$$A = \begin{bmatrix} 1 & 3 & 16 \\ 0 & -2 & 5 \end{bmatrix} \quad \text{then} \quad 4A = \begin{bmatrix} 4 & 12 & 64 \\ 0 & -8 & 20 \end{bmatrix}$$

Notice that the definitions of $A + A$ and $2A$ both give the same matrix

$$A + A = 2A = \begin{bmatrix} 2 & 6 & 32 \\ 0 & -4 & 10 \end{bmatrix}$$

as would seem reasonable.

▶ **EXAMPLE 4**   Find $5A + 2B$ if

$$A = \begin{bmatrix} 1 & 2 \\ 3 & 4 \end{bmatrix} \qquad \text{and} \qquad B = \begin{bmatrix} 5 & 6 \\ 7 & 8 \end{bmatrix}$$

Solution

$$5A + 2B = \begin{bmatrix} 5 & 10 \\ 15 & 20 \end{bmatrix} + \begin{bmatrix} 10 & 12 \\ 14 & 16 \end{bmatrix} = \begin{bmatrix} 15 & 22 \\ 29 & 36 \end{bmatrix}$$ ◀

If each element of a matrix is 0, the matrix is called a **zero matrix,** and it is written 0. It is the identity for matrix addition *when that addition is defined* since

$$A + 0 = A \qquad \text{for any matrix } A$$

We have seen how to multiply a number and a matrix, and we will now discuss multiplying two matrices. **The product of two matrices A and B** is written AB, and it is defined if and only if the number of columns in A is equal to the numbers of rows in B. For instance, if A is a 2×4 matrix and B is a 4×3 matrix (as in Example 7 below), then AB is defined, and it is a 2×3 matrix. In general the product of an $m \times n$ matrix A and an $n \times p$ matrix B is defined, and it is an $m \times p$ matrix AB. The element c_{ij} in the ith row and jth column of the product AB is

$$c_{ij} = a_{i1}b_{1j} + a_{i2}b_{2j} + \cdots + a_{in}b_{nj}$$

To multiply the two matrices, multiply each element in row i of A by the corresponding element in column j of B, and then add these products.

$A \times B$

$$\begin{bmatrix} a_{11} & a_{12} & \cdots & a_{1n} \\ \vdots & \vdots & & \vdots \\ a_{i1} & a_{i2} & \cdots & a_{in} \\ \vdots & \vdots & & \vdots \\ a_{m1} & a_{m2} & \cdots & a_{mn} \end{bmatrix} \begin{bmatrix} b_{11} & \cdots & b_{1j} & \cdots & b_{1p} \\ b_{21} & \cdots & b_{2j} & \cdots & b_{2p} \\ \vdots & & \vdots & & \vdots \\ b_{n1} & \cdots & b_{nj} & \cdots & b_{np} \end{bmatrix}$$

Briefly, to find each element in the product:

> *Multiply a row in the first matrix by a column in the*
> *second matrix, element by element, and add products*

This is possible since, by assumption, the number of elements in each row of A is n and the number of elements in each column of B is n.

▶ **EXAMPLE 5**   Find the products AB and BA if

$$A = \begin{bmatrix} 3 & -2 \\ 1 & 4 \end{bmatrix} \qquad \text{and} \qquad B = \begin{bmatrix} 5 & 1 \\ -6 & 3 \end{bmatrix}$$

Solution

$$AB = \begin{bmatrix} (3)(5) + (-2)(-6) & (3)(1) + (-2)(3) \\ (1)(5) + (4)(-6) & (1)(1) + (4)(3) \end{bmatrix}$$

$$= \begin{bmatrix} 27 & -3 \\ -19 & 13 \end{bmatrix}$$

Similarly, we find that

$$BA = \begin{bmatrix} 5 & 1 \\ -6 & 3 \end{bmatrix}\begin{bmatrix} 3 & -2 \\ 1 & 4 \end{bmatrix}$$

$$= \begin{bmatrix} (5)(3) + (1)(1) & (5)(-2) + (1)(4) \\ (-6)(3) + (3)(1) & (-6)(-2) + (3)(4) \end{bmatrix}$$

$$= \begin{bmatrix} 16 & -6 \\ -15 & 24 \end{bmatrix}$$

and in this case we see that $AB \neq BA$.

In general, even if both AB and BA are defined, they may or may not be equal. **Matrix multiplication is not commutative.**

It is however always true that $A(B + C) = AB + AC$, when all sums and products are defined. **The distributive law does hold.**

▶ **EXAMPLE 6**   Verify the distributive law for the matrices below.

Solution   If

$$A = \begin{bmatrix} 1 & 0 \\ 4 & 3 \end{bmatrix} \quad B = \begin{bmatrix} 2 & -5 \\ 1 & 3 \end{bmatrix} \quad \text{and} \quad C = \begin{bmatrix} 4 & 7 \\ -2 & 0 \end{bmatrix}$$

then

$$A(B + C) = \begin{bmatrix} 1 & 0 \\ 4 & 3 \end{bmatrix}\begin{bmatrix} 6 & 2 \\ -1 & 3 \end{bmatrix} = \begin{bmatrix} 6 & 2 \\ 21 & 17 \end{bmatrix}$$

and

$$AB + AC = \begin{bmatrix} 2 & -5 \\ 11 & -11 \end{bmatrix} + \begin{bmatrix} 4 & 7 \\ 10 & 28 \end{bmatrix} = \begin{bmatrix} 6 & 2 \\ 21 & 17 \end{bmatrix}$$

▶ **EXAMPLE 7**   What are AB and BA if

$$A = \begin{bmatrix} 3 & 1 & 4 & 2 \\ 5 & 0 & 2 & 6 \end{bmatrix} \quad \text{and} \quad B = \begin{bmatrix} 3 & 1 & 3 \\ 2 & 2 & 5 \\ 1 & 2 & 4 \\ 4 & 0 & 3 \end{bmatrix}$$

Solution   Since A is 2×4 and B is 4×3, the product AB is defined because $4 = 4$, and AB is a 2×3 matrix. We have

$$AB = \begin{bmatrix} (9 + 2 + 4 + 8) & (3 + 2 + 8 + 0) & (9 + 5 + 16 + 6) \\ (15 + 0 + 2 + 24) & (5 + 0 + 4 + 0) & (15 + 0 + 8 + 18) \end{bmatrix}$$

$$= \begin{bmatrix} 23 & 13 & 36 \\ 41 & 9 & 41 \end{bmatrix}$$

However BA is not defined since B is a 4×3 matrix, A is a 2×4 matrix, and $3 \neq 2$. ◢

If A is an $m \times n$ matrix and A^T is its transpose, then:

(i) $A \cdot A^T$ is a square matrix of order m since A is $m \times n$ and A^T is $n \times m$.

(ii) $A^T \cdot A$ is a square matrix of order n since A^T is $n \times m$ and A is $m \times n$.

If A is an $n \times n$ matrix and if each entry in the **main diagonal** is 1 (the diagonal from upper left to lower right) and all other elements are zero, the matrix is called an **identity matrix** since it acts as an identity for matrix multiplication. It is designated by I or I_n. Thus

$$I_2 = \begin{bmatrix} 1 & 0 \\ 0 & 1 \end{bmatrix} \quad \text{and} \quad I_3 = \begin{bmatrix} 1 & 0 & 0 \\ 0 & 1 & 0 \\ 0 & 0 & 1 \end{bmatrix}$$

are identity matrices.

Now that we have defined matrix addition and multiplication, we want to emphasize the different conditions under which each operation can be performed. The sum $A + B$ is defined if and only if A and B have (i) the same number of rows and (ii) the same number of columns. The number of rows may be different from the number of columns.

$$\begin{array}{ccc} A & + & B \\ m \times n & & m \times n \end{array}$$

Conditions for sum to exist

The product AB is defined if and only if the number of columns in A equals the number of rows in B.

$$\begin{array}{ccc} A & \times & B \\ m \times n & & n \times p \end{array}$$

Conditions for product to exist

The $n \times n$ Matrices Do Not Form a Field

In order to briefly discuss the *field properties* (Chap. 1), we will suppose now that A, B, and C are $n \times n$ matrices. Then the sum of any two is defined, the product of any two is also defined, and each is an $n \times n$ matrix. The associative laws

$$(A + B) + C = A + (B + C) \qquad \text{and} \qquad (AB)C = A(BC)$$

are true. For addition it is easy to prove, while for multiplication it is hard to prove. The matrix 0 is the identity for addition, and $I = I_n$ is the identity for multiplication, as mentioned earlier. The additive inverse of $A = (a_{ij})$ is $-A = (-a_{ij})$ since $A + (-A) = (a_{ij} - a_{ij}) = (0) = 0$. Addition is commutative since

$$A + B = (a_{ij}) + (b_{ij}) = (a_{ij} + b_{ij}) = (b_{ij} + a_{ij}) = (b_{ij}) + (a_{ij}) = B + A$$

The distributive law $A(B + C) = AB + AC$ also holds (see Prob. 44).

The two field properties which **do not hold** are the commutative law for multiplication and the existence of a multiplicative inverse. Example 5 shows that AB is not always equal to BA. Determinants will be presented later in this chapter, and with their help it can be shown that the $n \times n$ matrix A has an inverse if and only if the determinant of A is not zero. We will also present two methods for finding A^{-1} when it exists.

The matrix product $A \cdot A$ is written A^2. For A^3, we can write either $(A \cdot A) \cdot A$ or $A \cdot (A \cdot A)$. They have the same value because of the associative law of multiplication for matrices.

The definition of matrix multiplication seems artificial at first, but there are many reasons for its definition. One reason is its utility, illustrated in Example 8 below. Another is that it allows for compact notation in many cases. For instance if

$$ A = [a \quad b \quad c] \qquad X = \begin{bmatrix} x \\ y \\ z \end{bmatrix} \qquad \text{and} \qquad k \text{ is a constant} $$

Then $AX = k$ is the same equation as $ax + by + cz = k$.

Matrices are used in many ways in science, business, and government to *organize data systematically*. Frequently the number of rows or columns in "real world" matrices is so large that computers must be used to handle them efficiently. In fact there are currently hand-held calculators which can efficiently handle matrices with as many as 20 rows and columns, and when you read this, it will be many more.

▶ **EXAMPLE 8** Suppose that a car dealer sells cars, vans, and trucks at two locations, A and B. Then the vehicles received for January, February, and March may be written as the matrices J, F, and M:

$$ J = \begin{array}{c} \\ \\ \end{array}\begin{array}{ccc} C & V & T \\ \begin{bmatrix} 38 & 9 & 22 \\ 49 & 14 & 24 \end{bmatrix} \end{array}\begin{array}{c} A \\ B \end{array} \quad F = \begin{array}{ccc} C & V & T \\ \begin{bmatrix} 33 & 7 & 21 \\ 45 & 9 & 21 \end{bmatrix} \end{array}\begin{array}{c} A \\ B \end{array} \quad M = \begin{array}{ccc} C & V & T \\ \begin{bmatrix} 43 & 10 & 28 \\ 51 & 8 & 26 \end{bmatrix} \end{array}\begin{array}{c} A \\ B \end{array} $$

For example, there were 49 cars at location B in January and 10 vans at A in March. Then the total number of each type of vehicle received for the 3 months is given by

$$ J + F + M = \begin{array}{ccc} C & V & T \\ \begin{bmatrix} 114 & 26 & 71 \\ 145 & 31 & 71 \end{bmatrix} \end{array}\begin{array}{c} A \\ B \end{array} $$

Suppose that the costs are given in dollars by the matrix D:

$$ D = \begin{array}{cc} \text{Purchase} & \text{Overhead} \\ \begin{bmatrix} 9{,}300 & 340 \\ 15{,}400 & 500 \\ 22{,}900 & 660 \end{bmatrix} \end{array}\begin{array}{c} C \\ V \\ T \end{array} $$

Then for January, the matrix product

$$ JD = \begin{bmatrix} 38 & 9 & 22 \\ 49 & 14 & 24 \end{bmatrix}\begin{bmatrix} 9{,}300 & 340 \\ 15{,}400 & 500 \\ 22{,}900 & 660 \end{bmatrix} = \begin{array}{cc} \text{Purchase} & \text{Overhead} \\ \begin{bmatrix} 995{,}800 & 31{,}940 \\ 1{,}220{,}900 & 39{,}500 \end{bmatrix} \end{array}\begin{array}{c} A \\ B \end{array} $$

shows, for instance, that location A had \$995,800 in purchase prices and \$31,940 in overhead costs. Larger matrices would clearly be needed for a complete analysis.

Problems 65 to 68 ask further questions about this example. Problems 69 to 72 deal with another application of matrices.

It can be shown that if each entry in a square matrix is positive and the sum of the elements in each row is one, then A^n approaches a square matrix in which each row is the same. We will illustrate this in the next example.

EXAMPLE 9 For the matrix A below, calculate A^2, A^4, A^8, and A^{16}.

Solution We retain four digits in all calculations below, and use

$$A^4 = (A^2)^2 \qquad A^8 = (A^4)^2 \qquad A^{16} = (A^8)^2$$

Then

$$A = \begin{bmatrix} 0.6 & 0.4 \\ 0.2 & 0.8 \end{bmatrix}$$

$$A^2 = \begin{bmatrix} 0.6 & 0.4 \\ 0.2 & 0.8 \end{bmatrix}\begin{bmatrix} 0.6 & 0.4 \\ 0.2 & 0.8 \end{bmatrix} = \begin{bmatrix} 0.44 & 0.56 \\ 0.28 & 0.72 \end{bmatrix}$$

$$A^4 = \begin{bmatrix} 0.44 & 0.56 \\ 0.28 & 0.72 \end{bmatrix}\begin{bmatrix} 0.44 & 0.56 \\ 0.28 & 0.72 \end{bmatrix} = \begin{bmatrix} 0.3504 & 0.6496 \\ 0.3248 & 0.6752 \end{bmatrix}$$

$$A^8 = \begin{bmatrix} 0.3504 & 0.6496 \\ 0.3248 & 0.6752 \end{bmatrix}\begin{bmatrix} 0.3504 & 0.6496 \\ 0.3248 & 0.6752 \end{bmatrix} = \begin{bmatrix} 0.3338 & 0.6662 \\ 0.3331 & 0.6669 \end{bmatrix}$$

$$A^{16} = \begin{bmatrix} 0.3338 & 0.6662 \\ 0.3331 & 0.6669 \end{bmatrix}\begin{bmatrix} 0.3338 & 0.6662 \\ 0.3331 & 0.6669 \end{bmatrix} = \begin{bmatrix} 0.3333 & 0.6667 \\ 0.3333 & 0.6667 \end{bmatrix}$$

A theorem, which we will not prove, allows the following business interpretation of the calculations above. Suppose that from each month to the next, company C retains 60 percent = 0.6 of its customers, and loses 40 percent = 0.4 of its customers to the competition. That is why the first row in A is [0.6   0.4]. Furthermore suppose that the competition loses 20 percent of its customers to company C and retains 80 percent of its own customers. Thus the second row of A is [0.2   0.8]. In each row, the number in the **main diagonal** position gives the fraction of its **own customers** that are retained from one month to the next. Then the theorem says that in the long run, company C will have one-third of the total market share and the competition will have two-thirds of the total market share, since these (approximately) are the two numbers in the nearly identical rows of A^n for large values of n. The powers of A above show that the "long run" in this situation occurs after about 8 months, and it is close to that even after 4 months.

EXERCISE 10.1

Find the values of a, b, c, and d so that the statement in each of Probs. 1 to 4 is true.

1. $\begin{bmatrix} 2 & 3 \\ -2 & a \end{bmatrix} = \begin{bmatrix} b & c \\ d & 0 \end{bmatrix}$

2. $\begin{bmatrix} 1 & a & 3 \\ c & 4 & -2 \end{bmatrix} = \begin{bmatrix} b & -5 & d \\ 0 & 4 & -2 \end{bmatrix}$

3. $\begin{bmatrix} a & 3 & 2 \\ 5 & 0 & 6 \end{bmatrix} = \begin{bmatrix} -1 & 5 \\ 3 & 0 \\ 2 & 6 \end{bmatrix}$

4. $\begin{bmatrix} 2 & a \\ -1 & 0 \\ b & 7 \end{bmatrix} = \begin{bmatrix} c & 3 \\ -1 & 0 \\ 6 & d \end{bmatrix}$

State the order and find the transpose of the matrix in each of Probs. 5 to 8.

5. $\begin{bmatrix} 2 & 1 & 5 \\ 3 & -6 & 2 \end{bmatrix}$ **6.** $\begin{bmatrix} -1 & 4 & 0 \\ 4 & 5 & 2 \\ 0 & 2 & 3 \end{bmatrix}$

7. $\begin{bmatrix} 3 & -2 \\ 1 & 5 \\ 0 & 4 \end{bmatrix}$ **8.** $\begin{bmatrix} 3 & 4 \\ 5 & 8 \end{bmatrix}$

Use $A = \begin{bmatrix} 3 & -1 & 2 \\ 4 & 0 & 5 \end{bmatrix}$ and $B = \begin{bmatrix} -2 & 3 & 0 \\ 1 & 5 & -4 \end{bmatrix}$ to evaluate the matrices called for in Probs. 9 to 16. If the matrix asked for is not defined, say so.

9. $2A$ **10.** $B^T + A$ **11.** $-B$
12. $-3A$ **13.** $A^T + B$ **14.** $4B - A$
15. $3A + 2B$ **16.** $2A - 5B$

Find the matrix X in each of Probs. 17 to 20.

17. $X - \begin{bmatrix} 3 & 1 \\ 0 & -2 \end{bmatrix} = \begin{bmatrix} 4 & 1 \\ 0 & 3 \end{bmatrix}$

18. $X - 2\begin{bmatrix} 2 & -1 \\ 3 & 5 \end{bmatrix} = 3\begin{bmatrix} 1 & 2 \\ -2 & -3 \end{bmatrix}$

19. $2X - 3\begin{bmatrix} 2 & 0 \\ 4 & -8 \end{bmatrix} = 2\begin{bmatrix} -3 & 5 \\ -7 & 12 \end{bmatrix}$

20. $3X + \begin{bmatrix} 3 & -8 \\ 11 & 0 \end{bmatrix} = 3\begin{bmatrix} 1 & -3 \\ 4 & -2 \end{bmatrix}$

Verify the equations in Probs. 21 to 32 for these matrices.

$A = \begin{bmatrix} 3 & -1 \\ 2 & 1 \end{bmatrix}$ $B = \begin{bmatrix} 4 & 1 \\ 2 & 7 \end{bmatrix}$ and $C = \begin{bmatrix} 6 & -6 \\ 2 & -3 \end{bmatrix}$

21. $(A + 3B) + 4C = A + (3B + 4C)$
22. $A + (2B + 4C) = (A + 4C) + 2B$
23. $(3A)^T = 3(A^T)$
24. $(B + C)^T = B^T + C^T$
25. $(2A)(B) = A(2B)$
26. $(A - B)C = AC - BC$
27. $(AC)B = A(CB)$
28. $A(2B + 3C) = 2AB + 3AC$
29. $A(B^2) = (AB)B$ **30.** $A(BA) = (AB)A$

31. $(A^T)^2 = (A^2)^T$ **32.** $(AB)^T = B^T A^T$

Perform the indicated calculations to verify the inequalities in Probs. 33 to 36, if

$A = \begin{bmatrix} 3 & 0 & 1 \\ 2 & -1 & 4 \\ -2 & 3 & 5 \end{bmatrix}$ and $B = \begin{bmatrix} -1 & 4 & -3 \\ 3 & -2 & 5 \\ 0 & 1 & 2 \end{bmatrix}$

33. $AB \neq BA$
34. $(A + B)(A - B) \neq A^2 - B^2$
35. $(AB)^2 \neq A^2 B^2$
36. $(A + B)^2 \neq A^2 + 2AB + B^2$

Find the indicated products in each of Probs. 37 to 40.

37. $\begin{bmatrix} 2 & 1 & -3 \\ 3 & 0 & 1 \\ -2 & 2 & 5 \end{bmatrix}\begin{bmatrix} 2 \\ 0 \\ 1 \end{bmatrix}$ **38.** $\begin{bmatrix} 1 & -2 \\ 4 & 3 \\ 3 & 5 \end{bmatrix}\begin{bmatrix} 3 \\ 2 \end{bmatrix}$

39. $\begin{bmatrix} 1 & 2 & 4 \\ 3 & -1 & 0 \end{bmatrix}\begin{bmatrix} 1 & 3 \\ 2 & -1 \\ 4 & 0 \end{bmatrix}$

40. $\begin{bmatrix} 4 & -2 \\ 1 & 3 \\ 0 & 5 \end{bmatrix}\begin{bmatrix} 2 & -1 \\ 3 & 0 \end{bmatrix}$

Prove the statements in Probs. 41 to 48 if h and k are real numbers and A, B, and C are the matrices below.

$A = \begin{bmatrix} a & b \\ c & d \end{bmatrix}$ $B = \begin{bmatrix} p & q \\ r & s \end{bmatrix}$ $C = \begin{bmatrix} w & x \\ y & z \end{bmatrix}$

41. $(AB)^T = B^T A^T$ **42.** $(A + B)^T = A^T + B^T$
43. $A(B + C) = AB + AC$
44. $A(BC) = (AB)C$
45. $h(A + B) = hA + hB$
46. $(h + k)A = hA + kA$
47. $hk(A) = h(kA)$ **48.** $hk(AB) = (hA)(kB)$

In Probs. 49 to 52, let

$A = \begin{bmatrix} 0.1 & 0.3 & 0.6 \\ 0.4 & 0.4 & 0.2 \\ 0.7 & 0.2 & 0.1 \end{bmatrix}$ $B = \begin{bmatrix} 0.5 & 0.2 & 0.3 \\ 0.2 & 0.2 & 0.6 \\ 0.6 & 0.3 & 0.1 \end{bmatrix}$

$C = \begin{bmatrix} 0.8 & 0.1 & 0.1 \\ 0.3 & 0.3 & 0.4 \\ 0.5 & 0.4 & 0.1 \end{bmatrix}$

Notice that for each matrix, the sum of the elements in each row is one. Show by calculation that the same thing is true for each matrix below.

49. AB **50.** C^2 **51.** $(AC)^2$ **52.** CBA
53. Show that for the matrix below, the product of all three numbers in each row and in each column always has the same value.

$$\begin{bmatrix} 2 & 3 & 20 \\ 5 & 4 & 6 \\ 12 & 10 & 1 \end{bmatrix}$$

54. Show that if $w^3 = 1$ but $w \neq 1$, then $w^2 + w + 1 = 0$ and

$$\begin{bmatrix} 1 & 1 & 1 \\ 1 & w & w^2 \\ 1 & w^2 & w \end{bmatrix} \cdot \begin{bmatrix} 1 & 1 & 1 \\ 1 & w^2 & w \\ 1 & w & w^2 \end{bmatrix} = \begin{bmatrix} 3 & 0 & 0 \\ 0 & 3 & 0 \\ 0 & 0 & 3 \end{bmatrix}$$

In Probs. 55 and 56, use the matrices P, Q, and R below.

$$P = \begin{bmatrix} 0 & a & b \\ 0 & 0 & c \\ 0 & 0 & 0 \end{bmatrix} \quad Q = \begin{bmatrix} 0 & f & g \\ 0 & 0 & h \\ 0 & 0 & 0 \end{bmatrix} \quad R = \begin{bmatrix} 0 & x & y \\ 0 & 0 & z \\ 0 & 0 & 0 \end{bmatrix}$$

55 Prove that $PQR = 0$ (= the zero matrix).
56. Show that $(PQ)^2 = P^2Q^2$.

In Probs. 57 to 60, calculate A^2, A^4, and A^8. In each problem, the matrices A^n will approach a matrix with each row being the same. See Example 9.

57. $A = \begin{bmatrix} 0.7 & 0.3 \\ 0.2 & 0.8 \end{bmatrix}$ **58.** $A = \begin{bmatrix} 0.6 & 0.4 \\ 0.3 & 0.7 \end{bmatrix}$

59. $A = \begin{bmatrix} 0.5 & 0.5 \\ 0.1 & 0.9 \end{bmatrix}$ **60.** $A = \begin{bmatrix} 0.9 & 0.1 \\ 0.3 & 0.7 \end{bmatrix}$

In Probs. 61 to 64, let

$$A = \begin{bmatrix} 7 & 9 \\ 3 & 4 \end{bmatrix} \quad \text{and} \quad B = \begin{bmatrix} 5 & 3 \\ 12 & 7 \end{bmatrix}$$

61. Find a 2×2 matrix M for which $AM = I$, where I is the 2×2 identity matrix.
62. Find a 2×2 matrix F for which $FB = I$, where I is the 2×2 identity matrix.

63. Find the product below, and describe in words its relationship to A.

$$A\begin{bmatrix} 0 & 1 \\ 1 & 0 \end{bmatrix}$$

64. Find the product below, and describe in words its relationship to B.

$$\begin{bmatrix} 0 & 1 \\ 1 & 0 \end{bmatrix}B$$

In Probs. 65 to 68, refer to the business situation described in Example 8. Answer each question, and state which matrix product should be used to do so.

65. For February, what was the total overhead cost at B?
66. For March, what was the total purchase cost at location A?
67. For the three months combined, what was the total purchase cost at locations A and B combined?
68. For the three months combined, what was the total overhead cost at location B?

In Probs. 69 to 72, suppose that the mall store L and the college store C sell these types of pizzas: pepperoni P, mushroom M, and all the rest R. Assume that the number of pizzas, in hundreds, sold in September S and October T are

$$S = \begin{bmatrix} P & M & R \\ 33 & 19 & 47 \\ 54 & 21 & 46 \end{bmatrix} \begin{matrix} L \\ C \end{matrix} \quad T = \begin{bmatrix} P & M & R \\ 36 & 12 & 41 \\ 73 & 34 & 89 \end{bmatrix} \begin{matrix} L \\ C \end{matrix}$$

Suppose that the cost per pizza of ingredients I and delivery D is given by the matrix

$$A = \begin{bmatrix} I & D \\ 3.45 & 0.90 \\ 2.90 & 0.90 \\ 3.80 & 0.90 \end{bmatrix} \begin{matrix} P \\ M \\ R \end{matrix}$$

69. What do the entries of the matrix $\frac{1}{31}T$ tell us?
70. What do the entries of the matrix $S + T$ tell us?
71. Use the matrix SA to find the total ingredient cost in September at the college store.
72. Use the matrix TA to find the total cost of ingredients in October for the two stores combined.

10.2 Matrices and Systems of Linear Equations

In Chap. 9, we studied several methods for solving a system of linear equations, primarily elimination and substitution. We will now consider a procedure adapted to matrices. Suppose we have the following system of n linear equations in the n variables $x_1, x_2, \ldots, x_n$:

$$a_{11}x_1 + a_{12}x_2 + \cdots + a_{1n}x_n = k_1$$

$$a_{21}x_1 + a_{22}x_2 + \cdots + a_{2n}x_n = k_2$$

$$\cdots\cdots\cdots\cdots\cdots\cdots\cdots\cdots\cdots$$

$$a_{n1}x_1 + a_{n2}x_2 + \cdots + a_{nn}x_n = k_n$$

(10.1)

Then each of the following operations will produce a system which is **equivalent** to the given system (10.1). That is, the systems have the same solutions.

Operations which produce equivalent systems

1. Interchange any two equations.
2. Multiply any equation by a nonzero constant.
3. Add a multiple of any equation to any other equation.

The matrix whose elements are the coefficients of the given system of equations, in the same relative position, is called the **coefficient matrix.** If the constant terms are included on the right of the coefficient matrix as another column, the new matrix is called the **augmented matrix.** Thus for the system

$$x + y + z = 2$$

$$2x + 5y + 3z = 1$$

$$3x - y - 2z = -1$$

(1)

the coefficient matrix A is

$$A = \begin{bmatrix} 1 & 1 & 1 \\ 2 & 5 & 3 \\ 3 & -1 & -2 \end{bmatrix}$$

and the augmented matrix B is

$$B = \begin{bmatrix} 1 & 1 & 1 & 2 \\ 2 & 5 & 3 & 1 \\ 3 & -1 & -2 & -1 \end{bmatrix}$$

If we have the augmented matrix, we know each equation of the given system of equations just as clearly as if the variables and equality signs were written in. We may use the same operations on the rows of the augmented matrix as we did on the equations in the given system (10.1). When used on a matrix, they are called either **elementary row operations** or **elementary row transformations.**

For the augmented matrix of a system of linear equations, applying the elementary row operations below will produce the matrix of an equivalent system of linear equations.

1.   Interchange any two rows of the augmented matrix.
2.   Multiply any row of the augmented matrix by a nonzero constant.
3.   Add a nonzero multiple of any row to any other row, term by term.

These elementary row operations will be abbreviated as

$$R_i \longleftrightarrow R_j \qquad k \cdot R_i \qquad R_i + k \cdot R_j$$

We will use elementary row operations to change the augmented matrix into one which represents an equivalent set of equations, but which is easier to solve. The **main diagonal** of the matrix is the diagonal starting at the top left element and proceeding down and to the right. The goal is to produce a new matrix in which:

Only 0 occurs below the main diagonal

Only 1 or 0 occurs on the main diagonal, 1 if possible

This method of solution is called **gaussian elimination** after the German mathematician Karl Gauss (1777–1855). It produces a matrix which allows the corresponding system of equations to be solved by **back substitution,** which means substituting known values back into previous equations.

▶ **EXAMPLE 1**   Solve the system of two equations in two variables

$$3x + 2y = -17$$
$$7x + 5y = -41$$

Solution   The augmented matrix is

$$\begin{bmatrix} 3 & 2 & -17 \\ 7 & 5 & -41 \end{bmatrix}$$

We first multiply row 1 by $\frac{1}{3}$.

$$\begin{bmatrix} 1 & \frac{2}{3} & -\frac{17}{3} \\ 7 & 5 & -41 \end{bmatrix} \qquad \frac{1}{3}R_1$$

$$\begin{bmatrix} 1 & \frac{2}{3} & -\frac{17}{3} \\ 0 & \frac{1}{3} & -\frac{4}{3} \end{bmatrix} \qquad R_2 - 7R_1$$

$$\begin{bmatrix} 1 & \frac{2}{3} & -\frac{17}{3} \\ 0 & 1 & -4 \end{bmatrix} \qquad 3R_2$$

This last matrix corresponds to the system of equations

$$x + \tfrac{2}{3}y = -\tfrac{17}{3}$$
$$y = -4$$

Using $y = -4$ in the first equation gives

$$x + \tfrac{2}{3}(-4) = -\tfrac{17}{3}$$

$$x = -\tfrac{17}{3} + \tfrac{8}{3} = -\tfrac{9}{3} = -3$$

The solution is $(-3, -4)$, which should be checked in the original equations. ◢

The next example shows the ease with which a system of three equations in three variables can be solved by back substitution after gaussian elimination has been used.

▶ **EXAMPLE 2**   Solve the system of equations

$$x + 9y - 8z = 9$$

$$y + 3z = 39$$

$$z = 10$$

Solution   The third equation tells us that $z = 10$. Substituting back into the second equation shows that

$$y = 39 - 3z = 39 - 3(10) = 39 - 30 = 9$$

Now using $z = 10$ and $y = 9$ in the first equation gives

$$x = 9 + 8z - 9y = 9 + 8(10) - 9(9) = 9 + 80 - 81 = 8$$

The solution is $(8, 9, 10)$, which can be checked in the given equations. ◢

Examples 3 through 5 show how to deal with gaussian elimination when there is one solution, no solutions, or an infinite number of solutions.

▶ **EXAMPLE 3**   We will solve the system (1) below, which we saw earlier on page 505:

One solution

$$x + y + z = 2$$

$$2x + 5y + 3z = 1 \qquad \textbf{(1)}$$

$$3x - y - 2z = -1$$

Solution   The matrix B is the augmented matrix for the system (1):

$$B = \begin{bmatrix} 1 & 1 & 1 & 2 \\ 2 & 5 & 3 & 1 \\ 3 & -1 & -2 & -1 \end{bmatrix}$$

We want to perform row operations on B so as to replace each element of the main diagonal by a 1 and the elements below the main diagonal by zeros. We do this **one column at a time, working from left to right.** We normally begin by getting a 1 as the first element in the main diagonal, but it is already 1. Thus we make each other element in the first column 0.

$$\begin{bmatrix} 1 & 1 & 1 & 2 \\ 0 & 3 & 1 & -3 \\ 0 & -4 & -5 & -7 \end{bmatrix} \quad \begin{matrix} \\ R_2 - 2R_1 \\ R_3 - 3R_1 \end{matrix}$$

We have now completed the first column since the main diagonal element is 1 and those below are 0. We now use row operations for the other columns also:

$$\begin{bmatrix} 1 & 1 & 1 & 2 \\ 0 & 1 & \frac{1}{3} & -1 \\ 0 & -4 & -5 & -7 \end{bmatrix} \quad \frac{1}{3}R_2$$

Second column complete
$$\begin{bmatrix} 1 & 1 & 1 & 2 \\ 0 & 1 & \frac{1}{3} & -1 \\ 0 & 0 & -\frac{11}{3} & -11 \end{bmatrix} \quad R_3 + 4R_2$$

$$\begin{bmatrix} 1 & 1 & 1 & 2 \\ 0 & 1 & \frac{1}{3} & -1 \\ 0 & 0 & 1 & 3 \end{bmatrix} \quad -\frac{3}{11}R_3$$

The last matrix represents the system of equations

$$x + y + z = 2 \qquad y + \frac{z}{3} = -1 \qquad z = 3$$

We may now use back substitution to solve the system. Starting with the last equation, we see that $z = 3$. From the second equation, we have $y + \frac{3}{3} = -1$; hence $y = -1 - 1 = -2$. Now the first equation gives $x + (-2) + 3 = 2$, and so $x = 2 + 2 - 3 = 1$. The solution $(1, -2, 3)$ may be checked by substituting in the given system (1).

◢

The matrix method of solution is valuable and systematic, but doing it with pencil and paper is often slow and detailed. It, like many other techniques, is ideal for the computer or a hand-held, programmable calculator.

▶ EXAMPLE 4 Solve $x + y + 2z = 5$, $2x - y + 3z = 4$, and $5x - y + 8z = 10$.

Solution We will use row operations on the augmented matrix.

No solution

$$\begin{bmatrix} 1 & 1 & 2 & 5 \\ 2 & -1 & 3 & 4 \\ 5 & -1 & 8 & 10 \end{bmatrix}$$

First column complete
$$\begin{bmatrix} 1 & 1 & 2 & 5 \\ 0 & -3 & -1 & -6 \\ 0 & -6 & -2 & -15 \end{bmatrix} \quad \begin{array}{l} R_2 - 2R_1 \\ R_3 - 5R_1 \end{array}$$

$$\begin{bmatrix} 1 & 1 & 2 & 5 \\ 0 & 1 & \frac{1}{3} & 2 \\ 0 & -6 & -2 & -15 \end{bmatrix} \quad -\frac{1}{3}R_2$$

Second column complete
$$\begin{bmatrix} 1 & 1 & 2 & 5 \\ 0 & 1 & \frac{1}{3} & 2 \\ 0 & 0 & 0 & -3 \end{bmatrix} \quad R_3 + 6R_2$$

Now the third row of the last matrix corresponds to the equation

$$0 \cdot x + 0 \cdot y + 0 \cdot z = -3$$

which is not satisfied by any values for x, y, and z. Hence the given system has **no solution.** ◢

Infinite number of solutions   Solving linear equations by row operations may be done also when there is more than one solution. We must take care in interpreting the equation corresponding to the last row of the matrix.

▶ **EXAMPLE 5**   Solve $x + 3y - z = 1$, $3x - y + z = 3$, and $5x - 5y + 3z = 5$.

Solution   We begin with the augmented matrix:

$$\begin{bmatrix} 1 & 3 & -1 & 1 \\ 3 & -1 & 1 & 3 \\ 5 & -5 & 3 & 5 \end{bmatrix}$$

First column complete
$$\begin{bmatrix} 1 & 3 & -1 & 1 \\ 0 & -10 & 4 & 0 \\ 0 & -20 & 8 & 0 \end{bmatrix} \quad \begin{matrix} \\ R_2 - 3R_1 \\ R_3 - 5R_1 \end{matrix}$$

$$\begin{bmatrix} 1 & 3 & -1 & 1 \\ 0 & -10 & 4 & 0 \\ 0 & 0 & 0 & 0 \end{bmatrix} \quad \begin{matrix} \\ \\ R_3 - 2R_2 \end{matrix}$$

The third row represents the equation

$$0 \cdot x + 0 \cdot y + 0 \cdot z = 0$$

which is satisfied by any x, y, and z. The second row represents $-10y + 4z = 0$, and solving for y gives

$$y = \frac{4z}{10} = \frac{2z}{5}$$

The first row corresponds to the equation

$$x + 3y - z = 1$$

$$x + 3\left(\frac{2z}{5}\right) - z = 1 \qquad \text{replacing } y \text{ by } \frac{2z}{5}$$

$$x = 1 + z - \frac{6z}{5} = 1 - \frac{z}{5} \qquad \text{solving for } x$$

This means that for any value of z, there are values for x and y such that (x, y, z) is a solution of the given system of equations. For instance,

$$\text{If } z = 2, \text{ then } y = \tfrac{4}{5} \text{ and } x = \tfrac{3}{5}$$

and
$$\text{If } z = 5, \text{ then } y = 2 \text{ and } x = 0$$

In fact, any solution has the form

$$\left(1 - \frac{z}{5}, \frac{2z}{5}, z\right) \tag{2}$$

for some value of z, and the system has an **infinite number of solutions.**
There are other ways to write the solutions also. The equation $-10y + 4z = 0$ could have been solved for z instead of y and given $z = 5y/2$. Then $x + 3y - z = 1$ shows that

$$x = 1 + z - 3y = 1 + \frac{5y}{2} - 3y = 1 - \frac{y}{2}$$

and so the solutions may also be written

$$\left(1 - \frac{y}{2}, y, \frac{5y}{2}\right) \tag{3}$$

Alternatively, using $z = 5t$ in (2) gives the solutions in the form $(1 - t, 2t, 5t)$ for any real number t. The values $z = 5$, $y = 2$, or $t = 1$ each yield the particular solution $(0, 2, 5)$.   ◢

NOTE   These same procedures will allow three equations in four variables to be solved, or m equations in n variables. We just have to be sure to

Interpret each row correctly as an equation

In Example 6, we show how using a calculator simplifies gaussian elimination. Not only is the arithmetic easier, but the only elementary row operations needed are

(a) Multiply a row by a constant.
(b) Subtract one row from another.

The same thing could, of course, be done with arithmetic by hand, but it would involve formidable calculations. For solving large systems on a computer, much more sophisticated methods are used to cut down the number of calculations as much as possible.

▶ **EXAMPLE 6**   Solve the system of equations

Solution by calculator

$$3x + 7y - 10z = -6$$
$$-9x + 14y - 5z = -14$$
$$6x - 7y + 5z = 12$$

Solution   We will use four decimal places in all calculations in this example. We begin with the augmented matrix:

$$\begin{bmatrix} 3 & 7 & -10 & -6 \\ -9 & 14 & -5 & -14 \\ 6 & -7 & 5 & 12 \end{bmatrix}$$

Next we perform elementary row operations:

$$\begin{bmatrix} 1 & 2.3333 & -3.3333 & -2.0000 \\ 1 & -1.5556 & 0.5556 & 1.5556 \\ 1 & -1.1667 & 0.8333 & 2.0000 \end{bmatrix} \quad \begin{matrix} \frac{1}{3}R_1 \\ -\frac{1}{9}R_2 \\ \frac{1}{6}R_3 \end{matrix}$$

$$\begin{bmatrix} 1 & 2.3333 & -3.3333 & -2.0000 \\ 0 & -3.8889 & 3.8889 & 3.5556 \\ 0 & -3.5000 & 4.1666 & 4.0000 \end{bmatrix} \quad \begin{matrix} \\ R_2 - R_1 \\ R_3 - R_1 \end{matrix}$$

This completes the first column.

$$\begin{bmatrix} 1 & 2.3333 & -3.3333 & -2.0000 \\ 0 & 1 & -1.0000 & -0.9143 \\ 0 & 1 & -1.1905 & -1.1429 \end{bmatrix} \quad \begin{matrix} \\ (-1/3.8889)R_2 \\ (-1/3.5000)R_3 \end{matrix}$$

$$\begin{bmatrix} 1 & 2.3333 & -3.3333 & -2.0000 \\ 0 & 1 & -1.0000 & -0.9143 \\ 0 & 0 & -0.1905 & -0.2286 \end{bmatrix} \quad \begin{matrix} \\ \\ R_3 - R_2 \end{matrix}$$

This completes the second column. The equation corresponding to the third row is $-0.1905z = -0.2286$, and therefore

$$z = \frac{-0.2286}{-0.1905} = 1.2000$$

Using this in the second row or equation gives

$$y = z - 0.9143 = 1.2000 - 0.9143 = 0.2857$$

From the first equation

$$x = -2.3333y + 3.3333z - 2.0000$$

$$= -2.3333(0.2857) + 3.3333(1.2000) - 2.0000 = 1.3333$$

The exact values are $x = \frac{4}{3}$, $y = \frac{2}{7}$, and $z = \frac{6}{5}$. ◢

EXERCISE 10.2

Use row operations on matrices to solve the system
of equations in each of Probs. 1 to 16.

1.
$$x - 2y = 0$$
$$2x + y = 5$$

2.
$$2x + 3y = 0$$
$$3x - y = 11$$

3.
$$2x + y = -9$$
$$x - 3y = 13$$

4.
$$5x - 4y = 7$$
$$4x - 3y = 5$$

5.
$$3x + 2y + z = 8$$
$$2x + y + 3z = 7$$
$$x + 3y + 2z = 9$$

6.
$$x + 3y + z = 4$$
$$x - 5y + 2z = 7$$
$$3x + y - 4z = -9$$

7.
$$2x + 3y + z = -1$$
$$5x + 7y - z = 5$$
$$4x + 3y = 5$$

8.
$$3x - 2y + 3z = 4$$
$$5x + 4z = 3$$
$$2x + 7y = -8$$

9.
$$x - 2y + 3z = -5$$
$$3x + y = 1$$
$$2x - 3y + z = -4$$

10.
$$3x - 4y + 2z = -6$$
$$4x + 3y - 2z = 18$$
$$2x - 3y + 4z = -10$$

11.
$$2x + 3y - 6z = -3$$
$$4x - 3y = 1$$
$$4x + 3y + 12z = 13$$

12.
$$x + 2z = 0$$
$$3x + 5y - 8z = 3$$
$$5x - 7y - 4z = 0$$

13.
$$x + z - w = 0$$
$$x - y - z = -2$$
$$x - y - w = -3$$
$$y + z - w = 1$$

14. $\begin{aligned} x \quad\; + 2z - \; w &= 6 \\ y + \; z - \; w &= 2 \\ z + 2w &= -1 \\ y + \; z + \; w &= 0 \end{aligned}$

15. $\begin{aligned} x - y - z - w &= -1 \\ x + y - z + w &= -5 \\ x + y + z + w &= 1 \\ x + y + z - w &= 9 \end{aligned}$

16. $\begin{aligned} x + y + z \quad\;\; &= 1 \\ x + y \quad\; + \; w &= 2 \\ x \quad\; + z + \; w &= 0 \\ y - z + 4w &= 3 \end{aligned}$

Use row operations on matrices to show that the system of equations in each of Probs. 17 to 20 has no solution.

17. $\begin{aligned} 2x + \; y - 3z &= 1 \\ 2x - 3y - 2z &= 2 \\ -2x + 11y \quad\;\; &= -3 \end{aligned}$

18. $\begin{aligned} x - \; 3y + 5z &= 6 \\ 3x + \; 2y + 2z &= 3 \\ -7x - 12y + 4z &= 5 \end{aligned}$

19. $\begin{aligned} 3x + 5y - \; z &= 2 \\ 4x + 3y + 2z &= 5 \\ -6x + \; y - 8z &= -1 \end{aligned}$

20. $\begin{aligned} 2x - \; y - \; z &= 0 \\ 5x + \; y + 2z &= 2 \\ 11x + 5y + 8z &= 4 \end{aligned}$

Each of Probs. 21 to 28 has an infinite number of solutions. Find them all.

21. $\begin{aligned} 2x + \; 6y + \; z &= 3 \\ x + \; 4y + 2z &= 4 \\ 4x + 10y - \; z &= 1 \end{aligned}$

22. $\begin{aligned} 4x - 2y + 3z &= 5 \\ 3x + \; y - \; z &= -4 \\ 18x - 4y + 7z &= 7 \end{aligned}$

23. $\begin{aligned} 4x + 6y + 5z &= 8 \\ x + 2y + \; z &= 6 \\ 3x + 2y + 5z &= -14 \end{aligned}$

24. $\begin{aligned} 3x + \; 5y + \; 7z &= 4 \\ x + \; y + \; z &= 1 \\ 11x + 15y + 19z &= 13 \end{aligned}$

25. $\begin{aligned} x + 2y + \; z &= 2 \\ 3x + \; y + 2z &= 3 \\ 5x + 5y + 4z &= 7 \\ 10x + 5y + 7z &= 11 \end{aligned}$

26. $\begin{aligned} 3x + \; y + \; z &= 1 \\ 2x + \; 3y + \; 4z &= 2 \\ 12x + 11y + 14z &= 8 \\ 5x - \; 3y - \; 5z &= -1 \end{aligned}$

27. $\begin{aligned} x + 2y + 2z + \; w &= 4 \\ 2x + 3y + 3z - \; w &= 2 \\ x - \; y - 2z + 2w &= 3 \end{aligned}$

28. $\begin{aligned} x + \; y + 2z + 3w &= 3 \\ 3x + 4y + 6z - \; w &= 2 \\ 2x + 3y + 5z - 2w &= 6 \end{aligned}$

29. For what values of a, b, and c does the parabola determined by $y = ax^2 + bx + c$ pass through $(-1, 5)$, $(6, 4)$, and $(2, -4)$?

30. For what values of D, E, and F does the circle determined by

$$x^2 + y^2 + Dx + Ey = F$$

pass through $(-1, 5)$, $(6, 4)$, and $(2, -4)$?

10.3 Determinants of Order Two and Three

We saw in Sec. 10.2 that a matrix is a rectangular array of numbers. If the matrix is square, we may assign a number to the matrix, called the **determinant** of the matrix. The solution of some systems of linear equations can be handled by the use of determinants, and we will later present Cramer's rule for this purpose. But we must first define determinants and show how to evaluate them efficiently. Unless stated otherwise

All matrices are square matrices

in the rest of this chapter.

If A is the 2×2 matrix $\begin{bmatrix} a & b \\ c & d \end{bmatrix}$ the value of its determinant is defined to be

$$\text{Det } A = |A| = ad - bc$$

▶ **EXAMPLE 1** Find the value of each determinant below.

Solution

$$\begin{vmatrix} 2 & 4 \\ 7 & 3 \end{vmatrix} = 2(3) - 4(7) = 6 - 28 = -22$$

$$\begin{vmatrix} -8 & 4 \\ 12 & -6 \end{vmatrix} = -8(-6) - (4)(12) = 48 - 48 = 0$$

$$\begin{vmatrix} 6 & 3 \\ -5 & 4 \end{vmatrix} = 6(4) - 3(-5) = 24 + 15 = 39$$

◀

NOTE As we see from Example 1, $|A|$ may be positive, negative, or zero. The symbol $|A|$ means **determinant,** *not absolute value*.

To work systematically with determinants of order 3 in this section and order n in the next section, as well as finding the inverse of a square matrix in Sec. 10.6, we will write the matrices with the double subscript notation $A = (a_{ij})$. As in Sec. 10.1, this means that a_{ij} is the number in row i and column j. If $n = 1$, then $A = (a_{11})$ and we define $|A| = a_{11}$. For $n = 2$, a square matrix or order 2 will be written

$$A = \begin{bmatrix} a_{11} & a_{12} \\ a_{21} & a_{22} \end{bmatrix}$$

and its determinant is defined to be

$$\text{Det } A = |A| = a_{11}a_{22} - a_{12}a_{21}$$

▶ **EXAMPLE 2** Find the value of each determinant below.

Solution

$$\begin{vmatrix} 2 & -3 \\ 5 & 4 \end{vmatrix} = 2(4) - (-3)(5) = 8 + 15 = 23$$

$$\begin{vmatrix} -5 & 2 \\ -6 & 3 \end{vmatrix} = -5(3) - 2(-6) = -15 + 12 = -3$$

The calculations are done exactly as in Example 1.   ◀
If A is the 3×3 matrix

$$A = \begin{bmatrix} a_{11} & a_{12} & a_{13} \\ a_{21} & a_{22} & a_{23} \\ a_{31} & a_{32} & a_{33} \end{bmatrix}$$

the determinant D of A is written $|A|$ and is defined as

$$D = |A| = \begin{vmatrix} a_{11} & a_{12} & a_{13} \\ a_{21} & a_{22} & a_{23} \\ a_{31} & a_{32} & a_{33} \end{vmatrix}$$

$$D = |A| = a_{11}a_{22}a_{33} + a_{12}a_{23}a_{31} + a_{13}a_{21}a_{32} - a_{11}a_{23}a_{32} - a_{12}a_{21}a_{33} - a_{13}a_{22}a_{31}$$

$$= a_{11}(a_{22}a_{33} - a_{23}a_{32}) + a_{12}(a_{23}a_{31} - a_{21}a_{33}) + a_{13}(a_{21}a_{32} - a_{22}a_{31})$$

Hence, we may write this by using second-order determinants as

$$D = |A| = a_{11}\begin{vmatrix} a_{22} & a_{23} \\ a_{32} & a_{33} \end{vmatrix} - a_{12}\begin{vmatrix} a_{21} & a_{23} \\ a_{31} & a_{33} \end{vmatrix} + a_{13}\begin{vmatrix} a_{21} & a_{22} \\ a_{31} & a_{32} \end{vmatrix} \qquad \textbf{(10.2)}$$

A careful look at the subscripts in the definition shows that each of the six products consists of exactly one element from each row and exactly one from each column. Three of these products are preceded by a plus sign and the other three by a minus sign.

In Eq. (10.2), a_{11} is multiplied by the 2×2 determinant which remains from the given 3×3 determinant after crossing out the row and the column containing a_{11}. Similarly for a_{12} and a_{13}. Equation (10.2) is called the **expansion in terms of the first row** since the first row consists of a_{11}, a_{12}, and a_{13}.

We may expand $|A|$ in terms of any row or any column

The expansion in terms of the second column is

$$D = -a_{12}\begin{vmatrix} a_{21} & a_{23} \\ a_{31} & a_{33} \end{vmatrix} + a_{22}\begin{vmatrix} a_{11} & a_{13} \\ a_{31} & a_{33} \end{vmatrix} - a_{32}\begin{vmatrix} a_{11} & a_{13} \\ a_{21} & a_{23} \end{vmatrix}$$

The pattern of signs in front of the numbers a_{ij} is

$$\begin{matrix} + & - & + \\ - & + & - \\ + & - & + \end{matrix}$$

Another way of saying this is

The sign in front of a_{ij} is $(-1)^{i+j}$

▶ **EXAMPLE 3** Expand the following determinant by the first row and also by the second column.

First row   **Solution**

$$D = \begin{vmatrix} 2 & -4 & -5 \\ 1 & 0 & 4 \\ 2 & 3 & -6 \end{vmatrix} = +(2)\begin{vmatrix} 0 & 4 \\ 3 & -6 \end{vmatrix} - (-4)\begin{vmatrix} 1 & 4 \\ 2 & -6 \end{vmatrix} + (-5)\begin{vmatrix} 1 & 0 \\ 2 & 3 \end{vmatrix}$$

$$= 2(0 - 12) + 4(-6 - 8) - 5(3 - 0) = -24 - 56 - 15 = -95$$

We will now show that the value is also -95 when expanding by the second column.

Second column

$$D = -(-4)\begin{vmatrix} 1 & 4 \\ 2 & -6 \end{vmatrix} + 0\begin{vmatrix} 2 & -5 \\ 2 & -6 \end{vmatrix} - (3)\begin{vmatrix} 2 & -5 \\ 1 & 4 \end{vmatrix}$$

$$= 4(-6 - 8) + 0 - 3(8 + 5) = -56 - 39 = -95$$

The value, -95, is the same either way.   ◀

EXAMPLE 4   Use the first column to expand the following determinant.

Solution   The numbers in the first column are 2, 0, and -2, and the value of the determinant is

$$D = \begin{vmatrix} 2 & 3 & 0 \\ 0 & -2 & 1 \\ -2 & 4 & 3 \end{vmatrix} = 2 \begin{vmatrix} -2 & 1 \\ 4 & 3 \end{vmatrix} - 0 \begin{vmatrix} 3 & 0 \\ 4 & 3 \end{vmatrix} + (-2) \begin{vmatrix} 3 & 0 \\ -2 & 1 \end{vmatrix}$$

$$= 2(-6 - 4) - 0 - 2(3 + 0)$$

$$= -20 - 6 = -26$$

The determinant that remains after eliminating the row and column in which an element lies is called the **minor** of that element. Thus, in Example 4, the minor of 4 is $\begin{vmatrix} 2 & 0 \\ 0 & 1 \end{vmatrix}$ and the minor of 1 is $\begin{vmatrix} 2 & 3 \\ -2 & 4 \end{vmatrix}$.

The **cofactor** A_{ij} of an element a_{ij} of a determinant is the minor preceded by a positive sign if $i + j$ is an even number and by a negative sign if $i + j$ is an odd number. Consequently, the cofactor of 4 in D of Example 4 is $-\begin{vmatrix} 2 & 0 \\ 0 & 1 \end{vmatrix}$ since the element 4 is in the third row and second column and $3 + 2 = 5$ is an odd number.

By definition then, the minor M_{ij} of the element a_{ij} is a determinant, and the *cofactor* is

$$A_{ij} = (-1)^{i+j} M_{ij}$$

EXAMPLE 5   Evaluate the determinant

$$\begin{bmatrix} 4 & 2 & -1 \\ 5 & 3 & 6 \\ -2 & -4 & 1 \end{bmatrix}$$

in terms of the third row, using cofactors.

Solution   We have $-2 = a_{31}$, $-4 = a_{32}$, and $1 = a_{33}$. For the minors we get

$$M_{31} = \begin{vmatrix} 2 & -1 \\ 3 & 6 \end{vmatrix} = 12 - (-3) = 15$$

$$M_{32} = \begin{vmatrix} 4 & -1 \\ 5 & 6 \end{vmatrix} = 24 - (-5) = 29$$

$$M_{33} = \begin{vmatrix} 4 & 2 \\ 5 & 3 \end{vmatrix} = 12 - 10 = 2$$

The cofactors are

$$A_{31} = (-1)^{3+1} M_{31} = (+1)(15) = 15$$

$$A_{32} = (-1)^{3+2} M_{32} = (-1)(29) = -29$$

$$A_{33} = (-1)^{3+3} M_{33} = (+1)(2) = 2$$

The value of the determinant is

$$a_{31}A_{31} + a_{32}A_{32} + a_{33}A_{33} = (-2)(15) + (-4)(-29) + (1)(2)$$
$$= -30 + 116 + 2 = 88$$

For any square matrix A of order 2 or 3, we have defined a specific number $|A|$ called the determinant of A. In other words, we may define a **function** by setting

$$f(A) = |A|$$

Here A is a square matrix and $f(A)$ is a real number. We may find the value of $f(A)$ by expanding the determinant $|A|$ along any row or any column.

▶ **EXAMPLE 6**   For any two square matrices A and B of the same order, it is true that

$$|AB| = |A| \cdot |B|$$

Verify this in the particular case

$$A = \begin{bmatrix} 2 & 4 \\ 1 & 6 \end{bmatrix} \quad \text{and} \quad B = \begin{bmatrix} 3 & 2 \\ 8 & 5 \end{bmatrix}$$

Solution   Since

$$AB = \begin{bmatrix} 38 & 24 \\ 51 & 32 \end{bmatrix}$$

then $|AB| = 38(32) - 24(51) = -8$ while

$$|A| \cdot |B| = \begin{vmatrix} 2 & 4 \\ 1 & 6 \end{vmatrix} \cdot \begin{vmatrix} 3 & 2 \\ 8 & 5 \end{vmatrix} = (12 - 4)(15 - 16) = -8$$

EXERCISE 10.3

Evaluate the determinant in each of Probs. 1 to 8.

1. $\begin{vmatrix} 3 & 2 \\ 5 & 4 \end{vmatrix}$ **2.** $\begin{vmatrix} 4 & 1 \\ -7 & 0 \end{vmatrix}$ **3.** $\begin{vmatrix} 7 & -3 \\ 2 & -4 \end{vmatrix}$

4. $\begin{vmatrix} 6 & 7 \\ 8 & 9 \end{vmatrix}$ **5.** $\begin{vmatrix} 2 & a \\ 6 & 4 \end{vmatrix}$ **6.** $\begin{vmatrix} -2 & -1 \\ a & -3 \end{vmatrix}$

7. $\begin{vmatrix} 2 & b \\ -3 & a \end{vmatrix}$ **8.** $\begin{vmatrix} -3 & 2 \\ b & a \end{vmatrix}$

Find the cofactors of the elements in the second column in each of Probs. 9 to 12.

9. $\begin{vmatrix} 3 & 2 & 1 \\ 2 & 3 & 6 \\ 5 & 7 & 2 \end{vmatrix}$ **10.** $\begin{vmatrix} 3 & 0 & 4 \\ 1 & 1 & 4 \\ 4 & 4 & 1 \end{vmatrix}$

11. $\begin{vmatrix} 2 & 2 & -1 \\ 3 & 0 & -3 \\ 1 & 0 & -2 \end{vmatrix}$ **12.** $\begin{vmatrix} 2 & 5 & 4 \\ 1 & 4 & 3 \\ 2 & 3 & 1 \end{vmatrix}$

Expand the determinant in each of Probs. 13 to 24 by cofactors or minors of the elements of some row or column.

13. $\begin{vmatrix} 2 & 5 & 4 \\ 3 & 1 & 6 \\ 9 & 4 & 2 \end{vmatrix}$ **14.** $\begin{vmatrix} -3 & 7 & -2 \\ 3 & 2 & 4 \\ 5 & 6 & -4 \end{vmatrix}$

15. $\begin{vmatrix} 1 & 2 & 3 \\ -3 & 2 & 4 \\ -2 & -3 & 2 \end{vmatrix}$ **16.** $\begin{vmatrix} 3 & -4 & 1 \\ 2 & 0 & -2 \\ -1 & 4 & 3 \end{vmatrix}$

17. $\begin{vmatrix} 2 & 5 & 0 \\ 1 & 4 & 2 \\ 2 & 3 & 5 \end{vmatrix}$ **18.** $\begin{vmatrix} 1 & 1 & 3 \\ 0 & 4 & 6 \\ 2 & 9 & -1 \end{vmatrix}$

19. $\begin{vmatrix} 2 & 3 & 4 \\ -4 & 1 & 3 \\ -2 & -3 & 2 \end{vmatrix}$ **20.** $\begin{vmatrix} 2 & -5 & 0 \\ 3 & 1 & -1 \\ -2 & 3 & 6 \end{vmatrix}$

21. $\begin{vmatrix} 0 & 0 & 5 \\ 6 & 2 & -8 \\ 1 & 1 & 4 \end{vmatrix}$ **22.** $\begin{vmatrix} 6 & 3 & 0 \\ 4 & -7 & 0 \\ 2 & 1 & 2 \end{vmatrix}$

23. $\begin{vmatrix} 9 & -1 & -2 \\ 0 & 5 & 0 \\ 7 & -3 & 6 \end{vmatrix}$ **24.** $\begin{vmatrix} 2 & 0 & 5 \\ 1 & -1 & -8 \\ 4 & 0 & -7 \end{vmatrix}$

Find the value of each determinant in Probs. 25 to 28. Leave the variables in the answer.

25. $\begin{vmatrix} 3 & 1 & x \\ 2 & -2 & 5 \\ 4 & 3 & 6 \end{vmatrix}$ **26.** $\begin{vmatrix} 4 & x & 1 \\ 0 & -2 & 3 \\ 5 & y & 2 \end{vmatrix}$

27. $\begin{vmatrix} i & j & k \\ 3 & 5 & -1 \\ 2 & -2 & 7 \end{vmatrix}$ **28.** $\begin{vmatrix} i & j & k \\ 3 & 4 & 5 \\ 1 & -4 & 2 \end{vmatrix}$

Solve each equation in Probs. 29 to 32 by first expanding the determinant.

29. $\begin{vmatrix} 2 & x \\ 1 & 5 \end{vmatrix} = 7$ **30.** $\begin{vmatrix} x & 2 \\ -1 & 6 \end{vmatrix} = 4$

31. $\begin{vmatrix} 2 & 0 & 4 \\ 1 & x & 2 \\ 3 & -1 & 3 \end{vmatrix} = -12$ **32.** $\begin{vmatrix} 3 & x & 2 \\ 4 & 2 & 9 \\ 2 & 5 & x \end{vmatrix} = -83$

The area of the triangle with vertices (a, b), (c, d), and (e, f) is the absolute value of

$$\frac{1}{2} \begin{vmatrix} 1 & a & b \\ 1 & c & d \\ 1 & e & f \end{vmatrix}$$

Use this in Probs. 33 to 36 to find the areas of the triangles with the following vertices.

33. $(2, 3)$, $(4, -1)$, $(6, 6)$
34. $(1, -1)$, $(2, 4)$, $(-8, 5)$
35. $(4, 5)$, $(6, 7)$, $(8, 9)$
36. $(2, -1)$, $(-4, 3)$, $(5, 4)$

By direct calculation, verify the general properties in Probs. 37 to 40 for the 3×3 matrices A and B below.

$$A = \begin{bmatrix} 3 & 4 & 5 \\ 2 & 3 & 2 \\ 5 & 7 & 8 \end{bmatrix} \quad \text{and} \quad B = \begin{bmatrix} 4 & 1 & -2 \\ 3 & 4 & 1 \\ 2 & 5 & 3 \end{bmatrix}$$

37. $|AB| = |A| \cdot |B|$ **38.** $|B| = |B^T|$
39. $|2A| = 8|A|$ **40.** $|B^2| = |B|^2$

Show that the value of each of these determinants is zero.

41. $\begin{vmatrix} 4 & 7 & 9 \\ 0 & 0 & 0 \\ 6 & -8 & -3 \end{vmatrix}$ **42.** $\begin{vmatrix} x & 3 & x \\ y & -8 & y \\ z & 12 & z \end{vmatrix}$

43. $\begin{vmatrix} 2 & 4 & 6 \\ 3 & 6 & 9 \\ a & b & c \end{vmatrix}$ **44.** $\begin{vmatrix} x & a & 5a \\ y & b & 5b \\ z & c & 5c \end{vmatrix}$

45. Show that if a, b, and c are any real numbers, then the roots of the quadratic equation below are never complex numbers.

$$\begin{vmatrix} a - x & b \\ b & c - x \end{vmatrix} = 0$$

46. Find the value of $\begin{vmatrix} \log 125 & 3 \\ \log 25 & 2 \end{vmatrix}$.

47. Verify that $|A + B| \neq |A| + |B|$ for

$$A = \begin{bmatrix} 3 & 8 \\ 6 & 1 \end{bmatrix} \quad \text{and} \quad B = \begin{bmatrix} 4 & 9 \\ 2 & 6 \end{bmatrix}$$

48. Verify that $|A + B| \neq |A| + |B|$ for

$$A = \begin{bmatrix} 4 & 3 & 1 \\ 3 & -2 & 5 \\ -1 & 5 & 4 \end{bmatrix} \quad \text{and} \quad B = \begin{bmatrix} 0 & 3 & 7 \\ 4 & -3 & 2 \\ 6 & 1 & -2 \end{bmatrix}$$

49. (a) Show that the polynomial $|A - xI|$ is $x^2 - 7x + 2$ if

$$A = \begin{bmatrix} 4 & 2 \\ 5 & 3 \end{bmatrix} \quad \text{and} \quad I = \begin{bmatrix} 1 & 0 \\ 0 & 1 \end{bmatrix}$$

(b) Show that $A^2 - 7A + 2I$ is the zero matrix.

50. (a) Show that the polynomial $|A - xI|$ is $x^2 - 14x - 3$ if

$$A = \begin{bmatrix} 9 & 8 \\ 6 & 5 \end{bmatrix} \quad \text{and} \quad I = \begin{bmatrix} 1 & 0 \\ 0 & 1 \end{bmatrix}$$

(b) Show that $A^2 - 14A - 3I$ is the zero matrix.

In Probs. 51 and 52, (a) find the polynomial $|A - xI|$ where I is the identity matrix of order two and (b) find the solutions of the equation $|A - xI| = 0$.

51. $\begin{bmatrix} 4 & 2 \\ 1 & 5 \end{bmatrix}$ **52.** $\begin{bmatrix} 5 & -2 \\ 3 & 1 \end{bmatrix}$

Prove the results stated in Problems 53 to 64 by expanding the determinant.

53. $\begin{vmatrix} 1 & 1 & 1 \\ a & b & c \\ a^2 & b^2 & c^2 \end{vmatrix} = (a - b)(b - c)(c - a)$

54. $\begin{vmatrix} 1 & 1 & 1 \\ a & b & c \\ a^3 & b^3 & c^3 \end{vmatrix} = (a - b)(b - c)(c - a)(a + b + c)$

55. $\begin{vmatrix} a & x & y \\ 0 & b & z \\ 0 & 0 & c \end{vmatrix} = abc$

56. $\begin{vmatrix} ka & kb & kc \\ kd & ke & kf \\ kg & kh & ki \end{vmatrix} = k^3 \begin{vmatrix} a & b & c \\ d & e & f \\ g & h & i \end{vmatrix}$

57. $\begin{vmatrix} a & b \\ c & d \end{vmatrix} = - \begin{vmatrix} c & d \\ a & b \end{vmatrix}$ **58.** $\begin{vmatrix} a & b \\ ka & kb \end{vmatrix} = 0$

59. $\begin{vmatrix} a + A & b + B \\ c & d \end{vmatrix} = \begin{vmatrix} a & b \\ c & d \end{vmatrix} + \begin{vmatrix} A & B \\ c & d \end{vmatrix}$

60. $\begin{vmatrix} a & b \\ c + ka & d + kb \end{vmatrix} = \begin{vmatrix} a & b \\ c & d \end{vmatrix}$

61. $\begin{vmatrix} b + c & a - b & a \\ c + a & b - c & b \\ a + b & c - a & c \end{vmatrix} = 3abc - a^3 - b^3 - c^3$

62. $\begin{vmatrix} a - b - c & 2a & 2a \\ 2b & b - c - a & 2b \\ 2c & 2c & c - a - b \end{vmatrix}$
$$= (a + b + c)^3$$

63. If $w^3 = 1$, show
$$\begin{vmatrix} 1 & w & w^2 \\ w & w^2 & 1 \\ w^2 & 1 & w \end{vmatrix} = 0$$

64. If $w^3 = 1$, and $w \neq 1$, show
$$\begin{vmatrix} 1 & 1 & w^2 \\ 1 & 1 & w \\ w^2 & w & 1 \end{vmatrix} = 3$$

Hint: $0 = w^3 - 1 = (w - 1)(w^2 + w + 1)$.

10.4 Properties of Determinants

We will give some definitions and notation for use in connection with determinants of order n, where n may be 1, 2, 3, 4, ... These and the properties in this section will make it possible to efficiently evaluate determinants of any order.

The **minor** of the element a_{ij} is the determinant of the matrix of order $n - 1$ that remains after deleting the ith row and the jth column, and it is written M_{ij}.

The cofactor of a_{ij} is the minor of a_{ij} if $i + j$ is an even number and the negative of the minor if $i + j$ is an odd number. The cofactor of a_{ij} is written A_{ij}, and it is defined as follows:

The cofactor of the element a_{ij} is
$$A_{ij} = (-1)^{i+j} M_{ij} \tag{10.3}$$

The pattern of signs formed by $(-1)^{i+j}$ is a checkerboard of alternating $+$ and $-$ signs with a $+$ in the upper left corner.

Expansion of a Determinant by Minors and Cofactors

The expansion of the determinant of a square matrix of order n can be expressed in terms of the minors or the cofactors of the elements of the ith row in the following way:

Expansion by the ith row

Below is the determinant of $A = (a_{ij})$ expressed in terms of minors of the ith row:

$$|A| = (-1)^{i+1}a_{i1}M_{i1} + (-1)^{i+2}a_{i2}M_{i2} + \cdots + (-1)^{i+n}a_{in}M_{in} \quad \textbf{(10.4)}$$

By (10.3) we can express the determinant in terms of cofactors:

$$|A| = a_{i1}A_{i1} + a_{i2}A_{i2} + \cdots + a_{in}A_{in} \quad \textbf{(10.5)}$$

Similarly the expansion of a determinant in terms of the minors or cofactors of the elements of the jth column is as follows:

Expansion by the jth column

Below is the determinant of A in terms of minors of the jth column.

$$|A| = (-1)^{1+j}a_{1j}M_{1j} + (-1)^{2+j}a_{2j}M_{2j} + \cdots + (-1)^{n+j}a_{nj}M_{nj} \quad \textbf{(10.6)}$$

In terms of cofactors this is

$$|A| = a_{1j}A_{1j} + a_{2j}A_{2j} + \cdots + a_{nj}A_{nj} \quad \textbf{(10.7)}$$

These different ways of expansion of a determinant, using rows or columns, give the same value, but the proof is difficult and will be omitted. Using $n = 4$ with the first row we have

$$|A| = a_{11}A_{11} + a_{12}A_{12} + a_{13}A_{13} + a_{14}A_{14}$$

while with the second column, for instance,

$$|A| = a_{12}A_{12} + a_{22}A_{22} + a_{32}A_{32} + a_{42}A_{42}$$

In words, **to find the value of a determinant:**
1. Choose any row or column.
2. Multiply each element in that row or column by its cofactor.
3. Add these products.

▶ **EXAMPLE 1** Find the value of the determinant

$$D = \begin{vmatrix} 2 & 5 & 4 & 3 \\ 3 & 2 & 5 & 1 \\ 4 & 0 & 2 & 1 \\ 3 & 0 & 3 & 2 \end{vmatrix}$$

Solution We expand in terms of the **second column** since it has two zeros:

$$D = (-1)^{1+2}(5)\begin{vmatrix} 3 & 5 & 1 \\ 4 & 2 & 1 \\ 3 & 3 & 2 \end{vmatrix} + (-1)^{2+2}(2)\begin{vmatrix} 2 & 4 & 3 \\ 4 & 2 & 1 \\ 3 & 3 & 2 \end{vmatrix} + 0 + 0$$

First row

We next expand each of the third-order determinants in terms of the elements of the first row.

$$D = -5[3(4-3) - 5(8-3) + 1(12-6)] + 2[2(4-3) - 4(8-3) + 3(12-6)]$$

$$= -5(3 - 25 + 6) + 2(2 - 20 + 18)$$

$$= -5(-16) + 2(0) = 80$$

◢

Introduce zeros

As Example 1 illustrates, it is a big advantage to have lots of zeros in a determinant. We will see, in property 6 below, how to make all but one element in any row or column equal to 0 without changing the value of the determinant.

Having zeros in a determinant is essential for efficient computation, because if an $n \times n$ determinant is expanded completely, there will be a large number of terms, specifically $n!$ terms. Each of these terms has n factors, and the terms may be found (except for the sign) by forming every possible product of one and only one factor from each row and each column.

Properties of Determinants

Although the expansion of a determinant by minors enables us to express the determinant in terms of determinants of lower order, the computation in calculating the value of a determinant of order 4 or more by this method would be very tedious. The computation can be greatly simplified if we use the following properties of determinants.

See Probs. 1 and 2

> 1. If the rows of one determinant are the same as the columns of another, and in the same order, the two determinants are equal. That is
> $$|A| = |A^T|$$

This is because a determinant can be expanded by any row or column.

▶ **EXAMPLE 2**   Show that $|A| = |A^T|$ for the matrix A below.

Solution

$$\begin{vmatrix} 3 & 5 \\ 6 & 8 \end{vmatrix} = \begin{vmatrix} 3 & 6 \\ 5 & 8 \end{vmatrix} = 24 - 30 = -6$$

◢

We will prove some of the properties in the remainder of this section. Some proofs will be outlined in the exercise. The arguments used, however, are general and

Can be applied to a determinant of any given order

See Probs. 3 and 4

> 2. If two columns (or rows) of a determinant are interchanged, the value of the resulting determinant is equal to the negative of the value of the given determinant.

Proof   By (10.7), with $n = 4$, the expansion of the determinant in terms of the cofactors of the elements of the jth column is

$$|A| = a_{1j}A_{1j} + a_{2j}A_{2j} + a_{3j}A_{3j} + a_{4j}A_{4j}$$

Recall that $A_{ij} = (-1)^{i+j}M_{ij}$.

Now if we interchange the jth column with the *adjacent column* immediately to the left, we obtain a new determinant D'. This operation changes neither the elements of the original jth column nor the cofactors of the elements. It does, however, decrease the number of the original column by 1; hence, the jth column of D becomes the $(j - 1)$th column of D'. Therefore, the expansion of D' will be the same as the expansion of D except that the exponent of -1 in each term will be decreased by 1. Since $(-1)^{i+j-1} = -[(-1)^{i+j}]$, then $D = -D'$.

If the two columns interchanged are not adjacent, it can be proved that this interchange can be accomplished by an odd number of interchanges of adjacent columns. Thus if two nonadjacent columns of a determinant are interchanged, the value of the determinant obtained will be the negative of the value of the original determinant. ◢

EXAMPLE 3 The first determinant below is the negative of the second one since the second one is obtained by interchanging columns 3 and 2 of the first one.

Solution

$$\begin{vmatrix} 3 & 2 & 4 \\ 0 & 3 & 5 \\ 0 & 7 & 0 \end{vmatrix} = -\begin{vmatrix} 3 & 4 & 2 \\ 0 & 5 & 3 \\ 0 & 0 & 7 \end{vmatrix} = -(3)(5)(7) = -105$$ ◢

See Probs. 5 and 6

3. If two columns (or rows) of a determinant are identical, the value of the determinant is zero.

Proof If any two columns of the determinant D are identical and the determinant D' is obtained by interchanging these two columns, then by property 2, $D = -D'$. On the other hand, since the two columns interchanged are identical, $D = D'$. Therefore, $D = -D$, and it follows that $D = 0$. ◢

EXAMPLE 4 The value of the determinant below is zero since the second and third columns are equal.

Solution

$$\begin{vmatrix} 6 & 5 & 5 \\ 7 & 3 & 3 \\ 8 & 1 & 1 \end{vmatrix} = 0$$ ◢

See Probs. 7 and 8

4. If the elements of a column (or row) of a determinant are multiplied by k, the value of the determinant is multiplied by k.

Proof To prove this statement, we multiply the elements of the jth column of the determinant D by k and call the new determinant D''. If we expand D'' in terms of the cofactors of the elements of the jth column, we obtain

$$D'' = (ka_{1j})A_{1j} + (ka_{2j})A_{2j} + (ka_{3j})A_{3j} + (ka_{4j})A_{4j}$$

$$= k(a_{1j}A_{1j} + a_{2j}A_{2j} + a_{3j}A_{3j} + a_{4j}A_{4j}) = kD$$ ◢

▶ **EXAMPLE 5**   Use property 4 below with $k = 5$ in the first row.

Solution

$$\begin{vmatrix} 10 & 15 & 25 \\ 0 & 2 & 1 \\ 0 & 4 & 7 \end{vmatrix} = (5)\begin{vmatrix} 2 & 3 & 5 \\ 0 & 2 & 1 \\ 0 & 4 & 7 \end{vmatrix} = (5)(2)(14 - 4) = 100$$

◀

See Probs. 9 and 10

5. If the elements of the jth column of a determinant D are the sums $a_{ij} + b_{ij}$, then D is the sum of the determinants D' and D'' in which all the columns of $D, D',$ and D'' are the same except the jth; furthermore, the jth column of D' is a_{ij}, $i = 1, 2, 3, 4, \ldots, n$, and the jth column of D'' is b_{ij}, $i = 1, 2, 3, 4, \ldots, n$. Similarly for rows.

▶ **EXAMPLE 6**   Write the first determinant below as the sum of two other determinants using property 5 on the first column.

Solution

$$\begin{vmatrix} 3+4 & 2 & 5 \\ 5+1 & 3 & 7 \\ 2+7 & 4 & 1 \end{vmatrix} = \begin{vmatrix} 3 & 2 & 5 \\ 5 & 3 & 7 \\ 2 & 4 & 1 \end{vmatrix} + \begin{vmatrix} 4 & 2 & 5 \\ 1 & 3 & 7 \\ 7 & 4 & 1 \end{vmatrix} = 13 - 89 = -76$$

◀

See Probs. 11 and 12

6. The value of a determinant is not changed if a column is replaced by that column plus a multiple of another column. Similarly for rows.

Property 6 for determinants corresponds to one of the elementary row operations for matrices, in which a row was replaced by that row plus a multiple of another row. For determinants, this applies to columns also.

By a repeated application of property 6 to a determinant D of order n, we can obtain a determinant in which **all elements except one of some row or column are zero,** and the determinant thus obtained will be equal to D. We may then expand the determinant in terms of the row or column that contains the zeros and thus get the given determinant equal to the product of one constant and a determinant of order $n - 1$. We will illustrate the method with two examples.

We will use the notation $C_k + tC_j$ to indicate that each element in the jth column is multiplied by t, and the product is added to the corresponding element of the kth column. We have used a similar notation for rows when working with matrices.

▶ **EXAMPLE 7**   Find the value of

$$D = \begin{vmatrix} 2 & 1 & 4 & 1 \\ 4 & 2 & 6 & 2 \\ 3 & 5 & 2 & 3 \\ 7 & 3 & 1 & 3 \end{vmatrix}$$

Solution   We first notice that the second and fourth columns have three elements in common; hence, we replace C_2 by $C_2 - C_4$ and get

$$D = \begin{vmatrix} 2 & 0 & 4 & 1 \\ 4 & 0 & 6 & 2 \\ 3 & 2 & 2 & 3 \\ 7 & 0 & 1 & 3 \end{vmatrix}$$

Now we expand by the second column and get

$$D = (-2)\begin{vmatrix} 2 & 4 & 1 \\ 4 & 6 & 2 \\ 7 & 1 & 3 \end{vmatrix}$$

Finally, we replace R_2 by $R_2 - 2R_1$, expand the resulting determinant in terms of the elements of the second row and get

$$D = (-2)\begin{vmatrix} 2 & 4 & 1 \\ 0 & -2 & 0 \\ 7 & 1 & 3 \end{vmatrix} = (-2)(-2)\begin{vmatrix} 2 & 1 \\ 7 & 3 \end{vmatrix} = 4(6 - 7) = -4$$

▸ **EXAMPLE 8** Obtain the value of the determinant

$$D = \begin{vmatrix} 2 & 3 & 5 & 1 \\ 4 & 2 & 3 & 5 \\ 3 & 1 & 4 & 2 \\ 5 & 4 & 2 & 3 \end{vmatrix}$$

Solution If we examine the above determinant, we see that we cannot obtain a determinant with three zeros in either one row or one column by adding or subtracting corresponding terms in either rows or columns. Since $a_{14} = 1$, we can, however, obtain a determinant in which the elements in the first row are 0, 0, 0, 1 by performing successively the operations

$$C_1 - 2C_4 \qquad C_2 - 3C_4 \qquad \text{and} \qquad C_3 - 5C_4$$

and then writing column 4 unchanged. Thus we get

$$D = \begin{vmatrix} 0 & 0 & 0 & 1 \\ -6 & -13 & -22 & 5 \\ -1 & -5 & -6 & 2 \\ -1 & -5 & -13 & 3 \end{vmatrix}$$

We now expand in terms of the elements of the first row:

$$D = (-1)\begin{vmatrix} -6 & -13 & -22 \\ -1 & -5 & -6 \\ -1 & -5 & -13 \end{vmatrix}$$

Now we notice that the first two terms in the second and third rows are the same; so we perform the operation $R_2 - R_3$ and get

$$D = - \begin{vmatrix} -6 & -13 & -22 \\ 0 & 0 & 7 \\ -1 & -5 & -13 \end{vmatrix}$$

$$= (-1)(-7) \begin{vmatrix} -6 & -13 \\ -1 & -5 \end{vmatrix} = 7(30 - 13) = 119$$ ◢

If all entries below the main diagonal are zero, the value of the determinant is the product of the elements on the main diagonal (see Prob. 55 in the last section). For instance using the first column below gives

$$\begin{vmatrix} 3 & 1 & 8 \\ 0 & 4 & 7 \\ 0 & 0 & 5 \end{vmatrix} = (3)(4 \cdot 5 - 7 \cdot 0) + 0 + 0 = (3)(4)(5) = 60$$

Thus we can evaluate a determinant by using the above six properties for rows (or columns) to make all elements below the main diagonal zero:

The value changes only in sign by interchanging two rows

The value does not change by adding a multiple of one row to another row

◤ **EXAMPLE 9**   Find the value of

$$D = \begin{vmatrix} 5 & 3 & 2 & 4 \\ 11 & 5 & 7 & 6 \\ 9 & 2 & 9 & 2 \\ 6 & 3 & 2 & 4 \end{vmatrix}$$

Solution   First interchange columns 1 and 4 to change the sign of the determinant:

$$D = - \begin{vmatrix} 4 & 3 & 2 & 5 \\ 6 & 5 & 7 & 11 \\ 2 & 2 & 9 & 9 \\ 4 & 3 & 2 & 6 \end{vmatrix}$$

Now replace C_1 by $C_1 - C_2$ to get a 1 in the top left position:

$$D = - \begin{vmatrix} 1 & 3 & 2 & 5 \\ 1 & 5 & 7 & 11 \\ 0 & 2 & 9 & 9 \\ 1 & 3 & 2 & 6 \end{vmatrix}$$

Now do two row operations to get zeros in the first column:

$$D = - \begin{vmatrix} 1 & 3 & 2 & 5 \\ 0 & 2 & 5 & 6 \\ 0 & 2 & 9 & 9 \\ 0 & 0 & 0 & 1 \end{vmatrix} \quad \begin{matrix} \\ R_2 - R_1 \\ \\ R_4 - R_1 \end{matrix}$$

Now do another row operation to get another zero in the second column:

$$D = -\begin{vmatrix} 1 & 3 & 2 & 5 \\ 0 & 2 & 5 & 6 \\ 0 & 0 & 4 & 3 \\ 0 & 0 & 0 & 1 \end{vmatrix} \qquad R_3 - R_2$$

Since there are only zeros below the main diagonal, the value of the determinant is the product of the main diagonal elements:

$$D = -(1)(2)(4)(1) = -8$$

◢

EXERCISE 10.4

By use of the properties of determinants, prove the statement in each of Probs 1 to 16 without expanding.

Property 1

1. $\begin{vmatrix} s & e & e \\ b & o & y \\ r & u & n \end{vmatrix} = \begin{vmatrix} s & b & r \\ e & o & u \\ e & y & n \end{vmatrix}$

2. $\begin{vmatrix} 8 & a & m \\ g & e & t \\ o & u & t \end{vmatrix} = \begin{vmatrix} 8 & g & o \\ a & e & u \\ m & t & t \end{vmatrix}$

Property 2

3. $\begin{vmatrix} 1 & 4 & 3 \\ 2 & 1 & 8 \\ 3 & 2 & 5 \end{vmatrix} = -\begin{vmatrix} 1 & 4 & 3 \\ 3 & 2 & 5 \\ 2 & 1 & 8 \end{vmatrix}$

4. $\begin{vmatrix} 3 & 1 & 7 \\ 2 & 0 & 3 \\ 4 & 5 & 6 \end{vmatrix} = -\begin{vmatrix} 3 & 7 & 1 \\ 2 & 3 & 0 \\ 4 & 6 & 5 \end{vmatrix}$

Property 3

5. $\begin{vmatrix} 1 & 3 & 1 \\ 5 & 0 & 5 \\ 2 & 7 & 2 \end{vmatrix} = 0$

6. $\begin{vmatrix} 8 & 1 & 4 \\ 6 & 7 & 3 \\ 6 & 7 & 3 \end{vmatrix} = 0$

Property 4

7. $2\begin{vmatrix} b & a & t \\ b & o & y \\ s & i & d \end{vmatrix} = \begin{vmatrix} 2b & a & t \\ 2b & o & y \\ 2s & i & d \end{vmatrix}$

8. $6\begin{vmatrix} s & h & o \\ v & e & r \\ h & i & g \end{vmatrix} = \begin{vmatrix} 6s & 6h & 6o \\ v & e & r \\ h & i & g \end{vmatrix}$

Property 5

9. $\begin{vmatrix} 2 & 1 & 3 \\ 1 & 5 & 7 \\ 5 & 2 & 4 \end{vmatrix} = \begin{vmatrix} 2 & 1 & 3 \\ 1 & 1 & 2 \\ 5 & 2 & 4 \end{vmatrix} + \begin{vmatrix} 2 & 1 & 3 \\ 0 & 4 & 5 \\ 5 & 2 & 4 \end{vmatrix}$

10. $\begin{vmatrix} 1 & 2 & 3 \\ 4 & 5 & 6 \\ 7 & 8 & 9 \end{vmatrix} = \begin{vmatrix} 1 & 2 & 2 \\ 4 & 5 & 2 \\ 7 & 8 & 2 \end{vmatrix} + \begin{vmatrix} 1 & 2 & 1 \\ 4 & 5 & 4 \\ 7 & 8 & 7 \end{vmatrix}$

Property 6

11. $\begin{vmatrix} 3 & 6 & 2 \\ 1 & 1 & 5 \\ 4 & 3 & 8 \end{vmatrix} = \begin{vmatrix} 3 & 6 & 20 \\ 1 & 1 & 8 \\ 4 & 3 & 17 \end{vmatrix}$

12. $\begin{vmatrix} 4 & 3 & 2 \\ 6 & 1 & 6 \\ 5 & 9 & 4 \end{vmatrix} = \begin{vmatrix} 4 & 3 & 2 \\ 22 & 13 & 14 \\ 5 & 9 & 4 \end{vmatrix}$

13. $\begin{vmatrix} a & b & c \\ d & e & f \\ g & h & i \end{vmatrix} = -\begin{vmatrix} a & g & d \\ b & h & e \\ c & i & f \end{vmatrix}$

14. $\begin{vmatrix} a & b & c \\ d & e & f \\ g & h & i \end{vmatrix} = \begin{vmatrix} a+b+c & b & c \\ d+e+f & e & f \\ g+h+i & h & i \end{vmatrix}$

15. $\begin{vmatrix} x_1 & y_1 & z_1 \\ x_2 & y_2 & z_2 \\ x_3 & y_3 & z_3 \end{vmatrix} = \begin{vmatrix} x_1+ax_2 & y_1+ay_2 & z_1+az_2 \\ x_2 & y_2 & z_2 \\ x_3 & y_3 & z_3 \end{vmatrix}$

16. $\begin{vmatrix} a & b \\ c & d \end{vmatrix} = \begin{vmatrix} a+2b & b \\ c+2d & d \end{vmatrix} = \begin{vmatrix} a & b-7a \\ c & d-7c \end{vmatrix}$

In Probs. 17 to 20, assume that $\begin{vmatrix} L & S & U \\ T & I & G \\ E & R & Z \end{vmatrix} = 7$, and find the value of each determinant.

17. $\begin{vmatrix} L & U & S \\ E & Z & R \\ T & G & I \end{vmatrix}$

18. $\begin{vmatrix} L & -2U & S \\ T & -2G & I \\ E & -2Z & R \end{vmatrix}$

19. $\begin{vmatrix} L & S & U \\ T & I & G \\ E-T & R-I & Z-G \end{vmatrix}$

20. $\begin{vmatrix} 2L & 2S & 2U \\ 3T & 3I & 3G \\ -E & -R & -Z \end{vmatrix}$

Use property 6 (properties of determinants) to find the value of the determinant in each of Probs. 21 to 28.

21. $\begin{vmatrix} 1 & 8 & 1 \\ 1 & 3 & 3 \\ 8 & 3 & 24 \end{vmatrix}$

22. $\begin{vmatrix} 1 & -1 & 1 \\ 4 & 4 & -7 \\ -2 & -3 & 4 \end{vmatrix}$

23. $\begin{vmatrix} 2 & 9 & 4 \\ 8 & 2 & -3 \\ -2 & 1 & 2 \end{vmatrix}$

24. $\begin{vmatrix} 6 & 2 & 10 \\ 2 & 0 & 5 \\ 2 & 3 & -4 \end{vmatrix}$

25. $\begin{vmatrix} 1 & 1 & 2 \\ 2 & 2 & 1 \\ 3 & 1 & 3 \end{vmatrix}$

26. $\begin{vmatrix} 2 & 1 & 2 \\ 3 & 2 & 4 \\ 5 & 1 & 2 \end{vmatrix}$

27. $\begin{vmatrix} a & b & c \\ 0 & a & b \\ a & 0 & b \end{vmatrix}$

28. $\begin{vmatrix} x & y & 0 \\ 0 & x & y \\ x & 0 & y \end{vmatrix}$

Find the value or values of x so that the statement in each of Probs. 29 to 32 is true.

29. $\begin{vmatrix} 3 & 5 & -1 \\ 2 & 1 & 1 \\ 4 & x & 2 \end{vmatrix} = 0$

30. $\begin{vmatrix} 5 & 2 & x \\ 1 & 3 & -1 \\ x & 2 & 1 \end{vmatrix} = -4$

31. $\begin{vmatrix} 2 & 0 & x \\ 3 & 1 & x \\ x & 2 & 1 \end{vmatrix} = -13$

32. $\begin{vmatrix} x & 1 & x \\ 1 & x & 2 \\ 3 & x & 1 \end{vmatrix} = -7$

In each of Probs. 33 to 36, select the row (or column) that contains the most zeros, then expand the determinant in terms of this row (or column), and find the value of the determinant.

33. $\begin{vmatrix} 2 & 0 & 0 & 0 \\ 3 & 0 & 1 & 0 \\ 4 & 2 & 0 & 1 \\ 0 & 0 & 5 & 3 \end{vmatrix}$

34. $\begin{vmatrix} 4 & 1 & 0 & 2 \\ 0 & 3 & 0 & 0 \\ 2 & 0 & 1 & 0 \\ 4 & 0 & 1 & 2 \end{vmatrix}$

35. $\begin{vmatrix} 2 & 0 & 3 & 2 \\ 0 & 1 & 0 & 4 \\ 0 & 0 & 5 & 0 \\ 1 & 2 & 0 & 0 \end{vmatrix}$

36. $\begin{vmatrix} 3 & 2 & 0 & 5 \\ 0 & 2 & 0 & 1 \\ 1 & 6 & 3 & 4 \\ 0 & 1 & 0 & 2 \end{vmatrix}$

Verify these equations.

37. $\begin{vmatrix} 2 & 1 & 0 & 0 \\ 3 & 4 & 0 & 0 \\ 0 & 0 & 1 & 2 \\ 0 & 0 & 4 & 5 \end{vmatrix} = \begin{vmatrix} 2 & 1 \\ 3 & 4 \end{vmatrix} \cdot \begin{vmatrix} 1 & 2 \\ 4 & 5 \end{vmatrix}$

38. $\begin{vmatrix} 0 & 0 & 2 & 4 \\ 0 & 0 & 3 & 1 \\ 5 & 4 & 0 & 0 \\ 3 & 2 & 0 & 0 \end{vmatrix} = \begin{vmatrix} 2 & 4 \\ 3 & 1 \end{vmatrix} \cdot \begin{vmatrix} 5 & 4 \\ 3 & 2 \end{vmatrix}$

39. $\begin{vmatrix} a & 0 & b & 0 \\ 0 & x & 0 & y \\ x & 0 & b & 0 \\ 0 & a & 0 & y \end{vmatrix} = \begin{vmatrix} a & b \\ x & b \end{vmatrix} \cdot \begin{vmatrix} x & y \\ a & y \end{vmatrix}$

40. $\begin{vmatrix} a & 0 & 0 & b \\ 0 & a & b & 0 \\ 0 & b & a & 0 \\ b & 0 & 0 & a \end{vmatrix} = \begin{vmatrix} a & b \\ b & a \end{vmatrix}^2$

Find the value of the determinants in Probs. 41 to 48. See Examples 7, 8, and 9.

41. $\begin{vmatrix} 2 & 5 & 2 & 3 \\ 3 & 2 & 3 & 4 \\ 1 & 5 & 1 & 3 \\ 4 & 1 & 2 & 2 \end{vmatrix}$

42. $\begin{vmatrix} 2 & 4 & 1 & 3 \\ 1 & 3 & 5 & 2 \\ 3 & 1 & 2 & 1 \\ 1 & 3 & 5 & 3 \end{vmatrix}$

43. $\begin{vmatrix} 3 & 2 & 1 & 1 \\ 2 & 4 & 3 & 4 \\ 1 & 2 & 4 & 2 \\ 1 & 2 & 1 & 2 \end{vmatrix}$

44. $\begin{vmatrix} 2 & 5 & 1 & 3 \\ 1 & 3 & 2 & -1 \\ -2 & 1 & -1 & 3 \\ 2 & 5 & 1 & 6 \end{vmatrix}$

45. $\begin{vmatrix} 2 & 1 & 0 & 3 & 4 \\ 0 & 2 & 0 & 0 & 0 \\ 0 & 4 & 2 & 1 & 0 \\ 0 & 5 & 1 & 3 & 2 \\ 0 & 2 & 3 & 2 & 1 \end{vmatrix}$

46. $\begin{vmatrix} 3 & 5 & 0 & 0 & 1 \\ 1 & 2 & 5 & 0 & 0 \\ 0 & 1 & 0 & 0 & 0 \\ 2 & 3 & 1 & 4 & 2 \\ 1 & 3 & 4 & 0 & 2 \end{vmatrix}$

47. $\begin{vmatrix} 1 & 2 & 1 & 3 & 4 & 1 \\ 0 & 0 & 0 & 0 & 1 & 0 \\ 3 & 0 & 1 & 0 & 2 & 0 \\ 1 & 0 & 2 & 4 & 0 & 2 \\ 2 & 0 & 3 & 1 & 4 & 0 \\ 1 & 0 & 1 & 0 & 2 & 1 \end{vmatrix}$

48. $\begin{vmatrix} 2 & 1 & 0 & 0 & 0 & 0 \\ 1 & 2 & 0 & 0 & 0 & 0 \\ 0 & 0 & 1 & 1 & 0 & 0 \\ 0 & 0 & 2 & 1 & 0 & 0 \\ 0 & 0 & 0 & 0 & 3 & 1 \\ 0 & 0 & 0 & 0 & 1 & 3 \end{vmatrix}$

Verify the equations in Probs. 49 to 52.

49. $\begin{vmatrix} 0 & 0 & Q & 0 \\ S & 0 & 0 & 0 \\ 0 & 0 & 0 & R \\ 0 & P & 0 & 0 \end{vmatrix} = -SPQR$

50. $\begin{vmatrix} A & X & Y & Z \\ 0 & B & P & Q \\ 0 & 0 & C & R \\ 0 & 0 & 0 & D \end{vmatrix} = ABCD$

51. $\begin{vmatrix} a & b & w & x \\ c & d & y & z \\ 0 & 0 & e & f \\ 0 & 0 & g & h \end{vmatrix} = \begin{vmatrix} a & b \\ c & d \end{vmatrix} \cdot \begin{vmatrix} e & f \\ g & h \end{vmatrix}$

52. $\begin{vmatrix} 0 & x & a & b \\ y & 0 & c & d \\ 0 & 0 & 0 & u \\ 0 & 0 & t & 0 \end{vmatrix} = tuxy$

53. Show $\begin{vmatrix} a & b & c \\ b & c & a \\ c & a & b \end{vmatrix}$

$$= (a + b + c)(ab + bc + ca - a^2 - b^2 - c^2).$$

54. Show $\begin{vmatrix} x & y & z \\ x^2 & y^2 & z^2 \\ yz & zx & xy \end{vmatrix}$

$$= (x - y)(y - z)(z - x)(xy + yz + zx).$$

55. Show $\begin{vmatrix} a & b & c & d \\ b & a & d & c \\ c & d & a & b \\ d & c & b & a \end{vmatrix}$

$$= (a + b + c + d)(a - b + c - d) \cdot$$
$$(a - b - c + d)(a + b - c - d).$$

56. Show $\begin{vmatrix} 1 & 1 & 1 & 1 \\ a & b & c & d \\ a^2 & b^2 & c^2 & d^2 \\ a^3 & b^3 & c^3 & d^3 \end{vmatrix}$

$$= (a - b)(a - c)(a - d)(b - c)(b - d)(c - d).$$

57. Let $A = \begin{bmatrix} a & b \\ c & d \end{bmatrix}$ and $B = \begin{bmatrix} v & x \\ y & z \end{bmatrix}$. Show that $|AB| = |A| \cdot |B|$.

58. Use the notation and result of Prob. 57 to show that $|A^2| = |A|^2$ and $|A^3| = |A|^3$.

59. Suppose A is an $n \times n$ matrix. Show $|kA| = k^n|A|$.

60. Suppose A is an $n \times n$ matrix. Use Prob. 59 to show $|-A| = (-1)^n|A|$.

61. Prove that property 5 is valid for a determinant of the fourth order in which the third column is of the form $a_{ij} + b_{ij}$:

$$D = \begin{vmatrix} a_{11} & a_{12} & a_{13} + b_{13} & a_{14} \\ a_{21} & a_{22} & a_{23} + b_{23} & a_{24} \\ a_{31} & a_{32} & a_{33} + b_{33} & a_{34} \\ a_{41} & a_{42} & a_{43} + b_{43} & a_{44} \end{vmatrix}$$

Hint: Expand D in terms of the elements of the third column.

62. Prove that property 6 is true for a determinant D of order 4 in which we multiply each element of the fourth column by t and add the product to the corresponding element of the second column. Use the determinants

$$D = \begin{vmatrix} a_{11} & a_{12} & a_{13} & a_{14} \\ a_{21} & a_{22} & a_{23} & a_{24} \\ a_{31} & a_{32} & a_{33} & a_{34} \\ a_{41} & a_{42} & a_{43} & a_{44} \end{vmatrix}$$

and
$$D' = \begin{vmatrix} a_{11} & a_{12} + ta_{14} & a_{13} & a_{14} \\ a_{21} & a_{22} + ta_{24} & a_{23} & a_{24} \\ a_{31} & a_{32} + ta_{34} & a_{33} & a_{34} \\ a_{41} & a_{42} + ta_{44} & a_{43} & a_{44} \end{vmatrix}$$

Hint: Expand by the second column, and use properties 4 and 5.

63. If each element of a row is multiplied by the cofactor of the corresponding element of another row and the products are added, the sum is zero. Prove this for the third-order determinant

$$D = \begin{vmatrix} a_{11} & a_{12} & a_{13} \\ a_{21} & a_{22} & a_{23} \\ a_{31} & a_{32} & a_{33} \end{vmatrix} = a_{11}A_{11} + a_{12}A_{12} + a_{13}A_{13}$$

Hint: Use the elements of the first row multiplied by the cofactors of the elements of the third row and prove that

$$a_{11}A_{31} + a_{12}A_{32} + a_{13}A_{33} = 0 \qquad (1)$$

by showing that the left member of (1) is the expansion of

$$\begin{vmatrix} a_{11} & a_{12} & a_{13} \\ a_{11} & a_{12} & a_{13} \\ a_{21} & a_{22} & a_{23} \end{vmatrix}$$

in terms of the elements of the first row. Why is the value of the last determinant equal to zero?

10.5 **Cramer's Rule**

In the eighteenth century the Swiss mathematician Cramer devised a rule for solving a system of n linear equations in n variables, assuming that the determinant of the coefficient matrix is not zero. We will now prove Cramer's rule

For $n = 2$ using the elimination method

and   *For $n = 3$ using properties of determinants*

For $n = 2$, suppose the system of equations is

$$ax + by = e$$
$$cx + dy = f$$

Multiplying the first by d and the second by b gives

$$adx + bdy = de$$
$$bcx + bdy = bf$$

Subtracting gives

$$(ad - bc)x = de - bf$$

If $ad - bc$ is not zero, we can divide by it and get

Cramer's rule for $n = 2$
$$x = \frac{de - bf}{ad - bc} = \frac{\begin{vmatrix} e & b \\ f & d \end{vmatrix}}{\begin{vmatrix} a & b \\ c & d \end{vmatrix}} \qquad \text{if } ad - bc \neq 0 \qquad (10.8a)$$

In the same way, we may solve for y:

$$y = \frac{\begin{vmatrix} a & e \\ c & f \end{vmatrix}}{\begin{vmatrix} a & b \\ c & d \end{vmatrix}} \qquad \text{if } ad - bc \neq 0 \qquad \textbf{(10.8b)}$$

The above formulas for x and y are called **Cramer's rule.** The two denominators are the same, namely, the determinant of the coefficient matrix. The numerator in the formula for x can be obtained from the denominator by replacing the coefficients of x, namely, a and c, by the constant terms, namely, e and f. Similarly for y.

▶ **EXAMPLE 1**   Use Cramer's rule to find the solution of the equations

$$3x - 6y - 2 = 0 \qquad \textbf{(1)}$$

$$4x + 7y + 3 = 0 \qquad \textbf{(2)}$$

Solution   We first add 2 to each side of (1) and -3 to each member of (2), to put the system in the proper form:

$$3x - 6y = 2$$

$$4x + 7y = -3$$

We now obtain the solution by the following steps:

STEP 1   Form the determinant D of the coefficient matrix:

$$D = \begin{vmatrix} 3 & -6 \\ 4 & 7 \end{vmatrix} = 21 + 24 = 45$$

STEP 2   Replace the coefficients of x in D by the constant terms:

$$N(x) = \begin{vmatrix} 2 & -6 \\ -3 & 7 \end{vmatrix} = 14 - 18 = -4$$

STEP 3   Replace the coefficients of y in D by the constant terms:

$$N(y) = \begin{vmatrix} 3 & 2 \\ 4 & -3 \end{vmatrix} = -9 - 8 = -17$$

STEP 4   By Cramer's rule,

$$x = \frac{N(x)}{D} = \frac{-4}{45} = -\frac{4}{45}$$

$$y = \frac{N(y)}{D} = \frac{-17}{45} = -\frac{17}{45}$$

The solution is $(-\frac{4}{45}, -\frac{17}{45})$, and we will check it:

$$3(-4/45) - 6(-17/45) - 2 = (-12 + 102)/45 - 2 = 90/45 - 2 = 0$$

$$4(-4/45) + 7(-17/45) + 3 = (-16 - 119)/45 + 3 = -135/45 + 3 = 0 \quad \blacktriangleleft$$

Proof for n = 3

We will now prove Cramer's rule for a system of three linear equations by using properties of determinants. The method used is applicable regardless of the number of equations. We will consider the system

$$a_1 x + b_1 y + c_1 z = d_1 \tag{3}$$

$$a_2 x + b_2 y + c_2 z = d_2 \tag{4}$$

$$a_3 x + b_3 y + c_3 z = d_3 \tag{5}$$

The numbers d_1, d_2, and d_3 are called the **constants** of the system. The determinant of the coefficient matrix is

$$D = \begin{vmatrix} a_1 & b_1 & c_1 \\ a_2 & b_2 & c_2 \\ a_3 & b_3 & c_3 \end{vmatrix}$$

We now define three determinants $N(x)$, $N(y)$, and $N(z)$. To form each one, replace the coefficients of x (or y or z) by the constant terms:

$$N(x) = \begin{vmatrix} d_1 & b_1 & c_1 \\ d_2 & b_2 & c_2 \\ d_3 & b_3 & c_3 \end{vmatrix} \qquad N(y) = \begin{vmatrix} a_1 & d_1 & c_1 \\ a_2 & d_2 & c_2 \\ a_3 & d_3 & c_3 \end{vmatrix} \qquad N(z) = \begin{vmatrix} a_1 & b_1 & d_1 \\ a_2 & b_2 & d_2 \\ a_3 & b_3 & d_3 \end{vmatrix}$$

If we multiply the first column in D by x, then by property 4 the value of the determinant is multiplied by x and the first equality is given below:

$$xD = \begin{vmatrix} a_1 x & b_1 & c_1 \\ a_2 x & b_2 & c_2 \\ a_3 x & b_3 & c_3 \end{vmatrix} = \begin{vmatrix} a_1 x + b_1 y & b_1 & c_1 \\ a_2 x + b_2 y & b_2 & c_2 \\ a_3 x + b_3 y & b_3 & c_3 \end{vmatrix}$$

The second determinant above comes from the first one by replacing c_1 by $c_1 + yc_2$. In the second determinant above, we now replace c_1 by $c_1 + zc_3$ and get

$$xD = \begin{vmatrix} a_1 x + b_1 y + c_1 z & b_1 & c_1 \\ a_2 x + b_2 y + c_2 z & b_2 & c_2 \\ a_3 x + b_3 y + c_3 z & b_3 & c_3 \end{vmatrix}$$

$$= \begin{vmatrix} d_1 & b_1 & c_1 \\ d_2 & b_2 & c_2 \\ d_3 & b_3 & c_3 \end{vmatrix} \qquad \text{since } a_i x + b_i y + c_i z = d_i, \text{ for } i = 1, 2, 3$$

$$= N(x)$$

Consequently, $x = N(x)/D$, if $D \neq 0$. By a similar argument, we can find y and z. This is called **Cramer's rule** for $n = 3$.

Cramer's rule for n = 3

If $D \neq 0$, the solution of the system (3), (4), (5) of three equations in three variables is

$$x = \frac{N(x)}{D} \qquad y = \frac{N(y)}{D} \qquad z = \frac{N(z)}{D}$$

where D is the determinant of the coefficient matrix, $N(x)$ is found by replacing the coefficients of x in D by the constant terms, and $N(y)$ and $N(z)$ are found similarly.

NOTE   If the determinant of coefficients $D = 0$, **we cannot use Cramer's rule.** If $D = 0$, the system of equations is not independent, and we may solve the system (if there is a solution) by row operations as in Sec. 10.2. In fact it may be shown that if D is 0, the equations are

Dependent if $N(x) = N(y) = N(z) = 0$

and   *Inconsistent if at least one of them is not 0*

▶ EXAMPLE 2   Use Cramer's rule to solve the system of equations

$$3x + y - 2z = -3$$
$$2x + 7y + 3z = 9$$
$$4x - 3y - z = 7$$

Solution   The terms on the left-hand sides are arranged in the proper order, and only the constant terms appear on the right. Hence, we calculate the various determinants:

STEP 1

$$D = \begin{vmatrix} 3 & 1 & -2 \\ 2 & 7 & 3 \\ 4 & -3 & -1 \end{vmatrix}$$

$$= 3 \begin{vmatrix} 7 & 3 \\ -3 & -1 \end{vmatrix} - 1 \begin{vmatrix} 2 & 3 \\ 4 & -1 \end{vmatrix} + (-2) \begin{vmatrix} 2 & 7 \\ 4 & -3 \end{vmatrix}$$

$$= 3(-7 + 9) - 1(-2 - 12) - 2(-6 - 28)$$

$$= 6 + 14 + 68 = 88$$

STEP 2

$$N(x) = \begin{vmatrix} -3 & 1 & -2 \\ 9 & 7 & 3 \\ 7 & -3 & -1 \end{vmatrix}$$

$$= (-3) \begin{vmatrix} 7 & 3 \\ -3 & -1 \end{vmatrix} - 1 \begin{vmatrix} 9 & 3 \\ 7 & -1 \end{vmatrix} + (-2) \begin{vmatrix} 9 & 7 \\ 7 & -3 \end{vmatrix}$$

$$= -3(-7 + 9) - 1(-9 - 21) - 2(-27 - 49)$$

$$= -6 + 30 + 152 = 176$$

STEP 3
$$N(y) = \begin{vmatrix} 3 & -3 & -2 \\ 2 & 9 & 3 \\ 4 & 7 & -1 \end{vmatrix}$$

$$= 3\begin{vmatrix} 9 & 3 \\ 7 & -1 \end{vmatrix} - (-3)\begin{vmatrix} 2 & 3 \\ 4 & -1 \end{vmatrix} + (-2)\begin{vmatrix} 2 & 9 \\ 4 & 7 \end{vmatrix}$$

$$= 3(-9 - 21) + 3(-2 - 12) - 2(14 - 36)$$

$$= -90 - 42 + 44 = -88$$

STEP 4
$$N(z) = \begin{vmatrix} 3 & 1 & -3 \\ 2 & 7 & 9 \\ 4 & -3 & 7 \end{vmatrix}$$

$$= 3\begin{vmatrix} 7 & 9 \\ -3 & 7 \end{vmatrix} - 1\begin{vmatrix} 2 & 9 \\ 4 & 7 \end{vmatrix} + (-3)\begin{vmatrix} 2 & 7 \\ 4 & -3 \end{vmatrix}$$

$$= 3(49 + 27) - 1(14 - 36) - 3(-6 - 28)$$

$$= 228 + 22 + 102 = 352$$

STEP 5
$$x = \frac{N(x)}{D} = \frac{176}{88} = 2$$

$$y = \frac{N(y)}{D} = \frac{-88}{88} = -1$$

$$z = \frac{N(z)}{D} = \frac{352}{88} = 4$$

by Cramer's rule. Hence the solution is $(2, -1, 4)$; it can be checked in the original equations.   ◢

EXAMPLE 3   Show that the following equations are not consistent:

$$5x + 4y + 11z = 3$$
$$6x - 4y + 2z = 1$$
$$x + 3y + 5z = 2$$

Solution
$$D = \begin{vmatrix} 5 & 4 & 11 \\ 6 & -4 & 2 \\ 1 & 3 & 5 \end{vmatrix} = 5\begin{vmatrix} -4 & 2 \\ 3 & 5 \end{vmatrix} - 4\begin{vmatrix} 6 & 2 \\ 1 & 5 \end{vmatrix} + 11\begin{vmatrix} 6 & -4 \\ 1 & 3 \end{vmatrix}$$

$$= 5(-20 - 6) - 4(30 - 2) + 11(18 + 4)$$

$$= -130 - 112 + 242 = 0$$

Hence, since $D = 0$, the equations are not consistent and Cramer's rule does not apply. Row operations will show that no solution exists. This is also shown by calculating that $N(x) = 6$, which is not zero (see just before Example 2).   ◢

Cramer's rule can be extended to n linear equations in n variables, but its use is limited by the large number of calculations required. Gaussian elimination needs fewer calculations in general, and this is important even when using a computer where time is literally money. Furthermore, gaussian elimination handles all situations with m equations in n variables, whereas Cramer's rule only treats n equations in n variables when the determinant of the coefficient matrix is not zero.

As one example of the use of linear equations and determinants, we will now present the **method of least squares** for finding the line which "best fits" n given points. The coordinates of the n points are often found as the result of an experiment. If the n points are

$$(x_1, y_1), (x_2, y_2), \ldots, (x_n, y_n)$$

the method of least squares shows how to find the line $y = mx + b$ which gives the smallest value for the sum

$$[y_1 - (mx_1 + b)]^2 + [y_2 - (mx_2 + b)]^2 + \cdots + [y_n - (mx_n + b)]^2$$

Making the above sum as small as possible is the reason the method is called "least squares."

To find the line, **we must find m and b.** The method, which we present without proof, requires that we find two equations in the two variables m and b, and then solve these equations. For the data points below, the first number might be the number of fishermen on a charter boat, and the second number might be the average number of fish caught per fisherman on a day trip. Suppose that the points are

$$A(4, 21), B(6, 19), C(8, 16), D(10, 19), \text{ and } E(12, 15)$$

as in Fig. 10.1. We must

1. Substitute the coordinates of each point in $y = mx + b$ and get one set of equations in m and b.
2. Multiply each equation from (1) by the coefficient of m and get another set of equations in m and b.
3. Add each of these two sets of equations.

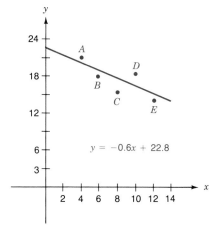

FIGURE 10.1

The two resulting equations are then solved for m and b.

Substitute given points	**Multiply by coefficient of m**
$21 = 4m + b$	$84 = 16m + 4b$
$19 = 6m + b$	$114 = 36m + 6b$
$16 = 8m + b$	$128 = 64m + 8b$
$19 = 10m + b$	$190 = 100m + 10b$
$15 = 12m + b$	$180 = 144m + 12b$
$90 = 40m + 5b$	$696 = 360m + 40b$

Adding

These two equations simplify to

$$8m + b = 18$$

$$45m + 5b = 87$$

and by Cramer's rule, the values for m and b are

$$m = \frac{\begin{vmatrix} 18 & 1 \\ 87 & 5 \end{vmatrix}}{\begin{vmatrix} 8 & 1 \\ 45 & 5 \end{vmatrix}} = \frac{90 - 87}{40 - 45} = \frac{3}{-5} = -0.6$$

$$b = \frac{\begin{vmatrix} 8 & 18 \\ 45 & 87 \end{vmatrix}}{\begin{vmatrix} 8 & 1 \\ 45 & 5 \end{vmatrix}} = \frac{696 - 810}{40 - 45} = \frac{-114}{-5} = 22.8$$

Therefore the **least-squares line** of best fit for the five given points is

$$y = -0.6x + 22.8$$

or $3x + 5y = 114$. Again, this line is shown in Fig. 10.1.

The same type of procedure may be used to fit a parabola $y = ax^2 + bx + c$ to n given points. The method would require solving three equations in the three variables a, b, and c.

EXERCISE 10.5

Use Cramer's rule to solve the systems of linear equations in Probs. 1 to 16.

1. $2x - y = 3$
$x + y = 3$

2. $3x + y = 2$
$2x + 3y = -1$

3. $2x + 3y = 3$
$3x + 2y = 7$

4. $3x - y = 9$
$4x + 3y = -1$

5. $7x + 3y = 1$
$3x - 4y = 11$

6. $5x + 3y = 7$
$4x + 5y = 3$

7. $5x - 4y = 2$
$3x - 5y = 9$

8. $6x + 7y = -11$
$3x + 5y = -4$

9. $x + 5y = 3$
$3x - 2y = 9$

10. $7x + 2y = 1$
$5x + 3y = 7$

11. $2x - 3y = 4$
$3x - 4y = 5$

12. $4x - 5y = 7$
$3x + 4y = -18$

13. $2x - y = 2a - b$
$3x + 2y = 3a + 2b$

14. $5x + 3y = 10a - 2b$
$4x - 5y = 8a - 9b$

15. $ax + by = a^2 + b^2$
$bx - 2ay = -ab$

16. $ax + by = a^2 + b^2$
$2ax - by = 2a^2 + 3ab - b^2$

In Probs. 17 to 28, use Cramer's rule to solve each system of three equations in three variables.

17. $3x + 2y + z = 8$
$2x + y + 3z = 7$
$5x - 3y + 4z = 3$

18. $2x - 3y - 2z = 10$
$3x - 4y + 3z = 8$
$4x - 5y + 4z = 10$

19. $7x + 3y + 4z = 15$
$2x + 6y + 3z = 1$
$7x + 3y + 2z = 13$

20. $2x - 5y - 8z = 12$
$5x - y + 3z = 7$
$3x + 4y + 5z = 7$

21. $6x + 5y + 4z = 8$
$7x - 5y + 3z = 26$
$5x - 2y - 6z = -9$

22. $3x + y + 4z = 13$
$6x + 2y - 3z = -29$
$2x + 3y + 2z = 3$

23. $3x + 5y + 4z = 2$
$5x + 4y + 3z = 7$
$4x + 2y + 5z = 3$

24. $7x + 5y + 9z = 10$
$6x + 4y + 7z = 7$
$5x + 3y + 4z = 1$

25. $3x + y = 9$
$2x + 3z = -2$
$3y - z = 11$

26. $3x + z = 7$
$2x - 3y = -1$
$2y + 3z = -9$

27. $5x + 3z = 1$
$3x + 2y = 4$
$4y - 5z = 11$

28. $y + 4z = -14$
$3x + 2y = 11$
$2x + 3z = 1$

In Probs. 29 to 32, use Cramer's rule to solve each system of four equations in four variables.

29. $x + y + z = 0$
$y + z - 2w = -5$
$2x - y + 3w = 9$
$x + 3z - w = -1$

30. $2x - y + z - w = 5$
$2y - z + 2w = -4$
$x + y - 3w = 0$
$3y + 2z - 2w = 1$

31. $x + 2y + 4z + 6w = -5$
$x - y - 2z + w = 0$
$2x + 3y + 2z + 2w = -8$
$x - y - 2z - 3w = 4$

32. $x + 2y - z + w = -1$
$x + 4y - z + 2w = -1$
$3x - 2y - 2z - w = 1$
$2x + y - z + w = 1$

Solve for any one variable in Probs. 33 to 36.

33. $x + y + z + w + t = 12$
$x + y - t = 1$
$y + z + w + t = 10$
$x - y - w - t = -4$
$x - z + w - t = -1$

34. $x + y - z - w + t = 5$
$x + z + w - t = 3$
$x + y - w - t = 0$
$x - y + z + t = 5$
$x + y + z - w = 4$

35. $x + 2y - w = 9$
$2x + y + w = 12$
$y + z + w = 6$
$y - z + 2t = 1$
$z - 2w + t = 0$

36. $x + z + t = 9$
$2x - z - 3t = -6$
$y + 2z - 4w = 3$
$z - 3w + 3t = 9$
$w + 2t = 7$

Use the method of least squares to find the line which best fits the following points. A calculator is useful, but not essential.

37. $(6, 16), (7, 20), (8, 21), (9, 24)$

38. $(6, 16), (7, 14), (8, 8), (9, 6)$

39. $(5.8, 19.2), (6.4, 20.2), (7.7, 22.4), (8.1, 23.2)$

40. $(18.3, 48.2), (18.7, 47.9), (19.1, 47.7), (19.9, 47.2)$

Show that Cramer's rule does not apply in Probs. 41 to 44 by verifying that the determinant of the coefficient matrix is 0.

41. $3x - 7y + z = 10$
$4x + 2y - 5z = -7$
$-6x - 20y + 17z = 8$

42. $6x + y - z = 10$
$2x + 11y + 9z = 17$
$4x - 2y - 3z = 15$

43. $6x + y - 2z = 11$
$3x + 5y + 5z = 1$
$3x - y - 3z = -4$

44. $-7x - 11y + 4z = 3$
$4x - 4y + 5z = 10$
$5x + y + 2z = 12$

10.6 Inverse of a Square Matrix

Recall from Sec. 10.1 that the $n \times n$ square matrix I_n is called an *identity* if it has a 1 in each position of the *main diagonal* (top left to bottom right) and 0 everywhere else. Thus

$$I_2 = \begin{bmatrix} 1 & 0 \\ 0 & 1 \end{bmatrix} \quad \text{and} \quad I_3 = \begin{bmatrix} 1 & 0 & 0 \\ 0 & 1 & 0 \\ 0 & 0 & 1 \end{bmatrix}$$

are identity matrices of order two and three. Usually the dimension of I_n is clear from the context, the subscript is omitted and the identity matrix is simply written as I. The identity I is the **multiplicative identity,** since $AI = A = IA$ for each $n \times n$ matrix A.

If A is an $n \times n$ matrix and a matrix B exists such that

$$AB = I = BA$$

then B is called the **inverse** of A, and we write $B = A^{-1}$. It can be shown that if either $AB = I$ or $BA = I$ for a square matrix A, then $B = A^{-1}$. Thus only one of the above equations needs to be checked.

▶ **EXAMPLE 1** If

$$A = \begin{bmatrix} 2 & 1 \\ 9 & 5 \end{bmatrix} \quad \text{then} \quad A^{-1} = \begin{bmatrix} 5 & -1 \\ -9 & 2 \end{bmatrix}$$

since

$$A \cdot A^{-1} = \begin{bmatrix} 2 & 1 \\ 9 & 5 \end{bmatrix} \begin{bmatrix} 5 & -1 \\ -9 & 2 \end{bmatrix} = \begin{bmatrix} 1 & 0 \\ 0 & 1 \end{bmatrix} = I$$

It is also true that

$$A^{-1} \cdot A = \begin{bmatrix} 5 & -1 \\ -9 & 2 \end{bmatrix} \begin{bmatrix} 2 & 1 \\ 9 & 5 \end{bmatrix} = \begin{bmatrix} 1 & 0 \\ 0 & 1 \end{bmatrix} = I$$

◀

▶ **EXAMPLE 2** For the matrices A and A^{-1} below, show that A^{-1} is actually the inverse of A.

Solution If

$$A = \begin{bmatrix} 3 & 1 & 2 \\ 2 & 1 & 2 \\ 6 & 2 & 5 \end{bmatrix} \quad \text{then} \quad A^{-1} = \begin{bmatrix} 1 & -1 & 0 \\ 2 & 3 & -2 \\ -2 & 0 & 1 \end{bmatrix}$$

since calculation yields $A \cdot A^{-1} = I = I_3$.   ◀

The question naturally arises about how to find the inverse of a square matrix A. For 2×2 matrices, we can use the method below. In fact, if

$$A = \begin{bmatrix} a_{11} & a_{12} \\ a_{21} & a_{22} \end{bmatrix} \quad \text{and} \quad A^{-1} = \begin{bmatrix} b & c \\ d & e \end{bmatrix}$$

we have by definition of the inverse of a matrix

$$\begin{bmatrix} a_{11} & a_{12} \\ a_{21} & a_{22} \end{bmatrix} \begin{bmatrix} b & c \\ d & e \end{bmatrix} = \begin{bmatrix} 1 & 0 \\ 0 & 1 \end{bmatrix}$$

Therefore

$$\begin{bmatrix} a_{11}b + a_{12}d & a_{11}c + a_{12}e \\ a_{21}b + a_{22}d & a_{21}c + a_{22}e \end{bmatrix} = \begin{bmatrix} 1 & 0 \\ 0 & 1 \end{bmatrix}$$

Using matrix equality now gives the two systems of equations

$$a_{11}b + a_{12}d = 1 \qquad a_{11}c + a_{12}e = 0$$

$$a_{21}b + a_{22}d = 0 \qquad a_{21}c + a_{22}e = 1$$

To solve each system using augmented matrices, we begin with

$$\begin{bmatrix} a_{11} & a_{12} & 1 \\ a_{21} & a_{22} & 0 \end{bmatrix} \quad \text{and} \quad \begin{bmatrix} a_{11} & a_{12} & 0 \\ a_{21} & a_{22} & 1 \end{bmatrix}$$

Since the coefficient matrices are the same, these two matrices may be combined into the 2 × 4 matrix

$$\begin{bmatrix} a_{11} & a_{12} & 1 & 0 \\ a_{21} & a_{22} & 0 & 1 \end{bmatrix} \tag{1}$$

If the first system of equations is solved for b and d and the second for c and e, using either elimination or Cramer's rule, we find (provided $|A| \neq 0$) that

$$b = \frac{a_{22}}{a_{11}a_{22} - a_{12}a_{21}} = \frac{a_{22}}{|A|} \qquad c = \frac{-a_{12}}{|A|}$$

$$d = \frac{-a_{21}}{|A|} \qquad e = \frac{a_{11}}{|A|}$$

Therefore, we may find the inverse of a 2 × 2 matrix in the following manner, if $|A| \neq 0$:

Inverse of a 2 × 2 matrix

> If $A = (a_{ij})$ and $|A| \neq 0$, then the inverse of A is
>
> $$A^{-1} = \frac{1}{|A|} \begin{bmatrix} a_{22} & -a_{12} \\ -a_{21} & a_{11} \end{bmatrix}$$

Thus we interchange the elements on the main diagonal, change the sign of the other two elements, and divide the matrix by $|A|$.

▶ **EXAMPLE 3**   Use the above formula to find the inverse of the matrix below.

Solution   If

$$A = \begin{bmatrix} 12 & -5 \\ 9 & -7 \end{bmatrix} \quad \text{then} \quad |A| = -84 + 45 = -39$$

and

$$A^{-1} = \frac{-1}{39} \begin{bmatrix} -7 & 5 \\ -9 & 12 \end{bmatrix}$$

◢

Remember that the inverse of a 2×2 matrix involves dividing by $|A|$. We will not prove it, but the following theorem is true:

The $n \times n$ matrix A has an inverse if and only if $|A| \neq 0$.

▶ **EXAMPLE 4**   Show that the matrix below does not have an inverse.

Solution   The matrix $\begin{bmatrix} 6 & 9 \\ 2 & 3 \end{bmatrix}$ does not have an inverse since its determinant is $6(3) - 9(2) = 0$.   ◢

To find the **inverse of a 3×3 matrix,** we will present a method whose proof, although omitted, is based on Eq. (1) above in the method for a 2×2 matrix. A similar method would work for $n \times n$ matrices.

Matrix inverse

Let A be a 3×3 matrix with $|A| \neq 0$.
(a) Write the 3×6 matrix $[A|I]$.
(b) Use elementary row operations to get a 3×6 matrix $[I|B]$.
(c) Then $A^{-1} = B$.

▶ **EXAMPLE 5**   Apply the method above to find the inverse of the matrix

$$A = \begin{bmatrix} 1 & 3 & -2 \\ 3 & 10 & -1 \\ -2 & -6 & 5 \end{bmatrix}$$

Solution   We first write the matrix $[A|I]$

$$\begin{bmatrix} 1 & 3 & -2 & 1 & 0 & 0 \\ 3 & 10 & -1 & 0 & 1 & 0 \\ -2 & -6 & 5 & 0 & 0 & 1 \end{bmatrix}$$

and then do these row operations.

$$\begin{bmatrix} 1 & 3 & -2 & 1 & 0 & 0 \\ 0 & 1 & 5 & -3 & 1 & 0 \\ 0 & 0 & 1 & 2 & 0 & 1 \end{bmatrix} \quad \begin{matrix} \\ R_2 - 3(R_1) \\ R_3 + 2(R_1) \end{matrix}$$

$$\begin{bmatrix} 1 & 0 & -17 & 10 & -3 & 0 \\ 0 & 1 & 5 & -3 & 1 & 0 \\ 0 & 0 & 1 & 2 & 0 & 1 \end{bmatrix} \quad \begin{matrix} R_1 - 3(R_2) \\ \\ \end{matrix}$$

$$\begin{bmatrix} 1 & 0 & 0 & 44 & -3 & 17 \\ 0 & 1 & 0 & -13 & 1 & -5 \\ 0 & 0 & 1 & 2 & 0 & 1 \end{bmatrix} \quad \begin{matrix} R_1 + 17(R_3) \\ R_2 - 5(R_3) \\ \end{matrix}$$

This last 3×6 matrix has the form $[I|B]$, and it follows that

$$A^{-1} = \begin{bmatrix} 44 & -3 & 17 \\ -13 & 1 & -5 \\ 2 & 0 & 1 \end{bmatrix}$$

which can be checked by calculating that $A \cdot A^{-1} = I$.

There is another method for finding the inverse of a square matrix which is shorter to state, but longer to apply. We will present it because it is a standard method, and it involves concepts we have discussed, namely, cofactors, transposes, and determinants.

If $A = (a_{ij})$ is a square matrix with $|A| \neq 0$ and A_{ij} is the cofactor of a_{ij}, then

$$A^{-1} = \frac{1}{|A|} (A_{ij})^T$$

The use of the inverse of a square matrix enables us to solve a system of n linear equations in n variables, assuming that the determinant of the coefficient matrix is not zero. The system of equations

$$a_{11}x_1 + a_{12}x_2 + \cdots + a_{1n}x_n = b_1$$

$$a_{21}x_1 + a_{22}x_2 + \cdots + a_{2n}x_n = b_2$$

$$\cdots\cdots\cdots\cdots\cdots\cdots\cdots\cdots\cdots\cdots$$

$$a_{n1}x_1 + a_{n2}x_2 + \cdots + a_{nn}x_n = b_n$$

can be written in matrix form

$$\begin{bmatrix} a_{11} & a_{12} & \cdots & a_{1n} \\ a_{21} & a_{22} & \cdots & a_{2n} \\ \multicolumn{4}{c}{\cdots\cdots\cdots\cdots} \\ a_{n1} & a_{n2} & \cdots & a_{nn} \end{bmatrix} \begin{bmatrix} x_1 \\ x_2 \\ \cdot \\ x_n \end{bmatrix} = \begin{bmatrix} b_1 \\ b_2 \\ \cdot \\ b_n \end{bmatrix}$$

An equivalent form is

$$AX = B$$

where A is the coefficient matrix and X and B are the column matrices with n elements. The left side is the product of an $n \times n$ and $n \times 1$ matrix, and the right is an $n \times 1$ column matrix. With the help of A^{-1} and the properties of matrices, we may solve the system above.

$AX = B$	given equations
$A^{-1}(AX) = A^{-1}B$	multiply on left by A^{-1}
$(A^{-1}A)X = A^{-1}B$	associative law
$IX = A^{-1}B$	$A^{-1}A = I = $ identity
$X = A^{-1}B$	$IX = X$

> The solution of the matrix equation $AX = B$ is $X = A^{-1}B$, where A is a square matrix of order n with $|A| \neq 0$.

▶ **EXAMPLE 6**   Solve the system of equations

$$8x + 9y = -13$$
$$6x + 7y = -11$$

Solution   First form the matrix $[A|I]$, where A is the coefficient matrix, and then do the indicated row operations.

$$\begin{bmatrix} 8 & 9 & 1 & 0 \\ 6 & 7 & 0 & 1 \end{bmatrix} \qquad \text{using coefficient matrix and } I$$

$$\begin{bmatrix} 1 & \frac{9}{8} & \frac{1}{8} & 0 \\ 6 & 7 & 0 & 1 \end{bmatrix} \qquad \frac{1}{8}R_1$$

$$\begin{bmatrix} 1 & \frac{9}{8} & \frac{1}{8} & 0 \\ 0 & \frac{1}{4} & -\frac{3}{4} & 1 \end{bmatrix} \qquad R_2 - 6R_1$$

$$\begin{bmatrix} 1 & \frac{9}{8} & \frac{1}{8} & 0 \\ 0 & 1 & -3 & 4 \end{bmatrix} \qquad 4R_2$$

$$\begin{bmatrix} 1 & 0 & \frac{7}{2} & -\frac{9}{2} \\ 0 & 1 & -3 & 4 \end{bmatrix} \qquad R_1 - \frac{9}{8}R_2$$

Therefore

$$A^{-1} = \begin{bmatrix} \frac{7}{2} & -\frac{9}{2} \\ -3 & 4 \end{bmatrix}$$

and

$$A^{-1}B = \begin{bmatrix} \frac{7}{2} & -\frac{9}{2} \\ -3 & 4 \end{bmatrix}\begin{bmatrix} -13 \\ -11 \end{bmatrix}$$

$$= \begin{bmatrix} -\frac{91}{2} + \frac{99}{2} \\ 39 - 44 \end{bmatrix} = \begin{bmatrix} 4 \\ -5 \end{bmatrix}$$

The solution is $x = 4$ and $y = -5$. It checks in the original equations since

$$8(4) + 9(-5) = 32 - 45 = -13$$

and

$$6(4) + 7(-5) = 24 - 35 = -11$$

◀

▶ **EXAMPLE 7**   Solve the system of equations

$$x + 3y - 2z = -22$$
$$3x + 10y - z = -24$$
$$-2x - 6y + 5z = 53$$

Solution   In Example 5, we found the inverse of the coefficient matrix

$$A = \begin{bmatrix} 1 & 3 & -2 \\ 3 & 10 & -1 \\ -2 & -6 & 5 \end{bmatrix}$$

Using the inverse, the solution of $AX = B$ is

$$X = A^{-1}B = \begin{bmatrix} 44 & -3 & 17 \\ -13 & 1 & -5 \\ 2 & 0 & 1 \end{bmatrix}\begin{bmatrix} -22 \\ -24 \\ 53 \end{bmatrix}$$

$$= \begin{bmatrix} -968 + 72 + 901 \\ 286 - 24 - 265 \\ -44 - 0 + 53 \end{bmatrix} = \begin{bmatrix} 5 \\ -3 \\ 9 \end{bmatrix}$$

The solution is $x = 5$, $y = -3$, and $z = 9$.

EXERCISE 10.6

Find the inverse of the matrix in each of Probs. 1 to 12.

1. $\begin{bmatrix} 2 & 4 \\ 3 & 7 \end{bmatrix}$

2. $\begin{bmatrix} -1 & 0 \\ 2 & 3 \end{bmatrix}$

3. $\begin{bmatrix} 3 & 5 \\ -2 & -1 \end{bmatrix}$

4. $\begin{bmatrix} 0 & -5 \\ 2 & 6 \end{bmatrix}$

5. $\begin{bmatrix} 1 & 3 & 2 \\ 2 & -1 & 3 \\ -2 & 4 & 1 \end{bmatrix}$

6. $\begin{bmatrix} 0 & 1 & -1 \\ 2 & -2 & 3 \\ -3 & -1 & 1 \end{bmatrix}$

7. $\begin{bmatrix} 1 & 7 & -3 \\ 2 & 0 & 1 \\ -3 & 3 & 2 \end{bmatrix}$

8. $\begin{bmatrix} 0 & 2 & 0 \\ 3 & 0 & 1 \\ 2 & -1 & 3 \end{bmatrix}$

9. $\begin{bmatrix} 2 & 3 & 6 \\ 5 & 6 & 10 \\ 3 & 4 & 7 \end{bmatrix}$

10. $\begin{bmatrix} 5 & 2 & 8 \\ 8 & 3 & 12 \\ 5 & 1 & 5 \end{bmatrix}$

11. $\begin{bmatrix} 1 & 0 & 1 & -1 \\ 1 & -1 & -1 & 0 \\ 0 & -1 & 0 & -1 \\ 0 & 1 & 1 & -1 \end{bmatrix}$

12. $\begin{bmatrix} 1 & 1 & 0 & 1 \\ 0 & -1 & -1 & 0 \\ -1 & -1 & 1 & -1 \\ -1 & 0 & 1 & 0 \end{bmatrix}$

Use the matrix-inverse method to solve the equations in Probs. 13 to 24.

13. $5x + 7y = -11$
$3x + 4y = -6$

14. $x + 2y = 6$
$2x + 5y = 13$

15. $-3x + y = -7$
$-8x + 5y = -14$

16. $6x + 7y = -1$
$-4x - 5y = 1$

17. $x + 2y + 2z = 18$
$2x + 3y + 3z = 29$
$x - y - 2z = -6$

18. $x + 2y - z = 2$
$-3x - 4y - 4z = -37$
$-2x + 3y + 2z = 10$

19. $2x + 2y + 3z = 9$
$3x + 3y + 4z = 13$
$x + 2y + 4z = 9$

20. $3x + 2y + 2z = 12$
$4x + 3y + 3z = 17$
$5x + 2y + 3z = 17$

21. $x + y + 2z = 7$
$3x + 4y + 6z = 21$
$2x + 3y + 5z = 16$

22. $x + 3y + 2z = 5$
$2x + 7y + 6z = 11$
$2x + 6y + 5z = 10$

23. $x + z - w = -2$
$x - y - z = -4$
$x - y - w = -10$
$y + z - w = 0$

24. $x + y + w = 6$
$-y - z = -5$
$-x - y + z - w = -3$
$-x + z = 0$

In Probs. 25 to 28, use the matrices

$$A = \begin{bmatrix} 3 & 7 \\ 2 & 5 \end{bmatrix} \quad \text{and} \quad B = \begin{bmatrix} 8 & 9 \\ 6 & 7 \end{bmatrix}$$

to verify the stated property.

25. $(AB)^{-1} = B^{-1}A^{-1}$

26. $(A^T)^{-1} = (A^{-1})^T$

27. $(A^2)^{-1} = (A^{-1})^2$

28. $(A + B)^{-1} \neq A^{-1} + B^{-1}$

In Probs. 29 to 32, use the matrices

$$A = \begin{bmatrix} 1 & 2 & 3 \\ 3 & 5 & 7 \\ -1 & 2 & 4 \end{bmatrix} \quad \text{and} \quad B = \begin{bmatrix} 5 & 12 & 6 \\ 3 & 7 & 4 \\ 5 & 13 & 2 \end{bmatrix}$$

to verify the stated property

29. $(BA)^{-1} = A^{-1}B^{-1}$ **30.** $(A^T)^{-1} = (A^{-1})^T$

31. $(B^2)^{-1} = (B^{-1})^2$

32. $(A + B)^{-1} \neq B^{-1} + A^{-1}$

In Probs. 33 and 34, show that $A^{-1} = A^T$. *Note:* This is true only for certain matrices.

33. $A = \begin{bmatrix} \frac{5}{13} & \frac{12}{13} \\ \frac{12}{13} & -\frac{5}{13} \end{bmatrix}$ **34.**

$$A = \frac{1}{3}\begin{bmatrix} 1 & 2 & -2 \\ 2 & 1 & 2 \\ 2 & -2 & -1 \end{bmatrix}$$

Problems 35 and 36 show an alternative way to find the inverse of a square matrix A by using the polynomial $|A - xI|$.

35. Let

$$A = \begin{bmatrix} 3 & 7 \\ 2 & 5 \end{bmatrix}$$

Show that $|A - xI| = x^2 - 8x + 1$. Show that $A^2 - 8A + I = 0$ (the zero matrix). Show from this that $I = 8A - A^2 = A(8I - A)$, and

$$A^{-1} = 8I - A = \begin{bmatrix} 5 & -7 \\ -2 & 3 \end{bmatrix}$$

36. If

$$A = \begin{bmatrix} 5 & 4 & 8 \\ 1 & 2 & 3 \\ 5 & 5 & 9 \end{bmatrix}$$

then $|A - xI| = -x^3 + 16x^2 - 14x - 1$.

(a) Show that $-A^3 + 16A^2 - 14A - I = 0$ (the zero matrix).

(b) Use (a) to show that $A(-A^2 + 16A - 14I) = I$ and hence

$$A^{-1} = -A^2 + 16A - 14I$$

(c) Use (b) or any other method to show

$$A^{-1} = \begin{bmatrix} -3 & -4 & 4 \\ -6 & -5 & 7 \\ 5 & 5 & -6 \end{bmatrix}$$

37. (a) Show that if M has an inverse and $MP = MQ$, then $P = Q$.

(b) Use (a) to show that if there is an inverse for a matrix, then there is only one. *Hint:* If P and Q are inverses for M, then $MP = I = MQ$. Now use part (a).

38. Show that $(A^{-1})^{-1} = A$, if A^{-1} exists.

In Probs. 39 and 40, let

$$A = \begin{bmatrix} 1 & 0 & 1 \\ 0 & 1 & 2 \end{bmatrix}$$

Find these inverses, if they exist.

39. $(A \cdot A^T)^{-1}$ **40.** $(A^T A)^{-1}$

10.7 Key Concepts

Be certain that you understand and can use each of the following important words and ideas.

Matrix (p. 496)

Square matrix (p. 496)

Element, order, equal matrices (p. 496)

Column matrix (p. 496)

Row matrix (p. 496)

Transpose (p. 497)

$A + B$ (p. 497)

kA (p. 497)

Zero matrix (p. 498)

AB (p. 498)

Identity matrix (p. 500)

Coefficient matrix (p. 505)

Augmented matrix (p. 505)

Elementary row operations (p. 506)

Gaussian elimination (p. 506)

Determinant (p. 513)

Minor (p. 515)

Cofactor (p. 515)

Properties of determinants (p. 520)

Cramer's rule (p. 529)   Matrix inverse (p. 536)

(10.3) $A_{ij} = (-1)^{i+j} M_{ij}$
(10.4) $|A| = a_{i1}A_{i1} + a_{i2}A_{i2} + \cdots + a_{in}A_{in}$
(10.6) $|A| = a_{1j}A_{1j} + a_{2j}A_{2j} + \cdots + a_{nj}A_{nj}$

$$(10.8) \quad x = \frac{\begin{vmatrix} e & b \\ f & d \end{vmatrix}}{\begin{vmatrix} a & b \\ c & d \end{vmatrix}} \text{ and } y = \frac{\begin{vmatrix} a & e \\ c & f \end{vmatrix}}{\begin{vmatrix} a & b \\ c & d \end{vmatrix}} \qquad (10.9) \quad x = \frac{N(x)}{D} \quad y = \frac{N(y)}{D} \quad z = \frac{N(z)}{D}$$

EXERCISE 10.7   Review

1. Find x and y so that

$$\begin{bmatrix} 2x + y & -4 \\ 14 & 5 \end{bmatrix} = \begin{bmatrix} 7 & x - 2y \\ 14 & 5 \end{bmatrix}$$

2. Find x, y, and z so that

$$\begin{bmatrix} x + y & 7 & 0 \\ 2 & y - z & 6 \\ -1 & 5 & 8 \end{bmatrix} = \begin{bmatrix} 3 & 7 & 0 \\ 2 & 3 & 6 \\ x + 2z & 5 & 8 \end{bmatrix}$$

Perform the operations indicated in Probs. 3 to 6.

3. $\begin{bmatrix} 2 & x - y & 4 \\ 3 & y & -6 \end{bmatrix} + \begin{bmatrix} -2 & y + x & x - 4 \\ 0 & 1 - y & x + 6 \end{bmatrix}$

4. $\begin{bmatrix} 2 & 4 \\ 0 & 3 \\ 1 & -2 \end{bmatrix} \begin{bmatrix} 0 & 1 & 4 & 2 \\ -3 & 2 & 7 & 5 \end{bmatrix}$

5. $\begin{bmatrix} a & 5 & b \\ b & -2 & 0 \\ c & 1 & 3 \end{bmatrix} + \begin{bmatrix} 1 - a & -5 & 1 - b \\ 2 - b & 2 & a \\ 3 - c & -2 & -4 \end{bmatrix}$

6. $\begin{bmatrix} 1 & 0 & 2 \\ 3 & -1 & 4 \end{bmatrix} \begin{bmatrix} 2 & 3 & -1 & 5 \\ 1 & 0 & 2 & -3 \\ -3 & 4 & 1 & 0 \end{bmatrix}$

Use

$$A = \begin{bmatrix} 3 & 2 & -2 \\ 0 & -1 & 3 \\ 1 & 4 & 5 \end{bmatrix} \quad \text{and} \quad B = \begin{bmatrix} 2 & -1 & -1 \\ 12 & -7 & -2 \\ -5 & 3 & 1 \end{bmatrix}$$

to find the quantities called for in Probs. 7 to 9.

7. $(AB)^T$ **8.** $A^T B^T$ **9.** B^{-1}
10. Prove that the value of B^{-1} found in Prob. 9 is correct by showing that $BB^{-1} = I$.
11. Show that I is its own inverse.

Find the value of the determinant in each of Probs. 12 to 17.

12. $\begin{vmatrix} 3 & 2 \\ 1 & 4 \end{vmatrix}$ **13.** $\begin{vmatrix} 5 & 0 \\ -1 & 3 \end{vmatrix}$ **14.** $\begin{vmatrix} -2 & 3 \\ 4 & 6 \end{vmatrix}$

15. $\begin{vmatrix} 1 & 2 & 3 \\ 1 & 2 & 3 \\ 3 & 2 & 1 \end{vmatrix}$ **16.** $\begin{vmatrix} 1 & 3 & 5 \\ 3 & 1 & 3 \\ 5 & 3 & 1 \end{vmatrix}$

17. $\begin{vmatrix} 0 & 2 & 1 \\ 0 & 1 & 0 \\ 1 & 2 & 2 \end{vmatrix}$

Prove the statements in Probs. 18 to 23 by using the properties of determinants, or by expanding.

18. $\begin{vmatrix} 2 & 5 & 0 \\ 1 & 4 & -2 \\ 3 & 0 & 6 \end{vmatrix} = \begin{vmatrix} 2 & 1 & 3 \\ 5 & 4 & 0 \\ 0 & -2 & 6 \end{vmatrix}$

19. $\begin{vmatrix} 3 & 4 & -2 \\ 1 & 0 & 7 \\ 6 & 5 & 8 \end{vmatrix} = -1 \begin{vmatrix} 1 & 3 & 6 \\ 0 & 4 & 5 \\ 7 & -2 & 8 \end{vmatrix}$

20. $\begin{vmatrix} 3 & 0 & 6 \\ -1 & 4 & -2 \\ 5 & 0 & 10 \end{vmatrix} = \begin{vmatrix} 3 & 3 & 9 \\ -1 & 3 & -3 \\ 5 & 5 & 15 \end{vmatrix}$

21. $6\begin{vmatrix} 3 & 5 & -1 \\ 2 & 4 & 3 \\ 1 & 0 & 2 \end{vmatrix} = \begin{vmatrix} 9 & 15 & -3 \\ 2 & 4 & 3 \\ 2 & 0 & 4 \end{vmatrix}$

22. $\begin{vmatrix} 3 & 5 & 2 \\ 1 & 3 & -4 \\ 0 & 2 & 6 \end{vmatrix} = \begin{vmatrix} 3 & 4 & 2 \\ 1 & 1 & -4 \\ 0 & -1 & 6 \end{vmatrix} + \begin{vmatrix} 3 & 1 & 2 \\ 1 & 2 & -4 \\ 0 & 3 & 6 \end{vmatrix}$

23. $\begin{vmatrix} 2 & 3 & 1 \\ 1 & -1 & 2 \\ -3 & 2 & 3 \end{vmatrix} = \begin{vmatrix} 2 & 9 & 1 \\ 1 & 2 & 2 \\ -3 & -7 & 3 \end{vmatrix}$

Find values for x, y, and z by use of determinants, so that the statements in Probs. 24 to 30 are true.

24. $\begin{vmatrix} x & 5 \\ 4 & 3 \end{vmatrix} = 1$

25. $\begin{vmatrix} x & 1 & 3 \\ 2 & -1 & 5 \\ 2 & -3 & 4 \end{vmatrix} = 1$

26. $\begin{vmatrix} x & 0 & 3 \\ -1 & 2 & x \\ 4 & -2 & 1 \end{vmatrix} = 6$

27. $3x + y = 3$
$2x - 3y = 13$

28. $2x - 3y = -9$
$3x + y = 14$

29. $x + y + z = 4$
$x + 2z = 11$
$2x - y = 4$

30. $2x + 3y - z = 10$
$3x - 2y + 4z = -7$
$x + 5y - 2z = 11$

31. Solve the system of Prob. 29 by using row operations on matrices.

32. Solve the system of Prob. 30 by using a matrix inverse.

33. Is it true that $AB = BA$ if

$$A = \begin{bmatrix} 1 & 2 \\ 3 & 4 \end{bmatrix} \quad \text{and} \quad B = \begin{bmatrix} 5 & 4 \\ 6 & 11 \end{bmatrix}$$

34. Let $A = \begin{bmatrix} 1 & 3 \\ 2 & 6 \end{bmatrix}$ and $B = \begin{bmatrix} -15 & -12 \\ 5 & 4 \end{bmatrix}$

Show that $AB = 0$ (the zero matrix).

35. Define A as in Prob. 33. Show that $|A|^2 = |A^2|$.

36. Show that if $A = \begin{bmatrix} \frac{3}{5} & \frac{4}{5} \\ \frac{4}{5} & -\frac{3}{5} \end{bmatrix}$

then $A^{-1} = A^T$.

37. Show that if $A^2 - 3A - 18I = 0$, then $A^{-1} = \frac{1}{18}(A - 3I)$.

38. If $A = \begin{bmatrix} 4 & 4 & 7 \\ 8 & 5 & 2 \\ 3 & 6 & 6 \end{bmatrix}$ and $B = \begin{bmatrix} 4 & 5 & 9 \\ 11 & 6 & 1 \\ 3 & 7 & 8 \end{bmatrix}$

then A and B are magic squares since each row and column has the same sum (although a different sum for each matrix). Show that the product AB is also a magic square.

39. Show that the equation of the line through the points (a, b) and (c, d) is

$$\begin{vmatrix} 1 & 1 & 1 \\ x & a & c \\ y & b & d \end{vmatrix} = 0$$

40. The complex number $a + bi$ can be identified with the matrix

$$\begin{bmatrix} a & b \\ -b & a \end{bmatrix}$$

by writing $\begin{bmatrix} a & b \\ -b & a \end{bmatrix} = aI + bJ$

where $I = \begin{bmatrix} 1 & 0 \\ 0 & 1 \end{bmatrix}$ and $J = \begin{bmatrix} 0 & 1 \\ -1 & 0 \end{bmatrix}$

(a) Show that $\begin{bmatrix} a & b \\ -b & a \end{bmatrix} = aI + bJ$.

(b) Show that $J^2 = -I$. Note the parallel between this and $i^2 = -1$.

(c) Show that $(3 + 2i)(1 - i)$ is identified with $(3I + 2J)(I - J)$, by multiplying out each product.

41. Show that the equation of the circle through the points (x_1, y_1), (x_2, y_2), and (x_3, y_3) is

$$\begin{vmatrix} x^2 + y^2 & x & y & 1 \\ x_1^2 + y_1^2 & x_1 & y_1 & 1 \\ x_2^2 + y_2^2 & x_2 & y_2 & 1 \\ x_3^2 + y_3^2 & x_3 & y_3 & 1 \end{vmatrix} = 0$$

42. Use the method of least squares to find the line which best fits the points $(-2, -10)$, $(0, -4)$, $(1, -1)$, and $(4, 8)$.

43. If $A = \begin{bmatrix} 0.9 & 0.1 \\ 0.2 & 0.8 \end{bmatrix}$

then it can be shown that A^n gets closer and closer to the matrix

$$\begin{bmatrix} \frac{2}{3} & \frac{1}{3} \\ \frac{2}{3} & \frac{1}{3} \end{bmatrix}$$

as n gets larger and larger. Calculate

$$A^2 \qquad A^4 = (A^2)^2 \qquad A^8 = (A^4)^2 \qquad A^{16} = (A^8)^2$$

using four decimal places in the calculations.

44. When considering the inputs in parts and assemblies that go into an output assembly, we are led to a square matrix N and the expression

$$T = I + N + N^2 + N^3$$

for the total requirements matrix T at stage 3. Find T for

$$I = \begin{bmatrix} 1 & 0 & 0 \\ 0 & 1 & 0 \\ 0 & 0 & 1 \end{bmatrix} \quad \text{and} \quad N = \begin{bmatrix} 0 & 4 & 1 \\ 0 & 0 & 0 \\ 3 & 2 & 0 \end{bmatrix}$$

45. For the final total requirements matrix S and the assembly matrix N, we have $S = NS + I$. Show that $S = (I - N)^{-1}$.

Problems 46, 47 and 48 show how to find the inverse of an $n \times n$ matrix A by using multiples of I, A, A^2, A^3, ..., A^{n-1}.

46. If A is an $n \times n$ matrix and I is the $n \times n$ identity, then det $(A - xI)$ is a polynomial of degree n. Verify this for the matrix

$$A = \begin{bmatrix} 3 & 2 & 1 \\ 6 & 5 & 2 \\ 2 & 1 & 1 \end{bmatrix}$$

by showing it is $-x^3 + 9x^2 - 7x + 1$.

47. If the polynomial in Prob. 46 is

$$\text{Det } (A - xI) = a_n x^n + a_{n-1} x^{n-1} + \cdots$$
$$+ a_2 x^2 + a_1 x + a_0$$

then it is true (but not proved here) that

$$a_n A^n + a_{n-1} A^{n-1} + \cdots + a_2 A^2 + a_1 A + a_0 I = 0$$

(the zero matrix). Verify this for the matrix of Prob. 46 by showing that

$$-A^3 + 9A^2 - 7A + I = 0$$

48. Justify the following steps in finding A^{-1}

$$-A^3 + 9A^2 - 7A + I = 0 \qquad \text{from Prob. 47}$$
$$A(A^2 - 9A + 7I) = I$$
$$A^{-1} = A^2 - 9A + 7I$$

Now also verify that

$$A^{-1} = \begin{bmatrix} 3 & -1 & -1 \\ -2 & 1 & 0 \\ -4 & 1 & 3 \end{bmatrix}$$

11 Sequences and Series

In this chapter we will work with two important types of sequences. Arithmetic sequences are formed by addition, while geometric sequences are formed by multiplication. We will also consider infinite geometric sequences. Sequences and series have numerous applications such as in calculating the position and speed of a falling body, depreciation, number of bacteria in a culture, and compound interest and annuities, which is the subject of the final section of the chapter.

11.1 Arithmetic Sequences

Earlier in the book, we studied functions such as

$$f(x) = x^3 + 3x^2 + 8x - 4 \qquad \text{polynomial}$$

$$g(x) = 10^x \qquad \text{exponential}$$

$$h(x) = \ln x \qquad \text{for } x > 0 \qquad \text{logarithm}$$

$$r(x) = \frac{2x - 1}{x^2 - 1} \qquad \text{for } x \neq \pm 1 \qquad \text{rational function}$$

Each function above has for its domain a set of real numbers. We will now study a new type of function.

> A function whose domain is a set of positive integers is called a **sequence.** The sequence is an **infinite sequence** if the domain is the set of positive integers $\{1, 2, 3, \ldots, n, \ldots\}$, and the sequence is a **finite sequence** if the domain is a finite subset of the positive integers.

The value of the sequence, or the value of the function, at n is $f(n)$, and the standard notation is $f(n) = a_n$. For instance, if $f(n) = n^2$, then the values of the sequence are written

$$f(1) = 1^2 = 1, f(2) = 2^2 = 4, f(3) = 3^2 = 9, \ldots, f(n) = n^2, \ldots$$

or using a_n instead of $f(n)$

$$a_1 = 1, a_2 = 4, a_3 = 9, \ldots, a_n = n^2, \ldots$$

or simply $\quad\quad\quad\quad\quad 1, 4, 9, 16, 25, 36, \ldots, n^2, \ldots$

The range of a sequence in this book will be a set of real numbers. The elements in the range are called **terms,** with

$$f(1) = a_1 \text{ being the } \textit{\textbf{first term}}$$

and $\quad\quad\quad\quad\quad\quad f(n) = a_n \text{ the } \textit{\textbf{nth term}} \text{ or } \textit{\textbf{general term}}$

Two important types of sequences are arithmetic and geometric sequences. The sequence above, whose general term is $a_n = n^2$, is neither arithmetic nor geometric. When speaking of arithmetic sequences, the word is pronounced arith*met*ic.

> An **arithmetic sequence** is one in which the same number is added to any term to get the next term. Thus if $a_1, a_2, a_3, \ldots, a_n, \ldots$ is an arithmetic sequence with **common difference** d, then
>
> $$a_{n+1} = a_n + d$$
>
> where the real number d may be positive, negative, or zero.

▶ **EXAMPLE 1**   Verify that each of the following sequences is actually an arithmetic sequence.

Falling body   ***Solution***   (a) 16, 48, 80, 112, 144, 176, . . . (here $a_1 = 16$ and $d = 32$). These numbers are approximately the distance in feet that a body would fall in a vacuum in each successive second.

Simple interest   (b) 650, 715, 780, 845, 910, . . . (here $a_1 = 650$ and $d = 65$). These numbers are the values of $650 invested at 10 percent simple interest per year.

Population   (c) 8546, 8346, 8146, 7946, 7746, . . . (here $a_1 = 8546$ and $d = -200$). These numbers could be the population of a town which is losing 200 people per year.   ◀

Arithmetic sequences are also called **arithmetic progressions** and the following notation is used:

d = common difference = $a_2 - a_1 = a_3 - a_2 = \cdots = a_n - a_{n-1}$
a = first term = $a_1 = f(1)$
n = number of the term
a_n = nth term = $f(n)$
S_n = sum of the first n terms = $a_1 + a_2 + a_3 + \cdots + a_n$

With this notation, the general arithmetic sequence is

Value of a_n: $a, a + d, a + 2d, a + 3d, a + 4d, a + 5d, \ldots$

Value of n: 1   2   3   4   5   6

Notice that d has the coefficient 1 in the second term. This coefficient then increases by 1 as we move from each term to the next. Hence the coefficient of d in any term is 1 less than the number of that term in the sequence. For instance:

The fifth term is $a + 4d$; the eighth term is $a + 7d$

and the nth term is $a + (n - 1)d$. This leads to the formula for the general term:

nth term of an arithmetic sequence

$$a_n = a + (n - 1)d \qquad \text{(11.1)}$$

▶ **EXAMPLE 2**   If the first three terms of an arithmetic sequence are 2, 6, and 10, find the 38th term.

Solution   Since the first and second terms, as well as the second and third, differ by 4, it follows that $d = 6 - 2 = 4$. We also know that $a_1 = 2$ and are given that $n = 38$. If we substitute these values in the formula for a_n, we obtain

$$a_{38} = 2 + (38 - 1)(4) = 2 + (37)(4) = 2 + 148 = 150 \qquad ◢$$

▶ **EXAMPLE 3**   If the first term of an arithmetic sequence is -3 and the eighth term is 11, find d and write the first 10 terms of the sequence.

Solution   In this problem, $a = -3$, $n = 8$, and $a_8 = 11$. If these values are substituted in the formula for a_n, we have

$$a_8 = -3 + (8 - 1)d$$

$$11 = -3 + 7d$$

$$14 = 7d$$

$$2 = d$$

Therefore, since $a = -3$, the first 10 terms of the sequence are

$$-3, -1, 1, 3, 5, 7, 9, 11, 13, 15$$

The general term is $a_n = -3 + (n - 1)(2) = 2n - 5$. ◢

Sum of an Arithmetic Sequence

A famous story about Gauss is that one of his teachers decided to keep him occupied by making him add all the integers from 1 to 100. He found a method to do this much more quickly than the teacher expected by writing

$$1 + 2 + 3 + 4 + \cdots + 97 + 98 + 99 + 100$$

$$= (1 + 100) + (2 + 99) + (3 + 98) + (4 + 97) + \cdots + (50 + 51)$$

$$= 101 + 101 + 101 + 101 + \cdots + 101 \qquad \text{with 50 terms}$$

$$= (50)(101) = 5050$$

His method is similar to our proof below of the formula for S_n. Both use a trick to obtain a repeated sum of one number.

The sum of the finite arithmetic sequence 1, 5, 9, 13 may be written starting with the first term as

$$1 + (1 + 4) + (1 + 2 \cdot 4) + (1 + 3 \cdot 4)$$

or starting with the last term as

$$13 + (13 - 4) + (13 - 2 \cdot 4) + (13 - 3 \cdot 4)$$

In a similar way, we may write the sum of the first n terms of any arithmetic sequence as

$$S_n = a + (a + d) + (a + 2d) + \cdots + [a + (n - 1)d]$$

and also as

$$S_n = a_n + (a_n - d) + (a_n - 2d) + \cdots + [a_n - (n - 1)d]$$

When we add corresponding terms of these two equations, the parts involving d cancel and leave

$$2S_n = (a + a_n) + (a + a_n) + \cdots + (a + a_n) = n(a + a_n)$$

Dividing by 2, we get the following formula:

S_n using n, a, and a_n

> The sum of the first n terms of an arithmetic sequence with first term a and nth term a_n is
>
> $$S_n = \frac{n}{2}(a + a_n) \qquad\qquad (11.2)$$

This formula may also be written

$$S_n = n\left(\frac{a + a_n}{2}\right)$$

It can be remembered easily in this form as "the number of terms multiplied by the mean (or average) value of the first and last terms."

There is also a second formula for S_n. Since $a + a_n = a + [a + (n - 1)d] = 2a + (n - 1)d$, we may substitute in (11.2) and obtain the following formula for S_n.

> For an arithmetic sequence with first term a and common difference d, the sum of the first n terms is
>
> $$S_n = \frac{n}{2}[2a + (n-1)d] \qquad (11.3)$$

S_n using a, n, and d

EXAMPLE 4 Find the sum of all the odd integers from 1 to 1111, inclusive.

Solution Since the odd integers 1, 3, 5, etc., taken in order, form an arithmetic sequence with $d = 2$, we can first find n from the formula for the nth term

$$1111 = a_n = 1 + (n - 1)(2) = 2n - 1$$

Thus $n = 556$, $a = 1$, and $a_n = 1111$, and by Eq. (11.2)

$$S_{556} = \frac{556}{2}(1 + 1111) = 278(1112) = 309{,}136$$

If any three of the quantities d, a, n, a_n, and S_n are known, the other two can be found by using Eqs. (11.2) and (11.3) for the sum and formula (11.1) for the nth term, either separately or by solving two of them simultaneously.

EXAMPLE 5 If $a = 4$, $n = 10$, and $a_{10} = 49$, find d and S_n.

Solution If we substitute the given values for a, n, and a_n in the formula $a_n = a + (n - 1)d$, we get

$$49 = 4 + (10 - 1)d = 4 + 9d$$

Thus $\qquad\qquad\qquad 45 = 9d \qquad$ and $\qquad 5 = d$

Similarly, by using Eq. (11.2), $S_n = n(a + a_n)/2$, we have

$$S_n = S_{10} = 10\left(\frac{4 + 49}{2}\right)$$

$$= 5(53) = 265$$

EXAMPLE 6 If $a_n = 23$, $d = 3$, and $S_n = 98$, find a and n.

Solution If we substitute these values in formula (11.1) for a_n, we obtain

$$23 = a + (n - 1)3 \qquad (1)$$

while the first formula for S_n gives

$$98 = \frac{n}{2}(a + 23) \qquad (2)$$

We will solve the system (1) and (2) for a and n. From (1)

$$a = 23 - 3(n - 1) = 26 - 3n \qquad (3)$$

Substituting this expression for a in Eq. (2) gives

$$98 = \frac{n}{2}(26 - 3n + 23)$$

$$196 = n(49 - 3n) \qquad \text{multiplying by 2}$$

$$196 = 49n - 3n^2 \qquad \text{combining similar terms}$$

$$3n^2 - 49n + 196 = 0 \qquad \text{quadratic equation}$$

$$(3n - 28)(n - 7) = 0 \qquad \text{factoring}$$

Since n cannot be a fraction, we discard $n = \frac{28}{3}$ and thus have $n = 7$. If we substitute 7 for n in Eq. (3), we have

$$a = 26 - (3 \cdot 7) = 26 - 21 = 5$$

Hence, the sequence consists of the seven terms

$$5, 8, 11, 14, 17, 20, \text{ and } 23 \qquad \blacktriangleleft$$

In 1837, at the age of 32, Peter Dirichlet presented a proof of the following interesting result dealing with arithmetic sequences to the Prussian Academy of Sciences. If a and d are two positive integers with no factor in common (except 1, of course), then there are an **infinite number of primes in the arithmetic sequence**

$$a, a + d, a + 2d, a + 3d, a + 4d, a + 5d, \ldots$$

For instance, there are an infinite number of primes in the arithmetic sequence

$$15, 23, 31, 39, 47, 55, 63, 71, \ldots$$

since $a = 15 = 5 \cdot 3$ and $d = 8 = 2 \cdot 2 \cdot 2$ have no common factors.

The Arithmetic Means between Two Numbers and the Arithmetic Mean of Several Numbers

The arithmetic mean between two numbers a and b is defined to be $(a + b)/2$. This is sometimes called the average of a and b, although there are other averages. Notice that

$$a, \frac{a + b}{2}, b$$

is an arithmetic sequence whose common difference is

$$\frac{a + b}{2} - a = \frac{b - a}{2} \qquad \text{or} \qquad b - \frac{a + b}{2} = \frac{b - a}{2}$$

Instead of inserting just one arithmetic mean between two given numbers $a = a_1$ and $b = a_n$, we can insert $n - 2$ numbers, called **arithmetic means,** between them so that the n numbers form an arithmetic sequence of n terms. In fact, if $a_1, a_2, \ldots, a_{n-1}, a_n$ is an arithmetic sequence, then $a_2, \ldots, a_{n-1}$ are called arithmetic means between a_1 and a_n. We may then find d from the formula

$$a_n = a_1 + (n - 1)d$$

which shows that the common difference for the arithmetic sequence $a_1, a_2, \ldots, a_n$ is

$$d = \frac{a_n - a_1}{n - 1} = \frac{b - a}{n - 1}$$

EXAMPLE 7 Insert four arithmetic means between 4 and 10.

Solution Counting the two numbers 4 and 10 and the four arithmetic means between them, we have $n = 6$. We also have $a = 4$ and $b = 10$, so

$$d = \frac{b - a}{n - 1} = \frac{10 - 4}{6 - 1} = \frac{6}{5}$$

and the arithmetic sequence is

$$4 = \tfrac{20}{5}, \tfrac{26}{5}, \tfrac{32}{5}, \tfrac{38}{5}, \tfrac{44}{5}, \tfrac{50}{5} = 10$$

The four arithmetic means between 4 and 10 are $\frac{26}{5}, \frac{32}{5}, \frac{38}{5}$, and $\frac{44}{5}$.

The arithmetic mean of any n numbers $c_1, c_2, c_3, \ldots, c_n$ is defined as

$$\frac{c_1 + c_2 + c_3 + \cdots + c_n}{n}$$

whether or not the n numbers are an arithmetic sequence. The arithmetic mean of the seven numbers 13, 15, 16, 16, 18, 20, and 21 is

$$\frac{13 + 15 + 16 + 16 + 18 + 20 + 21}{7} = \frac{119}{7} = 17$$

NOTE Finding the arithmetic mean of n given numbers is one thing. It is an entirely different thing to insert $n - 2$ numbers between two given ones so that the resulting n numbers are an arithmetic sequence.

Harmonic Sequences

The sequence formed by the reciprocals of the terms of an arithmetic sequence is called a **harmonic sequence.** For example, since

$$2, 5, 8, 11, 14 \text{ is an arithmetic sequence}$$

then

$$\tfrac{1}{2}, \tfrac{1}{5}, \tfrac{1}{8}, \tfrac{1}{11}, \tfrac{1}{14} \text{ is a harmonic sequence}$$

In general, if $w, x, y, \ldots, z$ is an arithmetic sequence with no term equal to zero, then

$$\frac{1}{w}, \frac{1}{x}, \frac{1}{y}, \ldots, \frac{1}{z}$$

is a harmonic sequence.

It is interesting that if strings of the same weight are subjected to the same tension, they will produce a harmonious or pleasing sound **if their lengths are in harmonic progression.** Briefly, this is owing to several facts. Two notes make a pleasing sound if, for instance, they have frequencies whose ratios are 5 to 4 for a major third, 4 to 3 for a fourth, 3 to 2 for a fifth, and 2 to 1 for an octave. The frequency (vibrations per second) and the period of a tone are reciprocals of each other, except for a constant multiple. For a given string, the period is proportional to the length. Thus if the lengths are in harmonic progression, the periods will also be in harmonic progression, and the frequencies will be in arithmetic progression, such as 500, 400, 300, 200, and 100.

From the definition of a harmonic progression, we can derive the following rule:

Rule for finding nth term of a harmonic sequence

> To determine the *n*th term of a harmonic sequence, we write the corresponding arithmetic sequence, find the *n*th term of the arithmetic sequence, and take its reciprocal.

The terms between any two terms of a harmonic sequence are called **harmonic means.**

▶ **EXAMPLE 8**   What is the tenth term of a harmonic sequence if the first and third terms are $\frac{1}{2}$ and $\frac{1}{6}$? What is the harmonic mean of $\frac{1}{2}$ and $\frac{1}{6}$?

Solution   The first and third terms of the corresponding arithmetic sequence are 2 and 6. Hence, $a_n = a + (n-1)d$ with $n = 3$ becomes $6 = 2 + 2d$, and consequently $d = 2$. Therefore, when $n = 10$, $a_{10} = 2 + (10-1)2 = 20$. Taking the reciprocal of 20, we find that the tenth term of the harmonic sequence is $\frac{1}{20}$. Since $d = 2$, the first three terms of the arithmetic sequence are 2, 4, and 6, and so the harmonic mean of $\frac{1}{2}$ and $\frac{1}{6}$ is $\frac{1}{4}$. Notice that the arithmetic mean of $\frac{1}{2}$ and $\frac{1}{6}$ is

$$\frac{\frac{1}{2} + \frac{1}{6}}{2} = \frac{\frac{3}{6} + \frac{1}{6}}{2} = \frac{\frac{4}{6}}{2} = \frac{1}{3}$$ ◀

Here is one use of harmonic means. Suppose that the distance between two campsites is 9 mi. If the trip in one direction is made at 20 mi/h, and in the other direction at 30 mi/h, what is the average speed for the whole trip? Using distance = (rate)(time) as $r = d/t$ and $t = d/r$ gives

$$\text{Average speed} = \frac{\text{total distance}}{\text{total time}} = \frac{9 + 9}{\text{time one way} + \text{time other way}}$$

$$= \frac{18}{\frac{9}{20} + \frac{9}{30}} = \frac{2}{\frac{1}{20} + \frac{1}{30}} \cdot \frac{60}{60} = \frac{120}{3 + 2} = 24$$

The average speed is the harmonic mean of 20 and 30. See also Prob. 66 in Sec. 11.2.

The Sigma Notation for Summation

If we want to indicate the sum of several numbers, we can use the following shorthand notation for the addition:

$$\sum_{k=1}^{n} a_k = a_1 + a_2 + a_3 + \cdots + a_n$$

The symbol Σ is the Greek capital letter **sigma.** The letter k is called the **index of summation,** and it could be replaced by i or j or any other letter. To find the indicated sum, simply replace k by 1, 2, . . . , n, and add the terms:

$$\sum_{k=1}^{4} k^3 = 1^3 + 2^3 + 3^3 + 4^3 = 1 + 8 + 27 + 64 = 100$$

$$\sum_{i=1}^{3} \frac{i}{i+1} = \frac{1}{2} + \frac{2}{3} + \frac{3}{4} = \frac{6+8+9}{12} = \frac{23}{12}$$

$$\sum_{j=1}^{4} (2j + 5) = (2 + 5) + (4 + 5) + (6 + 5) + (8 + 5)$$

$$= 7 + 9 + 11 + 13 = 40$$

The formula for the sum of the first n terms of an arithmetic progression can be written in the form

$$S_n = \sum_{k=1}^{n} a_k = \sum_{k=1}^{n} [a + (k - 1)d] = \frac{n}{2}(a + a_n)$$

because we have

$$\sum_{k=1}^{n} [a + (k - 1)d] = (a) + (a + d) + (a + 2d) + \cdots + [a + (n - 1)d]$$

which is in fact the sum of the first n terms of an arithmetic sequence. This notation can also be used for polynomials by writing

$$\sum_{k=0}^{n} a_k x^k = a_0 + a_1 x + a_2 x^2 + a_3 x^3 + \cdots + a_n x^n$$

Sometimes most of the terms cancel each other, such as in the **telescoping sum**

$$\sum_{k=1}^{n} \left(\frac{1}{k} - \frac{1}{k+1} \right) = \left(\frac{1}{1} - \frac{1}{2} \right) + \left(\frac{1}{2} - \frac{1}{3} \right) + \left(\frac{1}{3} - \frac{1}{4} \right) + \cdots + \left(\frac{1}{n} - \frac{1}{n+1} \right)$$

$$= 1 - \frac{1}{n+1}$$

In Sec. 11.3, we will discuss infinite series by treating the sequence of partial sums.

EXERCISE 11.1

Write the n terms of the arithmetic sequence described in each of Probs. 1 to 12.

1. $a_1 = 3$, $d = 4$, $n = 5$
2. $a_1 = 2$, $d = 5$, $n = 4$
3. $a_1 = 7$, $d = -3$, $n = 4$
4. $a_1 = 17$, $d = -2$, $n = 6$
5. $a_1 = 5$, $a_2 = 7$, $n = 5$

6. $a_1 = -2$, $a_3 = -8$, $n = 4$
7. $a_1 = -5$, $a_3 = 1$, $n = 4$
8. $a_1 = 11$, $a_2 = 8$, $n = 5$
9. $a_3 = 8$, $a_4 = 11$, $n = 5$
10. $a_2 = 3$, $a_4 = -3$, $n = 6$
11. $a_2 = 0$, $a_5 = -6$, $n = 6$
12. $a_3 = 7$, $a_6 = 13$, $n = 7$

In Probs. 13 to 24, find the quantity at the right by using the given values in the formulas for the nth term and the sum of an arithmetic sequence.

13. $a = 1$, $n = 6$, $d = 2$; a_n
14. $a_n = -5$, $a = 7$, $n = 7$; d
15. $n = 5$, $d = 4$, $a_n = 5$; a
16. $a = 13$, $d = -4$, $a_n = -7$; n
17. $a = 2$, $a_n = 14$, $n = 7$, S_n
18. $a = 14$, $a_n = 2$, $S_n = 56$; n
19. $S_n = 51$, $n = 6$, $a = 1$; a_n
20. $n = 7$, $a_n = 20$, $S_n = 77$; a
21. $a = 9$, $d = -3$, $S_n = 0$; n
22. $S_n = 15$, $n = 6$, $a = 10$; d
23. $n = 7$, $d = -3$, $S_n = 28$; a
24. $a = 17$, $S_n = 35$, $d = -4$; n

Find the two quantities a_n, a, n, d, and S_n that are missing in each of Probs. 25 to 36.

25. $a = -6$, $d = 3$, $n = 7$
26. $a = 12$, $d = -3$, $n = 7$
27. $a = 18$, $n = 6$, $a_n = -2$
28. $a = 19$, $a_n = -11$, $d = -5$
29. $a = 12$, $a_n = 3$, $S_n = 52.5$
30. $n = 8$, $a_n = \frac{17}{3}$, $S_n = \frac{80}{3}$
31. $a = -\frac{4}{5}$, $d = -\frac{3}{5}$, $S_n = -\frac{116}{5}$
32. $a = \frac{19}{7}$, $d = -\frac{2}{7}$, $S_n = 13$
33. $d = -3$, $a_n = -7$, $S_n = 3$
34. $d = 5$, $a_n = 7$, $S_n = -2$
35. $a_n = 16$, $d = 3$, $S_n = 51$
36. $a_n = -10$, $d = -4$, $S_n = 0$
37. Find the sum of all even integers between 5 and 29.
38. Find the sum of all multiples of 3 between 2 and 43.
39. Find the sum of the first n positive multiples of 4.
40. Find the sum of the first n positive multiples of 5.
41. Find the value of x if $2x + 1$, $x - 2$, and $3x + 4$ are consecutive terms of an arithmetic sequence.
42. Find the value of x if $3x - 1$, $1 - 2x$, and $2x - 5$ are consecutive terms of an arithmetic sequence.
43. Find the values of x and y if

$$3x - y, \ 2x + y, \ 4x + 3, \ \text{and} \ 3x + 3y$$

are consecutive terms of an arithmetic sequence.

44. Show that if a, b, c, and x, y, z are two arithmetic sequences, then $a + x$, $b + y$, $c + z$ is an arithmetic sequence.
45. How many times will a clock strike in 24 h if it strikes only at the hours, and strikes once at 1, twice at 2, thrice at three, . . . ?

46. If a compact body falls vertically 16 ft during the first second, 48 ft during the next second, 80 ft during the third, and so on, how far will it fall during the seventh second? During the first 7 s?
47. A bomb was dropped from an altitude of 10,000 ft. Neglecting air resistance, find the time required for it to reach the ground. See Prob. 46.
48. Susan made a grade of 64 on the first test and did 7 points better on each succeeding test than on the previous one. What was her score on the fifth test, and what was her average grade on the five tests?
49. A machine that cost $5800 depreciated 15 percent the first year, 13.5 percent the second, 12 percent the third, and so on. What was its value at the end of 9 years if all percentages apply to the original cost?
50. If Owen buys a painting on June 14, 1988, for $7000 and sells it on June 14, 1992, for $15,400 and the increase in value each year is $100 more than that of the previous year, find the value of the painting on June 14, 1994.
51. Find the approximate length of a motion picture film 0.01 cm thick if it is wound on a reel 6 cm in diameter that has a central core 2 cm in diameter. Consider the film as being wound in concentric circles.
52. A display of cans has 18 cans on the bottom row, 17 on the row above, 16 on the next row, and so on. If there are 12 rows of cans, how many cans are there in all?
53. Find three arithmetic means between 3 and 15.
54. Find five arithmetic means between 3 and 15.
55. Insert four arithmetic means between 10 and -10.
56. Insert six arithmetic means between 18 and 7.5.

In Probs. 57 to 64, use the corresponding arithmetic sequence.

57. Find the sixth term of the harmonic sequence

$$\tfrac{1}{4}, \ \tfrac{1}{8}, \ \tfrac{1}{12}, \ \ldots$$

58. Find the eighth term of the harmonic sequence

$$\tfrac{3}{5}, \ \tfrac{3}{7}, \ \tfrac{1}{3}, \ \ldots$$

59. Find the seventh term of the harmonic sequence

$$\tfrac{2}{3}, \ \tfrac{4}{9}, \ \tfrac{1}{3}, \ \ldots$$

60. Find the sixth term of the harmonic sequence 3, 1, $\tfrac{3}{5}$, ...
61. What is the first term of a harmonic sequence whose third term is $\tfrac{1}{5}$ and ninth term is $\tfrac{1}{8}$?

62. What is the eighth term of a harmonic sequence whose second term is 2 and fifth term is -2?

63. What is the sixth term of a harmonic sequence whose third term is -1 and eighth term is $\frac{1}{9}$?

64. What is the thirteenth term of a harmonic sequence whose third term is 12 and eighth term is 2?

65. Show that the harmonic mean between a and b is

$$\frac{2ab}{a+b}$$

66. Show that

$$\log 2, \log 6, \log 18, \log 54, \log 162$$

is an arithmetic sequence.

67. If $\sqrt{3}, \sqrt{6}$ is an arithmetic sequence, what is d?

68. If $\sqrt{2}, a_2, \sqrt{18}$ is a harmonic sequence, find a_2.

69. The second term of an arithmetic sequence is equal to -5, and the difference between the sixth and the fourth term is 6. Show that the sum of the first 10 terms of the sequence is 55.

70. Show that the sum

$$1 - 3 + 5 - 7 + 9 - 11 + \cdots - 171 + 173 = 87$$

71. Prove that if the numbers

$$\frac{2}{b+c}, \frac{2}{a+c}, \frac{2}{a+b}$$

form an arithmetic sequence, then the numbers a^2, b^2, c^2 also constitute an arithmetic sequence.

72. Show that if a, b, c, d, e form an arithmetic sequence, then

$$a - 4b + 6c - 4d + e = 0$$

In Probs. 73 to 76, show that the arithmetic mean of the roots of $f(x) = 0$ is the same as the arithmetic mean of the roots of $g(x) = 0$.

73. $f(x) = x^3 + 4x^2 + x - 6$
$\qquad = (x - 1)(x + 2)(x + 3) = 0$
$\quad g(x) = 3x^2 + 8x + 1 = 0$

74. $f(x) = 2x^3 + x^2 - 18x - 9$
$\qquad = (2x + 1)(x - 3)(x + 3) = 0$
$\quad g(x) = 6x^2 + 2x - 18 = 0$

75. $f(x) = 12x^3 - 8x^2 - 3x + 2$
$\qquad = (3x - 2)(2x - 1)(2x + 1) = 0$
$\quad g(x) = 36x^2 - 16x - 3 = 0$

76. $f(x) = 6x^3 + 5x^2 - 7x - 4$
$\qquad = (3x + 4)(2x + 1)(x - 1) = 0$
$\quad g(x) = 18x^2 + 10x - 7$

11.2 Geometric Sequences

The inventor of chess, so it is said, asked that he be rewarded with one grain of wheat for the first square of the board, two grains for the second, four for the third, eight for the fourth, and so on for the 64 squares. Fortunately, this apparently modest request was examined before it was granted. By the twentieth square, the reward for that single square would have amounted to more than a million grains of wheat. By the sixty-fourth square, the total number for the whole board would have been astronomical, and the amount would have exceeded all the grain in the kingdom. The actual number of grains would have been more than the distance in millimeters that light travels in one year. By the end of this section, you should be able to verify that.

Arithmetic sequences are formed by addition, whereas **geometric sequences** are formed by multiplication. Geometric sequences are also called **geometric progressions.**

A geometric sequence is one in which each term is multiplied by the same number to get the next term. Thus for a given **common ratio** r, the terms in the sequence $a_1, a_2, a_3, \ldots, a_n, \ldots$ satisfy

$$r \cdot a_n = a_{n+1} \qquad \text{for } n = 1, 2, 3, \ldots$$

where r may be positive or negative. We will write a for a_1.

Therefore the ratio is $r = a_2/a_1 = a_3/a_2 = \cdots = a_{n+1}/a_n$.

▶ **EXAMPLE 1**   Verify that each of the following sequences is actually a geometric sequence.

Bacteria

Solution   (a) 7000   14,000   28,000   56,000   112,000   224,000

Here $a = 7000$ and $r = 2$. This sequence may represent the number of bacteria in a culture where the number of bacteria doubles every 4 h.

Vacuum pump

(b) 729   486   324   216   144   96   64

Here $a = 729$ and $r = \frac{2}{3}$. This sequence could be the number of cubic centimeters of air in a bell jar if a pump removes $\frac{1}{3}$ of the air in it with each stroke and thus leaves $\frac{2}{3}$ of it.

Compound interest

(c) 1000   1100   1210   1331   1464.10   1610.51

Here $a = 1000$ and $r = 1.10$. This is the value of a \$1000 savings account at the end of each year if it earns 10 percent interest compounded each year.   ◀

The following special terminology is used for geometric sequences:

r = common ratio = $a_2/a_1 = a_3/a_2 = \cdots = a_n/a_{n-1}$
a = first term = $a_1 = f(1)$
n = number of the term
a_n = nth term = $f(n)$
S_n = sum of the first n terms

$$= \sum_{k=1}^{n} a_k = a_1 + a_2 + a_3 + \cdots + a_n$$

With this notation, the terms of a geometric sequence may be written as follows:

Value of a_n	a	ar	ar^2	ar^3	ar^4	ar^5
Value of n	1	2	3	4	5	6

Notice that the exponent of r in the second term is 1. This exponent increases by 1 as we go from one term to the next. This leads to the formula for the general term:

The nth term

$$a_n = ar^{n-1} \tag{11.4}$$

▶ **EXAMPLE 2**   Find the twelfth term of the geometric sequence which begins with the two terms $\frac{7}{8}$ and $\frac{7}{4}$.

Solution   The ratio is

$$r = \frac{\frac{7}{4}}{\frac{7}{8}} = \frac{7}{4} \cdot \frac{8}{7} = 2$$

and using $n = 12$ gives

$$a_{12} = \tfrac{7}{8}(2^{12-1}) = \tfrac{7}{8}(2^{11}) = 7(2^8) = 7(256) = 1792$$

Finite Geometric Series, or the Partial Sum of a Geometric Sequence

The definition of S_n is

$$S_n = a + ar + ar^2 + ar^3 + \cdots + ar^{n-2} + ar^{n-1}$$

which is the sum of the first n terms of the geometric sequence. In order to derive a formula for S_n, we can multiply both sides by r and get

$$rS_n = ar + ar^2 + ar^3 + ar^4 + \cdots + ar^{n-1} + ar^n$$

If we now subtract the second equation from the first, all but two of the terms on the right side of the equation cancel, and we obtain

$$S_n - rS_n = a - ar^n$$

$$S_n(1 - r) = a(1 - r^n)$$

Solving this equation for S_n gives the following formula:

S_n using r, a, and n

> The sum of the first n terms of a geometric sequence with first term a and common ratio $r \neq 1$ is
>
> $$S_n = \frac{a(1 - r^n)}{1 - r} = \frac{a(r^n - 1)}{r - 1} \qquad\qquad \textbf{(11.5)}$$

EXAMPLE 3   Find the sum of the terms 2, -6, 18, -54, 162, -486, and 1458.

Solution   These are the first seven terms of the geometric sequence with $r = -3$ and $a = 2$. Using $n = 7$ gives us $r^n = (-3)^7 = -2187$. So

$$S_7 = \frac{2(1 + 2187)}{1 - (-3)} = \frac{2(2188)}{4} = \frac{2188}{2} = 1094$$

The formula for the nth term is $a_n = ar^{n-1}$. Using this term in the numerator of formula (11.5) for S_n, we obtain

$$a(1 - r^n) = a - ar^n = a - r(ar^{n-1}) = a - ra_n$$

This gives an alternative formula for the sum of the first n terms:

S_n using r, a, and a_n

$$S_n = \frac{a - ra_n}{1 - r}$$ (11.6)

EXAMPLE 4 Ethel decided to celebrate her birthday for the whole month of May by giving to her church 1¢ on May 1, 2¢ on May 2, 4¢ on May 3, 8¢ on May 4, 16¢ on May 5, and so on through the whole month, doubling the amount every day.
(a) How much money will she give on May 11, on May 21, and on May 31?
(b) How much will she give during the whole month?

Solution (a) Using the formula $a_n = ar^{n-1}$ with $r = 2$ and $a = 1$ gives the following amounts in pennies:

May 11: $n = 11$: $a_{11} = (1)(2^{11-1}) = 2^{10} = 1024$, or $10.24
May 21: $n = 21$: $a_{21} = 2^{21-1} = 2^{20} = 1,048,576$, or $10,485.76
May 31: $n = 31$: $a_{31} = 2^{30} = 1,073,741,824$, or $10,737,418.24

(b) Using the formula

$$S_n = \frac{a(r^n - 1)}{r - 1}$$

we see first that $r - 1 = 2 - 1 = 1$, and since $a = 1$, we have

$$S_{31} = 2^{31} - 1 = 2,147,483,647$$

which means that the total amount of money given during the month is $21,474,836.47. Had she celebrated in February, the total would have been only

$$S_{28} = 2^{28} - 1 = \$2,684,354.55$$

EXAMPLE 5 The first term of a geometric sequence is 3 and the fourth term is -24. Find the tenth term and the sum of the first 10 terms.

Solution We are given $a = 3$. If we first use $n = 4$ in the formula $a_n = ar^{n-1}$, we obtain

$$-24 = (3)(r^{4-1}) = 3(r^3)$$

$$-8 = r^3 \quad \text{and thus} \quad r = -2$$

We next use $n = 10$ in the formulas for a_n and S_n, and get

$$a_{10} = (3)(-2)^{10-1} = 3(-2)^9 = 3(-512) = -1536$$

$$S_{10} = \frac{a - ra_n}{1 - r} = \frac{3 - (-2)(-1536)}{1 - (-2)} = \frac{-3069}{3} = -1023$$

EXAMPLE 6 Find r and a if $S_5 = 61$ and $a_5 = 81$.

Solution If we use the formula for a_n and then the second equation for S_n, we get the equations

$$81 = ar^4 \quad \text{and} \quad 61 = \frac{a - 81r}{1 - r}$$

Solving the second equation for a, we obtain

$$61 - 61r = a - 81r \qquad \text{and thus} \qquad a = 61 + 20r$$

Substituting this value in the first equation gives

$$81 = (61 + 20r)r^4 = 61r^4 + 20r^5$$

$$20r^5 + 61r^4 - 81 = 0 \qquad \text{collecting terms}$$

By using the theorem on rational zeros of polynomial functions, we find the solutions to be $r = 1$ and $r = -3$. We must discard $r = 1$ because of division by zero, and thus the only solution is $r = -3$. Using

$$a = 61 + 20r = 61 + 20(-3) = 61 - 60$$

gives $a = 1$. Thus the first five terms of the geometric sequence are 1, -3, 9, -27, 81.

Geometric Means

If a and b are positive numbers, then

$$a, \sqrt{ab}, b \text{ is a geometric sequence of three terms}$$

and $\sqrt{ab}$ is called the **geometric mean** of a and b. If $a_1, a_2, \ldots, a_{n-1}, a_n$ is a geometric sequence, the numbers

$$a_2, a_3, \ldots, a_{n-1}$$

are called **geometric means of a_1 and a_n.**

▶ **EXAMPLE 7** Find the five geometric means between 3 and 192.

Solution We are given $a_1 = 3$ and $a_7 = 192$. Thus

$$192 = 3(r^{7-1}) \qquad \text{using the formula for } a_n$$

$$r^6 = \tfrac{192}{3} = 64$$

$$r = \pm\sqrt[6]{64} = \pm 2$$

If $r = 2$, the five geometric means are 6, 12, 24, 48, 96.
If $r = -2$, the five geometric means are -6, 12, -24, 48, -96.

At the beginning of the section, we told a story about the inventor of chess. The total number of grains of wheat for all the squares on the board would be

$$S_{64} = 1 + 2 + 4 + \cdots + 2^{63} = 2^{64} - 1 \approx 1.84(10^{19})$$

Since the speed of light is approximately 186,000 mi/s, or $3(10^5)$ km/s, the number of millimeters that light travels in a year is approximately

$$3(10^5)\frac{\text{km}}{\text{s}}(10^6)\frac{\text{mm}}{\text{km}}\left(60\frac{\text{s}}{\text{min}}\right)\left(60\frac{\text{min}}{\text{h}}\right)\left(24\frac{\text{h}}{\text{day}}\right)\left(365\frac{\text{days}}{\text{year}}\right) \approx 9.46(10^{18})\frac{\text{mm}}{\text{year}}$$

which is indeed less than the total number of grains of wheat.

EXERCISE 11.2

Write the n terms of the geometric sequence described in each of Probs. 1 to 8.

1. $a_1 = 3, r = 2, n = 5$
2. $a_1 = 2, r = 3, n = 5$
3. $a_1 = 5, r = -2, n = 4$
4. $a_1 = -5, r = -2, n = 4$
5. $a_1 = 243, a_4 = 9, n = 5$
6. $a_1 = 256, a_4 = -32, n = 6$
7. $a_2 = 8, a_4 = 2, n = 6$
8. $a_6 = \frac{3}{16}, a_2 = 3, n = 6$

In Probs. 9 to 20, find the quantity on the right.

9. $a = 2, r = 3, n = 5, a_n$
10. $a = 3, r = 2, a_n = 96, n$
11. $r = -1, n = 7, a_n = -1, a$
12. $a_n = 81, a = 1, r = 3, n$
13. $a = 2, r = 4, n = 4, S_n$
14. $a = \frac{1}{3}, r = 3, n = 5, S_n$
15. $r = -4, n = 6, S_n = -819, a$
16. $a = -1, a_n = 243, r = -3, n$
17. $a = 64, r = \frac{1}{2}, a_n = 1, S_n$
18. $a = 27, a_n = \frac{16}{3}, r = \frac{2}{3}, S_n$
19. $a = 125, r = -\frac{1}{5}, S_n = 104\frac{1}{5}, a_n$
20. $a = 64, a_n = 1, S_n = 43, r$

In Probs. 21 to 36, find the two quantities $S_n, n, a, r,$ and a_n that are missing.

21. $a = 2, r = 3, n = 5$ 22. $a = 3, r = 2, n = 5$
23. $a = 8, r = -\frac{3}{2}, a_n = \frac{81}{2}$
24. $a = 162, r = -\frac{1}{3}, a_n = 2$
25. $a = 343, r = \frac{1}{7}, a_n = 1$
26. $n = 4, r = 3, a_n = 3$
27. $n = 9, a = 256, a_n = 1$
28. $n = 7, a = \frac{1}{8}, a_n = 8$
29. $S_n = 242, a = 2, r = 3$
30. $S_n = 781, n = 5, r = \frac{1}{5}$
31. $S_n = 400, r = \frac{1}{7}, a_n = 1$
32. $S_n = 1, n = 7, a_n = 1$
33. $a_n = 12, S_n = 9, n = 3$
34. $r = -\frac{3}{2}, a_n = \frac{81}{2}, S_n = \frac{55}{2}$
35. $a = 5, n = 3, S_n = 65$
36. $a = 8, a_n = \frac{1}{8}, S_n = \frac{127}{8}$
37. Find the sum of all of the integral powers of 2 between 5 and 500.
38. Find the sum of the first seven integral powers of 3 starting with 3.
39. Find the sum $1 + 2 + 4 + 8 + \cdots + 2^n$.
40. Find the sum

$$\frac{1}{4} + \frac{1}{16} + \frac{1}{64} + \cdots + \frac{1}{4^n}$$

41. For which values of k are $2k$, $5k + 2$, and $20k - 4$ consecutive terms of a geometric sequence?
42. If 1, 4, and 19 are added to the first, second, and third terms, respectively, of an arithmetic sequence with $d = 3$, then a geometric sequence is obtained. Find the arithmetic sequence and the common ratio of the geometric sequence.
43. Show that if

$$\frac{1}{y - x}, \frac{1}{2y}, \frac{1}{y - z}$$

form an arithmetic sequence, then x, y, and z form a geometric sequence.

44. Show that if a, b, c, and x, y, z are two geometric sequences, then ax, by, cz is also a geometric sequence.
45. Twelve people are fishing. If the first is worth $1000, the second $2000, the third $4000, and so on, how many of them are millionaires?
46. Mrs. Lewis willed one-third of her estate to one person, one-third of the remainder to a second, and so on, until the fifth received $25,600. What was the value of the estate?
47. The number of bacteria in a culture doubles every 2 h. If there were n bacteria present at noon one day, how many were there at noon the next day?
48. The first stroke of a pump removes one-fourth of the air from a bell jar, and each stroke thereafter removes one-fourth of the remaining air. What part of the original amount is left after six strokes?
49. Mr. Thiele loses $1 on the first poker hand, $2 on the second, $4 on the third, and so on, the amount doubling every time. If he loses nine hands in a row, how much does he lose altogether? If he then wins the tenth hand, what is his net profit or loss?
50. If $100 is put in a savings account at the end of each 6 months, how much money is in the account at the

end of 6 years if the bank pays 6 percent interest per year compounded semiannually?

51. If there were no duplications, how many ancestors did Jennifer have in the immediately preceding seven generations?

52. Each year, a $30,000 machine depreciates by 20 percent of its value at the beginning of that year. Find its value at the end of the fifth year.

53. What are the two geometric means between 2 and 54?

54. What are the four geometric means between $\frac{2}{9}$ and $\frac{27}{16}$?

55. Find two sets of three geometric means between 2 and 32.

56. Find two sets of five geometric means between 2 and $\frac{1}{32}$.

Classify the sequence in each of Probs. 57 to 64 as arithmetic, geometric, or harmonic and give the next two terms.

57. $\frac{2}{3}, \frac{4}{9}, \frac{8}{27}, \frac{16}{81}$ **58.** $\frac{2}{3}, \frac{4}{9}, \frac{1}{3}, \frac{4}{15}$

59. $\frac{2}{3}, \frac{4}{9}, \frac{2}{9}, 0$ **60.** $\frac{1}{20}, \frac{3}{10}, \frac{11}{20}, \frac{4}{5}$

61. $\frac{1}{4}, 1, -\frac{1}{2}, -\frac{1}{5}$ **62.** $2, 3, \frac{9}{2}, \frac{27}{4}$

63. $\frac{1}{6}, \frac{2}{3}, \frac{7}{6}, \frac{5}{3}$ **64.** $\frac{1}{7}, \frac{2}{11}, \frac{1}{4}, \frac{2}{5}$

65. Show that if $0 < a < b$ and the plus sign is used for the geometric mean, then the harmonic mean of a and b is less than their geometric mean, and their geometric mean is less than their arithmetic mean. *Hint:* Show that

$$\frac{2ab}{a+b} \le \sqrt{ab} \quad \text{and} \quad \sqrt{ab} \le \frac{a+b}{2}$$

66. Suppose the distance between two houses is d mi and the trip in one direction is made with an average speed of v mi/h. Show that if w is the average speed in the other direction, then the average speed for the round trip is at most $(v + w)/2$. *Hint:* The total distance is clearly $2d$. Show that the total time is $d/v + d/w$, and then use

$$\frac{\text{Total distance}}{\text{Total time}} = \text{average speed}$$

67. Three numbers form a geometric sequence. If 8 is added to the second number, then these numbers will constitute an arithmetic sequence. If 64 is then added to the third number, the resulting numbers will form a geometric sequence once again. Find the three given numbers.

68. Prove that

$$\log \sqrt{ab} = \frac{\log a + \log b}{2}$$

In words, this says that "the logarithm of the geometric mean is equal to the arithmetic mean of the logarithms."

Any integer from 1 to 127 can be written by adding some or all of the numbers 1, 2, 4, 8, 16, 32, and 64, each of these being used at most once. For instance, $87 = 1 + 2 + 4 + 16 + 64$. Write the numbers below in this manner.

69. 30   **70.** 111   **71.** 59   **72.** 95

Any integer from 1 to 121 can be written by adding or subtracting some or all of the numbers 1, 3, 9, 27, and 81, each of these being used at most once. For instance, $58 = 81 - 27 + 3 + 1$. Write the numbers below in this manner.

73. 53   **74.** 44   **75.** 111   **76.** 95

11.3 Infinite Geometric Series

The **infinite geometric sequence** with first term a and ratio r is

$$a, ar, ar^2, ar^3, ar^4, \ldots, ar^{n-1}, \ldots$$

The associated **infinite geometric series** is the indicated sum

$$a + ar + ar^2 + ar^3 + ar^4 + \cdots$$

We cannot literally "add" an infinite number of terms, but we can most certainly add a finite number of the terms. As we have seen in Sec. 11.2, the sum of the first n terms is denoted by S_n, and that sum is

$$S_n = \frac{a - ar^n}{1 - r} = \frac{a(1 - r^n)}{1 - r} = \frac{a}{1 - r}(1 - r^n)$$

By definition, as n becomes larger, the value of S_n approaches the "sum" of the infinite geometric series. This definition is necessarily incomplete; a rigorous definition using limits is presented in a calculus course. However, it is true that

If $-1 < r < 1$, *then* r^n *approaches* 0

as n becomes larger and larger (see Prob. 49). For instance if $r = \frac{2}{3}$, then the sequence

$$\frac{2}{3} \qquad \frac{4}{9} \qquad \frac{8}{27} \qquad \frac{16}{81} \qquad \frac{32}{243} \qquad \frac{64}{729}$$

approaches 0. It follows that as $n \to \infty$, then

$$1 - r^n \longrightarrow 1 - 0 = 1$$

and S_n approaches

$$\frac{a}{1 - r}(1 - 0) = \frac{a}{1 - r}$$

These ideas are treated much more fully in a calculus course. The standard notation for this is shown below.

If $-1 < r < 1$, then the infinite geometric series

$$\sum_{i=1}^{\infty} a \cdot r^{i-1} = a + ar + ar^2 + ar^3 + \cdots + ar^{n-1} + \cdots$$

has the sum

$$S = \lim_{n \to \infty} S_n = \frac{a}{1 - r} \tag{11.7}$$

► **EXAMPLE 1**   Find the sum of the infinite geometric series

$$\tfrac{1}{2} + \tfrac{1}{4} + \tfrac{1}{8} + \tfrac{1}{16} + \cdots$$

Solution   In the series, $a = \frac{1}{2}$ and $r = \frac{1}{2}$. Using the formula for the sum of an infinite geometric series, we obtain

$$S = \frac{a}{1 - r} = \frac{\frac{1}{2}}{1 - \frac{1}{2}} = \frac{\frac{1}{2}}{\frac{1}{2}} = 1$$

The 1×1 square in Fig. 11.1 gives a compelling geometric argument that the "sum" of the series is indeed 1. The unit square is partitioned into pieces of area $\frac{1}{2}$, $\frac{1}{4}$, $\frac{1}{8}$, $\frac{1}{16}$, and so on.   ◢

► **EXAMPLE 2**   Find the ratio r of an infinite geometric series if the sum $S = 2$ and $a = \frac{1}{2}$.

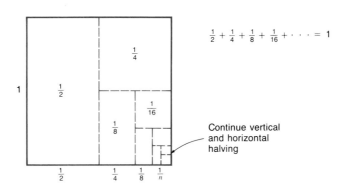

$\frac{1}{2} + \frac{1}{4} + \frac{1}{8} + \frac{1}{16} + \cdots = 1$

Continue vertical
and horizontal
halving

FIGURE 11.1

Solution Substituting the given values in the formula $S = a/(1 - r)$ gives

$$2 = \frac{\frac{1}{2}}{1 - r}$$

and so $2 - 2r = \frac{1}{2}$, $\frac{3}{2} = 2r$, $r = \frac{3}{4}$. ◢

A nonterminating, repeating decimal fraction is an illustration of an infinite geometric series with $-1 < r < 1$. For example

$$0.232323\cdots = 0.23 + 0.0023 + 0.000023 + \cdots$$

The terms on the right form a geometric series with $a = 0.23$ and $r = \frac{1}{100} = 0.01$.

We can use the formula for the sum of an infinite geometric series to express any repeating decimal fraction as a common fraction. The method is illustrated in the following example. In fact, the decimal form of a number is repeating (or terminating)

If and only if the number is a rational number

◤ **EXAMPLE 3** Write $0.636363\cdots$ as a quotient of positive integers.

Solution The decimal fraction $0.6363\cdots$ can be expressed as the series

$$0.63 + 0.0063 + 0.000063 + \cdots$$

in which $a = 0.63$ and $r = 0.01$. Hence we can write the sum as

$$S = \frac{a}{1 - r} = \frac{0.63}{1 - 0.01} = \frac{0.63}{0.99} = \frac{63}{99} = \frac{7}{11}$$ ◢

Some results related to this are in Probs. 29 to 32. In particular we show there that $0.99999\cdots = 1$.

◤ **EXAMPLE 4** Express $3.2181818\cdots$ as a fraction.

Solution The given number can be expressed as 3.2 plus an infinite geometric series with $a = 0.018$ and $r = 0.01$. Thus we can write the decimal as

$$3.2181818\cdots = 3.2 + 0.018 + 0.00018 + 0.0000018 + \cdots$$

$$= 3.2 + \frac{0.018}{1 - 0.01} = 3.2 + \frac{0.018}{0.990}$$

$$= \frac{16}{5} + \frac{18}{990} = \frac{16}{5} + \frac{1}{55} = \frac{177}{55}$$

EXAMPLE 5   Terry loses 18 lb in 6 months, 12 lb in the next 6 months, 8 in the next 6 months, and so on for a long time. What is the maximum total weight loss?

Solution   The amounts lost form a geometric sequence with $a = 18$ lb and $r = \frac{2}{3}$. Thus

$$S = \frac{18}{1 - \frac{2}{3}} = \frac{18}{\frac{1}{3}} = 54$$

EXAMPLE 6   Find the sum of the geometric series

$$2x + 3 + \frac{(2x + 3)^2}{4} + \frac{(2x + 3)^3}{16} + \cdots$$

and also the values of x for which the sum exists.

Solution   In this series

$$a = 2x + 3 \qquad \text{and} \qquad r = \frac{2x + 3}{4}$$

We can write the sum using $S = a/(1 - r)$.

$$\frac{2x + 3}{1 - \dfrac{2x + 3}{4}} = \frac{4(2x + 3)}{4 - (2x + 3)} = \frac{8x + 12}{1 - 2x}$$

The sum exists if and only if $|r| < 1$, and thus we need

$$\left| \frac{2x + 3}{4} \right| < 1 \qquad \text{or} \qquad |2x + 3| < 4$$

$$-4 < 2x + 3 < 4 \qquad \text{equivalent inequality}$$

$$-7 < 2x < 1 \qquad \text{subtracting 3}$$

$$-\tfrac{7}{2} < x < \tfrac{1}{2} \qquad \text{dividing by 2}$$

EXAMPLE 7   There is a phenomenon in economics which is known as the *multiplier effect*. Assume that a company invests \$6,000,000 in a community and that 75 percent of the money is spent and 25 percent saved. Of the 75 percent, or \$4,500,000, again 75 percent is spent. If this spending chain reaction is continued repeatedly, find the total amount of spending caused by the initial \$6,000,000, including the initial amount. What is the ratio of the total to \$6,000,000?

The multiplier effect

Solution The amounts spent form a geometric series with $a = 6,000,000$ and $r = 0.75$, and their sum is

$$6,000,000 + 6,000,000(0.75) + 6,000,000(0.75)(0.75) + \cdots$$

$$= 6,000,000(1 + 0.75 + 0.75^2 + 0.75^3 + \cdots) = 6,000,000\left(\frac{1}{1 - 0.75}\right)$$

$$= 6,000,000\left(\frac{1}{0.25}\right) = 6,000,000(4) = 24,000,000$$

The total spending is $24,000,000, and the ratio in economics is called the *multiplier*, which in this example is $24,000,000/$6,000,000 = 4$. In general

$$\textit{The multiplier is } \frac{1}{1 - r}$$

where r is the ratio spent at each stage. This gives the cumulative effect of an initial investment. ◀

EXERCISE 11.3

Find the sum of the infinite geometric sequence described in each of Probs. 1 to 12.

1. $a_1 = 5, r = \frac{4}{5}$
2. $a_1 = 5, r = \frac{2}{5}$
3. $a_1 = 5, r = -\frac{4}{5}$
4. $a_1 = 5, r = -\frac{1}{5}$
5. $a_1 = 18, r = \frac{1}{2}$
6. $a_1 = 12, r = -\frac{1}{2}$
7. $a_1 = 11, r = -\frac{1}{10}$
8. $a_1 = 11, r = \frac{1}{12}$
9. $a_1 = 12, a_2 = 8$
10. $a_1 = 27, a_4 = 1$
11. $a_2 = 24, a_3 = 12$
12. $a_2 = 24, a_3 = -12$

Find a or r, whichever is missing.

13. $r = \frac{1}{3}, S = \frac{9}{2}$
14. $r = -\frac{2}{5}, S = \frac{25}{7}$
15. $a = 16, S = 10$
16. $a = 7, S = 9$

If n is a positive integer, find the sum of all the numbers of the form given in each of Probs. 17 to 20.

17. $(\frac{1}{3})^n$
18. $(\frac{2}{3})^n$
19. $(-\frac{2}{5})^n$
20. $(-\frac{3}{4})^n$

Express the repeating decimal in each of Probs. 21 to 28 as a rational number in lowest terms.

21. $0.444\cdots$
22. $0.2424\cdots$
23. $2.343434\cdots$
24. $1.414141\cdots$
25. $4.1222\cdots$
26. $2.2111\cdots$
27. $6.54848\cdots$
28. $2.0124124\cdots$

Problems 29 to 32 give four different ways of showing that

$$0.999\cdots = 1$$

29. Treat $0.999\cdots$ as in Probs. 21 to 28 or Examples 3 and 4.

30. Let $x = 0.999\cdots$, so $10x = 9.999\cdots$. Then subtract and solve for x.

31. Show that if $(a + b)/2 = a$, then $a = b$. Apply this with

$$a = 0.999\cdots \quad \text{and} \quad b = 1.000\cdots$$

32. Multiply both members of $0.333\cdots = \frac{1}{3}$ by 3.

In each of Probs. 33 to 36, find the sum S of the series. Verify by calculation that the sum of any odd number of terms is larger than S, and the sum of any even number of terms is less than S.

33. $1 - \dfrac{1}{3} + \dfrac{1}{3^2} - \dfrac{1}{3^3} + \cdots$

34. $1 - \dfrac{1}{4} + \dfrac{1}{4^2} - \dfrac{1}{4^3} + \cdots$

35. $\frac{2}{5} - (\frac{2}{5})^2 + (\frac{2}{5})^3 - (\frac{2}{5})^4 + \cdots$

36. $2 - 1 + \frac{1}{2} - \frac{1}{4} + \cdots$

37. *Physics* If the first arc made by the tip of a pendulum is 12 cm and each arc thereafter is 0.995 as long as the one just before it, how far does the tip move before coming to rest?

38. *Physics* If a ball rebounds three-fifths as far as it

falls, how far will it travel before coming to rest when dropped from a height of 30 m?

39. *Engineering* The motion of a particle through a certain medium is such that it moves two-thirds as far each second as in the preceding second. If it moves 6 m the first second, how far will it move before coming to rest?

40. *Finance* An alumna gave an oil field to her university. If the university received $230,000 from the field the first year and two-thirds as much as in the immediately preceding year each year thereafter, how much did the college realize?

41. *Agriculture* Assume that potatoes shrink one-half as much each week as during the previous week. If a dealer stores 1000 kg when the price is p cents per kilogram and the weight decreases to 950 kg during the first week, for which values of p can he afford to hold the potatoes until the price rises to $p + 1$ cents per kilogram?

42. *Biology* A hamster receives a dose of 3 mg of a compound and then two-thirds as much as the previous dose at the end of every 3 h. What is the maximum amount of the compound it will receive?

43. *Geometry* A series of squares is drawn by connecting the midpoints of the sides of a given square, then the midpoints of the square thus drawn, and so on. Find the sum of the areas of all the squares if the original square had sides of 10 in.

44. *Geometry* Find the sum of the perimeters of the squares of Prob. 43.

Infinite Series

Find the values for x in each of Probs. 45 to 48 in order for the sum to exist. Also find the sum.

45. $\dfrac{3x - 1}{2} + \dfrac{(3x - 1)^2}{4} + \dfrac{(3x - 1)^3}{8} + \cdots$

46. $\dfrac{x - 5}{3} - \dfrac{(x - 5)^2}{9} + \dfrac{(x - 5)^3}{27} - + \cdots$

47. $\dfrac{2x + 1}{4} + \dfrac{(2x + 1)^2}{16} + \dfrac{(2x + 1)^3}{64} + \cdots$

48. $\dfrac{5x + 2}{2} - \dfrac{(5x + 2)^2}{4} + \dfrac{(5x + 2)^3}{8} - + \cdots$

49. We stated in this section that if $|r| < 1$, then r^n approaches 0 as n becomes larger and larger. Verify the following steps, which show that

$$\text{If } n > 52, \text{ then } (0.7)^n < 10^{-8}$$

Given: $(0.7)^n < 10^{-8}$

If and only if: $\log (0.7)^n < \log (10^{-8})$

If and only if: $n \log 0.7 < -8$

If and only if: $n(\log 7 - 1) < -8$

If and only if: $n > \dfrac{-8}{\log 7 - 1} \approx 51.6$

50. Find the sum of the geometric series

$$\tfrac{1}{3} + \tfrac{2}{9} + \tfrac{4}{27} + \tfrac{8}{81} + \cdots$$

Economics

In Probs. 51 and 52, use the result in Example 7 to find the multiplier if the ratio r of spending at each stage is the number given.

51. $r = 0.80$ **52.** $r = 0.90$

11.4 Compound Interest and Annuities

Borrowing and lending money are everyday occurrences in modern life. A borrower pays a lender (either an individual or a business) interest for the use of the lender's money. The amount of interest paid depends on several things:

The principal, which is the amount of money borrowed
The interest rate per period, expressed as a decimal
The number of interest periods
The use of simple or compound interest

Simple interest for one interest period is the product of the principal and the interest rate per period. The interest is paid at the end of each interest period.

Compound interest for one interest period is also the product of the principal and the interest rate per period. However the interest for a period is added to the principal at the end of the period, and their sum is used as the new principal for the next interest period. For both simple and compound interest, the principal plus the interest is called the **accumulated value.**

EXAMPLE 1   Find the accumulated value after each of the first four years if $32,000 is invested at 5 percent per year. Use simple interest and also compound interest.

Solution

	Simple interest	Compound interest
Principal	32,000	32,000
Year 1 interest	$1,600 = 0.05(32,000)$	$1,600 = 0.05(32,000)$
Accumulated value	$33,600 = 32,000 + 1,600$	$33,600 = 32,000 + 1,600$
Principal	32,000	33,600
Year 2 interest	$1,600 = 0.05(32,000)$	$1,680 = 0.05(33,600)$
Accumulated value	$35,200 = 33,600 + 1,600$	$35,280 = 33,600 + 1,680$
Principal	32,000	35,280
Year 3 interest	$1,600 = 0.05(32,000)$	$1,764 = 0.05(35,280)$
Accumulated value	$36,800 = 35,200 + 1,600$	$37,044 = 35,280 + 1,764$
Principal	32,000	37,044
Year 4 interest	$1,600 = 0.05(32,000)$	$1,852.20 = 0.05(37,044)$
Accumulated value	$38,400 = 36,800 + 1,600$	$38,896.20 = 37,044 + 1,852.20$

In Example 1, the accumulated values for the simple interest form an **arithmetic sequence** with the

$$\text{Common difference} = 1,600 = 33,600 - 32,000 = 35,200 - 33,600$$

With compound interest, the accumulated values form a **geometric sequence** with the

$$\text{Common ratio} = 1.05 = \frac{33,600}{32,000} = \frac{35,280}{33,600} = \cdots$$

In general, if the principal is P and the interest rate per period is r, then the simple interest each period is Pr. Moreover, if there are t interest periods and I is the total interest, then

Simple-interest formula

$$I = Prt$$

If A is the accumulated value at simple interest, then

$$A = P + I = P + Prt = P(1 + rt)$$

Now suppose that a principal of P is invested at compound interest for n interest periods at the rate i per period. If S is the accumulated value, then for the first period

$$S = P + Pi = P(1 + i)$$

for the second period

$$S = P(1 + i) + [P(1 + i)]i = P(1 + i)^2$$

for the third period

$$S = P(1 + i)^2 + [P(1 + i)^2]i = P(1 + i)^3$$

and so on until the nth period, when S equals $P(1 + i)^n$.

Compound-interest formula

> If P is compounded using an interest rate of i per period for n periods, then it will accumulate to $S = P(1 + i)^n$.   **(11.8)**

▶ **EXAMPLE 2**   Find the accumulated value if $4588 is invested at 6 percent per period for eight periods. Use simple and compound interest.

Solution   With simple interest, $P = 4588$, $r = 0.06$, and $t = 8$, and so

$$A = P(1 + rt)$$

$$= 4588(1 + 0.48) = 4588(1.48) = 6790.24$$

With compound interest, we use $P = 4588$, $i = 0.06$, $n = 8$ and get

$$S = P(1 + i)^n = 4588(1 + 0.06)^8 = 4588(1.06)^8$$

$$= 4588(1.59385) = 7312.58 \quad \blacktriangleleft$$

If a principal P is invested at 8 percent per year compounded quarterly, this means that the interest rate for each of the four quarters is 2 percent. The *stated annual rate* (8 percent here) is called the **nominal rate,** and the *rate per period* (2 percent) is called the **periodic rate.** In general, if the nominal rate is j and if it is compounded m times per year, then the rate per period is j/m. Using $P = 1$, $i = j/m$, and $n = m$ shows that

$$\textit{The accumulated value of 1 in 1 year is } \left(1 + \frac{j}{m}\right)^m$$

and the interest rate for 1 year is

$$E = \left(1 + \frac{j}{m}\right)^m - 1 \quad \text{(11.9)}$$

The number E is called the **effective rate,** or effective annual interest rate, and it is the simple-interest rate which gives the same interest after 1 year as the nominal rate j compounded m times per year.

▶ **EXAMPLE 3**   Find the effective rate corresponding to 12 percent compounded 6 times per year.

Solution   Using $j = 12$ percent $= 0.12$ and $m = 6$ gives $j/m = 0.12/6 = 0.02$, and thus

$$E = (1.02)^6 - 1 = 1.1262 - 1 = 0.1262 = 12.62 \text{ percent} \quad \blacktriangleleft$$

Suppose that we invest P dollars at a nominal or annual rate of j compounded m times a year, for a period of n years. Then the periodic rate is j/m, while the number of periods is mn. Using the compound-interest formula shows that the accumulated value after n years is

$$S = P\left(1 + \frac{j}{m}\right)^{mn} \tag{11.10}$$

This equation is solved for S, but it also involves P, j, m, and n. If any four of these five values are known, the remaining value can be found. The values that are used in this section can be found by either a calculator or tables.

EXAMPLE 4 How much must be invested at 8 percent compounded quarterly for 5 years in order to have \$11,070 at the end of the 5 years?

Solution We are given $j = 8$ percent, $m = 4$, $S = 11{,}070$, and $n = 5$. Hence $j/m = 0.08/4 = 0.02$ and $mn = 20$, and using these values gives, to the nearest dollar,

$$11{,}070 = P(1 + 0.02)^{(4)(5)} = P(1.02)^{20} = P(1.4859)$$

$$P = \frac{11{,}070}{1.4859} = 7450$$

EXAMPLE 5 If \$22,100 is invested at 6 percent compounded semiannually, how long will it take to accumulate to \$60,375?

Solution In this case, $P = 22{,}100$, $j = 0.06$, $m = 2$, and $S = 60375$. Hence $j/m = 0.06/2 = 0.03$ and $mn = 2n$. Thus

$$60{,}375 = 22{,}100(1.03)^{2n}$$

$$1.03^{2n} = \frac{60{,}375}{22{,}100} = 2.7319$$

Using Appendix II Table A.3, we obtain

$$2n = 34 \qquad \text{and} \qquad n = 17$$

By algebra and calculator

$$\log 2.7319 = \log (1.03^{2n}) = 2n \log 1.03$$

$$2n = \frac{\log 2.7319}{\log 1.03} = \frac{0.436465}{0.012837} = 34$$

$$n = 17$$

Ordinary Annuities

Sometimes it is desirable to pay for an item in several payments over a period of time. A sequence of equal payments at equal intervals is called an **annuity.** Monthly payments on a house or a car are annuities. The time between consecutive payments is called the **payment interval** or **period.** If each payment is made at the end of the payment period, we have an **ordinary annuity.** The **term,** or **length,** of an annuity is found by multiplying the number of payments by the payment period.

▶ EXAMPLE 6   Find the term and interest rate per period of the ordinary annuity described below.

Solution   If a payment is made at the end of each quarter, the payment period is 3 months. If there are a total of 22 payments, the term is 22(3) = 66 months, or $5\frac{1}{2}$ years. If the interest rate is 12 percent compounded quarterly, the periodic interest rate is

$$\frac{0.12}{4} = 0.03$$ ◢

To derive a formula for the value of an annuity at the end of its term, suppose that $1 is invested at the end of each period for n periods and the rate of interest is i per period. The first payment draws interest compounded for $n - 1$ periods, and its accumulated value using formula (11.8) is

$$P(1 + i)^{n-1} = (1 + i)^{n-1}$$

The second payment draws interest for $n - 2$ periods, and its accumulated value is

$$(1 + i)^{n-2}$$

The third payment's accumulated value is $(1 + i)^{n-3}$. This process can be continued until the last payment, whose value is just 1 since it is deposited at the very end. The sum of these accumulated values is

$$(1 + i)^{n-1} + (1 + i)^{n-2} + (1 + i)^{n-3} + \cdots + (1 + i)^2 + (1 + i) + 1$$

This is a finite geometric series. If we write the series in reverse order, we have $a = 1$ and $r = 1 + i$. Its sum is

$$\frac{a(r^n - 1)}{r - 1} = \frac{(1 + i)^n - 1}{(1 + i) - 1} = \frac{(1 + i)^n - 1}{i}$$

If the periodic payment is R instead of 1, then each term in the geometric series above is multiplied by R.

Accumulated value of an annuity

> If R dollars are invested each period at a rate of i per period, then the accumulated value of the annuity after n periods is
>
> $$S = R\left[\frac{(1 + i)^n - 1}{i}\right]$$ (11.11)

▶ EXAMPLE 7   How much did Grandpa accumulate by depositing $1500 at the end of each quarter for 9 years if he got 8 percent interest compounded quarterly?

Solution   These payments form an ordinary annuity with $R = \$1500$, $i = 0.08/4 = 0.02$, and $n = 9(4) = 36$. The value at the end of the annuity is

$$1500\left(\frac{1.02^{36} - 1}{0.02}\right)$$

Using Appendix II Table A.4, this equals $(1500)(51.9944) = 77,991.60$. Using 8 digits in a calculator, we find

$$1500\left(\frac{2.0398873 - 1}{0.02}\right) = (1500)(51.994367) = 77,991.55$$

EXAMPLE 8   Suppose that you buy a house for $125,000, make a down payment of $25,000, and must pay off the remaining $100,000 on time. If the interest rate is 12 percent compounded monthly, and the term is 30 years, what must your monthly payment be?

Solution   Instead of loaning you the $100,000, the bank could invest it at 1 percent a month for $(12)(30) = 360$ months. The accumulated value of this investment at the end of the 30 years is

$$100,000(1.01)^{360} = 100,000(35.949641) = 3,594,964.10$$

in dollars (yes, it is over $3\frac{1}{2}$ million dollars). You must pay into an annuity whose value at the end of the term is also this same $3,594,964.10. Thus we must solve this equation for R:

$$100,000(1.01)^{360} = R\left(\frac{1.01^{360} - 1}{0.01}\right)$$

$$3,594,964.10 = R\left(\frac{34.949641}{0.01}\right) = R(3494.9641)$$

$$R = \frac{3,594,964.10}{3494.9641} = 1028.61$$

You must pay $1,028.61 each month for 30 years. Your total payments are $(360)(1028.61) = 370,299.60$, and these payments plus the interest they draw over the 30 years total the aforementioned $3\frac{1}{2}$ million plus dollars.

You should repeat Example 8 yourself using 20 years instead of 30 years. You will probably be surprised to learn that the monthly payment only needs to be increased to $1101.09, which is an increase of only $72.48, or about 7 percent.

Sometimes we need to know the value of an annuity at the beginning of its term. This is called the **present value** of the annuity even though it refers to the beginning, not the "present" time. The relation between the accumulated value S and the present value A is, by definition,

$$S = A(1 + i)^n$$

EXAMPLE 9   Find the present value of an annuity of $240 per quarter for 12 years if the rate is 12 percent compounded quarterly.

Solution   Using $i = 0.12/4 = 0.03$ and $n = 4(12) = 48$ gives the accumulated value

$$S = 240\left(\frac{1.03^{48} - 1}{0.03}\right) = 240(104.4084) = 25,058.02$$

Therefore we need to solve

$$25{,}058.02 = A(1.03)^{48} = A(4.1323)$$

$$A = \frac{25{,}058.02}{4.1323} \approx 6064$$

This means that having $6064 now is equivalent to receiving the annuity over the next 12 years.   ◀

EXERCISE 11.4

In Probs. 1 to 4, find the accumulated value using both compound and simple interest.

  1. $15,000 at 5 percent per year for 18 years
  2. $240,000 at 6 percent per year for 13 years
  3. $78,500 at 4 percent per year for 25 years
  4. $186,000 at 5 percent per year for 7 years

Find the accumulated value at compound interest in Probs. 5 to 8.

  5. $18,400 at 3 percent per period for 38 periods
  6. $96,600 at 2 percent per period for 46 periods
  7. $1,480,000 at $2\frac{1}{2}$ percent per period for 34 periods
  8. $765,000 at 3 percent per period for 29 periods

Find the effective rate in Probs. 9 to 12.

  9. $j = 8$ percent, $m = 4$ **10.** $j = 6$ percent, $m = 2$
  11. $j = 12$ percent, $m = 6$
  12. $j = 10$ percent, $m = 4$

Find the value of the one of S, P, and n that is missing in each of Probs. 13 to 24, which deal with compound interest. The answers were found by using a calculator. Answers from the appendix tables in this book should be very close.

  13. $P = \$560$, $j = 6$ percent, $m = 2$, $n = 17$ years
  14. $P = \$2350$, $j = 5$ percent, $m = 2$, $n = 20$ years
  15. $P = \$4600$, $j = 6$ percent, $m = 4$, $n = 12$ years
  16. $P = \$7500$, $j = 8$ percent, $m = 4$, $n = 9$ years
  17. $S = \$5200$, $j = 5$ percent, $m = 2$, $n = 8$ years
  18. $S = \$2100$, $j = 8$ percent, $m = 2$, $n = 23$ years
  19. $S = \$1120$, $j = 6$ percent, $m = 4$, $n = 11$ years
  20. $S = \$480$, $j = 8$ percent, $m = 4$, $n = 7$ years
  21. $P = \$1000$, $S = \$1194.10$, $j = 6$ percent, $m = 2$
  22. $P = \$1800$, $S = \$2771.10$, $j = 8$ percent, $m = 2$
  23. $P = \$540$, $S = \$2836.78$, $j = 10$ percent, $m = 2$
  24. $P = \$770$, $S = \$1768.84$, $j = 4$ percent, $m = 2$

In Probs. 25 to 32, find the accumulated value of the annuity at the end of the term and also the present value A at the beginning of the term. Assume that j is the nominal or annual rate compounded m times per year and R is the periodic payment.

  25. $j = 6$ percent, $m = 2$, term $= 19$ years, $R = \$2000$
  26. $j = 5$ percent, $m = 2$, term $= 23$ years, $R = \$7200$
  27. $j = 8$ percent, $m = 2$, term $= 24$ years, $R = \$1250$
  28. $j = 4$ percent, $m = 2$, term $= 16$ years, $R = \$540$
  29. $j = 8$ percent, $m = 4$, term $= 11$ years, $R = \$270$
  30. $j = 10$ percent, $m = 4$, term $= 7$ years, $R = \$460$
  31. $j = 6$ percent, $m = 4$, term $= 12$ years, $R = \$950$
  32. $j = 8$ percent, $m = 4$, term $= 5$ years, $R = \$1800$
  33. Johannes bought a car for $28,000 and put down $5,000. What is his monthly payment if the interest rate is 18 percent compounded monthly and the term is 3 years?
  34. Nguyen bought a house for $220,000 and made a down payment of $40,000. What is his semiannual payment for 25 years if the interest rate is 12 percent compounded semiannually?
  35. Maria bought a condominium for $385,000 with a down payment of $75,000. What is her quarterly payment if the interest rate is 10 percent compounded quarterly and the term is 12 years?
  36. Shelly bought a partnership in a business for $663,000 with a down payment of $83,000. What is her quarterly payment if the interest rate is 8 percent compounded quarterly and the term is 12 years?
  37. How long will it take for P dollars to double at 8 percent compounded quarterly?
  38. How long will it take for P dollars to double at 10 percent compounded quarterly?
  39. How long will it take for P dollars to quintuple at 10 percent compounded semiannually?
  40. How long will it take for P dollars to triple at 8 percent compounded semiannually?

11.5 Key Concepts

Be sure that you understand the following important words and ideas.

Arithmetic sequence (p. 548)
Common difference (p. 548)
Arithmetic means (p. 552)
Harmonic sequence (p. 553)
Harmonic means (p. 554)
Geometric sequence (p. 558)
Common ratio (p. 558)
Sum of the terms of a geometric sequence (p. 559)
Geometric means (p. 561)

Infinite geometric series (p. 564)
Simple interest (p. 569)
Compound interest (p. 569)
Accumulated value (p. 570)
Nominal rate (p. 570)
Periodic rate (p. 570)
Effective rate (p. 570)
Annuity (p. 571)
Period (p. 571)
Term (p. 572)

(11.1) $a_n = a + (n - 1)d$ nth term of an arithmetic sequence

(11.2) $S_n = \dfrac{n}{2}(a + a_n)$ Sum of the first n terms of an arithmetic sequence

(11.3) $S_n = \dfrac{n}{2}[2a + (n - 1)d]$ Sum of the first n terms of an arithmetic sequence

(11.4) $a_n = ar^{n-1}$ nth term of a geometric sequence

(11.5) $S_n = \dfrac{a(1 - r^n)}{1 - r}, \; r \neq 1$ Sum of the first n terms of a geometric sequence

(11.6) $S_n = \dfrac{a - ra_n}{1 - r}, \; r \neq 1$ Sum of the first n terms of a geometric sequence

(11.7) $S = \dfrac{a}{1 - r}, \; |r| < 1$ Sum of an infinite geometric series

(11.8) $S = P(1 + i)^n$ Compound interest, i per period for n periods

(11.9) $E = \left(1 + \dfrac{j}{m}\right)^m - 1$ Effective rate of interest

(11.10) $S = P\left(1 + \dfrac{j}{m}\right)^{mn}$ Compound interest, nominal rate j compounded m times per year for n years

(11.11) $S = R\left[\dfrac{(1 + i)^n - 1}{i}\right]$ Value of an annuity, compounded at i per period for n periods, periodic payment of R

EXERCISE 11.5   Review

1. Write the five terms of an arithmetic sequence with $a_2 = 3$ and $d = \frac{1}{2}$.

2. Write the five terms of a geometric sequence with $a_2 = 3$ and $r = \frac{1}{2}$.

3. Write the five terms of a harmonic sequence with the first two terms being $\frac{1}{5}$ and $\frac{1}{3}$.

4. If a, b, c, d is an arithmetic sequence then $1/a$, $1/b$, $1/c$, $1/d$ is by definition a harmonic sequence. Show that if x, y, z, w is a geometric sequence, then $1/x$, $1/y$, $1/z$, $1/w$ is also a geometric sequence.

5. Find the sixth term and the sum of the six terms of the geometric sequence that begins 2, $\frac{2}{3}$, ...

6. Find the seventh term and the sum of the seven terms of the arithmetic sequence that begins $\frac{1}{12}$, $\frac{5}{24}$, ...

7. If the second and fourth terms of an arithmetic sequence are $\frac{3}{4}$ and $\frac{7}{4}$ and $n = 5$, find a, d, a_n, and S_n.

8. If the second and fifth terms of a geometric sequence are $\frac{1}{2}$ and 32 and $S_n = \frac{341}{8}$, find a, r, a_n, and n.

9. Find the sum of all integers between 8 and 800 that are multiples of 7.

10. Find all values of k such that $2k + 2$, $5k - 11$, and $7k - 13$ is a geometric sequence.

11. If \$1000 is put in a savings account and left for 6 years, how much is in the account at the end of that time if the bank pays 6 percent interest compounded semiannually?

12. Express $0.5151\cdots$ as a ratio of two integers.

13. Find the sum of all numbers of the form $(-\frac{1}{6})^n$, where n is a positive integer.

14. Show that if a, b, c, d is an arithmetic sequence and x is a real number, then $a + x$, $b + x$, $c + x$, $d + x$ is also an arithmetic sequence.

15. Show that if a, b, c, d is a geometric sequence and y is a real number, then ay, by, cy, dy is also a geometric sequence.

16. Show that p^2, q^2, r^2 is a geometric sequence if p, q, r is.

17. Show that $\frac{1}{4}$, $\frac{3}{4}$, $\frac{9}{4}$, $\frac{27}{4}$ is a geometric sequence and

$$\log \tfrac{1}{4}, \ \log \tfrac{3}{4}, \ \log \tfrac{9}{4}, \ \log \tfrac{27}{4}$$

is an arithmetic sequence.

18. Show that if a^2, b^2, c^2 is an arithmetic sequence, then $a + b$, $a + c$, $b + c$ is a harmonic sequence.

19. Prove that if each term of a geometric sequence is added to 9 times the term, if any, that follows it, the resulting sums form a geometric sequence.

20. Find an arithmetic sequence of three terms whose sum is 18, if the product of all three terms is 210.

21. Find a geometric sequence of three terms whose sum is 26 and whose product is 216.

22. Find r for an infinite geometric series in which each term after the first is twice the sum of all the terms that follow it.

23. Find three geometric means between 4 and 16.

24. Find three arithmetic means between 4 and 16.

25. Find three harmonic means between 4 and 16.

26. In Prob. 65 of Exercise 11.2, a proof was requested that the arithmetic mean exceeds the geometric mean for positive, unequal numbers a and b. Show that the difference is

$$\frac{(\sqrt{a} - \sqrt{b})^2}{2}$$

27. Let $f(x) = x^3 - 2x^2 - x + 2$ and $g(x) = 3x^2 - 4x - 1$. Show that the arithmetic average of the roots of $f(x) = 0$ equals the arithmetic average of the roots of $g(x) = 0$.

28. Find the infinite geometric sequence whose sum is $\frac{4}{3}$ and the sum of whose first three terms is $\frac{3}{2}$.

Classify the sequence in each of Probs. 29 to 33, and give the next two terms.

29. $\frac{1}{12}$, $\frac{1}{4}$, $\frac{5}{12}$, $\frac{7}{12}$

30. $\frac{3}{5}$, $\frac{2}{5}$, $\frac{4}{15}$, $\frac{8}{45}$

31. $\frac{1}{9}$, $\frac{5}{18}$, $\frac{4}{9}$, $\frac{11}{18}$

32. $\frac{3}{2}$, $\frac{6}{5}$, 1, $\frac{6}{7}$

33. $\frac{4}{3}$, $\frac{8}{7}$, 1, $\frac{8}{9}$

34. About 1200, Leonardo of Pisa introduced the Fibonacci sequence, defined by $a_1 = 1$, $a_2 = 1$, and for $n \geq 3$,

$$a_n = a_{n-1} + a_{n-2}$$

Find the first eight terms in the sequence. Verify by calculation that

$$a_4 \text{ is a factor of } a_8$$

$$a_7 \text{ is prime}$$

$$(a_6)^2 + 1 = a_7 a_5$$

$$(a_7)^2 - 1 = a_8 a_6$$

35. Show that if $0 < a < b < c$ and a, b, c form
(a) An arithmetic sequence, then $b^2 > ac$.
(b) A geometric sequence, then $b^2 = ac$.
(c) A harmonic sequence, then $b^2 < ac$.

36. The formula $C = \frac{5}{9}(F - 32)$ converts degrees Fahrenheit to degrees Celsius. Show that if F_1, F_2, F_3 is an arithmetic sequence in degrees Fahrenheit, then the corresponding numbers C_1, C_2, C_3 in degrees Celsius also form an arithmetic sequence.

37. What effective rate corresponds to 12 percent compounded quarterly?

38. What sum must be repaid if $13,750 is borrowed for 5 years at 10 percent compounded semiannually?

39. How much could the Thrifties accumulate toward their daughter's educational expenses by depositing $300 at the end of each 6 months into a fund that accumulates at 8 percent compounded semiannually? Assume that the first payment is made when she is 6 months old and the last when she is 18 years of age.

40. The Koonce family made a down payment of 10 percent of the cash value of a house and finished paying for it with a payment of $2000 at the end of each 6 months for 20 years. What was the cash price if money is worth 8 percent, $m = 2$?

41. If $2000 is invested for a year at the nominal rate of 12 percent, find the accumulated value if interest is compounded annually, semiannually, and quarterly.

42. A brokerage firm advertises an average of 18 percent growth compounded yearly over 5 years. How long will it take for P dollars to triple at that rate?

In Probs. 43 to 46, use $S = P(1 + i)^n$.

43. Find S if $P = 1200$, $i = 0.06$, and $n = 12$.

44. Find P if $S = 28,153$, $i = 0.06$, and $n = 15$.

45. Find i if $S = 68,851.50$, $P = 46,600$, and $n = 8$.

46. Find n if $S = 121,014$, $P = 28,000$, and $i = 0.05$.

47. How much money is accumulated after 12 years if $83,000 is invested at 8 percent compounded quarterly?

48. How much money is accumulated after 12 years if $1950 is invested at the end of each quarter at 8 percent compounded quarterly?

49. The Indians were paid $24 for Manhattan Island in 1626. If this had been invested at 3 percent compounded annually, what would it be worth in 1991, to the nearest dollar? How much at 4 percent? How much at 5 percent?

50. How much must be invested by a person's insurance company on the twenty-first birthday to be able to pay $200,000 on the sixty-fifth birthday assuming a 2.5 percent quarterly rate?

12 Topics in Algebra

Some statements are true for all positive integers, but verifying the statements for 10 or even 10,000 numbers will not prove this. To do so, we need mathematical induction. Special methods of quickly counting large subsets occupy the next two sections. These methods are then used in each of the last two sections in order to expand powers of binomials and calculate probabilities.

12.1 Mathematical Induction

Many statements, equations, and inequalities can be made using positive integers. Some examples are

$n^2 - n + 41$ is prime	False
$2^{n+1} < n^3$	False
$1 + 3 + 5 + \cdots + (2n - 1) = n^2$	True
$4^n - 1$ is divisible by 3	True

The **last two statements** above are true for every positive integer n. This will be proved by *mathematical induction* in Examples 1 and 3 below; no number of special cases will suffice to prove them.

Each of the **first two statements** above is false because we cannot answer yes to the question:

"Is the statement true for all positive integers?"

A counterexample, a specific positive integer, is all that is needed to make either of these statements false.

If we let $q(n) = n^2 - n + 41$, we find that $q(1) = 41$, $q(2) = 43$, $q(3) = 47$, and $q(4) = 53$, all of which are prime numbers. In fact $q(n)$ will be prime for all integers n 1 to 40. For instance

$$q(20) = 400 - 20 + 41 = 421$$

which is prime, and

$$q(40) = 1601$$

which is also prime. However, $q(41) = 41^2 - 41 + 41 = (41)(41)$, which is certainly not prime. Thus even though $q(n)$ is prime for the first 40 positive integers, it is not always prime. It is interesting to observe that $q(n + 1) = q(-n)$. The second statement above is false, for instance, if n is 1, 2, 8, or 9.

On the other hand, we can calculate

$$1 = 1^2 \qquad\qquad 1 + 3 = 4 = 2^2$$

$$1 + 3 + 5 = 9 = 3^2 \qquad 1 + 3 + 5 + 7 = 16 = 4^2$$

These results *suggest* that the sum of the first n odd positive integers is n^2. That is

$$1 + 3 + 5 + \cdots + (2n - 1) = n^2 \tag{1}$$

Verifying this equation for particular values of n does not constitute a proof for all values of n. We will prove it by using **mathematical induction.**

Principle of mathematical induction

> Let $P(n)$ be a statement or proposition involving the positive integer n. Suppose that $P(n)$ satisfies the following two properties:
>
> (a) The statement $P(1)$ is true.
> (b) Assuming that the statement $P(k)$ is true, then the statement $P(k + 1)$ is also true.
>
> Then the statement $P(n)$ is true for every positive integer n.

Here is the idea behind the principle of mathematical induction. By (a), $P(n)$ is true for $n = 1$. By (b), $P(2)$ is true since $P(1)$ is true. Again by (b), $P(3)$ is true since $P(2)$ is true. Continuing in this manner would show that $P(4)$, $P(5)$, . . . are all true. A complete argument is beyond this course.

EXAMPLE 1   Prove that for all positive integers n

$$1 + 3 + 5 + \cdots + (2n - 1) = n^2 \qquad P(n)$$

Solution   Remember that the left side of $P(n)$ is the sum of the first n odd positive integers.
(a) The statement $P(1)$ is true since $1 = 1^2$.
(b) We now *assume* that $P(k)$ is true and write

GIVEN:
$$1 + 3 + 5 + \cdots + (2k - 1) = k^2 \qquad P(k)$$

Next we write $P(n)$ for $n = k + 1$ and have

$$1 + 3 + 5 + \cdots + [2(k + 1) - 1] = (k + 1)^2$$

which simplifies to

TO PROVE:
$$1 + 3 + 5 + \cdots + (2k + 1) = (k + 1)^2 \qquad P(k + 1)$$

Now to verify part (b), we will prove that the assumption of $P(k)$ implies the truth of $P(k + 1)$. To do this, add $2k + 1$ to both sides of $P(k)$. The left-hand side is

$$[1 + 3 + 5 + \cdots + (2k - 1)] + (2k + 1)$$

which is exactly the left-hand side of $P(k + 1)$. The right-hand side is

$$k^2 + (2k + 1) = k^2 + 2k + 1 = (k + 1)^2$$

which is the right-hand side of $P(k + 1)$. This completes (b), and we have already shown (a). Hence we have shown by mathematical induction that the statement $P(n)$ is true for every positive integer n. Thus, for instance, using $n = 432$ and $2n - 1 = 863$ gives

$$1 + 3 + 5 + \cdots + 861 + 863 = 432^2 = 186{,}624 \qquad \blacktriangleleft$$

NOTE   In all mathematical induction proofs, we must know clearly what the statements $P(k)$ and $P(k + 1)$ say, whether in an equation, an inequality, or words. And then we have to figure out some way to use the statement $P(k)$, which we are **assuming** is true, to help show the statement $P(k + 1)$ is also true.

No general directions can be given for carrying out step (b) in the principle of mathematical induction because of the variety of statements involving positive integers n. The examples give some typical procedures.

▶ **EXAMPLE 2**   Prove that

$$(1)(2) + (3)(4) + (5)(6) + \cdots + (2n - 1)(2n) = \frac{n(n + 1)(4n - 1)}{3} \qquad P(n)$$

Notice that the left-hand side consists of the product of the first odd and even positive integers, plus the product of the second odd and even positive integers, and so on, to the product of the nth odd and even positive integers.

Solution   (a) For $n = 1$, the left-hand side is $(1)(2) = 2$, and the right side is $(1)(2)(3)/3 = 2$. Hence the statement $P(1)$ is true.

(b) We now *assume* that $P(k)$ is true. That is, we assume

GIVEN:
$$1(2) + 3(4) + 5(6) + \cdots + (2k - 1)(2k) = \frac{k(k + 1)(4k - 1)}{3} \qquad P(k)$$

We are trying to prove $P(n)$ for $n = k + 1$ is true, namely,

$$1(2) + 3(4) + 5(6) + \cdots + [2(k + 1) - 1][2(k + 1)]$$

$$= \frac{(k + 1)[(k + 1) + 1][(4(k + 1) - 1]}{3}$$

which simplifies to

TO PROVE:
$$1(2) + 3(4) + 5(6) + \cdots + (2k + 1)(2k + 2) = \frac{(k + 1)(k + 2)(4k + 3)}{3} \qquad P(k + 1)$$

In comparing $P(k)$ and $P(k + 1)$, we see that if we add $(2k + 1)(2k + 2)$ to both sides of $P(k)$, we have

$$1(2) + 3(4) + \cdots + (2k - 1)(2k) + (2k + 1)(2k + 2)$$
$$= \frac{k(k + 1)(4k - 1)}{3} + (2k + 1)(2k + 2)$$

whose left-hand side is the left-hand side of $P(k + 1)$. Now the right-hand side above is

$$\frac{k(k + 1)(4k - 1)}{3} + (2k + 1)(2k + 2) = \frac{1}{3}[k(k + 1)(4k - 1) + 3(2k + 1)(2)(k + 1)]$$

$$= \frac{k + 1}{3}[(4k^2 - k) + (12k + 6)] \qquad \text{factoring}$$

$$= \frac{k + 1}{3}(4k^2 + 11k + 6)$$

$$= \frac{(k + 1)(k + 2)(4k + 3)}{3}$$

which is also the right-hand side of $P(k + 1)$. We have shown (a) and (b), which proves by mathematical induction that $P(n)$ is true for every positive integer n. The statement $P(50)$ is

$$1 \cdot 2 + 3 \cdot 4 + \cdots + 99 \cdot 100 = \frac{50(51)(199)}{3} = 169{,}150 \qquad \blacktriangleleft$$

◢ **EXAMPLE 3**   Prove that for every positive integer n

$$4^n - 1 \text{ is divisible by } 3 \qquad \text{\small P(n)}$$

Solution   (a) For $n = 1$, the statement is that $4 - 1$ is divisible by 3, which is certainly true.
(b) Supposing that $P(n)$ is true for $n = k$, we have

$$4^k - 1 = 3q \qquad \text{for some integer } q \qquad \text{\small P(k)}$$

Now for $n = k + 1$ we may write

$$4^{k+1} - 1 = 4^{k+1} - 4^k + (4^k - 1) \qquad \text{\small adding and subtracting } 4^k$$

$$= 4^k(4 - 1) + 3q \qquad \text{\small using P(k)}$$

$$= 3(4^k + q) \qquad \text{\small common factor of 3}$$

which shows that $P(n)$ is true for $n = k + 1$ if it is true for $n = k$. We have shown (a) and (b), which proves by mathematical induction that $P(n)$ is true for every positive integer n. ◢

The statement in Example 4 below is false for $n = 1, 2, 3, 4, 5,$ and 6, but it is true for $n \geq 7$. The following corollary of the principle of mathematical induction allows us to handle this situation.

Generalized principle of mathematical induction

(a) Show that $P(M)$ is true for some positive integer M.
(b) For $k \geq M$, show that if $P(k)$ is true, then $P(k + 1)$ is true.

The conclusion is that the statement $P(n)$ is true for all positive integers n which are equal to or greater than M.

Therefore the statement $P(n)$ will be true for

$$M, M + 1, M + 2, M + 3, \ldots$$

in other words for all integers $n \geq M$.

▶ **EXAMPLE 4** Show that for $n \geq 7$

$$3^n < n! \qquad P(n)$$

Solution (a) For $n = 7$, we have

$$3^7 = 3 \cdot 3 \cdot 3 \cdot 3 \cdot 3 \cdot 3 \cdot 3 = 9 \cdot 9 \cdot 9 \cdot 3 = 81 \cdot 27 = 2187$$

and $\qquad 7! = 7 \cdot 6 \cdot 5 \cdot 4 \cdot 3 \cdot 2 \cdot 1 = 42(20)(6) = 42(120) = 5040$

and so the inequality $P(7)$ is true. It is false for $n = 1, 2, 3, 4, 5,$ and 6.
(b) We suppose now that $k \geq 7$ and $P(k)$ is true, hence

$$3^k < k! \qquad P(k)$$

We must show that $P(k + 1)$ is true, that is, $3^{k+1} < (k + 1)!$. Now

$$
\begin{aligned}
3^{k+1} &= 3(3^k) & &\text{by laws of exponents} \\
&< 3(k!) & &\text{true for } n = k \text{ by assumption} \\
&< (k + 1)(k!) & &k \geq 7 \text{ implies that } k + 1 \geq 8 > 3 \\
&= (k + 1)! & &\text{definition of factorial}
\end{aligned}
$$

◀

Many of the statements in this section can be written using the sigma notation for summation. For instance the statement $P(n)$ in Example 1 is

$$1 + 3 + 5 + \cdots + (2n - 1) = n^2$$

which can also be written

$$\sum_{k=1}^{n} (2k - 1) = n^2$$

EXERCISE 12.1

By mathematical induction, show that the equation in each of Probs. 1 to 36 is true for all positive integers. *Hint:* Add the $(k + 1)$th term of the formula under consideration to each side of the equation.

1. $1 + 2 + 3 + \cdots + n = n(n + 1)/2$
2. $3 + 5 + 7 + \cdots + (2n + 1) = n(n + 2)$
3. $1 + 4 + 7 + \cdots + (3n - 2) = n(3n - 1)/2$
4. $5 + 9 + 13 + \cdots + (4n + 1) = n(2n + 3)$
5. $3 + 7 + 11 + \cdots + (4n - 1) = n(2n + 1)$
6. $7 + 13 + 19 + \cdots + (6n + 1) = n(3n + 4)$

7. $2 + 9 + 16 + \cdots + (7n - 5) = n(7n - 3)/2$

8. $a + (a + d) + (a + 2d) + \cdots + [a + (n - 1)d] = (n/2)[2a + (n - 1)d]$

9. $2 + 6 + 18 + \cdots + 2(3^{n-1}) = 3^n - 1$

10. $\frac{1}{2} + \frac{1}{4} + \frac{1}{8} + \cdots + (\frac{1}{2})^n = 1 - (\frac{1}{2})^n$

11. $7 + 7^2 + 7^3 + \cdots + 7^n = 7(7^n - 1)/6$

12. $1 + 6 + 6^2 + \cdots + 6^{n-1} = (6^n - 1)/5$

13. $\frac{1}{3} + \frac{2}{9} + \frac{4}{27} + \cdots + \frac{1}{3}(\frac{2}{3})^{n-1} = 1 - (\frac{2}{3})^n$

14. $\frac{1}{4} + \frac{3}{16} + \frac{9}{64} + \cdots + \frac{1}{4}(\frac{3}{4})^{n-1} = 1 - (\frac{3}{4})^n$

15. $1 - \frac{1}{2} + \frac{1}{4} - \frac{1}{8} + \cdots + (-\frac{1}{2})^{n-1} = \frac{2}{3}[1 - (-\frac{1}{2})^n]$

16. $a + ar + ar^2 + \cdots + ar^{n-1} = \dfrac{a(1 - r^n)}{1 - r}$

17. $2 + 6 + 12 + \cdots + n(n + 1) = n(n + 1)(n + 2)/3$

18. $4 + 10 + 18 + \cdots + n(n + 3) = n(n + 1)(n + 5)/3$

19. $2 + 14 + 36 + \cdots + n(5n - 3) = n(n + 1)(5n - 2)/3$

20. $-3 - 2 + 3 + \cdots + n(2n - 5) = n(n + 1)(4n - 13)/6$

21. $(1)(3) + (2)(4) + (3)(5) + \cdots + (n)(n + 2) = n(n + 1)(2n + 7)/6$

22. $(1)(2)(3) + (2)(3)(4) + (3)(4)(5) + \cdots + n(n + 1)(n + 2) = n(n + 1)(n + 2)(n + 3)/4$

23. $2(4) + 5(7) + 8(10) + \cdots + (3n - 1)(3n + 1) = \dfrac{n}{2}(6n^2 + 9n + 1)$

24. $3(5) + 7(9) + 11(13) + \cdots + (4n - 1)(4n + 1) = n(4n + 1)(4n + 5)/3$

25. $\dfrac{1}{(1)(2)} + \dfrac{1}{(2)(3)} + \dfrac{1}{(3)(4)} + \cdots + \dfrac{1}{n(n + 1)} = \dfrac{n}{n + 1}$

26. $\dfrac{1}{(1)(2)(3)} + \dfrac{1}{(2)(3)(4)} + \dfrac{1}{(3)(4)(5)} + \cdots + \dfrac{1}{(n)(n + 1)(n + 2)} = \dfrac{n(n + 3)}{4(n + 1)(n + 2)}$

27. $\dfrac{1}{1(3)} + \dfrac{1}{3(5)} + \dfrac{1}{5(7)} + \cdots + \dfrac{1}{(2n - 1)(2n + 1)} = \dfrac{n}{2n + 1}$

28. $\dfrac{3}{4} + \dfrac{5}{36} + \dfrac{7}{144} + \cdots + \dfrac{2n + 1}{[n(n + 1)]^2} = 1 - \dfrac{1}{(n + 1)^2}$

29. $1^2 + 2^2 + 3^2 + \cdots + n^2 = n(n + 1)(2n + 1)/6$

30. $1^2 + 3^2 + 5^2 + \cdots + (2n - 1)^2 = n(2n - 1)(2n + 1)/3$

31. $1^3 + 2^3 + 3^3 + \cdots + n^3 = [n(n + 1)/2]^2$

32. $1^3 + 3^3 + 5^3 + \cdots + (2n - 1)^3 = 2n^4 - n^2$

33. $1 \cdot 2^1 + 2 \cdot 2^2 + 3 \cdot 2^3 + 4 \cdot 2^4 + \cdots + n \cdot 2^n = 2[1 + (n - 1) \cdot 2^n]$

34. $1 \cdot 3^1 + 2 \cdot 3^2 + 3 \cdot 3^3 + 4 \cdot 3^4 + \cdots + n \cdot 3^n = \frac{3}{4}[1 + (2n - 1) \cdot 3^n]$

35. $1 \cdot 4^1 + 2 \cdot 4^2 + 3 \cdot 4^3 + 4 \cdot 4^4 + \cdots + n \cdot 4^n = \frac{4}{9}[1 + (3n - 1) \cdot 4^n]$

36. Prove that if $x \neq 1$, then
$$1 + 2x + 3x^2 + 4x^3 + \cdots + nx^{n-1} = \dfrac{1 - x^n}{(1 - x)^2} - \dfrac{nx^n}{1 - x}$$

37. Show that $5^n - 1$ is divisible by 4.

38. Show that $3^{2n+1} + 1$ is divisible by 4.

39. Show that $4^{2n} - 1$ is divisible by 3.

40. Show that $2^{3n} - 1$ is divisible by 7.

41. Show that $x^{2n+1} + y^{2n+1}$ is divisible by $x + y$.

42. Show that $x^{2n-1} - y^{2n-1}$ is divisible by $x - y$.

43. Show that $x^{2n} - y^{2n}$ is divisible by $x - y$.

44. Show that $x^{2n} - y^{2n}$ is divisible by $x + y$.

45. Show that $n < 2^n$.

46. Show that $n^2 < 2^n$ if $n \geq 5$.

47. Show that $2^{n-1} \leq n!$.

48. Show that $2n + 1 < n^2$ for $n \geq 3$.

49. Show that
$$\left(1 + \frac{1}{1}\right)\left(1 + \frac{1}{2}\right)\left(1 + \frac{1}{3}\right)\cdots\left(1 + \frac{1}{n}\right) = n + 1$$

50. Show that for $n \geq 2$,
$$\left(1 - \frac{1}{2^2}\right)\left(1 - \frac{1}{3^2}\right)\left(1 - \frac{1}{4^2}\right)\cdots\left(1 - \frac{1}{n^2}\right) = \dfrac{n + 1}{2n}$$

51. Show that
$$\frac{1}{n + 1} + \frac{1}{n + 2} + \frac{1}{n + 3} + \cdots + \frac{1}{2n} \geq \frac{1}{2}$$

52. Show that
$$\frac{1}{\sqrt{1}} + \frac{1}{\sqrt{2}} + \frac{1}{\sqrt{3}} + \cdots + \frac{1}{\sqrt{n}} > \sqrt{n}$$

Problems 53 to 56 serve to emphasize that when using the principle of mathematical induction, **you**

must actually verify the statement $P(1)$. Showing that $P(k)$ implies $P(k + 1)$ is not enough.

53. Show that if
$$2 + 5 + 8 + \cdots + (3n - 1) = \frac{(3n + 4)(n - 1)}{2}$$
is true for $n = k$, then it is true for $n = k + 1$. Nevertheless, try any positive integer n and observe that the formula fails.

54. Repeat Prob. 53 for
$$2 + 7 + 12 + \cdots + (5n - 3) = \frac{(5n + 4)(n - 1)}{2}$$

55. Repeat Prob. 53 for
$$6 + 11 + 16 + \cdots + (5n + 1) = \frac{(5n + 2)(n + 1)}{2}$$

56. Let $P(n)$ be the statement $n = n + 1$. Show that if it is true for $n = k$, then it is also true for $n = k + 1$.

Problems 57 to 60 emphasize that **you must show that if $P(k)$ is true, then $P(k + 1)$ is also true.** It is not enough to verify that $P(k)$ is true for a few values of k.

57. Show that $1 + 3 + 5 + \cdots + (2n - 1) = 3n - 2$ holds for $n = 1$ and $n = 2$, but not for all n.

58. Let $p_1 = 2$, $p_2 = 3$, $p_3 = 5$, $\ldots$ be the primes in order. Show that the product
$$p_1 p_2 p_3 \cdots p_n + 1$$
is prime for $n = 1, 2$, and 3 but not for all n. *Hint:* For $n = 6$, try 59 as a factor.

59. Show that $n^3 > 2^n$ for $n = 2, 3, 4, 5, 6, 7, 8$, and 9, but not for $n = 10$.

60. Let $f(n) = n^2 - n + 2$. Show that $f(n) = 2^n$ for $n = 1, 2$, and 3, but not for $n = 4$.

61. Show that the number of subsets (counting the empty set) of a set with n elements is 2^n.

62. Show that
$$\frac{1}{n} + \frac{1}{n + 1} + \frac{1}{n + 2} + \cdots + \frac{1}{2n - 1} =$$
$$1 - \frac{1}{2} + \frac{1}{3} - \frac{1}{4} + \cdots + \frac{1}{2n - 1}$$

63. Show by mathematical induction that for any real numbers a and b, $(ab)^n = a^n b^n$, $n = 1, 2, 3, \ldots$.

64. Show that for $a > 0$, $(1 + a)^n \geq 1 + na$.

12.2 Permutations

In Secs. 12.2 and 12.3, we will begin with a set of n distinct elements, and we will then choose a subset of r of them where $r \leq n$. Depending upon whether the order of choice matters and whether repetition is allowed within the subset, the r elements will be called a permutation, combination, sample, or selection.

For instance, the n distinct elements may be the 7 letters on the bottom row of a typewriter keyboard: Z, X, C, V, B, N, and M. Four of these 7 letters may be typed ($r = 4$) in a variety of ways.

Permutation
If repetition is not allowed and order matters, we have a **permutation:**

BCMN, NBMC, CBNM, ZVXN, and BVCZ are permutations.
BBCV, ZVVB, and XXXM are not permutations.
BCMN, NMCB, and CNBM are all different permutations even though they have the same four letters.

Combination
If repetition is not allowed and order does not matter, we have a **combination:**

MNBC, MNBZ, XBNZ, CBNZ, and NVZX are combinations.
CCCC, ZXVV, and NZZV are not combinations.
ZXCV, ZXVC, and VXCZ are the same combination.

Sample

If repetition is allowed and order matters, we have a **sample:**

BCMN, BCNM, CBCB, CCCB, and ZZZZ are different samples.
CCNV, NCVC, and VCCN are all different samples even though they use the same four letters.

Selection

If repetition is allowed and order does not matter, we have a **selection:**

ZVCV, BNZZ, CCNZ, XXXV, and MCXX are selections.
ZZXC, ZZCX, and ZXCZ are the same selection, but they are different samples.

Many other examples can be found. Formulas to be given in the next two sections will show that of the various ways of typing 4 of these 7 letters, there are

$$(7)(6)(5)(4) = 840 \text{ permutations}$$

$$\frac{(7)(6)(5)}{(3)(2)(1)} = 35 \text{ combinations}$$

$$(7)(7)(7)(7) = 2401 \text{ samples}$$

$$\frac{(10)(9)(8)(7)}{(4)(3)(2)(1)} = 210 \text{ selections}$$

It is not always immediately obvious which formula to use in the next two sections. You must decide whether repetition is allowed, and also whether order matters. See Fig. 12.1.

EXAMPLE 1   Write out each of the 4 ways of choosing 2 letters from the 4 letters S, P, Q, and R.

Solution   (a) 12 permutations: no repetition, order matters

SP, SQ, SR, PS, PQ, PR, QS, QP, QR, RS, RP, RQ

(b) 6 combinations: no repetition, order does not matter

SP, SQ, SR, PQ, PR, QR

(c) 16 samples: repetition allowed, order matters

SS, SP, SQ, SR, PS, PP, PQ, PR, QS, QP, QQ, QR, RS, RP, RQ, RR

(d) 10 selections: repetition allowed, order does not matter

SS, SP, SQ, SR, PP, PQ, PR, QQ, QR, RR

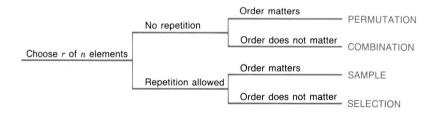

FIGURE 12.1

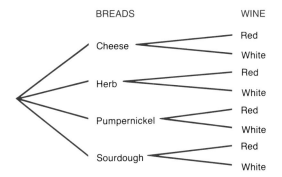

BREADS   WINE

FIGURE 12.2

The Fundamental Principle of Counting

In *The Rubaiyat of Omar Khayyam* by Edward Fitzgerald, there is the unforgettable phrase, "A Jug of Wine, a Loaf of Bread—and Thou." Let's assume that the "Thou" is predetermined, there is red and white wine, and the available breads are cheese, herb, pumpernickel, and sourdough. Then the possible menus can be illustrated by a tree diagram as shown in Fig. 12.2. There are 8 menus possible. The number is found by multiplying 4 and 2.

A **tree diagram** is effective visually and conceptually, but the total number of branches can be drawn and counted efficiently only when the number of results is fairly small. The fundamental principle of counting, given below, makes it easy to count the number of branches in any tree diagram since it may be extended to three or more events. It applies provided that the outcome of one event does not affect the outcome of the other event.

Fundamental principle of counting

> If one event can occur in m ways and a second one can occur in n ways, then the number of ways both can occur is mn.

▶ **EXAMPLE 2**   In how many ways can a fountain and a mountain be chosen from 8 fountains in Rome and 5 mountains in Switzerland?

Solution   The fountain can be chosen in 8 ways, and the mountain can be chosen in 5 ways. By the fundamental principle, the answer is

$$8 \cdot 5 = 40$$ ◀

▶ **EXAMPLE 3**   How many automobile license plates of six symbols can be made if each one begins with 3 different letters and ends with any 3 digits?

Solution   Because the letters must be different, but the numbers can be repeated, the number of plates is

$$(26)(25)(24)(10)(10)(10) = 15,600,000$$ ◀

If a set has n elements and we choose a **sample** of r elements, we allow repetition and the order of the elements matters. We may choose the first element in n ways since any of the n elements is eligible. Since repetition is allowed, the second element may also be chosen in n ways. The same is true for the third, fourth, and so on all the way to the rth element. Thus by the fundamental principle, the total number of samples of r elements chosen from n elements is

Formula for samples

$$(n)(n)(n) \cdots (n) = n^r$$

EXAMPLE 4   How many "words" of 4 symbols may be formed for a code which uses the 5 letters V, I, D, E, O and the 3 characters #, *, & if any symbol may be repeated?

Solution   We are dealing with a sample since any of the 8 symbols may be used and repeated, and order clearly matters for a code word. Using the formula for samples with $n = 8$ and $r = 4$ gives the answer

$$n^r = 8^4 = (8)(8)(8)(8) = 4096$$

EXAMPLE 5   (a) How many 3-digit area codes are there for the telephone company to use if there are no restrictions on the digits?
(b) How many 3-digit area codes are there if the first digit may not be 0 or 1 and the second digit must be 0 or 1?

Solution   (a) This is a sample of 3 digits chosen from the 10 digits 0, 2, . . . , 9. The answer is $10 \cdot 10 \cdot 10 = 1000$.
(b) There are eight choices for the first digit, two for the second, and ten for the third. By the fundamental principle of counting, the answer is $8 \cdot 2 \cdot 10 = 160$.

Permutations of n Different Elements Taken r at a Time

A **permutation** of n distinct elements consists of r of those elements arranged in some order where $1 \le r \le n$. We do not allow repetition, and order does matter.

In Example 1 we wrote out the 12 permutations of 4 letters taken 2 at a time. There are 6 permutations of the 3 letters a, b, c taken 2 at a time:

$$ab, \ ba, \ ac, \ ca, \ bc, \ cb$$

EXAMPLE 6   How many 5-digit postal ZIP codes are there
(a) If no digit is repeated?
(b) If digits may be repeated?

Solution   (a) These are **permutations** since we begin with 10 different digits ($n = 10$), the order of the digits matters (70124 and 12047 are different ZIP codes), and in (a) we specified no repetition. By the fundamental principle of counting, the answer is

$$(10)(9)(8)(7)(6) = 30,240$$

(b) These are **samples** because order matters and repetition is allowed. Using the formula for samples gives

$$n^r = 10^5 = 100,000$$

possible ZIP codes, even though the U.S. Postal Service may not use some of them, for example, 00000.

We will let $P(n, r)$ represent the number of permutations of n elements taken r at a time, and we will develop a formula for evaluating this number. We can fill position 1 in the arrangement in n ways. After position 1 has been filled, we have $n - 1$ choices for position 2, then $n - 2$ choices for position 3, and finally, $n - (r - 1)$ choices for position r. Since

$$n - (r - 1) = n - r + 1$$

the fundamental principle of counting gives this formula:

Number of permutations

$$P(n, r) = n(n - 1)(n - 2) \cdots (n - r + 1) \qquad \text{(12.1a)}$$

NOTE This is a product of r factors, which are consecutive integers starting with n and going down.

▶ EXAMPLE 7 Evaluate $P(9, 3)$ and $P(6, 4)$.

Solution The formula for $P(n, r)$ gives

$$P(9, 3) = 9 \cdot 8 \cdot 7 = 504 \qquad \text{three factors}$$

$$P(6, 4) = 6 \cdot 5 \cdot 4 \cdot 3 = 360 \qquad \text{four factors} \qquad \blacktriangleleft$$

Remember that with a permutation, it is assumed that we are working with a set of n elements which can be distinguished one from another.

Sometimes it is convenient to write and use the formula for $P(n, r)$ in an alternative form. Recall that the definition of $n!$ is

$$n! = n(n - 1)(n - 2) \cdots (3)(2)(1)$$

Thus

$$3! = 3 \cdot 2 \cdot 1 = 6$$

$$5! = 5 \cdot 4 \cdot 3 \cdot 2 \cdot 1 = 120$$

$$8! = 8 \cdot 7 \cdot 6 \cdot 5 \cdot 4 \cdot 3 \cdot 2 \cdot 1 = 40,320$$

$$12! = 479,001,600$$

We define $0! = 1$ because that makes some formulas easier to use. In order to give the alternative form for $P(n, r)$, notice first that we can write

$$P(8, 3) = 8 \cdot 7 \cdot 6 = \frac{8 \cdot 7 \cdot 6 \cdot 5 \cdot 4 \cdot 3 \cdot 2 \cdot 1}{5 \cdot 4 \cdot 3 \cdot 2 \cdot 1} = \frac{8!}{5!} = \frac{8!}{(8 - 3)!}$$

In the same way we may multiply and divide by $(n - r)!$ and get

$$P(n, r) = n(n - 1)(n - 2) \cdots (n - r + 1) \left[\frac{(n - r)!}{(n - r)!} \right] = \frac{n!}{(n - r)!}$$

Alternative form for $P(n, r)$

$$P(n, r) = \frac{n!}{(n - r)!} \qquad \text{(12.1b)}$$

Using $r = n$ in either formula for $P(n, r)$ gives

$$P(n, n) = n!$$

which is the number of permutations of n elements taken n at a time. This is just the number of different arrangements of all n elements.

▶ **EXAMPLE 8**   (a) How many ways are there to seat 9 people in a row of 9 chairs?
(b) How many ways are there to seat 6 of 9 people in a row of 6 chairs?

Solution   (a) The order of seating matters, and each chair holds only one person, so the answer is $P(9, 9) = 9! = 362,880$.
(b) There are 9 choices for the first chair, 8 for the second chair, etc., and so the answer is

$$P(9, 6) = 9 \cdot 8 \cdot 7 \cdot 6 \cdot 5 \cdot 4 = 60,480$$ ◀

▶ **EXAMPLE 9**   If 20 people won prizes in a state lottery, how many ways were there for these 20 to win first, second, third, and fourth prizes? Assume there were no ties.

Solution   Here we are choosing 4 out of 20 people, order matters, and no ties means no repetitions. The answer is thus

$$P(20, 4) = 20 \cdot 19 \cdot 18 \cdot 17 = 116,280$$ ◀

EXERCISE 12.2

Find each of the following numbers.

1. $P(5, 3)$
2. $P(11, 2)$
3. $P(8, 5)$
4. $P(13, 3)$
5. $P(33, 1)$
6. $P(10, 4)$
7. $P(6, 6)$
8. $P(9, 7)$

Which number is larger?

9. 3^7 or 13^3
10. 6^4 or 11^3
11. 7^4 or 14^3
12. 2^9 or 5^5

Decide whether the situation is a permutation or a sample in Probs. 13 to 16.

13. Make a 5-letter "word" using any letters.
14. Make a 7-letter "word" using 7 different letters.
15. George and Marie each choose one of five soups.
16. Warren and Carol each choose a different spring cleaning job from their list of 8.
17. How many license plates can be made if each has 3 different digits followed by 2 different letters?
18. How many license plates can be made if each has 3 letters followed by 3 digits.
19. How many 3-letter "words" may be formed from the alphabet, excluding K, Q, X, Y, and Z?

20. How many 5-letter "words" may be made using the 12 letters of the Hawaiian alphabet?
21. How many integers between 1000 and 9000 may be formed from the digits 2, 4, 5, 6, and 7?
22. How many 4-digit even numbers can be formed from 7, 6, 4, and 2?
23. How many results are possible if 2 standard dice are thrown? Assume the dice are not distinguishable.
24. In how many ways may a true-false test of 12 questions be answered?
25. How many 3-letter "words" can be made from the first 8 consonants if no letter is repeated?
26. In how many ways can 4 suspects be arranged in a lineup?
27. How many ways are there for the Louvre to arrange 3 of 10 paintings in 3 places in a row on a wall?
28. After having selected the 9 starters, how many batting orders can a Little League coach have if the pitcher bats fourth?
29. How many 4-digit numbers may be made using 1, 2, 4, 5, 7, and 8 if no digit is repeated?
30. How many radio station call signals of 4 different

letters may be formed if the first letter must be W or K? How many if letters may be repeated?

31. In how many ways may 9 people be seated for a picture of 5 of them if there are only 5 chairs?

32. In how many ways may 8 people line up for a picture if Mr. Kitchen insists on being on the left end?

33. The Greek alphabet has 24 letters. How many organizations can there be whose name consists of either 2 or 3 Greek letters if no name has a letter repeated? *Hint:* Do 2 letters, then 3 letters, and then add.

34. In how many different ways can a video rental store arrange 11 different movies on a shelf?

35. If Stan, a person in the signal corps, has 8 different flags, how many signals can be made by putting the flags on a pole?

36. How many permutations are there of all 6 letters in the word "sample"?

Derangement

A **derangement** of $1, 2, 3, \ldots, n$ is a permutation of all n elements which leaves no element in its original position. The number of derangements is

$$D_n = n!\left[\frac{1}{2!} - \frac{1}{3!} + \cdots + \frac{(-1)^n}{n!}\right]$$

37. Write out all derangements of 1, 2, 3, and 4.
38. Calculate D_5, D_6, and D_7.

39. Chefs from China, Italy, Greece, New Zealand, Mexico, and Sweden each prepare one national specialty. In how many ways may they each eat a national specialty they did not prepare?

40. Six people are scheduled for one operation each, all different operations. In how many ways may the operations be performed so that at least one person gets the correct operation?

Show that each of these is true for all positive integers n.

41. $P(n, n-1) = P(n, n)$
42. $P(n, 2) + P(n, 3) = (n-1)P(n, 2)$
43. $P(n, 4) = (n^2 - 5n + 6)P(n, 2)$
44. $P(n, n) - P(n-1, n-2) =$
$$(n-1)^2 P(n-2, n-3)$$

Solve each of these equations.

45. $P(n, 2) = 72$ **46.** $P(n, 3) = 210$
47. $P(n-1, 5) = 3P(n, 4)$
48. $P(n, 4) = 8P(n-1, 3)$
49. How many ways are there for Abigail, Faith, Prudence, Jill, and Bill to sit in a row for a picture if Jill and Bill must sit next to each other? *Hint:* First think of Jill and Bill as a single person, and find the number of arrangements of the four things "Jill/Bill," Abigail, Faith, and Prudence. Next allow Jill and Bill to switch places, and use the fundamental principle of counting.

12.3 Combinations

If we begin with a set of n distinct elements, a subset of r of these elements is called a **combination** of n things taken r at a time.

NOTE   For a combination the order of the elements in the subset does not matter, but for a permutation it does.

EXAMPLE 1   There are 24 permutations of the 4 letters a, b, c, and d, taken 3 at a time since $4 \cdot 3 \cdot 2 = 24$. Write the 6 which use the 3 letters a, b, and d.

Solution   The permutations abd, adb, bad, bda, dab, and dba are all different permutations of the 4 letters a, b, c, d, taken 3 at a time. However they are all the same combination since, for instance, the sets {a, b, d} and {d, b, a} are the same set.

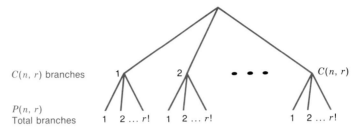

C(n, r) branches

P(n, r)
Total branches   1   2 ... r!   1   2 ... r!   1   2 ... r!

FIGURE 12.3

To get a combination, merely choose r of the n elements.

To get a permutation, choose r of the n elements and then arrange them in some order.

For both permutations and combinations, there is no repetition allowed when choosing the r elements from the n given ones.

We will let $C(n, r)$ represent the number of combinations of n elements taken r at a time. Since a permutation involves choosing r elements (a combination) and then arranging these r elements in one of the r! possible ways, the fundamental principle of counting gives

$$P(n, r) = C(n, r) \cdot r!$$

See Fig. 12.3. Using the formula $P(n, r) = n!/(n - r)!$, we have the following formula:

$$C(n, r) = \frac{1}{r!} \cdot \frac{n!}{(n - r)!} = \frac{n!}{r!(n - r)!} \qquad (12.2)$$

Notice that the formula for $C(n, r)$ involves r! and $(n - r)!$ on the bottom and n! on the top, and the sum of r and $n - r$ is n.

EXAMPLE 2   Calculate $C(11, 4)$ and $C(8, 5)$.

Solution

$$C(11, 4) = \frac{11!}{4!7!} = \frac{11 \cdot 10 \cdot 9 \cdot 8 \cdot (7!)}{4 \cdot 3 \cdot 2 \cdot 1 \cdot (7!)} = \frac{11 \cdot 10 \cdot 9 \cdot 8}{4 \cdot 3 \cdot 2 \cdot 1} = 330$$

$$C(8, 5) = \frac{8!}{5!3!} = \frac{8 \cdot 7 \cdot 6 \cdot (5!)}{3 \cdot 2 \cdot 1 \cdot (5!)} = \frac{8 \cdot 7 \cdot 6}{3 \cdot 2 \cdot 1} = 56$$

Aid to calculation

The calculations are done most efficiently if the larger factorial in the denominator is used to cancel out most of the numerator.

EXAMPLE 3   How many committees of 7 women can be formed from a group of 25 women?

Solution   The number of committees is equal to the number of combinations of 25 elements taken 7 at a time. Hence it is

$$C(25, 7) = \frac{25!}{18!7!} = \frac{25 \cdot 24 \cdot 23 \cdot 22 \cdot 21 \cdot 20 \cdot 19 \cdot (18!)}{(18!) \cdot 7 \cdot 6 \cdot 5 \cdot 4 \cdot 3 \cdot 2 \cdot 1} = 480,700$$

► EXAMPLE 4   A Broadway show wants to hire 6 women and 3 men. In how many ways can the choice be made if 9 women and 5 men are available?

Solution   The 6 women can be selected from the 9 in $C(9, 6)$ ways, and the 3 men from the 5 in $C(5, 3)$ ways. Hence by the fundamental principle the number of ways in which the choice of the employees can be made is

$$C(9, 6) \cdot C(5, 3) = \frac{9!}{3!6!} \cdot \frac{5!}{2!3!}$$

$$= \frac{9 \cdot 8 \cdot 7 \cdot (6!)}{3 \cdot 2 \cdot (6!)} \cdot \frac{5 \cdot 4 \cdot (3!)}{2 \cdot (3!)}$$

$$= 840 \qquad \blacktriangleleft$$

If we choose r elements from a set of n elements with repetition allowed and without any regard for the order of the r elements, we have a **selection.** In Example 1 of Sec. 12.2, we wrote out the 10 selections of 4 elements taken 2 at a time. The 6 selections of APT taken 2 at a time are

AA, AP, AT, PP, PT, TT

It can be shown that the number of selections of n distinct elements taken r at a time is

$$C(n + r - 1, r)$$

► EXAMPLE 5   How many throws of a pair of dice are there if we consider 5, 6 and 6, 5 the same, 2, 4 and 4, 2 the same, etc.?

Solution   This is a selection since repetition is allowed and order does not matter. Using $n = 6$ and $r = 2$ gives

$$C(6 + 2 - 1, 2) = C(7, 2) = \frac{7!}{2!5!} = \frac{7 \cdot 6}{2 \cdot 1} = 21 \qquad \blacktriangleleft$$

In working with permutations, combinations, samples, and selections, we begin with n distinct elements which can be distinguished one from another. Suppose however that we start with 7 red rings, 5 white rings, and 4 blue rings. These 16 rings have 16! permutations, but many of them look the same. It can be shown that if we begin with a collection of n elements split into k groups with n_1 alike of one type, n_2 alike of another type, . . . , and n_k alike of another type, then the number of **distinguishable permutations** of the n elements taken n at a time is

$$\frac{n!}{n_1!n_2!\cdots n_k!}$$

Thus the number of distinguishable permutations of the red, white, and blue rings mentioned above is $16!/7!5!4! = 1,441,440$.

► EXAMPLE 6   In how many ways can the letters of the word "abracadabra" be arranged?

Solution   The solution of this problem involves two factors: (1) the number of permutations of 11 letters taken 11 at a time and (2) the letters b and r must be used 2 times and the letter a 5 times. Hence, the number of distinguishable arrangements is given by

$$\frac{11!}{5!2!2!1!1!} = \frac{11 \cdot 10 \cdot 9 \cdot 8 \cdot 7 \cdot 6 \cdot 5!}{5! \cdot 2 \cdot 2} = 83,160 \qquad \blacktriangleleft$$

EXERCISE 12.3

Find each of these numbers.
1. $C(7, 5)$
2. $C(12, 3)$
3. $C(9, 7)$
4. $C(10, 4)$
5. It is true that $C(n, r) = C(n, n - r)$. Verify that $C(11, 7) = C(11, 4)$.
6. It is true that $C(n + 1, r) = C(n, r) + C(n, r - 1)$. Verify that $C(8, 3) = C(7, 3) + C(7, 2)$.
7. It is true that

$$C(n, 0) + C(n, 1) + \cdots + C(n, n) = 2^n$$

Verify by calculations that

$$C(5, 0) + C(5, 1) + C(5, 2) + C(5, 3) +$$
$$C(5, 4) + C(5, 5) = 2^5$$

8. Verify that $C(8, 4) = C^2(4, 0) + C^2(4, 1) + C^2(4, 2) + C^2(4, 3) + C^2(4, 4)$.
9. How many groups of 3 letters can be chosen from 9 letters if (a) repetition is not allowed and (b) repetition is allowed? Assume that order does not matter.
10. How many groups of 4 numbers can be chosen from 6 numbers if (a) repetition is not allowed and (b) repetition is allowed? Assume that order does not matter.
11. How many groups of 3 cars can be chosen from 7 models of cars if (a) no model may be chosen twice and (b) any models are allowed?
12. How many groups of 5 fruit juices can be chosen from 10 types of fruit juice if repetition is (a) not allowed and (b) allowed?

Find the number of combinations described in Probs. 13 to 20.
13. How many ways are there to choose 5 basketball players from the 9 people on the team?
14. How many triangles can be made from 10 points?
15. How many bridge hands (of 13 cards) are possible from a standard deck of 52 cards?
16. In how many ways can 4 NCAA Final Four basketball team finalists be chosen from 64 teams?

17. How many poker hands of 5 cards are there from a standard deck?
18. In how many ways may a buyer choose 6 dresses from a rack of 18?
19. How many ways are there for a teacher to give 3 A's in a class of 26 students?
20. In how many ways can a bear catch half of a school of 10 fish?
21. In how many ways can 2 men and 2 women be chosen for a debate team from 5 men and 6 women?
22. In how many ways can 2 short players (guards) and 3 tall players (forwards and centers) be chosen for a basketball team from 12 short players and 9 tall ones?
23. How many committees of 5 Republicans and 4 Democrats can be chosen from a group of 12 Republican and 10 Democratic senators?
24. How many groups of 3 red dresses and 2 black ones can be chosen from 12 red and 8 black dresses?

Find the number of selections described in Probs. 25 to 28.
25. A commodities trader deals in wheat, corn, pork bellies, gold, and silver. In how many ways may she buy 4 contracts on Monday if order does not matter? Suppose that she may buy several contracts in the same commodity.
26. Schizophrenia has 5 main characteristics. In how many ways may 3 people each exhibit precisely one such characteristic? Suppose that the profiles are done anonymously.
27. A car has 8 basic systems. A test is run on 5 similar cars to see which system breaks down first. How many results are possible? Assume that the order in which the cars are tested is irrelevant.
28. A light bulb has 5 essential components. If any of the 5 fail, the bulb goes out. In how many ways may 4 bulbs fail? Ignore the order in which the bulbs are tested.

29. Find the number of distinguishable permutations of the letters in "referee."

30. In how many ways may a teacher give 6 A's, 5 B's, 7 C's, 3 D's, and 1 F in a class of 22?

31. In how many ways may 9 women split into 3 groups of 2, 3, and 4 women, to meet in the red, green, and blue rooms, respectively?

32. How many ways are there for a football team to win 7 games, lose 2, and tie 2 if their schedule is 11 games?

33. Prove that $C(10, 7) \cdot C(7, 2) = C(10, 2) \cdot C(8, 5)$. This is a special case of

$$C(n, k) \cdot C(k, r) = C(n, r) \cdot C(n - r, k - r)$$

which is true for $r \le k \le n$.

34. For every positive integer n,

$$\sum_{k=1}^{n} \frac{k(k!)}{n^k} C(n, k) = n$$

Verify this by calculation for $n = 3$ and $n = 4$.

12.4 The Binomial Theorem

In Chap. 1, we dealt with formulas for

$$(x + y)^2 \quad \text{and} \quad (x + y)^3$$

There are many occasions when we have to deal with expressions of the form $(x + y)^n$, a power of a binomial. In *Principia Mathematica* Sir Isaac Newton developed a formula for this, which he then used to help develop calculus. We will not only give the complete formula, but we will be able to write any particular term in the expansion. In this section we shall develop a formula that will enable us to express any *positive integral power* of a binomial as a polynomial. This polynomial is called the **expansion** of the power of the binomial.

By actual multiplication, we obtain the following expansions of the first, second, third, fourth, and fifth powers of $x + y$:

$$(x + y)^1 = x + y$$
$$(x + y)^2 = x^2 + 2xy + y^2$$
$$(x + y)^3 = x^3 + 3x^2y + 3xy^2 + y^3$$
$$(x + y)^4 = x^4 + 4x^3y + 6x^2y^2 + 4xy^3 + y^4$$
$$(x + y)^5 = x^5 + 5x^4y + 10x^3y^2 + 10x^2y^3 + 5xy^4 + y^5$$

By referring to these expansions, we can readily verify the fact that the following properties of $(x + y)^n$ hold for $n = 1, 2, 3, 4,$ and 5. The terms must be kept in the order where the exponents of x decrease.

1. The first term in the expansion is x^n.
2. The second term is $nx^{n-1}y$.
3. The exponent of x decreases by 1 and the exponent of y increases by 1 as we move from left to right.
4. There are $n + 1$ terms in the expansion.
5. The nth, or next to last, term of the expansion is nxy^{n-1}.

6. The $(n + 1)$th, or last, term is y^n.
7. If we multiply the coefficient of any term by the exponent of x in that term and then divide the product by the number of the term in the expansion, we obtain the coefficient of the next term.
8. The sum of the exponents of x and y in any term is n.

If we assume that these eight properties hold for all positive integrals n, we can write the first five terms in the expansion of $(x + y)^n$ as follows:

First term $= x^n$	By property 1
Second term $= nx^{n-1}y$	By property 2
Third term $= \dfrac{n(n-1)}{2}x^{n-2}y^2$	By properties 7, 3
Fourth term $= \dfrac{n(n-1)(n-2)}{3 \cdot 2}x^{n-3}y^3$	By properties 7, 3
Fifth term $= \dfrac{n(n-1)(n-2)(n-3)}{4 \cdot 3 \cdot 2}x^{n-4}y^4$	By properties 7, 3

We can continue this process until we have

nth term $= nxy^{n-1}$	By property 5
$(n + 1)$th term $= y^n$	By property 6

We are now in a position to form the sum of the above terms and obtain the binomial formula. Notice that $4 \cdot 3 \cdot 2 = 4 \cdot 3 \cdot 2 \cdot 1 = 4!$, $3 \cdot 2 = 3 \cdot 2 \cdot 1 = 3!$, and $2 = 2 \cdot 1 = 2!$, and write

$$(x + y)^n = x^n + nx^{n-1}y + \frac{n(n-1)}{2!}x^{n-2}y^2 + \frac{n(n-1)(n-2)}{3!}x^{n-3}y^3$$

$$+ \frac{n(n-1)(n-2)(n-3)}{4!}x^{n-4}y^4 + \cdots + nxy^{n-1} + y^n$$

This equation is called the **binomial theorem.** We will present its proof later in this section.

EXAMPLE 1   Use the binomial theorem to obtain the expansion of $(2a + b)^6$.

Solution   Using $x = 2a$, $y = b$, and $n = 6$ gives

$$(2a + b)^6 = (2a)^6 + 6(2a)^5b + \frac{6 \cdot 5}{2!}(2a)^4b^2 + \frac{6 \cdot 5 \cdot 4}{3!}(2a)^3b^3$$

$$+ \frac{6 \cdot 5 \cdot 4 \cdot 3}{4!}(2a)^2b^4 + \frac{6 \cdot 5 \cdot 4 \cdot 3 \cdot 2}{5!}(2a)b^5 + \frac{6 \cdot 5 \cdot 4 \cdot 3 \cdot 2 \cdot 1}{6!}b^6$$

Now simplifying the coefficients, and raising $2a$ to the indicated powers, we obtain

$$(2a + b)^6 = 64a^6 + 6(32a^5)b + 15(16a^4)b^2 + 20(8a^3)b^3 + 15(4a^2)b^4 + 6(2a)b^5 + b^6$$

Finally, we perform the indicated multiplication in each term and get

$$(2a + b)^6 = 64a^6 + 192a^5b + 240a^4b^2 + 160a^3b^3 + 60a^2b^4 + 12ab^5 + b^6 \quad \blacktriangleleft$$

The computation of the coefficients can, in most cases, be performed mentally by use of property 7, and thus we can avoid writing the first step in the expansion in the above example.

▶ **EXAMPLE 2**   Expand $(a - 3b)^5 = [a + (-3b)]^5$.

Solution   We use $x = a$, $y = -3b$, and $n = 5$. The first term in the expansion is a^5, and the second is $5a^4(-3b)$. To get the coefficient of the third, we multiply 5 by 4, divide the product by 2, and thus obtain 10. Hence, the third term is $10a^3(-3b)^2$. Similarly, the fourth term is

$$\tfrac{30}{3} a^2(-3b)^3 = 10a^2(-3b)^3$$

By continuing this process, we obtain the following expansion:

$$(a - 3b)^5 = a^5 + 5a^4(-3b) + 10a^3(-3b)^2 + 10a^2(-3b)^3 + 5a(-3b)^4 + (-3b)^5$$

$$= a^5 - 15a^4b + 90a^3b^2 - 270a^2b^3 + 405ab^4 - 243b^5$$

We carry the second term of the binomial, $-3b$, through the first step of the expansion as a single term. Then we raise $-3b$ to the indicated powers and simplify the result.   ◀

▶ **EXAMPLE 3**   Expand $(2x - 5y)^4$.

Solution   We shall carry through the expansion with $2x$ as the first term and $-5y$ as the second and get

$$(2x - 5y)^4 = (2x)^4 + 4(2x)^3(-5y) + 6(2x)^2(-5y)^2 + 4(2x)(-5y)^3 + (-5y)^4$$

$$= 16x^4 + 4(8x^3)(-5y) + 6(4x^2)(25y^2) + 4(2x)(-125y^3) + 625y^4$$

$$= 16x^4 - 160x^3y + 600x^2y^2 - 1000xy^3 + 625y^4 \quad \blacktriangleleft$$

The General Term, or the *r*th Term

In the preceding examples, we explained the method for obtaining any term of a binomial expansion from the term just before it. However, by use of this method, it is impossible to obtain any specific term of the expansion without first computing all the terms which precede it. We shall now develop a formula for finding the general, or *r*th, term without using the other terms. In order to find the *r*th term, we shall prove the binomial theorem.

Proof of the binomial theorem   By definition the product of n factors of $(x + y)$ is

$$(x + y)^n = (x + y)(x + y) \cdots (x + y) \tag{1}$$

To multiply out the right-hand side of (1), we must take either x or y from each of the n factors $(x + y)$. If, for a particular term, y is chosen r times and x is chosen $n - r$ times, the resulting term will be $x^{n-r}y^r$. But by the definition of a combination from Sec. 12.3, there are $C(n, r)$ ways of choosing r of the y's from the n y's in the n factors $(x + y)$. Thus the term involving $x^{n-r}y^r$ is $C(n, r)x^{n-r}y^r$.

Alternative form of binomial theorem

It is therefore true that

$$(x + y)^n = C(n, 0)x^n + C(n, 1)x^{n-1}y + C(n, 2)x^{n-2}y^2 + \cdots$$

$$+ C(n, r)x^{n-r}y^r + \cdots + C(n, n-1)xy^{n-1} + C(n, n)y^n$$

$$= \sum_{r=0}^{n} C(n, r)x^{n-r}y^r \qquad (12.3)$$

You should show that (12.3) is the same as the binomial theorem given earlier.

The numbers $C(n, r)$ are called **binomial coefficients** because of their appearance above in the binomial formula. If we call $C(n, 0)x^n$ the first term, $C(n, 1)x^{n-1}y$ the second term, and so on, then:

NOTE   *The rth term will involve $C(n, r - 1)$*

The *r*th term of the expansion of $(x + y)^n$ is

$$C(n, r-1)x^{n-r+1}y^{r-1} = \frac{n!}{(r-1)!(n-r+1)!}x^{n-r+1}y^{r-1}$$

$$= \frac{n(n-1)(n-2)\cdots(n-r+2)}{(r-1)!}x^{n-r+1}y^{r-1} \quad (2)$$

First note that the exponents on x and y add up to n. Notice also that the numerator and denominator of the coefficient in (2) are each the product of $r - 1$ consecutive integers. The **largest** factor in the numerator is n, the **smallest** in the denominator is 1.

◤ **EXAMPLE 4**   Find the first four terms in the expansion of

$$(2x + y)^{37}$$

Solution   By the binomial formula with $n = 37$, the first four terms are

$$(2x)^{37} + 37(2x)^{36}y + \frac{(37)(36)(2x)^{35}y^2}{2!} + \frac{(37)(36)(35)(2x)^{34}y^3}{3!}$$ ◢

◤ **EXAMPLE 5**   Find the fourth term in the expansion of $(2a - b)^9$.

Solution   In this problem, $x = 2a$, $y = -b$, $n = 9$, and $r = 4$. Therefore by Eq. (2), the fourth term is

$$C(9, 3)(2a)^6(-b)^3 = \frac{9 \cdot 8 \cdot 7}{3 \cdot 2 \cdot 1}(2a)^6(-b)^3$$

$$= 84(64)a^6(-b^3)$$

$$= -5376a^6b^3$$

The first form $(9 \cdot 8 \cdot 7)/(3 \cdot 2 \cdot 1)$ of the coefficient checks with the statement in the note just before Example 4.   ◢

▶ **EXAMPLE 6**   What is the sixth term of $(3x - 4y)^8$?

Solution   The value of r is 6, hence the coefficient is

$$C(8, 5) = \frac{8 \cdot 7 \cdot 6}{3 \cdot 2 \cdot 1} = 56$$

Consequently, the sixth term is

$$56(3x)^3(-4y)^5 = 56(27x^3)(-1024y^5)$$
$$= -1,548,288x^3y^5 \qquad ◢$$

The triangular array of numbers below is called **Pascal's triangle.** Except for those on the end, each number in Pascal's triangle is the sum of the two numbers just above it. See Prob. 36. The numbers in each row are

The coefficients of $(x + y)^n$

for $n = 0, 1, 2, 3, 4, \ldots$. While Pascal's triangle is useful for small values of n, for large values of n it is more efficient to use the binomial theorem.

$$
\begin{array}{llccccccccccccccccc}
n = 0 & & & & & & & & & 1 \\
n = 1 & & & & & & & & 1 & & 1 \\
n = 2 & & & & & & & 1 & & 2 & & 1 \\
n = 3 & & & & & & 1 & & 3 & & 3 & & 1 \\
n = 4 & & & & & 1 & & 4 & & 6 & & 4 & & 1 \\
n = 5 & & & & 1 & & 5 & & 10 & & 10 & & 5 & & 1 \\
n = 6 & & & 1 & & 6 & & 15 & & 20 & & 15 & & 6 & & 1 \\
n = 7 & & 1 & & 7 & & 21 & & 35 & & 35 & & 21 & & 7 & & 1 \\
n = 8 & 1 & & 8 & & 28 & & 56 & & 70 & & 56 & & 28 & & 8 & & 1 \\
\end{array}
$$

EXERCISE 12.4

Find the expansion in Probs. 1 to 12 by the binomial formula.

1. $(x + y)^4$
2. $(x + t)^7$
3. $(b - y)^5$
4. $(a - w)^6$
5. $(3x - y)^5$
6. $(2a - b)^6$
7. $(x + 3w)^4$
8. $(a + 4x)^3$
9. $(2x + 3y)^4$
10. $(3s - 4t)^4$
11. $(2x - 5y)^3$
12. $(5a + 3b)^5$

Find the first four terms of the expansion of the binomial in each of Probs. 13 to 16.

13. $(a + y)^{33}$
14. $(x - y)^{51}$
15. $(m - 2y)^{101}$
16. $(b + 3c)^{42}$

Find the indicated power of the number in each of Probs. 17 to 20, and round off to four decimal places.

17. $(1 + 0.04)^5$
18. 1.05^4
19. 1.03^6
20. 1.06^3

Find the specified term of the expansion in each of Probs. 21 to 32.

21. Fifth term of $(x - 2y)^7$
22. Fourth term of $(2a - c)^6$
23. Sixth term of $(3x + y)^9$
24. Third term of $(x + 4y)^8$
25. Fourth term of $(a - a^{-1})^7$
26. Sixth term of $(2x - x^{-2})^9$
27. Seventh term of $(x^2 + 2y)^{11}$
28. Fifth term of $(3x + y^3)^8$
29. Middle term of $(x + 2y^{1/2})^6$
30. Middle term of $(x - 3y^{1/4})^8$
31. The term in $(x + 2y)^{10}$ that involves x^7.
32. The term in $(3x - y^{1/2})^{13}$ that involves y^4.
33. Show that

$$C(n, 0) + C(n, 1) + C(n, 2) + \cdots + C(n, n) = 2^n$$

for every positive integer n. *Hint:* Use the binomial theorem with $x = y = 1$.

34. Show that

$$C(n, 0) - C(n, 1) + C(n, 2) - C(n, 3) + \cdots$$
$$+ (-1)^n C(n, n) = 0$$

for every positive integer n. *Hint:* Use $x = 1$ and $y = -1$.

35. Show that

$$C(n, 0) + 2C(n, 1) + 2^2 C(n, 2) + 2^3 C(n, 3) + \cdots$$
$$+ 2^n C(n, n) = 3^n$$

for every positive integer n. *Hint:* Use $x = 1$ and $y = 2$.

36. It is true that

$$C(2n, n) = C^2(n, 0) + C^2(n, 1) + C^2(n, 2) + \cdots$$
$$+ C^2(n, n) \quad (*)$$

for every positive integer n. This can be proved by looking at the middle term in

$$(x + y)^{2n} = (x + y)^n (x + y)^n$$

Verify formula $(*)$ for $n = 4$ and $n = 5$.

Problems 37 to 40 give the outline of an alternative proof of the binomial theorem which is based on mathematical induction.

37. Show that the binomial formula (12.3) holds for $n = 1$.

38. Assuming that the binomial formula (12.3) holds for $n = k$, multiply both sides of the equation by $x + y$. Why is the rth term of $(x + y)^{k+1}$ equal to

$$C(k + 1, r - 1)x^{k-r+2}y^{r-1}$$

39. Continuing Prob. 38, show that after the right side of (12.3) is multiplied by $x + y$, the terms involving y^{r-1} are

$$C(k, r - 1)x^{k-r+2}y^{r-1} + C(k, r - 2)x^{k-r+2}y^{r-1}$$

40. Show that $C(k + 1, r - 1) = C(k, r - 1) + C(k, r - 2)$. How does this allow you to complete the proof of the binomial theorem by mathematical induction? *Hint:* $n! = n(n - 1)!$.

12.5 Probability

Probability had its beginnings in the middle of the seventeenth century because of a disagreement over a dice game. A wealthy patron, Antoine Gombaud, the Chevalier de Méré, asked Blaise Pascal a question about rolling a total of 12 with two dice. Pascal and Fermat then had a correspondence which was in essence the beginning of probability theory. It has grown into a varied discipline with applications in the social and natural sciences and is now used not only by gamblers, but also by statisticians, economists, insurance companies, engineers, and others.

There are 52 possible results if one card is drawn from a standard deck of cards. There are

$$C(52, 5) = \frac{52!}{5!47!} = 2{,}598{,}960$$

ways in which five cards can be drawn from a deck. There are three possible outcomes at the end of regulation time in a basketball game.

In general, there is a set of possible results if an event or experiment occurs. The set of all possible results is called the **sample space.** Each element of the sample space is called a sample point or **outcome.** Any subset of a sample space is called an **event.** For instance, if a die is cast, it may stop with 1, 2, 3, 4, 5, or 6 on top. Hence, $\{1, 2, 3, 4, 5, 6\}$ is the sample space, and any one of these elements is an outcome or sample point. Furthermore, any combination or subset of them is an event.

If a die is made accurately and rolled honestly, it is as likely to stop with one number up as another. Thus, each of the outcomes is **equally likely,** and we say the outcome is **random.** In this section we shall *assume* that:

All outcomes of experiments are equally likely

We will use the following notation in this section:

Symbol	Meaning
S	The sample space of all possible outcomes
$n(S)$	The number of elements in S
E	A set of outcmes in S, called an event; hence E is a subset of S
$n(E)$	The number of elements is E
$p(E)$	The probability that E will happen, or more briefly, the probability of E

We will only consider sample spaces with a **finite number of outcomes,** so that by assumption $n(S)$ is finite. Under the presumption that **each outcome is equally likely,** we define the probability of an **event E** as

$$p(E) = \frac{n(E)}{n(S)} \qquad (12.4)$$

This is equivalent to saying that the probability of each *outcome* is $1/n(S)$. Since $0 \le n(E) \le n(S)$, it follows that

$$0 \le p(E) \le 1 \qquad \text{for every event } E$$

▶ **EXAMPLE 1** If one card is drawn from a standard deck of 52 cards, find the probability that the card will be a jack.

Solution Here $S = \{x|x$ is a card in a deck of 52 cards$\}$. Hence $n(S) = 52$. Furthermore, $E = \{$club jack, diamond jack, heart jack, spade jack$\}$; so $n(E) = 4$. Thus

$$p(E) = \frac{n(E)}{n(S)} = \frac{4}{52} = \frac{1}{13} \qquad \blacktriangleleft$$

▶ **EXAMPLE 2** Find the probability of throwing a prime number total with (a) 1 die and (b) 2 dice.

Solution (a) We have $n(S) = 6$, $E = \{2, 3, 5\}$, and $n(E) = 3$, and so $p(E) = \frac{3}{6} = \frac{1}{2}$.
(b) The chart below lists all the possibilities. We have $n(S) = 6 \cdot 6 = 36$. The primes from 2 to 12 are 2, 3, 5, 7, and 11, and each prime sum in the chart is underlined. We can count that $n(E) = 15$. It follows that $p(E) = \frac{15}{36} = \frac{5}{12}$.

	1	2	3	4	5	6
1	2	3	4	5	6	7
2	3	4	5	6	7	8
3	4	5	6	7	8	9
4	5	6	7	8	9	10
5	6	7	8	9	10	11
6	7	8	9	10	11	12

$\blacktriangleleft$

The counting methods of Secs. 12.3 and 12.4 can be valuable tools in calculating probabilities. Remember that a combination is a subset without regard to order.

EXAMPLE 3   Find the probability of drawing 5 black cards if 5 cards are drawn from a deck of 52 cards without replacement.

Solution   The total number of ways to draw 5 cards from all 52 is $C(52, 5)$. Since there are 26 black cards in a deck, we can draw 5 black ones in $C(26, 5)$ ways. Therefore

$$p(E) = \frac{C(26, 5)}{C(52, 5)} = \frac{26!}{5!21!} \cdot \frac{5!47!}{52!} = \frac{26 \cdot 25 \cdot 24 \cdot 23 \cdot 22}{52 \cdot 51 \cdot 50 \cdot 49 \cdot 48} = \frac{7,893,600}{311,875,200}$$

which is about 0.0253. It occurs about 1 time in 40.

EXAMPLE 4   If 6 balls are drawn without replacement from a bag that contains 7 black and 5 white balls, what is the probability that 4 will be black and 2 white?

Solution   There are $C(12, 6)$ ways in which 6 balls can be drawn from a bag that contains 12. Furthermore, 4 black balls can be drawn from the 7 in $C(7, 4)$ ways and 2 white balls can be drawn from 5 in $C(5, 2)$ ways. Therefore the probability of drawing the stated combination is

$$\frac{C(7, 4) \cdot C(5, 2)}{C(12, 6)} = \frac{\dfrac{7!}{3!4!} \cdot \dfrac{5!}{3!2!}}{\dfrac{12!}{6!6!}} = \frac{7!5!6!6!}{3!4!3!2!12!} = \frac{25}{66} = 0.37878 \cdots$$

It occurs about 3 times in 8.

There are several theorems in probability which we shall now present and use. We have already seen that for any event E, $0 \le p(E) \le 1$; moreover $p(\emptyset) = 0$ and $p(S) = 1$. If A and B are **disjoint events,** then by definition $A \cap B = \emptyset$ and it follows that $n(A) + n(B) = n(A \cup B)$. Thus

$$p(A \cup B) = \frac{n(A \cup B)}{n(S)} = \frac{n(A)}{n(S)} + \frac{n(B)}{n(S)} = p(A) + p(B) \tag{1}$$

for events which are disjoint, or mutually exclusive.

EXAMPLE 5   Suppose that x is the estimated profit of a business for this year expressed as a percent of last year's profit, as given by a market analyst. The following table summarizes all of the estimates.

$x \le 50$	$50 < x \le 75$	$75 < x \le 100$	$100 < x \le 125$	$x > 125$
.12	.17	.26	.29	.16

Find the probability that this year's profit is not more than last year's profit.

Solution   Since the events are disjoint, the probability is the sum

$$.12 + .17 + .26 = .55$$

The theorem on disjoint events can be extended to any finite number of events by considering $(E_1 \cup E_2)$ as an event and adding a third event E_3 and then considering $(E_1 \cup E_2 \cup E_3)$ as an event and adding another. If this is continued, we reach the following conclusion:

> The probability that one of a set of pairwise mutually exclusive events will occur in a single trial is the sum of the probabilities of the separate events.
>
> $$p(E_1 \cup E_2 \cup \cdots \cup E_n) = p(E_1) + p(E_2) + \cdots + p(E_n) \qquad (2)$$

EXAMPLE 6   In a race for mayor, four candidates A, B, C, and D have probabilities .15, .16, .24, and .42 of winning, respectively. What is the probability that A, B, C, or D will win?

Solution   Only one of the candidates will win, so

$$p(A \cup B \cup C \cup D) = p(A) + p(B) + p(C) + p(D)$$
$$= .15 + .16 + .24 + .42 = .97$$

Notice that this probability is less than 1, and thus there is at least one other candidate in the race.

If E is an event and E' the complementary event, then by definition E' happens precisely when E does not happen. Hence E and E' are **disjoint** and

$$1 = p(S) = p(E \cup E') = p(E) + p(E')$$

In other words, $p(E') = 1 - p(E)$.

EXAMPLE 7   What is the probability of throwing less than 11 with two dice?

Solution   The probability of throwing less than 11 is one minus the probability of throwing either 11 or 12. Using the chart in Example 2 shows that

$$1 - p(11 \text{ or } 12) = 1 - \tfrac{2}{36} - \tfrac{1}{36} = 1 - \tfrac{1}{12} = \tfrac{11}{12}$$

Repeated Trials of an Event

Suppose that a player's batting average is .250 for the season, and in a certain game he comes to bat 5 times. If H represents a hit and A is anything else, then the probability that he will get 2 hits in the order

$$H\,H\,A\,A\,A \text{ is } (\tfrac{1}{4})(\tfrac{1}{4})(\tfrac{3}{4})(\tfrac{3}{4})(\tfrac{3}{4}) = (\tfrac{1}{4})^2(\tfrac{3}{4})^3$$

or

$$A\,H\,A\,H\,A \text{ is } (\tfrac{3}{4})(\tfrac{1}{4})(\tfrac{3}{4})(\tfrac{1}{4})(\tfrac{3}{4}) = (\tfrac{1}{4})^2(\tfrac{3}{4})^3$$

or

$$A\,A\,H\,A\,H \text{ is } (\tfrac{3}{4})(\tfrac{3}{4})(\tfrac{1}{4})(\tfrac{3}{4})(\tfrac{1}{4}) = (\tfrac{1}{4})^2(\tfrac{3}{4})^3$$

In fact the number of ways in which he can get exactly 2 hits in his 5 times at bat in this game is just the number of ways of choosing 2 things from 5 things, which is

$$C(5,\ 2) = \frac{5!}{2!3!} = 10$$

As indicated above, the probability of any one of the 10 things happening is $(\frac{1}{4})^2(\frac{3}{4})^3$, and since they are disjoint events, the probability of **exactly** 2 hits in 5 times at bat is

$$(\tfrac{1}{4})^2(\tfrac{3}{4})^3 + (\tfrac{1}{4})^2(\tfrac{3}{4})^3 + \cdots + (\tfrac{1}{4})^2(\tfrac{3}{4})^3 = C(5,\,2) \cdot (\tfrac{1}{4})^2(\tfrac{3}{4})^3 = \frac{10 \cdot 1^2 \cdot 3^3}{4^5} = \frac{270}{1024} = .264$$

In a similar way, we can find that in 5 times at bat the probability of *exactly*

0 hits is $\frac{243}{1024} \approx .237$
1 hit is $\frac{405}{1024} \approx .396$
2 hits is $\frac{270}{1024} \approx .264$, as above
3 hits is $\frac{90}{1024} \approx .088$
4 hits is $\frac{15}{1024} \approx .015$
5 hits is $\frac{1}{1024} \approx .001$

The decimals, which are approximations, add up to 1.001, while the fractions, which are exact, add up to 1. This corresponds to the fact mentioned earlier that $p(S) = 1$.

The same method as that above can be used to show that if p is the probability that an event will occur in one trial, then the probability that the event will occur exactly r times in n identically repeated trials is

$$C(n,\,r)p^r(1 - p)^{n-r} \tag{12.5}$$

EXAMPLE 8   If the probability that a missile will hit the target is $\frac{3}{5}$, find the probability of
(a) Exactly 4 hits out of 6 tries
(b) Exactly 8 hits out of 12 tries

Solution   (a) Using $n = 6$ and $r = 4$ gives

$$C(6,\,4)(\tfrac{3}{5})^4(\tfrac{2}{5})^2 = \frac{15(3^4)(2^2)}{5^6} \approx .311$$

(b) Here we use $n = 12$ and $r = 8$ and get

$$C(12,\,8)(\tfrac{3}{5})^8(\tfrac{2}{5})^4 = \frac{495(3^8)(2^4)}{5^{12}} \approx .213$$

There are many topics related to these in probability, but we will not have time to develop them. For instance

$$p(A \cup B) = p(A) + p(B) - p(A \cup B)$$

whether or not A and B are disjoint. And remember that each outcome does not need to be equally likely—just consider a pair of loaded dice.

Summary of Formulas

$p(E) = n(E)/n(S)$ $0 \le p(E) \le 1$
$p(\emptyset) = 0$ $p(S) = 1$
$p(A \cup B) = p(A) + p(B)$ if A and B are disjoint
$p(E') = 1 - p(E)$
$C(n,\,r)p^r(1 - p)^{n-r}$ is the probability of exactly r occurrences in n repeated trials if p
    is the probability in one trial

EXERCISE 12.5

1. If 1 card is drawn from a standard deck of 52 cards, what is the probability it will be a diamond? A red card?

2. If only 1 of a pair of dice is thrown, what is the probability the number will be even? What is the probability the number will have 4 letters in its English spelling?

3. What is the probability that a card drawn from a standard deck will be a 5, 6, or 7? Will be a black face card?

4. If 1 die is thrown, what is the probability that the number x on top will satisfy $x^2 > 22$? Will satisfy $7x + 3 < 19$?

5. What is the probability that the English spelling of the name of a month has the letter "R" in it?

6. What is the probability that an integer from 1 to 20 has 3 letters in its English spelling?

7. What is the probability that a color chosen from red, orange, yellow, green, blue, indigo, and violet has the letter "E" in its spelling?

8. What is the probability of choosing a vowel if 1 letter is chosen from the words "a quick fox jumped over the lazy brown dogs"?

In Probs. 9 to 12, assume that 2 fair dice are thrown.

9. Find the probability of throwing a sum of (a) 8 and (b) 12.

10. What is the probability of a sum of (a) 9 and (b) 5?

11. Find the probability the sum will be 7 or 11.

12. What is the probability of the sum being 2, 3, or 12?

Assume that in Math 1234 there were 16 A's, 35 B's, 63 C's, 40 D's, and 26 F's. Find the probabilities of the events in Probs. 13 to 16 for a random student.

13. An A or a B
14. Not an F
15. A B, an A, or a D
16. Not a C

17. A bridge hand of 13 cards is drawn from a deck. Find the probability of getting a hand with every card 8 or lower if aces are high.

18. A poker hand of 5 cards is drawn from a deck. What is the probability that every card wil be a 10, jack, queen, king, or ace?

19. Three people are to be chosen randomly from a group of 12 men and 8 women. What is the probability all 3 will be men?

20. Five dogs will be in the finals of a dog show containing 8 poodles, 10 terriers, and 14 bulldogs. What is the probability none of the finalists is a poodle?

21. If 8 people are chosen in all, what is the probability of choosing 3 Mexicans and 5 Canadians out of 6 Mexicans and 12 Canadians?

22. If there are 10 people with June anniversaries and 6 people with August anniversaries, what is the probability of choosing 4 people with June anniversaries and 2 people with August anniversaries if 6 are chosen?

23. If 5 balls are drawn from a bag containing 8 green and 7 yellow balls, what is the probability that 3 will be green and 2 yellow?

24. Out of 15 people, 8 have disease A and 7 have disease B. If 5 are chosen, what is the probability that 3 will have A and 2 will have B?

25. If candidates P, Q, R, and S are in an election and the probabilities of winning are $\frac{1}{2}$ for P, $\frac{1}{3}$ for Q, and $\frac{1}{24}$ for R, find the probability that S will win if there are no other candidates.

26. The probability that a contract will go to company W is $\frac{1}{2}$, to X is $\frac{1}{4}$, and to Y is $\frac{1}{20}$. What is the probability none of these three gets it?

27. A box contains lavender, turquoise, magenta, silver, and scarlet scarves. If the probabilities of choosing one of the first 4 are respectively $\frac{1}{4}$, $\frac{1}{9}$, $\frac{1}{12}$, and $\frac{1}{18}$, what is the probability of getting a scarlet scarf?

28. The 7 dwarfs are working in the forest, and the probabilities of each one doing the most work are $\frac{1}{3}$ for Doc, $\frac{1}{5}$ for Grumpy, $\frac{1}{6}$ for Happy, $\frac{1}{7}$ for Sneezy, $\frac{1}{10}$ for Dopey, and $\frac{1}{30}$ for Bashful. What is the probability that Sleepy will do the most work?

In Probs. 29 to 32, find the probability of an event occurring exactly r times in n trials if p is the probability it will occur in one trial.

29. $r = 3$, $n = 6$, $p = \frac{1}{3}$
30. $r = 2$, $n = 5$, $p = \frac{1}{2}$
31. $r = 3$, $n = 4$, $p = \frac{2}{7}$
32. $r = 4$, $n = 8$, $p = \frac{3}{4}$

33. Find the probability of throwing, in 5 tosses of a coin, (a) exactly 3 heads and (b) at least 3 heads.

34. The probability that a boy will be on time for a meal is .2. Find the probability that he will be on time (a) exactly 4 times in 2 days and (b) at least 4 times.

35. A bag contains 3 white, 4 red, and 5 black balls. Five withdrawals of 1 ball each are made, and the ball is replaced after each. Find the probability that all 5 will be red.

36. If the probability that a certain basketball team will

win the conference championship in any given year is $\frac{2}{5}$, find the probability that it will win exactly 3 championships in 5 years.

Problems 37 to 40 refer to Example 5, which expressed this year's profit as x percent of last year's. The table is reproduced below:

$x \leq 50$	$50 < x \leq 75$	$75 < x \leq 100$	$100 < x \leq 125$	$x > 125$
.12	.17	.26	.29	.16

37. What is the probability that $x \leq 75$?
38. What is the probability that $x > 50$?
39. What is the probability that $75 < x \leq 125$?
40. What is the probability that $50 < x \leq 100$?
41. If 3 dice are tossed, what is the probability the sum will be 5?

12.6 Key Concepts

Be sure you understand the following important words and ideas.

Principle of mathematical induction (p. 580)
Generalized principle of mathematical induction (p. 583)
Repetition (p. 585)
Order (p. 585)
Permutation (p. 585)
Combination (p. 585)
Sample (p. 586)
Selection (p. 586)
Tree diagram (p. 587)
Fundamental principle of counting (p. 587)

Distinguishable permutation (p. 593)
Binomial theorem (p. 596)
Binomial coefficients (p. 598)
The rth term of the binomial theorem (p. 598)
Pascal's triangle (p. 599)
Sample space (p. 600)
Event (p. 600)
Equally likely events (p. 601)
Probability of an event (p. 601)
Disjoint events (p. 602)
Repeated trials of an event (p. 602)

(12.1) $P(n, r) = n(n - 1)(n - 2) \cdots (n - r + 1) = \dfrac{n!}{(n - r)!}$

n^r = number of samples

(12.2) $C(n, r) = \dfrac{n!}{r!(n - r)!}$

$C(n + r - 1, r)$ = number of selections

(12.3) $(x + y)^n = \displaystyle\sum_{r=0}^{n} C(n, r)x^{n-r}y^r$

(12.4) $p(E) = \dfrac{n(E)}{n(S)}$

(12.5) $C(n, r)p^r(1 - p)^{n-r}$

EXERCISE 12.6   Review

Use mathematical induction to prove the following statements for every positive n.

1. $3 + 7 + 11 + \cdots + (4n - 1) = n(2n + 1)$
2. $5 + 8 + 11 + \cdots + (3n + 2) = n(3n + 7)/2$
3. $\frac{1}{6} + \frac{1}{12} + \frac{1}{24} + \cdots + (\frac{1}{6})(\frac{1}{2})^{n-1} = (1 - 2^{-n})/3$
4. $\frac{2}{5} - \frac{1}{10} + \frac{1}{40} - \frac{1}{160} + \cdots + (\frac{2}{5})(-\frac{1}{4})^{n-1} =$
   $\frac{8}{25}[1 - (-\frac{1}{4})^n]$
5. $0 + 3 + 8 + 15 + \cdots + (n^2 - 1) =$
   $n(n - 1)(2n + 5)/6$
6. $(2)(1) + (3)(3) + (4)(5) + \cdots + (n + 1)(2n - 1) =$
   $n(4n^2 + 9n - 1)/6$
7. $(1)(4) + (2)(9) + (3)(16) + \cdots + n(n + 1)^2 =$
   $n(n + 1)(n + 2)(3n + 5)/12$
8. $1 + 2(\frac{1}{2}) + 3(\frac{1}{2})^2 + 4(\frac{1}{2})^3 + \cdots + n(\frac{1}{2})^{n-1} =$

$$4 - \frac{1}{2^{n-2}} - \frac{n}{2^{n-1}}$$

Verify by calculation the statements in Probs. 9 to 12.

9. $C(8, 6) < C(8, 5) < C(8, 4) < P(8, 4) <$
   $P(8, 5) < P(8, 6)$
10. $C(6, 3) = P(5, 2) = C(5, 3) + C(4, 2) +$
    $C(3, 1) + C(2, 0)$
11. $C(4, 1) + 2C(4, 2) + 3C(4, 3) + 4C(4, 4) =$
    $(4)(2^3)$
12. $C(4, 1) + 4C(4, 2) + 9C(4, 3) + 16C(4, 4) =$
    $(4)(5)(2^2)$
13. How many ways are there to choose 3 numbers from the set

$$\{\tfrac{1}{4}, \tfrac{3}{4}, \tfrac{1}{5}, \tfrac{2}{5}, \tfrac{3}{5}, \tfrac{4}{5}\}$$

if numbers may not be repeated and order does not matter?
14. Repeat Prob. 13 if numbers may not be repeated and order matters.
15. How many 3-digit numbers are there using the digits 1, 3, 5, 7, and 9?
16. How many 3-digit numbers are there with different digits using the digits 1, 3, 5, 7, and 9?
17. How many ways are there of choosing 3 different odd digits?
18. How many ways are there of choosing 3 odd digits?
19. In how many ways may a coach keep 2 centers, 4 forwards, and 4 guards from a group of tryouts of 5 centers, 7 forwards, and 9 guards?
20. Two cards are drawn from the 12 face cards without replacement. In how many ways may this be done with 3 decks?
21. How many permutations are there of the letters in the word "seventeenth"?
22. In how many ways may a board of directors of 8 people reach a majority decision?
23. How many triangles are formed by n lines in a plane if no 2 of the lines are parallel and no 3 pass through a common point?
24. The probability of throwing exactly n heads in $2n$ tosses of a fair coin is

$$\frac{C(2n, n)}{2^{2n}} = \frac{(2n)!}{n!n!2^{2n}}$$

(a) Show that this is approximately $1/\sqrt{n\pi}$, by using Sterling's formula, which says

$$\frac{k!}{k^{k+1/2} \cdot e^{-k} \cdot \sqrt{2\pi}} \approx 1$$

for large enough values of k.
(b) Calculate $1/\sqrt{n\pi}$ for $n = 32$.
25. Show that $2 \cdot 4 \cdot 6 \cdots \cdot (2n) = 2^n \cdot (n!)$.
26. Show that $1 \cdot 3 \cdot 5 \cdot 7 \cdots \cdot (2n - 1) = (2n)!/2^n(n!)$.
27. Show that if $f(n) = [1 \cdot 3 \cdot 5 \cdots \cdot (2n - 1)]/[2 \cdot 4 \cdot 6 \cdots \cdot (2n)]$,

then $\quad \dfrac{f(n + 1)}{f(n)} = \dfrac{2n + 1}{2n + 2}$

28. Show that if $f(n) = n^n/n!$, then $f(n + 1)/f(n) = (1 + 1/n)^n$.

Use the binomial formula in Probs. 29 to 32.

29. Find the expansion of $(x + 3y)^5$.
30. Find the expansion of $(3x - 2y)^4$.
31. Find the first four terms of $(x - y)^{15}$.
32. Find the first four terms of $(2x + y)^{12}$.

Find the specified term of the expansion in Probs. 33 to 36.

33. Fifth term of $(x - 3y)^{10}$
34. Sixth term of $(4x + y)^{12}$
35. Fourth term of $(x - x^{-1})^{18}$
36. Fifth term of $(x^2 + 3y)^{15}$
37. What is the probability that the letter "U" is in the English spelling of the name of one of the 7 days of the week?

38. What is the probability that an integer from 10 to 50 inclusive is not divisible by 3?

39. What is the probability of throwing a total of 6 with (a) one die, (b) two dice, and (c) three dice?

40. If 3 fair coins are tossed, what is the probability that the result will not be 3 heads?

41. If 6 balls are chosen from a bag with 5 black balls and 4 white ones, what is the probability that 4 are black and 2 are white?

42. If 5 patients are chosen for an experiment from 6 with colds and 4 with the flu, what is the probability that 3 will have a cold and 2 will have the flu?

43. Five disjoint events have probabilities of $\frac{1}{3}$, $\frac{1}{4}$, $\frac{1}{5}$, $\frac{1}{8}$, and $\frac{1}{15}$. What is the probability that none of these 5 will happen?

44. The probability that an airport detector will find

item G is $\frac{2}{5}$, item B is $\frac{3}{8}$, item D is $\frac{1}{9}$, and item X is $\frac{1}{10}$. What is the probability of finding none of these 4 items?

45. Find the probability of getting exactly 3 heads in 6 flips of a fair coin.

46. Find the probability of throwing exactly 2 sevens in 5 tosses of a pair of dice.

47. Find the probability of getting at least 2 heads in 6 tosses of a fair coin.

48. With a certain group of symptoms, the probability of contracting a particular disease is $\frac{2}{3}$. If 8 people have these symptoms, what is the probability that at least two-thirds of them have that disease?

49. Suppose that each member of a team has a batting average of .250. Find the probability that 27 consecutive batters will not get a hit.

13

The Conics

Certain figures in a plane are created by the intersection of a plane and a right circular cone. The type of figure depends on the relative position of the plane and the cone. We will briefly describe two ways of thinking of these intersections. One way is to keep the cone fixed, as in Fig. 13.1, and rotate a plane through it, giving successively a circle, an ellipse, a parabola, and a hyperbola. The other way is to keep the plane fixed and rotate the cone, which can perhaps best be visualized by beginning with a flashlight pointed straight down at the floor, and then rotating the flashlight to and beyond the horizontal position. Here too the curves occur in the order of circle, ellipse, parabola, and hyperbola. By passing the plane through the vertex of the cone, certain degenerate cases can occur, namely, a point, a line, or two intersecting lines.

Although conics were extensively studied and understood by the Greeks over two millennia ago, they continue to be applicable even in today's technology. For instance, they are used in satellite dishes which receive TV signals (parabolas), in dissolving kidney stones (ellipses), and in navigation devices (hyperbolas). They also remain vital in many traditional areas.

13.1 Parabolas

If a plane is parallel to an edge of a cone, but does not go through the vertex of the cone, the curve of intersection is called a **parabola.** See Fig. 13.1c for a geometric version. An algebraic definition is given below:

Definition of parabola

A **parabola** is the set of all points in a plane that are equidistant from a fixed point and a fixed line. The fixed point is called the **focus,** and the fixed line the **directrix.** The focus is not allowed to be on the directrix.

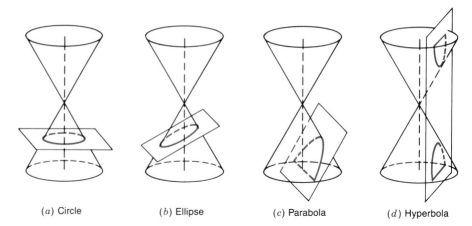

FIGURE 13.1   (*a*) Circle   (*b*) Ellipse   (*c*) Parabola   (*d*) Hyperbola

The line through the focus and perpendicular to the directrix is called the **axis of symmetry,** or just the axis of the parabola. The line segment through the focus and perpendicular to the axis of symmetry which is cut off by the parabola is called the **focal chord** or **latus rectum,** and its length is the **focal width.** The point of intersection of the axis of symmetry and the parabola is called the **vertex.** It then follows by definition that the vertex is equidistant from the focus and the directrix. These lines and points are shown in Fig. 13.2.

In this section we will treat only parabolas whose axis of symmetry is parallel to either the *x* axis or the *y* axis. To allow *any* axis of symmetry requires rotating the axes.

We will now derive the equation of a parabola from the definition above. It is convenient to place the vertex at the point $V(h, k)$ as in Fig. 13.3, and then choose

The vertical line with equation $x = h - p$ as directrix, and the point $F(h + p, k)$ as the focus

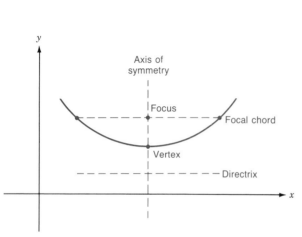

FIGURE 13.2

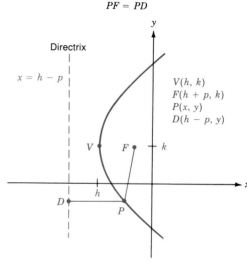

FIGURE 13.3

NOTE

where p is some real number with $p \neq 0$. Notice that $|p|$ is the distance from the vertex to either **the focus or the directrix.** Next we let $P(x, y)$ be any point on the parabola, and draw the line segment PF from P to the focus. We also draw the line segment PD from P perpendicular to the directrix, intersecting it at D. The coordinates of the point D are $(h - p, y)$ since it is on the directrix and has the same ordinate as P. Then by the definition of a parabola, $PF = PD$.

Now the distance formula shows that

$$PF = \sqrt{[x - (h + p)]^2 + (y - k)^2}$$
$$= \sqrt{[(x - h) - p]^2 + (y - k)^2} \qquad \text{by associative axiom}$$
$$= \sqrt{(x - h)^2 - 2p(x - h) + p^2 + (y - k)^2} \qquad \text{squaring the first expression inside}$$

Similarly by the distance formula

$$PD = \sqrt{[x - (h - p)]^2 + (y - y)^2} = \sqrt{(x - h)^2 + 2p(x - h) + p^2}$$

But since $PF = PD$, it follows that $(PF)^2 = (PD)^2$, and thus

$$(x - h)^2 - 2p(x - h) + p^2 + (y - k)^2 = (x - h)^2 + 2p(x - h) + p^2$$

Canceling identical terms gives

$$-2p(x - h) + (y - k)^2 = 2p(x - h)$$
$$(y - k)^2 = 4p(x - h)$$

Consequently, we have the following conclusion:

Standard forms of the equations of a parabola

An equation of the parabola with its vertex at (h, k) and focus at $(h + p, k)$ is

$$(y - k)^2 = 4p(x - h) \qquad \textbf{(13.1)}$$

Remember that p may be positive or negative. In a similar manner, we can show that an equation of the parabola with the vertex at (h, k) and focus at $(h, k + p)$ is

$$(x - h)^2 = 4p(y - k) \qquad \textbf{(13.2)}$$

The axis of symmetry of the parabola (13.1) is parallel to the x axis, and the graph opens to the right if $p > 0$ and to the left if $p < 0$. The axis of symmetry of (13.2) is parallel to the y axis, and the graph opens up if $p > 0$, and down if $p < 0$.

Since the axis of symmetry goes through the vertex (h, k), the **equation of the axis of symmetry** of (13.1) is

$$y = k \qquad \textbf{(13.3)}$$

with directrix $x = h - p$. The **equation of the axis of symmetry** of (13.2) is

$$x = h \qquad \textbf{(13.3a)}$$

with directrix $y = k - p$.

Equations (13.1) and (13.2) are called the **standard forms** of the equations of a parabola. If the vertex (h, k) is at the origin, then $h = k = 0$ and the equations reduce to the following special forms:

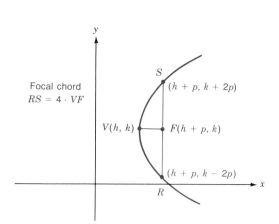

Focal chord
$RS = 4 \cdot VF$

S
$(h + p, k + 2p)$

$V(h, k)$ $F(h + p, k)$

$(h + p, k - 2p)$

R

FIGURE 13.4

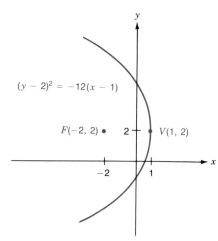

$(y - 2)^2 = -12(x - 1)$

$F(-2, 2)$ • $V(1, 2)$

-2 1

FIGURE 13.5

$$y^2 = 4px \qquad \text{(13.1a)}$$

and $$x^2 = 4py \qquad \text{(13.2a)}$$

We can find the **length of the focal chord** by solving the equation of the line along which it lies simultaneously with that of the parabola, and then using the distance formula. For (13.1), these equations are

$$x = h + p \qquad \text{and} \qquad (y - k)^2 = 4p(x - h)$$

If we substitute the expression for x from the first equation into the second one, we have

$$(y - k)^2 = 4p(h + p - h) = 4p^2$$
$$y - k = \pm 2p \qquad \text{and thus} \qquad y = k \pm 2p$$

Hence the ends of the focal chords are at

$$(h + p, k + 2p) \qquad \text{and} \qquad (h + p, k - 2p)$$

as shown in Fig. 13.4. The distance between them is $4|p|$ whether $p > 0$ or $p < 0$.

The focal width of the parabola (13.1) or (13.2) is $4|p|$.

It is worth pointing out once again that

the distance between vertex and focus is $|p|$

EXAMPLE 1   Find the equation and focal width of the parabola with vertex at $(1, 2)$ and focus at $(-2, 2)$.

Solution   In this problem, the vertex and focus are the same distance from the x axis; therefore the line $y = 2$ is the axis of symmetry. See Fig. 13.5. Hence the form of the equation is

$(y - k)^2 = 4p(x - h)$, with $h = 1$ and $k = 2$. Since the focus is 3 units to the left of the vertex, then $p = -3$ and $4p = -12$. Consequently the equation of the parabola is

$$(y - 2)^2 = -12(x - 1)$$

and the focal width is $|-12| = 12$.   ◢

EXAMPLE 2 Put $x^2 - 6x - 8y + 25 = 0$ in standard form, and find the vertex, focus, directrix, and focal width.

Solution We complete the square of the quadratic in x by adding 9 to each side, and thus have

$$x^2 - 6x + 9 = 8y - 25 + 9 \qquad \text{transposing } -8y + 25$$
$$(x - 3)^2 = 8y - 16$$
$$(x - 3)^2 = 8(y - 2)$$

This is the standard form, which shows that the vertex is $(h, k) = (3, 2)$, and $4p = 8$. The axis of symmetry is $x = 3$. Since $p = 2 > 0$, the parabola opens up and

The focus is $(h, k + p) = (3, 4)$

The directrix is $y = k - p = 2 - 2 = 0$

The focal width is $|4p| = |8| = 8$. See Fig. 13.6.   ◢

EXAMPLE 3 Find an equation of the parabola with vertex at $(-2, 3)$, axis parallel to the x axis, and going through $(4, 9)$.

Solution The form of the equation must be

$$(y - 3)^2 = 4p(x + 2)$$

Substituting $x = 4$ and $y = 9$ gives $36 = 4p(6)$, and so $4p = 6$. The equation is thus $(y - 3)^2 = 6(x + 2)$.   ◢

Reflection property

Every parabola has a remarkable **reflection property.** Suppose a light ray begins at the focus, and then goes toward any point on the parabola. It will bounce off the parabola as if it were bouncing off the tangent line to the parabola at that point on the parabola. The new direction of the ray will always be parallel to the axis of symmetry

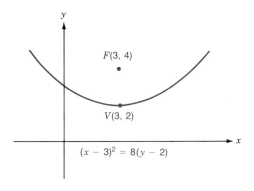

FIGURE 13.6

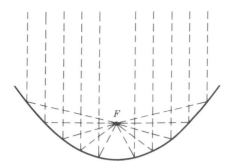

FIGURE 13.7

of the parabola. See Fig. 13.7. This reflection property is the basis for flashlights and car headlights.

The reflection property works in reverse too. That is, any ray parallel to the axis of symmetry will be reflected off the parabola and go through the focus. This is the basis for the satellite dishes which collect TV signals. Each one is made by revolving a parabolic segment about its axis of symmetry.

Summary

> The parabola whose equation is $(x - h)^2 = 4p(y - k)$
>
> *opens up if $p > 0$, and opens down if $p < 0$*
>
> The parabola whose equation is $(y - k)^2 = 4p(x - h)$
>
> *opens to the right if $p > 0$, to the left if $p < 0$*
>
> The vertex is always (h, k).
> The distance from the vertex to the focus is $|p|$.
> The shortest distance from the vertex to the directrix is $|p|$.
> The length of the focal chord is $4|p|$.

EXERCISE 13.1

Find the equation of and sketch each parabola described in Probs. 1 to 20.

1. Vertex at $(5, 1)$, focus at $(7, 1)$
2. Vertex at $(8, 4)$, focus at $(8, 8)$
3. Focus at $(11, 4)$, vertex at $(9, 4)$
4. Focus at $(6, -4)$, vertex at $(6, -3)$
5. Vertex at $(8, 3)$, $y = 7$ as directrix
6. Vertex at $(5, 0)$, $y = -8$ as directrix
7. Directrix $x = 4$, vertex at $(0, 3)$
8. Directrix $x = -3$, vertex at $(5, 2)$
9. Focus at $(7, 2)$, $x = 11$ as directrix
10. Focus at $(6, 3)$, $x = 2$ a directrix
11. Directrix $y = 3$, focus at $(5, -1)$
12. Directrix $y = -2$, focus at $(4, 6)$
13. Vertex at $(5, 2)$, ends of focal chord at $(3, 6)$ and $(3, -2)$
14. Vertex at $(3, 5)$, ends of focal chord at $(5, 6)$ and $(1, 6)$
15. Ends of focal chord at $(-1, 1)$ and $(15, 1)$, vertex at $(7, -3)$
16. Ends of focal chord at $(3, 12)$ and $(3, -4)$, vertex at $(-1, 4)$
17. Vertex at $(5, 2)$, axis parallel to x axis, through $(9, 6)$
18. Vertex at $(6, -1)$, axis parallel to x axis, through $(2, 3)$
19. Axis parallel to the y axis, vertex at $(1, 1)$, through $(-3, 3)$

20. Axis parallel to the y axis, vertex at $(0, 0)$, through $(-6, -3)$

Put each of the equations in Probs. 21 to 28 in standard form and give the vertex and focus.

21. $y^2 - 4y - 4x = 0$
22. $y^2 + 2y + 6x - 17 = 0$
23. $x^2 + 6x + 4y - 3 = 0$
24. $x^2 - 8x - 8y + 8 = 0$
25. $x^2 - 4x - 4y - 8 = 0$
26. $x^2 + 6x + 8y + 41 = 0$
27. $y^2 + 4y + 4x + 8 = 0$
28. $y^2 - 6y - 8x - 7 = 0$

Find the equation of the set of points equidistant from the point and line given in Probs. 29 to 32.

29. $(6, 3)$, $x = 2$ **30.** $(6, 1)$, $x = -2$

31. $(1, 7)$, $y = -1$ **32.** $(5, -2)$, $y = 6$
33. Locate the focus of a parabolic reflector that is 12 in wide and 4 in deep.
34. Find the equation satisfied by the centers of the set of circles such that each is tangent to $x^2 + y^2 = 9$ and to $x = 5$.
35. If a ball is thrown vertically upward from the ground with an initial velocity of V_0 feet per second (ft/s), its distance above the ground after t seconds is given approximately by $y = V_0 t - 16t^2$. To what height will it rise if thrown up at 40 ft/s?
36. If a ball is thrown at an angle of $45°$, with the horizontal and an initial velocity of V_0 feet per second, it follows a path whose equation is approximately $y = x - 32x^2/V_0^2$. If V_0 is 96, find the horizontal distance traveled and the greatest height reached by the ball.

13.2 Ellipses

As indicated in Fig. 13.1b, an ellipse is obtained by cutting a right circular cone with a plane that cuts through one nappe of the cone and is not perpendicular to the axis of symmetry. In addition to this geometric version, the algebraic definition is given below:

Definition of an ellipse

An **ellipse** is the set of all points in a plane such that the sum of the distances of each point from two fixed points is the same. The fixed points are called the **foci,** and the line through the foci is the **axis of symmetry.**

In this section we will choose the axis of symmetry to be parallel to either the x axis or the y axis. To derive the equation of an ellipse, we will take the axis of symmetry to be parallel to the x axis, and choose the foci to be at

$$F_1(h - c, k) \qquad \text{and} \qquad F_2(h + c, k)$$

as shown in Fig. 13.8.

If we let $P(x, y)$ be any point on the ellipse and $2a$ be the sum of its distances from the foci, then by definition we have

$$F_1 P + F_2 P = 2a \tag{1}$$

By the distance formula

$$F_1 P = \sqrt{[x - (h - c)]^2 + (y - k)^2}$$
$$= \sqrt{[(x - h) + c]^2 + (y - k)^2}$$

Similarly,

$$F_2 P = \sqrt{[(x - h) - c]^2 + (y - k)^2}$$

13 The Conics

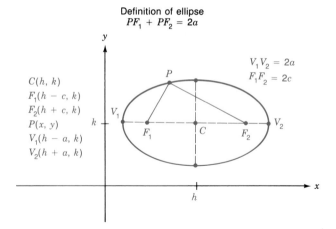

Definition of ellipse
$PF_1 + PF_2 = 2a$

$C(h, k)$
$F_1(h - c, k)$
$F_2(h + c, k)$
$P(x, y)$
$V_1(h - a, k)$
$V_2(h + a, k)$

$V_1V_2 = 2a$
$F_1F_2 = 2c$

FIGURE 13.8

Consequently, we have by Eq. (1)

$$\sqrt{[(x - h) + c]^2 + (y - k)^2} + \sqrt{[(x - h) - c]^2 + (y - k)^2} = 2a$$

We shall eliminate the two radicals one at a time, first transposing one term and squaring:

$$\sqrt{[(x - h) + c]^2 + (y - k)^2} = 2a - \sqrt{[(x - h) - c]^2 + (y - k)^2}$$

Now square each side above, then solve for the remaining radical on the right, denoted by R:

$$(x - h)^2 + 2c(x - h) + c^2 + (y - k)^2 =$$
$$4a^2 - 2(2a)(R) + (x - h)^2 - 2c(x - h) + c^2 + (y - k)^2$$

Thus $\qquad 4aR = -4c(x - h) + 4a^2$

Dividing by 4 and replacing R by its value gives

$$a\sqrt{[(x - h) - c]^2 + (y - k)^2} = a^2 - c(x - h)$$

Now square each of the sides above and combine similar terms:

$$a^2[(x - h)^2 - 2c(x - h) + c^2 + (y - k)^2] = a^4 - 2a^2c(x - h) + c^2(x - h)^2$$

Combining terms gives

$$(a^2 - c^2)(x - h)^2 + a^2(y - k)^2 = a^4 - a^2c^2$$

Now divide both sides by $a^4 - a^2c^2 = a^2(a^2 - c^2)$:

$$\frac{(x - h)^2}{a^2} + \frac{(y - k)^2}{a^2 - c^2} = 1$$

The distance between $F_1(h - c, k)$ and $F_2(h + c, k)$ is $2c$, and the sum of the distances PF_1 and PF_2 in Fig. 13.8 is $2a$. Since the sum of two sides of a triangle is greater than the third side, then $2a > 2c$ and it follows that $a^2 - c^2$ is positive. Letting $a^2 - c^2 = b^2$ above gives

$$\frac{(x-h)^2}{a^2} + \frac{(y-k)^2}{b^2} = 1 \qquad (2)$$

in which $b = \sqrt{a^2 - c^2} < a$.

The ratio c/a is called the **eccentricity** of the ellipse. The point (h, k) midway between the foci is called the **center.** The intersection points of an ellipse and the line through the foci are known as the **vertices.** The line segment joining the vertices is the **major axis.** The part of the line through the center, perpendicular to the major axis, which is intercepted by the ellipse is the **minor axis.** We have proved the following theorem:

Standard forms of the equation of an ellipse

$$\frac{(x-h)^2}{a^2} + \frac{(y-k)^2}{b^2} = 1 \qquad (13.4)$$

is an equation of the ellipse with center at (h, k), vertices at $(h \pm a, k)$, foci at $(h \pm c, k)$, major axis parallel to the x axis, and semiaxes of length a and b. Also

$$\frac{(y-k)^2}{a^2} + \frac{(x-h)^2}{b^2} = 1 \qquad (13.5)$$

is an equation of the ellipse with center at (h, k), vertices at $(h, k \pm a)$, foci at $(h, k \pm c)$, major axis parallel to the y axis, and semiaxes of length a and b.

Equations (13.4) and (13.5) are called **standard forms** of the equation of an ellipse. The vertical line test shows that the graph of an ellipse is not the graph of a function.

If the center is at $(h, k) = (0, 0)$, the equations above have the form

$$\frac{x^2}{a^2} + \frac{y^2}{b^2} = 1 \qquad \text{and} \qquad \frac{y^2}{a^2} + \frac{x^2}{b^2} = 1$$

In each case, $b^2 = a^2 - c^2$, which implies $a^2 = b^2 + c^2$, and thus

$$a > b \qquad \text{and} \qquad a > c$$

Also, for every ellipse,

Each vertex is a units from the center

EXAMPLE 1 Find the equation of the ellipse with center at $(3, 4)$, a focus at $(6, 4)$, and a vertex at $(8, 4)$. Sketch the graph.

Solution We can write the equation of an ellipse if we know the center, the semiaxes, and which of the two standard forms to use. With the given data, we must use Eq. (13.4) since the center, focus, and vertex are on a line parallel to the x axis. See Fig. 13.9. Furthermore, since a is the distance between the center and the vertex, we have

$$a = 8 - 3 = 5$$

Also c is the distance between the center and the focus, and it follows that $c = 6 - 3 = 3$. To determine the value of b, use the relation

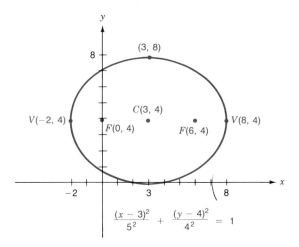

FIGURE 13.9

$$b^2 = a^2 - c^2 = 25 - 9 = 16 \qquad \text{and hence} \qquad b = 4$$

Therefore, the desired equation is

$$\frac{(x - 3)^2}{5^2} + \frac{(y - 4)^2}{4^2} = 1$$

and the sketch is shown in Fig. 13.9.

EXAMPLE 2 Put $16x^2 + 9y^2 - 96x - 18y + 9 = 0$ in standard form, and find the center, vertices, and foci.

Solution To complete the squares, begin by factoring out the coefficients of the second-degree terms:

$$16(x^2 - 6x) + 9(y^2 - 2y) = -9$$

Now complete the square inside each pair of parentheses, remembering that adding 9 inside the first pair actually adds $16(9) = 144$ to the whole left-hand side.

$$16(x^2 - 6x + 9) + 9(y^2 - 2y + 1) = -9 + 144 + 9$$
$$16(x - 3)^2 + 9(y - 1)^2 = 144$$
$$\frac{(x - 3)^2}{3^2} + \frac{(y - 1)^2}{4^2} = 1 \qquad \text{dividing by 144}$$

Consequently, the center is at $(3, 1)$, $a = 4$, $b = 3$, and the axis of symmetry is parallel to the y axis. Using $b^2 = a^2 - c^2$ gives

$$c^2 = a^2 - b^2 = 16 - 9 = 7 \qquad \text{and} \qquad c = \sqrt{7}$$

Therefore the vertices are at

$$(3, 1 \pm 4) \qquad \text{that is } (3, -3) \text{ and } (3, 5)$$

and the foci are at

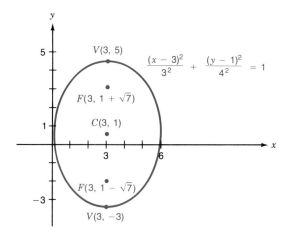

FIGURE 13.10

$$(3, 1 \pm \sqrt{7}) \qquad \text{that is } (3, 1 - \sqrt{7}) \text{ and } (3, 1 + \sqrt{7})$$

See Fig. 13.10. ◀

▶ **EXAMPLE 3** Find an equation of the set of all points such that the sum of the distances of each point from (2, 5) and (2, −3) is 14.

Solution By definition of an ellipse, the given points are the foci, and $2a$ is 14, giving $a = 7$. The center is the midpoint of the line segment joining the foci, namely, (2, 1). Since $2c = 5 - (-3) = 8$, we have $c = 4$. Thus $b^2 = 7^2 - 4^2 = 49 - 16 = 33$, and the equation is

$$\frac{(y - 1)^2}{49} + \frac{(x - 2)^2}{33} = 1 \qquad ◀$$

Circles   For an ellipse, $a > b$. The standard equation of a circle can be found by letting b approach a in the standard equation of an ellipse. Remember that $a^2 = b^2 + c^2$. In fact if b approaches a, then c will approach 0 and the two foci will approach a common point. This point is the center of a circle whose center is (h, k) and radius is a:

$$(x - h)^2 + (y - k)^2 = a^2$$

A **latus rectum,** or **focal chord,** of an ellipse is a chord that passes through a focus and is perpendicular to the major axis. Hence in the ellipse determined by Eq. (13.4), whose major axis is parallel to the x axis, a focal chord passes through the focus $(h + c, k)$. Thus we replace x by $h + c$ in Eq. (13.4) and solve for y:

$$\frac{(h + c - h)^2}{a^2} + \frac{(y - k)^2}{b^2} = 1$$

$$\frac{(y - k)^2}{b^2} = 1 - \frac{c^2}{a^2} = \frac{a^2 - c^2}{a^2} = \frac{b^2}{a^2}$$

$$(y - k)^2 = \frac{b^4}{a^2} \qquad \text{and hence} \qquad y = k \pm \frac{b^2}{a}$$

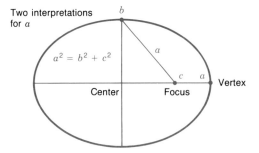

Two interpretations for a

$a^2 = b^2 + c^2$

Center   Focus   Vertex

FIGURE 13.11

So the coordinates of the endpoints of one of the focal chords are $(h + c, k \pm b^2/a)$, and it follows that

The length of a focal chord is $\dfrac{2b^2}{a}$

An ellipse may be drawn on a piece of paper easily with a piece of string and two tacks or pins. Use the tacks to fasten the ends of the string to the paper, and then use the pencil point to pull the string tight. Now move the pencil point, always keeping the string tight. The length of the string is the constant $2a$ in the definition of an ellipse, and the pencil point at P traces out an ellipse. See Fig. 13.8.

In Fig. 13.11, there are two geometric interpretations for the constant a. Recall that $2a$ was the constant in the definition of an ellipse, and that a occurs in the standard forms of the equation of an ellipse. The number a is the distance

From the center to either vertex, and also
from either focus to the end of the semiminor axis

The first statement follows most easily from the standard form. For the second one, use the relation $a^2 = b^2 + c^2$.

Reflection property

Every ellipse enjoys a remarkable **reflection property.** Suppose a ray of light, for instance, starts at one focus and goes in a straight line toward any point on the ellipse. The ray will bounce off the ellipse as though it were bouncing off the tangent line to the ellipse at that point. It will then travel in another straight line, always in a direction which will take it through the other focus. See Fig. 13.12.

This reflection property is the basis for the recent ''ultrasound'' method for

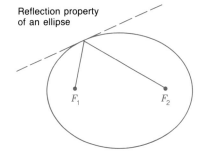

Reflection property of an ellipse

F_1 F_2

FIGURE 13.12

dissolving kidney stones. A tub is made by revolving an ellipse about its major axis. The patient is placed in the tub so that the kidney stone is at one focus. A vibration source is placed at the other focus. When the vibrator is turned on, all of the vibrations are reflected off the walls of the tub and concentrated at the kidney stone. The stone is broken up by the vibrations.

Summary

In the standard forms, $a^2 > b^2$.
The center, foci, and vertices are all on the major axis.
If a^2 is under $(x - h)^2$, the major axis is parallel to the x axis.
If a^2 is under $(y - k)^2$, the major axis is parallel to the y axis.
$b^2 = a^2 - c^2$.
The distance from the center to each vertex is a.
The distance from the center to each focus is c.

EXERCISE 13.2

Sketch the ellipse whose equation is given in each of Probs. 1 to 8 after finding the coordinates of the center, foci, and vertices.

1. $\dfrac{(x - 2)^2}{5^2} + \dfrac{(y + 1)^2}{3^2} = 1$

2. $\dfrac{(x + 5)^2}{5^2} + \dfrac{(y - 3)^2}{4^2} = 1$

3. $\dfrac{(y + 3)^2}{13^2} + \dfrac{(x + 2)^2}{5^2} = 1$

4. $\dfrac{(y - 1)^2}{17^2} + \dfrac{(x - 2)^2}{8^2} = 1$

5. $\dfrac{(y - 2)^2}{25^2} + \dfrac{(x + 1)^2}{24^2} = 1$

6. $\dfrac{(y + 4)^2}{5^2} + \dfrac{(x - 2)^2}{4^2} = 1$

7. $\dfrac{(x + 1)^2}{13^2} + \dfrac{(y - 2)^2}{12^2} = 1$

8. $\dfrac{(x - 3)^2}{5^2} + \dfrac{(y - 2)^2}{3^2} = 1$

Find the standard form of the equation of each ellipse described in Probs. 9 to 24.

9. Major axis parallel to the x axis, center at $(3, 2)$, $a = 5$, $b = 4$.

10. Major axis parallel to the x axis, center at $(-1, 4)$, $a = 17$, $b = 15$.

11. Major axis parallel to the y axis, center at $(5, -3)$, $a = 13$, $b = 12$.

12. Major axis parallel to the y axis, center at $(-2, -6)$, $a = 5$, $b = 3$.

13. Center at $(-1, 1)$, a focus at $(3, 1)$, a vertex at $(4, 1)$.

14. Center at $(1, -1)$, a focus at $(1, 7)$, a vertex at $(1, 16)$.

15. Center at $(4, 0)$, a focus at $(4, 5)$, a vertex at $(4, -13)$.

16. Center at $(3, -2)$, a focus at $(7, -2)$, a vertex at $(-2, -2)$.

17. Vertices at $(-1, 1)$ and $(9, 1)$, a focus at $(4 - \sqrt{21}, 1)$.

18. Vertices at $(-2, -6)$ and $(-2, 8)$, a focus at $(-2, 1 - \sqrt{13})$.

19. Foci at $(2, -2 - \sqrt{17})$ and $(2, -2 + \sqrt{17})$, a vertex at $(2, 7)$.

20. Foci at $(-\sqrt{11}, 5)$ and $(\sqrt{11}, 5)$, a vertex at $(6, 5)$.

21. Ends of the minor axis at $(-4, 3)$ and $(6, 3)$, a vertex at $(1, 10)$.

22. Ends of the minor axis at $(5, -2)$ and $(1, -2)$, a vertex at $(3, 3)$.

23. A vertex at $(3, 2)$, a focus at $(7 + \sqrt{7}, 2)$, an end of the minor axis at $(7, -1)$. *Hint:* First find the coordinates of the center.

24. A vertex at $(0, 2)$, a focus at $(-7 + 2\sqrt{6}, 2)$, an end of the minor axis at $(-7, -3)$. *Hint:* First find the coordinates of the center.

Find an equation that is satisfied by the points described in each of Probs. 25 to 32.

25. The distance of each point from (6, 0) is one-half its distance from the y axis.
26. The distance of each point from (0, 7) is two-fifths its distance from the x axis.
27. The distance of each point from (3, −5) is three-fourths its distance from $y = 1$.
28. The distance of each point from (4, 6) is three-sevenths its distance from $x = -3$.
29. The sum of the distances of each point from (4, 7) and (4, 10) is 9.
30. The sum of the distances of each point from (5, 9) and (2, 9) is 4.
31. The sum of the distances of each point from (1, 3) and (4, 4) is 5.
32. The sum of the distances of each point from (−1, 6) and (2, −1) is 8.

Put the equation in each of Probs. 33 to 40 in standard form and find the center, vertices, and foci.
33. $9x^2 + 4y^2 - 36x - 8y + 4 = 0$
34. $9x^2 + 16y^2 + 54x - 64y + 1 = 0$
35. $9x^2 + 4y^2 + 18x - 32y + 37 = 0$
36. $16x^2 + 4y^2 + 32x + 16y - 32 = 0$
37. $9x^2 + 25y^2 - 18x + 100y = 116$
38. $16x^2 + 25y^2 + 64x - 50y = 311$
39. $169x^2 + 144y^2 + 676x - 864y = 22{,}364$
40. $169x^2 + 25y^2 - 676x + 100y = 3449$

13.3 Hyperbolas

As indicated in Fig. 13.1d, the hyperbola is obtained by cutting a right circular cone by a plane that cuts both nappes, or halves, of the cone. In addition to this geometric picture, we give an algebraic definition below:

Definition of a hyperbola

A **hyperbola** is the set of all points in a plane such that the difference of the distances of each from two fixed points is a constant. The fixed points are called the **foci** and the line through them is the **axis of symmetry.**

For the hyperbola the *difference* of the distances is used, while the *sum* is used for the ellipse.

To find the equation of a hyperbola, we shall choose the position of the coordinate axes so that the two foci are at

$$F_1(h - c, k) \qquad \text{and} \qquad F_2(h + c, k)$$

as shown in Fig. 13.13. If we let $P(x, y)$ be any point on the hyperbola, and $2a$ be the difference of its distances from the foci, then the definition of a hyperbola can be written

$$F_1 P - F_2 P = \pm 2a \qquad \qquad \text{1)}$$

We shall now express these equations in terms of x, y, and the constants a, c, h, k by the procedure below:

$$F_1 P = \pm 2a + F_2 P \qquad \text{Eq. (1)}$$

Now the distance formula with the coordinates for P, F_1, and F_2 gives the equation

$$\sqrt{[x - (h - c)]^2 + (y - k)^2} = \pm 2a + \sqrt{[x - (h + c)]^2 + (y - k)^2}$$

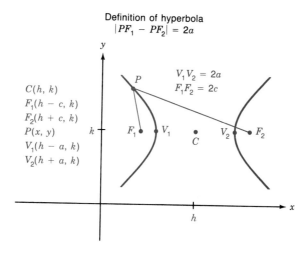

Definition of hyperbola
$|PF_1 - PF_2| = 2a$

$C(h, k)$
$F_1(h - c, k)$
$F_2(h + c, k)$
$P(x, y)$
$V_1(h - a, k)$
$V_2(h + a, k)$

$V_1V_2 = 2a$
$F_1F_2 = 2c$

FIGURE 13.13

We can simplify this as we did with the ellipse by squaring, combining similar terms, isolating the radical, and squaring again. This will eliminate the $\pm$ sign, and yield the equation

$$\frac{(x - h)^2}{a^2} - \frac{(y - k)^2}{c^2 - a^2} = 1$$

For the hyperbola, $c > a$. In fact, using the triangle inequality with the triangle F_1F_2P in Fig. 13.13, we have

$$F_1P + F_1F_2 > F_2P$$

or in other words

$$F_1F_2 > F_2P - F_1P$$

However $F_1F_2 = 2c$ and $F_2P - F_1P = \pm 2a$, which shows that $c > a$. It follows that $c^2 - a^2 > 0$, and we will let

$$b^2 = c^2 - a^2$$

with b positive. We have shown that if (x, y) are the coordinates of a point P on the hyperbola, then (x, y) satisfies the equation

$$\frac{(x - h)^2}{a^2} - \frac{(y - k)^2}{b^2} = 1$$

Reversing the steps would show that if (x, y) satisfies the above equation, then $P(x, y)$ is on the hyperbola.

The ratio c/a is called the **eccentricity** of the hyperbola. The point (h, k), midway between the foci, is called the **center.** The intersection points of a hyperbola and the line through the foci are known as the **vertices.** The line segment joining the vertices is called the **transverse axis.** The line segment of length $2b$, through the center, bisected by and perpendicular to the transverse axis, is called the **conjugate axis.**

a, b, and c

Remember that $c^2 - a^2 = b^2$ for a hyperbola, but $a^2 - c^2 = b^2$ for an ellipse.

*Standard forms of the equations
of the hyperbola*

The equation of the hyperbola with center at (h, k), transverse axis parallel to the x axis, foci at $(h \pm c, k)$, and vertices $(h \pm a, k)$ is

$$\frac{(x - h)^2}{a^2} - \frac{(y - k)^2}{b^2} = 1 \qquad (13.6)$$

It can be shown similarly that

$$\frac{(y - k)^2}{a^2} - \frac{(x - h)^2}{b^2} = 1 \qquad (13.7)$$

is the equation of the hyperbola with center at (h, k), transverse axis parallel to the y axis, foci at $(h, k \pm c)$, and vertices at $(h, k \pm a)$.

Equations (13.6) and (13.7) are called **standard forms** of the equations of the hyperbola.

EXAMPLE 1   Find the equation of the hyperbola with center at $C(3, 4)$, a focus at $F(8, 4)$, and a vertex at $V(6, 4)$.

Solution   With the given data, we must use Eq. (13.6) since the center, vertex, and focus are on a line parallel to the x axis. Furthermore, the distance from the center to a vertex is $a = 6 - 3 = 3$, and the distance from the center to a focus is $c = 8 - 3 = 5$. Now we need to determine b, which can be done by the relation

$$b = \sqrt{c^2 - a^2} \qquad \text{that is} \qquad b = \sqrt{25 - 9} = 4$$

Therefore the desired equation is

$$\frac{(x - 3)^2}{3^2} - \frac{(y - 4)^2}{4^2} = 1$$

See Fig. 13.14.

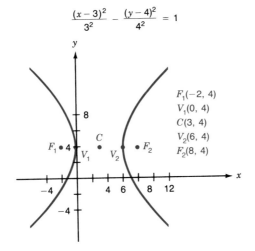

FIGURE 13.14

Notice that $a^2 < b^2$ in Example 1, whereas for every ellipse, $a^2 > b^2$. The relations between a, b, and c for hyperbolas and for ellipses are similar, yet different.

Summary for both hyperbola standard forms

> The center, foci, and vertices are all on the transverse axis.
> a^2 is under the term with the positive sign.
> If a^2 is under $(x - h)^2$, the transverse axis is parallel to the x axis.
> If a^2 is under $(y - k)^2$, the transverse axis is parallel to the y axis.
> $b^2 = c^2 - a^2$.
> The distance from the center (h, k) to each vertex is a.
> The distance from the center (h, k) to each focus is c.

Writing Eq. (13.6) as $(x - h)^2/a^2 = 1 + (y - k)^2/b^2$ shows that $(x - h)^2/a^2 \geq 1$. Thus we must have $|x - h| \geq a$. This means that there are no points on the hyperbola which are between the vertical lines through the vertices. Similar comments apply to Eq. (13.7) and horizontal lines through the vertices. The graph of a hyperbola has two separated, symmetric halves.

The Asymptotes of a Hyperbola

If we solve Eq. (13.6) for $y - k$, we get

$$y - k = \pm \frac{b}{a} \sqrt{(x - h)^2 - a^2}$$

$$= \pm \frac{b}{a}(x - h) \sqrt{1 - \frac{a^2}{(x - h)^2}}$$

by multiplying and dividing the right-hand side by $x - h$. If the value of h is fixed, then $x - h$ becomes increasingly larger as x increases. Hence the value of $a^2/(x - h)^2$ approaches zero as x becomes increasingly larger. Consequently, the radical expression in the last equation approaches 1, and it follows that the hyperbola (13.6) approaches the lines

$$y - k = \pm \frac{b}{a}(x - h) \tag{13.8}$$

as $|x|$ becomes increasingly larger. These lines are called the **asymptotes** of the hyperbola (13.6), and they are of considerable help in sketching the curve.

These equations do not need to be remembered since they can be obtained readily by replacing the 1 in the right-hand side of the standard form by 0, and then solving for $y - k$. The asymptotes of the hyperbola (13.7) can be obtained in a similar manner.

The asymptotes of a hyperbola are two lines which intersect at the center of the hyperbola. Their slopes are

$$\frac{b}{a} \ and \ \frac{-b}{a} \ for \ (13.6) \qquad and \qquad \frac{a}{b} \ and \ \frac{-a}{b} \ for \ (13.7)$$

A simple way to draw the asymptotes if the equation is in standard form is to first draw a rectangle with center (h, k). The four corners of the rectangle are found by

(i)   Starting at the center, go a units to one vertex, then b units in each perpendicular direction.

(ii)   Starting again at the center, go a units to the other vertex, and b units in each perpendicular direction.

The asymptotes are then the lines drawn through opposite corners of the rectangle.

▶ **EXAMPLE 2**   Sketch the graph of

$$\frac{(x - 2)^2}{4^2} - \frac{(y + 1)^2}{3^2} = 1$$

Solution   This equation is in the standard form (13.6). Consequently, the axis of symmetry is parallel to the x axis. Furthermore, the center is at $(2, -1)$ and $a = 4$, $b = 3$. Therefore the vertices are at

$$(2 + 4, -1) = (6, -1) \qquad \text{and} \qquad (2 - 4, -1) = (-2, -1)$$

The ends of the conjugate axes are 3 units above and below the center, at

$$(2, -1 + 3) = (2, 2) \qquad \text{and} \qquad (2, -1 - 3) = (2, -4)$$

To find the foci, we can use the relation

$$c^2 = a^2 + b^2 \qquad \text{that is} \qquad c = \sqrt{16 + 9} = 5$$

Hence the foci are at

$$(2 + 5, -1) = (7, -1) \qquad \text{and} \qquad (2 - 5, -1) = (-3, -1)$$

The equations of the asymptotes are found by solving

$$\frac{(x - 2)^2}{4^2} - \frac{(y + 1)^2}{3^2} = 0$$

for $y + 1$. The solution is $y + 1 = \pm\frac{3}{4}(x - 2)$. The center, vertices, foci, asymptotes, and hyperbola are shown in Fig. 13.15.   ◀

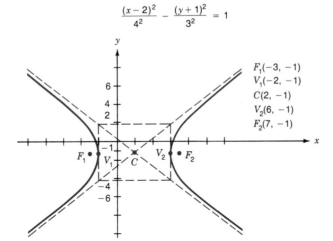

FIGURE 13.15

▶ **EXAMPLE 3** Change $25x^2 - 4y^2 + 50x + 8y + 121 = 0$ to standard form. Find the center, vertices, foci, asymptotes, and sketch the graph.

Solution

$$25x^2 + 50x - 4y^2 + 8y = -121$$

$$25(x^2 + 2x + 1) - 4(y^2 - 2y + 1) = -121 + 25 - 4$$

$$25(x + 1)^2 - 4(y - 1)^2 = -100$$

$$\frac{(y - 1)^2}{25} - \frac{(x + 1)^2}{4} = 1$$

Hence the transverse axis is parallel to the y axis. The center is $(-1, 1)$, and $a = 5$, $b = 2$. The asymptotes are $y - 1 = \pm\frac{5}{2}(x + 1)$. The vertices are

$$(-1, 1 \pm 5) \qquad \text{that is} \qquad (-1, -4) \text{ and } (-1, 6)$$

Since $c^2 = a^2 + b^2 = 25 + 4 = 29$, then $c = \sqrt{29}$ and the foci are

$$(-1, 1 \pm \sqrt{29}) \qquad \text{that is} \qquad (-1, 1 + \sqrt{29}) \text{ and } (-1, 1 - \sqrt{29})$$

The graph is shown in Fig. 13.16. ◀

A **latus rectum,** or **focal chord,** of a hyperbola is a chord passing through a focus and perpendicular to the transverse axis. By solving simultaneously the equation of the line along which the focal chord lies and the equation of the hyperbola, and then

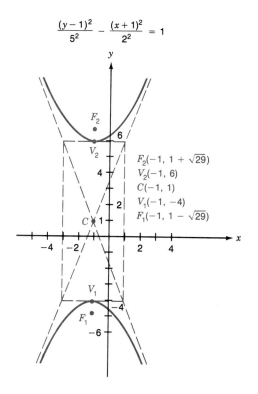

FIGURE 13.16

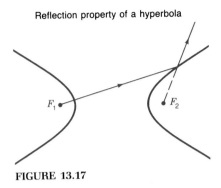

Reflection property of a hyperbola

FIGURE 13.17

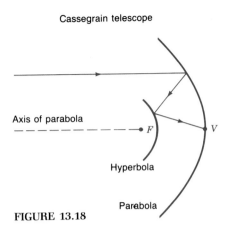

Cassegrain telescope

Axis of parabola

F V

Hyperbola

Parabola

FIGURE 13.18

using the distance formula, we can find that the length of the focal chord is $2b^2/a$. This is the same expression that we found for the length of the focal chord of an ellipse.

Reflection property

Hyperbolas, as well as parabolas and ellipses, have a nice **reflection property.** Suppose a ray of light starts at one focus of a hyperbola, and then goes in a straight line toward any point on the other "half" of the hyperbola. The ray will bounce off the hyperbola as though it were bouncing off the tangent line to the hyperbola at that point. The ray will then travel away from the hyperbola in a line, but that line extended in the opposite direction will pass through the other focus. See Fig. 13.17.

This reflection property of hyperbolas is used in modern navigation devices. Suppose there are two transmitters, each sending out a signal. If you are in a location and receive the signals at slightly different times, these differences determine a hyperbola that you are on. If a third transmitter is added, it can be paired with each of the first two, thereby determining two more hyperbolas on which you lie. The intersection of these three hyperbolas determines your position.

In Fig. 13.18, we show how the reflection properties of parabolas and hyperbolas have been combined to create a Cassegrain telescope. Begin with a parabola, whose vertex is at V and focus at F. Then determine the hyperbola whose two foci are at V and F. Part of one-half of this hyperbola is actually used in the telescope, as in Fig. 13.18. Any light ray coming in parallel to the axis of the parabola will be reflected toward its focus F, by the reflection property of parabolas. But since F and V are also foci of the hyperbola, its reflection property guarantees that the light ray will be reflected off of the hyperbola and toward its focus V. The net effect is that light coming in to the parabola is concentrated at its vertex, not its focus.

EXERCISE 13.3

Sketch the hyperbola whose equation is given in each of Probs. 1 to 8 after finding the coordinates of the center, foci, vertices, and asymptotes.

1. $\dfrac{(x-2)^2}{4^2} - \dfrac{(y+1)^2}{3^2} = 1$

2. $\dfrac{(x+5)^2}{3^2} - \dfrac{(y-3)^2}{4^2} = 1$

3. $\dfrac{(y+3)^2}{12^2} - \dfrac{(x+2)^2}{5^2} = 1$

4. $\dfrac{(y-1)^2}{8^2} - \dfrac{(x-2)^2}{15^2} = 1$

5. $\dfrac{(y-2)^2}{7^2} - \dfrac{(x+1)^2}{24^2} = 1$

6. $\dfrac{(y+4)^2}{3^2} - \dfrac{(x-2)^2}{4^2} = 1$

7. $\dfrac{(x+1)^2}{5^2} - \dfrac{(y-2)^2}{12^2} = 1$

8. $\dfrac{(x-3)^2}{4^2} - \dfrac{(y-2)^2}{3^2} = 1$

Find an equation of the hyperbola described in each of Probs. 9 to 24.

9. Transverse axis parallel to the x axis, center at $(3, 2)$, $a = 3$, $b = 4$

10. Transverse axis parallel to the x axis, center at $(-1, 4)$, $a = 8$, $b = 15$

11. Transverse axis parallel to the y axis, center at $(5, -3)$, $a = 5$, $b = 12$

12. Transverse axis parallel to the y axis, center at $(-2, -6)$, $a = 4$, $b = 3$

13. Center at $(-1, 1)$, a focus at $(4, 1)$, a vertex at $(3, 1)$

14. Center at $(1, -1)$, a focus at $(1, 16)$, a vertex at $(1, 7)$

15. Center at $(4, 0)$, a focus at $(4, 13)$, a vertex at $(4, 5)$

16. Center at $(3, -2)$, a focus at $(8, -2)$, a vertex at $(7, -2)$

17. Vertices at $(9, 1)$ and $(-1, 1)$, a focus at $(4 - \sqrt{29}, 1)$

18. Vertices at $(-2, 8)$ and $(-2, -6)$, a focus at $(-2, 26)$

19. Foci at $(2, -2 + \sqrt{145})$ and $(2, -2 - \sqrt{145})$, a vertex at $(2, 7)$

20. Foci at $(\sqrt{61}, 5)$ and $(-\sqrt{61}), 5)$, a vertex at $(6, 5)$

21. Ends of conjugate axis at $(6, 3)$ and $(-4, 3)$, a vertex at $(1, 10)$

22. Ends of conjugate axis at $(5, -2)$ and $(1, -2)$, a vertex at $(3, 3)$

23. A vertex at $(11, 2)$, a focus at $(12, 2)$, an end of the conjugate axis at $(7, 5)$

24. A vertex at $(0, 2)$, a focus at $(-7 + \sqrt{74}, 2)$, an end of the conjugate axis at $(-7, 7)$

Find an equation that is satisfied by the coordinates of the points in the set described in each of Probs. 25 to 32.

25. The distance of each point from $(1, -3)$ is twice its distance from $y = 3$.

26. The distance of each point from $(6, 2)$ is 1.5 times its distance from $x = 2$.

27. The distance of each point from $(4, -1)$ is four-thirds its distance from $x = 3$.

28. The distance of each point from $(4, 3)$ is five-thirds its distance from $y = -2$.

29. The difference of the distances of each point from $(4, 4)$ and $(4, -2)$ is 2.

30. The difference of the distances of each point from $(2, 6)$ and $(2, 1)$ is 3.

31. The difference of the distances of each point from $(1, 6)$ and $(4, 2)$ is 3.

32. The difference of the distances of each point from $(-2, 6)$ and $(-2, -1)$ is 2.

Change each of the following equations to standard form and find the center, vertices, foci, and asymptotes.

33. $9x^2 - 4y^2 - 36x + 8y - 4 = 0$

34. $9x^2 - 16y^2 + 54x + 64y - 127 = 0$

35. $-9x^2 + 4y^2 - 18x + 32y + 19 = 0$

36. $-16x^2 + 4y^2 - 32x + 16y - 64 = 0$

37. $9x^2 - 64y^2 - 18x - 128y = 631$

38. $16x^2 - 9y^2 + 32x + 18y = 137$

39. $144y^2 - 25x^2 - 100x - 288y = 3556$

40. $25y^2 - 144x^2 + 576x + 100y = 4076$

13.4 Rotation of Axes

We have already treated horizontal and vertical translation of graphs in Chap. 3. Now we shall figure out the effect on an equation of leaving the origin fixed and rotating both axes through the same angle about the origin. If this is done, we say that the axes have been **rotated.**

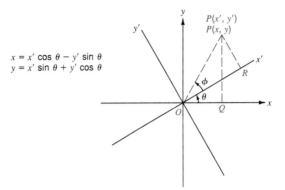

$x = x' \cos \theta - y' \sin \theta$
$y = x' \sin \theta + y' \cos \theta$

FIGURE 13.19

Rotation of axes

If (x, y) are the coordinates of a point before the axes are rotated, and if (x', y') are the coordinates of the same point after the axes are rotated through an angle θ, then

$$x = x' \cos \theta - y' \sin \theta \qquad (13.9)$$

and
$$y = x' \sin \theta + y' \cos \theta \qquad (13.10)$$

In order to show that Eqs. (13.9) and (13.10) are valid, we will use Fig. 13.19. It is constructed by first drawing a pair of coordinate axes labeled x and y, and then drawing a second pair of coordinate axes, called x' and y', with the same origin as the first pair, but making an angle of θ with the first pair. We then select any point P in the plane, and let its coordinates be (x, y) relative to the first pair of axes, and (x', y') relative to the second pair. Now drop perpendiculars from P to the x and x' axes, and call their feet Q and R, respectively. Connect P and O and call the angle ROP ϕ. Then the identity

$$\cos (\phi + \theta) = \cos \phi \cos \theta - \sin \phi \sin \theta$$

for the cosine of the sum of two angles becomes

$$\frac{OQ}{OP} = \frac{OR}{OP} \cos \theta - \frac{RP}{OP} \sin \theta$$

when we use the definitions of the sine and cosine of an angle. Now multiplying by OP, we have

$$OQ = OR \cos \theta - RP \sin \theta$$

Hence

$$x = x' \cos \theta - y' \sin \theta$$

since $OQ = x$, $OR = x'$, and $RP = y'$. This completes the proof of the expression for x. The expression for y can be found similarly by starting with

$$\sin (\phi + \theta) = \sin \phi \cos \theta + \cos \phi \sin \theta$$

Solving Eqs. (13.9) and (13.10) for x' and y' gives the alternative formulas below:

Alternative formulas for rotation of axes

$$x' = x \cos \theta + y \sin \theta \qquad y' = y \cos \theta - x \sin \theta$$

▶ **EXAMPLE 1**   What does the equation $xy - 2 = 0$ become if the axes are rotated through $\pi/4$?

Solution   For $\theta = \pi/4$, the rotation formulas become

$$x = x' \cos \frac{\pi}{4} - y' \sin \frac{\pi}{4} \qquad \text{and} \qquad y = x' \sin \frac{\pi}{4} + y' \cos \frac{\pi}{4}$$

After putting $1/\sqrt{2}$ for $\sin (\pi/4)$ and for $\cos (\pi/4)$, we have

$$x = \frac{x' - y'}{\sqrt{2}} \qquad y = \frac{x' + y'}{\sqrt{2}}$$

If we replace x and y in $xy - 2 = 0$ by these expressions, we get

$$\left(\frac{x' - y'}{\sqrt{2}}\right)\left(\frac{x' + y'}{\sqrt{2}}\right) - 2 = 0$$

This can be put in the form

$$x'^2 - y'^2 - 4 = 0$$

which by Sec. 13.3 is the equation of a hyperbola.   ◀

Simplification by Rotation

The most frequent use of rotation in connection with a quadratic in two variables is to eliminate the term that involves xy. We shall now prove a theorem for use in that connection:

The term that involves xy is eliminated from

$$Ax^2 + Bxy + Cy^2 + Dx + Ey + F = 0$$

if the axes are rotated through an angle θ determined by

$$\cot 2\theta = \frac{A - C}{B} \qquad B \neq 0 \qquad \text{(13.11)}$$

If $B = 0$, no rotation is necessary.

In order to show that the above statement is true, we would begin by putting $x = x' \cos \theta - y' \sin \theta$ and $y = x' \sin \theta + y' \cos \theta$ in the given equation. We will not carry out the details, but if this were done and we then collected the coefficients of $x'y'$, we would see that we need to have

$$B(\cos^2 \theta - \sin^2 \theta) + (C - A)(2 \sin \theta \cos \theta) = 0$$

to be able to eliminate the xy term. Using the identities for the cosine and sine of twice an angle, we can put this equation in the form

$$B \cos 2\theta + (C - A) \sin 2\theta = 0$$

Now dividing by $B \sin 2\theta$, using $(\cos 2\theta)/(\sin 2\theta) = \cot 2\theta$, and solving for $\cot 2\theta$ gives

$$\cot 2\theta = \frac{A - C}{B}$$

in order to eliminate the xy term as stated above. If $B = 0$, there is no xy term to eliminate.

There are infinitely many angles which satisfy the equation $\cot (2\theta) = (A - C)/B$, and any one of them enables us to eliminate the product term. Normally we will choose the smallest possible positive angle. Hence we ordinarily rotate the axes through a positive acute angle θ since **there is always an angle θ between 0 and $\pi/2$** which satisfies Eq. (13.11). Note that $0 < \theta < \pi/2$ if and only if

$$0 < 2\theta < \pi, \text{ and the cotangent function has period } \pi$$

Although Eq. (13.11) gives the value of $\cot 2\theta$, we must have the exact values of $\sin \theta$ and of $\cos \theta$ to apply the rotation formulas. These can be found from the equation

$$\cot 2\theta = \frac{1 - \tan^2 \theta}{2 \tan \theta} \tag{1}$$

This identity enables us to find $\tan \theta$ if $\cot 2\theta$ is known. Then a right triangle can be used to find $\sin \theta$ and $\cos \theta$ after $\tan \theta$ is determined. This is done in Example 2 below.

Another way to find $\sin \theta$ and $\cos \theta$ is to first find $\cos 2\theta$ from $\cot 2\theta$ by using a right triangle, and then use

$$\cos^2 \theta = \frac{1 + \cos 2\theta}{2} \qquad \text{and} \qquad \sin^2 \theta = \frac{1 - \cos 2\theta}{2}$$

to find $\cos \theta$ and $\sin \theta$.

EXAMPLE 2 Find the sine and cosine of the angle θ through which the axes must be rotated to eliminate the product term from

$$9x^2 + 24xy + 2y^2 - 3 = 0$$

and then obtain the transformed equation.

Solution We have to rotate the axes through an angle θ determined by

$$\cot 2\theta = \frac{A - C}{B} = \frac{9 - 2}{24} = \frac{7}{24}$$

Consequently, by the identity in Eq. (1), we have

$$\frac{1 - \tan^2 \theta}{2 \tan \theta} = \frac{7}{24}$$

$12 - 12 \tan^2 \theta = 7 \tan \theta \qquad$ multiplying by 24 tan θ

$12 \tan^2 \theta + 7 \tan \theta - 12 = 0 \qquad$ adding $-7 \tan \theta$

$(4 \tan \theta - 3)(3 \tan \theta + 4) = 0 \qquad$ factoring

Therefore tan θ is $\frac{3}{4}$ or $-\frac{4}{3}$, and we will use tan $\theta = \frac{3}{4}$ since we want to rotate through a positive acute angle. Note that

$$\theta = \tan^{-1} \tfrac{3}{4} \approx 36.9°$$

We have the exact values sin $\theta = \frac{3}{5}$ and cos $\theta = \frac{4}{5}$, and hence the rotation formulas are

$$x = \frac{4x' - 3y'}{5} \qquad \text{and} \qquad y = \frac{3x' + 4y'}{5}$$

We now substitute these expressions for x and y in

$$9x^2 + 24xy + 2y^2 - 3 = 0$$

$$9\left(\frac{4x' - 3y'}{5}\right)^2 + 24\left(\frac{4x' - 3y'}{5}\right)\left(\frac{3x' + 4y'}{5}\right) + 2\left(\frac{3x' + 4y'}{5}\right)^2 - 3 = 0$$

If we perform the indicated operations in this equation and combine similar terms, we have

$$x'^2\left(\frac{144 + 288 + 18}{25}\right) + x'y'\left(\frac{-216 + 168 + 48}{25}\right)$$

$$+ y'^2\left(\frac{81 - 288 + 32}{25}\right) - 3 = 0$$

which becomes $\qquad 18x'^2 - 7y'^2 - 3 = 0$

This shows that the graph is a hyperbola. Its standard form is

$$\frac{x'^2}{\frac{1}{6}} - \frac{y'^2}{\frac{3}{7}} = 1$$

See Fig. 13.20. ◢

Types of Conic from the Discriminant

It can be shown that if

$$Ax^2 + Bxy + Cy^2 + Dx + Ey + F = 0$$

becomes $\qquad A'x^2 + B'xy + C'y^2 + D'x + E'y + F' = 0$

as a result of replacing x and y by their values from the rotation formulas, then

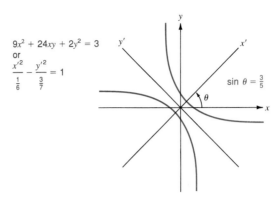

$9x^2 + 24xy + 2y^2 = 3$
or
$\dfrac{x'^2}{\frac{1}{6}} - \dfrac{y'^2}{\frac{3}{7}} = 1$

$\sin \theta = \frac{3}{5}$

FIGURE 13.20

$$A' = A \cos^2 \theta + B \sin \theta \cos \theta + C \sin^2 \theta$$
$$B' = -2A \sin \theta \cos \theta + B \cos^2 \theta - B \sin^2 \theta + 2C \sin \theta \cos \theta$$
$$C' = A \sin^2 \theta - B \sin \theta \cos \theta + C \cos^2 \theta$$
$$D' = D \cos \theta + E \sin \theta$$
$$E' = -D \sin \theta + E \cos \theta$$

Straightforward but lengthy calculations would show that

$$B^2 - 4AC = B'^2 - 4A'C' \tag{2}$$

This is described by saying that $B^2 - 4AC$ is invariant under a rotation.

EXAMPLE 3   Show that Eq. (2) above holds for the equation $9x^2 + 24xy + 2y^2 = 3$ of Example 2.

Solution   We found in Example 2 that $9x^2 + 24xy + 2y^2 = 3$ becomes

$$18x'^2 - 7y'^2 = 3$$

after eliminating the product term. Therefore

$$B^2 - 4AC = 24^2 - 4(9)2 = 576 - 72 = 504$$

and $$B'^2 - 4A'C' = 0^2 - 4(18)(-7) = 504$$

and so Eq. (2) does hold.

The standard forms show that the equation

$$Ax^2 + Cy^2 + Dx + Ey + F = 0$$

except for degenerate cases, represents

An ellipse if A and C have the same sign, or	$-4AC < 0$
A parabola if A or C, but not both, is 0, or	$-4AC = 0$
A hyperbola if A and C have opposite signs, or	$-4AC > 0$

By rotating the axes and making $B' = 0$, we will have

$$B^2 - 4AC = B'^2 - 4A'C' = -4A'C'$$

Applying the results above shows that a conic is

Classification of conics

An ellipse if $B^2 - 4AC < 0$
A parabola if $B^2 - 4AC = 0$
A hyperbola if $B^2 - 4AC > 0$

For this reason, the expression $B^2 - 4AC$ is called the **discriminant** of the general second-degree equation

$$Ax^2 + Bxy + Cy^2 + Dx + Ey + F = 0$$

▶ **EXAMPLE 4** What type of conic is represented by
(a) $5x^2 - 9xy + 5y^2 = 123$?
(b) $5x^2 - 10xy + 5y^2 = 456$?
(c) $5x^2 - 11xy + 5y^2 = 789$?

Solution We shall evaluate $B^2 - 4AC$ since its value determines the type of conic.
(a) An ellipse since $B^2 - 4AC = (-9)^2 - 4(5)5 = -19 < 0$
(b) A parabola since $B^2 - 4AC = (-10)^2 - 4(5)5 = 0$
(c) A hyperbola since $B^2 - 4AC = (-11)^2 - 4(5)5 = 21 > 0$ ◀

EXERCISE 13.4

Find the equation into which the one given in each of Probs. 1 to 8 is transformed if the axes are rotated through the given angle.

1. $x^2 + 2\sqrt{3}xy - y^2 = 2$, 30° or $\pi/6$
2. $x^2 + 2\sqrt{3}xy - y^2 = 2$, 120° or $2\pi/3$
3. $16x^2 + 24xy + 9y^2 = 3$, θ an acute angle whose sine is 0.6
4. $2x^2 - 3\sqrt{3}xy - y^2 = 5$, θ an acute angle whose cosine is 0.5
5. $2x^2 + \sqrt{3}xy + y^2 = 5$, 60° or $\pi/3$
6. $2x^2 + \sqrt{3}xy - y^2 = 5$, 150° or $5\pi/6$
7. $16x^2 + 24xy + 9y^2 = 3$, $\sin\theta = \frac{3}{5}$ and θ in quadrant II
8. $2x^2 - 3\sqrt{3}xy + y^2 = 5$, $\cos\theta = -\frac{1}{2}$ and θ in quadrant II

Find the sine and the cosine of the smallest positive angle through which the axes can be rotated so as to eliminate the xy term in each of Probs. 9 to 20.

9. $7x^2 - 6xy - y^2 = 3$
10. $5x^2 + 2\sqrt{3}xy + 3y^2 = 7$
11. $9x^2 - 7\sqrt{3}xy + 2y^2 = 2$
12. $-5x^2 + 24xy - 12y^2 = 5$
13. $19x^2 + 24xy + 12y^2 = 47$
14. $37x^2 + 35xy + 25y^2 = 31$
15. $43x^2 + 72xy - 22y^2 = 11$

16. $x^2 + 336xy + y^2 = 17$
17. $2x^2 + 24xy - 5y^2 = 9$
18. $x^2 + 24xy - 6y^2 = 5$
19. $xy = 9$
20. $x^2 - 4xy - 2y^2 = 3$

Remove the product term in each of Probs. 21 to 24 by rotating the axes.

21. $x^2 + 2xy + y^2 - 8\sqrt{2}x + 8 = 0$
22. $41x^2 + 24xy + 34y^2 + 25x + 50y - 25 = 0$
23. $31x^2 + 10\sqrt{3}xy + 21y^2 - 144 = 0$
24. $3x^2 - 8xy - 3y^2 - 2\sqrt{5}x - 4\sqrt{5} = 0$

Determine the type of conic represented by each of the following equations by using the discriminant. Remove the product term by means of rotation.

25. $x^2 + 2xy + y^2 - 4\sqrt{2}x - 2\sqrt{2}y + 2 = 0$
26. $2x^2 + 24xy - 5y^2 + 3x - y - 9 = 0$
27. $xy = a^2$
28. $3x^2 - 2xy + 3y^2 - 7 = 0$
29. $2x^2 + 7xy - 22y^2 + 14 = 0$
30. $14x^2 - 7xy - 10y^2 - 1 = 0$
31. $2x^2 + 24xy - 5y^2 - 4x + 2y + 2 = 0$
32. $17x^2 + 8xy + 2y^2 - 5 = 0$

Use $Ax^2 + Bxy + Cy^2 + Dx + Ey + F = 0$ in Probs. 33 to 36.

33. Prove that $B^2 - 4AC$ is unchanged by a rotation.
34. Prove that $A - C + F$ is unchanged by a rotation.
35. Prove that $B^2 - 4AC$ is unchanged by a translation.
36. Prove that if $A = C$, then the product term can be eliminated by rotating through $\pi/4$.

In Probs. 37 to 40, two foci are given for an ellipse, along with the constant sum $2a$ from the definition. (a) Write the equation of the ellipse using the definition; this will have the sum of two radicals equal to $2a$.

(b) Rewrite the equation in the form

$$Ax^2 + Bxy + Cy^2 + Dx + Ey + F = 0$$

by isolating a radical, squaring, collecting terms, and repeating if necessary.
(c) Find the value of $B^2 - 4AC$ (it should be negative).
37. $F_1 = (2, 0),\ F_2 = (0, 2),\ 2a = 3$
38. $F_1 = (1, 0),\ F_2 = (0, -1),\ 2a = 2$
39. $F_1 = (4, 4),\ F_2 = (1, 1),\ 2a = 5$
40. $F_1 = (1, -2),\ F_2 = (3, 0),\ 2a = 4$

13.5   Polar Equations of Conics

In order to derive the polar form of the equation of a conic, we will use the concept of eccentricity defined below. This concept allows us to give one definition of conics which includes all three basic cases.

Ellipses, parabolas, and hyperbolas

Note that the symbol e used in the definition below may be any *positive real number;* in particular it is not the base of natural logarithms.

Alternative definition of conics

Let the **focus** F be a given point, and the **directrix** D be a given line. The set of points P in a plane such that

$$\frac{PF}{PD} = e$$

is called a **conic.** The number e may have any positive value.

The definition is illustrated in Fig. 13.21. We will not do so, but it can be shown that this definition and the one (about two foci) given earlier in this chapter are equivalent. The constant e is called the **eccentricity** of the conic. Furthermore, the type of conic depends solely on the value of e.

If $0 < e < 1$, the conic is an ellipse.
If $e = 1$, the conic is a parabola.
If $e > 1$, the conic is a hyperbola.

It can be shown that

NOTE

$$e = \frac{c}{a}$$

for any hyperbola, and also for any ellipse.

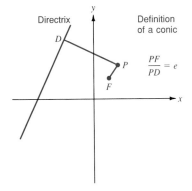

FIGURE 13.21

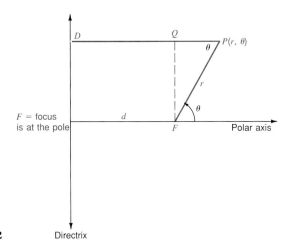

FIGURE 13.22

In deriving the equation of a conic, we shall choose the pole as a focus, and choose a line perpendicular to the polar axis and d units to the left of the pole as the directrix. This is shown in Fig. 13.22.

Now, applying the definition above, we get

$$FP = eDP$$
$$r = e(DQ + QP)$$
$$= e(d + r \cos \theta)$$

since $DQ = d$ and $\cos FPQ = \cos \theta = QP/r$. Solving this equation for r gives the standard polar form of the equation of a conic:

$$r = \frac{de}{1 - e \cos \theta} \tag{13.12}$$

is the standard polar form of the equation of the noncircular conic with eccentricity e, a focus at the pole, and corresponding directrix perpendicular to the polar axis and d units to the left of the pole. Similarly

$$r = \frac{de}{1 + e \cos \theta} \tag{13.13}$$

is the equation of the noncircular conic with eccentricity e, a focus at the pole, and corresponding directrix perpendicular to the polar axis and d units to the right of the pole.

Furthermore, it can be shown that

$$r = \frac{de}{1 - e \sin \theta} \quad \text{or} \quad r = \frac{de}{1 + e \sin \theta} \tag{13.14}$$

is the equation of the noncircular conic with eccentricity e, a focus at the pole, and corresponding directrix perpendicular to the normal axis and d units below or above the pole.

► **EXAMPLE 1**   Identify the type of conic if

(a) $r = \dfrac{7}{1 - 6 \cos \theta}$ (b) $r = \dfrac{11}{1 - \sin \theta}$

Solution   Since the constant in the denominator in each case is 1, we can tell immediately from the standard forms that

   (a) represents a hyperbola since $e = 6 > 1$

   (b) is a parabola since the coefficient of $\sin \theta$ is $e = 1$ ◄

► **EXAMPLE 2**   Identify and sketch the graph of

$$r = \frac{4}{3 - \sin \theta}$$

Solution   We begin by dividing numerator and denominator by 3 since, in standard form, the constant in the denominator must be 1. Thus, we get

$$r = \frac{\frac{4}{3}}{1 - \frac{1}{3} \sin \theta}$$

Now, by comparing this with the standard form, we see that $e = \frac{1}{3}$ and $d = 4$. Hence the graph is an ellipse with a focus at the pole and corresponding directrix 4 units below the pole. The major axis of the ellipse is perpendicular to the polar axis. By substitution we find that the points

$$(\tfrac{4}{3}, 0) \qquad (2, \pi/2) \qquad (\tfrac{4}{3}, \pi) \qquad (1, 3\pi/2)$$

are on the ellipse, and thus the two vertices are at $(2, \pi/2)$ and $(1, 3\pi/2)$. Since one of these is above the pole and the other below, we have $2a = 2 + 1 = 3$ and so $a = \frac{3}{2}$. Knowing the two vertices shows that the center is at $(\frac{1}{2}, \pi/2)$. Furthermore, $e = c/a$ gives $c = ae = (\frac{3}{2})(\frac{1}{3}) = \frac{1}{2}$. Thus the foci are at $(\frac{1}{2} \pm \frac{1}{2}, \pi/2)$, and these points are $(1, \pi/2)$ and $(0, \pi/2)$, verifying that one focus is indeed at the pole. See Fig. 13.23.

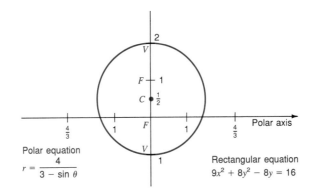

FIGURE 13.23

Changing the given equation from polar form to rectangular form also shows that we have an ellipse. In fact

$$r = \frac{4}{3 - \sin \theta}$$

$$3r - r \sin \theta = 4 \qquad \text{multiplying by the denominator}$$

$$3r = 4 + r \sin \theta = 4 + y$$

$$9r^2 = 16 + 8y + y^2 \qquad \text{squaring}$$

$$9x^2 + 9y^2 = 16 + 8y + y^2$$

$$9x^2 + 8y^2 - 8y = 16 \qquad \text{combining like terms}$$

which is indeed an ellipse in rectangular form. Its standard form is

$$\frac{x^2}{(\sqrt{2})^2} + \frac{(y - \frac{1}{2})^2}{(\frac{3}{2})^2} = 1$$

EXAMPLE 3 Find the equation of the ellipse with eccentricity $\frac{1}{4}$, a focus at the pole, and corresponding directrix perpendicular to the polar axis and 6 units to the right of the pole.

Solution This description fits the conic whose equation is given by (13.13); hence we must use that standard form, namely,

$$r = \frac{de}{1 + e \cos \theta}$$

Furthermore, since $d = 6$, then $de = 6(\frac{1}{4}) = \frac{3}{2}$, and the equation is

$$r = \frac{\frac{3}{2}}{1 + \frac{1}{4} \cos \theta} = \frac{6}{4 + \cos \theta}$$

See Fig. 13.24.

There are also standard forms for the polar equations of a line and a circle. The first merely uses the definition of the cosine of an angle, while the second uses the law of cosines. See Probs. 21 to 28.

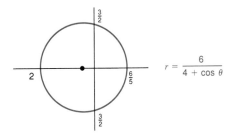

$$r = \frac{6}{4 + \cos \theta}$$

FIGURE 13.24

EXERCISE 13.5

Identify and sketch the conic represented in Probs. 1 to 12.

1. $r = \dfrac{3}{1 + \cos \theta}$

2. $r = \dfrac{2}{1 - \cos \theta}$

3. $r = \dfrac{4}{1 - \sin \theta}$

4. $r = \dfrac{4}{1 + \sin \theta}$

5. $r = \dfrac{4}{3 + \cos \theta}$

6. $r = \dfrac{8}{3 - 2 \sin \theta}$

7. $r = \dfrac{6}{4 + 3 \sin \theta}$

8. $r = \dfrac{2}{2 - \cos \theta}$

9. $r = \dfrac{6}{2 - 3 \sin \theta}$

10. $r = \dfrac{6}{2 + 7 \sin \theta}$

11. $r = \dfrac{10}{2 - 5 \cos \theta}$

12. $r = \dfrac{12}{3 + 4 \cos \theta}$

Write the equation of each conic described in Probs. 13 to 20.

	Focus at	Directrix perpendicular to the	Directrix	Eccentricity
13.	pole	normal axis	4 above pole	1
14.	pole	normal axis	2 above pole	2
15.	pole	polar axis	6 to right of pole	0.5
16.	pole	polar axis	12 to left of pole	1
17.	pole	polar axis	4 to left of pole	3
18.	pole	polar axis	10 to right of pole	0.2
19.	pole	normal axis	8 below pole	1.5
20.	pole	normal axis	4 below pole	0.75

For a given line L, let ON be the perpendicular line segment from the pole O to L. Suppose that the length of ON is p, and that the angle from the polar axis to ON is ϕ. See Fig. 13.25. Then the polar form of the equation of the line L is

$$r \cos(\theta - \phi) = p$$

The rectangular form is $x \cos \phi + y \sin \phi = p$. Write the polar form of the equations of the lines described in Probs. 21 to 24.

21. $\phi = \pi/3$, $p = 5$ **22.** $\phi = 2\pi/3$, $p = 3$

23. $\phi = 5\pi/4$, $p = 8$ **24.** $\phi = 3\pi/4$, $p = 6$

Suppose that a given circle has radius a and center (R, ϕ), as in Fig. 13.26. Then the law of cosines shows that its polar equation is

$$a^2 = r^2 + R^2 - 2Rr \cos (\theta - \phi)$$

Some special cases are

$r = \pm a$ if the center is at the origin

$r = \pm 2a \cos \theta$ if the center is on the polar axis (x axis)

$r = \pm 2a \sin \theta$ if the center is on the normal axis (y axis)

Write the polar form of the equations of the circles in each of Probs. 25 to 28.

25. center $= (3, \pi/4)$, radius $= 2$

26. center $= (7, 5\pi/4)$, radius $= 4$

27. center $= (9, 5\pi/3)$, radius $= 1$

28. center $= (5, 4\pi/3)$, radius $= 2$

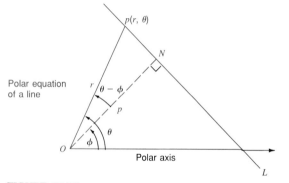

Polar equation of a line

FIGURE 13.25

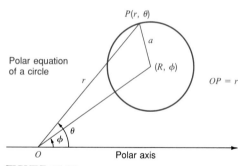

Polar equation of a circle

$OP = r$

FIGURE 13.26

13.6 Key Concepts

You should know the meaning of each term listed below and be able to use each equation.

Parabola (p. 609)
Focus (p. 609)
Directrix (p. 609)
Vertex (pp. 610, 617, 623)
Focal chord (pp. 610, 619, 627)
Ellipse (p. 615)
Major axis (p. 617)
Center (p. 617)
Hyperbola (p. 622)
Asymptote (p. 625)
Rotation of axes (p. 630)
Type of conic from the discriminant $B^2 - 4AC$ (p. 634)
Polar form of conic (p. 636)
Eccentricity (p.636)

(13.4) $(x - h)^2/a^2 + (y - k)^2/b^2 = 1$
(13.5) $(y - k)^2/a^2 + (x - h)^2/b^2 = 1$
(13.6) $(x - h)^2/a^2 - (y - k)^2/b^2 = 1$
(13.7) $(y - k)^2/a^2 - (x - h)^2/b^2 = 1$
(13.8) $y - k = \pm(b/a)(x - h)$
(13.9) $x = x' \cos \theta - y' \sin \theta$
(13.10) $y = x' \sin \theta + y' \cos \theta$
(13.11) $\cot 2\theta = (A - C)/B$

(13.12) $r = \dfrac{de}{1 - e \cos \theta}$

(13.13) $r = \dfrac{de}{1 + e \cos \theta}$

(13.14) $r = \dfrac{de}{1 - e \sin \theta}$

or $r = \dfrac{de}{1 + e \sin \theta}$

(13.1) $(y - k)^2 = 4p(x - h)$
(13.2) $(x - h)^2 = 4p(y - k)$

EXERCISE 13.6 Review

Find the equation of the conic described in Probs. 1 to 18.

1. Parabola with vertex at (4, 2), focus at (6, 2)
2. Parabola with vertex at (4, −1), focus at (4, −2)
3. Parabola with focus at (5, 0) and $y = 4$ as directrix
4. Parabola with vertex at (1, 3) and $x = 5$ as directrix
5. Parabola with the ends of the focal chord at (5, 9) and (5, −7) and vertex at (1, 1)
6. Each point is equidistant from the line $x = -1$ and the point (3, 3)
7. Ellipse with its major axis parallel to the x axis, center at (3, 2), $a = 5$, $b = 3$
8. Ellipse with its major axis parallel to the y axis, center at (3, 2), $a = 5$, $b = 3$
9. Ellipse with center at (1, −2), a focus at (1, 6), and a vertex at (1, 15)
10. Ellipse with vertices at (1, 0) and (11, 0), a focus at $(6 - \sqrt{21}, 0)$

11. Ellipse with ends of the minor axis at (2, 1) and (2, −1), a vertex at (6, 0)
12. Distance of (x, y) from (3, 1) is one-half its distance from the line $y = 7$
13. Transverse axis is parallel to the x axis, center at (2, 3), $a = 4$, $b = 3$
14. Transverse axis parallel to the y axis, center at (1, −2), $a = 3$, $b = 4$
15. Center at (4, −1), a focus at (9, −1), a vertex at (8, −1)
16. Foci at $(\sqrt{38}, 3)$ and $(-\sqrt{38}, 3)$, a vertex at (6, 3)
17. The distance of each point (x, y) from (4, 2) is twice its distance from the line $y = 8$
18. The differences of the distances of (x, y) from (1, 2) and from (1, −4) is 2

Put each equation in Probs. 19, 20, and 21 in standard form.
19. $y^2 - 6y - 2x + 7 = 0$

20. $9x^2 + 16y^2 - 36x - 32y = 92$

21. $9x^2 - 16y^2 - 18x + 64y = 199$

22. Remove the product term from $5x^2 - 8xy - 10y^2 = 17$ by rotation of axes.

23. Remove the product term from $x^2 + 4xy - 2y^2 = 9$ by rotation of axes.

In Probs. 24 to 27, use the discriminant to determine the type of conic represented by the equation.

24. $5x^2 - 6xy - 2y^2 = 6$

25. $9x^2 - 6xy + 4y^2 = 13$

26. $9x^2 - 6xy + y^2 = 6$

27. $xy = -3$

28. Find the equation in polar form of the conic with focus at the pole, directrix perpendicular to the normal axis and 6 units above the pole if the eccentricity is 2.

29. Find the equation in polar form of the conic with focus at the pole, directrix perpendicular to the polar axis and 4 units to the left of the pole if the eccentricity is $\frac{1}{4}$.

In Probs. 30 to 33, draw the graph of each conic.

30. $r = \dfrac{4}{3 - 5 \cos \theta}$

31. $r = \dfrac{3}{2 + 2 \sin \theta}$

32. $r = \dfrac{1}{4 + \cos \theta}$

33. $r = \dfrac{2}{5 - 2 \sin \theta}$

Appendixes

I Interpolation, Tables, and Calculators

Table A.1 gives the values of the mantissa of $\log x$, which have been rounded off to four decimal places, for values of x from 1.00 to 9.99. Table A.2 gives decimal approximations for e^x, e^{-x}, and $\ln x$ for certain values of x, and it is less extensive than Table A.1. In Chap. 5, we have already seen how to find values in the tables, but we will briefly review it here. Then we will see how to use interpolation to find approximations to values not in the tables. We also include some comments on the use of calculators.

To find $\log 328$ by Table A.1, find 32 in the left-hand column, then find 8 in the top row. The number at the intersection of this column and row is 5159, and it is the mantissa without its decimal point. Thus

$$\log 328 = \text{mantissa} + \text{characteristic}$$

$$= 0.5159 + 2 = 2.5159$$

Similarly, $\log 328{,}000 = 0.5159 + 5 = 5.5159$.

To use Table A.2 is even easier because there is no mantissa or characteristic to worry about when finding e^x, e^{-x}, and $\ln x$. Just read the value directly from the table.

643

FIGURE A.1 $y = \log x$ and straight line joining two points

$$e^{0.16} = 1.1735 \qquad e^{-0.16} = 0.8521 \qquad \ln 0.16 = -1.8326$$

$$e^{1.40} = 4.0552 \qquad e^{-1.40} = 0.2466 \qquad \ln 1.40 = 0.3365$$

Calculators also give good approximations for these values, and the values of x are not limited to three digits. For instance

$$\log 21.4407 = 1.331239 \qquad \ln 8.884422 = 2.184299$$

$$e^{2.998765} = 20.060747 \qquad e^{-0.643991} = 0.525192$$

If a number x is not in the table, we may approximate $\log x$ in two ways. The first way is by using the closest value in the table. For instance, $\log 336.8$ is closest to $\log 337$, whose value is 2.5276. However we will get a better approximation if we use a procedure known as **linear interpolation.** This term is used because the method is based on replacing a small part of the graph of $y = \log x$ by a straight line. See Fig. A.1.

▶ EXAMPLE 1   Use interpolation to find an approximation to $\log 59.56$.

Solution   If we are asked to find $\log 59.56$ directly from the table, we cannot do it since there are four significant digits in 59.56. However since $f(x) = \log x$ is increasing, we know that

$$\log 59.50 < \log 59.56 < \log 59.60$$

Furthermore, since 59.56 is $\frac{6}{10}$ of the way from 59.50 to 59.60, we will assume that $\log 59.56$ is also $\frac{6}{10}$ of the way from $\log 59.50$ to $\log 59.60$, that is, $\frac{6}{10}$ of the way from 1.7745 to 1.7752. Now to four decimal places

$$\tfrac{6}{10}(1.7752 - 1.7745) = \tfrac{6}{10}(0.0007) \approx 0.0004$$

Therefore we have

$$\log 59.56 \approx \log 59.50 + 0.0004 \approx 1.7745 + 0.0004 \approx 1.7749$$

This work is summarized in the following format:

$$0.10 \left[0.06 \left[\begin{array}{cc} x & \log x \\ \overline{59.50} & \overline{1.7745} \\ 59.56 & \end{array} \right] d \\ 59.60 \quad 1.7752 \end{array} \right] 0.0007$$

$$\frac{0.06}{0.10} = \frac{d}{0.0007} \qquad d = \left(\frac{6}{10}\right)(0.0007) \approx 0.0004$$

Then as above,

$$\log 59.56 \approx \log 59.50 + d \approx 1.7745 + 0.0004 \approx 1.7749 \qquad \blacktriangleleft$$

We may use interpolation for any of the tables, and in the next example we do so for the ln x table.

EXAMPLE 2 Find an approximation to ln 2.13 by interpolation.

Solution Since $f(x) = \ln x$ is increasing, we know that

$$\ln 2.10 < \ln 2.13 < \ln 2.20$$

Therefore ln 2.13 $\approx$ ln 2.10 + d, where d is determined below:

$$0.10 \left[0.03 \left[\begin{array}{cc} x & \ln x \\ \overline{2.10} & \overline{0.7419} \\ 2.13 & \end{array} \right] d \right] 0.0466$$
$$\begin{array}{cc} 2.20 & 0.7885 \end{array}$$

$$\frac{0.03}{0.10} = \frac{d}{0.0466} \qquad d = \left(\frac{3}{10}\right)(0.0466) \approx 0.0140$$

Then as above

$$\ln 2.13 \approx \ln 2.10 + d \approx 0.7419 + 0.0140 = 0.7559 \qquad \blacktriangleleft$$

We may also use interpolation for numbers with negative logarithms.

EXAMPLE 3 Find an approximation to log 0.02844 by interpolation.

Solution Since $f(x) = \log x$ is increasing, we know that

$$\log 0.02840 < \log 0.02844 < \log 0.02850$$

Therefore log 0.02844 $\approx$ log 0.02840 + d, where d is determined below:

$$10 \left[4 \left[\begin{array}{cc} x & \log x \\ \overline{0.02840} & \overline{8.4533 - 10} \\ 0.02844 & \end{array} \right] d \right] 0.0015$$
$$\begin{array}{cc} 0.02850 & 8.4548 - 10 \end{array}$$

For the differences on the left, we wrote 4 and 10 since $\frac{4}{10} = 0.00004/0.00010$:

$$\frac{4}{10} = \frac{d}{0.0015} \qquad d = \frac{4}{10}(0.0015) = 0.0006$$

Then as above

$$\log 0.02844 \approx \log 0.02840 + d$$

$$\approx (8.4533 - 10) + 0.0006 = 8.4539 - 10 \quad \blacktriangleleft$$

We may also use interpolation to find x if $\log x$ is given to four decimal places and the value is not in the table.

▶ EXAMPLE 4   Find x if $\log x = 2.9256$.

Solution   The nearest entries in the table are $\log 842.0 = 2.9253$ and $\log 843.0 = 2.9258$:

$$1.0 \begin{bmatrix} d \begin{bmatrix} \begin{array}{cc} x & \log x \\ \hline 842.0 & 2.9253 \\ & 2.9256 \end{array} \end{bmatrix} 0.0003 \\ \\ 843.0 \quad 2.9258 \end{bmatrix} 0.0005$$

Writing the corresponding ratios gives

$$\frac{d}{1.0} = \frac{0.0003}{0.0005} \qquad d = \frac{3}{5}(1.0) \approx 0.6$$

and thus

$$x \approx 842.0 + d \approx 842.0 + 0.6 = 842.6$$

Remember that if $\log x = 2.9256$, then

$$x = 10^{2.9256} \approx 842.6$$

Sometimes x is called the *antilog* of 2.9265.   ◢

▶ EXAMPLE 5   Find x if $\log x = 9.4835 - 10$.

Solution   The nearest entries in the table are $\log 0.304 = 9.4829 - 10$ and $\log 0.305 = 9.4843 - 10$. Since in equating ratios, we only use the differences in the values of $\log x$, we could write down $9.4835 - 10$, or -0.5165, or even just the mantissa 0.4835. We choose to write the mantissa in order to save space:

$$0.001 \begin{bmatrix} d \begin{bmatrix} \begin{array}{cc} x & \text{mantissa of } \log x \\ \hline 0.304 & 0.4829 \\ & 0.4835 \end{array} \end{bmatrix} 0.0006 \\ \\ 0.305 \quad 0.4843 \end{bmatrix} 0.0014$$

Writing the corresponding ratios gives

$$\frac{d}{0.001} = \frac{0.0006}{0.0014} \qquad d = \frac{6}{14}(0.001) \approx 0.0004$$

and thus $\qquad x \approx 0.304 + d \approx 0.304 + 0.0004 = 0.3044$ ◢

We have done most of our examples with the log x table because results with it are more accurate than with the ln x, e^x, and e^{-x} tables in this book. That is because these last three tables are much shorter than the log x table. One way to alleviate this for the ln x table is to use the change-of-base formula proved in Chap. 5, namely,

$$\ln x = (\ln 10) \cdot \log x \approx 2.3026 \log x$$

For instance, $\qquad \ln 2.13 \approx (2.3026) \log 2.13$

$$\approx (2.3026)(0.3284) \approx 0.756174 \approx 0.7562$$

compared to the value we found in Example 2, ln $2.13 \approx 0.7559$. A calculator gives ln $2.13 \approx 0.756122 \approx 0.7561$.

If we use interpolation with the e^x table when x is 1.36, we get 3.9008 (try it yourself). This result is not very good because this table does not have many entries. However we can get better results by using properties of exponential functions and values actually in the table. For instance

$$e^{1.36} = e^{1.3} \cdot e^{0.06} \approx 3.6693(1.0618) \approx 3.8961$$

A calculator gives $e^{1.36} \approx 3.8962$. Similarly

$$e^{4.87} = e^{4.50} \cdot e^{0.30} \cdot e^{0.07}$$

$$\approx (90.0171)(1.3499)(1.0725) \approx 130.324$$

whereas a calculator gives

$$e^{4.87} \approx 130.321$$

The same method may be used for the e^{-x} table. For instance

$$e^{-0.78} = e^{-0.70} \cdot e^{-0.08} \approx 0.4966(0.9231) \approx 0.4584$$

which agrees with the value from a calculator to four decimal places.

When using interpolation with the trigonometric functions, it is important to know whether the function is increasing or decreasing. This will determine whether to add or subtract the difference we have called d.

▶ **EXAMPLE 6**   Use interpolation to find sin 28.52°.

Solution   The nearest values in the table are sin $28.5° = 0.4772$ and sin $28.6° = 0.4787$. Moreover since $f(x) = \sin x$ is increasing, we know that

$$\sin 28.50° < \sin 28.52° < \sin 28.60°$$

Furthermore, since 28.52 is $\frac{2}{10}$ of the way from 28.50 to 28.60, we will assume that sin 28.52° is also $\frac{2}{10}$ of the way from sin 28.50° to sin 28.60°; that is, $\frac{2}{10}$ of the way from 0.4772 to 0.4787. We will put this information in the usual format.

$$\begin{array}{c} x \qquad \sin x \\ 0.10 \left[0.02 \left[\begin{array}{c} \overline{28.50} \quad \overline{0.4772} \\ 28.52 \end{array} \right] d \right] 0.0015 \\ 28.60 \qquad 0.4787 \end{array}$$

$$\frac{0.02}{0.10} = \frac{d}{0.0015} \qquad d = \left(\frac{2}{10}\right)(0.0015) = 0.0003$$

Now we *add* d since $\sin x$ is increasing,

$$\sin 28.52° \approx \sin 28.50° + d \approx 0.4772 + 0.0003 \approx 0.4775 \qquad \blacktriangleleft$$

The same basic technique would work with the tangent function since it is also increasing in the first quadrant. However, the cosine function is decreasing in the first quadrant, and we must subtract d, as in the next example.

▶ **EXAMPLE 7**   Use interpolation to find $\cos 156.23°$.

Solution   The reference angle is $180° - 156.23° = 23.77°$, and $\cos 156.23° = -\cos 23.77°$. From the table, we find that $\cos 23.7° = 0.9157$ and $\cos 23.8° = 0.9150$. Now since $f(x) = \cos x$ is decreasing, we know that

$$\cos 23.70° > \cos 23.77° > \cos 23.80°$$

Furthermore, 23.77 is $\frac{7}{10}$ of the way from 23.70 to 23.80, and we will assume that $\cos 23.77°$ is also $\frac{7}{10}$ of the way from $\cos 23.70°$ to $\cos 23.80°$; that is, $\frac{7}{10}$ of the way from 0.9157 to 0.9150. We will put this information in the usual format.

$$\begin{array}{c} x \qquad \cos x \\ 0.10 \left[0.07 \left[\begin{array}{c} \overline{23.70} \quad \overline{0.9157} \\ 23.77 \end{array} \right] d \right] 0.0007 \\ 23.80 \qquad 0.9150 \end{array}$$

$$\frac{0.07}{0.10} = \frac{d}{0.0007} \qquad d = \left(\frac{7}{10}\right)(0.0007) \approx 0.0005$$

Now we *subtract* d since $\cos x$ is decreasing.

$$\cos 23.77° \approx \cos 23.70° - d \approx 0.9157 - 0.0005 \approx 0.9152$$

Thus $\cos 156.23° = -\cos 23.77° = -0.9152$.   ◀

▶ **EXAMPLE 8**   Use interpolation to approximate $\tan 0.6713$.

Solution   The angle is in radians, and the nearest values from the table are $\tan 0.6702 = 0.7926$ and $\tan 0.6720 = 0.7954$.

$$\begin{array}{c} x \qquad \tan x \\ 18 \left[11 \left[\begin{array}{c} \overline{0.6702} \quad \overline{0.7926} \\ 0.6713 \end{array} \right] d \right] 0.0028 \\ 0.6720 \qquad 0.7954 \end{array}$$

$$\frac{11}{18} = \frac{d}{0.0028} \qquad d = \left(\frac{11}{18}\right)(0.0028) \approx 0.0017$$

Now we *add d* since tan x is increasing.

$$\tan 0.6713 \approx \tan 0.6702 + d \approx 0.7926 + 0.0017 \approx 0.7943 \qquad \blacktriangleleft$$

We can also use interpolation to find the angle if a function value is given.

EXAMPLE 9   Find x in radians if cos 0.5937, where $0 < x < 2n$.

Solution   We will first find the angle in the first quadrant. From the table, cos 0.9338 = 0.5948 and cos 0.9355 = 0.5934.

$$0.0017 \left[d \left[\begin{array}{cc} x & \cos x \\ \overline{0.9338} & \overline{0.5948} \\ & 0.5937 \end{array} \right] 0.0011 \right] 0.0014$$
$$0.9355 \quad 0.5934$$

Writing the corresponding ratios gives

$$\frac{d}{0.0017} = \frac{0.0011}{0.0014} \qquad d = \left(\frac{11}{14}\right)(0.0017) = 0.0013$$

Although cos x decreases, x increases in the chart above, and so we add d to find the first quadrant angle.

$$x \approx 0.9338 + d \approx 0.9338 + 0.0013 \approx 0.9351$$

There is also a fourth quadrant angle y with cos y = 0.5937. The reference angle of y is x, and

$$y = 2n - x \approx 2(3.1416) - 0.9351 = 5.3481$$

Therefore cos 0.9351 = 0.5937 = cos 5.3481 $\qquad \blacktriangleleft$

EXAMPLE 10   Find x in degrees if sin x = 0.0743, and $0° < x < 360°$.

Solution   From the table, sin 4.2° = 0.0732 and sin 4.3° = 0.0750.

$$0.10° \left[d \left[\begin{array}{cc} x & \sin x \\ \overline{4.20°} & \overline{0.0732} \\ & 0.0743 \end{array} \right] 0.0011 \right] 0.0018$$
$$4.30° \quad 0.0750$$

Writing the corresponding ratios gives

$$\frac{d}{0.10} = \frac{0.0011}{0.0018} \qquad d = \left(\frac{11}{18}\right)(0.10) \approx 0.06$$

From the chart above, we add d to 4.20°. The first quadrant angle is

$$x \approx 4.20° + d \approx 4.20° + 0.06 = 4.26°$$

The second quadrant angle is $180° - 4.26° = 175.74°$. Thus

$$\sin 4.26° = 0.0743 = \sin 175.74°$$ ◢

You must be careful when using a calculator to have it in the right mode for degrees or radians, to use parentheses and the memory if necessary to make sure that the operations are done in the correct order, and to understand the various inverse operations. Sometimes it helps to use the "=" key, if there is one, as an intermediate step to complete a part of the calculation. Here are some calculations which you should verify by actually doing them on a calculator.

$$2.1^3 + 4.3(6.6^2) = 196.569$$

$$\frac{9.7 - 5.5}{2.5 + 3.7} \approx 0.67742$$

$$\sqrt{77(77 - 33)(77 - 56)(77 - 65)} = 924$$

$$\log(18.1^2 + 1) \approx 2.5167$$

$$\frac{\ln 64}{\ln 16} = 1.5$$

$$\sin^2 17.3° + \cos^2 17.3° = 1$$

$$\frac{\sin 23° + \tan 44°}{1.4 + \cos 70°} \approx 1.0107$$

$$\sec^2 33° \approx 1.4217$$

$$(\sin^{-1} 0.66)^3 \approx 0.3745$$

$$\frac{16.2 \sin 0.48}{\sin 0.74} \approx 11.09$$

$$3^2 + 5^2 - 2(3)(5) \cos 2.0944 = 49.00$$

$$\tan^{-1} 1.23 + \cot 1.23 \approx 1.2428$$

EXERCISES   Appendix I

Use interpolation to find $\log x$ for each value of x given in Probs. 1 to 12.

1.	3.574	**2.**	57.43	**3.**	74.35
4.	4357	**5.**	6732	**6.**	5.986
7.	80.27	**8.**	159.8	**9.**	0.03175
10.	0.006007	**11.**	0.7243	**12.**	0.6245

Use interpolation to find x to four digits if $\log x$ is given in Probs. 13 to 24.

13.	0.5961	**14.**	1.8727	**15.**	3.4238
16.	2.5434	**17.**	1.4850	**18.**	3.8823
19.	2.6047	**20.**	0.2017	**21.**	$9.1234 - 10$
22.	$8.7615 - 10$	**23.**	-1.3599	**24.**	-2.5434

Find the function value in Probs. 25 to 40 by interpolation.

25.	$\cos 38.34°$	**26.**	$\tan 64.37°$	**27.**	$\cot 81.52°$
28.	$\sec 58.88°$	**29.**	$\csc 42.26°$	**30.**	$\sin 85.75°$
31.	$\cos 13.23°$	**32.**	$\sin 64.47°$	**33.**	$\tan 0.4356$

34.	$\cot 1.2333$	**35.**	$\sec 1.4574$	**36.**	$\csc 0.4164$
37.	$\sin 1.4357$	**38.**	$\cos 1.1129$	**39.**	$\cos 0.3572$
40.	$\sin 1.3627$				

Find the number of degrees in the angle in Probs. 41 to 48 in the interval $[0°, 360°)$.

41.	$\sin x = 0.2364$	**42.**	$\cos x = 0.5793$
43.	$\tan x = 2.347$	**44.**	$\cot x = 2.347$
45.	$\sec \theta = 2.3118$	**46.**	$\csc \theta = 4.2337$
47.	$\cos \theta = 1.0024$	**48.**	$\sin \theta = 0.1469$

Find the number of radians in Probs. 49 to 56 in the interval $[0, 2\pi)$.

49.	$\cos x = 0.9134$	**50.**	$\tan x = 1.234$
51.	$\cot x = 0.4576$	**52.**	$\sec x = 2.338$
53.	$\csc s = 5.432$	**54.**	$\sin s = 0.2647$
55.	$\sin s = 0.7643$	**56.**	$\cos s = 0.5876$

▌ Tables

TABLE A.1
COMMON LOGARITHMS

N	0	1	2	3	4	5	6	7	8	9
10	0000	0043	0086	0128	0170	0212	0253	0294	0334	0374
11	0414	0453	0492	0531	0569	0607	0645	0682	0719	0755
12	0792	0828	0864	0899	0934	0969	1004	1038	1072	1106
13	1139	1173	1206	1239	1271	1303	1335	1367	1399	1430
14	1461	1492	1523	1553	1584	1614	1644	1673	1703	1732
15	1761	1790	1818	1847	1875	1903	1931	1959	1987	2014
16	2041	2068	2095	2122	2148	2175	2201	2227	2253	2279
17	2304	2330	2355	2380	2405	2430	2455	2480	2504	2529
18	2553	2577	2601	2625	2648	2672	2695	2718	2742	2765
19	2788	2810	2833	2856	2878	2900	2923	2945	2967	2989
20	3010	3032	3054	3075	3096	3118	3139	3160	3181	3201
21	3222	3243	3263	3284	3304	3324	3345	3365	3385	3404
22	3424	3444	3464	3483	3502	3522	3541	3560	3579	3598
23	3617	3636	3655	3674	3692	3711	3729	3747	3766	3784
24	3802	3820	3838	3856	3874	3892	3909	3927	3945	3962
25	3979	3997	4014	4031	4048	4065	4082	4099	4116	4133
26	4150	4166	4183	4200	4216	4232	4249	4265	4281	4298
27	4314	4330	4346	4362	4378	4393	4409	4425	4440	4456
28	4472	4487	4502	4518	4533	4548	4564	4579	4594	4609
29	4624	4639	4654	4669	4683	4698	4713	4728	4742	4757
30	4771	4786	4800	4814	4829	4843	5857	4871	4886	4900
31	4914	4928	4942	4955	4969	4983	4997	5011	5024	5038
32	5051	5065	5079	5092	5105	5119	5132	5145	5159	5172
33	5185	5198	5211	5224	5237	5250	5263	5276	5289	5302
34	5315	5328	5340	5353	5366	5378	5391	5403	5416	5428
35	5441	5453	5465	5478	5490	5502	5514	5527	5539	5551
36	5563	5575	5587	5599	5611	5623	5635	5647	5658	5670
37	5682	5694	5705	5717	5729	5740	5752	5763	5775	5786
38	5798	5809	5821	5832	5843	5855	5866	5877	5888	5899
39	5911	5922	5933	5944	5955	5966	5977	5988	5999	6010
40	6021	6031	6042	6053	6064	6075	6085	6096	6107	6117
41	6128	6138	6149	6160	6170	6180	6191	6201	6212	6222
42	6232	6243	6253	6263	6274	6284	6294	6304	6314	6325
43	6335	6345	6355	6365	6375	6385	6395	6405	6415	6425
44	6435	6444	6454	6464	6474	6484	6493	6503	6513	6522
45	6532	6542	6551	6561	6571	6580	6590	6599	6609	6618
46	6628	6637	6646	6656	6665	6675	6684	6693	6702	6712
47	6721	6730	6739	6749	6758	6767	6776	6785	6794	6803
48	6812	6821	6830	6839	6849	6857	6866	6875	6884	6893
49	6902	6911	6920	6928	6937	6946	6955	6964	6972	6981
50	6990	6998	7007	7016	7024	7033	7042	7050	7059	7067
51	7076	7084	7093	7101	7110	7118	7126	7135	7143	7152
52	7160	7168	7177	7185	7193	7202	7210	7218	7226	7235
53	7243	7251	7259	7267	7275	7284	7292	7300	7308	7316
54	7324	7332	7340	7348	7356	7364	7372	7380	7388	7396
N	0	1	2	3	4	5	6	7	8	9

N	0	1	2	3	4	5	6	7	8	9
55	7404	7412	7419	7427	7435	7443	7451	7459	7466	7474
56	7482	7490	7497	7505	7513	7520	7528	7536	7543	7551
57	7559	7566	7574	7582	7589	7597	7604	7612	7619	7627
58	7634	7642	7649	7657	7664	7672	7679	7686	7694	7701
59	7709	7716	7723	7731	7738	7745	7752	7760	7767	7774
60	7782	7789	7796	7803	7810	7818	7825	7832	7839	7846
61	7853	7860	7868	7875	7882	7889	7896	7903	7910	7917
62	7924	7931	7938	7945	7952	7959	7966	7973	7980	7987
63	7993	8000	8007	8014	8021	8028	8035	8041	8048	8055
64	8062	8069	8075	8082	8089	8096	8102	8109	8116	8122
65	8129	8136	8142	8149	8156	8162	8169	8176	8182	8189
66	8195	8202	8209	8215	8222	8228	8235	8241	8248	8254
67	8261	8267	8274	8280	8287	8293	8299	8306	8312	8319
68	8325	8331	8338	8344	8351	8357	8363	8370	8376	8382
69	8388	8395	8401	8407	8414	8420	8426	8432	8439	8445
70	8451	8457	8463	8470	8476	8482	8488	8494	8500	8506
71	8513	8519	8525	8531	8537	8543	8549	8555	8561	8567
72	8573	8579	8585	8591	8597	8603	8609	8615	8621	8627
73	8633	8639	8645	8651	8657	8663	8669	8675	8681	8686
74	8692	8698	8704	8710	8716	8722	8727	8733	8739	8745
75	8751	8756	8762	8768	8774	8779	8785	8791	8797	8802
76	8808	8814	8820	8825	8831	8837	8842	8848	8854	8859
77	8865	8871	8876	8882	8887	8893	8899	8904	8910	8915
78	8921	8927	8932	8938	8943	8949	8954	8960	8965	8971
79	8976	8982	8987	8993	8998	9004	9009	9015	9020	9025
80	9031	9036	9042	9047	9053	9058	9063	9069	9074	9079
81	9085	9090	9096	9101	9106	9112	9117	9122	9128	9133
82	9138	9143	9149	9154	9159	9165	9170	9175	9180	9186
83	9191	9196	9201	9206	9212	9217	9222	9227	9232	9238
84	9243	9248	9253	9258	9263	9269	9274	9279	9284	9289
85	9294	9299	9304	9309	9315	9320	9325	9330	9335	9340
86	9345	9350	9355	9360	9365	9370	9375	9380	9385	9390
87	9395	9400	9405	9410	9415	9420	9425	9430	9435	9440
88	9445	9450	9455	9460	9465	9469	9474	9479	9484	9489
89	9494	9499	9504	9509	9513	9518	9523	9528	9533	9538
90	9542	9547	9552	9557	9562	9566	9571	9576	9581	9586
91	9590	9595	9600	9605	9609	9614	9619	9624	9628	9633
92	9638	9643	9647	9652	9657	9661	9666	9671	9675	9680
93	9685	9689	9594	9699	9703	9708	9713	9717	9722	9727
94	9731	9736	9741	9745	9750	9754	9759	9763	9768	9773
95	9777	9782	9786	9791	9795	9800	9805	9809	9814	9818
96	9823	9827	9832	9836	9841	9845	9850	9854	9859	9863
97	9868	9872	9877	9881	9886	9890	9894	9899	9903	9908
98	9912	9917	9921	9926	9930	9934	9939	9943	9948	9952
99	9956	9961	9965	9969	9974	9978	9983	9987	9991	9996
N	0	1	2	3	4	5	6	7	8	9

TABLE A.2 e^x, e^{-x} AND $\ln x$

x	e^x	e^{-x}	$\ln x$	x	e^x	e^{-x}	$\ln x$
0.00	1.0000	1.0000		1.60	4.9530	0.2019	0.4700
0.01	1.0101	0.9900	−4.6052	1.70	5.4739	0.1827	0.5306
0.02	1.0202	0.9802	−3.9120	1.80	6.0496	0.1653	0.5878
0.03	1.0305	0.9704	−3.5066	1.90	6.6859	0.1496	0.6419
0.04	1.0408	0.9608	−3.2189	2.00	7.3891	0.1353	0.6931
0.05	1.0513	0.9512	−2.9957				
				2.10	8.1662	0.1225	0.7419
0.06	1.0618	0.9418	−2.8134	2.20	9.0250	0.1108	0.7885
0.07	1.0725	0.9324	−2.6593	2.30	9.9742	0.1003	0.8329
0.08	1.0833	0.9231	−2.5257	2.40	11.0232	0.0907	0.8755
0.09	1.0942	0.9139	−2.4079	2.50	12.1825	0.0821	0.9163
0.10	1.1052	0.9048	−2.3026				
				2.60	13.4637	0.0743	0.9555
0.11	1.1163	0.8958	−2.2073	2.70	14.8797	0.0672	0.9933
0.12	1.1275	0.8869	−2.1203	2.80	16.4446	0.0608	1.0296
0.13	1.1388	0.8781	−2.0402	2.90	18.1741	0.0550	1.0647
0.14	1.1503	0.8694	−1.9661	3.00	20.0855	0.0498	1.0986
0.15	1.1618	0.8607	−1.8971				
				3.50	33.1155	0.0302	1.2528
0.16	1.1735	0.8521	−1.8326	4.00	54.5982	0.0183	1.3863
0.17	1.1853	0.8437	−1.7720	4.50	90.0171	0.0111	1.5041
0.18	1.1972	0.8353	−1.7148				
0.19	1.2092	0.8270	−1.6607	5.00	148.4132	0.0067	1.6094
				5.50	224.6919	0.0041	1.7047
0.20	1.2214	0.8187	−1.6094				
0.30	1.3499	0.7408	−1.2040	6.00	403.4288	0.0025	1.7918
0.40	1.4918	0.6703	−0.9163	6.50	665.1416	0.0015	1.8718
0.50	1.6487	0.6065	−0.6931				
				7.00	1096.6332	0.00091	1.9459
0.60	1.8221	0.5488	−0.5108	7.50	1808.0424	0.00055	2.0149
0.70	2.0138	0.4966	−0.3567				
0.80	2.2255	0.4493	−0.2231	8.00	2980.9580	0.00034	2.0794
0.90	2.4596	0.4066	−0.1054	8.50	4914.7688	0.00020	2.1401
1.00	2.7183	0.3679	0.0000	9.00	8130.0839	0.00012	2.1972
1.10	3.0042	0.3329	0.0953	9.50	13359.7268	0.00007	2.2513
1.20	3.3201	0.3012	0.1823				
1.30	3.6693	0.2725	0.2624	10.00	22026.4658	0.00005	2.3026
1.40	4.0552	0.2466	0.3365				
1.50	4.4817	0.2231	0.4055				

TABLE A.3
ACCUMULATED VALUE:
$(1 + i)^n$

$n \backslash i$	$1\frac{1}{2}\%$	2%	$2\frac{1}{2}\%$	3%	4%	5%	6%
1	1.0150	1.0200	1.0250	1.0300	1.0400	1.0500	1.0600
2	1.0302	1.0404	1.0506	1.0609	1.0816	1.1025	1.1236
3	1.0457	1.0612	1.0769	1.0927	1.1249	1.1576	1.1910
4	1.0614	1.0824	1.1038	1.1255	1.1699	1.2155	1.2625
5	1.0773	1.1041	1.1314	1.1593	1.2167	1.2763	1.3382
6	1.0934	1.1262	1.1597	1.1941	1.2653	1.3401	1.4185
7	1.1098	1.1487	1.1887	1.2299	1.3159	1.4071	1.5036
8	1.1265	1.1717	1.2184	1.2668	1.3686	1.4775	1.5938
9	1.1434	1.1951	1.2489	1.3048	1.4233	1.5513	1.6895
10	1.1605	1.2190	1.2801	1.3439	1.4802	1.6289	1.7908
11	1.1779	1.2434	1.3121	1.3842	1.5395	1.7103	1.8983
12	1.1956	1.2682	1.3449	1.4258	1.6010	1.7959	2.0122
13	1.2136	1.2936	1.3785	1.4685	1.6651	1.8856	2.1329
14	1.2318	1.3195	1.4130	1.5126	1.7317	1.9799	2.2609
15	1.2502	1.3459	1.4483	1.5580	1.8009	2.0789	2.3966
16	1.2690	1.3728	1.4845	1.6047	1.8730	2.1829	2.5404
17	1.2880	1.4002	1.5216	1.6528	1.9479	2.2920	2.6928
18	1.3073	1.4282	1.5597	1.7024	2.0258	2.4066	2.8543
19	1.3270	1.4568	1.5987	1.7535	2.1068	2.5270	3.0256
20	1.3469	1.4859	1.6386	1.8061	2.1911	2.6533	3.2071
21	1.3671	1.5157	1.6796	1.8603	2.2788	2.7860	3.3996
22	1.3876	1.5460	1.7216	1.9161	2.3699	2.9253	3.6035
23	1.4084	1.5769	1.7646	1.9736	2.4647	3.0715	3.8197
24	1.4295	1.6084	1.8087	2.0328	2.5633	3.2251	4.0489
25	1.4509	1.6406	1.8539	2.0938	2.6658	3.3864	4.2919
26	1.4727	1.6734	1.9003	2.1566	2.7725	3.5557	4.5494
27	1.4948	1.7069	1.9478	2.2213	2.8834	3.7335	4.8223
28	1.5172	1.7410	1.9965	2.2879	2.9987	3.9201	5.1117
29	1.5400	1.7758	2.0464	2.3566	3.1187	4.1161	5.4184
30	1.5631	1.8114	2.0976	2.4273	3.2434	4.3219	5.7435
31	1.5865	1.8476	2.1500	2.5001	3.3731	4.5380	6.0881
32	1.6103	1.8845	2.2038	2.5751	3.5081	4.7649	6.4534
33	1.6345	1.9222	2.2589	2.6523	3.6484	5.0032	6.8406
34	1.6590	1.9607	2.3153	2.7319	3.7943	5.2533	7.2510
35	1.6839	1.9999	2.3732	2.8139	3.9461	5.5160	7.6861
36	1.7091	2.0399	2.4325	2.8983	4.1039	5.7918	8.1473
37	1.7348	2.0807	2.4933	2.9852	4.2681	6.0814	8.6361
38	1.7608	2.1223	2.5557	3.0748	4.4388	6.3855	9.1543
39	1.7872	2.1647	2.6196	3.1670	4.6164	6.7048	9.7035
40	1.8140	2.2080	2.6851	3.2620	4.8010	7.0400	10.2857
41	1.8412	2.2522	2.7522	3.3599	4.9931	7.3920	10.9029
42	1.8688	2.2972	2.8210	3.4607	5.1928	7.7616	11.5570
43	1.8969	2.3432	2.8915	3.5645	5.4005	8.1497	12.2505
44	1.9253	2.3901	2.9638	3.6715	5.6165	8.5572	12.9855
45	1.9542	2.4379	3.0379	3.7816	5.8412	8.9850	13.7646
46	1.9835	2.4866	3.1139	3.8950	6.0748	9.4343	14.5905
47	2.0133	2.5363	3.1917	4.0119	6.3178	9.9060	15.4659
48	2.0435	2.5871	3.2715	4.1323	6.5705	10.4013	16.3939
49	2.0741	2.6388	3.3533	4.2562	6.8333	10.9213	17.3775
50	2.1052	2.6916	3.4371	4.3839	7.1067	11.4674	18.4202

$n \backslash i$	$1\frac{1}{2}\%$	2%	$2\frac{1}{2}\%$	3%	4%	5%	6%
1	1.0000	1.0000	1.0000	1.0000	1.0000	1.0000	1.0000
2	2.0150	2.0200	2.0250	2.0300	2.0400	2.0500	2.0600
3	3.0452	3.0604	3.0756	3.0909	3.1216	3.1525	3.1836
4	4.0909	4.1216	4.1525	4.1836	4.2465	4.3101	4.3746
5	5.1523	5.2040	5.2563	5.3091	5.4163	5.5256	5.6371
6	6.2296	6.3081	6.3877	6.4684	6.6330	6.8019	6.9753
7	7.3230	7.4343	7.5474	7.6625	7.8983	8.1420	8.3938
8	8.4328	8.5830	8.7361	8.8923	9.2142	9.5491	9.8975
9	9.5593	9.7546	9.9545	10.1591	10.5828	11.0266	11.4913
10	10.7027	10.9497	11.2034	11.4639	12.0061	12.5779	13.1808
11	11.8633	12.1687	12.4835	12.8078	13.4864	14.2068	14.9716
12	13.0412	13.4121	13.7956	14.1920	15.0258	15.9171	16.8699
13	14.2368	14.6803	15.1404	15.6178	16.6268	17.7130	18.8821
14	15.4504	15.9739	16.5190	17.0863	18.2919	19.5986	21.0151
15	16.6821	17.2934	17.9319	18.5989	20.0236	21.5786	23.2760
16	17.9324	18.6393	19.3802	20.1569	21.8245	23.6575	25.6725
17	19.2014	20.0121	20.8647	21.7616	23.6975	25.8404	28.2129
18	20.4894	21.4123	22.3863	23.4144	25.6454	28.1324	30.9057
19	21.7967	22.8406	23.9460	25.1169	27.6712	30.5390	33.7600
20	23.1237	24.2974	25.5447	26.8704	29.7781	33.0660	36.7853
21	24.4705	25.7833	27.1833	28.6765	31.9692	35.7193	39.9927
22	25.8376	27.2990	28.8629	30.5368	34.2480	38.5052	43.3923
23	27.2251	28.8450	30.5844	32.4529	36.6179	41.4305	46.9958
24	28.6335	30.4219	32.3490	34.4265	39.0826	44.5020	50.8156
25	30.0630	32.0303	34.1578	36.4593	41.6459	47.7271	54.8645
26	31.5140	33.6709	36.0117	38.5530	44.3117	51.1135	59.1564
27	32.9867	35.3443	37.9120	40.7096	47.0842	54.6691	63.7058
28	34.4815	37.0512	39.8598	42.9309	49.9676	58.4026	68.5281
29	35.9987	38.7922	41.8563	45.2189	52.9663	62.3227	73.6398
30	37.5387	40.5681	43.9027	47.5754	56.0849	66.4388	79.0582
31	39.1018	42.3794	46.0003	50.0027	59.3283	70.7608	84.8017
32	40.6883	44.2270	48.1503	52.5028	62.7015	75.2988	90.8898
33	42.2986	46.1116	50.3540	55.0778	66.2095	80.0638	97.3432
34	43.9331	48.0338	52.6129	57.7302	69.8579	85.0670	104.1838
35	45.5921	49.9945	54.9282	60.4621	73.6522	90.3203	111.4348
36	47.2760	51.9944	57.3014	63.2759	77.5983	95.8363	119.1209
37	48.9851	54.0343	59.7339	66.1742	81.7022	101.6281	127.2681
38	50.7199	56.1149	62.2273	69.1594	85.9703	107.7095	135.9042
39	52.4807	58.2372	64.7830	72.2342	90.4091	114.0950	145.0585
40	54.2679	60.4020	67.4026	75.4013	95.0255	120.7998	154.7620
41	56.0819	62.6100	70.0876	78.6633	99.8265	127.8398	165.0477
42	57.9231	64.8622	72.8398	82.0232	104.8196	135.2318	175.9505
43	59.7920	67.1595	75.6608	85.4839	110.0124	142.9933	187.5076
44	61.6889	69.5027	78.5523	89.0484	115.4129	151.1430	199.7580
45	63.6142	71.8927	81.5161	92.7199	121.0294	159.7002	212.7435
46	65.5684	74.3306	84.5540	96.5015	126.8706	168.6852	226.5081
47	67.5519	76.8172	87.6679	100.3965	132.9454	178.1194	241.0986
48	69.5652	79.3535	90.8596	104.4084	139.2632	188.0254	256.5645
49	71.6087	81.9406	94.1311	108.5406	145.8337	198.4267	272.9584
50	73.6828	84.5794	97.4843	112.7969	152.6671	209.3480	290.3359

656

TABLE A.5   TRIGONOMETRIC FUNCTIONS: ANGLES EVERY 0.1 DEGREE (AND RADIANS)

θ deg	radians	sin θ	cos θ	tan θ	csc θ	sec θ	cot θ		
0.0	.0000	0.0000	1.0000	0.0000	No value	1.0000	No value	**1.5708**	90.0
0.1	.0017	0.0017	1.0000	0.0017	572.96	1.0000	572.96	**1.5691**	89.9
0.2	.0035	0.0035	1.0000	0.0035	286.48	1.0000	286.48	**1.5673**	89.8
0.3	.0052	0.0052	1.0000	0.0052	190.99	1.0000	190.98	**1.5656**	89.7
0.4	.0070	0.0070	1.0000	0.0070	143.24	1.0000	143.24	**1.5638**	89.6
0.5	.0087	0.0087	1.0000	0.0087	114.59	1.0000	114.59	**1.5621**	89.5
0.6	.0105	0.0105	0.9999	0.0105	95.495	1.0001	95.490	**1.5603**	89.4
0.7	.0122	0.0122	0.9999	0.0122	81.853	1.0001	81.847	**1.5586**	89.3
0.8	.0140	0.0140	0.9999	0.0140	71.622	1.0001	71.615	**1.5568**	89.2
0.9	.0157	0.0157	0.9999	0.0157	63.665	1.0001	63.657	**1.5551**	89.1
1.0	.0175	0.0175	0.9998	0.0175	57.299	1.0002	57.290	**1.5533**	89.0
1.1	.0192	0.0192	0.9998	0.0192	52.090	1.0002	52.081	**1.5516**	88.9
1.2	.0209	0.0209	0.9998	0.0209	47.750	1.0002	47.740	**1.5499**	88.8
1.3	.0227	0.0227	0.9997	0.0227	44.077	1.0003	44.066	**1.5481**	88.7
1.4	.0244	0.0244	0.9997	0.0244	40.930	1.0003	40.917	**1.5464**	88.6
1.5	.0262	0.0262	0.9997	0.0262	38.202	1.0003	38.188	**1.5446**	88.5
1.6	.0279	0.0279	0.9996	0.0279	35.815	1.0004	35.801	**1.5429**	88.4
1.7	.0297	0.0297	0.9996	0.0297	33.708	1.0004	33.694	**1.5411**	88.3
1.8	.0314	0.0314	0.9995	0.0314	31.836	1.0005	31.821	**1.5394**	88.2
1.9	.0332	0.0332	0.9995	0.0332	30.161	1.0005	30.145	**1.5376**	88.1
2.0	.0349	0.0349	0.9994	0.0349	28.654	1.0006	28.636	**1.5359**	88.0
2.1	.0367	0.0366	0.9993	0.0367	27.290	1.0007	27.271	**1.5341**	87.9
2.2	.0384	0.0384	0.9993	0.0384	26.050	1.0007	26.031	**1.5324**	87.8
2.3	.0401	0.0401	0.9992	0.0402	24.918	1.0008	24.898	**1.5307**	87.7
2.4	.0419	0.0419	0.9991	0.0419	23.880	1.0009	23.859	**1.5289**	87.6
2.5	.0436	0.0436	0.9990	0.0437	22.926	1.0010	22.904	**1.5272**	87.5
2.6	.0454	0.0454	0.9990	0.0454	22.044	1.0010	22.022	**1.5254**	87.4
2.7	.0471	0.0471	0.9989	0.0472	21.229	1.0011	21.205	**1.5237**	87.3
2.8	.0489	0.0488	0.9988	0.0489	20.471	1.0012	20.446	**1.5219**	87.2
2.9	.0506	0.0506	0.9987	0.0507	19.766	1.0013	19.740	**1.5202**	87.1
3.0	.0524	0.0523	0.9986	0.0524	19.107	1.0014	19.081	**1.5184**	87.0
3.1	.0541	0.0541	0.9985	0.0542	18.492	1.0015	18.464	**1.5167**	86.9
3.2	.0559	0.0558	0.9984	0.0559	17.914	1.0016	17.886	**1.5149**	86.8
3.3	.0576	0.0576	0.9983	0.0577	17.372	1.0017	17.343	**1.5132**	86.7
3.4	.0593	0.0593	0.9982	0.0594	16.862	1.0018	16.832	**1.5115**	86.6
3.5	.0611	0.0610	0.9981	0.0612	16.380	1.0019	16.350	**1.5097**	86.5
3.6	.0628	0.0628	0.9980	0.0629	15.926	1.0020	15.895	**1.5080**	86.4
3.7	.0646	0.0645	0.9979	0.0647	15.496	1.0021	15.464	**1.5062**	86.3
3.8	.0663	0.0663	0.9978	0.0664	15.089	1.0022	15.056	**1.5045**	86.2
3.9	.0681	0.0680	0.9977	0.0682	14.703	1.0023	14.669	**1.5027**	86.1
4.0	.0698	0.0698	0.9976	0.0699	14.336	1.0024	14.301	**1.5010**	86.0
4.1	.0716	0.0715	0.9974	0.0717	13.987	1.0026	13.951	**1.4992**	85.9
4.2	.0733	0.0732	0.9973	0.0734	13.654	1.0027	13.617	**1.4975**	85.8
4.3	.0750	0.0750	0.9972	0.0752	13.337	1.0028	13.300	**1.4957**	85.7
4.4	.0768	0.0767	0.9971	0.0769	13.035	1.0030	12.996	**1.4940**	85.6
4.5	.0785	0.0785	0.9969	0.0787	12.746	1.0031	12.706	**1.4923**	85.5
4.6	.0803	0.0802	0.9968	0.0805	12.469	1.0032	12.429	**1.4905**	85.4
4.7	.0820	0.0819	0.9966	0.0822	12.204	1.0034	12.163	**1.4888**	85.3
4.8	.0838	0.0837	0.9965	0.0840	11.951	1.0035	11.909	**1.4870**	85.2
4.9	.0855	0.0854	0.9963	0.0857	11.707	1.0037	11.665	**1.4853**	85.1
	cos θ	sin θ	cot θ	sec θ	csc θ	tan θ	radians	θ deg

Adapted by permission of the publisher from TRIGONOMETRY: AN ANALYTIC APPROACH, Fourth Edition, by Irving Drooyan, Walter Hadel, and Charles C. Carico (New York: Macmillan Publishing Company), Table III. pp. 324–332.

TABLE A.5 TRIGONOMETRIC FUNCTIONS: ANGLES EVERY 0.1 DEGREE (AND RADIANS) *(Continued)*

θ deg	radians	sin θ	cos θ	tan θ	csc θ	sec θ	cot θ		
5.0	.0873	0.0872	0.9962	0.0875	11.474	1.0038	11.430	**1.4835**	85.0
5.1	.0890	0.0889	0.9960	0.0892	11.249	1.0040	11.205	**1.4818**	84.9
5.2	.0908	0.0906	0.9959	0.0910	11.034	1.0041	10.988	**1.4800**	84.8
5.3	.0925	0.0924	0.9957	0.0928	10.826	1.0043	10.780	**1.4783**	84.7
5.4	.0942	0.0941	0.9956	0.0945	10.626	1.0045	10.579	**1.4765**	84.6
5.5	.0960	0.0958	0.9954	0.0963	10.433	1.0046	10.385	**1.4748**	84.5
5.6	.0977	0.0976	0.9952	0.0981	10.248	1.0048	10.199	**1.4731**	84.4
5.7	.0995	0.0993	0.9951	0.0998	10.069	1.0050	10.019	**1.4713**	84.3
5.8	.1012	0.1011	0.9949	0.1016	9.8955	1.0051	9.8448	**1.4696**	84.2
5.9	.1030	0.1028	0.9947	0.1033	9.7283	1.0053	9.6768	**1.4678**	84.1
6.0	.1047	0.1045	0.9945	0.1051	9.5668	1.0055	9.5144	**1.4461**	84.0
6.1	.1065	0.1063	0.9943	0.1069	9.4105	1.0057	9.3573	**1.4643**	83.9
6.2	.1082	0.1080	0.9942	0.1086	9.2593	1.0059	9.2052	**1.4626**	83.8
6.3	.1100	0.1097	0.9940	0.1104	9.1129	1.0061	9.0579	**1.4608**	83.7
6.4	.1117	0.1115	0.9938	0.1122	8.9711	1.0063	8.9152	**1.4591**	83.6
6.5	.1134	0.1132	0.9936	0.1139	8.8337	1.0065	8.7769	**1.4573**	83.5
6.6	.1152	0.1149	0.9934	0.1157	8.7004	1.0067	8.6428	**1.4556**	83.4
6.7	.1169	0.1167	0.9932	0.1175	8.5711	1.0069	8.5126	**1.4539**	83.3
6.8	.1187	0.1184	0.9930	0.1192	8.4457	1.0071	8.3863	**1.4521**	83.2
6.9	.1204	0.1201	0.9928	0.1210	8.3238	1.0073	8.2636	**1.4504**	83.1
7.0	.1222	0.1219	0.9925	0.1228	8.2055	1.0075	8.1444	**1.4486**	83.0
7.1	.1239	0.1236	0.9923	0.1246	8.0905	1.0077	8.0285	**1.4469**	82.9
7.2	.1257	0.1253	0.9921	0.1263	7.9787	1.0079	7.9158	**1.4451**	82.8
7.3	.1274	0.1271	0.9919	0.1281	7.8700	1.0082	7.8062	**1.4434**	82.7
7.4	.1292	0.1288	0.9917	0.1299	7.7642	1.0084	7.6996	**1.4416**	82.6
7.5	.1309	0.1305	0.9914	0.1317	7.6613	1.0086	7.5958	**1.4399**	82.5
7.6	.1326	0.1323	0.9912	0.1334	7.5611	1.0089	7.4947	**1.4382**	82.4
7.7	.1344	0.1340	0.9910	0.1352	7.4635	1.0091	7.3962	**1.4364**	82.3
7.8	.1361	0.1357	0.9907	0.1370	7.3684	1.0093	7.3002	**1.4347**	82.2
7.9	.1379	0.1374	0.9905	0.1388	7.2757	1.0096	7.2066	**1.4329**	82.1
8.0	.1396	0.1392	0.9903	0.1405	7.1853	1.0098	7.1154	**1.4312**	82.0
8.1	.1414	0.1409	0.9900	0.1423	7.0972	1.0101	7.0264	**1.4294**	81.9
8.2	.1431	0.1426	0.9898	0.1441	7.0112	1.0103	6.9395	**1.4277**	81.8
8.3	.1449	0.1444	0.9895	0.1459	6.9273	1.0106	6.8548	**1.4259**	81.7
8.4	.1466	0.1461	0.9893	0.1477	6.8454	1.0108	6.7720	**1.4242**	81.6
8.5	.1484	0.1478	0.9890	0.1495	6.7655	1.0111	6.6912	**1.4224**	81.5
8.6	.1501	0.1495	0.9888	0.1512	6.6874	1.0114	6.6122	**1.4207**	81.4
8.7	.1518	0.1513	0.9885	0.1530	6.6111	1.0116	6.5350	**1.4190**	81.3
8.8	.1536	0.1530	0.9882	0.1548	6.5366	1.0119	6.4596	**1.4172**	81.2
8.9	.1553	0.1547	0.9880	0.1566	6.4637	1.0122	6.3859	**1.4155**	81.1
9.0	.1571	0.1564	0.9877	0.1584	6.3925	1.0125	6.3138	**1.4137**	81.0
9.1	.1588	0.1582	0.9874	0.1602	6.3228	1.0127	6.2432	**1.4120**	80.9
9.2	.1606	0.1599	0.9871	0.1620	6.2547	1.0130	6.1742	**1.4102**	80.8
9.3	.1623	0.1616	0.9869	0.1638	6.1880	1.0133	6.1066	**1.4085**	80.7
9.4	.1641	0.1633	0.9866	0.1655	6.1227	1.0136	6.0405	**1.4067**	80.6
9.5	.1658	0.1650	0.9863	0.1673	6.0589	1.0139	5.9758	**1.4050**	80.5
9.6	.1676	0.1668	0.9860	0.1691	5.9963	1.0142	5.9124	**1.4032**	80.4
9.7	.1693	0.1685	0.9857	0.1709	5.9351	1.0145	5.8502	**1.4015**	80.3
9.8	.1710	0.1702	0.9854	0.1727	5.8751	1.0148	5.7894	**1.3998**	80.2
9.9	.1728	0.1719	0.9851	0.1745	5.8164	1.0151	5.7297	**1.3980**	80.1
		cos θ	sin θ	cot θ	sec θ	csc θ	tan θ	radians	θ deg

TABLE A.5   TRIGONOMETRIC FUNCTIONS: ANGLES EVERY 0.1 DEGREE (AND RADIANS) *(Continued)*

θ deg	radians	sin θ	cos θ	tan θ	csc θ	sec θ	cot θ		
10.0	.1745	0.1736	0.9848	0.1763	5.7588	1.0154	5.6713	**1.3963**	80.0
10.1	.1763	0.1754	0.9845	0.1781	5.7023	1.0157	5.6140	**1.3945**	79.9
10.2	.1780	0.1771	0.9842	0.1799	5.6470	1.0161	5.5578	**1.3928**	79.8
10.3	.1798	0.1788	0.9839	0.1817	5.5928	1.0164	5.5027	**1.3910**	79.7
10.4	.1815	0.1805	0.9836	0.1835	5.5396	1.0167	5.4486	**1.3893**	79.6
10.5	.1833	0.1822	0.9833	0.1853	5.4874	1.0170	5.3955	**1.3875**	79.5
10.6	.1850	0.1840	0.9829	0.1871	5.4362	1.0174	5.3435	**1.3858**	79.4
10.7	.1868	0.1857	0.9826	0.1890	5.3860	1.0177	5.2924	**1.3840**	79.3
10.8	.1885	0.1874	0.9823	0.1908	5.3367	1.0180	5.2422	**1.3823**	79.2
10.9	.1902	0.1891	0.9820	0.1926	5.2883	1.0184	5.1929	**1.3806**	79.1
11.0	.1920	0.1908	0.9816	0.1944	5.2408	1.0187	5.1446	**1.3788**	79.0
11.1	.1937	0,1925	0.9813	0.1962	5.1942	1.0191	5.0970	**1.3771**	78.9
11.2	.1955	0.1942	0.9810	0.1980	5.1484	1.0194	5.0504	**1.3753**	78.8
11.3	.1972	0.1959	0.9806	0.1998	5.1034	1.0198	5.0045	**1.3736**	78.7
11.4	.1990	0.1977	0.9803	0.2016	5.0593	1.0201	4.9595	**1.3718**	78.6
11.5	.2007	0.1994	0.9799	0.2035	5.0159	1.0205	4.9152	**1.3701**	78.5
11.6	.2025	0.2011	0.9796	0.2053	4.9732	1.0209	4.8716	**1.3683**	78.4
11.7	.2042	0.2028	0.9792	0.2071	4.9313	1.0212	4.8288	**1.3666**	78.3
11.8	.2059	0.2045	0.9789	0.2089	4.8901	1.0216	4.7867	**1.3648**	78.2
11.9	.2077	0.2062	0.9785	0.2107	4.8496	1.0220	4.7453	**1.3631**	78.1
12.0	.2094	0.2079	0.9781	0.2126	4.8097	1.0223	4.7046	**1.3614**	78.0
12.1	.2112	0.2096	0.9778	0.2144	4.7706	1.0227	4.6646	**1.3596**	77.9
12.2	.2129	0.2113	0.9774	0.2162	4.7321	1.0231	4.6252	**1.3579**	77.8
12.3	.2147	0.2130	0.9770	0.2180	4.6942	1.0235	4.5864	**1.3561**	77.7
12.4	.2164	0.2147	0.9767	0.2199	4.6569	1.0239	4.5483	**1.3544**	77.6
12.5	.2182	0.2164	0.9763	0.2217	4.6202	1.0243	4.5107	**1.3526**	77.5
12.6	.2199	0.2181	0.9759	0.2235	4.5841	1.0247	4.4737	**1.3509**	77.4
12.7	.2217	0.2198	0.9755	0.2254	4.5486	1.0251	4.4374	**1.3491**	77.3
12.8	.2234	0.2215	0.9751	0.2272	4.5137	1.0255	4.4015	**1.3474**	77.2
12.9	.2251	0.2232	0.9748	0.2290	4.4793	1.0259	4.3662	**1.3456**	77.1
13.0	.2269	0.2250	0.9744	0.2309	4.4454	1.0263	4.3315	**1.3439**	77.0
13.1	.2286	0.2267	0.9740	0.2327	4.4121	1.0267	4.2972	**1.3422**	76.9
13.2	.2304	0.2284	0.9736	0.2345	4.3792	1.0271	4.2635	**1.3404**	76.8
13.3	.2321	0.2300	0.9732	0.2364	4.3469	1.0276	4.2303	**1.3387**	76.7
13.4	.2339	0.2317	0.9728	0.2382	4.3150	1.0280	4.1976	**1.3369**	76.6
13.5	.2356	0.2334	0.9724	0.2401	4.2837	1.0284	4.1653	**1.3352**	76.5
13.6	.2374	0.2351	0.9720	0.2419	4.2528	1.0288	4.1335	**1.3334**	76.4
13.7	.2391	0.2368	0.9715	0.2438	4.2223	1.0293	4.1022	**1.3317**	76.3
13.8	.2409	0.2385	0.9711	0.2456	4.1923	1.0297	4.0713	**1.3299**	76.2
13.9	.2426	0.2402	0.9707	0.2475	4.1627	1.0302	4.0408	**1.3282**	76.1
14.0	.2443	0.2419	0.9703	0.2493	4.1336	1.0306	4.0108	**1.3265**	76.0
14.1	.2461	0.2436	0.9699	0.2512	4.1048	1.0311	3.9812	**1.3247**	75.9
14.2	.2478	0.2453	0.9694	0.2530	4.0765	1.0315	3.9520	**1.3230**	75.8
14.3	.2496	0.2470	0.9690	0.2549	4.0486	1.0320	3.9232	**1.3212**	75.7
14.4	.2513	0.2487	0.9686	0.2568	4.0211	1.0324	3.8947	**1.3195**	75.6
14.5	.2531	0.2504	0.9681	0.2586	3.9939	1.0329	3.8667	**1.3177**	75.5
14.6	.2548	0.2521	0.9677	0.2605	3.9672	1.0334	3.8391	**1.3160**	75.4
14.7	.2566	0.2538	0.9673	0.2623	3.9408	1.0338	3.8118	**1.3142**	75.3
14.8	.2583	0.2554	0.9668	0.2642	3.9147	1.0343	3.7849	**1.3125**	75.2
14.9	.2601	0.2571	0.9664	0.2661	3.8890	1.0348	3.7583	**1.3107**	75.1
	cos θ	**sin θ**	**cot θ**	**sec θ**	**csc θ**	**tan θ**	**radians**	**θ deg**	

TABLE A.5   TRIGONOMETRIC FUNCTIONS: ANGLES EVERY 0.1 DEGREE (AND RADIANS) *(Continued)*

θ deg	radians	sin θ	cos θ	tan θ	csc θ	sec θ	cot θ		
15.0	.2618	0.2588	0.9659	0.2679	3.8637	1.0353	3.7321	**1.3090**	75.0
15.1	.2635	0.2605	0.9655	0.2698	3.8387	1.0358	3.7062	**1.3073**	74.9
15.2	.2653	0.2622	0.9650	0.2717	3.8140	1.0363	3.6806	**1.3055**	74.8
15.3	.2670	0.2639	0.9646	0.2736	3.7897	1.0367	3.6554	**1.3038**	74.7
15.4	.2688	0.2656	0.9641	0.2754	3.7657	1.0372	3.6305	**1.3020**	74.6
15.5	.2705	0.2672	0.9636	0.2773	3.7420	1.0377	3.6059	**1.3003**	74.5
15.6	.2723	0.2689	0.9632	0.2792	3.7186	1.0382	3.5816	**1.2985**	74.4
15.7	.2740	0.2706	0.9627	0.2811	3.6955	1.0388	3.5576	**1.2968**	74.3
15.8	.2758	0.2723	0.9622	0.2830	3.6727	1.0393	3.5339	**1.2950**	74.2
15.9	.2775	0.2740	0.9617	0.2849	3.6502	1.0398	3.5105	**1.2933**	74.1
16.0	.2793	0.2756	0.9613	0.2867	3.6280	1.0403	3.4874	**1.2915**	74.0
16.1	.2810	0.2773	0.9608	0.2886	3.6060	1.0408	3.4646	**1.2898**	73.9
16.2	.2827	0.2790	0.9603	0.2905	3.5843	1.0413	3.4420	**1.2881**	73.8
16.3	.2845	0.2807	0.9598	0.2924	3.5629	1.0419	3.4197	**1.2863**	73.7
16.4	.2862	0.2823	0.9593	0.2943	3.5418	1.0424	3.3977	**1.2846**	73.6
16.5	.2880	0.2840	0.9588	0.2962	3.5209	1.0429	3.3759	**1.2828**	73.5
16.6	.2897	0.2857	0.9583	0.2981	3.5003	1.0435	3.3544	**1.2811**	73.4
16.7	.2915	0.2874	0.9578	0.3000	3.4800	1.0440	3.3332	**1.2793**	73.3
16.8	.2932	0.2890	0.9573	0.3019	3.4598	1.0446	3.3122	**1.2776**	73.2
16.9	.2950	0.2907	0.9568	0.3038	3.4399	1.0451	3.2914	**1.2758**	73.1
17.0	.2967	0.2924	0.9563	0.3057	3.4203	1.0457	3.2709	**1.2741**	73.0
17.1	.2985	0.2940	0.9558	0.3076	3.4009	1.0463	3.2506	**1.2723**	72.9
17.2	.3002	0.2957	0.9553	0.3096	3.3817	1.0468	3.2305	**1.2706**	72.8
17.3	.3019	0.2974	0.9548	0.3115	3.3628	1.0474	3.2106	**1.2689**	72.7
17.4	.3037	0.2990	0.9542	0.3134	3.3440	1.0480	3.1910	**1.2671**	72.6
17.5	.3054	0.3007	0.9537	0.3153	3.3255	1.0485	3.1716	**1.2654**	72.5
17.6	.3072	0.3024	0.9532	0.3172	3.3072	1.0491	3.1524	**1.2636**	72.4
17.7	.3089	0.3040	0.9527	0.3191	3.2891	1.0497	3.1334	**1.2619**	72.3
17.8	.3107	0.3057	0.9521	0.3211	3.2712	1.0503	3.1146	**1.2601**	72.2
17.9	.3124	0.3074	0.9516	0.3230	3.2536	1.0509	3.0961	**1.2584**	72.1
18.0	.3142	0.3090	0.9511	0.3249	3.2361	1.0515	3.0777	**1.2566**	72.0
18.1	.3159	0.3107	0.9505	0.3268	3.2188	1.0521	3.0595	**1.2549**	71.9
18.2	.3176	0.3123	0.9500	0.3288	3.2017	1.0527	3.0415	**1.2531**	71.8
18.3	.3194	0.3140	0.9494	0.3307	3.1848	1.0533	3.0237	**1.2514**	71.7
18.4	.3211	0.3156	0.9489	0.3327	3.1681	1.0539	3.0061	**1.2497**	71.6
18.5	.3229	0.3173	0.9483	0.3346	3.1515	1.0545	2.9887	**1.2479**	71.5
18.6	.3246	0.3190	0.9478	0.3365	3.1352	1.0551	2.9714	**1.2462**	71.4
18.7	.3264	0.3206	0.9472	0.3385	3.1190	1.0557	2.9544	**1.2444**	71.3
18.8	.3281	0.3223	0.9466	0.3404	3.1030	1.0564	2.9375	**1.2427**	71.2
18.9	.3299	0.3239	0.9461	0.3424	3.0872	1.0570	2.9208	**1.2409**	71.1
19.0	.3316	0.3256	0.9455	0.3443	3.0716	1.0576	2.9042	**1.2392**	71.0
19.1	.3334	0.3272	0.9449	0.3463	3.0561	1.0583	2.8878	**1.2374**	70.9
19.2	.3351	0.3289	0.9444	0.3482	3.0407	1.0589	2.8716	**1.2357**	70.8
19.3	.3368	0.3305	0.9438	0.3502	3.0256	1.0595	2.8556	**1.2339**	70.7
19.4	.3386	0.3322	0.9432	0.3522	3.0106	1.0602	2.8397	**1.2322**	70.6
19.5	.3403	0.3338	0.9426	0.3541	2.9957	1.0608	2.8239	**1.2305**	70.5
19.6	.3421	0.3355	0.9421	0.3561	2.9811	1.0615	2.8083	**1.2287**	70.4
19.7	.3438	0.3371	0.9415	0.3581	2.9665	1.0622	2.7929	**1.2270**	70.3
19.8	.3456	0.3387	0.9409	0.3600	2.9521	1.0628	2.7776	**1.2252**	70.2
.9.9	.3473	0.3404	0.9403	0.3620	2.9379	1.0635	2.7625	**1.2235**	70.1
		cos θ	sin θ	cot θ	sec θ	csc θ	tan θ	radians	θ deg

TABLE A.5 TRIGONOMETRIC FUNCTIONS: ANGLES EVERY 0.1 DEGREE (AND RADIANS) *(Continued)*

θ deg	radians	sin θ	cos θ	tan θ	csc θ	sec θ	cot θ		
20.0	.3491	0.3420	0.9397	0.3640	2.9238	1.0642	2.7475	**1.2217**	70.0
20.1	.3508	0.3437	0.9391	0.3659	2.9099	1.0649	2.7326	**1.2200**	69.9
20.2	.3526	0.3453	0.9385	0.3679	2.8960	1.0655	2.7179	**1.2182**	69.8
20.3	.3543	0.3469	0.9379	0.3699	2.8824	1.0662	2.7034	**1.2165**	69.7
20.4	.3560	0.3486	0.9373	0.3719	2.8688	1.0669	2.6889	**1.2147**	69.6
20.5	.3578	0.3502	0.9367	0.3739	2.8555	1.0676	2.6746	**1.2130**	69.5
20.6	.3595	0.3518	0.9361	0.3759	2.8422	1.0683	2.6605	**1.2113**	69.4
20.7	.3613	0.3535	0.9354	0.3779	2.8291	1.0690	2.6464	**1.2095**	69.3
20.8	.3630	0.3551	0.9348	0.3799	2.8161	1.0697	2.6325	**1.2078**	69.2
20.9	.3648	0.3567	0.9342	0.3819	2.8032	1.0704	2.6187	**1.2060**	69.1
21.0	.3665	0.3584	0.9336	0.3839	2.7904	1.0711	2.6051	**1.2043**	69.0
21.1	.3683	0.3600	0.9330	0.3859	2.7778	1.0719	2.5916	**1.2025**	68.9
21.2	.3700	0.3616	0.9323	0.3879	2.7653	1.0726	2.5782	**1.2008**	68.8
21.3	.3718	0.3633	0.9317	0.3899	2.7529	1.0733	2.5649	**1.1990**	68.7
21.4	.3735	0.3649	0.9311	0.3919	2.7407	1.0740	2.5517	**1.1973**	68.6
21.5	.3752	0.3665	0.9304	0.3939	2.7285	1.0748	2.5386	**1.1956**	68.5
21.6	.3770	0.3681	0.9298	0.3959	2.7165	1.0755	2.5257	**1.1938**	68.4
21.7	.3787	0.3697	0.9291	0.3979	2.7046	1.0763	2.5129	**1.1921**	68.3
21.8	.3805	0.3714	0.9285	0.4000	2.6927	1.0770	2.5002	**1.1903**	68.2
21.9	.3822	0.3730	0.9278	0.4020	2.6811	1.0778	2.4876	**1.1886**	68.1
22.0	.3840	0.3746	0.9272	0.4040	2.6695	1.0785	2.4751	**1.1868**	68.0
22.1	.3857	0.3762	0.9265	0.4061	2.6580	1.0793	2.4627	**1.1851**	67.9
22.2	.3875	0.3778	0.9259	0.4081	2.6466	1.0801	2.4504	**1.1833**	67.8
22.3	.3892	0.3795	0.9252	0.4101	2.6354	1.0808	2.4383	**1.1816**	67.7
22.4	.3910	0.3811	0.9245	0.4122	2.6242	1.0816	2.4262	**1.1798**	67.6
22.5	.3927	0.3827	0.9239	0.4142	2.6131	1.0824	2.4142	**1.1781**	67.5
22.6	.3944	0.3843	0.9232	0.4163	2.6022	1.0832	2.4023	**1.1764**	67.4
22.7	.3962	0.3859	0.9225	0.4183	2.5913	1.0840	2.3906	**1.1746**	67.3
22.8	.3979	0.3875	0.9219	0.4204	2.5805	1.0848	2.3789	**1.1729**	67.2
22.9	.3997	0.3891	0.9212	0.4224	2.5699	1.0856	2.3673	**1.1711**	67.1
23.0	.4014	0.3907	0.9205	0.4245	2.5593	1.0864	2.3559	**1.1694**	67.0
23.1	.4032	0.3923	0.9198	0.4265	2.5488	1.0872	2.3445	**1.1676**	66.9
23.2	.4049	0.3939	0.9191	0.4286	2.5384	1.0880	2.3332	**1.1659**	66.8
23.3	.4067	0.3955	0.9184	0.4307	2.5282	1.0888	2.3220	**1.1641**	66.7
23.4	.4084	0.3971	0.9178	0.4327	2.5180	1.0896	2.3109	**1.1624**	66.6
23.5	.4102	0.3987	0.9171	0.4348	2.5078	1.0904	2.2998	**1.1606**	66.5
23.6	.4119	0.4003	0.9164	0.4369	2.4978	1.0913	2.2889	**1.1589**	66.4
23.7	.4136	0.4019	0.9157	0.4390	2.4879	1.9021	2.2781	**1.1572**	66.3
23.8	.4154	0.4035	0.9150	0.4411	2.4780	1.0929	2.2673	**1.1554**	66.2
23.9	.4171	0.4051	0.9143	0.4431	2.4683	1.0938	2.2566	**1.1537**	66.1
24.0	.4189	0.4067	0.9135	0.4452	2.4586	1.0946	2.2460	**1.1519**	66.0
24.1	.4206	0.4083	0.9128	0.4473	2.4490	1.0955	2.2355	**1.1502**	65.9
24.2	.4224	0.4099	0.9121	0.4494	2.4395	1.0963	2.2251	**1.1484**	65.8
24.3	.4241	0.4115	0.9114	0.4515	2.4301	1.0972	2.2148	**1.1467**	65.7
24.4	.4259	0.4131	0.9107	0.4536	2.4207	1.0981	2.2045	**1.1449**	65.6
24.5	.4276	0.4147	0.9100	0.4557	2.4114	1.0989	2.1943	**1.1432**	65.5
24.6	.4294	0.4163	0.9092	0.4578	2.4022	1.0998	2.1842	**1.1414**	65.4
24.7	.4311	0.4179	0.9085	0.4599	2.3931	1.1007	2.1742	**1.1397**	65.3
24.8	.4328	0.4195	0.9078	0.4621	2.3841	1.1016	2.1642	**1.1380**	65.2
24.9	.4346	0.4210	0.9070	0.4642	2.3751	1.1025	2.1543	**1.1362**	65.1
		cos θ	**sin θ**	**cot θ**	**sec θ**	**csc θ**	**tan θ**	**radians**	**θ deg**

TABLE A.5 TRIGONOMETRIC FUNCTIONS: ANGLES EVERY 0.1 DEGREE (AND RADIANS) *(Continued)*

θ deg	radians	sin θ	cos θ	tan θ	csc θ	sec θ	cot θ		
25.0	.4363	0.4226	0.9063	0.4663	2.3662	1.1034	2.1445	**1.1345**	65.0
25.1	.4381	0.4242	0.9056	0.4684	2.3574	1.1043	2.1348	**1.1327**	64.9
25.2	.4398	0.4258	0.9048	0.4706	2.3486	1.1052	2.1251	**1.1310**	64.8
25.3	.4416	0.4274	0.9041	0.4727	2.3400	1.1061	2.1155	**1.1292**	64.7
25.4	.4433	0.4289	0.9033	0.4748	2.3314	1.1070	2.1060	**1.1275**	64.6
25.5	.4451	0.4305	0.9026	0.4770	2.3228	1.1079	2.0965	**1.1257**	64.5
25.6	.4468	0.4321	0.9018	0.4791	2.3144	1.1089	2.0872	**1.1240**	64.4
25.7	.4485	0.4337	0.9011	0.4813	2.3060	1.1098	2.0778	**1.1222**	64.3
25.8	.4503	0.4352	0.9003	0.4834	2.2976	1.1107	2.0686	**1.1205**	64.2
25.9	.4520	0.4368	0.8996	0.4856	2.2894	1.1117	2.0594	**1.1188**	64.1
26.0	.4538	0.4384	0.8988	0.4877	2.2812	1.1126	2.0503	**1.1170**	64.0
26.1	.4555	0.4399	0.8980	0.4899	2.2730	1.1136	2.0413	**1.1153**	63.9
26.2	.4573	0.4415	0.8973	0.4921	2.2650	1.1145	2.0323	**1.1135**	63.8
26.3	.4590	0.4431	0.8965	0.4942	2.2570	1.1155	2.0233	**1.1118**	63.7
26.4	.4608	0.4446	0.8957	0.4964	2.2490	1.1164	2.0145	**1.1100**	63.6
26.5	.4625	0.4462	0.8949	0.4986	2.2412	1.1174	2.0057	**1.1083**	63.5
26.6	.4643	0.4478	0.8942	0.5008	2.2333	1.1184	1.9970	**1.1065**	63.4
26.7	.4660	0.4493	0.8934	0.5029	2.2256	1.1194	1.9883	**1.1048**	63.3
26.8	.4677	0.4509	0.8926	0.5051	2.2179	1.1203	1.9797	**1.1030**	63.2
26.9	.4695	0.4524	0.8918	0.5073	2.2103	1.1213	1.9711	**1.1013**	63.1
27.0	.4712	0.4540	0.8910	0.5095	2.2027	1.1223	1.9626	**1.0996**	63.0
27.1	.4730	0.4555	0.8902	0.5117	2.1952	1.1233	1.9542	**1.0978**	62.9
27.2	.4747	0.4571	0.8894	0.5139	2.1877	1.1243	1.9458	**1.0961**	62.8
27.3	.4765	0.4586	0.8886	0.5161	2.1803	1.1253	1.9375	**1.0943**	62.7
27.4	.4782	0.4602	0.8878	0.5184	2.1730	1.1264	1.9292	**1.0926**	62.6
27.5	.4800	0.4617	0.8870	0.5206	2.1657	1.1274	1.9210	**1.0908**	62.5
27.6	.4817	0.4633	0.8862	0.5228	2.1584	1.1284	1.9128	**1.0891**	62.4
27.7	.4835	0.4648	0.8854	0.5250	2.1513	1.1294	1.9047	**1.0873**	62.3
27.8	.4852	0.4664	0.8846	0.5272	2.1441	1.1305	1.8967	**1.0856**	62.2
27.9	.4869	0.4679	0.8838	0.5295	2.1371	1.1315	1.8887	**1.0838**	62.1
28.0	.4887	0.4695	0.8829	0.5317	2.1301	1.1326	1.8807	**1.0821**	62.0
28.1	.4904	0.4710	0.8821	0.5339	2.1231	1.1336	1.8728	**1.0804**	61.9
28.2	.4922	0.4726	0.8813	0.5362	2.1162	1.1347	1.8650	**1.0786**	61.8
28.3	.4939	0.4741	0.8805	0.5384	2.1093	1.1357	1.8572	**1.0769**	61.7
28.4	.4957	0.4756	0.8796	0.5407	2.1025	1.1368	1.8495	**1.0751**	61.6
28.5	.4974	0.4772	0.8788	0.5430	2.0957	1.1379	1.8418	**1.0734**	61.5
28.6	.4992	0.4787	0.8780	0.5452	2.0890	1.1390	1.8341	**1.0716**	61.4
28.7	.5009	0.4802	0.8771	0.5475	2.0824	1.1401	1.8265	**1.0699**	61.3
28.8	.5027	0.4818	0.8763	0.5498	2.0758	1.1412	1.8190	**1.0681**	61.2
28.9	.5044	0.4833	0.8755	0.5520	2.0692	1.1423	1.8115	**1.0664**	61.1
29.0	.5061	0.4848	0.8746	0.5543	2.0627	1.1434	1.8040	**1.0647**	61.0
29.1	.5079	0.4863	0.8738	0.5566	2.0562	1.1445	1.7966	**1.0629**	60.9
29.2	.5096	0.4879	0.8729	0.5589	2.0598	1.1456	1.7893	**1.0612**	60.8
29.3	.5114	0.4894	0.8721	0.5612	2.0434	1.1467	1.7820	**1.0594**	60.7
29.4	.5131	0.4909	0.8712	0.5635	2.0371	1.1478	1.7747	**1.0577**	60.6
29.5	.5149	0.4924	0.8704	0.5658	2.0308	1.1490	1.7675	**1.0559**	60.5
29.6	.5166	0.4939	0.8695	0.5681	2.0245	1.1501	1.7603	**1.0542**	60.4
29.7	.5184	0.4955	0.8686	0.5704	2.0183	1.1512	1.7532	**1.0524**	60.3
29.8	.5201	0.4970	0.8678	0.5727	2.0122	1.1524	1.7461	**1.0507**	60.2
29.9	.5219	0.4985	0.8669	0.5750	2.0061	1.1535	1.7391	**1.0489**	60.1
		cos θ	**sin θ**	**cot θ**	**sec θ**	**csc θ**	**tan θ**	**radians**	**θ deg**

TABLE A.5 TRIGONOMETRIC FUNCTIONS: ANGLES EVERY 0.1 DEGREE (AND RADIANS) *(Continued)*

θ deg	radians	sin θ	cos θ	tan θ	csc θ	sec θ	cot θ	
30.0	.5236	0.5000	0.8660	0.5774	2.0000	1.1547	1.7321	**1.0472**	60.0
30.1	.5253	0.5015	0.8652	0.5797	1.9940	1.1559	1.7251	**1.0455**	59.9
30.2	.5271	0.5030	0.8643	0.5820	1.9880	1.1570	1.7182	**1.0437**	59.8
30.3	.5288	0.5045	0.8634	0.5844	1.9821	1.1582	1.7113	**1.0420**	59.7
30.4	.5306	0.5060	0.8625	0.5867	1.9762	1.1594	1.7045	**1.0402**	59.6
30.5	.5323	0.5075	0.8616	0.5890	1.9703	1.1606	1.6977	**1.0385**	59.5
30.6	.5341	0.5090	0.8607	0.5914	1.9645	1.1618	1.6909	**1.0367**	59.4
30.7	.5358	0.5105	0.8599	0.5938	1.9587	1.1630	1.6842	**1.0350**	59.3
30.8	.5376	0.5120	0.8590	0.5961	1.9530	1.1642	1.6775	**1.0332**	59.2
30.9	.5393	0.5135	0.8581	0.5985	1.9473	1.1654	1.6709	**1.0315**	59.1
31.0	.5411	0.5150	0.8572	0.6009	1.9416	1.1666	1.6643	**1.0297**	59.0
31.1	.5428	0.5165	0.8563	0.6032	1.9360	1.1679	1.6577	**1.0280**	58.9
31.2	.5445	0.5180	0.8554	0.6056	1.9304	1.1691	1.6512	**1.0263**	58.8
31.3	.5463	0.5195	0.8545	0.6080	1.9249	1.1703	1.6447	**1.0245**	58.7
31.4	.5480	0.5210	0.8536	0.6104	1.9194	1.1716	1.6383	**1.0228**	58.6
31.5	.5498	0.5225	0.8526	0.6128	1.9139	1.1728	1.6319	**1.0210**	58.5
31.6	.5515	0.5240	0.8517	0.6152	1.9084	1.1741	1.6255	**1.0193**	58.4
31.7	.5533	0.5255	0.8508	0.6176	1.9031	1.1753	1.6191	**1.0175**	58.3
31.8	.5550	0.5270	0.8499	0.6200	1.8977	1.1766	1.6128	**1.0158**	58.2
31.9	.5568	0.5284	0.8490	0.6224	1.8924	1.1779	1.6066	**1.0140**	58.1
32.0	.5585	0.5299	0.8480	0.6249	1.8871	1.1792	1.6003	**1.0123**	58.0
32.1	.5603	0.5314	0.8471	0.6273	1.8818	1.1805	1.5941	**1.0105**	57.9
32.2	.5620	0.5329	0.8462	0.6297	1.8766	1.1818	1.5880	**1.0088**	57.8
32.3	.5637	0.5344	0.8453	0.6322	1.8714	1.1831	1.5818	**1.0071**	57.7
32.4	.5655	0.5358	0.8443	0.6346	1.8663	1.1844	1.5757	**1.0053**	57.6
32.5	.5672	0.5373	0.8434	0.6371	1.8612	1.1857	1.5697	**1.0036**	57.5
32.6	.5690	0.5388	0.8425	0.6395	1.8561	1.1870	1.5637	**1.0018**	57.4
32.7	.5707	0.5402	0.8415	0.6420	1.8510	1.1883	1.5577	**1.0001**	57.3
32.8	.5725	0.5417	0.8406	0.6445	1.8460	1.1897	1.5517	**.9983**	57.2
32.9	.5742	0.5432	0.8396	0.6469	1.8410	1.1910	1.5458	**.9966**	57.1
33.0	.5760	0.5446	0.8387	0.6494	1.8361	1.1924	1.5399	**.9948**	57.0
33.1	.5777	0.5461	0.8377	0.6519	1.8312	1.1937	1.5340	**.9931**	56.9
33.2	.5794	0.5476	0.8368	0.6544	1.8263	1.1951	1.5282	**.9913**	56.8
33.3	.5812	0.5490	0.8358	0.6569	1.8214	1.1964	1.5224	**.9896**	56.7
33.4	.5829	0.5505	0.8348	0.6594	1.8166	1.1978	1.5166	**.9879**	56.6
33.5	.5847	0.5519	0.8339	0.6619	1.8118	1.1992	1.5108	**.9861**	56.5
33.6	.5864	0.5534	0.8329	0.6644	1.8070	1.2006	1.5051	**.9844**	56.4
33.7	.5882	0.5548	0.8320	0.6669	1.8023	1.2020	1.4994	**.9826**	56.3
33.8	.5899	0.5563	0.8310	0.6694	1.7976	1.2034	1.4938	**.9809**	56.2
33.9	.5917	0.5577	0.8300	0.6720	1.7929	1.2048	1.4882	**.9791**	56.1
34.0	.5934	0.5592	0.8290	0.6745	1.7883	1.2062	1.4826	**.9774**	56.0
34.1	.5952	0.5606	0.8281	0.6771	1.7837	1.2076	1.4770	**.9756**	55.9
34.2	.5969	0.5621	0.8271	0.6796	1.7791	1.2091	1.4715	**.9739**	55.8
34.3	.5986	0.5635	0.8261	0.6822	1.7745	1.2105	1.4659	**.9721**	55.7
34.4	.6004	0.5650	0.8251	0.6847	1.7700	1.2120	1.4605	**.9704**	55.6
34.5	.6021	0.5664	0.8241	0.6873	1.7655	1.2134	1.4550	**.9687**	55.5
34.6	.6039	0.5678	0.8231	0.6899	1.7610	1.2149	1.4496	**.9669**	55.4
34.7	.6056	0.5693	0.8221	0.6924	1.7566	1.2163	1.4442	**.9652**	55.3
34.8	.6074	0.5707	0.8211	0.6950	1.7522	1.2178	1.4388	**.9634**	55.2
34.9	.6091	0.5721	0.8202	0.6976	1.7478	1.2193	1.4335	**.9617**	55.1
		cos θ	**sin θ**	**cot θ**	**sec θ**	**csc θ**	**tan θ**	**radians**	**θ deg**

TABLE A.5   TRIGONOMETRIC FUNCTIONS: ANGLES EVERY 0.1 DEGREE (AND RADIANS) *(Continued)*

θ deg	radians	sin θ	cos θ	tan θ	csc θ	sec θ	cot θ		
35.0	.6109	0.5736	0.8192	0.7002	1.7434	1.2208	1.4281	**.9599**	55.0
35.1	.6126	0.5750	0.8181	0.7028	1.7391	1.2223	1.4229	**.9582**	54.9
35.2	.6144	0.5764	0.8171	0.7054	1.7348	1.2238	1.4176	**.9564**	54.8
35.3	.6161	0.5779	0.8161	0.7080	1.7305	1.2253	1.4124	**.9547**	54.7
35.4	.6178	0.5793	0.8151	0.7107	1.7263	1.2268	1.4071	**.9530**	54.6
35.5	.6196	0.5807	0.8141	0.7133	1.7221	1.2283	1.4019	**.9512**	54.5
35.6	.6213	0.5821	0.8131	0.7159	1.7179	1.2299	1.3968	**.9495**	54.4
35.7	.6231	0.5835	0.8121	0.7186	1.7137	1.2314	1.3916	**.9477**	54.3
35.8	.6248	0.5850	0.8111	0.7212	1.7095	1.2329	1.3865	**.9460**	54.2
35.9	.6266	0.5864	0.8100	0.7239	1.7054	1.2345	1.3814	**.9442**	54.1
36.0	.6283	0.5878	0.8090	0.7265	1.7013	1.2361	1.3764	**.9425**	54.0
36.1	.6301	0.5892	0.8080	0.7292	1.6972	1.2376	1.3713	**.9407**	53.9
36.2	.6318	0.5906	0.8070	0.7319	1.6932	1.2392	1.3663	**.9390**	53.8
36.3	.6336	0.5920	0.8059	0.7346	1.6892	1.2408	1.3613	**.9372**	53.7
36.4	.6353	0.5934	0.8049	0.7373	1.6852	1.2424	1.3564	**.9355**	53.6
36.5	.6370	0.5948	0.8039	0.7400	1.6812	1.2440	1.3514	**.9338**	53.5
36.6	.6388	0.5962	0.8028	0.7427	1.6772	1.2456	1.3465	**.9320**	53.4
36.7	.6405	0.5976	0.8018	0.7454	1.6733	1.2472	1.3416	**.9303**	53.3
36.8	.6423	0.5990	0.8007	0.7481	1.6694	1.2489	1.3367	**.9285**	53.2
36.9	.6440	0.6004	0.7997	0.7508	1.6655	1.2505	1.3319	**.9268**	53.1
37.0	.6458	0.6018	0.7986	0.7536	1.6616	1.2521	1.3270	**.9250**	53.0
37.1	.6475	0.6032	0.7976	0.7563	1.6578	1.2538	1.3222	**.9233**	52.9
37.2	.6493	0.6046	0.7965	0.7590	1.6540	1.2554	1.3175	**.9215**	52.8
37.3	.6510	0.6060	0.7955	0.7618	1.6502	1.2571	1.3127	**.9198**	52.7
37.4	.6528	0.6074	0.7944	0.7646	1.6464	1.2588	1.3079	**.9180**	52.6
37.5	.6545	0.6088	0.7934	0.7673	1.6427	1.2605	1.3032	**.9163**	52.5
37.6	.6562	0.6101	0.7923	0.7701	1.6390	1.2622	1.2985	**.9146**	52.4
37.7	.6580	0.6115	0.7912	0.7729	1.6353	1.2639	1.2938	**.9128**	52.3
37.8	.6597	0.6129	0.7902	0.7757	1.6316	1.2656	1.2892	**.9111**	52.2
37.9	.6615	0.6143	0.7891	0.7785	1.6279	1.2673	1.2846	**.9093**	52.1
38.0	.6632	0.6157	0.7880	0.7813	1.6243	1.2690	1.2799	**.9076**	52.0
38.1	.6650	0.6170	0.7869	0.7841	1.6207	1.2708	1.2753	**.9058**	51.9
38.2	.6667	0.6184	0.7859	0.7869	1.6171	1.2725	1.2708	**.9041**	51.8
38.3	.6685	0.6198	0.7848	0.7898	1.6135	1.2742	1.2662	**.9023**	51.7
38.4	.6702	0.6211	0.7837	0.7926	1.6099	1.2760	1.2617	**.9006**	51.6
38.5	.6720	0.6225	0.7826	0.7954	1.6064	1.2778	1.2572	**.8988**	51.5
38.6	.6737	0.6239	0.7815	0.7983	1.6029	1.2796	1.2527	**.8971**	51.4
38.7	.6754	0.6252	0.7804	0.8012	1.5994	1.2813	1.2482	**.8954**	51.3
38.8	.6772	0.6266	0.7793	0.8040	1.5959	1.2831	1.2437	**.8936**	51.2
38.9	.6789	0.6280	0.7782	0.8069	1.5925	1.2849	1.2393	**.8919**	51.1
39.0	.6807	0.6293	0.7771	0.8098	1.5890	1.2868	1.2349	**.8901**	51.0
39.1	.6824	0.6307	0.7760	0.8127	1.5856	1.2886	1.2305	**.8884**	50.9
39.2	.6842	0.6320	0.7749	0.8156	1.5822	1.2904	1.2261	**.8866**	50.8
39.3	.6859	0.6334	0.7738	0.8185	1.5788	1.2923	1.2218	**.8849**	50.7
39.4	.6877	0.6347	0.7727	0.8214	1.5755	1.2941	1.2174	**.8831**	50.6
39.5	.6894	0.6361	0.7716	0.8243	1.5721	1.2960	1.2131	**.8814**	50.5
39.6	.6912	0.6374	0.7705	0.8273	1.5688	1.2978	1.2088	**.8796**	50.4
39.7	.6929	0.6388	0.7694	0.8302	1.5655	1.2997	1.2045	**.8779**	50.3
39.8	.6946	0.6401	0.7683	0.8332	1.5622	1.3016	1.2002	**.8762**	50.2
39.9	.6964	0.6414	0.7672	0.8361	1.5590	1.3035	1.1960	**.8744**	50.1
		cos θ	sin θ	cot θ	sec θ	csc θ	tan θ	radians	θ deg

TABLE A.5 TRIGONOMETRIC FUNCTIONS: ANGLES EVERY 0.1 DEGREE (AND RADIANS) *(Continued)*

θ deg	radians	sin θ	cos θ	tan θ	csc θ	sec θ	cot θ		
40.0	.6981	0.6428	0.7660	0.8391	1.5557	1.3054	1.1918	.8727	50.0
40.1	.6999	0.6441	0.7649	0.8421	1.5525	1.3073	1.1875	.8709	49.9
40.2	.7016	0.6455	0.7638	0.8451	1.5493	1.3092	1.1833	.8692	49.8
40.3	.7034	0.6468	0.7627	0.8481	1.5461	1.3112	1.1792	.8674	49.7
40.4	.7051	0.6481	0.7615	0.8511	1.5429	1.3131	1.1750	.8657	49.6
40.5	.7069	0.6494	0.7604	0.8541	1.5398	1.3151	1.1708	.8639	49.5
40.6	.7086	0.6508	0.7593	0.8571	1.5366	1.3171	1.1667	.8622	49.4
40.7	.7103	0.6521	0.7581	0.8601	1.5335	1.3190	1.1626	.8604	49.3
40.8	.7121	0.6534	0.7570	0.8632	1.5304	1.3210	1.1585	.8587	49.2
40.9	.7138	0.6547	0.7559	0.8662	1.5273	1.3230	1.1544	.8570	49.1
41.0	.7156	0.6561	0.7547	0.8693	1.5243	1.3250	1.1504	.8552	49.0
41.1	.7173	0.6574	0.7536	0.8724	1.5212	1.3270	1.1463	.8535	48.9
41.2	.7191	0.6587	0.7524	0.8754	1.5182	1.3291	1.1423	.8517	48.8
41.3	.7208	0.6600	0.7513	0.8785	1.5151	1.3311	1.1383	.8500	48.7
41.4	.7226	0.6613	0.7501	0.8816	1.5121	1.3331	1.1343	.8482	48.6
41.5	.7243	0.6626	0.7490	0.8847	1.5092	1.3352	1.1303	.8465	48.5
41.6	.7261	0.6639	0.7478	0.8878	1.5062	1.3373	1.1263	.8447	48.4
41.7	.7278	0.6652	0.7466	0.8910	1.5052	1.3393	1.1224	.8430	48.3
41.8	.7295	0.6665	0.7455	0.8941	1.5003	1.3414	1.1184	.8412	48.2
41.9	.7313	0.6678	0.7443	0.8972	1.4974	1.3435	1.1145	.8395	48.1
42.0	.7330	0.6691	0.7431	0.9004	1.4945	1.3456	1.1106	.8378	48.0
42.1	.7348	0.6704	0.7420	0.9036	1.4916	1.3478	1.1067	.8360	47.9
42.2	.7365	0.6717	0.7408	0.9067	1.4887	1.3499	1.1028	.8343	47.8
42.3	.7383	0.6730	0.7396	0.9099	1.4859	1.3520	1.0990	.8325	47.7
42.4	.7400	0.6743	0.7385	0.9131	1.4830	1.3542	1.0951	.8308	47.6
42.5	.7418	0.6756	0.7373	0.9163	1.4802	1.3563	1.0913	.8290	47.5
42.6	.7435	0.6769	0.7361	0.9195	1.4774	1.3585	1.0875	.8273	47.4
42.7	.7453	0.6782	0.7349	0.9228	1.4746	1.3607	1.0837	.8255	47.3
42.8	.7470	0.6794	0.7337	0.9260	1.4718	1.3629	1.0799	.8238	47.2
42.9	.7487	0.6807	0.7325	0.9293	1.4690	1.3651	1.0761	.8221	47.1
43.0	.7505	0.6820	0.7314	0.9325	1.4663	1.3673	1.0724	.8203	47.0
43.1	.7522	0.6833	0.7302	0.9358	1.4635	1.3696	1.0686	.8186	46.9
43.2	.7540	0.6845	0.7290	0.9391	1.4608	1.3718	1.0649	.8168	46.8
43.3	.7557	0.6858	0.7278	0.9424	1.4581	1.3741	1.0612	.8151	46.7
43.4	.7575	0.6871	0.7266	0.9457	1.4554	1.3763	1.0575	.8133	46.6
43.5	.7592	0.6884	0.7354	0.9490	1.4527	1.3786	1.0538	.8116	46.5
43.6	.7610	0.6896	0.7242	0.9523	1.4501	1.3809	1.0501	.8098	46.4
43.7	.7627	0.6909	0.7230	0.9556	1.4474	1.3832	1.0464	.8081	46.3
43.8	.7645	0.6921	0.7218	0.9590	1.4448	1.3855	1.0428	.8063	46.2
43.9	.7662	0.6934	0.7206	0.9623	1.4422	1.3878	1.0392	.8046	46.1
44.0	.7679	0.6947	0.7193	0.9657	1.4396	1.3902	1.0355	.8029	46.0
44.1	.7697	0.6959	0.7181	0.9691	1.4370	1.3925	1.0319	.8011	45.9
44.2	.7714	0.6972	0.7169	0.9725	1.4344	1.3949	1.0283	.7994	45.8
44.3	.7732	0.6984	0.7157	0.9759	1.4318	1.3972	1.0247	.7976	45.7
44.4	.7749	0.6997	0.7145	0.9793	1.4293	1.3996	1.0212	.7959	45.6
44.5	.7767	0.7009	0.7133	0.9827	1.4267	1.4020	1.0176	.7941	45.5
44.6	.7784	0.7022	0.7120	0.9861	1.4242	1.4044	1.0141	.7924	45.4
44.7	.7802	0.7034	0.7108	0.9896	1.4217	1.4069	1.0105	.7906	45.3
44.8	.7819	0.7046	0.7096	0.9930	1.4192	1.4093	1.0070	.7889	45.2
44.9	.7837	0.7059	0.7083	0.9965	1.4167	1.4118	1.0035	.7871	45.1
45.0	.7854	0.7071	0.7071	1.0000	1.4142	1.4142	1.0000	.7854	45.0
		cos θ	sin θ	cot θ	sec θ	csc θ	tan θ	radians	θ deg

Answers to Selected Problems

EXERCISE 1.1

1 Same digits in each side **2** Same digits in each side **3** Each nonzero digit is used just once **5** Yes, no **6** No, yes
7 Yes, yes **9** 3530.98 **10** 2232.72 **11** 44.8 **13** $-3 \neq 3$ **14** $2 \neq \frac{1}{2}$ **15** $12 \neq \frac{4}{3}$ **17** -36 **18** 96 **19** 6 **21** 8
22 -15 **23** -14 **25** 7 **26** 0 **27** -9 **29** 8 **30** 4 **31** -7 **33** -1 **34** 1 **35** 7 **37** True **38** True **39** True
41 Yes **42** Yes **43** Yes **45** $4 - \pi$ **46** $\pi - 3$ **47** $10 - x$ **49** 5, -6 **50** 18, -3 **51** 1, 2, 13
53 $-5.33 < -5.3 < -5 + 0.33$ **54** $-8 < -7 < 7$ **55** $-8 < -2 < 2$ **77** Positive, negative **78** Positive, negative
79 Negative, positive **81** False unless $a = 1$ **82** False unless $c = 0$ **83** False **89** $A \cup B = \{12, 13, 14, 15, 16, 18, 20, 22\}$,
$A \cap B = \{12, 18\}$ **90** $A \cup B = \{3, 5, 7, 8, 11, 14, 15, 17, 19, 20, 23\}$, $A \cap B = \{11, 23\}$ **91** $\{1, 5, 9, 13, 17, 21, 25, 29\}$
93 $(5, 9]$ **94** $[4, 12)$ **95** $(2, 8]$

EXERCISE 1.2

1 128 **2** 25 **3** 64 **5** $6x^3y^4$ **6** $-14x^5y^7$ **7** $-6x^7y^7$ **9** $4x^3y$ **10** $9x^3y^3$ **11** $6xy$ **13** $8a^6b^3c^9$ **14** $9a^6b^4c^8$ **15** $625a^4b^8c^{16}$
17 $\dfrac{a^6b^4}{4c^6d^8}$ **18** $\dfrac{a^{12}b^9c^3}{8d^6}$ **19** $\dfrac{4x^8y^6}{9w^4z^2}$ **21** $324a^8b^6$ **22** $108a^{13}b^9$ **23** $200c^8d^{13}$ **25** $\dfrac{uv}{2w^2}$ **26** $\dfrac{3b^6}{4c}$ **27** $\dfrac{4y^6}{11x^6z^5}$ **29** ac^2d^3
30 $\dfrac{c^4}{b^{10}}$ **31** $\dfrac{b^7c^9}{108a^5}$ **33** $\frac{1}{27}$ **34** $\frac{1}{5}$ **35** $\frac{1}{81}$ **37** $\dfrac{18}{p^5q^2}$ **38** $\dfrac{q^2}{3p}$ **39** $\dfrac{6b^3}{a^5}$ **41** $\dfrac{b^6}{a^4}$ **42** $a^{12}b^3$ **43** $\dfrac{1}{a^6b^2}$ **45** $\dfrac{1}{a^2b^4}$
46 $\dfrac{a^4}{b^2}$ **47** $\dfrac{b^3}{a^9}$ **49** $\dfrac{n}{a^4t^3}$ **50** $\dfrac{u^{10}}{b^6g^6}$ **51** $\dfrac{a^6}{s^8t^6}$ **53** $2b^2$ **54** $\dfrac{1}{a^2}$ **55** $-c^3$ **57** $1 - (\frac{2}{11})^8$ **58** $3/(50a^2)$ **59** 4.70 and 2.29
61 $7.82(10^{11})$ **62** $2.64(10^{31})$ **63** $9.51(10^{21})$ **65** $6.0(10^{26})$ **66** $7.7(10^{12})$ **67** $7.42(10^{58})$ **69** 35.98 **70** 260.684
71 1085.9 **73** 60.1 **74** 142.3 **75** 14.53 **77** 4, 0.64 **78** 0.57 **79** 0.28, 0.0038 **81** $7 + 9$, $31 + 33$, $127 + 129$
82 $1 + 3 + 5 + 7 + 9 = 25$, $21 + 23 + 25 + 27 + 29 = 125$, $121 + 123 + 125 + 127 + 129 = 625$ **83** Each is 2592
85 $x^{46} = x^2x^4x^8x^{32}$ **86** $x^{55} = x^1x^2x^4x^{16}x^{32}$ **87** $x^{33} = \dfrac{x^9x^{27}}{x^3}$ **89** 1.3125 **90** 3.735

EXERCISE 1.3

1 33 **2** $\frac{9}{5}$ **3** $\frac{17}{5}$ **5** $-25x + 13t$ **6** $n + b + a$ **7** $5ax - 4bx - 3ay - 2by$ **9** $-5y + 3z$ **10** $-3y + 2z$ **11** $2x - 5b$
13 $4b$ **14** $6a + 4b$ **15** $6a + b + c$ **17** $4a - 4ab - 2bc - 2c$ **18** $2a^3 + 10a^2$ **19** $4a - 7b - 3ab$ **21** $-6x + 4y + 4z$
22 $-3a - 5b + 6c$ **23** $12d - 6e - 6f$ **25** $x^3 + 4x^2 - 6x + 3$ **26** $-x^3 + 7x^2 + 5x - 2$ **27** $x^4 + 3x^3 - 4x^2 + 6x - 1$
29 $9ab^2 + 6ab - 6a^2b$ **30** $-xy + 2xy^2 + 3xy^3$ **31** $p^2q + 2pq + pq^2$ **33** $-a - b - 7c$ **34** $a + b - c$ **35** $-2x + 4y - 9z$
37 $-6x^3y^5 + 4x^4y^4$ **38** $-6x^3y^5 + 15x^4y^3$ **39** $10x^4y^6 - 20x^6y^5$ **41** $-4x^3y + 3xy^3$ **42** $-2x^2y + 11x^3y^2$ **43** $2x^3y^4 + 13x^2y^6$
45 $2x^4 - 3x^3y - 8x^2y^2 + 15xy^3 - 6y^4$ **46** $6x^4 - 5x^3y + 6x^2y^2 - xy^3 - 6y^4$ **47** $10x^4 - x^3y + 15x^2y^2 + 5xy^3 + 3y^4$
49 $8x^2 + 22x + 15$ **50** $6x^2 + x - 15$ **51** $10x^2 - 29x + 10$ **53** $6x^2 - 7xy - 20y^2$ **54** $28x^2 - 33xy - 28y^2$

55 $30x^2 + 17xy - 35y^2$ **57** $4a^2 + 4ab + b^2$ **58** $9a^2 + 12ab + 4b^2$ **59** $36a^2 + 60ab + 25b^2$ **61** $x^3 + 6x^2y + 12xy^2 + 8y^3$
62 $27x^3 + 135x^2y + 225xy^2 + 125y^3$ **63** $8x^3 + 12x^4 + 6x^5 + x^6$ **65** $125x^3 - 75x^2y + 15xy^2 - y^3$
66 $216x^3 - 540x^2y + 450xy^2 - 125y^3$ **67** $343x^3 - 294x^2 + 84x - 8$ **69** $x^2 - 16$ **70** $x^2 - 49$ **71** $9x^2 - 25$ **73** $4x^2 - 25y^2$
74 $9x^2 - 16y^2$ **75** $49x^2 - 36y^2$ **77** $4a^4 - 9b^4$ **78** $4a^4 - 25b^4$ **79** $25a^4 - 49b^6$ **81** $x^2 + y^2 + z^2 + 2xy + 2xz + 2yz$
82 $4x^2 + y^2 + z^2 - 4xy + 4xz - 2yz$ **83** $x^2 + y^2 + 9z^2 - 2xy + 6xz - 6yz$ **85** $x^6 + x^4 + 3x^2 - 1$ **86** $x^4 - x^6 + x^2 - 1$
87 $4x^8 + 8x^5 + x^2 - x^6 - 4x^4$ **89** $3x^2 - 2x + 1, 1$ **90** $2x^2 - x + 2, 1$ **91** $3x^2 + 6x + 1, 13$ **93** $2x^2 + x - 1, 6x - 2$
94 $x^2 - 2x + 2, -1$ **95** $2x^3 - x^2 + x - 3, -3$ **102** $(2n + 1)(2k + 1) = 2n(2k + 1) + 2k + 1 = 2(2nk + n + k) + 1$
103 $(3k + 2)^2 = 9k^2 + 12k + 4 = 3(3k^2 + 4k + 1) + 1$ **105** $125,000 + 22,500x + 1350x^2 + 27x^3; 274,625$
106 $75[1 - 4/(3 + x)^2] = 75\dfrac{(x + 1)(x + 5)}{(3 + x)^2}, \dfrac{225}{4}, \dfrac{200}{3}$ **107** $-x^2 + 84x - 1440$

EXERCISE 1.4

1 $3(x + 3)$ **2** $7(x - 4)$ **3** $5(x + 6)$ **5** $x(x + 3)$ **6** $x(x - 4)$ **7** $x^2(x + 6)$ **9** $(x - 1)(2x + 1)$ **10** $(2x + 3)(7x + 5)$
11 $(x + 1)(x + 2)(3x + 4)$ **13** $(a + x)(a - x)$ **14** $(3 + y)(3 - y)$ **15** $(x + 5)(x - 5)$ **17** $(4y + 5a)(4y - 5a)$
18 $(8x + 7y)(8x - 7y)$ **19** $(4x + 9y)(4x - 9y)$ **21** $(x + y + 1)(x - y - 1)$ **22** $(2x + 3y + 2)(2x - 3y - 2)$
23 $(2x - 3 + 3y)(2x - 3 - 3y)$ **25** $z(x - 2y)(x^2 + 2xy + 4y^2)$ **26** $c^2(3a + b)(9a^2 - 3ab + b^2)$
27 $k(2a + 5b)(4a^2 - 10ab + 25b^2)$ **29** $(x + y - 1)(x^2 + 2xy + y^2 + x + y + 1)$
30 $(2x - y - 2)(4x^2 - 4xy + y^2 + 4x - 2y + 4)$ **31** $(3x + 2y + 3)(9x^2 + 12xy + 4y^2 - 9x - 6y + 9)$
33 $(4x^2 + y^2)(2x + y)(2x - y)$ **34** $(x^2 + 9y^2)(x + 3y)(x - 3y)$ **35** $(9x^2 + 25y^2)(3x + 5y)(3x - 5y)$ **37** $b(2a - 1)^2$
38 $d(3b + 1)^2$ **39** $(5x + 1)^2$ **41** $(2x - 3)^2$ **42** $y^2(3x + 4)^2$ **43** $(5x + 6)^2k$ **45** $(3x + 1)(x + 2)$ **46** $(2x + 1)(x + 2)$
47 $(2x + 3)(3x - 1)$ **49** $(7x - 3)(x - 1)x$ **50** $(3x - 2)(x + 5)x^2$ **51** $(2x - 1)(2x + 3)x^3$ **53** 65 **54** -4 **55** -104 **57** 153
58 40 **59** 161 **61** $(x + 5)(x - 1)$ **62** $(5x - 1)(x + 1)$ **63** $(2x + 3)(x - 3)$ **65** $(x - 4y)(2x + 7y)$ **66** $(x - 3y)(3x + 8y)$
67 $(x - 3y)(5x + 6y)$ **69** $(4x - 5y)(5x + 7y)$ **70** $(12x - 5y)(2x + 3y)$ **71** $(7x - 5y)(6x + 5y)$ **73** $(6x - 7y)(5x + 7y)$
74 $(6x - 5y)(9x + 7y)$ **75** $(15x - 4y)(2x + 3y)$ **77** $(x + 3)(y + 1)$ **78** $(x + 4)(y - 2)$ **79** $(x - 3)(y + 4)$
81 $(2x - 1)(x + 2y)$ **82** $(3x + 2)(x - 4y)$ **83** $(x + 2)(2x - 3y)$ **85** $(x + 1)(x - 1)(3x + 2)$ **86** $(2x - 1)(x^2 + 2)$
87 $(x^2 + 3)(2x - 5)$ **89** $(x + 2y + z)(x + 2y - z)$ **90** $(2x - y + 3z)(2x - y - 3z)$ **91** $(x + 3y - z)(x - 3y + z)$
95 $3k^2 + 6k + 4$ **97** $t^2(18 - t), (b - a)(18b + 18a - b^2 - ab - a^2)$ **98** $75[1 - 2/(3 + x)][1 + 2/(3 + x)], \frac{125}{3}, 63$
99 $(b - a)(130 - b - a)$ **101** $60(b - a)(b + a + 6)$ **102** $8(T - t)(2T + 2t - 5)$ **103** $(p + 30)(p - 20)$
105 If $t = (1 - b)p = p - bp$, then $1 - t = 1 - p + bp = (1 - b)(1 - p) + b$ **106** $6(b - a)(3b + 3a + 2)$
107 $n(n + 1)(2n + 1) + 6(n + 1)^2 = (n + 1)[n(2n + 1) + 6(n + 1)] = (n + 1)(2n^2 + 7n + 6) = (n + 1)(n + 2)(2n + 3)$

EXERCISE 1.5

1 $4xy^2$ **2** $\dfrac{2y}{x}$ **3** $\dfrac{3x^2}{5y}$ **5** $\dfrac{x - 2}{x - 1}$ **6** $\dfrac{x - 1}{x - 3}$ **7** $\dfrac{2x - 1}{2x + 1}$ **9** $\dfrac{(x - 2)^2}{(x - 1)(x + 3)}$ **10** $\dfrac{x - 3}{x - 1}$ **11** $\dfrac{x - 2}{x + 1}$ **13** $\dfrac{32xy^3}{15z^2}$ **14** $\dfrac{4y^3}{5xv^3}$
15 $\dfrac{x}{3v}$ **17** $\dfrac{5}{9}$ **18** $\dfrac{xw}{2y}$ **19** 1 **21** $\dfrac{y(2x - y)}{2x}$ **22** $\dfrac{y(x + 4)}{2}$ **23** $\dfrac{x^2}{y(2x - 3y)}$ **25** $\dfrac{w^2}{z^2}$ **26** $\dfrac{q}{p^2}$ **27** $\dfrac{3xz}{y^2(x - 7y)^2}$ **29** $\dfrac{y^3}{x}$
30 $\dfrac{x(x + y)}{y - x}$ **31** $\dfrac{(x - y)(y + z)}{(y - z)(x + z)}$ **33** $2x$ **34** $\dfrac{1}{x + 3y}$ **35** x **37** $\dfrac{18x - 7}{6x + 1}$ **38** $\dfrac{-(8x + 1)}{x^2 + 11}$ **39** $\dfrac{6a + 7b - 9c}{d - 1}$ **41** $\dfrac{-a}{b}$
42 0 **43** $\dfrac{a^2 + b^2}{5ab}$ **45** $\dfrac{15x^2 + 9xy - 2y^2}{2y(3x + y)}$ **46** $\dfrac{3x^2 - 2y^2}{x(2x + y)}$ **47** $\dfrac{9x^2 + 4y^2}{2y(3x + 2y)}$ **49** $\dfrac{6xy}{(x - y)(x + y)}$ **50** $\dfrac{5x^2 - 9xy + 3y^2}{(2x - y)(3x - y)}$
51 $\dfrac{9x^2 - 62xy + 34y^2}{(3x - 8y)(2x - 5y)}$ **53** $\dfrac{1}{r - s}$ **54** $\dfrac{r + s}{s}$ **55** $\dfrac{r + s}{r}$ **57** $\dfrac{2x + 3}{y(x + y)}$ **58** $\dfrac{2x - 3y}{x(3x + 2y)}$ **59** $\dfrac{2(x + 2y)}{y(x - 2y)}$ **61** $\dfrac{1}{(x - y)(x - 2y)}$
62 $\dfrac{4(a + 2b)}{(a + b)(a - 2b)(a + 3b)}$ **63** $\dfrac{7}{(a + 5b)(a - 4b)}$ **65** $(3x^2 + 8x)/(x + 1)^3$ **66** $(4x^2 - 19x + 23)/(x - 2)^3$
67 $(x^2 + 8x + 3)/(3 + x)^2(1 - x)$ **69** $(y - x)/(y + x)$ **70** $(y - x)/(y + 2x)$ **71** $(a - 2)/(a - 4)$ **73** $1/(p + q)$
74 $-2p/3(p - 1)$ **75** $(3x + 2)/(x + 3)$ **77** $-3/7(3x + 5)$ **78** $-4/5(4x - 5)$ **79** $(2 - x)/10(x^2 + 6)$ **81** $(2x + 1)/(7x + 3)$
82 $(68x - 115)/(13x - 22)$ **83** $(35x + 156)/(11x + 49)$ **85** $2x - 17$ **86** $47x + 10$ **87** $2xy/(x^2 - 4y^2)$

91 $\frac{12}{78}, \frac{11}{78}, \frac{10}{78}, \frac{9}{78}, \frac{8}{78}, \frac{7}{78}, \frac{6}{78}, \frac{5}{78}, \frac{4}{78}, \frac{3}{78}, \frac{2}{78}, \frac{1}{78}$; sum is 1　**95** $(x - y)(3xy - 480,000)/xy$　**97** $(b - a)[2\pi ab(a + b) - 200]/ab$
99 0.492　**101** $7x^3 - 20x^2 + 45x - 17$　**102** $27x^2 + 88x - 98$

EXERCISE 1.6

1 Real　**2** Not real　**3** Real　**5** $3\sqrt{2}$, $\sqrt{105}$　**6** $9\sqrt{2}$, $5\sqrt{7}$　**7** $8\sqrt{3}$, $(-3) \cdot \sqrt[3]{5}$　**9** $3a^3b^2 \cdot \sqrt{7a}$　**10** $7a^3b^2 \cdot \sqrt{3b}$
11 $5b^2 \cdot \sqrt{7}$　**13** $-2ab^3 \cdot \sqrt[3]{3}$　**14** $3a^2b^2 \cdot \sqrt[4]{4b}$　**15** $3ab \cdot \sqrt[4]{3a^2b}$　**17** $6 \cdot \sqrt{6}$　**18** $3 \cdot \sqrt[4]{5}$　**19** $9 \cdot \sqrt{5}$　**21** $3x^2y\sqrt{6y}$
22 $11x^2y^2 \cdot \sqrt{7y}$　**23** $6xy^2 \cdot \sqrt{5x}$　**25** $2x^2y \cdot \sqrt[3]{3}$　**26** $2x^2y \cdot \sqrt[3]{20x^2y}$　**27** $2y \cdot \sqrt[4]{27x^3y}$　**29** $\sqrt[4]{2}$　**30** $\sqrt[5]{5}$　**31** $\sqrt[8]{3}$
33 $\sqrt[6]{a^2} = \sqrt[3]{a}$　**34** $\sqrt[8]{a}$　**35** $\sqrt[20]{a^2} = \sqrt[10]{a}$　**37** $-\sqrt{3}$　**38** $7\sqrt{5}$　**39** $-\sqrt[3]{2}$　**41** $5\sqrt{2} + \sqrt[3]{2}$　**42** $\sqrt{3} + 5\sqrt[3]{2}$
43 $11\sqrt{2} - 3\sqrt[3]{3}$　**45** $3a\sqrt{b} - b\sqrt{a}$　**46** $(r + 3t^2)\sqrt{2rt} + r(r - t)\sqrt{r}$　**47** $(2c + 3d)\sqrt[3]{c^2d} + cd(3 - c)\sqrt[3]{cd^2}$　**49** $x^2\sqrt{15xy}/5y$
50 $\sqrt{6xy}/4y^2$　**51** $x\sqrt{xy}/5y^3$　**53** $9x^2y\sqrt{y}/7$　**54** $2xy^2\sqrt{y}/3$　**55** $xy\sqrt[4]{42y}/6$　**57** $3x\sqrt[3]{2y}/2y$　**58** $5\sqrt[3]{12x^2y^2}/6y$　**59** $x\sqrt[4]{24xy^2}/3y$
61 $7x^2y^2\sqrt{xy}/9$　**62** $x^4y^3\sqrt[3]{102y}/6$　**63** $3x^2y^5\sqrt{2}/14$　**65** $-1 - \sqrt{3}$　**66** $-(\sqrt{2} + 3)$　**67** $3(\sqrt{5} - 2)$　**69** $2(\sqrt{5} + \sqrt{2})$
70 $-(\sqrt{3} + \sqrt{7})/2$　**71** $\sqrt{10} + \sqrt{5}$　**73** $(2\sqrt{5} + 2\sqrt{3} + \sqrt{15} + 3)/2$　**74** $(\sqrt{3} - \sqrt{5} + 2\sqrt{15} - 10)/(-2)$　**75** $-7 - 3\sqrt{6}$
77 $1/(\sqrt{x + h + 3} + \sqrt{x + 3})$　**78** $2/(\sqrt{2x + 2h - 5} + \sqrt{2x - 5})$　**79** $3/(\sqrt{3x - 2} + \sqrt{10})$　**81** $6\sqrt{35} \approx 35.5$　**82** 681 days
83 $\sqrt{(L + 2m)/m}$　**85** 10.71　**86** -6.53　**87** 5.30　**89** 1.85, 1.96, 1.99　**90** 2.91, 2.98, 3.00　**91** 3.932, 3.992, 3.999
93 $(3 + \sqrt{7})/2 + (3 - \sqrt{7})/2 + 2\sqrt{(9 - 7)/4} = 3 + \sqrt{2}$　**94** $(4 + \sqrt{11})/2 + (4 - \sqrt{11})/2 + 2\sqrt{(16 - 11)/4} = 4 + \sqrt{5}$
95 $(5 + \sqrt{14})/2 + (5 - \sqrt{14})/2 + 2\sqrt{(25 - 14)/4} = 5 + \sqrt{11}$　**97** $2 + \sqrt{3} + 2 - \sqrt{3} = 4$
98 $2 + \sqrt{3} - (2 - \sqrt{3}) = 2\sqrt{3}$　**99** $\sqrt{3} + \sqrt{2} - (\sqrt{3} - \sqrt{2}) = 2\sqrt{2}$
101 $(\sqrt{m} + \sqrt{n} + \sqrt{p})(\sqrt{m} + \sqrt{n} - \sqrt{p})(m + n - p - 2\sqrt{mn}) = (m + n - p + 2\sqrt{mn})(m + n - p - 2\sqrt{mn}) = m^2 + n^2 + p^2 + 2mn - 2mp - 2np - 4mn = m^2 + n^2 + p^2 - 2mn - 2mp - 2np$　**103** (a) $\sqrt[12]{16}$, $\frac{5}{4}$ (b) $\sqrt[12]{32}$, $\frac{4}{3}$ (c) $\sqrt[12]{128}$, $\frac{3}{2}$　**105** 0.671
106 4350, 4341.65, 4346

EXERCISE 1.7

1 5　**2** 7　**3** 4　**5** 9　**6** 8　**7** 256　**9** $\frac{1}{2}$　**10** $\frac{1}{8}$　**11** $\frac{1}{8}$　**13** $\frac{8}{125}$　**14** $\frac{256}{81}$　**15** $\frac{9}{4}$　**17** $\frac{9}{7}$　**18** $\frac{5}{6}$　**19** $\frac{9}{25}$　**21** 64　**22** 25　**23** 8
25 $4ab^2$　**26** $3a^2b^3$　**27** $7a^3b^4$　**29** $3pq^2$　**30** $4p^3q^2$　**31** $2p^2q$　**33** $5a/b^2c^3$　**34** $2a^2/bc^3$　**35** $a^2b/3$　**37** $\sqrt[5]{xy^3}$　**38** $\sqrt[3]{x^2y}$
39 $\sqrt[6]{x^4y^5}$　**41** $\sqrt[12]{x^8/y^3}$　**42** $\sqrt[6]{y^4/x^3}$　**43** $\sqrt[15]{1/x^9y^{10}}$　**45** $6x^{5/6}$　**46** $10x^{7/12}$　**47** $12x^{7/10}$　**49** $4x^{1/3}y^{3/4}/y$　**50** $3x^{1/5}y^{1/6}/y$
51 $5x^{1/2}y^{1/2}/y^2$　**53** $4x^{1/8}y^{4/5}/y$　**54** $ab^{2/3}/3b$　**55** $a^{1/3}b^{6/7}/3b$　**57** $9y^{14/9}/4x^6$　**58** $3x^{5/6}y^{11/12}/xy$　**59** $x^{1/6}y^{1/4}/2y$　**61** $\frac{4}{3}$　**62** $3/5a^3b$
63 $4^{1/3}a^{1/3}/4a^3b^4$　**65** $(60x + 29)(5x + 3)^{1/2}/(10x + 6)$　**66** $(1 - 9x)(5 - 3x)^{1/2}/(10 - 6x)$　**67** $(21x - 24)(2x - 5)^{3/4}/(4x - 10)$
69 $(14x + 5)(x + 1)^{1/2}(2x - 1)^{2/3}/6(x + 1)(2x - 1)$　**70** $(35x + 26)(x + 1)^{1/2}(5x + 2)^{2/3}/6(x + 1)(5x + 2)$
71 $(9x + 8)(3x - 1)^{1/2}(2x + 3)^{1/4}/2(3x - 1)(2x + 3)$　**73** $x^{4/b}$　**74** x^a　**75** x^{4ab}　**77** $2.5\sqrt{5}$　**78** 21.1　**79** $S = S_0 + \sqrt{R/k}$
81 (a) 19,280 (b) 12,929　**82** 8176　**83** 32.15, 32.61　**85** $(x^2 + 25)^{3/2}$　**86** $(4x^2 + 49)^{5/2}$　**87** $(16x^2 - 1)^{3/2}$
89 $(x + 2y)^{3/4}$, $(x^3 + 2y^3)^{1/4}$　**90** $x^{4/5} + y^{4/5}$, $(x + y)^{4/5}$　**91** $(3x - y)^{5/6}$, $(3x)^{5/6} - y^{5/6}$　**93** $(2x + 1/8x)^2$　**94** $(x^{2/3} + 1/4x^{2/3})^2$
95 $(\sqrt{x} + 1/4\sqrt{x})^2$

EXERCISE 1.8

1 $460 = 2^2 \cdot 5 \cdot 23$　**2** Distributive　**3** No integral factors except itself and 1　**4** $\frac{3}{2}$, -5　**5** 8　**6** It is, it is　**7** $54 = (\frac{3}{2})36$
8 472 and 853　**9** Yes, no　**10** $\frac{2}{11}$, 3.141414 $\cdots$　**11** -81, 81　**12** 1296, $\frac{125}{343}$　**13** $\frac{1}{9}$, $\frac{1}{8}$, $-\frac{1}{8}$　**14** $16c^4d^3a^2/3$
15 $2c^2/a^3t^3$　**16** $5.83(10^2)$, $5.83(10^{-3})$, $5.083(10)$, $(2.03)10^{-3}$　**17** 73.6, 73.7, 0.0737, $7.37(10^5)$　**18** $1.14(10^3)$, 0.725
19 8.539, 5.860　**20** $12a^3 - 24a^2 - 10a - 3$　**21** $15x^2 + 2xy - 8y^2$　**22** $9x^2 - 25y^2$　**23** $27x^3 - 135x^2y + 225xy^2 - 125y^3$
24 $x^2 + 4y^2 + 9z^2 - 4xy + 6xz - 12yz$　**25** $4x^2 - 25y^2 + 70yz - 49z^2$　**26** $3x^2 - 5x + 4$, 19
27 $2x^4 + x^3y - 18x^2y^2 + 13xy^3 - 2y^4$　**28** $(3a - 2b)(9a^2 + 6ab + 4b^2)$　**29** $(2a - b + 3)(2a - b - 3)$　**30** $(2a + 3b)(3a - 5b)$
31 $D = 337$ is not a positive perfect square　**32** $(2x + 2y - 3)(2x - 2y + 3)$　**33** $(x^2 + 2 + x)(x^2 + 2 - x)$　**34** $8x^3/3y$
35 $2x + 3$　**36** $(10x^3 - 9x^2 - 13x - 15)/(3x - 1)(x + 3)(2x + 3)$　**37** $-(7x + 9)/(8x^2 + 18x + 9)$　**38** 1　**39** 3　**40** -3
41 $6\sqrt{2}$　**42** $0.6\sqrt[4]{2}$　**43** $(2xy)\sqrt[3]{9x^2z^2}$　**44** $(3xy^2)\sqrt[5]{7y}$　**45** $\dfrac{-1 - \sqrt{15}}{2}$　**46** $\sqrt[6]{6a}$　**47** $\sqrt[3]{6}$　**48** $(2ab - 3a^2 - 2b)\sqrt{2a}$
49 $\sqrt[3]{3} + 13\sqrt{2}$　**50** 37　**51** $\dfrac{2}{\sqrt{2x + 2h + 3} + \sqrt{2x + 3}}$　**52** 25, -5, -5, -5, not real　**53** $\sqrt[5]{a^2b^3}$, $\sqrt[6]{b^2/a^3}$　**54** $a/5b^{1/3}$

55 $(8x - 9)/(2x - 1)^{1/3}(x + 2)^{1/2}$ **56** x^a **57** $\sqrt[5]{\frac{10}{3}} = 1.27$ **58** $-3/2(3x + 4)$ **60** 9.67 **61** $(x^2 + 25)^{3/2}$ **62** $(x^{3/5} + 1/4x^{3/5})^2$
63 $32.37 = 3^{\sqrt{10}} > (\sqrt{10})^3 = 31.62$ **64** $\frac{11}{15}$ **65** (a) $\dfrac{mP - 1}{mQ - 1}$ (b) 0.205 **66** $8.471 < 8.485 < 8.5 < 8.515$
69 Multiply both sides by pq. **70** Multiply both sides by $abcd$, then transpose two terms and factor.

EXERCISE 2.1

1 Identity **2** Conditional equation **3** Conditional equation **5** Conditional equation **6** Identity **7** Identity **9** No **10** Yes
11 No **13** -2 **14** -1 **15** 3 **17** 1 **18** -1 **19** 1 **21** 10 **22** -8 **23** 12 **25** 6 **26** 4 **27** 5 **29** 4 **30** 6 **31** 12
33 1 **34** -2 **35** -3 **37** -1 **38** 3 **39** 9 **41** 5 **42** 8 **43** 4 **45** 2 **46** -2 **47** 7 **49** -2 **50** -4 **51** -3 **53** 4
54 3 **55** 7 **57** 1 **58** 3 **59** 3 **61** 5 **62** -4 **63** -7 **65** 6 **66** 8 **67** 5 **69** $F = 1.8C + 32$ **70** $d = Ak/4\pi C$
71 $f = pq/(p + q)$ **73** $p = [c - m(1 - d)]/c$ **74** $r = (Ne - IR)/IN$ **75** $a = S(1 - r)/(1 - r^n)$ **77** $-\frac{5}{2}$ **78** $-\frac{11}{2}$
79 (a) $H = z(x^2 + W^2)/Wx$ (b) $H = 2zW^2/(2Wx - x^2)$ (c) $H = W(y + z)/x$ **85** \$115.38 **86** \$180 **87** \$184.21

EXERCISE 2.2

1 $x + (x + 1) + (x + 2) = 75$; 24, 25, 26 **2** $x + 4x/3 = 224$, \$96, \$128 **3** $41,209 = 2x - 5015$; 18,097 increase
5 $x + (x + 195) = 625$; \$215, \$410 **6** $2898 = 210 + x/2$; 5376 **7** $x/3 + 2 = x/2$; 12 problems **9** Sal 1526, Bruce 1210
10 532 **11** 83 **13** 12 **14** 16 weeks **15** 252 **17** 680 mi **18** \$15,500 at 9 percent, \$16,250 at 10 percent
19 \$728 on living room carpet, \$760 on bedroom carpet **21** \$400, \$350 **22** \$10,000 at 12 percent, \$11,600 at 10 percent
23 \$24,000 at 12.5 percent, \$26,000 at 14 percent **25** 11, 14 **26** $25Q$, $75D$, $50N$ **27** 10 mi **29** 3.6 min **30** 46 mi/h
31 100 s, 160 m, 190 m **33** 625 mi/h **34** 10 mi **35** 1.5 h **37** $\frac{100}{3}$ min **38** $\frac{100}{3}$ min **39** 3.25 h **41** 17.5 min
42 5:05 P.M. **43** 10 min **45** 19.2 h **46** 2 **47** 4 at \$3.94; 3 at \$1.89 **49** 40 lb
50 1125 lb of 9.3 percent; 3375 lb of 11.3 percent **51** 50 **53** 24 yd^3 **54** 20 **55** 300 **57** 50 ml **58** 112 mi
59 Bus, 40 mi/h; plane, 660 mi/h **61** 12 mph **62** 20 km **63** 1.4 h **65** \$7000 at 10 percent, \$11,000 at 7 percent **66** \$80
67 120 yd, \$6.50 per yard

EXERCISE 2.3

1 $9 + 5i$ **2** $9 + 7i$ **3** $-1 - 3i$ **5** $-1 - i$ **6** $13 + 2i$ **7** $-11 + i$ **9** $17 - 6i$ **10** $53 + 26i$ **11** 13 **13** $54 + 10i$
14 $84 - 13i$ **15** $-26 - 36i$ **17** $(-7 - 22i)/41$ **18** $-i$ **19** $(58 - 11i)/85$ **21** $(-33 + 56i)/65$ **22** $2 + 3i$ **23** $1 + 7i$
25 $-2(17 + 6i)/325$ **26** $32i/25$ **27** $\frac{4}{5}$ **29** 5 **30** 5 **31** 13 **41** $|9 + i| = \sqrt{82} \le \sqrt{34} + \sqrt{52}$
42 $|18 + 7i - 11 + i| = \sqrt{113} \le |18 + 7i| + |-11 + i| = \sqrt{373} + \sqrt{122}$
43 $|6 + 5i - 12 - 10i| = \sqrt{61} \le |6 + 5i| + |-12 - 10i| = \sqrt{61} + 2\sqrt{61}$ **49** (3, 2) **50** (4, 7) **51** (6, 2) **53** (2, 1)
54 (6, 1) **55** (3, 3) **65** Both are $40 - 10i$ **67** Both are $40 + 20i$

EXERCISE 2.4

1 $3, -3$ **2** $5, -5$ **3** $\frac{1}{2}, -\frac{1}{2}$ **5** $0, 3$ **6** $0, 4$ **7** $0, 2$ **9** $i, -i$ **10** $6i, -6i$ **11** $5i/3, -5i/3$ **13** $2, 3$ **14** $1, -2$
15 $3, -4$ **17** $3, 4$ **18** $3, -1$ **19** $4, -3$ **21** $\frac{1}{2}, 3$ **22** $2, -\frac{1}{2}$ **23** $\frac{2}{3}, 1$ **25** $\frac{1}{2}, -\frac{2}{3}$ **26** $\frac{2}{3}, -\frac{3}{2}$ **27** $\frac{5}{3}, -\frac{1}{4}$ **29** $3, \frac{2}{5}$
30 $2, \frac{1}{3}$ **31** $2, \frac{3}{7}$ **33** $1 \pm \sqrt{3}$ **34** $2 \pm \sqrt{5}$ **35** $3 \pm \sqrt{2}$ **37** $(2 \pm \sqrt{3})/2$ **38** $(3 \pm \sqrt{2})/3$ **39** $(2 \pm \sqrt{3})/3$ **41** $4 \pm \sqrt{21}$
42 $-2 \pm \sqrt{10}$ **43** $(3 \pm \sqrt{23})/2$ **45** $2 \pm 3i$ **46** $3 \pm 2i$ **47** $4 \pm 2i$ **49** $(3 \pm i)/2$ **50** $(2 \pm i)/3$ **51** $(3 \pm 2i)/5$
53 1; rational, unequal; 5, 6 **54** 121; rational, unequal; $\frac{5}{12}, -\frac{1}{6}$ **55** 0; rational, equal; 6, 9 **57** 72; real, unequal; 6, -9
58 84; real, unequal; $-\frac{1}{2}, -\frac{5}{4}$ **59** -76; conjugate imaginary; $-\frac{1}{2}, \frac{5}{4}$ **61** $x^2 - 3x + 2 = 0$ **62** $x^2 - 2x - 3 = 0$
63 $15x^2 - 2x - 8 = 0$ **65** $x^2 - 4x - 1 = 0$ **66** $x^2 - 6x + 7 = 0$ **67** $x^2 - 10x + 29 = 0$ **69** $-0.74, -2.39$
70 $1.97, -0.77$ **71** $1.65, -0.70$ **73** $3i + 2, 3i - 2$ **74** $4i + 3, 4i - 3$ **75** $-2i + 3, -2i - 3$ **77** 5400 **78** 16
79 11,647 **81** $(B + C) \pm \sqrt{(B - C)^2 + 4AD})/2$, discriminant is positive, or 0 **82** $(1 \pm \sqrt{5})/4$ **83** 0.766
85 $y = (-2x \pm \sqrt{4 - 2x^2})/2$ **86** $y = (3x + i\sqrt{8 + 39x^2})/4$ **87** $x = (-5y \pm \sqrt{89y^2 + 32})/4$ **89** $t = (v \pm \sqrt{v^2 - 64s})/32$
90 $r = (-\pi h \pm \sqrt{\pi^2 h^2 + 4A})/\pi$ **91** $n = (-1 \pm \sqrt{1 + 8S})/2$ **93** $4, -2 \pm 2i\sqrt{3}$ **94** $-3, 1.5(1 \pm i\sqrt{3})$
95 $-\frac{5}{2}, 1.25(1 \pm i\sqrt{3})$ **97** $10, -2$ **98** $-4 \pm 2\sqrt{43})/3$

EXERCISE 2.5

1 ± 1, ± 2 **2** ± 3, $\pm 2i$ **3** ± 3, $\pm i$ **5** $\pm 2i/3$, $\pm\frac{1}{2}$ **6** $\pm\frac{2}{3}$, $\pm 3i$ **7** ± 2, $\pm 2i/3$ **9** $\pm\frac{1}{8}$, $\pm\frac{1000}{27}$ **10** $\pm\frac{1}{8}$, $\pm\frac{1}{27}$
11 ± 125, ± 27 **13** 2, 4, ± 1 **14** -1, 1, 1, 3 **15** -2, -2, $-2\pm 2\sqrt{3}$ **17** 7, 1 **18** 7, 1 **19** $-\frac{5}{8}$, $-\frac{3}{2}$ **21** $\frac{10}{3}$, 0 **22** $-\frac{1}{3}$
23 $\frac{21}{4}$, -1 **25** 3, $-\frac{11}{18}$ **26** 2, -1 **27** 1, $-\frac{2}{3}$ **29** 2 **30** $\frac{7}{4}$ **31** 0 **33** $\frac{56}{9}$ **34** 1, 5 **35** -1 **37** 0 **38** 1 **39** -1 **41** 13
42 18 **43** 3, -4 **45** -1.5 **46** -4 **47** 0 **49** 2, $-4\pm 2i\sqrt{3}$ **50** $\frac{1}{2}$, $(4\pm i\sqrt{3})/2$ **51** 2.5 $(19\pm 3i\sqrt{3})/4$

EXERCISE 2.6

1 $x(x+1)-2x-1=19$; 5, 6; -4, -3 **2** $x^2-4x-21=0$; 7, 9; -3, -1 **3** $x(x-8)=273$; 21, 13; -21, -13
5 $x^2-7x=18$, 9 **6** $x^2+5x=14$; -7 **7** $(x+6)^2=4x^2$, 6 **9** $x^2+(x+3)^2=117$, 96 **10** $x^2+(x+4)^2=26$, 51
11 $(x-10)(1560/x+24)=1520$, 30 **13** $24/x+24/(x+20)=1$, 40 min **14** $(72/r-200)(r-0.01)=50$, 0.06
15 $(100-400t)^2+(200-300t)^2=100^2$, 0.4 h **17** 75 by 100 ft or 50 by 150 ft **18** 90 by 60 m **19** 5 ft, 12 ft
21 3 by 24 ft **22** 9 by 12 ft **23** 4 m/h **25** 9, 12, 15 **26** 16, 30, 34 **27** 10, 24, 26 **29** 4 in **30** 320
31 (a) 2536.8, (b) 99.29° or 102.4° **33** 2, 1 **34** $(5\pm\sqrt{7})/2$ **35** Cannot make 39.

EXERCISE 2.7

1 $x<2$ **2** $x>3$ **3** $x<-7$ **5** $x>2$ **6** $x>-1$ **7** $x<-3$ **9** $x\le 2$ **10** $x\le -3$ **11** $x\ge 4$ **13** $x<1$ **14** $x<-2$
15 $x>-2$ **17** $x<4$ **18** $x<2$ **19** $x>-1$ **21** $x\ge -6$ **22** $x\le -1$ **23** $x\ge -7$ **25** $x<-1$ or $x>2$
26 $x<2$ or $x>4$ **27** $x\le -3$ or $x\ge -2$ **29** $-\frac{3}{2}\le x\le\frac{2}{5}$ **30** $-\frac{2}{7}\le x\le\frac{7}{2}$ **31** $-\frac{7}{2}<x<\frac{3}{5}$ **33** $x<1$ or $x>3$
34 $-3<x<2$ **35** Empty set **37** All x **38** $-4\le x\le -1.5$ **39** $-\frac{2}{3}\le x\le\frac{3}{2}$ **41** $x<-3$ or $x>1$ **42** $-4<x<2$
43 $-3<x<-\frac{1}{2}$ **45** $1<x\le 7$ **46** $x<-3$ or $x\ge -\frac{11}{5}$ **47** $x<\frac{4}{13}$ or $x>\frac{5}{8}$ **49** $x<1$ or $x>\frac{5}{3}$ **50** $x<-1$ or $x>1$
51 $-\frac{1}{2}<x<\frac{1}{2}$ **53** $-\frac{4}{3}<x<-1$ or $x>\frac{1}{2}$ **54** $-\frac{2}{3}<x<-\frac{1}{3}$ or $x>3$ **55** $-2\le x\le -\frac{2}{7}$ or $x\ge\frac{7}{3}$
57 $-2\le x\le -\frac{1}{2}$ or $\frac{5}{3}\le x\le 4$ **58** $-2\le x\le\frac{1}{5}$ or $1\le x\le\frac{8}{3}$ **59** $-3<x<-\frac{2}{7}$ or $\frac{7}{2}<x<4$
61 $x<-4-\sqrt{13}$ or $x>-4+\sqrt{13}$ **62** Empty set **63** $x<(-11-\sqrt{141})/2$ or $x>(-11+\sqrt{141})/2$
65 $k<(3-\sqrt{21})/2$ or $k>(3+\sqrt{21})/2$ **66** $(-3-5\sqrt{3})/4<x<(-3+5\sqrt{3})/4$ **67** $7-4\sqrt{3}<k<7+4\sqrt{3}$
69 $10-5\sqrt{2}<t<10+5\sqrt{2}$ **70** $x>2+\sqrt{29}$ **71** More than 145 **73** $20\le C\le 30$ **74** $R_2\le 30$ **75** $\frac{13}{16}\le F\le\frac{91}{16}$

EXERCISE 2.8

1 3, -3 **2** 1, -1 **3** 3, -3 **5** 5, -1 **6** 1 **7** 6, -2 **9** 2, $-\frac{2}{3}$ **10** 3, -6 **11** 2, $-\frac{8}{5}$ **13** $\frac{2}{3}$, 4 **14** -2, $-\frac{12}{7}$ **15** $\emptyset$
17 $\frac{1}{2}$ **18** 2 **19** All x **21** $\frac{1}{3}$, 9 **22** -10, $-\frac{4}{5}$ **23** -1, 1 **25** $-2<x<2$ **26** $-5<x<5$ **27** $x<-3$ or $x>3$
29 $-7<x<1$ **30** $-4<x<8$ **31** $2\le x\le 8$ **33** $x\le -2$ or $x\ge 3$ **34** $x\le\frac{4}{3}$ or $x\ge 2$ **35** $x<-2$ or $x>-\frac{2}{3}$
37 $-1<x<5$ **38** $-3\le x\le 2$ **39** $x\le 1$ or $x\ge\frac{7}{3}$ **41** $x<1$ **42** $x<2$ **43** $x>\frac{1}{2}$ **45** $x\le -\frac{1}{3}$ **46** $-1<x<1$
47 $x\le -2$ or $x\ge\frac{1}{3}$

EXERCISE 2.9

1 No **2** No **3** No **4** No **5** Yes **6** Yes **7** 3 **8** -2 **9** 2 **10** 5 **11** 6 **12** 8 **13** 15 **14** 18 **15** 1 **16** 24 **17** 4
18 3 **19** 6 **20** 12 **21** $\pm\frac{1}{4}$ **22** 0, $\frac{1}{16}$ **23** $\frac{4}{3}$, $-\frac{1}{2}$ **24** $(-3\pm\sqrt{7})/3$ **25** $2\pm\sqrt{3}$ **26** $(-3\pm\sqrt{6})/2$ **27** $2\pm i\sqrt{3}$
28 $(5\pm 3i)/2$ **29** $(-1\pm 2i)/4$ **30** $\frac{5}{6}$, $-\frac{3}{4}$ **31** $5\pm 3i\sqrt{3}$ **32** ± 3, ± 1 **33** $2\pm\sqrt{7}$, $(4\pm\sqrt{14})/2$ **34** 16 **35** 5 **36** 3
37 4, $-\frac{3}{4}$ **38** 5, $\frac{4}{3}$ **39** 1, -7 **40** -3, 4 **41** -1, 1 **42** $-\frac{4}{7}$, 4 **43** $5(F-32)/9$ **44** $(2S-na)/n$ **45** $x>3$ **46** $x<2$
47 $x<1$ **48** $x<4$ **49** $-\frac{7}{3}<x<\frac{1}{2}$ **50** $x<-\frac{1}{3}$ or $x>\frac{8}{5}$ **51** $x<-\frac{9}{5}$ or $x>\frac{5}{6}$ **52** $-\frac{3}{7}<x<\frac{7}{3}$ **53** $x<-\frac{9}{2}$ or $-2<x<4$
54 $-\frac{8}{3}<x<-\frac{3}{5}$ or $x>\frac{5}{2}$ **55** $-7<x<1$ **56** $x<-3$ or $x>4$ **57** $-1<x<1$ **58** $-1<x<5$
59 $|F-f|=|(F-50)/9|<5$ if $|F-50|<45$ **60** 7, 41 **61** 24, 24 **62** $\frac{57}{8}$ **63** $\frac{8}{3}$, $\frac{14}{3}$ **64** $-\frac{6}{5}$, $-\frac{9}{5}$ **65** All k
66 $\frac{2}{5}<x\le\frac{5}{2}$ **67** All x **68** $15x^2-11x-12=0$ **69** $x^2-4x+13=0$ **70** Yes, $D=146^2$
71 (a) $(9\pm 2\sqrt{14})/5$ (b) $\frac{181}{5}$ m at $\frac{9}{5}$ s **72** $\left(\dfrac{-b+\sqrt{b^2-4ac}}{2a}\right)\left(\dfrac{-b-\sqrt{b^2-4ac}}{2c}\right)=\dfrac{b^2-(b^2-4ac)}{4ac}=1$

73 $\left(\dfrac{-b + \sqrt{b^2 - 4a^2}}{2a}\right)\left(\dfrac{-b - \sqrt{b^2 - 4a^2}}{2a}\right) = \dfrac{b^2 - (b^2 - 4a^2)}{4a^2} = 1$ **74** $\dfrac{-b \pm \sqrt{b^2 - 4ac}}{2a} = (-1)\left(\dfrac{b \mp \sqrt{b^2 - 4ac}}{2a}\right)$

75 $\left(\dfrac{-b + \sqrt{b^2 - 4ac}}{2a} + \dfrac{-b - \sqrt{b^2 - 4ac}}{2a}\right) \Big/ 2 = \dfrac{1}{2}\left(-\dfrac{b}{2a} - \dfrac{b}{2a}\right) = \dfrac{-b}{2a}$ **76** Sum = product = $-b/a$

79 $\dfrac{-b \pm \sqrt{b^2 - 4ac}}{2a} - \dfrac{2c}{-b \mp \sqrt{b^2 - 4ac}} = \dfrac{b^2 - (b^2 - 4ac) - (2c)(2a)}{2a(-b \mp \sqrt{b^2 - 4ac})} = 0$

EXERCISE 3.1

1 4   **2** 1   **3** 2   **5** 3   **6** 4   **7** 3   **17** The x axis   **18** The negative y axis   **19** The fourth quadrant
21 All points above the line $y = 5$ **22** All points in the first or third quadrant
23 The line parallel to and two units to the left of the y axis   **25** $10\sqrt{2}$, $(-1, 3)$ **26** $4\sqrt{5}$, $(6, -1)$ **27** $4\sqrt{10}$, $(3, 6)$
29 13, $(5.5, 1)$ **30** 17, $(-8, -0.5)$ **31** 25, $(2.5, 10)$ **33** $\sqrt{61}$, $(-8, -0.5)$ **34** $\sqrt{58}$, $(6.5, 1.5)$ **35** $\sqrt{173}$, $(-2.5, 5)$
37 $(12, 2)$ **38** $(11, -6)$ **39** $(-2, 11)$ **41** The squares of the sides are 13, 13, and 26. The area is 6.5.
42 The squares of the sides are 34, 136, and 170. The area is 34.
43 The squares of the sides are 45, 45, and 90. The area is 22.5.   **45** $FS = \sqrt{5}$, $ST = 2\sqrt{5}$, and $FT = 3\sqrt{5}$
46 $FS = 2\sqrt{5}$, $ST = 3\sqrt{5}$, $TF = 5\sqrt{5}$ **47** $FS = \sqrt{13}$, $ST = 2\sqrt{13}$, $TF = 3\sqrt{13}$ **49** $(5, 6.5)$ **50** $(8, 9)$
51 $AB = BC = CD = DA = \sqrt{13}$, $DB = \sqrt{26}$ **53** $(5, 3.5)$ is the midpoint of each diagonal.
54 $(0.5, 0)$ is the midpoint of each diagonal.   **55** $AP = AQ = \sqrt{50}$, midpoint of PQ is $(5, 2) \neq (9, 5)$.

57 $(x - 5)^2 + (y + 10)^2 = 3^2$ **58** $5x - 11y = 8$ **59** $MP_1 = MP_2 = \sqrt{\left(\dfrac{x_1 - x_2}{2}\right)^2 + \left(\dfrac{y_1 - y_2}{2}\right)^2}$

EXERCISE 3.2

1 $3x + 5y = 15$

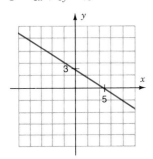

2 $x - 4y = 8$

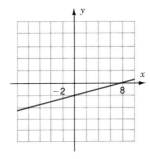

3 $-4x + 3y = 6$

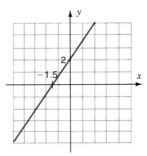

5 $4y = x^2 + 4x + 8$

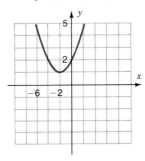

6 $4y = -x^2 + 2x - 7$

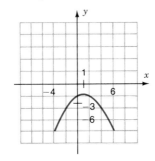

7 $2y = x^2 + 2x - 1$

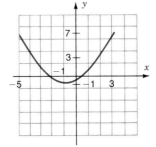

Answers to Selected Problems

9 $2x = -y^2 + 4y - 8$

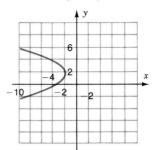

10 $4x = y^2 + 2y + 9$

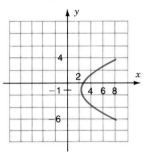

11 $8x = y^2 + 2y - 15$

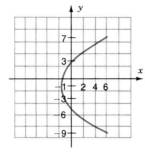

13 $y = x^3 - 2x^2 - x + 2$

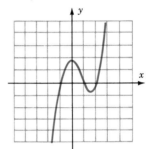

14 $y = x^3 + x^2 - 4x - 4$

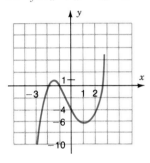

15 $4y = x^3 + 3x^2 + 3x - 8$

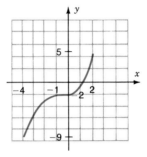

17 $2y = x^4 - 13x^2 + 36$

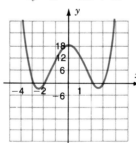

18 $4y = 4x^4 - 25x^2 + 21$

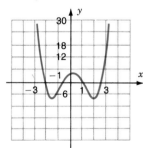

19 $y = x^4 - 15x^2 - 10x + 24$

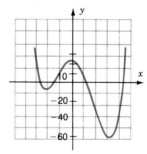

21 $y = x + |x|$

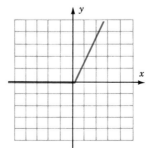

22 $y = x|x|$

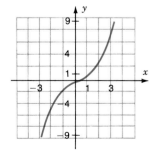

23 $y = |x + 2| + |x - 1|$

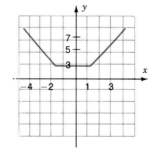

25 $y = \sqrt{-x}$

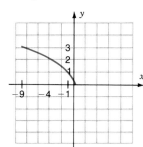

26 $y = \sqrt{3x}$

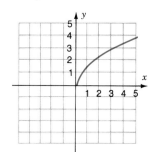

27 $y = [2x]$

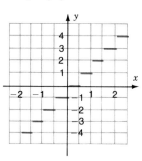

29 $(x - 3)^2 + (y + 5)^2 = 16$ **30** $(x + 12)^2 + (y + 7)^2 = 121$ **31** $(x + 4)^2 + (y - 2)^2 = 49$ **33** $(x - 7)^2 + (y - 4)^2 = 25$
34 $(x - 3)^2 + (y + 3)^2 = 169$ **35** $(x - 6)^2 + (y + 1)^2 = 40$

37 $(x - 4)^2 + (y - 5)^2 = 4 = 2^2$

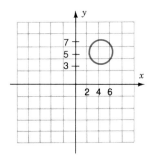

38 $(x - 2)^2 + (y + 3)^2 = 9 = 3^2$

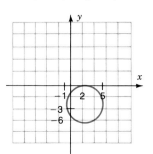

39 $(x + 5)^2 + (y - 1)^2 = 1$ **41** $x^2 + (y + 3)^2 = 4$ **42** $(x - 4)^2 + (y - 3)^2 = 25$

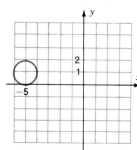
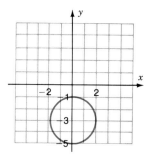
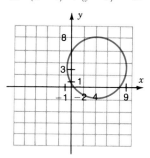

43 $(x - 6)^2 + y^2 = 36$ **45** $(x + 3)^2 + (y + 2)^2 = 16$ **46** $(x + 4)^2 + (y - 6)^2 = 25$

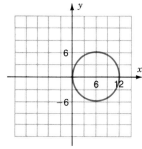
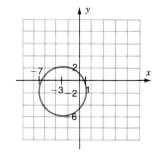
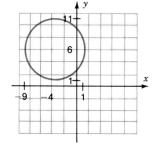

47 $(x - 2)^2 + (y + 4)^2 = 25$

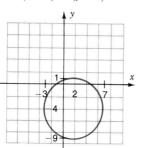

49 $(x + 1)^2 + (y - 2)^2 = 9$

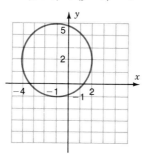

50 $(x + 2)^2 + (y + 4)^2 = 16$

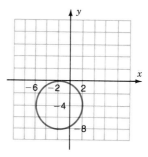

51 $(x - 1)^2 + (y - 2)^2 = 4$

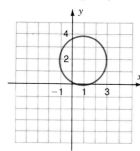

53 $y = \dfrac{x}{|x|}$

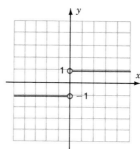

54 $y = 2^x$

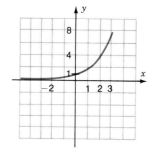

55 $y = \dfrac{6}{1 + x^2}$

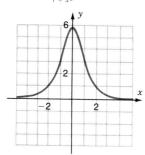

57 $[6.5 + 4] = [10.5] = 10$ and $[6.5] + [4] = 6 + 4 = 10;$
$[13.7 + 8.6] = [22.3] = 22$
and $[13.7] + [8.6] = 13 + 8 = 21$

EXERCISE 3.3

1 $4x^2 + 9y^2 = 36$

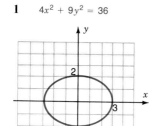

2 $9x^2 + y^2 = 9$

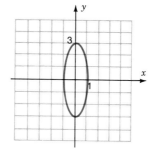

3 $x^2 + 36y^2 = 36$

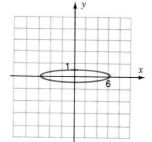

5 $25x^2 + 16y^2 = 400$

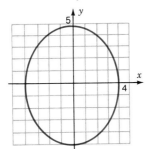

6 $16x^2 + y^2 = 16$

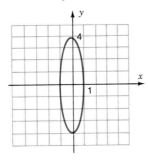

7 $9x^2 + 25y^2 = 225$

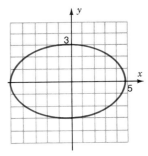

9 $x^2 - 4y^2 = 9$

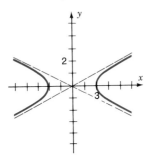

10 $4x^2 - 25y^2 = 16$

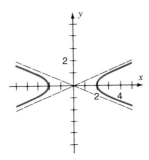

11 $9y^2 - x^2 = 36$

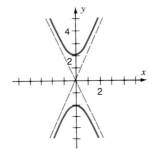

13 $25x^2 - 9y^2 = 81$

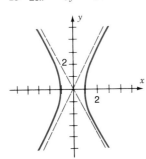

14 $16x^2 - 144y^2 = 49$

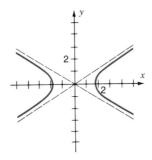

15 $81y^2 - 4x^2 = 36$

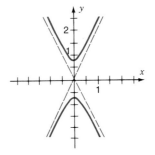

17 $xy = 4$

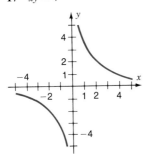

18 $xy = 7$

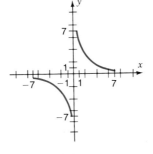

19 $xy = -3$

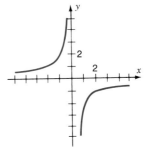

21 $y = 2x^2 - x - 10$

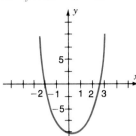

22 $y = -3x^2 + 4x + 7$

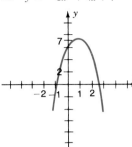

23 $x = 3y^2 + 7y - 6$

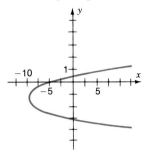

25 $x = y^2 - 6y + 12$

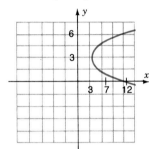

26 $x = -y^2 - 2y + 1$

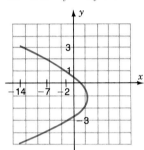

27 $y = -x^2 - 2x + 2$

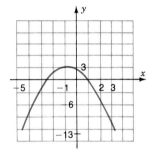

EXERCISE 3.4

1 $(3, 5)$, $(-3, 5)$ **2** $(-2, -1)$, $(2, -1)$ **3** $(-3, 8)$, $(3, 8)$ **5** $(-3, 2)$, $(2, 3)$ **6** $(-4, -1)$, $(-1, 4)$ **7** $(5, 6)$, $(6, -5)$
9 Both axes, the origin **10** y axis **11** $y = x$ **13** y axis **14** $y = x$ **15** $y = x$ **17** $xy(x + y) = 7$ **18** $xy(-x + y) = 7$
19 $xy(y - x) = 7$ **21** $(x - 3)^2 + (y - 5)^2 = 4$ **22** $(x + 2)^2 - (y + 3)^2 = 11$ **23** $x(y - 1) + x = 5$
25 $7(x - 3) - 2(y + 2) = 3$ **26** $(x - 3)(y - 5) = 15$ **27** $(x + 2)^2 + 3(x + 2) + 2(y - 3) = 4$

29

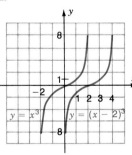

30

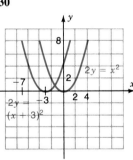

31

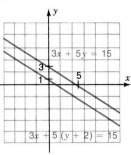

33

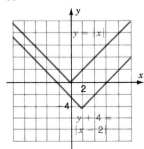

34

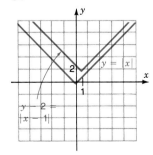

35

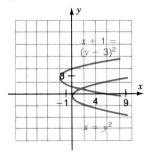

37

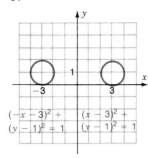

38

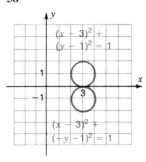

39

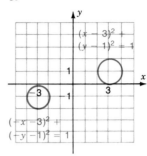

41 $y = (x + 3)^2$

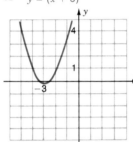

42 $y = (x + 2)^3$

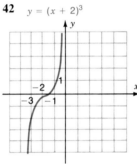

43 $x = (y - 1)^4$

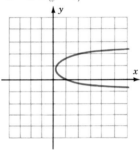

45 $y + 1 = |x - 4|$

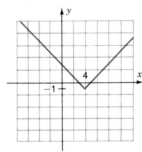

46 $y - 2 = -|x + 3|$

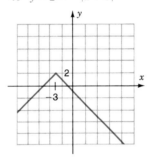

47 $x - 3 = -|y + 1|$

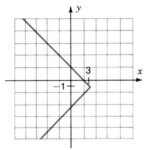

49 $-y = (x - 3)^2$

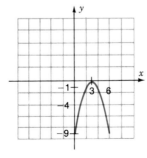

50 $-x = y^3$

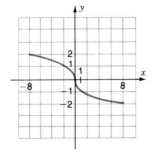

51 $-x = |y|$

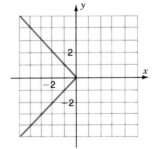

EXERCISE 3.5

1 $x \geq -\frac{1}{5}$ **2** All real x **3** All real x **5** $x \neq 2, -2$ **6** $x \neq 0$ **7** All real x **9** Yes **10** No **11** Yes **13** 7, -21
14 4, 34 **15** -8, 55 **17** 14, 2 **18** -67, 28 **19** 31, -14 **21** -11, 1.25 **22** -0.6, 12 **23** $\frac{2}{3}, -\frac{5}{4}$ **25** 2, 29
26 16, 17 **27** 1, 5 **29** $21t - 5$, $21t - 15$ **30** $a^2 + 2ab + b^2 + 3a + 3b + 1$, $a^2 + 3a + b^2 + 3b + 2$
31 $(1 + 3x)/(2 - x)$, $(2x - 1)/(x + 3)$ **33** 8 **34** $x + 8$ **35** $-2/7(7 + h)$ **37** $f(-x) = f(x)$ **38** $f(-x) = f(x)$
39 $f(-x) = -f(x)$ **45** 22 **46** 16 **47** -3 **49** -273 **50** Does not exist **51** 60 **53** -26 **54** -5 **55** 0 **57** $1/2(x^2 - 3)$
58 $1/5x$ **59** $2(5x^2 - 18)$ **61** $25x - 6$, -31 **62** $50x^2 - 20x - 5$, 385 **63** $1/(2x^2 - 6)$, $\frac{1}{2}$ **65** 0 **66** 0 **73** -55

75 $f(12, 18) = \dfrac{-4104}{468} = 6\left(\dfrac{-114}{13}\right) = 6f(2, 3)$ **77** 4700; 6700; 10,700 **78** \$3,700,000 **79** $C(33, 425) = \$488.33$

82 $q = \dfrac{f(b) - f(a)}{b - a}$ **83** $\frac{8}{3}$ **85** $(-5 \pm \sqrt{247})/3$ **86** $(3 \pm 2\sqrt{3})/3$ **87** $-2 \pm 2\sqrt{3}$

EXERCISE 3.6

1 $f(x) = \sqrt{x} - 2$

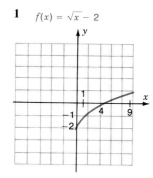

2 $f(x) = [x] + 3$

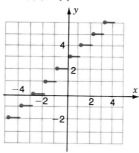

3 $f(x) = |x| - 4$

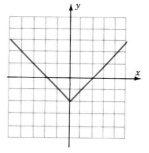

5 $g(x) = -[x]$

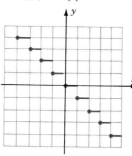

6 $g(x) = -x^3$

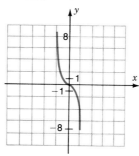

7 $g(x) = -\frac{1}{x}$

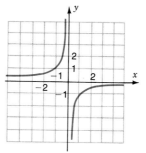

9 $h(x) = 2\sqrt{x}$

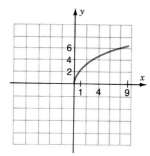

10 $h(x) = \frac{3}{x}$

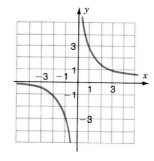

11 $h(x) = \frac{x^2}{4}$

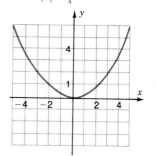

13 $E(x) = \frac{12|x|}{x^2 + 1}$

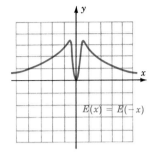

$E(x) = E(-x)$

14 $f(x) = \frac{x^4}{5} - 4x^2$

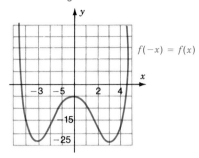

$f(-x) = f(x)$

15 $G(x) = x^3 - 8x$

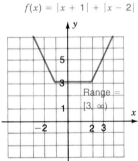

$G(-x) = -G(x)$

17 Range $= [-3, 3]$

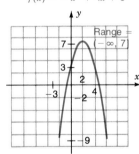

Range $= [-3, 3]$

18 Range $= [3, \infty)$

$f(x) = |x + 1| + |x - 2|$

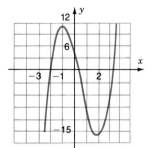

Range $= [3, \infty)$

19 Range $= (-\infty, 7]$

$f(x) = -x^2 + 4x + 3$

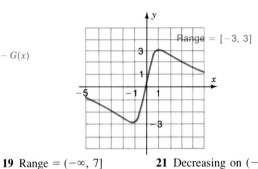

Range $= (-\infty, 7]$

21 Decreasing on $(-\infty, \frac{1}{2})$, increasing on $(\frac{1}{2}, \infty)$

$g(x) = |x + 2| + |2x - 1|$

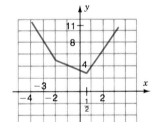

22 Increasing on $(-\infty, -1)$ and $(2, \infty)$, decreasing on $(-1, 2)$

$g(x) = 2x^3 - 3x^2 - 12x + 4$

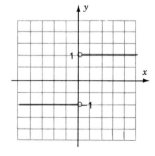

23 Constant on $(-\infty, 0)$ and also on $(0, \infty)$

$g(x) = \frac{|x|}{x}$

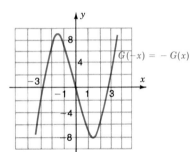

25

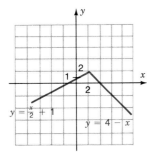

26

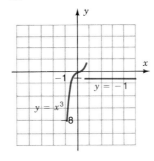

27

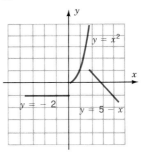

29 $f(x) = 3\sqrt{x - 2} + 4$

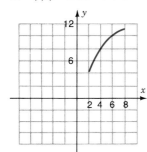

30 $f(x) = 4|x + 1| - 3$

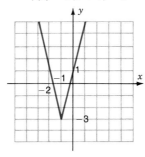

31 $f(x) = \dfrac{-1}{x - 3} + 1$

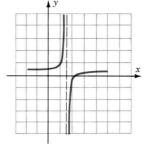

33 $g(x) = 3(x + 2)^2 - 3$

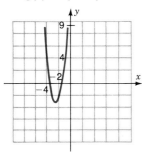

34 $g(x) = -4[x - 4] + 4$

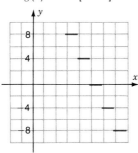

35 $h(x) = -3|x - 2| + 1$

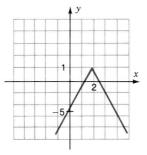

37

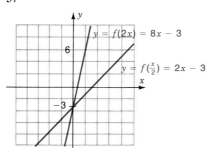

38

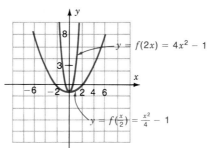

39

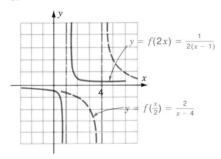

EXERCISE 3.7

1 1   **2** $-\frac{5}{9}$ **3** $\frac{1}{3}$ **5** $x + y = 7$ **6** $2x + y = 19$ **7** $2x - 3y = -13$ **9** $x - 2y + 3 = 0$ **10** $x + y = 4$ **11** $5x - 2y + 14 = 0$
13 $3x - y = 7$ **14** $3x + y = 16$ **15** $2x + 5y + 19 = 0$ **17** $y = 4x + 2$ **18** $y = -0.5x + 5$ **19** $y = -5x - 7$ **21** $2, -4$
22 $-3, 5$ **23** $\frac{1}{2}, -\frac{7}{2}$ **25** $a = 3, b = 5$ **26** $a = 4, b = -7$ **27** $a = 1.5, b = 8$ **29** Parallel   **30** Perpendicular
31 Perpendicular   **33** Perpendicular   **34** Neither   **35** Parallel   **37** The slope of the segment between each pair of points is 3.
38 The slope of the segment between each pair of points is -5.
39 The slope of the segment between each pair of points is 2.5   **41** $6x - 7y + 11 = 0$ **42** $2x + y + 9 = 0$
43 $2x - 3y + 10 = 0$ **45** $x/5 + y/5 = 1$ **46** $x - y = 7$ **47** $y = 6x - 5$ **49** $2.5\sqrt{5}$ **50** $7/\sqrt{58}$ **51** $20/\sqrt{26}$

53 $y = 3x + 1$

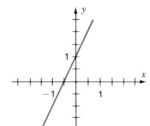

54 $y = -2x - 3$

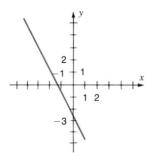

55 $2y = x - 5$

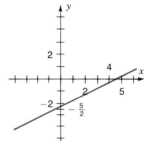

57 $6x + 5y + 14 = 0$

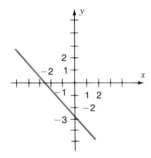

58 $5x + 6y - 23 = 0$

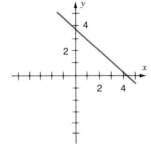

59 $4x - y = 6$

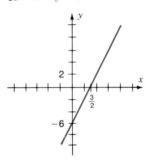

61 $y = 3x - 5$ **62** $x + 2y = 8$ **63** $3x + y - 8 = 0$ **65** $x + y = 7$ **66** $7x - 10y = 32.5$ **67** $4x + 38y = -183$
69 $5x - 12y + 169 = 0$ **70** $3x - 4y = 25$ **71** $8x + 15y = 289$ **73** $m_{23} = \frac{5}{6}, m_{13} = -\frac{6}{5}$ **74** $m_{12} = \frac{4}{3}, m_{23} = -\frac{3}{4}$ **75** $m_{12} = \frac{8}{3}$
77 $2x + h$ **78** $-4/x(x + h)$ **79** $3x^2 + 3hx + h^2$ **81** $450x + 6500$ **82** $y = -8000x + 132,000$ **83** $y = 320x + 6400$

EXERCISE 3.8

1 Yes **2** No **3** Yes **5** No **6** No **7** Yes **9** $y = (x - 2)/3$ **10** $y = (x + 1)/5$ **11** $y = (-x + 7)/2$ **13** $y = 3x - 4$ **14** $y = (7x + 1)/2$ **15** $y = (4x + 1)/12$ **17** $y = \sqrt[3]{x} - 1$ **18** $y = \sqrt[3]{x + 3}$ **19** $y = \sqrt[3]{x - 4}$ **21** $y = 6/x$ **22** $y = 3x/(4 - x)$ **23** $y = (1 + 3x)/2x$ **25** $f(2) = 5, f^{-1}(2) = 1$ **26** $f(-3.5) = 0, f^{-1}(-3.5) = -5.25$ **27** $f(1) = 1, f^{-1}(1) = 1$ **29** 1 **30** 4 **31** -2

33 $y = 2x - 4$

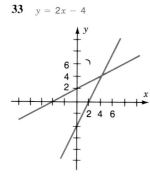

34 $f(x) = f^{-1}(x)$

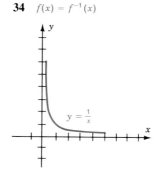

$y = \frac{1}{x}$

35 $y - 1 = (x + 1)^3$

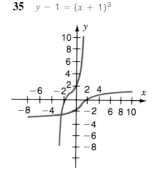

37 $f[f^{-1}(x)] = 3(x - 5)/3 + 5 = x, f^{-1}[f(x)] = (3x + 5 - 5)/3 = x$ **38** $f(x) = f^{-1}(x) = 3/x, f[f^{-1}(x)] = f^{-1}[f(x)] = \dfrac{3}{3/x} = x$

39 $f^{-1}(x) = (3 - 5x)/x, f[(3 - 5x)/x] = 3/(3/x) = x$, and $f^{-1}[3/(x + 5)] = (3x + 15 - 15)/3 = x$

41 For $a > -1$ and $b > 0$, $f(a + b) - f(a) = (a + b)^2 + 2(a + b) + 5 - a^2 - 2a - 5 = 2ab + b^2 + 2b = 2(a + 1)b + b^2 > 0$

42 For $b > 0$, $f(a + b) - f(a) = 3(a + b) + 5 - 3a - 5 = 3b > 0$ **43** If $b > a$, then $f(b) - f(a) = b^3 - a^3 + 2(b - a) > 0$

45 For $f(x)$ and $g(x)$ odd functions, $f(-x) = -f(x)$ and $g(-x) = -g(x)$. Hence, $f(-x) + g(-x) = -[f(x) + g(x)]$ is odd and $[-f(x)][-g(x)] = f(x)g(x)$ is even **46** If $f(-x) = -f(x)$ and $g(-x) = g(x)$, then $f(-x)g(-x) = -f(x)g(x)$ is odd **47** 3 **49** 3

50 1, 0 **51** 4, -2.5 **53** If $y = h(x) = (6x + 7)/(5x - 6)$, then $x = (6y + 7)/(5y - 6)$ and $y = h^{-1}(x) = (6x + 7)/(5x - 6)$; 2

54 $M^{-1}(x) = (x + 9)/(x - 1); x$ **55** $f(f(x)) = (a^2x + bcx)/(bc + a^2) = x$

EXERCISE 3.9

1 $m = kn^2$ **2** $s = k/t$ **3** $p = kqr^3$ **5** 14 **6** 6 **7** 2 **9** 100 **10** 40 **11** $\frac{7}{2}$ **13** 2816 in^3 **14** $\frac{340}{9}$

15 Intensity at 5 ft is $\frac{49}{25}$ of the intensity at 7 ft. **17** 50 barrels **18** 23.9 ft **19** 1280 lb **21** First is $\frac{9}{4}$ as strong as the second

22 $\frac{8}{1}$ **23** $\frac{4}{25}$ **25** 145 lb **26** 30 A **27** The first produces $\frac{4}{9}$ as much illumination as the second **29** 54 **30** \$62.50 **31** 8 in^3

33 128 **34** 1875 lb **35** 0.054 in **37** (a) $(W - 10)/3$ (b) $-\frac{2}{3}$ **38** I is multiplied by 8 **39** $V_1/V_2 = \frac{64}{343}$ **41** \$13.50

42 1.84 s **43** 1.45 times the first **45** 139.7 lb **46** 7 **47** 6 h

EXERCISE 3.10

1 (a) No (b) No (c) Yes (d) Yes **2** 2, -10, $6t - 4$ **3** $-2, -2, -2$ **4** 3, $\frac{1}{2}$ **5** 29 **6** No **7** $5x - 2y = 13$

8 $y = -3x + 2$ **9** $2x + 7y = 10$ **10** 3 **11** No **12** $-7, \frac{1}{2}$ **13** $f^{-1}(x) = (1 + 3x)/(2 - x)$ **16** $(\frac{7}{30}, \frac{8}{15})$

18

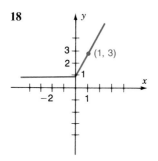

19

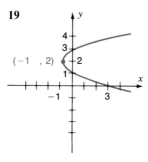

20

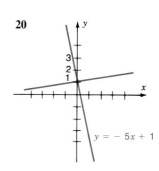

$y = -5x + 1$

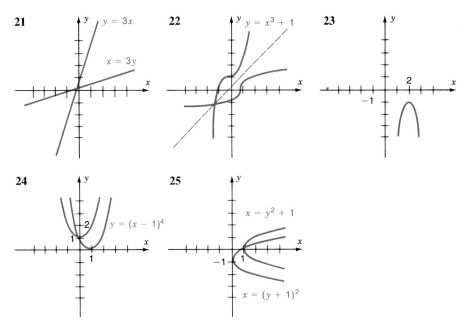

26 0　**27** *I*　**28** *U*　**29** *W*　**30** *V*　**31** *X*　**32** *M*　**33** *E*　**34** *C*　**35** *N*　**36** *S*　**37** *Z*　**40** 8.618　**41** 47.1　**42** 800　**43** $\frac{2}{9}h$
44 0.01 s　**45** They are the same　**46** Energy at 50 mi/h is 25 times that at 10 mi/h　**47** 671 days　**48** 64 lb

EXERCISE 4.1

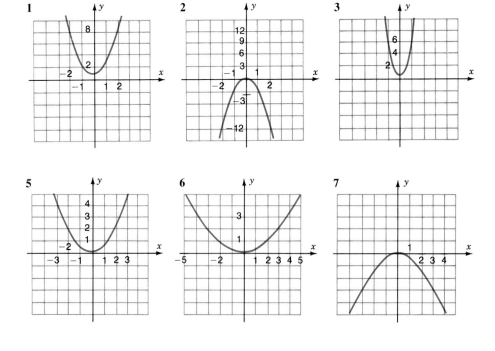

9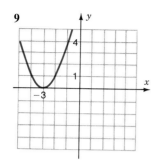

10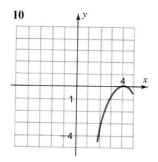

11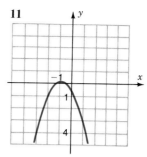

13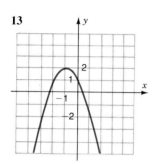

14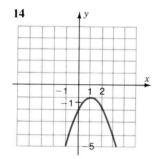

15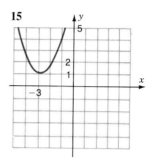

17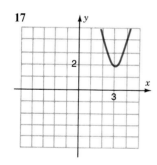

18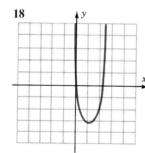

19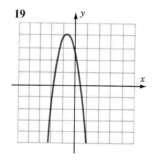

21 $y - 2 = 4(x - 1)^2$ **22** $y - 3 = 6(x - 2)^2$ **23** $y + 1 = -3(x - 3)^2$ **25** $x = 2$, $(2, 1)$ **26** $x = 3$, $(3, -2)$
27 $x = 1$, $(1, -1)$ **29** $y = 3$, $(3, 3)$ **30** $y = -2$, $(1, -2)$ **31** $y = 2$, $(-1, 2)$

33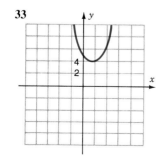

34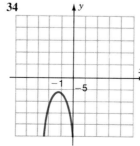

35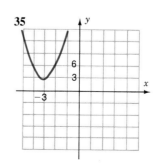

37 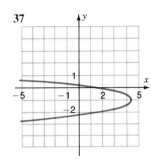   **38** 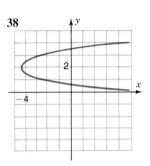   **39**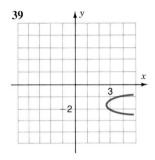

41 $f(4) = 105,\ 4 + \sqrt{21}$ **42** $f(5.2) = 152.2,\ (26 + \sqrt{761})/5$ **43** $f(3.6) = 106.8,\ (18 + \sqrt{534}/5$ **45** $-\frac{89}{8}$ **46** 8.05
47 $-\frac{13}{3}$ **49** -5.5 **50** 4.25   **51** 10.25   **53** $\frac{1}{4}$ **54** 12, 12   **55** 1 ft   **57** 6900; 10   **58** \$38.50   **59** 15
61 $0.005x(200 - x) + x/6$ **62** $0,\ \frac{700}{3}$ **63** $(\frac{350}{9})\sqrt{37}$

EXERCISE 4.2

1 $f(x) = (x - 2)(x - 1)(x + 2)$

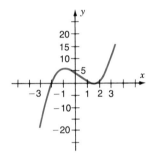

2 $f(x) = -(2x + 3)(x - 1)(3x - 7)$

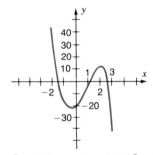

3 $f(x) = -(3x + 4)(2x - 1)(x - 2)$

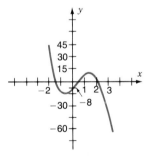

5 $f(x) = -(3x + 5)(2x^2 - 6x + 5)$

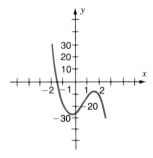

6 $f(x) = (x - 2)(2x^2 + 5x + 4)$

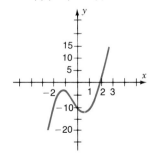

7 $f(x) = (2x - 1)(x^2 - x + 7)$

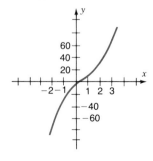

9 $f(x) = (x + 3)(x + 1)(x)(x - 2)$

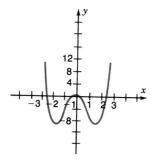

10 $f(x) = -(x + 2)(2x + 1)(x - 1)(x - 4)$

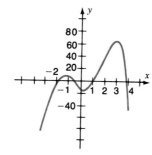

11 $f(x) = (x - 2)(2x - 3)(x^2 + 2x + 2)$

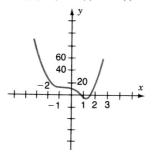

13 $f(x) = -(2x + 1)(x - 3)(x^2 - 4x + 5)$

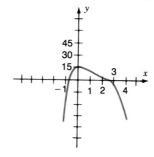

14 $f(x) = (3x + 4)(x - 1)(x^2 - 3x + 6)$

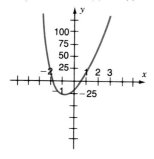

15 $f(x) = -(x + 3)(x + 2)(x - 1)(x - 4)$

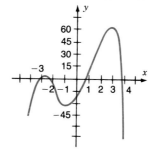

17 $f(x) = (x + 4)(x^2 - x - 6)(x^2 - 1)$

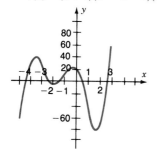

18 $f(x) = -(x - 3)(x^2 + x - 2)(x^2 + 5x + 8)$

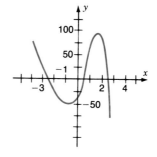

19 $f(x) = x(x^2 + 2x - 3)(x^2 - 2x - 8)$

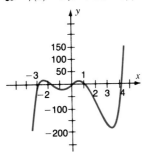

21 $f(x) = (x - 1)^2(x - 2)^3(x - 3)^2$

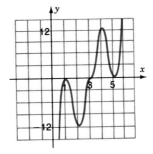

22 $f(x) = (x - 1)^2(x - 3)^2(x - 5)^2$

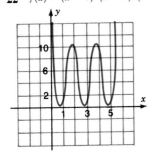

23 $f(x) = (x - 1)^3(x - 3)^2(x - 5)^3$

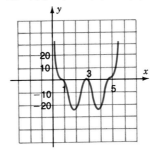

25 $f(x) = (x + 3)(x + 1)^2(x - 1)(x - 3)^3$

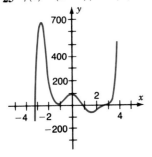

26 $f(x) = (x + 3)(x + 1)^3(x - 1)^3(x - 3)$

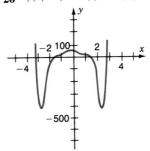

27 $f(x) = x^2(x + 2)(x - 2)^2(x - 1)^4$

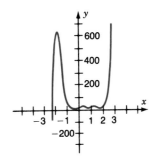

29 $C(x) = 0.001 x^4 + 0.037 x^3 + 0.117 x^2 + 0.12 x$
$C(x) \geq 200$ for approx. $21 \leq x \leq 36$

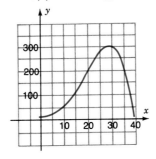

30 $D(x) = (-0.008)(x^3 + x^2 - 72x)$
$D(x) \geq 0.10$ for approx. $2 \leq x \leq 7$

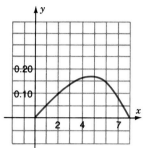

31 $V(x) = x(25 - 2x)(40 - 2x)$
$V(x) \geq 1950$ for approx. $3 \leq x \leq 7$

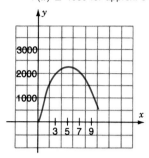

33 $(-\frac{3}{2}, 1) \cup (\frac{7}{3}, \infty)$ **34** $(-\infty, -2) \cup (-\frac{1}{2}, 1) \cup (4, \infty)$ **35** $(-\infty, -2) \cup (1, 3)$ **37** All points above the graph in Prob. 3
38 All points below the graph in Prob. 11 **39** All points above the graph in Prob. 19

EXERCISE 4.3

1 -1 **2** 2 **3** 1 **5** 3 **6** 5 **7** 2 **9** 1 **10** 84 **11** 1 **37** 3 **38** 2 **39** 3 **41** $R = 1$ **42** $R = -3$ **43** $R = 90$
45 $R = 0$ **46** $R = 0$ **47** $R = 0$ **49** $R = 0$ **50** $R = 0$ **51** $R = 0$ **53** $c^2 + 1 \neq 0$ for any real c **54** $c^4 + 3c^2 + 2 > 0$
55 $c^4 + 5c^2 + 3 > 0$ **57** -1.8627 **58** 17.84 **59** -2.6644 **61** $77 + 46\sqrt{3}$ **62** $138 - 104\sqrt{2}$ **63** $226 + 99\sqrt{5}$ **65** -9
66 7 **67** $c^n - c^n = 0$ **69** $x^2 + 6x + 4$, 1 **70** $-x^2 + 9x - 3$, -2 **71** $-3x^2 - 19x - 52$, -163 **73** $x^3 + 3x^2 + 6x + 9$, 24
74 $3x^3 - 7x^2 + 8x - 8$, 1 **75** $-2x^3 + 8x^2 - 27x + 111$, -447 **77** $2x^4 - x^3 + 7x^2 - x - 7$, -22 **78** $3x^4 + x^3 - 3x^2 - x$, 5
79 $x^5 + 5x^4 - x^3 + 2x^2 - x + 5$, -2

EXERCISE 4.4

1 10; $-4, -4, -4, -4, -4$; $-2, -2$; $3, 3, 3$ **2** 11; $-1, -1, -1, -1, -1$; $-2, -2, -2, -2$; $-3, -3$
3 9; $-16, -16, -16$; $3, 3$; $1, 1, 1$; -5 **5** 7; $-\frac{17}{3}, -\frac{17}{3}, -\frac{17}{3}$; $-4, -4, -4, -4$
6 9; $-25, -25, -25, -25, -25$; $-\frac{11}{4}, -\frac{11}{4}, -\frac{11}{4}, -\frac{11}{4}$ **7** 9; $-\frac{22}{3}, -\frac{22}{3}, -\frac{22}{3}, -\frac{22}{3}$; $-23, -23$; $-18.5, -18.5, -18.5$
9 $-1, 1, 2$ **10** $3, 1, -4$ **11** $2, -2, 3$ **13** $1, 1, -1, -2$ **14** $-1, -1, i, -i$ **15** $1, 2, 2i, -2i$ **17** $-1, i, -i$
18 $\frac{3}{2}, 2i, -2i$ **19** $-\frac{5}{3}, 2i, -2i$ **21** $-\frac{3}{2}, 1 + i, 1 - i$ **22** $-\frac{1}{4}, -1 + 2i, -1 - 2i$ **23** $\frac{3}{4}, 2 - i, 2 + i$
25 $2i, -2i, -1 + 2i, -1 - 2i$ **26** $3, -2 + i, -2 + i, -2 - i, -2 - i$ **27** $-1 + 2i, -1 + 2i, -1 - 2i, -1 - 2i, i, -i$
29 $3x^3 - 2x^2 - 3x + 2 = 0$ **30** $4x^3 - 13x^2 + 11x - 2 = 0$ **31** $3x^3 - 2x^2 + 3x - 2 = 0$ **33** $3x^3 - 5x^2 + 13x + 5 = 0$
34 $2x^3 + 5x^2 - 22x - 70 = 0$ **35** $x^3 - 5x^2 + 9x - 5 = 0$ **37** $3x^3 - 5x^2 - 5x - 1 = 0$ **38** $2x^3 + 5x^2 - 34x - 28 = 0$
39 $x^3 - 5x^2 + 6x - 2 = 0$ **41** $x^4 - 8x^3 + 26x^2 - 40x + 25 = 0$ **42** $x^4 + 4x^3 + 2x^2 - 4x + 1 = 0$
43 $x^4 - 8x^3 + 32x^2 - 64x + 64 = 0$ **45** $2(x - 1)(x - 3)(x - 6)$ **46** $3(x + 2)(x)(x - 3)$ **47** $(x + 3)(x - 1)(x - 3)(x - 4)$
49 $8(x^2 - 2)(x - 1)$ **50** $4(x^2 - 3)(x - 2)$ **51** $5(x^2 - 4x - 1)(x - 4)$ **53** $(x^2 + 4)(x - 1)$ **54** $3(x^2 + 9)(x + 2)$
55 $2(x^2 - 4x + 13)(x^2 - 6x + 13)$ **57** $5, -7$ **58** $-\frac{4}{3}, -2$ **59** 5 **61** 5, 6 **62** $-9, 3$ **63** -4 **69** 1 **70** $\frac{1}{2}, 4$ **71** No

EXERCISE 4.5

1 $1, -1$ **2** $2, -1$ **3** $2, -1$ **5** $2, -1$ **6** $3, -2$ **7** $1, -4$ **9** $6, -1$ **10** $11, -1$ **11** $2, -3$
13 2 or 0 positive, 1 negative **14** 1 positive, 2 or 0 negative **15** 0 positive, 3 or 1 negative
17 2 or 0 positive, 2 or 0 negative **18** 2 or 0 positive, 2 or 0 negative **19** 3 or 1 positive, 1 negative
21 4, 2, or 0 positive, 1 negative **22** 3 or 1 positive, 2 or 0 negative **23** 1 positive, 2 or 0 negative
25 -4 and -3, -1 and 0, 0 and 1 **26** 0 and 1, 1 and 2, 4 and 5 **27** 0 and 1, 3 and 4, 5 and 6
29 -2 and -1, 0 and 1, 3 and 4, 5 and 6 **30** -5 and -4, -3 and -2, -2 and -1, 4 and 5
31 -2 and -1, -1 and 0, 1 and 2, 4 and 5 **33** 3 and 4 **34** 0 and 1 **35** -1 and 0, 2 and 3
37 -1 and $-\frac{1}{2}$, $-\frac{1}{2}$ and 0, 2 and 3 **38** -2 and -1, 1 and $\frac{3}{2}$, $\frac{3}{2}$ and 2 **39** -2 and -1, 1 and $\frac{3}{2}$, $\frac{3}{2}$ and 2
41 No positive or negative roots **42** None positive, 1 negative **43** 1 positive, none negative

EXERCISE 4.6

1 $-2, 1, 3$ **2** $-2, -1, 4$ **3** $-1, 2, 3$ **5** $-2, 1, 1.5$ **6** $-2.5, -2, 3$ **7** $-\frac{2}{3}, -1, 4$ **9** $-3, -\frac{3}{2}, \frac{1}{2}$ **10** $-\frac{1}{2}, \frac{3}{2}, 2$
11 $\frac{2}{3}, 1, \frac{3}{2}$ **13** $1, 1 \pm \sqrt{3}$ **14** $-2, -1 \pm \sqrt{2}$ **15** $-1, 2 \pm \sqrt{2}$ **17** $\frac{1}{2}, 1 \pm \sqrt{5}$ **18** $-\frac{3}{2}, -2 \pm \sqrt{3}$ **19** $\frac{2}{3}, -3 \pm \sqrt{2}$
21 $\pm 1, \pm 2$ **22** $\pm 2, \pm 3$ **23** $-\frac{2}{3}, \frac{1}{2}, 1, 2$ **25** $-3, \frac{1}{2}, 2 \pm \sqrt{3}$ **26** $-\frac{2}{3}, 2, 3 \pm \sqrt{2}$ **27** $-1, \frac{5}{3}, -1 + 2i, -1 - 2i$
45 $0, -2, -1 + 5i, -1 - 5i$ **46** $1, -2, (-1 + i\sqrt{23})/2, (-1 - i\sqrt{23})/2$ **47** $0, 3, (3 + \sqrt{17})/2, (3 - \sqrt{17})/2$ **49** 15
50 8 **51** 10 A.M. and 4 P.M. **53** $\frac{2}{3}$ **54** $2, 2.42; 2.42$

EXERCISE 4.7

1 0.79 **2** 0.28 **3** 2.27 **5** 0.46 **6** 5.46 **7** 8.20 **9** 1.41 **10** 1.73 **11** 3.24 **13** 1.24 **14** 1.27 **15** 1.59
17 $2.732, -0.732$ **18** $6.236, 1.764$ **19** $5.449, 0.551$ **21** $-3.261, -1.340, 1.602$ **22** $-4.769, -3.116, 1.884$
23 $-0.262, 1.660, 4.602$ **25** $1 + \sqrt{3}, 1 - \sqrt{3}, 1 + \sqrt{5}, 1 - \sqrt{5}; 3.236$
26 $2 + \sqrt{5}, 2 - \sqrt{5}, -1 + i\sqrt{2}, -1 - i\sqrt{2}; 4.236$ **27** $3 + \sqrt{2}, 3 - \sqrt{2}, -2 + \sqrt{3}, -2 - \sqrt{3}; 4.414$
29 $i, -i, 4 - \sqrt{3}, 4 + \sqrt{3}; 5.732$ **30** $i\sqrt{3}, -i\sqrt{3}, 2 - \sqrt{6}, 2 + \sqrt{6}; 4.449$ **31** $2i, -2i, -3 - 2\sqrt{2}, -3 + 2\sqrt{2}; -0.172$
33 $(7 \pm \sqrt{5})/2, (3 \pm \sqrt{53})/2; 5.140$ **34** $-1 \pm i\sqrt{2}, -5 \pm 2\sqrt{7}; 0.292$ **35** $\pm 2i, -3 \pm \sqrt{13}; 0.606$
37 $A = \sqrt[3]{9}, B = -2\sqrt[3]{3}; A + B, A\omega + B\omega^2, A\omega^2 + B\omega$ **38** $A = \sqrt[3]{25}, B = -\sqrt[3]{5}; A + B, A\omega + B\omega^2, A\omega^2 + B\omega$
39 $A = \sqrt[3]{4}, B = \sqrt[3]{2}; A + B, A\omega + B\omega^2, A\omega^2 + B\omega$
41 $A = \sqrt[3]{-3 + \sqrt{10}}, B = \sqrt[3]{-3 - \sqrt{10}}; A + B, A\omega + B\omega^2, A\omega^2 + B\omega$
42 $A = \sqrt[3]{-2 + 2\sqrt{3}}, B = \sqrt[3]{-2 - 2\sqrt{3}}; A + B, A\omega + B\omega^2, A\omega^2 + B\omega$
43 $A = \sqrt[3]{-1 + 2\sqrt{7}}, B = \sqrt[3]{-1 - 2\sqrt{7}}; A + B, A\omega + B\omega^2, A\omega^2 + B\omega$

EXERCISE 4.8

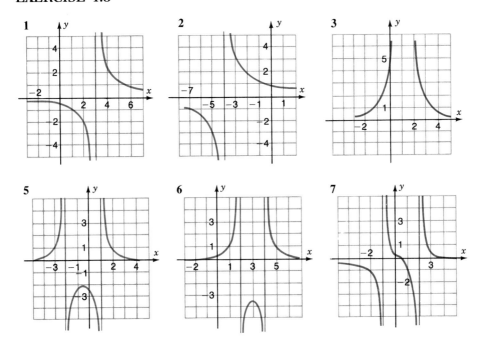

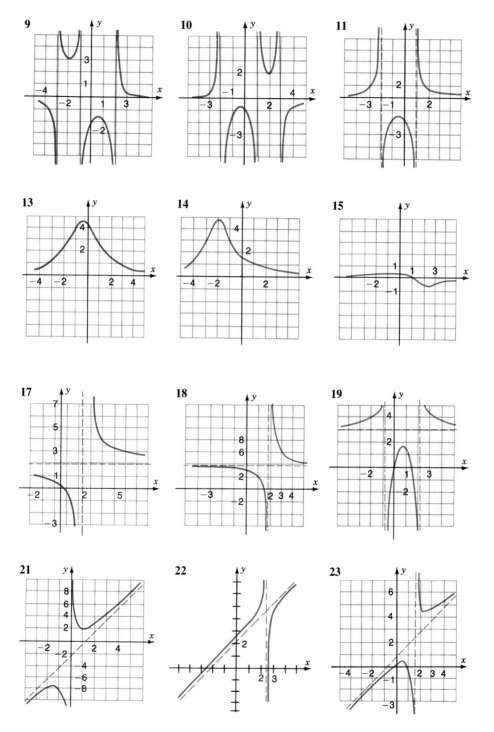

25 $(-\infty, -2) \cup (1, \infty)$ **26** $(-3, -1) \cup (2, \infty)$ **27** $(-\frac{1}{4}, \frac{3}{2})$ **29** $(-\infty, 0)$ **30** $(-\infty, -2) \cup (1, \infty)$ **31** $(-\infty, 1)$

EXERCISE 4.9

1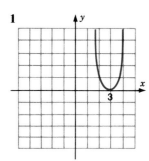

2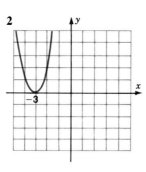

3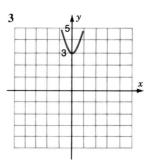

4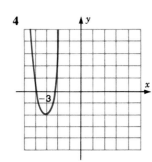

5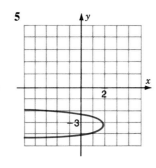

6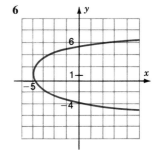

7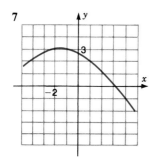

8 $(-1.5, 8)$, minimum   **9** $(2, 17)$, maximum   **10** $(0.5, 0.8125)$, minimum   **11** 14   **12** 20   **13** $d^4 - 2d^3 + 5d + 2$
14 $R = 0$ **15** $R = 0$ **16** $R = 0$ **17** $R = 0$ **18** $R = 0$ **19** $2x^2 + 4x + 13$, $R = 20$ **20** $3x^3 - x^2 + 4x - 2$, $R = 1$
21 2, 2, -3 **22** $\pm i\sqrt{2}$ **23** $x^3 - 8x^2 + 22x - 20 = 0$ **24** $x^3 - 5x^2 + 4x + 6$ **25** $x^4 + 2x^3 + 2x^2 + 10x + 25$
26 $x^4 - 8x^3 + 24x^2 - 32x + 7$ **27** 3   **28** 2   **29** Sum is 1, product is 1.   **30** Sum is 4, product is 16.
31 1 is an upper limit and -1 is a lower limit.   **32** There is one variation in sign.   **33** 1, 2, 3
34 $\sqrt[3]{4}$ is a root and ±4, ±2, ±1 are the only possible rational roots.
35 Equating right members gives $x^2 + 4x + 7 = 0$ and its roots are imaginary.   **36** 2, $\pm i$ **37** $-\frac{3}{2}$, $-\frac{3}{2}$, $\pm2i$
38 $\frac{5}{2}$, $\frac{1}{3}$, -2, $1 \pm i$ **39** $\frac{2}{3}$ **42** No   **43** -0.18 **44** 0.73, -2.73 **45** 1.618, -0.618, ±1.732 **46** $(1 \pm \sqrt{5})/2$, $\pm\sqrt{3}$
47 $A + B$, $A\omega + B\omega^2$, $A\omega^2 + B\omega$ where $A^3 = 18$, $B^3 = 12$, $\omega = (-1 + i\sqrt{3})/2$
48 $3 + A + B$, $3 + A\omega + B\omega^2$, $3 + A\omega^2 + B\omega$, where $A^3 = 72$, $B^3 = 24$, and $\omega = (-1 + i\sqrt{3})/2$

49 $f(x) = x^3 - 4x^2 + x + 6$

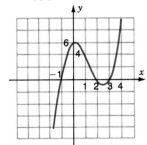

50 $f(x) = x^3 - 2x^2 - 5x + 6$

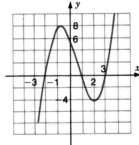

51 $f(x) = x^4 + 2x^3 - 7x^2 - 8x + 12$

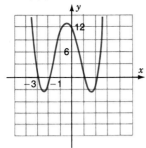

52 $f(x) = (x + 1)^2(x - 1)^2(x - 3)^3$

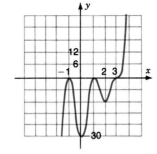

53 $f(x) = (x + 2)^3(x - 1)^2(x - 4)^3$

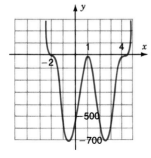

54 $f(x) = \frac{4}{x - 2}$

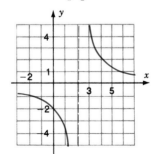

55 $f(x) = \frac{2}{(x + 1)(x - 2)}$

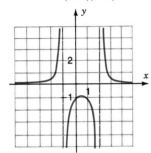

56 $f(x) = \frac{6x + 1}{3x - 2}$

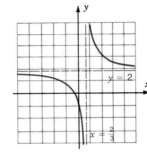

57 $f(x) = \frac{(x + 1)(x - 1)}{(x + 2)(x - 2)}$

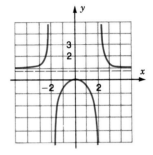

59 $x^4 + 4x^3 - 6x^2 + 52x + 169 = 0$, $S = 2 + 3i + 2 - 3i - 4 + \sqrt{3} - 4 - \sqrt{3} = -4$, and $P = (2 + 3i)(2 - 3i)(-4 + \sqrt{3})$
$(-4 - \sqrt{3}) = 13(13) = 169$ **62** $(-\infty, -4] \cup [-1, 3] \cup (5, \infty)$ **63** $[-5, -3] \cup [1, 3]$ **64** $[-2, -1] \cup [3, \infty)$
65 $(-1, 1) \cup (2, 4)$

EXERCISE 5.1

1 $y = 4^x$

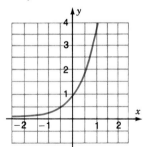

2 $y = 5^x$

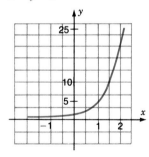

3 $y = e^x$

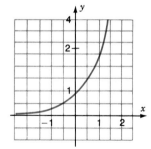

5 $y = \left(\frac{1}{3}\right)^x$

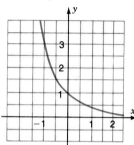

6 $y = \left(\frac{1}{4}\right)^x$

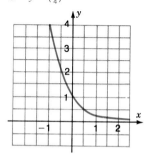

7 $y = \left(\frac{5}{6}\right)^x$

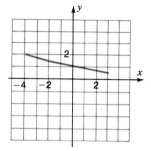

9 $y = 2^{-x}$

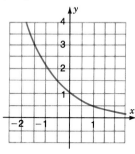

10 $y = -5^x$

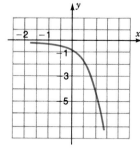

11 $y = -\left(\frac{1}{7}\right)^x$

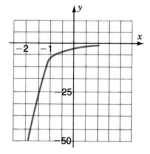

13 $y = (27)\,3^x$

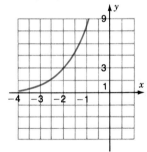

14 $y = \left(\frac{1}{27}\right)3^x$

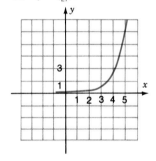

15 $y = -\left(\frac{2}{3}\right)^{x-5}$

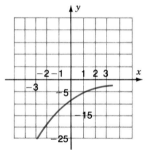

17 $\quad y = 2^{|x|}$

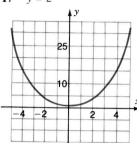

18 $\quad y = 2^{-x^2}$

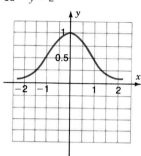

19 $\quad y = 2^x + 2^{-x}$

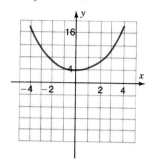

21 $-\frac{3}{4}$ **22** -3 **23** $-\frac{3}{2}$ **25** 10 **26** 10.5 **27** 2 **29** 4 **30** 16 **31** 13.5 **33** 196.608 **34** 3:1
35 6.25 percent simple interest **37** 7.355 lb/in^2 **38** $3555 **39** 3 min **41** False **42** False **43** True **45** 2401 **46** $\frac{1}{1024}$
47 6 **49** 16 **50** $\frac{1}{4}$ **51** $255\frac{255}{256}$ **53** 4^2 **54** Each is $(\frac{3}{2})^{27/4}$ **55** Each is $(\frac{5}{3})^{25\sqrt{5}/6\sqrt{3}}$ **57** 15.426, 16.242 **58** 11.212, 11.665
59 15.245, 15.673 **61** Subtract them **62** It approaches 50,000. **63** $\frac{5}{8}$ **65** $4^{y+2} - 4^y = 4^y(16 - 1) = 15(4^y)$
66 $5^t(5^2 + 15 - 40) = 0$ **67** Factor out 2^x

EXERCISE 5.2

1 $\log_3 9 = 2$ **2** $\log_3 81 = 4$ **3** $\log_3 \frac{1}{27} = -3$ **5** $\log_8 4 = \frac{2}{3}$ **6** $\log_{36} 216 = \frac{3}{2}$ **7** $\log_{1/3} 9 = -2$ **9** $2^4 = 16$ **10** $5^3 = 125$
11 $2^{-3} = \frac{1}{8}$ **13** $36^{3/2} = 216$ **14** $216^{2/3} = 36$ **15** $125^{2/3} = 25$ **17** 4 **18** 3 **19** 4 **21** $-\frac{3}{2}$ **22** $-\frac{3}{2}$ **23** $-\frac{7}{2}$ **25** 1.3 **26** 1
27 0 **29** 125 **30** 16 **31** 27 **33** 5 **34** 2 **35** 4

37

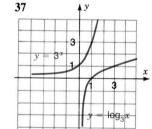

38

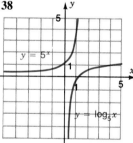

39

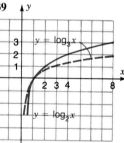

41 $\quad y = \log_5 (x^2)$

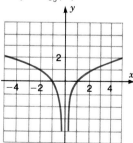

42 $\quad y = \log_5 (3x)$

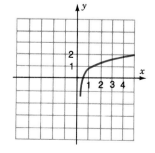

43 $\quad y = \log_2 (x - 3)$

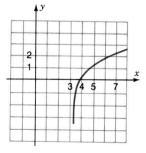

45

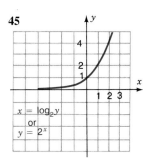

$x = \log_2 y$
or
$y = 2^x$

46

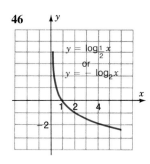

$y = \log_{\frac{1}{2}} x$
or
$y = -\log_2 x$

47

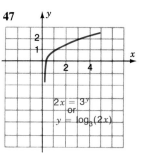

$2x = 3^y$
or
$y = \log_3 (2x)$

49 $2 \log_b x + 0.5 \log_b y - \log_b 5 - 3 \log_b z$ **50** $\log_b 8 + \log_b x + 4 \log_b y - \log_b 7 - \log_b z$
51 $\log_b 3 + 0.5 \log_b y - 3 \log_b x - 7 \log_b y$ **53** $\log_4 x + \log_4 (x^3 - 2) - \log_4 (5x + 3)$
54 $4 \log_5 x + \frac{2}{3} \log_5 (x + 1) - \log_5 (x + 23)$ **55** $\log_6 (x - 4) + 5 \log_6 (2x + 7) - \log_6 x - 3 \log_6 (3x + 8)$ **57** $\log_a 3x^2 y^9$
58 $\log_a (x^2 z^{1/3} / y^{1/2})$ **59** $\log_a (x^3)$ **61** $\log_{10} 1.5 x^7 y^4 z^6$ **62** $\log_9 [(2x + 3)/(2x - 3)]$ **63** $\log_7 (x^4 w^2 y^7)$ **65** 1.45   **66** 2.81
67 1.32   **69** True   **70** True   **71** False   **73** False   **74** True   **75** False   **85** $-2N \log_5 (1 - f)$
86 $-\log_2 N = \log_2 (1/N)$, $H = \frac{7}{4}$ **87** $S = N[1 - (1 - 1/N)^f]$ **89** $[\log (S/S_0)]/\log (1 + c)$
90 (a) $A = 10^{-d/c}$, (b) $x[c \log_{10} (A/x) + 1]$ **91** $\pm W \sqrt{5^{2A/WH} - 1}$ **93** If $(1/b)^P = x$, then $b^{-P} = x$.

EXERCISE 5.3

1 $y = e^{2x}$

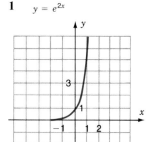

2 $y = e^{x^2}$

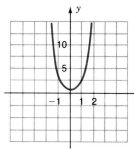

3 $y = e^{x + 3}$

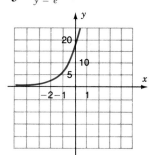

5 $y = 2 + e^x$

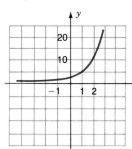

6 $y = 3 - e^{2x}$

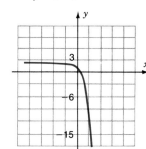

7 $y = (x + 1)e^x$

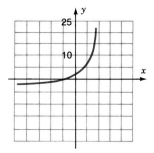

9 20.09, 0.04979, 1.0986   **10** 2.718, 0.3679, 0   **11** 66.69, 0.01500, 1.435   **13** $\ln 20.09 = 3$ **14** $x = \ln 37.6 = 3.6270$
15 $\ln 67.3 = 1.9066$ **17** $e^4 = 54.5982$ **18** $e^2 = 7.3891$ **19** $e^{2.303} = 10.0042$ **21** $(e^3 - 5)/2$, 7.5428
22 $(4e + 1)/3e$, 1.4560   **23** $(5 - e^{-2})/2$, 2.4323   **25** $0.2 \ln 2$, 0.1386   **26** $(2 - \ln 4)/6$, 0.1023   **27** $(\ln 3 - 5)/6$, -0.6502
29 1.3610   **30** 1.8563   **31** 3.0007   **33** 5.9   **34** 0.3   **35** 3.2   **37** $\ln y = \ln (2x - 1) + 0.5 \ln (x + 1) - \ln 5 - 2 \ln x$
38 $\ln y = 3 \ln (4x + 7) + 0.5 \ln (7 - x) - \ln 3 - 5 \ln x$ **39** $\ln y = \ln 6 + 0.2 \ln (2x + 3) - \ln 7 - 3 \ln x$ **41** $(-4 \pm \sqrt{10})/2$
42 $(-5 \pm \sqrt{73})/24$ **43** $(-17 \pm \sqrt{229})/6$ **45** 4.95 years   **46** 2.67 years   **47** $\frac{1}{4}$, 0.2643   **49** 0.98 min   **50** $14.7(10^{-0.1273})$

51 128,403; 164,872; 271,828 **53** 6885.64 **54** 5930.25 **55** 8.11 **57** 3.9656 **58** 2.6610 **59** 2.8614 **61** $e^{x \ln 2}$ **62** $e^{5x \ln 6}$
63 $e^{(x-2)\ln 7}$ **65** $L(\ln 30 - \ln I)/t$ **66** $(\ln P_0 - \ln P)/t$ **67** $e^{-P/0.43} = H$ **69** Log of a quotient **70** Log of a power
73 $(1 + 1/n)^n$: $(\frac{4}{3})^3 = 2.37037$, $(\frac{7}{6})^6 = 2.52163$, $(\frac{10}{9})^9 = 2.58117$; $(1 + 1/n)^{n+1}$:$(\frac{4}{3})^4 = 3.16049$, $(\frac{7}{6})^7 = 2.94190$, $(\frac{10}{9})^{10} = 2.86797$
74 2.70833, 2.71806, 2.71828 **75** 1.22140, 1.22133, 1.10517, 1.10517 **76** 0.2624 and 0.2550, 0.0953 and 0.0953
77 0.9917 **79** 4

EXERCISE 5.4

1 1, 0, −1 **2** 3, 1, 0 **3** 6, −2, 2 **5** 0.5340 **6** 0.6263 **7** 0.9523 **9** 0.9425 **10** 1.5403 **11** 2.7767 **13** 7.9557 − 10
14 8.0374 − 10 **15** 8.8007 − 10 **17** 40.3 **18** 9.51 **19** 653 **21** 0.205 **22** 0.0428 **23** 0.00863 **25** 7546 **26** 507
27 1.77 **29** 2.08 **30** 3.00 **31** 8.00 **33** 4.5 **34** 2.3333 **35** 2.5 **37** 0.6978 **38** −1.0925 **39** 0.1204
41 0.3010, 0.0669 **42** $\log 2 + \log \frac{3}{2} + \log \frac{4}{3} + \log \frac{5}{4} + \log \frac{6}{5} + \log \frac{7}{6} + \log \frac{8}{7} + \log \frac{9}{8} + \log \frac{10}{9} = 1$ **43** 17.875 > 17.34
45 210 **46** 924 **47** 20.97, 40.79 **49** 7722 **50** 1.55 g **51** 6991 **53** It is 1259 times as intense.
54 The first is $\frac{1}{32}$ as intense as the second. **55** 7.9 **57** 57.7 **58** 752.83, 829.41 **59** 6.3979 **61** 11.44 h = 11 h 26 min
62 50; 115,385 **63** 10.245 **65** 94 **66** 101 **67** First **69** Use the change-of-base formula
70 The graph of a polynomial of degree m **71** Use the change-of-base formula **73** 1121.01 **74** 231.066 **75** 16.1616
77 0.4493 **78** 2.2442 **79** 0.1735 **81** 22.2007 **82** 1.3791 **83** 0.1342 **85** 207.0570 **86** 33.2899 **87** 27.5978
89 7.2721 **90** 31.9049 **91** 2.7579

EXERCISE 5.5

1 5 **2** 3 **3** 1, 1 **5** $-\frac{1}{2}$, 1 **6** $-\frac{8}{3}$ **7** −6 **9** 4, 2 **10** 2, 0 **11** 1, 0 **13** 0.9735 **14** 2.0214 **15** −1.0268 **17** 2.7381
18 3.1505 **19** 2.0208 **21** −0.6158 **22** 21.7643 **23** 1.2002 **25** 3 **26** 4 **27** 5 **29** 3 **30** 1 **31** 2 **33** $x = \log y$
34 $x = \log (1/y)$ **35** $x = 0.5 \log (5/y)$ **37** $x = \ln (y \pm \sqrt{y^2 - 1})$ **38** $x = \ln (y + \sqrt{y^2 + 1})$ **39** $x = \ln \sqrt{(y + 1)/(y - 1)}$
41 $x < 1.5068$ **42** $x < 0.3895$ **43** $x > -1.1708$ **45** $x < 1.5509$ **46** $x < 1.0829$ **47** $x < 24.26$ **49** 3^{16} **50** 9
51 $10^{(1+\sqrt{17})/2}$ **52** 1 or e^2 **53** $10^{\sqrt{3}} = 53.96$ **54** 10,000, 1

EXERCISE 5.6

1

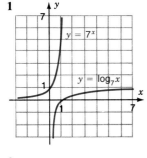

2

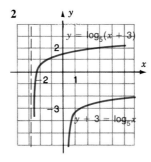

3

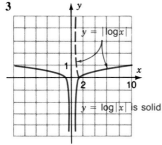

4

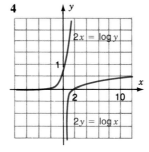

5 Raise each member to the power 40. **6** Square each member. **7** Each is $(\frac{6}{5})^{6^6/5^5}$ **8** $2^{\sqrt{2}} = 2.6651$, $(\sqrt{2})^2 = 2$
9 $5 \log_3 3 = 5 \cdot 1 = 5$ **10** $\log_b (b^8) = 8 = 2^3$ **11** Exponential form is $101^0 = 1$. **12** Exponential form is $(\frac{2}{5})^3 = \frac{8}{125}$
13 Exponential form is $9^{2.5} = 3^5 = 243$. **14** Exponential form is $4^{-3.5} = \frac{1}{128} = 2^{-7}$. **15** $30 = 2(3)5$; hence, the statement
16 $3x$ **17** $1 + y - 2x - z$ **18** $z/2 + y$ **19** 2.6857 **20** 1.8274 **21** $9.9886 - 10$ **22** 0.3347 **23** 55,195 **24** $8.4(10^{-6})$
25 0.0804 **26** 0.2160 **27** 3 **28** 1, -4 **29** 2.8229 **30** 8 **31** $\emptyset$ **32** -4.6072 **33** $3^{16} = 43,046,721$ **34** 0, 2
35 $x < 0.4348$ **36** 0.8848 **37** $x < \frac{1}{3}$ as seen from a graph **38** $\ln y = \ln (12x + 31) + 0.5 \ln (x^2 + 17) - \ln (5x^2 + 6)$
39 $(13 + \sqrt{229})/6$ **40** 18.05 min **41** 256 **42** $5.01, -3$ **43** 3.1415915 **44** 38.825, 36.403 **45** $10^{12.5}I_0 = I$ **46** 83,613
47 $2 g$ **48** 850, 1025 **49** $3.1622(10)^{-9}$ **50** First **51** 3 h, 4.75 h **52** Second is $10^{3.7} = 5012$ times as severe as the first
53 2217 years **54** $t > 14.33$ s. It approaches 120 ft/s. **55** 4226, 6308, 7214, 6428, 153, -72, $-12,826$ **56** $f(2) = 4.53$,
$f(3) = 4.55$, $f(4) = 4.58$, 5 **57** 915.13 **58** 0.07979 **60** 6.514 **61** 32 **64** 172.634 **65** 0.5756 **66** 1.442 **67** 27,797.13
68 0.3335 **69** 1.3869 **70** 4.3198 **71** 2.0814 **72** 0.9293 **73** 1.2118

EXERCISE 6.1

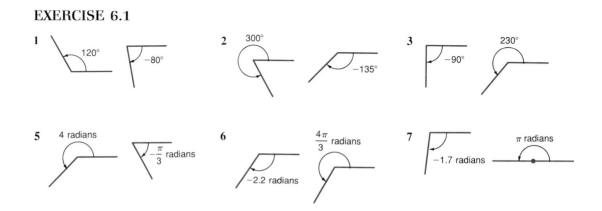

9 $\pi/5$ **10** $\pi/6$ **11** $\pi/20$ **13** $49\pi/720$ **14** $31\pi/270$ **15** $\pi/16$ **17** $751\pi/64,800$ **18** $269\pi/3000$ **19** $73\pi/12,000$
21 $31\pi/20$ **22** 0.85π **23** 3.4π **25** 0.541 **26** -0.209 **27** 0.855 **29** -0.157 **30** 0.195 **31** 0.475 **33** $45°$ **34** $15°$
35 $12°$ **37** $28°7'30''$ **38** $26°40'$ **39** $35°$ **41** $148°58'8''$ **42** $211°59'40''$ **43** $85°56'37''$ **45** $17\pi/6, -7\pi/6$
46 $7\pi/4, -9\pi/4$ **47** $\pi/2, -3\pi/2$ **49** $690°, -30°$ **50** $120°, -240°$ **51** $180°, -180°$ **53** 1.49 cm **54** 8.92 in **55** 32.0 cm
57 3.246 cm **58** 26.44 ft **59** 98.44 ft **61** 0.744 rad **62** 0.360 rad **63** 1.89 **65** 2.91 in **66** 15 seconds **67** 35.2
69 3.8 cm **70** $65°$ **71** 4 **73** 9.9 **74** 1.7 **75** 14.7 **77** 3142 mi **78** 977 mi **79** 5585 mi **82** $7\pi/8, 157.5°$ **83** 10.05

EXERCISE 6.2

The function values are given in the order sine, cosine, tangent, cotangent, secant, cosecant.
1 $\frac{4}{5}, \frac{3}{5}, \frac{4}{3}, \frac{3}{4}, \frac{5}{3}, \frac{5}{4}$ **2** $\frac{15}{17}, \frac{8}{17}, \frac{15}{8}, \frac{8}{15}, \frac{17}{8}, \frac{17}{15}$ **3** $\frac{5}{13}, \frac{12}{13}, \frac{5}{12}, \frac{12}{5}, \frac{13}{12}, \frac{13}{5}$ **5** $3/\sqrt{13}, 2/\sqrt{13}, \frac{3}{2}, \frac{2}{3}, \sqrt{13}/2, \sqrt{13}/3$ **6** $\sqrt{11}/6, \frac{5}{6}$,
$\sqrt{11}/5, 5/\sqrt{11}, \frac{6}{5}, 6/\sqrt{11}$ **7** $\sqrt{38}/7, \sqrt{11}/7, \sqrt{38}/\sqrt{11}, \sqrt{11}/\sqrt{38}, 7/\sqrt{11}, 7/\sqrt{38}$ **9** $-\frac{4}{5}, \frac{3}{5}, -\frac{4}{3}, -\frac{3}{4}, \frac{5}{3}, -\frac{5}{4}$ **10** $\frac{15}{17}, -\frac{8}{17}$,
$-\frac{15}{8}, -\frac{8}{15}, -\frac{17}{8}, \frac{17}{15}$ **11** $\frac{4}{5}, \frac{3}{5}, \frac{4}{3}, \frac{3}{4}, \frac{5}{3}, \frac{5}{4}$ **13** $-\frac{4}{5}, \frac{3}{5}, -\frac{4}{3}, -\frac{3}{4}, \frac{5}{3}, -\frac{5}{4}$ **14** $-\frac{15}{17}, \frac{8}{17}, -\frac{15}{8}, -\frac{8}{15}, \frac{17}{8}, -\frac{17}{15}$ **15** $\frac{24}{25}, \frac{7}{25}, \frac{24}{7}, \frac{7}{24}, \frac{25}{7}, \frac{25}{24}$
17 $\frac{4}{5}, \frac{3}{5}, \frac{4}{3}, \frac{3}{4}, \frac{5}{3}, \frac{5}{4}$ **18** $-\frac{12}{13}, \frac{5}{13}, -\frac{12}{5}, -\frac{5}{12}, \frac{13}{5}, -\frac{13}{12}$ **19** $-\frac{8}{17}, -\frac{15}{17}, \frac{8}{15}, \frac{15}{8}, -\frac{17}{15}, -\frac{17}{8}$ **21** $-\frac{12}{13}, \frac{5}{13}, -\frac{12}{5}, -\frac{5}{12}, \frac{13}{5}, -\frac{13}{12}$
22 $\frac{5}{13}, -\frac{12}{13}, -\frac{5}{12}, -\frac{12}{5}, -\frac{13}{12}, \frac{13}{5}$ **23** $-\frac{4}{5}, -\frac{3}{5}, \frac{4}{3}, \frac{3}{4}, -\frac{5}{3}, -\frac{5}{4}$ **25** $-\sqrt{5}/3, \frac{2}{3}, -\sqrt{5}/2, -2/\sqrt{5}, \frac{3}{2}, -3/\sqrt{5}$ **26** $-3/\sqrt{13}$,
$-2/\sqrt{13}, \frac{3}{2}, \frac{2}{3}, -\sqrt{13}/2, -\sqrt{13}/3$ **27** $\frac{7}{10}, -\sqrt{51}/10, -7/\sqrt{51}, -\sqrt{51}/7, -10/\sqrt{51}, \frac{10}{7}$ **29** $\frac{24}{25}, \pm\frac{7}{25}, \pm\frac{24}{7}, \pm\frac{7}{24}, \pm\frac{25}{7}, \frac{25}{24}$
30 $\pm\frac{8}{17}, \mp\frac{15}{17}, -\frac{8}{15}, -\frac{15}{8}, \mp\frac{17}{15}, \pm\frac{17}{8}$ **31** $\pm\frac{12}{13}, -\frac{5}{13}, \mp\frac{12}{5}, \mp\frac{5}{12}, -\frac{13}{5}, \pm\frac{13}{12}$ **33** $\frac{20}{29}$ **34** $-\frac{12}{5}$ **35** $-\sqrt{85}/7$ **37** $\frac{24}{7}$ **38** $\frac{4}{5}$
39 $-\frac{13}{5}$ **41** $\frac{8}{3}$ **42** $-\frac{11}{7}$ **43** $-\frac{14}{19}$

EXERCISE 6.3

1 $\frac{15}{17}, \frac{8}{17}, \frac{15}{8}, \frac{8}{15}, \frac{17}{8}, \frac{17}{15}$ **2** $\frac{4}{5}, \frac{3}{5}, \frac{4}{3}, \frac{3}{4}, \frac{5}{3}, \frac{5}{4}$ **3** $\frac{24}{25}, \frac{7}{25}, \frac{24}{7}, \frac{7}{24}, \frac{25}{7}, \frac{25}{24}$ **5** $\sqrt{2}/2, \sqrt{2}/2, 1, 1, \sqrt{2}, \sqrt{2}$ **6** $\frac{7}{25}, \frac{24}{25}, \frac{7}{24}, \frac{24}{7}, \frac{25}{24}, \frac{25}{7}$
7 $\frac{3}{5}, \frac{4}{5}, \frac{3}{4}, \frac{4}{3}, \frac{5}{4}, \frac{5}{3}$ **9** cos 61° **10** sin 43° **11** cot 3° **13** csc 0.5934 **14** sec 0.5411 **15** sin 1.3614 **17** $-\cos 33°$
18 $-\tan 33°$ **19** $-\sec 11°$ **21** $-\cot 37°$ **22** csc 36° **23** $-\sin 17°$ **33** 2 **34** 3 **35** 4 **37** False **38** False **39** True
41 True **42** True **43** False **45** False **46** True **47** True **49** 12° **50** 15° **51** 20.5° **53** 4.787 **54** 0.3038 **55** 0.3988
57 0.6455 **58** 0.9720 **59** 2.204 **61** 27.10° **62** 22.30° **63** 28.30° **65** 29.20° **66** 75.49° **67** 65.0° **69** 57.8° or 302.2°
70 26.7° or 153.3° **71** 32.1° or 212.1° **101** 0.6910

EXERCISE 6.4

1 $A = 60°, a = 6\sqrt{3}, b = 6$ **2** $B = 30°, a = 18\sqrt{3}, b = 18$ **3** $B = 30°, a = 16\sqrt{3}, c = 32$ **5** $A = 45°, b = 20, c = 20\sqrt{2}$
6 $A = 45°, a = 7\sqrt{2}, c = 14$ **7** $A = 45°, B = 45°, a = 17$ **9** $B = 16.3°, a = 251, c = 262$
10 $B = 21.2°, a = 110, c = 118$ **11** $A = 52.5°, b = 494, c = 812$ **13** $B = 48.8°, a = 607, b = 693$
14 $B = 57.5°, a = 4.37, b = 6.86$ **15** $A = 26.3°, a = 43.7, b = 88.4$ **17** $B = 47.1°, b = 33.7, c = 46.0$
18 $B = 20.4°, b = 1.85, c = 5.30$ **19** $A = 13.7°, a = 98.0, c = 414$ **21** $A = 39.91°, B = 50.09°, c = 88.50$
22 $A = 34.73°, B = 55.27°, c = 0.6540$ **23** $B = 35.30°, A = 54.70°, c = 4.563$ **25** $A = 46.11°, B = 43.89°, a = 6.847$
26 $A = 32.49°, B = 57.51°, b = 3.162$ **27** $A = 46.67°, B = 43.33°, b = 8.468$ **29** 13 m **30** 142 ft **31** 12.35 ft
33 3167 ft **34** 2.80 ft **35** 141 ft **37** Train by 0.0858 h = 5.1 min **38** $4.53(10^3)$ ft² **39** 21.6 **41** 154 mi **42** Yes
43 25.1 ft **45** 7.457 ft **46** 811 m S 66.0 W **47** 594 ft **49** 1003 m **50** 193 ft, 70 ft **51** 19 ft **53** 4.2° **54** 61.9°
55 13.4° **57** 36.9°, 53.1° **58** 22.6°, 67.4° **59** 43.6°, 46.4° **65** Each is approximately -0.2502. **66** 15.6°

EXERCISE 6.5

1 $\sqrt{3}/2$ **2** 1 **3** $\sqrt{3}/2$ **5** $-\sqrt{3}/3$ **6** $-\sqrt{3}/2$ **7** $\sqrt{2}$ **9** -2 **10** $-\sqrt{2}$ **11** 0 **13** tan 0.85 **14** $-\cot 0.45$ **15** sec 1.13
17 $-\sin \pi/4$ **18** $-\cos \pi/6$ **19** tan $2\pi/5$ **21** $-\sec 24°$ **22** csc 30° **23** $-\sin 10°$ **25** tan 21° **26** $-\sin 52°$ **27** $-\cot 4°$
29 $-\sin 0.60$ **30** $-\csc 0.56$ **31** csc 0.02 **33** sin $\pi/10$ **34** cot $\pi/6$ **35** cot $\pi/6$ **37** sec 14° **38** $-\cos 6°$ **39** sin 37°
41 sin 1.52 **42** $-\sin 1.50$ **43** $-\sin 1.42$ **45** $-1/2, -\sqrt{3}/2, 1/\sqrt{3}, \sqrt{3}, -2/\sqrt{3}, -2$ **46** 0, -1, 0, not defined, -1, not
defined **47** $\sqrt{3}/2, -1/2, -\sqrt{3}, -1/\sqrt{3}, -2, 2/\sqrt{3}$ **49** $1/2, -\sqrt{3}/2, -1/\sqrt{3}, -\sqrt{3}, -2/\sqrt{3}, 2$ **50** 1, 0, not defined, 0, not
defined, 1 **51** $\sqrt{2}/2, \sqrt{2}/2, 1, 1, \sqrt{2}, \sqrt{2}$ **65** 1 **66** 3 **67** 5 **73** $-1, 1, -1, 1$ **74** $-1, -1, 1, 1$ **75** 1, -1, 1, 1

EXERCISE 6.6

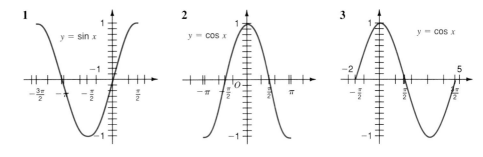

5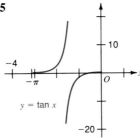

6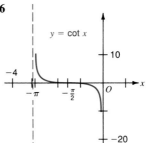

7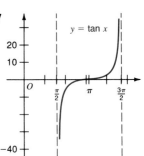

9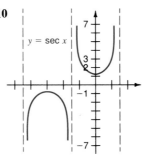

10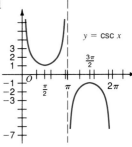

11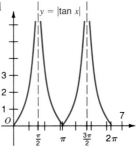

13 True   **14** False   **15** True   **17** $[0, \pi]$ **18** $[0, \pi/2), (\pi/2, 3\pi/2), (3\pi/2, 2\pi]$

19 $(0, \pi/2], [3\pi/2, 2\pi)$

21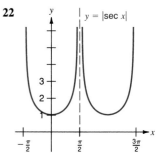

22

23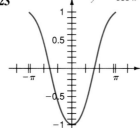

25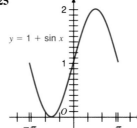

26 $y = -2 + \tan x$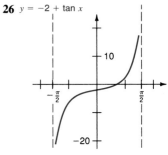

27

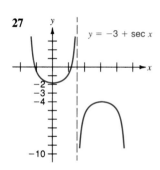

$y = -3 + \sec x$

29

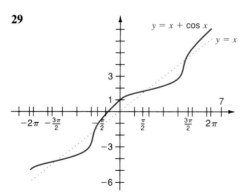

$y = x + \cos x$

$y = x$

30

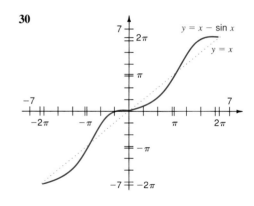

$y = x - \sin x$

$y = x$

31

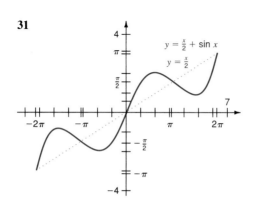

$y = \frac{x}{2} + \sin x$

$y = \frac{x}{2}$

33

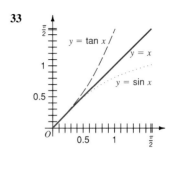

$y = \tan x$

$y = x$

$y = \sin x$

EXERCISE 6.7

1 None, $\pi/2$, none   **2** None, $\pi/3$, none   **3** None, $2\pi/5$, none   **5** 2, 4π, none   **6** 3, $4\pi/5$, none   **7** 0.2, 2, none
9 None, $\pi/2$, $\pi/2$ to the left   **10** None, $\pi/5$, 1.8 to the left   **11** None, $2\pi/3$, $\frac{7}{3}$ to the left   **13** 7, $\pi/3$, 1.5 to the right
14 2, π, $\pi/6$ to the right   **15** None, 2π, 12 to the right   **17** 2   **18** 2   **19** $2\pi/3$

21

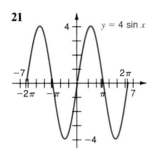

$y = 4 \sin x$

22

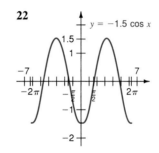

$y = -1.5 \cos x$

23

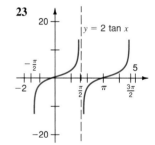

$y = 2 \tan x$

25
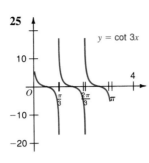
$y = \cot 3x$

26
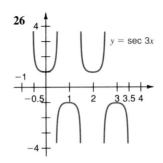
$y = \sec 3x$

27
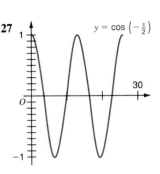
$y = \cos\left(-\frac{x}{2}\right)$

29
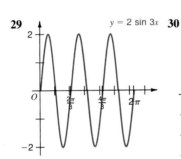
$y = 2 \sin 3x$

30
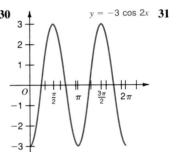
$y = -3 \cos 2x$

31
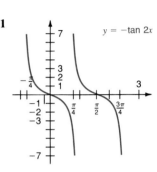
$y = -\tan 2x$

33
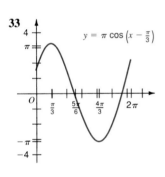
$y = \pi \cos\left(x - \frac{\pi}{3}\right)$

34
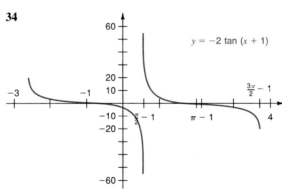
$y = -2 \tan (x + 1)$

35
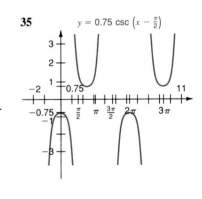
$y = 0.75 \csc\left(x - \frac{\pi}{2}\right)$

37
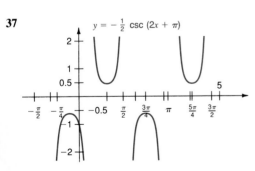
$y = -\frac{1}{2} \csc (2x + \pi)$

38
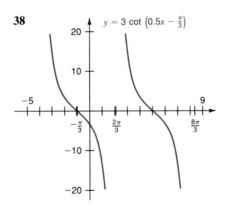
$y = 3 \cot\left(0.5x - \frac{\pi}{3}\right)$

39
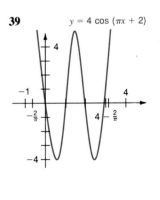
$y = 4 \cos (\pi x + 2)$

41 4, $2\pi/3$, $\frac{1}{2}$ to the left   **42** 3, π, 0.8 to the left   **43** 3.1, $2\pi/3$, $\pi/9$ to the right   **45** 3, π, 3.35 to the left
46 6.3, $2\pi/3$, 0.8 to the left   **47** 44.8, $\pi/4$, $\frac{7}{8}$ to the right

49 $y = \sin x + \cos x$
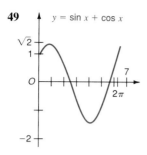

50 $y = 3 \sin x + 4 \cos x$
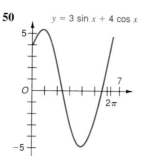

51 $y = 15 \sin x - 8 \cos x$
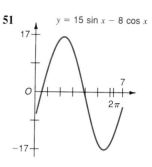

53 $y = e^{-x} \cos x$
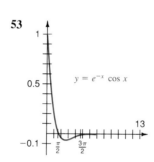

54 $y = \cos x$ $y = 1 - \frac{x^2}{2}$
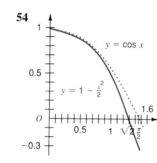

55 $y = \sin\left(x + \frac{\pi}{4}\right)$
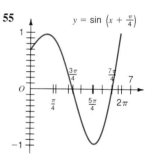

57 $y = 110 + 30 \cos\left(\frac{12\pi t}{5}\right)$
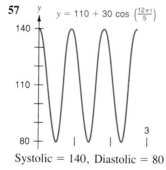
Systolic = 140, Diastolic = 80

58 $y = 12 + 4 \sin\left(\frac{2\pi t}{365}\right)$
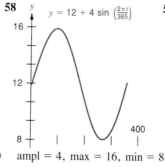
ampl = 4, max = 16, min = 8

59 $y = 20 + 5 \sin\left(2t - \frac{\pi}{2}\right)$
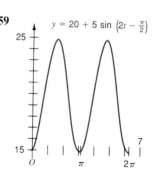

61 $y = 3 \cos x + \cos 3x$
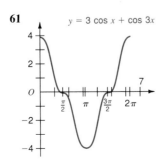

62 $y = 3 \sin 2x + 2 \sin 3x$
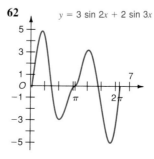

63 $f(x + 2\pi/3) = f(x)$

65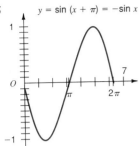

$y = \sin(x + \pi) = -\sin x$

66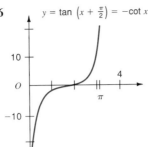

$y = \tan\left(x + \frac{\pi}{2}\right) = -\cot x$

67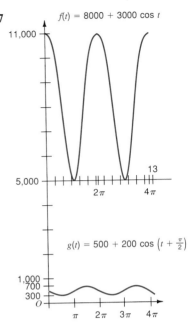

$f(t) = 8000 + 3000 \cos t$

$g(t) = 500 + 200 \cos\left(t + \frac{\pi}{2}\right)$

EXERCISE 6.8

1 $2\pi/5$ **2** $7\pi/10$ **3** $25\pi/12$ **4** $31\pi/540$ **5** $\pi/16$ **6** 7.8π **7** 0.820 **8** 0.303 **9** 0.599 **10** $7°30'$ **11** $23°20'$
12 $211.994° = 211°59'40''$ **13** 0.368 **14** 1.67 **15** 113 **16** 2164 mi
17 $4\sqrt{2}/7$, $\sqrt{17}/7$, $4\sqrt{2}/\sqrt{17}$, $\sqrt{17}/4\sqrt{2}$, $7/\sqrt{17}$, $7/4\sqrt{2}$ **18** $-\frac{8}{17}$, $-\frac{15}{17}$, $\frac{8}{15}$, $\frac{15}{8}$, $-\frac{17}{15}$, $-\frac{17}{8}$ **19** $\frac{21}{29}$, $\pm\frac{20}{29}$, $\pm\frac{21}{20}$, $\pm\frac{20}{21}$, $\pm\frac{29}{20}$, $\frac{29}{21}$
20 $\frac{1}{2} = \sqrt{2}(1/\sqrt{2})(\frac{1}{2}) + 0$ **21** $0.9205 + (-0.0872) + (-0.9744) + (-0.5150) + 0.6561 = 0$
22 $\sin 312° = -\sin 48° = -\cos 42°$ **23** $-\sqrt{2}/2$, $-1/\sqrt{3}$, 1 **24** $\frac{1}{2}$, -1, -1 **25** $-\sqrt{2}/2$, $\sqrt{2}/2$, $-\sqrt{3}$ **26** 7, $2\pi/5$, none
27 None, $\pi/9$, none   **28** 3, 0.8, none   **29** None, $3\pi/2$, none   **30** None, 2π, $\pi/2$ to the right   **31** 1, π, $\pi/8$ to the left

32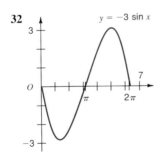

$y = -3 \sin x$

33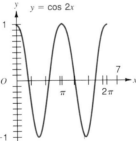

$y = \cos 2x$

34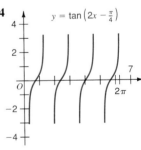

$y = \tan\left(2x - \frac{\pi}{4}\right)$

35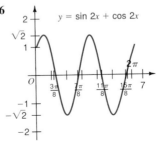

$y = 2\cos\left(3x + \frac{\pi}{2}\right)$

36

$y = \sin 2x + \cos 2x$

37 10.1 **38** Polynomial gives 0.8254, calculator gives 0.8253 **39** Polynomial gives 0.8417, calculator gives 0.8415
40 $\tan(3\pi/11) + 4\sin(2\pi/11) = 1.15406 + 4(0.54064) = 3.31662$ and so is $\sqrt{11}$ **42** The signs of the factors in the first
product are $+$, $-$, $-$ while those in the second are $-$, $+$, $+$ **43** $\sin^2 x + 2\sin x \cos x + \cos^2 x = 1 + 2\sin x \cos x > 1$ for
$0 < x < \pi/2$ **44** (a) sine, cosine, tangent, cotangent; (b) tangent, cotangent, secant, cosecant **45** 7, 5
46 (a) $\sin^{-1} 0.9 = 1.1198$, (b) $\sin^{-1} 0.8 = 0.9273$ **47** $-\frac{7}{25}$ **48** 4.19 ft/s **49** $7\pi/12$, $105°$ **50** There is no such angle **51** 1
52 $\arctan \frac{4}{9} + \arctan \frac{5}{13} = 0.4182 + 0.3672 = 0.7854 \approx \pi/4$

53

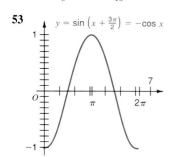

$y = \sin\left(x + \frac{3\pi}{2}\right) = -\cos x$

54 1.0730 **55** 0.434 **56** (a) They are opposite equal sides; (b) in triangle BAD, $A + B + D = \pi$, $B = D$, and $A = \pi - \theta$, so
$\pi - \theta + 2B = \pi$ implies $B = \theta/2$; (c) ABC is a right triangle; (d) $\tan(\theta/2) = BC/(DC) = BC/(DA + AC) = \sin\theta/(1 + \cos\theta)$
57 $B = 56.3°$, $a = 18.8$, $c = 33.9$ **58** $B = 28.8°$, $a = 571$, $b = 314$ **59** $B = 41.7°$, $c = 67.5$, $b = 44.9$
60 $c = 69.9$, $A = 28.8°$, $B = 61.2°$ **61** $a = 5.108$, $B = 50.42°$, $A = 39.58°$ **62** 41.7 ft **63** $3.20(10^4)$ **64** 33.9 mi
65 3600 m, S67.7°W **66** 498 ft **67** $61.9°$ and $28.1°$

EXERCISE 7.1

69 $\sin A / \pm\sqrt{1 - \sin^2 A}$ **70** $\pm\sqrt{1 - \sin^2 A}/\sin A$ **71** $\pm 1/\sqrt{1 - \sin^2 A}$ **73** $\pi/6$ **74** $\pi/4$ **75** $\pi/3$ **89** $6\cos\theta$ **90** $7\sec\theta$
91 $2\sin\theta$

EXERCISE 7.2

1 $-(\sqrt{2} + \sqrt{6})/4$ **2** $-(\sqrt{2} + \sqrt{6})/4$ **3** $(\sqrt{2} - \sqrt{6})/4$ **5** $(\sqrt{6} - \sqrt{2})/4$ **6** $(-\sqrt{2} + \sqrt{6})/4$ **7** $(\sqrt{2} - \sqrt{6})/4$ **9** $\sqrt{2}/2$
10 $\sqrt{2}/2$ **11** $-\sqrt{6}/2$ **13** $-\frac{3}{5}, \frac{117}{125}$ **14** $\frac{63}{65}, -\frac{33}{65}$ **15** $-1, \frac{7}{25}$ **17** $-\frac{7}{25}, -1$ **18** $\frac{33}{65}, \frac{63}{65}$
19 $-\frac{21}{221}, -\frac{171}{221}$ **21** $\frac{144}{125}$ **22** $-\frac{42}{125}$ **23** $\frac{176}{625}$ **33** $\cos 120°$ **34** $\cos 45°$ **35** $\sin 60°$ **37** $\sin 197°$ **38** $\sin 93°$ **39** $\cos 77°$
75 $\dfrac{-1 + \sqrt{5}}{4} \cdot \dfrac{\sqrt{6} + \sqrt{2}}{4} - \dfrac{\sqrt{10 + 2\sqrt{5}}}{4} \cdot \dfrac{\sqrt{6} - \sqrt{2}}{4}$

EXERCISE 7.3

1 $(\sqrt{2 + \sqrt{3}})/2$ **2** $(\sqrt{2 - \sqrt{3}})/2$ **3** $(\sqrt{2 + \sqrt{2}})/2$ **5** $\frac{1}{2}$ **6** $\sqrt{3}/2$ **7** $\frac{1}{2}$ **9** $\frac{7}{25}, 3/\sqrt{10}$ **10** $-\frac{527}{625}, -\frac{4}{5}$ **11** $\frac{119}{169}, -1/\sqrt{26}$
13 $\frac{7}{25}, 1/\sqrt{10}$ **14** $-\frac{119}{169}, 2/\sqrt{13}$ **15** $-\frac{119}{169}, -3/\sqrt{13}$ **17** $\frac{119}{169}, -1/\sqrt{26}$ **18** $-\frac{7}{25}, 2/\sqrt{5}$ **19** $\frac{527}{625}, -1/5\sqrt{2}$ **21** $\frac{120}{169}, 5/\sqrt{26}$
22 $-\frac{120}{169}, 1/\sqrt{26}$ **23** $-\frac{336}{625}, 7/5\sqrt{2}$ **25** $-\frac{24}{25}, 1/\sqrt{5}$ **26** $-\frac{120}{169}, 5/\sqrt{26}$ **27** $-\frac{120}{169}, 2/\sqrt{13}$ **29** $-\frac{120}{169}, 2/\sqrt{13}$ **30** $-\frac{24}{25}, 3/\sqrt{10}$
31 $\frac{120}{169}, 1/\sqrt{26}$ **77** $45°$

EXERCISE 7.4

1 $\dfrac{\sqrt{3}-1}{1+\sqrt{3}}$ **2** $\sqrt{3}$ **3** $2+\sqrt{3}$ **5** $\frac{16}{63}, \frac{56}{33}$ **6** $\frac{77}{36}, -\frac{13}{84}$ **7** $-\frac{240}{161}, 0$ **9** $-\frac{240}{161}, \frac{3}{5}$ **10** $\frac{336}{527}, \frac{4}{3}$ **11** $\frac{24}{7}, -\frac{1}{2}$ **41** $\frac{1}{3}$; $1/\sqrt{10}, 3/\sqrt{10}$
42 $\frac{2}{3}$; $2/\sqrt{13}, 3/\sqrt{13}$ **43** 4; $4/\sqrt{17}, 1/\sqrt{17}$ **45** $\frac{5}{3}$; $5/\sqrt{34}, 3/\sqrt{34}$ **46** 3; $3/\sqrt{10}, 1/\sqrt{10}$ **47** $\frac{1}{5}$; $-1/\sqrt{26}, 5/\sqrt{26}$
53 $\tan(\arctan 8/x - \arctan 3/x) = \dfrac{8/x - 3/x}{1 + 24/x^2} = \dfrac{5x}{x^2 + 24}$

EXERCISE 7.5

1 $2(\sin 115° - \sin 39°)$ **2** $-\cos 87° + \cos 5°$ **3** $3(\cos 221° + \cos 51°)$ **5** $\frac{1}{2}(-\cos 12x + \cos 2x)$ **6** $\frac{1}{2}(\sin 22x + \sin 14x)$
7 $\frac{1}{2}(\sin 19x - \sin 7x)$ **9** $\sin x + \sin 7x$ **10** $\cos 3x + \cos 15x$ **11** $-\cos 4x + \cos 6x$ **13** $2 \sin 21° \cos 6°$
14 $2 \cos 25° \sin 13°$ **15** $2 \cos 44° \cos 5°$ **17** $-2 \cos 5x \sin 2x$ **18** $2 \cos 7x \cos 2x$ **19** $-2 \sin 9x \sin 5x$ **21** $2 \cos x \cos 6x$
22 $-2 \sin 6x \sin 10x$ **23** $2 \sin 3x \cos 7x$ **37** $\sin 6x(2 \cos 2x + 1)$ **38** $\cos 5x(-2 \sin 3x + 1)$ **39** $\cos 6x(2 \cos 5x + 1)$
41 π **42** $2\pi/3$ **43** $\pi/2$

EXERCISE 7.6

1 False **2** True **3** True **5** $\pi/6$ **6** $\pi/3$ **7** $\pi/4$ **9** $\pi/6$ **10** 0 **11** 0 **13** $2\pi/3$ **14** $-\pi/4$ **15** $-\pi/3$ **17** $-60°$ **18** $60°$
19 $150°$ **21** $159°, 46°$ **22** $77°, -37°$ **23** $-16°, 40°$ **25** $55.0°$ or 0.9599 **26** $69.2°$ or 1.2078 **27** No such angle
29 $2, -1.1416$ **30** $0.99, 0.99$ **31** $-0.2, -0.2$ **33** $\frac{16}{65}$ **34** $\frac{84}{85}$ **35** $\frac{253}{325}$ **37** $u/\sqrt{1+u^2}$ **38** $\sqrt{1-u^2}$ **39** $1/u$ **41** $90°$
42 $90°$ **43** 0 **53** $(\pi/6)^2 + (\pi/3)^2 = 5\pi^2/36 \neq 1$ **54** First is 0.2293, $\arcsin 0.2334/\arccos 0.2334 = 0.2356/1.3352 = 0.1764$
55 $y = \text{arccot } x$ if and only if $\cot y = x$ where x may be any number and $0 < \text{arccot } x < \pi$ **57** $\pi/2 - 0.3821 \doteq 1.1887$
58 $\pi/2 - 0.3821 \doteq 1.1887$ **59** $52°$ **65** $100.57°$ **66** $2 \arcsin (1/M)$ **67** 4675 mi

EXERCISE 7.7

1 $120° + n \cdot 360°, 240° + n \cdot 360°$; $2\pi/3 + n \cdot 2\pi, 4\pi/3 + n \cdot 2\pi$ **2** $60° + n \cdot 360°, 240° + n \cdot 360°$; $\pi/3 + n \cdot 2\pi,$
$4\pi/3 + n \cdot 2\pi$ **3** $0° + n \cdot 360°$; $0 + n \cdot 2\pi$ **5** $45° + n \cdot 360°, 135° + n \cdot 360°, 225° + n \cdot 360°, 315° + n \cdot 360°$; $\pi/4 + n \cdot 2\pi,$
$3\pi/4 + n \cdot 2\pi, 5\pi/4 + n \cdot 2\pi, 7\pi/4 + n \cdot 2\pi$ **6** $45° + n \cdot 360°, 135° + n \cdot 360°, 225° + n \cdot 360°, 315° + n \cdot 360°$; $\pi/4 + n \cdot 2\pi,$
$3\pi/4 + n \cdot 2\pi, 5\pi/4 + n \cdot 2\pi, 7\pi/4 + n \cdot 2\pi$ **7** $60° + n \cdot 360°, 120° + n \cdot 360°, 240° + n \cdot 360°, 300° + n \cdot 360°$; $\pi/3 + n \cdot 2\pi,$
$4\pi/3 + n \cdot 2\pi, 5\pi/3 + n \cdot 2\pi$ **9** $45°, 225°$; $\pi/4, 5\pi/4$ **10** $30°, 150°, 210°, 330°$; $\pi/6, 5\pi/6, 7\pi/6, 11\pi/6$ **11** $20°, 80°, 140°,$
$200°, 260°, 320°$; $\pi/9, 4\pi/9, 7\pi/9, 10\pi/9, 13\pi/9, 16\pi/9$ **13** $30°, 150°$; $\pi/6, 5\pi/6$ **14** $0°$; 0 **15** $60°, 120°, 240°, 300°$; $\pi/3,$
$2\pi/3, 4\pi/3, 5\pi/3$ **17** $60°, 240°, 135°, 315°$; $\pi/3, 4\pi/3, 3\pi/4, 7\pi/4$ **18** $120°, 240°$; $2\pi/3, 4\pi/3$ **19** $60°, 120°, 63.4°, 243.4°$;
$\pi/3, 2\pi/3, 1.11, 4.25$ **21** No solution **22** $180°, 270°$; $\pi, 3\pi/2$ **23** $90°, 270°, 45°, 135°, 225°, 315°$; $\pi/2, 3\pi/2, \pi/4, 3\pi/4,$
$5\pi/4, 7\pi/4$ **25** $0°, 180°$; $0, \pi$ **26** $0°, 90°, 180°, 270°$; $0, \pi/2, \pi, 3\pi/2$ **27** $90°, 270°, 30°, 150°$; $\pi/2, 3\pi/2, \pi/6, 5\pi/6$
29 $0°, 180°, 90°, 270°$; $0, \pi, \pi/2, 3\pi/2$ **30** $30°, 90°, 150°, 210°, 270°, 330°$; $\pi/6, \pi/2, 5\pi/6, 7\pi/6, 3\pi/2, 11\pi/12$ **31** $0°,$
$180°, 90°, 270°$; $0, \pi, \pi/2, 3\pi/2$ **33** $0°, 60°, 120°, 180°, 240°, 300°, 30°, 150°, 210°, 330°$; $0, \pi/3, 2\pi/3, \pi, 4\pi/3, 5\pi/3, \pi/6,$
$5\pi/6, 7\pi/6, 11\pi/6$ **34** $30°, 90°, 150°, 210°, 270°, 330°$; $\pi/6, \pi/2, 5\pi/6, 7\pi/6, 3\pi/2, 11\pi/12$ **35** $20°, 100°, 140°, 220°, 260°,$
$340°, 45°, 135°, 225°, 315°$; $\pi/9, 5\pi/9, 7\pi/9, 11\pi/9, 13\pi/9, 17\pi/9, \pi/4, 3\pi/4, 5\pi/4, 7\pi/4$ **37** $36.4°, 323.6°, 97.9°, 262.1°$

38 46.6°, 226.6°, 176.6°, 356.6° **39** 186.5°, 353.5° **41** 61.9° **42** 337.4° **43** 126.9°, 270° **45** 11.1°, 62.7° **46** −15°, 105° **47** 337.0°, 68.2° **49** 90°, 210° **50** 60°, 180° **51** 232.6°, 352.6° **54** $\sqrt{61}$ < 8, no solution **55** $\sqrt{113}$ < 11, no solution **57** April 10 **58** 0.005 **59** −0.232; 1.338

EXERCISE 7.8

1 $-\frac{171}{221}$ **2** $\frac{119}{169}$ **3** $\frac{220}{221}$ **4** $-\frac{240}{289}$ **5** $-\frac{140}{171}$ **6** $\frac{1}{5}$ **7** $\frac{25}{34}$ **8** −3685/3757 **9** 28,560/28,561 **10** $(\sqrt{2} - \sqrt{6})/4$ **11** $\sqrt{2} + 1$
12 cos 83° **44** 3 cos θ **45** 4 sec θ **46** cos 7y(1 + 2 cos 2y) **47** 0.5(cos 8x − cos 20x) **48** 0.5(sin 22x + sin 10x)
49 −2 sin 6x sin 3x **50** −2 cos 7x sin 3x **52** (a) 90° (b) 2.1433 (c) 1/u **53** (a) $\frac{1}{4}$ (b) 0.3 **54** (a) 32° (b) $\frac{1}{7}$ **61** 270°
62 30°, 330°, 150°, 210° **63** 60°, 150°, 240°, 330° **64** 60°, 300°, 180° **65** 30°, 210°, 120°, 300°
66 0°, 180°, 56.3°, 236.3° **67** 210°, 330° **68** 0°, 180°, 135°, 315° **69** 60°, 300°, 180° **70** 0°, 180°
71 0°, 90°, 180°, 270° **72** 30°, 150° **73** 30°, 150° **74** 26.6°, 206.6°, 109.5°, 250.5° **75** 0°, 180°, 90°, 270° **76** 0°, 180°
77 0°, 180°, 120°, 240° **78** 36°, 108°, 180°, 252°, 324°, 60°, 300° **79** 0°, 180°, 45°, 135°, 225°, 315°
80 22.5°, 67.5°, 112.5°, 157.5°, 202.5°, 247.5°, 292.5°, 337.5°, 90°, 270° **81** 67.4° **82** 60° **83** 143.1° **84** 52.6°, 352.6°
85 61.3°, 151.3° **86** $5^2 + 8^2 > 9^2$, $5^2 + 8^2 < 10^2$

EXERCISE 8.1

1 C = 66.3°, b = 499, c = 470 **2** A = 55.9°, a = 228, c = 273 **3** B = 35.1°, a = 18.7, b = 12.0 **5** A = 54.4°, a = 4.38, c = 4.33 **6** B = 62.6°, a = 5.88, b = 6.84 **7** C = 27.9°, b = 59.4, c = 41.7 **9** B = 49.91°, a = 25.49, b = 23.06
10 C = 19.95°, b = 89.68, c = 31.19 **11** A = 119.85°, a = 98.07, c = 70.90 **13** C = 22.43°, b = 61.40, c = 47.20
14 A = 21.36°, a = 48.03, c = 60.32 **15** B = 63.17°, a = 45.89, b = 50.32 **17** One **18** Two **19** Two **21** No solution
22 B = 42.0°, 138.0°, A = 99.3°, 3.3°, a = 365, 21.3 **23** C = 41.8°, B = 93.1°, b = 306 **25** 129.6 m **26** 10.9 km
27 3.6 mi **29** 14.8 ft **30** 2.01 km, 2.14 km **31** 21.7, 29.3 **33** 6642 ft **34** 12,514, 34,919 **35** 2924

EXERCISE 8.2

1 27 **2** 141 **3** 16 **5** 100 **6** 357 **7** 283 **9** 42° **10** 90° **11** 75° **13** 142.1° **14** 61.6° **15** 53.5°
17 No usable c, no triangle **18** No usable b, no triangle **19** a = 17 ± $\sqrt{152}$, two triangles **21** −9 + 2$\sqrt{70}$, one triangle
22 No usable a, no triangle **23** 27 ± $\sqrt{486}$, two triangles **29** 53 **30** 346 mi/h at 234° **31** 53.2°, 58.0°, 68.8°
33 205 yards **34** 58 mi **35** 73.5° **45** 1.5(10²) **46** 4.0(10²) **47** 8.50(10⁴) **49** 2.0(10³) **50** 1.1(10³) **51** 3.16(10⁵)
53 3.4(10²) **54** 6.1(10²) **55** 2.81(10³) **57** 1.50(10⁵) **58** 1.84(10⁵) **59** 3.69(10⁴) **61** 11, 24
62 35.9, 94.1 **63** 72.2, 163 **65** 3.3 ft **66** S5.8°W, S48.2°W **67** 78.6°

EXERCISE 8.3

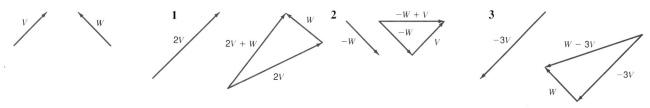

5 13, arctan($\frac{5}{12}$) ≈ 22.6°   **6** 25, arctan($-\frac{24}{7}$) ≈ −73.7°   **7** 5, 180° + arctan($\frac{4}{3}$) ≈ 233.1°   **9** 3$\sqrt{2}$, 45°   **10** 7i, 0°   **11** 2, −60°
13 3.3**i** + 2.3**j**   **14** −3.7**i** + 5.9**j**   **15** −3.7**i** − 3.3**j**   **17** 4**i** + 6.9**j**   **18** 7.5**i** + 4.33**j**   **19** 7**i** + 7**j**   **21** 83 lb, 18°
22 102 lb, 26°   **23** 282 mi/h, 25.5°   **25** 73.7°   **26** 101.1°   **27** 87.7°   **29** 21.3 g   **30** 65.6 g   **31** 157 lb   **33** 23°   **34** 27°
35 24°   **37** 297 mi/h, 184°   **38** 274 mi/h, 77°   **39** 363 mi/h, 200°

EXERCISE 8.4

1 2 cis 120°   **2** 8$\sqrt{3}$ cis 300°   **3** 5$\sqrt{2}$ cis 45°   **5** $\sqrt{85}$ cis 319.4°   **6** 2 cis 270°   **7** 13 cis 112.6°   **9** 6 cis 210°
10 10 cis 225°   **11** 35 cis 240°   **13** 4 cis 30°   **14** 5 cis 45°   **15** 11 cis 60°   **17** 4 cis 225°   **18** 2 cis 240°   **19** 2 cis 300°
21 4$\sqrt{2}$ cis 165°, $\sqrt{2}$ cis 105°   **22** 2 cis 330°, 2 cis 150°   **23** 4 cis 510°, 1 cis 90°   **25** 6$\sqrt{2}$ cis 315°, 1.5$\sqrt{2}$ cis (−225°)
26 4 cis 270°, 1 cis (−30°)   **27** 8$\sqrt{2}$ cis 555°, 2$\sqrt{2}$ cis (−105°)   **33** $\sqrt{1.5}$ cis 45°   **34** $\frac{1}{2}\sqrt{3}$ cis 35.3°   **35** cis (−40°)
41 |8 + i| = $\sqrt{65}$ = 8.06 < |3 + i| + |5| = $\sqrt{10}$ + 5 = 8.16   **42** |2 − 5i| = $\sqrt{29}$ = 5.39 < |−2 + 5i| + |4 − 10i| = 16.16
43 |12 + 19i| = $\sqrt{505}$ = 22.472 < |3 + 5i| + |9 + 14i| = $\sqrt{34}$ + $\sqrt{277}$ = 22.474   **45** 2 + i, −2 − i   **46** Second
47 Third, add 90° to the argument

EXERCISE 8.5

1 81 cis 108°   **2** 64 cis 264°   **3** 625 cis 128°   **5** 36$\sqrt{6}$ cis (5π/7)   **6** 256 cis (4π/5)   **7** 3$\sqrt{3}$ cis (3π/8)   **9** 128$\sqrt{2}$ cis 225°
10 64 cis 900°   **11** 16 cis 1200°   **13** −0.3090 + 0.9511i   **14** −0.9877 − 0.1564i   **15** −0.8090 + 0.5878i
17 0.9198 − 0.3923i   **18** −0.1316 + 0.9913i   **19** −0.2800 − 0.9600i   **21** 2 cis $\frac{1}{4}$(315° + k360°), k = 0, 1, 2, 3
22 3 cis (18° + k72°), k = 0, 1, 2, 3, 4   **23** 2 cis (40° + k60°), k = 0, 1, 2, 3, 4, 5   **25** 3 cis (42° + k120°), k = 0, 1, 2
26 3 cis (58° + k90°), k = 0, 1, 2, 3   **27** 5 cis (110° + k120°), k = 0, 1, 2   **29** cis k120°, k = 0, 1, 2
30 cis (22.5° + k90°), k = 0, 1, 2, 3   **31** cis (36° + k72°), k = 0, 1, 2, 3, 4   **33** 4 cis (60° + k120°), k = 0, 1, 2
34 3 cis k90°, k = 0, 1, 2, 3   **35** 2 cis (30° + k90°), k = 0, 1, 2, 3

EXERCISE 8.6

1 (−3, 340°), (3, −200°); (−4, 155°), (4, 335°)   **2** (4, 140°), (−4, 320°); (5,400°), (−5, −140°)
3 (−5, 98°), (5, 278°); (3, 347°), (−3, −193°)   **5** (2, 300°)   **6** ($\sqrt{10}$, 225°)   **7** ($\sqrt{5}$, 116.6°)   **9** (1.5, 1.5$\sqrt{3}$)
10 ($\sqrt{2}$, −$\sqrt{2}$)   **11** (−$\sqrt{3}$/2, −1.5)   **13** r(cos θ + 3 sin θ) = 2   **14** 9r^2 + 7r^2 $\sin^2$ θ = 144   **15** ar = sec θ $\tan^2$ θ
17 r cos θ = a(3 $\cos^2$ θ − $\sin^2$ θ)   **18** r^2 = a^2 sin 2θ   **19** r^2 $\cos^2$ θ − 4r^2 $\sin^2$ θ = 4   **21** x + 3y = 2   **22** 9x^2 + 16y^2 = 144
23 ax^3 = y^2 **25** x(x^2 + y^2) = a(3x^2 − y^2)   **26** (x^2 + y^2)^2 = 2a^2xy   **27** x^2 − 4y^2 = 4   **29** f(r, −θ) = f(r, θ)
30 f(r, 180° − θ) = f(r, θ)   **31** f(r, −θ) = f(r, 180° + θ) = f(r, 180° − θ) = f(r, θ)

33 r = 5   csc θ   **34** r = 3   sin θ   **35** r = 6   cos θ

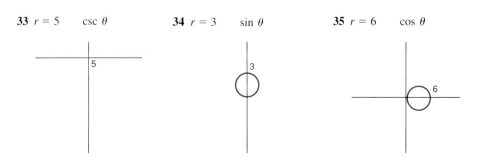

37 $r = \sin 2\theta$

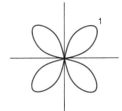

38 $r = \sin 3\theta$

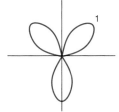

39 $r = 3 + 2\sin\theta$

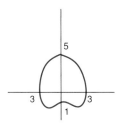

41 $r = 4$

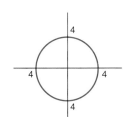

42 $\theta = \dfrac{\pi}{6}$

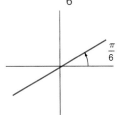

43 $r = 6\cos\theta + 8\sin\theta$

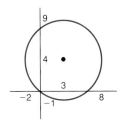

44

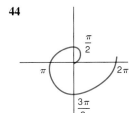

EXERCISE 8.7

1 30 cis 77°   **2** $4\sqrt{2}$ cis 165°   **3** 3 cis 90°   **4** cis 392°   **5** cis 720°   **6** 3 cis $(37° + k120°)$, $k = 0, 1, 2$
7 4 cis $(60° + k90°)$, $k = 0, 1, 2, 3$ **8** 41   **9** 83   **10** 53   **11** 230   **12** 692   **13** 45.9°   **14** 108.1°   **15** 126.2°   **19** None
20 None   **21** One solution   **22** Two solutions   **23** 47 mi   **24** 326 mi/h, 184°   **25** 0.89 mi   **27** 0.154   **28** 514   **29** 82.4°
30 19.3°   **31** $(-4, 4)$, $(\sqrt{10}, \arctan(-2/\sqrt{6}))$ **32** $2x - 3y = 5$, $r = 4\sec\theta\tan\theta$ **34** 3   **51** $a = -2\sqrt{2}$, $b = 2\sqrt{2}$
52 $19i$ **53** $\sqrt{122}$ **54** $2\sqrt{34} + 3\sqrt{13}$ **55** 44.3 kg, S77°E   **56** 20.6°   **57** $9\mathbf{i}$

EXERCISE 9.1

1 $(1, 2)$ **2** $(2, 1)$ **3** $(3, 1)$ **5** $(2, -1)$ **6** $(-3, 2)$ **7** $(-2, 3)$ **9** $(-1, -1)$ **10** $(-\frac{1}{2}, -\frac{1}{3})$ **11** $(-\frac{1}{5}, -\frac{1}{2})$ **13** $(2, 1, 1)$
14 $(1, 0, -2)$ **15** $(-4, -2, 3)$ **17** $(2, 1, 3)$ **18** $(-2, 1, -1)$ **19** $(3, -2, -1)$ **21** $(-1, 0, 1, 2)$ **22** $(-2, -1, 1, 3)$
23 $(-7, 4, 8, 1)$ **25** Consistent, $(2, 1)$ **26** Inconsistent   **27** Dependent   **29** Dependent   **30** Consistent, $(1, -2)$
31 Dependent   **33** $(1, 2)$ **34** $(2, 0)$ **35** $(0, 1)$ **37** Sucker, 10 cents; team roster, 15 cents
38 2 qt whipping cream, $\frac{1}{2}$ qt half-and-half   **39** 54, 36   **41** 1880, 500   **42** 200 mi, 220 mi
43 18, shorter hike; 17, longer hike   **45** Isabelle, $2\frac{1}{2}$ h; Ian, $1\frac{1}{2}$ h   **46** 19, 10, 3 of ages 18, 19, 20   **47** 12, 18, 24
49 $x^2 + y^2 - 4x + 6y - 12 = 0$ **50** $x^2 + y^2 - 8x + 10y - 128 = 0$ **51** 116

EXERCISE 9.2

1 $(1, 0), (-1, 0)$ **2** $(1, 1), (-1, 1), (-1, -1), (1, -1)$ **3** $(1, 1), (1, -1), (-1, 1), (-1, -1)$
5 $(2, 1), (2, -1), (-\frac{11}{3}, \frac{1}{3}\sqrt{26}), (-\frac{11}{3}, -\frac{1}{3}\sqrt{26})$ **6** $(3, 1), (3, -1)$ **7** $(2, 3), (-2, 3), (0, -1)$ **9** $(-1, 1), (-\frac{4}{5}, \frac{9}{5})$
10 $(2, 5), (-7, -\frac{10}{7})$ **11** $(-1, 1), (-\frac{1}{13}, \frac{109}{13})$ **13** $(7, 6), (3, 4)$ **14** $(\frac{1}{3}, 0), (\frac{1}{27}, -\frac{4}{9})$ **15** $(19, -6), (3, 2)$
17 $(10, 2), (-2, -2), (5, 1.5), (-4, -1.5)$ **18** $(1, -2), (-1, -4), (\sqrt{7}, 3 + \sqrt{7}), (-\sqrt{7}, 3 - \sqrt{7})$
19 $(20, 2), (-4, -2), (9 + 9\sqrt{2}, 1.5\sqrt{2}), (9 - 9\sqrt{2}, - 1.5\sqrt{2})$ **21** $(2, 1), (-2, -1), (0.5\sqrt{2}, 2\sqrt{2}), (-0.5\sqrt{2}, -2\sqrt{2})$
22 $(1, 3), (-1, -3), (1.5\sqrt{6}, \frac{1}{3}\sqrt{6}), (-1.5\sqrt{6}, -\frac{1}{3}\sqrt{6})$ **23** $(5, -1), (-5, 1), (\sqrt{2}, -2.5\sqrt{2}), (-\sqrt{2}, 2.5\sqrt{2})$
33 $(\frac{2}{3}, -\frac{1}{3}), (\frac{1}{2}, -\frac{1}{2})$ **34** $(-1, -2), (-\frac{9}{13}, -\frac{6}{13})$ **35** $(3, 2), (4, 1)$ **37** $(\pm 5, 2), (\pm 2\sqrt{7}, -1)$ **38** $(\pm 4, 3), (\pm \sqrt{11}, -2)$
39 $(\frac{8}{3}, -3), (2, -4)$ **41** $(1, 2), (-1, -2)$ **42** $(2, 3), (-2, -3), (2\sqrt{13}/13, -3\sqrt{13}/13), (-2\sqrt{13}/13, 3\sqrt{13}/13)$
43 $(3, 4), (-3, -4)$ **45** $(2, 3), (3, 2)$ **46** $(2, 2)$ **47** $(2, 1), (-\frac{13}{10}, -\frac{8}{3})$ **49** 4   **50** 4   **51** ± 5 **53** 8, 7   **54** 8, 7; $-8, -7$
55 Yes   **57** 15 by 15, 12 by 15   **58** Base, 6 by 6; height, 5   **59** 6 by 8   **61** 80 members, $12   **62** $4, $5
63 16 in, 14 in or 26.56 in, 7.28 in

EXERCISE 9.3

1 $\dfrac{2}{x + 1} + \dfrac{1}{2x + 3}$ **2** $\dfrac{1}{x + 2} + \dfrac{3}{3x - 4}$ **3** $\dfrac{3}{3x - 1} - \dfrac{4}{2x + 1}$ **5** $\dfrac{1}{x + 1} + \dfrac{2}{x - 2} - \dfrac{3}{2x - 3}$ **6** $\dfrac{4}{3x - 5} - \dfrac{1}{x + 2} + \dfrac{3}{x - 3}$

7 $\dfrac{3}{5x - 2} - \dfrac{2}{2x - 3} + \dfrac{1}{x + 4}$ **9** $\dfrac{2}{2x - 1} - \dfrac{5}{x - 4} + \dfrac{2}{(x - 4)^2}$ **10** $\dfrac{2}{2x + 3} - \dfrac{1}{3x - 1} + \dfrac{5}{(3x - 1)^2}$

11 $\dfrac{2}{5x + 2} - \dfrac{3}{2x - 7} - \dfrac{1}{(2x - 7)^2}$ **13** $\dfrac{1}{x - 1} - \dfrac{x + 3}{x^2 + 2}$ **14** $\dfrac{3}{x + 1} + \dfrac{2x - 1}{x^2 + 1}$ **15** $\dfrac{1}{x - 3} + \dfrac{2x - 5}{x^2 + x + 1}$

17 $\dfrac{2}{x - 1} - \dfrac{1}{2x + 1} + \dfrac{x - 4}{x^2 + 3}$ **18** $\dfrac{2}{x + 5} + \dfrac{3}{2x - 1} - \dfrac{x - 5}{x^2 + 3}$ **19** $\dfrac{2}{x - 3} + \dfrac{1}{3x + 1} - \dfrac{2x - 1}{x^2 - x + 2}$

21 $\dfrac{1}{x - 1} - \dfrac{2}{(x - 1)^2} + \dfrac{2x - 3}{x^2 + 1}$ **22** $\dfrac{2}{x - 2} + \dfrac{1}{(x - 2)^2} - \dfrac{3x + 1}{x^2 + 5}$ **23** $\dfrac{3}{x - 2} - \dfrac{1}{(x - 2)^2} + \dfrac{x - 3}{x^2 + x + 1}$

25 $\dfrac{3x - 1}{x^2 + 2} - \dfrac{x - 1}{x^2 + 3}$ **26** $\dfrac{2x - 5}{x^2 - 3x - 1} + \dfrac{x - 2}{x^2 + 1}$ **27** $\dfrac{x - 3}{x^2 - 5} + \dfrac{2x + 1}{x^2 - x + 3}$ **29** $\dfrac{x + 2}{x^2 + 2} + \dfrac{2x + 1}{(x^2 + 2)^2}$

30 $\dfrac{2x - 3}{x^2 + 3} - \dfrac{3x + 1}{(x^2 + 3)^2}$ **31** $\dfrac{2x + 1}{x^2 - x + 3} - \dfrac{11x + 11}{(x^2 - x + 3)^2}$ **33** $\dfrac{2}{x^2} + \dfrac{x - 1}{(x^2 + 3x - 1)^2}$ **34** $\dfrac{1}{x^2} + \dfrac{x + 1}{x^2 - x + 2} + \dfrac{x - 7}{(x^2 - x + 2)^2}$

35 $\dfrac{1}{x^2} - \dfrac{x + 2}{(x^2 + 1)^2}$ **37** $x - 4 + \dfrac{2}{x + 1} + \dfrac{5}{2x - 3}$ **38** $2x - 5 + \dfrac{1}{(x - 2)^2} - \dfrac{3}{3x + 2}$ **39** $2x - 5 + \dfrac{3}{x - 3} - \dfrac{4x - 6}{x^2 + x + 2}$

41 $x + 3 + \dfrac{4}{2x + 3} + \dfrac{3}{3x + 2}$ **42** $-2x + 1 + \dfrac{7}{5x - 3} - \dfrac{5}{4x + 1}$ **43** $3x - 5 + \dfrac{4}{4x + 3} + \dfrac{3}{2x - 1}$

45 $A = \dfrac{cr + d}{r - s}, B = \dfrac{cs + d}{s - r}$

EXERCISE 9.4

1 $y < 3x - 2$ **2** $y \geq -2x + 1$ **3** $y < x - 1$

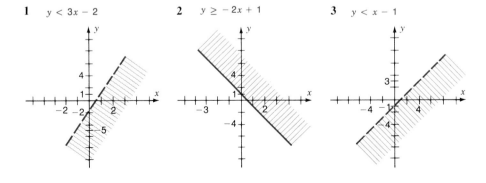

5 $y \le 2 - x^2$

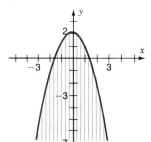

6 $x \ge y^2 - 1$

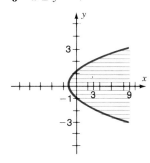

7 $3x > (y - 3)(y)(y - 2)$

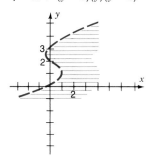

9 $x^2 + 4y^2 \le 16$

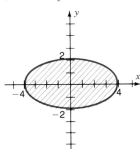

10 $x^2 + y^2 \le 2$

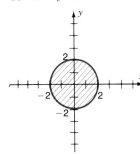

11 $x^2 + 9y^2 > 9$

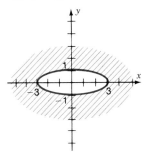

13

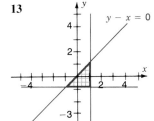

14

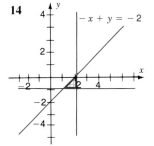

15

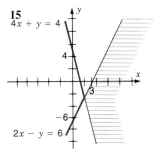

17

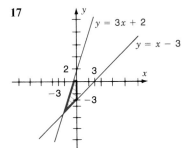

18

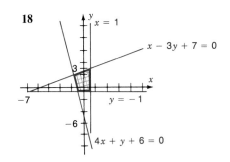

19

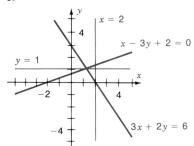

21

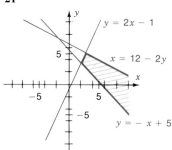

22

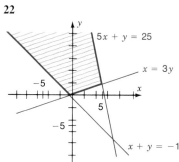

23

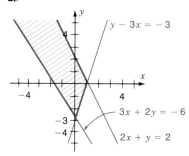

25

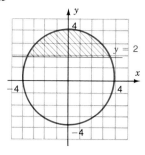

26

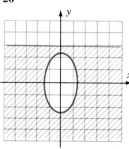

27

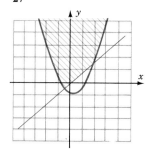

29

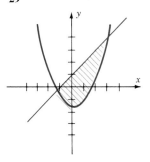

30

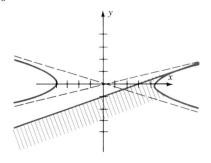

31

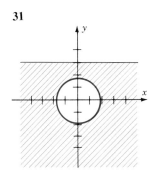

33

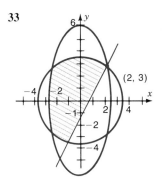

(2, 3)

34

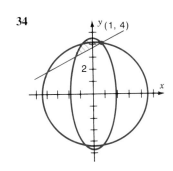

35

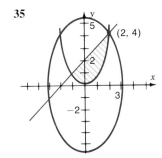

EXERCISE 9.5

1 Maximum is 4 at (1, 0), minimum is -2 at $(-1, 2)$.   **2** Maximum is 21 at (2, 2), minimum is -6 at $(-1, 1)$.
3 Maximum is 6 at (3, 1), minimum is -4 at $(-2, 1)$.   **5** Maximum is 32 at (3, 6), minimum is 4 at (0, 1).
6 Maximum is 28 at (9, 1), minimum is -1 at $(-2, -3)$.   **7** Maximum is 24 at (7, 1), minimum is -8 at $(-1, 1)$.
9 Maximum is 10 at (1, 0), minimum is -29 at $(-2, 3)$.   **10** Maximum is 14 at (3, 0), minimum is 0 at $(-1, 3)$.
11 Maximum is 21 at (2, 4) and at $(6, -2)$, minimum is -41 at $(-5, -1)$.
13 Maximum is 1 at (1, 2), minimum is -24 at $(-5, 3)$.   **14** Maximum is 28 at $(-3, 5)$, minimum is 0 at $(-1, -1)$.
15 Maximum is 29 at (0, 6), minimum is 5 at (1, 2).   **17** $M = 15$ at (0, 2), $m = 1$ at (0, 0)
18 $M = 13$ at (3, 0), $m = -2$ at (0, 0)   **19** $M = 18$ at (2, 2), $m = 2$ at (0, 0)
21 $M = 2$ at (1, 0) and (0, 1), $m = 0$ at $(-1, 0)$ and $(0, -1)$ **22** $M = 13$ at (3, 2), $m = 0$ at $(-1, 1)$
23 $m = -5$ at (0, 2), $M = 5$ at $(1, -1)$ **25** $m = 8$ at (0, 0), $M = 19$ at $(1, -2)$ **26** $m = -13$ at $(-2, 2)$, $M = -1$ at (0, 0)
27 $m = 5$ at (0, 1), $M = 17$ at $(2, -2)$ **29** $m = -13$ at $(0, -2)$, $M = 16$ at (2, 3)   **30** $m = -4$ at $(-1, 1)$, $M = 2$ at $(3, -1)$
31 $m = -13$ at $(0, -3)$, $M = 4$ at (2, 2)   **33** X, 42 units; Y, 60 units; Z, 100 units; profit, $11.120   **34** X, 63 units; Y, 45
units; Z, 100 units; profit, $11,420   **35** $4.04 for 4 bags of X and 2 of Y **37** Oxfords, 200 pairs; boots, 180 pairs; sandals, 120
pairs; $2290   **38** Oxfords, 200 pairs; boots, 180 pairs; sandals, 120 pairs; $2400   **39** 500 corn, 300 wheat   **41** 200 corn, 400
wheat, no beans; $50,000   **42** 300 corn, 500 wheat, no beans; $67,000   **43** 200 day lilies; $60,000   **45** 450 boxes of
chocolates, 200 designer jeans; $6550   **46** 450 boxes of chocolates, 200 designer jeans; $5500   **47** 1500 sheep, 9 cattle;
$17,670

EXERCISE 9.6

1 Dependent **2** Inconsistent **3** Consistent, $(2, 1)$ **4** $(3, 4, 5)$ **5** $(6, 5, 4)$ **6** $(-\frac{27}{7}, \frac{13}{3})$ **7** $x^2 + y^2 - 4x - 2y - 20 = 0$
8 $(2, 1)$, $(\frac{14}{23}, -\frac{41}{23})$ **9** $(\pm 3, 1)$, $(\pm\sqrt{619}/9, -\frac{1}{9})$ **10** $(4/\sqrt{3}, -\sqrt{3}/2)$, $(-4/\sqrt{3}, \sqrt{3}/2)$, $(1, -2)$, $(-1, 2)$
11 $(3, 2)$, $(-3, -2)$, $(2\sqrt{15}/3, 9/\sqrt{15})$, $(-2\sqrt{15}/3, -9/\sqrt{15})$ **12** $(1, 1)$, $(-\frac{18}{7}, -\frac{29}{21})$
13 $(1, -2)$, $(-1, 2)$, $(\frac{9}{26}\sqrt{13}, \frac{11}{26}\sqrt{13})$, $(-\frac{9}{26}\sqrt{13}, -\frac{11}{26}\sqrt{13})$ **14** No solutions to $y^2 + 6y + 10 = 0$ **15** 6
27 $(1, 1)$, $(5, 2)$, $(3, -2)$ **28** $m = -7$ at $(-1, 2)$, $M = 29$ at $(3, -2)$ **29** $m = -4$ at $(0, 0)$, $M = 10$ at $(4, 2)$ **30** 18 mi
31 $8, 7$ **32** 200 corn, 400 wheat, 100 soybeans; \$21,800 **33** $0.4/x + 2.4/(4x + 5)$ **34** $2/(x - 3) + 5/(x - 3)^2$
35 $2/(x + 1) + 3/(x + 2) + 4/(x + 3)$ **36** $4 + 3/(x + 2) + 2/(x + 3)$ **37** $2/(x + 1) + (3x - 1)/(x^2 + x + 3)$
38 $1/(x - 2) + (2x - 1)/(x^2 - x + 3) + (3x + 2)/(x^2 - x + 3)^2$

EXERCISE 10.1

1 $a = 0$, $b = 2$, $c = 3$, $d = -2$ **2** $a = -5$, $b = 1$, $c = 0$, $d = 3$ **3** These two matrices can not be equal. **5** 2×3, $\begin{bmatrix} 2 & 3 \\ 1 & -6 \\ 5 & 2 \end{bmatrix}$

6 3×3, $\begin{bmatrix} -1 & 4 & 0 \\ 4 & 5 & 2 \\ 0 & 2 & 3 \end{bmatrix}$ **7** 3×2, $\begin{bmatrix} 3 & 1 & 0 \\ -2 & 5 & 4 \end{bmatrix}$ **9** $\begin{bmatrix} 6 & -2 & 4 \\ 8 & 0 & 10 \end{bmatrix}$ **10** Not defined **11** $\begin{bmatrix} 2 & -3 & 0 \\ -1 & -5 & 4 \end{bmatrix}$ **13** Not defined

14 $\begin{bmatrix} -11 & 13 & -2 \\ 0 & 20 & -21 \end{bmatrix}$ **15** $\begin{bmatrix} 5 & 3 & 6 \\ 14 & 10 & 7 \end{bmatrix}$ **17** $\begin{bmatrix} 7 & 2 \\ 0 & 1 \end{bmatrix}$ **18** $\begin{bmatrix} 7 & 4 \\ 0 & 1 \end{bmatrix}$ **19** $\begin{bmatrix} 0 & 5 \\ -1 & 0 \end{bmatrix}$ **37** $\begin{bmatrix} 1 \\ 7 \\ 1 \end{bmatrix}$ **38** $\begin{bmatrix} -1 \\ 18 \\ 19 \end{bmatrix}$ **39** $\begin{bmatrix} 21 & 1 \\ 1 & 10 \end{bmatrix}$

57 $\begin{bmatrix} 0.55 & 0.45 \\ 0.30 & 0.70 \end{bmatrix} = A^2$, $\begin{bmatrix} 0.4375 & 0.5625 \\ 0.3750 & 0.6250 \end{bmatrix} = A^4$, $\begin{bmatrix} 0.40234375 & 0.59765625 \\ 0.3984375 & 0.6015625 \end{bmatrix} = A^8$

58 $\begin{bmatrix} 0.48 & 0.52 \\ 0.39 & 0.61 \end{bmatrix} = A^2$, $\begin{bmatrix} 0.4332 & 0.5668 \\ 0.4251 & 0.5749 \end{bmatrix} = A^4$, $\begin{bmatrix} 0.42860892 & 0.57139108 \\ 0.42854331 & 0.57145669 \end{bmatrix} = A^8$

59 $\begin{bmatrix} 0.30 & 0.70 \\ 0.14 & 0.86 \end{bmatrix} = A^2$, $\begin{bmatrix} 0.1880 & 0.8120 \\ 0.1624 & 0.8376 \end{bmatrix} = A^4$, $\begin{bmatrix} 0.1672128 & 0.8327872 \\ 0.1665574 & 0.8334426 \end{bmatrix} = A^8$ **61** $A^{-1} = \begin{bmatrix} 4 & -9 \\ -3 & 7 \end{bmatrix}$

62 $F = \begin{bmatrix} -7 & 3 \\ 12 & -5 \end{bmatrix}$ **63** $\begin{bmatrix} 9 & 7 \\ 4 & 3 \end{bmatrix}$, the columns are interchanged **65** 33,660 **66** 1,195,100 **67** \$6,538,300

69 The average number of hundreds of pizzas of each type sold each day in October at each location
70 The total number of hundreds of pizzas of each type sold at each location in September and October combined
71 $100[54(3.45) + 91(2.90) + 46(3.80)] = 62,500$

EXERCISE 10.2

1 $(2, 1)$ **2** $(3, -2)$ **3** $(-2, -5)$ **5** $(1, 2, 1)$ **6** $(1, 0, 3)$ **7** $(2, -1, -2)$ **9** $(0, 1, -1)$ **10** $(2, 2, -2)$ **11** $(\frac{1}{2}, \frac{1}{3}, \frac{5}{6})$
13 $(1, 2, 1, 2)$ **14** $(3, 0, 1, -1)$ **15** $(0, 2, 3, -4)$ **17** Row operations make the last row $0, 0, 0, \frac{1}{3}$
18 Row operations make the last row $0, 0, 0, 2$ **19** Row operations make the last row $0, 0, 0, 10$
21 x, any value; $y = (2 - 3x)/8$, $z = (6 + x)/4$ **22** x, any value; $y = -13x - 7$, $z = -3 - 10x$
23 y, any number; $x = 22 - 4y$, $z = 2y - 16$ **25** x, any value; $y = (1 + x)/3$, $z = (4 - 5x)/3$
26 x, any value; $y = 2 - 10x$, $z = 7x - 1$ **27** x, any value; $y = (11 - 13x)/5$, $z = 2x - 1$, $w = (8 + x)/5$
29 $a = \frac{5}{7}$, $b = -\frac{26}{7}$, $c = \frac{4}{7}$ **30** $D = -4$, $E = -2$, $F = 20$

EXERCISE 10.3

1 2 **2** 7 **3** -22 **5** $8 - 6a$ **6** $6 + a$ **7** $3b + 2a$ **9** $-\begin{vmatrix} 2 & 6 \\ 5 & 2 \end{vmatrix}, \begin{vmatrix} 3 & 1 \\ 5 & 2 \end{vmatrix}, -\begin{vmatrix} 3 & 1 \\ 2 & 6 \end{vmatrix}$ **10** $-\begin{vmatrix} 1 & 4 \\ 4 & 1 \end{vmatrix}, \begin{vmatrix} 3 & 4 \\ 4 & 1 \end{vmatrix}, -\begin{vmatrix} 3 & 4 \\ 1 & 4 \end{vmatrix}$

11 $-\begin{vmatrix} 3 & -3 \\ 1 & -2 \end{vmatrix}, \begin{vmatrix} 2 & -1 \\ 1 & -2 \end{vmatrix}, -\begin{vmatrix} 2 & -1 \\ 3 & -3 \end{vmatrix}$ **13** $2\begin{vmatrix} 1 & 6 \\ 4 & 2 \end{vmatrix} - 5\begin{vmatrix} 3 & 6 \\ 9 & 2 \end{vmatrix} + 4\begin{vmatrix} 3 & 1 \\ 9 & 4 \end{vmatrix} = 208$

14 $-3\begin{vmatrix} 2 & 4 \\ 6 & -4 \end{vmatrix} - 7\begin{vmatrix} 3 & 4 \\ 5 & -4 \end{vmatrix} - 2\begin{vmatrix} 3 & 2 \\ 5 & 6 \end{vmatrix} = 304$ **15** $1\begin{vmatrix} 2 & 4 \\ -3 & 2 \end{vmatrix} - 2\begin{vmatrix} -3 & 4 \\ -2 & 2 \end{vmatrix} + 3\begin{vmatrix} -3 & 2 \\ -2 & -3 \end{vmatrix} = 51$

17 $2\begin{vmatrix} 5 & 0 \\ 4 & 2 \end{vmatrix} - 3\begin{vmatrix} 2 & 0 \\ 1 & 2 \end{vmatrix} + 5\begin{vmatrix} 2 & 5 \\ 1 & 4 \end{vmatrix} = 23$ **18** $0\begin{vmatrix} 1 & 3 \\ 9 & -1 \end{vmatrix} + 4\begin{vmatrix} 1 & 3 \\ 2 & -1 \end{vmatrix} - 6\begin{vmatrix} 1 & 1 \\ 2 & 9 \end{vmatrix} = -70$

19 $4\begin{vmatrix} -4 & 1 \\ -2 & -3 \end{vmatrix} - 3\begin{vmatrix} 2 & 3 \\ -2 & -3 \end{vmatrix} + 2\begin{vmatrix} 2 & 3 \\ -4 & 1 \end{vmatrix} = 84$ **21** $0\begin{vmatrix} 2 & -8 \\ 1 & 4 \end{vmatrix} - 0\begin{vmatrix} 6 & -8 \\ 1 & 4 \end{vmatrix} + 5\begin{vmatrix} 6 & 2 \\ 1 & 1 \end{vmatrix} = 20$

22 $0\begin{vmatrix} 4 & -7 \\ 2 & 1 \end{vmatrix} - 0\begin{vmatrix} 6 & 3 \\ 2 & 1 \end{vmatrix} + 2\begin{vmatrix} 6 & 3 \\ 4 & -7 \end{vmatrix} = -108$ **23** $0\begin{vmatrix} -1 & -2 \\ -3 & 6 \end{vmatrix} + 5\begin{vmatrix} 9 & -2 \\ 7 & 6 \end{vmatrix} + 0\begin{vmatrix} 9 & -1 \\ 7 & -3 \end{vmatrix} = 340$ **25** $14x - 73$

26 $15x - 12y - 6$ **27** $33i - 23j - 16k$ **29** 3 **30** $\frac{1}{3}$ **31** 2 **33** 11 **34** 25.5 **35** 0 **41** A row of zeros
42 Two columns are equal. **43** One row is a multiple of another. **45** Discriminant $= (a - c)^2 + 4b^2 > 0$ **46** 0
47 $-87 \ne -39$ **49** $x^2 - 7x + 2$ **50** $x^2 - 14x - 3$ **51** (a) $x^2 - 9x + 18$, (b) 6, 3

EXERCISE 10.4

1 Rows and columns are interchanged. **2** Rows and columns are interchanged. **3** R2 and R3 are interchanged.
5 C1 and C3 are the same. **6** R2 and R3 are the same.
7 Each element of C1 of the second determinant is multiplied by 2 and so is the first determinant.
9 R1 and R3 are the same in all three determinants and property 5 applies to R2.
10 C1 and C2 are the same in all determinants and property 5 applies to C3. **11** Replace C3 by C3 + 3C2.
13 Interchange rows and columns, then interchange the new columns 2 and 3. **14** Replace C1 by C1 + C2 + C3.
15 Replace R1 by R1 + aR2. **17** 7 **18** 14 **19** 7 **21** 42 **22** -7 **23** -28 **25** -6 **26** 0 **27** $a(ab + b^2 - ac)$ **29** 2
30 3, -3 **31** 5, -3 **33** -12 **34** 12 **35** -90 **41** -28 **42** 46 **43** 0 **45** 12 **46** -116 **47** -54
57 $|AB| = (ad - bc)(vz - xy)$, $|A| = ad - bc$, $|B| = vz - xy$
59 Each element of kA is k times the corresponding element of A.

EXERCISE 10.5

1 (2, 1) **2** (1, -1) **3** (3, -1) **5** (1, -2) **6** (2, -1) **7** ($-2, -3$) **9** (3, 0) **10** ($-1, 4$) **11** ($-1, -2$) **13** (a, b)
14 ($2a - b, b$) **15** (a, b) **17** (1, 2, 1) **18** (1, $-2, -1$) **19** (2, $-1, 1$) **21** (1, $-2, 3$) **22** ($-2, -1, 5$) **23** (2, 0, -1)
25 (2, 3, -2) **26** (4, 3, -5) **27** (2, $-1, -3$) **29** (1, $-1, 0, 2$) **30** (1, $-1, 2, 0$) **31** (1, $-4, 2, -1$)
33 $x = 2$, $y = 1$, $z = 4$, $w = 3$, $t = 2$ **34** $x = 3$, $y = 2$, $z = 1$, $w = 2$, $t = 3$ **35** $x = 4$, $y = 3$, $z = 2$, $w = 1$, $t = 0$
37 $m = 2.5$, $b = 1.5$, $y = 2.5x + 1.5$ **38** $m = -3.6$, $b = 38$, $y = -3.6x + 38$
39 $m = 24.16/14$, $b = 128.38/14$, $14y = 24.16x + 128.38$

EXERCISE 10.6

1 $\frac{1}{2}\begin{bmatrix} 7 & -4 \\ -3 & 2 \end{bmatrix}$ **2** $-\frac{1}{3}\begin{bmatrix} 3 & 0 \\ -2 & -1 \end{bmatrix}$ **3** $\frac{1}{7}\begin{bmatrix} -1 & -5 \\ 2 & 3 \end{bmatrix}$ **5** $-\frac{1}{25}\begin{bmatrix} -13 & 5 & 11 \\ -8 & 5 & 1 \\ 6 & -10 & -7 \end{bmatrix}$ **6** $-\frac{1}{3}\begin{bmatrix} 1 & 0 & 1 \\ -11 & -3 & -2 \\ -8 & -3 & -2 \end{bmatrix}$

7 $-\frac{1}{70}\begin{bmatrix} -3 & -23 & 7 \\ -7 & -7 & -7 \\ 6 & -24 & -14 \end{bmatrix}$ **9** $\begin{bmatrix} 2 & 3 & -6 \\ -5 & -4 & 10 \\ 2 & 1 & -3 \end{bmatrix}$ **10** $\begin{bmatrix} -3 & 2 & 0 \\ -20 & 15 & -4 \\ 7 & -5 & 1 \end{bmatrix}$ **11** $\frac{1}{2}\begin{bmatrix} 1 & 1 & -1 & 0 \\ -1 & 1 & -1 & 2 \\ 2 & -2 & 0 & -2 \\ 1 & -1 & -1 & -2 \end{bmatrix}$ **13** $(2, -3)$ **14** $(4, 1)$

15 $(3, 2)$ **17** $(4, 4, 3)$ **18** $(3, 2, 5)$ **19** $(1, 2, 1)$ **21** $(3, 0, 2)$ **22** $(2, 1, 0)$ **23** $(4, 6, 2, 8)$ **39** $\frac{1}{6}\begin{bmatrix} 5 & -2 \\ -2 & 2 \end{bmatrix}$

EXERCISE 10.7

1 $(2, 3)$ **2** $(1, 2, -1)$ **3** $\begin{bmatrix} 0 & 2x & x \\ 3 & 1 & x \end{bmatrix}$ **4** $\begin{bmatrix} -12 & 10 & 36 & 24 \\ -9 & 6 & 21 & 15 \\ 6 & -3 & -10 & -8 \end{bmatrix}$ **5** $\begin{bmatrix} 1 & 0 & 1 \\ 2 & 0 & a \\ 3 & -1 & -1 \end{bmatrix}$ **6** $\begin{bmatrix} -4 & 11 & 1 & 5 \\ -9 & 25 & -1 & 18 \end{bmatrix}$

7 $\begin{bmatrix} 40 & -27 & 25 \\ -23 & 16 & -14 \\ -9 & 5 & -4 \end{bmatrix}$ **8** $\begin{bmatrix} 5 & 34 & -14 \\ 1 & 23 & -9 \\ -12 & -55 & 24 \end{bmatrix}$ **9** $\begin{bmatrix} 1 & 2 & 5 \\ 2 & 3 & 8 \\ -1 & 1 & 2 \end{bmatrix}$ **12** 10 **13** 15 **14** -24 **15** 0 **16** 48 **17** -1

18 The rows of the first are the columns of the second.
19 The columns of the second are the rows of the first but with 1 and 2 interchanged.
20 Columns 2 and 3 of the second are obtained by adding $C1$ to columns 2 and 3 of the first.
21 $R1$ of the second is $3R1$ of the first, $R3$ of the second is twice $R3$ of the first.
22 $C2$ of the second plus $C2$ of the third gives $C2$ of the first.
23 $C2$ of second is $C2$ of first plus $3(C1)$ **24** 7 **25** 1 **26** $(-4, 3)$ **27** $(2, -3)$ **28** $(3, 5)$ **29** $(1, -2, 5)$ **30** $(3, 0, -4)$
31 $(1, -2, 5)$ **32** $(3, 0, -4)$ **33** Yes, each is $\begin{bmatrix} 17 & 26 \\ 39 & 56 \end{bmatrix}$ **34** Find their product.

35 If $A = \begin{bmatrix} 1 & 2 \\ 3 & 4 \end{bmatrix}$, then $A^2 = \begin{bmatrix} 7 & 10 \\ 15 & 22 \end{bmatrix}$ and $|A|^2 = (-2)^2 = 4$ and $|A^2| = 154 - 150 = 4$.

37 $A^2 - 3A - 18I = 0$, $A^2 - 3A = 18I$, $\frac{1}{18}(A)(A - 3I) = I$, $A^{-1} = \frac{1}{18}(A - 3I)$

38 $AB = \begin{bmatrix} 81 & 93 & 96 \\ 93 & 84 & 93 \\ 96 & 93 & 81 \end{bmatrix}$ with row and column sums of 270

39 The equation is $(y - b)/(x - a) = (b - d)/(a - c)$ or $(a - c)y - (b - d)x - ad + bc = 0$ which is the expansion of the determinant.
42 $y = 3x - 4$

43 $A^2 = \begin{bmatrix} 0.83 & 0.17 \\ 0.34 & 0.66 \end{bmatrix}$, $A^4 = \begin{bmatrix} 0.7467 & 0.2533 \\ 0.5066 & 0.4934 \end{bmatrix}$, $A^8 = \begin{bmatrix} 0.6859 & 0.3141 \\ 0.6282 & 0.3718 \end{bmatrix}$, $A^{16} = \begin{bmatrix} 0.6678 & 0.3322 \\ 0.6644 & 0.3356 \end{bmatrix}$ **44** $\begin{bmatrix} 4 & 18 & 4 \\ 0 & 0 & 0 \\ 12 & 20 & 4 \end{bmatrix}$

EXERCISE 11.1

1 3, 7, 11, 15, 19 **2** 2, 7, 12, 17 **3** 7, 4, 1, -2 **5** 5, 7, 9, 11, 13 **6** $-2, -5, -8, -11$ **7** $-5, -2, 1, 4$
9 2, 5, 8, 11, 14 **10** 6, 3, 0, $-3, -6, -9$ **11** 2, 0, $-2, -4, -6, -8$ **13** 11 **14** -2 **15** -11 **17** 56 **18** 7 **19** 16
21 7 **22** -3 **23** 13 **25** $a_n = 12$, $s = 21$ **26** $a_n = -6$, $s = 21$ **27** $d = -4$, $s_n = 48$ **29** $d = -1.5$, $n = 7$
30 $a = 1$, $d = \frac{2}{3}$ **31** $a_n = -5$, $n = 8$ **33** $a = 8$, $n = 6$ **34** $a = -8$, $n = 4$ **35** $a = 1$, $n = 6$ **37** 204 **38** 315
39 $2n(n + 1)$ **41** -3 **42** $\frac{8}{9}$ **43** $x = 2$, $y = 3$ **45** 156 **46** 208 ft, 784 ft **47** 25 s **49** $1102 **50** $20,200 **51** 804π cm
53 6, 9, 12 **54** 5, 7, 9, 11, 13 **55** 6, 2, $-2, -6$ **57** $\frac{1}{24}$ **58** $\frac{3}{19}$ **59** $\frac{1}{6}$ **61** $\frac{1}{4}$ **62** $-\frac{2}{3}$ **63** $\frac{1}{5}$

65 $\left[\dfrac{1}{2}\left(\dfrac{1}{a}+\dfrac{1}{b}\right)\right]^{-1}=\dfrac{2ab}{a+b}$ **66** $d=\log 3$ **67** $d=\sqrt{6}-\sqrt{3}$ **69** $d=3,\ a=-8,\ S_{10}=55$

70 $-2-2-2-\cdots$ to 43 terms $=-86$ and $173-86=87$ **73** Both are $-\frac{4}{3}$ **74** Both are $-\frac{1}{6}$ **75** Both are $\frac{2}{9}$

EXERCISE 11.2

1 3, 6, 12, 24, 48 **2** 2, 6, 18, 54, 162 **3** 5, -10, 20, -40 **5** 243, 81, 27, 9, 3 **6** 256, -128, 64, -32, 16, -8
7 16, 8, 4, 2, 1, $\frac{1}{2}$ **9** 162 **10** 6 **11** -1 **13** 170 **14** $\frac{121}{3}$ **15** 1 **17** 127 **18** $\frac{211}{3}$ **19** $\frac{1}{5}$ **21** $a_n=162,\ s_n=242$
22 $a_n=48,\ s_n=93$ **23** $n=5,\ s_n=\frac{55}{2}$ **25** $s_n=400,\ n=4$ **26** $a=\frac{1}{9},\ s_n=\frac{40}{9}$ **27** $r=\frac{1}{2},\ s_n=511$ **29** $a_n=162,\ n=5$
30 $a=625,\ a_n=1$ **31** $a=343,\ n=4$ **33** $r=-2,\ a=3$ **34** $a=8,\ n=5$ **35** $r=3,\ a_n=45,\ r=-4,\ l=80$
37 504 **38** 3279 **39** $2^{n+1}-1$ **41** 2, $-\frac{2}{15}$ **42** 2, 5, 8; $r=3$ **45** 2 **46** \$129,600 **47** $4096n$ **49** \$511, \$1 profit
50 \$1419.20 **51** 254 **53** 6, 18 **54** $\frac{1}{3},\frac{1}{3},\frac{3}{4},\frac{9}{4}$ **55** 4, 8, 16 and -4, 8, -16 **57** Geometric, $\frac{32}{243},\frac{64}{729}$ **58** Harmonic, $\frac{2}{9},\frac{4}{21}$
59 Arithmetic, $-\frac{2}{9},-\frac{4}{9}$ **61** Harmonic, $-\frac{1}{8},-\frac{1}{11}$ **62** Geometric, $\frac{81}{8},\frac{243}{16}$ **63** Arithmetic, $\frac{13}{6},\frac{8}{3}$ **67** 4, 12, 36 or $\frac{4}{9},-\frac{20}{9},\frac{100}{9}$
69 $16+8+4+2$ **70** $64+32+8+4+2+1$ **71** $32+16+8+2+1$ **73** $81-27-1$ **74** $81-27-9-1$
75 $81+27+3$

EXERCISE 11.3

1 25 **2** $\frac{25}{3}$ **3** $\frac{25}{9}$ **5** 36 **6** 8 **7** 10 **9** 36 **10** $\frac{81}{2}$ **11** 96 **13** 3 **14** 5 **15** $-\frac{3}{5}$ **17** $\frac{1}{2}$ **18** 2 **19** $-\frac{2}{7}$ **21** $\frac{4}{9}$ **22** $\frac{8}{33}$
23 $\frac{232}{99}$ **25** $\frac{371}{90}$ **26** $\frac{199}{90}$ **27** $\frac{2161}{330}$ **33** $\frac{3}{4}$ **34** $\frac{4}{5}$ **35** $\frac{2}{7}$ **37** 2400 cm **38** 120 m **39** 18 m **41** $p<9$ **42** 9 mg
43 200 in^2 **45** $-\frac{1}{3}<x<1,\ (3x-1)/(3-3x)$ **46** $2<x<8,\ (x-5)/(x-2)$ **47** $-2.5<x<1.5,\ (2x+1)/(3-2x)$ **50** 1
51 5

EXERCISE 11.4

1 \$36,099.29, \$28,500 **2** \$511,902.78, \$427,200 **3** \$209,268.15, \$157,000 **5** \$56,576.02 **6** \$240,206.65
7 \$3,426,676.76 **9** 8.24 percent **10** 6.09 percent **11** 12.62 percent **13** \$1529.87 **14** \$6309.90 **15** \$9400.00
17 \$3502.85 **18** \$345.69 **19** \$581.72 **21** 3 years **22** 5.5 years **23** 17 years **25** \$138,318.80, \$44,984.90
26 \$608,788.80, \$195,510.20 **27** \$174,079; \$26,493.91 **29** \$18,765.73, \$7851.59 **30** \$18,335.51, \$9183.85
31 \$66,086.94, \$32,340.47 **33** \$831.50 **34** \$11,419.94 **35** \$11,161.85 **37** 8.75 years **38** 7 years **39** 16.5 years

EXERCISE 11.5

1 2.5, 3, 3.5, 4, 4.5 **2** 6, 3, 1.5, 0.75, 0.375 **3** $\frac{1}{5},\frac{1}{3}$, 1, -1, $-\frac{1}{3}$ **5** $\frac{2}{243},\frac{728}{243}$ **6** $\frac{5}{6},\frac{77}{24}$ **7** $a=\frac{1}{4},\ d=\frac{1}{2},\ a_n=\frac{9}{4},\ s_n=\frac{25}{4}$
8 $a=\frac{1}{8},\ r=4,\ a_n=32,\ n=5$ **9** 45,878 **10** $\frac{21}{11}$, 7 **11** \$1425.76 **12** $\frac{17}{33}$ **13** $-\frac{1}{7}$ **20** 5, 6, 7 or 7, 6, 5
21 2, 6, 18; 18, 6, 2 **22** $\frac{1}{3}$, 0 **23** $4\sqrt{2}$, 8, $8\sqrt{2}$ **24** 7, 10, 13 **25** $\frac{64}{13},\frac{32}{5},\frac{64}{7}$ **27** Each is $\frac{2}{3}$ **28** 2, $-1,\frac{1}{2},-\frac{1}{4},\ldots$
29 $\frac{3}{4},\frac{11}{12}$, arithmetic **30** $\frac{16}{135},\frac{32}{405}$, geometric **31** $\frac{7}{9},\frac{17}{18}$, arithmetic **32** $\frac{3}{4},\frac{2}{3}$, harmonic **33** $\frac{4}{5},\frac{8}{11}$, harmonic
34 1, 1, 2, 3, 5, 8, 13, 21 **37** 12.55% **38** \$22,397.30 **39** \$23,279.49 **40** \$43,983.94 **41** \$2240, \$2247.20, \$2251.02
42 About 6.64 years, or about 6 years, 233 days **43** \$2414.64 **44** \$11,747.26 **45** 5 percent **46** 30 **47** \$214,726.84
48 \$154,739.33 **49** \$1,163,585, \$39,571,279; 24(\$54,211,842) = \$1,301,084,198 **50** \$2591.97

EXERCISE 12.2

1 60 **2** 110 **3** 6720 **5** 33 **6** 5040 **7** 720 **9** 13^3 **10** 11^3 **11** 14^3 **13** Sample **14** Permutation **15** Sample
17 468,000 **18** 17,576,000 **19** 9261 **21** 625 **22** 192 **23** 36 **25** 336 **26** 24 **27** 720 **29** 360 **30** 27,600; 35,152
31 15,120 **33** 12,696 **34** 11! **35** 40,320 **37** 2143, 2341, 2413, 3142, 3421, 3412, 4123, 4312, 4321
38 $D_5=44,\ D_6=265,\ D_7=1854$ **39** 265 **45** 9 **46** 7 **47** 10 **49** 48

EXERCISE 12.3

1 21 **2** 220 **3** 36 **5** Yes, both are 330 **6** $56 = 35 + 21$ **7** Yes, both are 32 **9** (a) 84, (b) 165 **10** (a) 15, (b) 126
11 (a) 35, (b) 84 **13** 126 **14** 120 **15** $C(52, 13) \approx 6.35(10^{11})$ **17** 2,598,960 **18** 18,564 **19** 2600 **21** 150 **22** 5544
23 166,320 **25** 70 **26** 35 **27** 792 **29** 105 **30** 22!/6!5!7!3! **31** $9!/2!3!4! = 1260$

EXERCISE 12.4

1 $x^4 + 4x^3y + 6x^2y^2 + 4xy^3 + y^4$ **2** $x^7 + 7x^6t + 21x^5t^2 + 35x^4t^3 + 35x^3t^4 + 21x^2t^5 + 7xt^6 + t^7$
3 $b^5 - 5b^4y + 10b^3y^2 - 10b^2y^3 + 5by^4 - y^5$ **5** $243x^5 - 405x^4y + 270x^3y^2 - 90x^2y^3 + 15xy^4 - y^5$
6 $64a^6 - 192a^5b + 240a^4b^2 - 160a^3b^3 + 60a^2b^4 - 12ab^5 + b^6$ **7** $x^4 + 12x^3w + 54x^2w^2 + 108xw^3 + 81w^4$
9 $16x^4 + 96x^3y + 216x^2y^2 + 216xy^3 + 81y^4$ **10** $81s^4 - 432s^3t + 864s^2t^2 - 768st^3 + 256t^4$ **11** $8x^3 - 60x^2y + 150xy^2 - 125y^3$
13 $a^{33} + 33a^{32}y + 528a^{31}y^2 + 5456a^{30}y^3$ **14** $x^{51} - 51x^{50}y + 1275x^{49}y^2 - 20,825x^{48}y^3$
15 $m^{101} - 202m^{100}y + 20,200m^{99}y^2 - 1,333,200m^{98}y^3$ **17** 1.2167 **18** 1.2155 **19** 1.1941 **21** $560x^3y^4$ **22** $-160a^3c^3$
23 $10,206x^4y^5$ **25** $-35a$ **26** $-2016x^{-6}$ **27** $29,568x^{10}y^6$ **29** $160x^3y^{3/2}$ **30** $5670x^4y$ **31** $960x^7y^3$

EXERCISE 12.5

1 $\frac{1}{4}, \frac{1}{2}$ **2** $\frac{1}{2}, \frac{1}{3}$ **3** $\frac{3}{13}, \frac{3}{26}$ **5** $\frac{2}{3}$ **6** $\frac{1}{3}$ **7** $\frac{6}{7}$ **9** (a) $\frac{5}{36}$, (b) $\frac{1}{36}$ **10** (a) $\frac{1}{9}$ (b) $\frac{1}{9}$ **11** $\frac{2}{9}$ **13** $\frac{17}{60}$ **14** $\frac{77}{90}$ **15** $\frac{91}{180}$
17 $C(28, 13)/C(52, 13)$ **18** $C(20, 5)/C(52, 5)$ **19** $C(12, 3)/C(20, 3)$ **21** $C(6, 3)C(12, 5)/C(18, 8)$
22 $C(10, 4)C(6,2)/C(16, 6)$ **23** $C(8, 3)C(7, 2)/C(15, 5)$ **25** $\frac{1}{8}$ **26** $\frac{1}{5}$ **27** $\frac{1}{2}$ **29** $\frac{160}{729}$ **30** $\frac{5}{16}$ **31** $\frac{160}{2401}$ **33** (a) $\frac{5}{16}$ (b) $\frac{1}{2}$
34 (a) $\frac{48}{3125}$ (b) $\frac{73}{3125}$ **35** $(\frac{1}{3})^5$ **37** 0.29 **38** 0.88 **39** 0.55 **41** $\frac{1}{36}$

EXERCISE 12.6

9 $C(8, 6) = 28 < C(8, 5) = 56 < C(8, 4) = 70 < P(8, 4) = 1680 < P(8, 5) = 6720 < P(8, 6) = 20,160$
10 $C(6, 3) = P(5, 2) = 20, C(5, 3) + C(4, 2) + C(3, 1) + C(2, 0) = 10 + 6 + 3 + 1 = 20$
11 $C(4, 1) + 2C(4, 2) + 3C(4, 3) + 4C(4, 4) = 4 + 12 + 12 + 4 = 32 = 4(2^3)$
12 $C(4, 1) + 4C(4, 2) + 9C(4, 3) + 16C(4, 4) = 4 + 4(6) + 9(4) + 16(1) = 80 = 4(5)2^2$ **13** 20 **14** 120 **15** 125 **16** 60
17 10 **18** 125 **19** 44,100 **20** 287,496 **21** 415,800 **22** 93 **23** $C(n, 3)$ **24** (b) 0.09974
29 $x^5 + 15x^4y + 90x^3y^2 + 270x^2y^3 + 405xy^4 + 243y^5$ **30** $81x^4 - 216x^3y + 216x^2y^2 - 96xy^3 + 16y^4$
31 $x^{15} - 15x^{14}y + 105x^{13}y^2 - 455x^{12}y^3$ **32** $4096x^{12} + 24,576x^{11}y + 67,584x^{10}y^2 + 112,640x^9y^3$ **33** $17,010x^6y^4$
34 $12,976,128x^7y^5$ **35** $-816x^{12}$ **36** $110,565x^{22}y^4$ **37** $\frac{4}{7}$ **38** $\frac{28}{41}$ **39** (a) $\frac{1}{6}$, (b) $\frac{5}{36}$, (c) $\frac{5}{108}$ **40** $\frac{7}{8}$ **41** $\frac{5}{14}$ **42** $\frac{10}{21}$ **43** $\frac{1}{40}$
44 $\frac{1}{72}$ **45** $\frac{5}{16}$ **46** $\frac{625}{3888}$ **47** $\frac{57}{64}$ **48** $\frac{3072}{6561} = \frac{1024}{2187}$ **49** $(\frac{3}{4})^{27} = 0.0004$

EXERCISE 13.1

1 $(y - 1)^2 = 8(x - 5)$ **2** $(x - 8)^2 = 16(y - 4)$ **3** $(y - 4)^2 = 8(x - 9)$ **5** $(x - 8)^2 = -16(y - 3)$ **6** $(x - 5)^2 = 32y$
7 $(y - 3)^2 = -16x$ **9** $(y - 2)^2 = -8(x - 9)$ **10** $(y - 3)^2 = 8(x - 4)$ **11** $(x - 5)^2 = -8(y - 1)$ **13** $(y - 2)^2 = -8(x - 5)$
14 $(x - 3)^2 = 4(y - 5)$ **15** $(x - 7)^2 = 16(y + 3)$ **17** $(y - 2)^2 = 4(x - 5)$ **18** $(y + 1)^2 = -4(x - 6)$ **19** $(x - 1)^2 = 8(y - 1)$
21 $(y - 2)^2 = 4(x + 1)$, $(-1, 2)$, $(0, 2)$ **22** $(y + 1)^2 = -6(x - 3)$, $(3, -1)$, $(1.5, -1)$ **23** $(x + 3)^2 = -4(y - 3)$, $(-3, 3)$,
$(-3, 2)$ **25** $(x - 2)^2 = 4(y + 3)$, $(2, -3)$, $(2, -2)$ **26** $(x + 3)^2 = -8(y + 4)$, $(-3, -4)$, $(-3, -6)$ **27** $(y + 2)^2 = -4(x + 1)$,
$(-1, -2)$, $(-2, -2)$ **29** $(y - 3)^2 = 8(x - 4)$ **30** $(y - 1)^2 = 16(x - 2)$ **31** $(x - 1)^2 = 16(y - 3)$ **33** On the axis and 2.25 in
from the vertex **34** $y^2 = -16(x - 4)$, $y^2 = -4(x - 1)$ **35** 25 ft

EXERCISE 13.2

1 $(2, -1)$, $(2 \pm 4, -1)$, $(2 \pm 5, -1)$ **2** $(-5, 3)$, $(-5 \pm 3, 3)$, $(-5 \pm 5, 3)$ **3** $(-2, -3)$, $(-2, -3 \pm 12)$, $(-2, -3 \pm 13)$
5 $C(-1, 2)$, $F(-1, 2 \pm 7)$, $V(-1, 2 \pm 25)$ **6** $C(2, -4)$, $F(2, -4 \pm 3)$, $V(2, -4 \pm 5)$ **7** $C(-1, 2)$, $F(-1 \pm 5, 2)$,
$V(-1 \pm 13, 2)$ **9** $(x - 3)^2/5^2 + (y - 2)/4^2 = 1$ **10** $\dfrac{(x + 1)^2}{17^2} + \dfrac{(y - 4)^2}{15^2} = 1$ **11** $(y + 3)^2/13^2 + (x - 5)^2/12^2 = 1$

13 $\dfrac{(x+1)^2}{5^2} + \dfrac{(y-1)^2}{3^2} = 1$ **14** $(y+1)/17^2 + (x-1)^2/15^2 = 1$ **15** $y^2/13^2 + (x-4)^2/12^2 = 1$

17 $(x-4)^2/5^2 + (y-1)^2/2^2 = 1$ **18** $(y-1)^2/7^2 + (x+2)^2/6^2 = 1$ **19** $(y+2)^2/5^2 + (x-2)^2/(2\sqrt{2})^2 = 1$

21 $(y-3)^2/7^2 + (x-1)^2/5^2 = 1$ **22** $(y+2)^2/5^2 + (x-3)^2/2^2 = 1$ **23** $(x-7)^2/16 + (y-2)^2/9 = 1$

25 $4y^2 + 3x^2 - 48x + 144 = 0$ **26** $25x^2 + 21y^2 - 350y + 1225 = 0$ **27** $16x^2 - 96x + 7y^2 + 178y + 535 = 0$

29 $9x^2 + 8y^2 - 72x - 136y + 560 = 0$ **30** $28x^2 + 64y^2 - 196x - 1152y + 5415 = 0$

31 $64x^2 - 24xy + 96y^2 - 236x - 612y + 991 = 0$ **33** $(x-2)^2/4 + (y-1)^2/9 = 1$, $C(2,1)$, $V(2, 1\pm3)$, $F(2, 1\pm\sqrt5)$

34 $(x+3)^2/4^2 + (y-2)^2/3^2 = 1$, $C(-3,2)$, $V(-3\pm4, 2)$, $F(-3\pm\sqrt7, 2)$ **35** $(x+1)^2/4 + (y-4)^2/9 = 1$, $C(-1,4)$,
$V(-1, 4\pm3)$, $F(-1, 4\pm\sqrt5)$ **37** $(x-1)^2/25 + (y+2)^2/9 = 1$, $C(1,-2)$, $V(1\pm5, -2)$, $F(1\pm4, -2)$

38 $(x+2)^2/25 + (y-1)^2/16 = 1$, $C(-2,1)$, $V(-2\pm5, 1)$, $F(-2\pm3, 1)$ **39** $(x+2)^2/144 + (y-3)^2/169 = 1$, $C(-2,3)$,
$V(-2, 3\pm13)$, $F(-2, 3\pm5)$

EXERCISE 13.3

1 $C(2,-1)$, $F(2\pm5, -1)$, $V(2\pm4, -1)$, $y+1 = \pm0.75(x-2)$ **2** $C(-5,3)$, $F(-5\pm5, 3)$, $V(-5\pm3, 3)$,
$y-3 = \pm(\frac{4}{3})(x+5)$ **3** $C(-2,-3)$, $F(-2, -3\pm13)$, $V(-2, -3\pm12)$, $y+3 = \pm2.4(x+2)$ **5** $C(-1,2)$, $F(-1, 2\pm25)$,
$V(-1, 2\pm7)$, $y-2 = \pm(\frac{7}{24})(x+1)$ **6** $C(2,-4)$, $F(2, -4\pm5)$, $V(2, -4\pm3)$, $y+4 = \pm0.75(x-2)$ **7** $C(-1,2)$,
$F(-1\pm13, 2)$, $V(-1\pm5, 2)$, $y-2 = \pm2.4(x+1)$ **9** $(x-3)^2/3^2 - (y-2)^2/4^2 = 1$ **10** $(x+1)^2/5^2 - (y-4)^2/15^2 = 1$

11 $(y+3)^2/5^2 - (x-5)^2/12^2 = 1$ **13** $(x+1)^2/4^2 - (y-1)^2/3^2 = 1$ **14** $(y+1)^2/8^2 - (x-1)^2/15^2 = 1$

15 $y^2/5^2 - (x-4)^2/12^2 = 1$ **17** $(x-4)^2/5^2 - (y-1)^2/2^2 = 1$ **18** $(y-1)^2/7^2 - (x+2)^2/24^2 = 1$

19 $(y+2)^2/9^2 - (x-2)^2/8^2 = 1$ **21** $(y-3)^2/7^2 - (x-1)^2/5^2 = 1$ **22** $(y+2)^2/5^2 - (x-3)^2/2^2 = 1$

23 $(x-7)^2/4^2 - (y-2)^2/3^2 = 1$ **25** $3y^2 - 30y - x^2 + 2x + 26 = 0$ **26** $5x^2 + 12x - 4y^2 + 16y - 124 = 0$

27 $7x^2 - 24x - 9y^2 - 18y - 9 = 0$ **29** $8y^2 - 16y - x^2 + 8x - 16 = 0$ **30** $16y^2 - 9x^2 - 112y + 36x + 124 = 0$

31 $24xy - 7y^2 - 96x - 4y + 164 = 0$ **33** $(x-2)^2/2^2 - (y-1)^2/3^2 = 1$, $C(2,1)$, $V(2\pm2, 1)$, $F(2\pm\sqrt{13}, 1)$,
$y-1 = \pm1.5(x-2)$ **34** $(x+3)^2/4^2 - (y-2)^2/3^2 = 1$, $C(-3,2)$, $V(-3\pm4, 2)$, $F(-3\pm5, 2)$, $y-2 = \pm(\frac{3}{4})(x+3)$

35 $(y+4)^2/3^2 - (x+1)^2/2^2 = 1$, $C(-1,-4)$, $V(-1, -4\pm3)$, $F(-1, -4\pm\sqrt{13})$, $y+4 = \pm1.5(x+1)$

37 $(x-1)^2/8^2 - (y+1)^2/3^2 = 1$, $C(1,-1)$, $V(1\pm8, -1)$, $F(1\pm\sqrt{73}, -1)$, $y+1 = \pm(\frac{3}{8})(x-1)$

38 $(x+1)^2/3^2 - (y-1)^2/4^2 = 1$, $C(-1,1)$, $V(-1\pm3, 1)$, $F(-1\pm5, 1)$, $y-1 = \pm(\frac{4}{3})(x+1)$

39 $(y-1)^2/5^2 - (x+2)^2/12^2 = 1$, $C(-2,1)$, $V(-2, 1\pm5)$, $F(-2, 1\pm13)$, $y-1 = (\pm\frac{5}{12})(x+2)$

EXERCISE 13.4

1 $x^2 - y^2 = 1$ **2** $x^2 - y^2 = -1$ **3** $25x^2 = 3$ **5** $2x^2 - \sqrt3 xy + y^2 = 5$ **6** $x^2 + 4\sqrt3 xy + y^2 = 10$

7 $49x^2 + 336xy + 576y^2 = 75$ **9** $\cos\theta = 0.1\sqrt{10}$, $\sin\theta = 3\sqrt{10}$ **10** $\cos\theta = \sqrt3/2$, $\sin\theta = \frac{1}{2}$ **11** $\cos\theta = \frac{1}{2}$, $\sin\theta = \sqrt3/2$

13 $\cos\theta = 0.8$, $\sin\theta = 0.6$ **14** $\cos\theta = 7/\sqrt{74}$, $\sin\theta = 5/\sqrt{74}$ **15** $\cos\theta = 9/\sqrt{97}$, $\sin\theta = 4/\sqrt{97}$ **17** $\cos\theta = 0.8$,
$\sin\theta = 0.6$ **18** $\cos\theta = 0.8$, $\sin\theta = 0.6$ **19** $\cos\theta = \sin\theta = 0.5\sqrt2$ **21** $9x^2 - 4\sqrt2 x + 4\sqrt2 y + 4 = 0$

22 $2x^2 + y^2 + 2x + y = 1$ **23** $9x^2 + 4y^2 = 36$ **25** Parabola, $2x^2 - 6x + 2y + 2 = 0$ **26** Hyperbola,
$55x^2 - 70y^2 + 9x - 13y - 45 = 0$ **27** Hyperbola, $x^2 - y^2 = 2a^2$ **29** Hyperbola, $5x^2 - 45y^2 + 28 = 0$ **30** Hyperbola,
$21x^2 - 29y^2 + 2 = 0$ **31** Hyperbola, $11x^2 - 14y^2 - 2x + 4y + 2 = 0$ **37** $20x^2 + 32xy + 20y^2 - 72x - 72y - 63 = 0$,
$D = -576$ **38** $3x^2 + 3y^2 - 2xy - 4x + 4y = 0$, $D = -32$ **39** $64x^2 - 72xy + 64y^2 - 140x - 140y + 175 = 0$, $D = -11,200$

EXERCISE 13.5

1 Parabola **2** Parabola **3** Parabola **5** Ellipse **6** Ellipse **7** Ellipse **9** Hyperbola **10** Hyperbola **11** Hyperbola

13 $r = \dfrac{4}{1+\sin\theta}$ **14** $r = \dfrac{4}{1+2\sin\theta}$ **15** $r = \dfrac{6}{2+\cos\theta}$ **17** $r = \dfrac{12}{1-3\cos\theta}$ **18** $r = \dfrac{10}{5+\cos\theta}$ **19** $r = \dfrac{12}{1-1.5\sin\theta}$

21 $r\cos(\theta - \pi/3) = 5$ **22** $r\cos(\theta - 2\pi/3) = 3$ **23** $r\cos(\theta - 5\pi/4) = 8$ **25** $r^2 - 6r\cos(\theta - \pi/4) + 5 = 0$

26 $r^2 - 14\cos(\theta - 5\pi/4) + 33 = 0$ **27** $r^2 - 18r\cos(\theta - 5\pi/3) + 80 = 0$

EXERCISE 13.6

1 $(y - 2)^2 = 8(x - 4)$ **2** $(x - 4)^2 = -4(y + 1)$ **3** $(x - 5)^2 = -8(y - 2)$ **4** $(y - 3)^2 = -16(x - 1)$ **5** $(y - 1)^2 = 16(x - 1)$

6 $y^2 - 6y - 8x + 17 = 0$ **7** $\dfrac{(x - 3)^2}{5^2} + \dfrac{(y - 2)^2}{3^2} = 1$ **8** $\dfrac{(y - 2)^2}{5^2} + \dfrac{(x - 3)^2}{3^2} = 1$ **9** $\dfrac{(y + 2)^2}{17^2} + \dfrac{(x - 1)^2}{15^2} = 1$

10 $\dfrac{(x - 6)^2}{5^2} + \dfrac{y^2}{2^2} = 1$ **11** $\dfrac{(x - 2)^2}{4^2} + \dfrac{y^2}{1^2} = 1$ **12** $4x^2 + 3y^2 - 24x - 6y - 9 + 0$ **13** $\dfrac{(x - 2)^2}{4^2} - \dfrac{(y - 3)^2}{3^2} = 1$

14 $\dfrac{(y + 2)^2}{3^2} - \dfrac{(x - 1)^2}{4^2} = 1$ **15** $\dfrac{(x - 4)^2}{4^2} - \dfrac{(y + 1)^2}{3^2} = 1$ **16** $\dfrac{x^2}{6^2} - \dfrac{(y - 3)^2}{(\sqrt{2})^2} = 1$ **17** $x^2 - 8x - 3y^2 + 60y - 236 = 0$

18 $x^2 - 8y^2 - 2x - 16y + 1 = 0$ **19** $(y - 3)^2 = 2(x + 1)$ **20** $\dfrac{(x - 2)^2}{4^2} - \dfrac{(y - 1)^2}{3^2} = 1$ **21** $\dfrac{(x - 1)^2}{4^2} - \dfrac{(y - 2)^2}{3^2} = 1$

22 $6y^2 - 11x^2 = 17$ **23** $2x^2 - 3y^2 = 9$ **24** Hyperbola   **25** Ellipse   **26** Parabola   **27** Hyperbola   **28** $r = \dfrac{12}{1 + 2\sin\theta}$

29 $r = \dfrac{4}{4 - \cos\theta}$ **30** Hyperbola   **31** Parabola   **32** Ellipse   **33** Ellipse

APPENDIX I

1 0.5532   **2** 1.7591   **3** 1.8713   **4** 3.6392   **5** 3.8281   **6** 0.7771   **7** 1.9046   **8** 2.2036   **9** 8.5017 − 10   **10** 7.7787 − 10
11 9.8599 − 10   **12** 9.7955 − 10   **13** 3.945   **14** 74.59   **15** 2653   **16** 349.5   **17** 30.55   **18** 7626   **19** 402.4   **20** 1.591
21 0.1329   **22** 0.05774   **23** 0.04366   **24** 0.002862   **25** 0.7843   **26** 2.084   **27** 0.1491   **28** 1.935   **29** 1.487   **30** 0.9973
31 0.9735   **32** 0.9024   **33** 0.4654   **34** 0.3509   **35** 8.838   **36** 2.472   **37** 0.9909   **38** 0.4421   **39** 0.9369   **40** 0.9784
41 13.67°, 166.33°   **42** 54.60°, 305.40°   **43** 66.92°, 246.92°   **44** 23.08°, 203.08°   **45** 64.37°, 295.63°   **46** 13.66°, 166.34°
47 No such angle   **48** 8.45°, 171.55°   **49** 0.4192, 5.864   **50** 0.8898, 4.031   **51** 1.142, 4.284   **52** 1.129, 5.154
53 0.1852, 2.956   **54** 0.2679, 2.874   **55** 0.8700, 2.272   **56** 0.9427, 5.340

Index

(8.7) $\dfrac{a - b}{c} = \dfrac{\sin (A - B)/2}{\cos C/2}$ Mollweide's equation

(8.8) $a = b \cos C + c \cos B$

(8.9) $\dfrac{a - b}{a + b} = \dfrac{\tan [(A - B)/2]}{\tan [(A + B)/2]}$ Law of tangents

(8.10) $|V| = \sqrt{a^2 + b^2}$ (8.11) $\tan \theta = \dfrac{b}{a}$

(8.12) $z = x + yi = r(\cos \theta + i \sin \theta)$ (8.13) $x = r \cos \theta, \ y = r \sin \theta$

(8.14) $r^2 = x^2 + y^2, \ \tan \theta = \dfrac{y}{x}$

(8.15) $[r(\cos \theta + i \sin \theta)][R(\cos \phi + i \sin \phi)] = rR[\cos (\theta + \phi) + i \sin (\theta + \phi)]$

(8.16) $\dfrac{r(\cos \theta + i \sin \theta)}{s(\cos \phi + i \sin \phi)} = \dfrac{r}{s}[\cos (\theta - \phi) + i \sin (\theta - \phi)]$

(8.17) $[r(\cos \theta + i \sin \theta)]^n = r^n(\cos n\theta + i \sin n\theta)$

(10.3) $A_{ij} = (-1)^{i+j} M_{ij}$

(10.4) $|A| = a_{i1}A_{i1} + a_{i2}A_{i2} + \cdots + a_{in}A_{in}$ (10.6) $|A| = a_{1j}A_{1j} + a_{2j}A_{2j} + \cdots + a_{nj}A_{nj}$

(10.8) $x = \dfrac{\begin{vmatrix} e & b \\ f & d \end{vmatrix}}{\begin{vmatrix} a & b \\ c & d \end{vmatrix}}$ and $y = \dfrac{\begin{vmatrix} a & e \\ c & f \end{vmatrix}}{\begin{vmatrix} a & b \\ c & d \end{vmatrix}}$ (10.9) $x = \dfrac{N(x)}{D} \ y = \dfrac{N(y)}{D} \ z = \dfrac{N(z)}{D}$

(11.1) $a_n = a + (n - 1)d$ nth term of an arithmetic sequence

(11.2) $S_n = \dfrac{n}{2}(a + a_n)$ Sum of the first n terms of an arithmetic sequence

(11.3) $S_n = \dfrac{n}{2}[2a + (n - 1)d]$ Sum of the first n terms of an arithmetic sequence

(11.4) $a_n = ar^{n-1}$ nth term of a geometric sequence

(11.5) $S_n = \dfrac{a(1 - r^n)}{1 - r}, \ r \neq 1$ Sum of the first n terms of a geometric sequence

(11.6) $S_n = \dfrac{a - ra_n}{1 - r}, \ r \neq 1$ Sum of the first n terms of a geometric sequence

(11.7) $S = \dfrac{a}{1 - r}, \ |r| < 1$ Sum of an infinite geometric series

(11.8) $S = P(1 + i)^n$ Compound interest, i per period for n periods

(11.9) $E = \left(1 + \dfrac{j}{m}\right)^m - 1$ Effective rate of interest

(11.10) $S = P\left(1 + \dfrac{j}{m}\right)^{mn}$ Compound interest, nominal rate j compounded m times per year for n years

(11.11) $S = R\left[\dfrac{(1 + i)^n - 1}{i}\right]$ Value of an annuity, compounded at i per period for n periods, periodic payment of R